Zhaoying Zhou
Zhonglin Wang
Liwei Lin

Microsystems and Nanotechnology

Zhaoying Zhou
Zhonglin Wang
Liwei Lin

Microsystems and Nanotechnology

With 586 figures, 148 of them in color

TSINGHUA UNIVERSITY PRESS

Springer

Editors:
Zhaoying Zhou
Department of Precision Instruments & Mechanology
Tsinghua University
Beijing 100084, China
Tel &Fax: +86-10-6277-1478
E-mail: zhouzy@mail.tsinghua.edu.cn

Liwei Lin
Department of Mechanical Engineering
University of California at Berkeley
Berkeley, CA 94720-1740, USA
Tel: (510) 643-5495
Fax: (510) 643-5599
E-mail: lwlin@me.berkeley.edu

Zhonglin Wang
Center for Nanostructure Characterization and Fabrication (CNCF)
Georgia Institute of Technology
Atlanta, GA 30332-0245, USA
Tel: 404-894-8008; Fax: 404-894-9140
E-mail: zhong.wang@mse.gatech.edu

ISBN 978-7-302-24307-6
Tsinghua University Press, Beijing

ISBN 978-3-642-18292-1 e-ISBN 978-3-642-18293-8
Springer Heidelberg Dordrecht London New York

Library of Congress Control Number: 2011920981

Printed on acid-free paper

Springer is part of Springer Science+Business Media (www.springer.com)

From the Editors

It's a great honor for me to cooperate with Prof. Zhonglin Wang, Regents' Professor at the Georgia Institute of Technology and member of the European Academy of Sciences, and Prof. Liwei Lin, Co-Director of the Berkeley Sensor and Actuator Center, University of California at Berkeley, in the compilation and publication of this book. In this multi-disciplinary field characterized by rapid development it is extremely hard, if not impossible, for an individual to complete a comprehensive and accurate monograph, given that hundreds or even thousands of relevant papers might be submitted at some international conference. Hence, our decision to collaboration on this book.

Early in 2003, after much discussion, we decided on an outline of chapters divided into four sections: Fundamentals of MEMS and Nanotechnology, MEMS, Nanotechnology, and Applications of MEMS and Nanotechnology. Subsequently, more than forty experts and scholars were invited to cooperate in developing the book with us, among whom are Prof. Li Zhijian, Tsinghua University, Academician of the Chinese Academy of Sciences (CAS); Prof. Hou Jianguo, the University of Science & Technology of China, Academician of CAS; Prof. Chih-Ming Ho, University of California, Los Angeles, Member of the National Academy of Engineering; Prof. Yu-Chong Tai, California Institute of Technology; and Prof. Roland Zengerle from Germany, etc. Some authorities and experts of world-renown in this field, such as Academician Richard S. Muller from the US, Prof. Wolfgang Menz from Germany, Prof. Masayoshi Esashi from Japan as well as Dr. Geoff Beardmore from the UK, described their own experience of decades of research as well as their perspectives for the future of MEMS. Their views together with the achievements from the scientific and technological frontier constitute the substance of this book.

We are indebted to these more than 40 experts for their contributions to the book, and sincerely hope that this work will stimulate discussions and communications well into the future. We are also grateful to those experts and scholars who intended to contribute but failed to meet the deadline of publication of this book, and hope that their writing will enrich this book when reprinted afterwards.

MEMS and nanotechnology, or micro-nanotechnology, is a rising field of science and technology. Many scientific workers have been inspired by the prophecy of several Nobel Prize winners, such as Richard Feynman's famous speech at the California Institute of Technology (CIT) in 1959: "There's Plenty of Room at the Bottom." Many scientists and scientific and technological research contributors have incisively explained the problem using the inductive method. For instance, some people regard Biological Engineering, Information Technology and Micro-Nano technology as the three most important fields of the scientific frontier in the 21st century, whose combination and development will cause a new technological revolution. Some others think that science and technology develops towards two opposite extremes, with space technology at the large scale and micro-nanotechnology at the small scale. Because of its growing importance-nanotechnology has received strong support, but also sometimes too urgent demands, from governments as well as corporations. Confident in their knowledge of this field, the authors of this book have explained the stages of micro-nanotechnology development according to the developmental laws of science and technology, and thus responsibly promoting its development.

Many people have made contributions to the development of micro-nanotechnology, which is, according to the developmental laws of science, a long-term development. With the strong support of governments, micro-nanotechnology has been promoted, relevant mechanisms innovated, strong research teams formed, and a high level development platform for micro-nanotechnology is under construction. Surely, micro-nanotechnology has bright prospects. Therefore, the knowledge, experience and achievements of the authors of this book are well worth studying. My gratitude also goes to Miss Lijuan Wang and Miss Xiaoli Liu, who have helped sort through the contents, chapters, and pictures of the book.

During publication, we express our thanks to the support of National Science and Technology Publication Fund and the State Key Laboratory.

Zhaoying Zhou, Tsinghua University, Beijing, China

Over the past few decades, microelectronics has been developing following Moore's Law, which predicts that the number of electronic components that can be integrated onto a silicon chip doubles every 18 months. One of the important characteristics of microelectronic technology is the size of components, such as the 90-nanometer technology and the 60-nanometer technology. However, when its size shrinks to under 50 nanometers, the performance of the component may depend strongly on the device size due to surface and interface effects, thus electronics inevitably enters into the Nano Era.

Nanotechnology is the integration and application of functional systems at the atomic or molecular scale; the integration and application of nanometer-scale functional structures involves at least the one spacial dimension. It is one of the two technologies characterized by length scale, and its future development and application are mainly in the following three fields: the integration with micro-systems, life sciences and medical technology based on nano-processing technologies, and the application of nanomaterials in energy and environmental technologies. This book is about the integration of nanotechnology with micro-systems.

The dominant material of the first Industrial Revolution is steel. Silicon is the material for the second industrial revolution. When nanotechnology was first introduced, it was believed that it might replace micron technology and that silicon might be replaced by other materials. However, no matter on how small a scale the technology is based, even pico-scale technology, it has to be connected with the real world. In other words, a technology with practical importance should be the one based on multi-scales from nanometer to micrometer, and then to the millimeter, etc. Therefore, the application of nanotechnology in microsystems involves the integration of new nanomaterials, components and nanotechnology. This book is to present this subject as well as its prospects to the reader.

It's my honor to have collaborated with Prof. Zhou Zhaoying and Prof. Liwei Lin in editing this book. First I would extend my thanks to all the authors of this book, and I am indebted to Prof. Zhou for his leading role and elaborate planning of the editing. I hope that this book will be instrumental in promoting the integration of micro-nanotechnology world-wide.

Zhonglin Wang, Georgia Institute of Technology, Atlanta, USA

Over the past few decades, microelectronic technology has been applied in the manufacturing of micro-components of movable mechanical parts, which in turn has prompted research into micro/nanometer sensors and actuators. Multi-functionality of semiconductor materials and microminiaturization of VLSI technology provide the new system with higher performance and more reasonable performance/price ratio compared with traditional components. Key components and general components of such a system mainly depend on the following two factors. Firstly, various micro-manufacturing processes, such as surface processing, volume processing and hot embossing plastic mold and injection mold design, and manufacture of innovative concepts will be updated. As devices get better, multifunctional systems become cheaper. Secondly, new and existing basic sciences and technical basis prompt new discoveries. Earlier research results, such as micro-pressure sensors, acceleration sensors and gyroscopes, have become mature products.

With the research on MEMS and nanotechnology, significant capital and vast resources have been invested in many fields. Traditionally, the United States, Japan and Europe have been the three typical powerhouses, predominating in the research activities around the world. Research on MEMS and nanotechnology fields are no exception. However recent research in many fields in Asia have made rapid progress, which has brought remarkable progress on MEMS and nanotechnology. Korea, for instance, hosted the 13th International Conference of Solid-State Sensors, Actuators and Microsystems in 2005, which is the largest in the field of MEMS, held on a two-year rotational schedule in the United States, Europe and Asia. China is the host of this conference in 2011, which clearly demonstrates that the research carried out in China are well accepted worldwide. Now in China more than 100 universities and over 500 academic researchers are engaged in research on MEMS, and it is estimated that China will invest more than 150 million dollars in this field in the next five years. All these facts indicate that China will become one of the powerhouses for micro-nanotechnology activity in the near future.

With its emphasis on MEMS and nanotechnology, this book has integrated knowledge of mechanics, material science, manufacturing and products. I owe my gratitude to these senior researchers in MEMS and nanotechnology who have contributed different chapters to the book. Here I would like to extend my special thanks to Prof. Chih-Ming Ho from UCLA, who contributed Mechanics in MEMS, and Prof. Yu-Chong Tai from Caltech, author of the Introduction to MEMS; Prof. Ming Wu from UC Berkeley, who wrote Optical MEMS, and Prof. Yu-Chuan Su from Hsinchu Tsing Hua University, who provided MEMS Design; Prof. Mu Chiao from British Columbia University and Prof. Yu-Ting Cheng from Tainan Chiao-Tung University, co-authors of MEMS Packaging; Dr. Weijie Ynn, author of Microaccelerometer, and Dr. Scott Chang, who contributed MEMS in Automobiles. Obviously, this book could not have been produced without their contributions. And it might be important to know that these experts and other researchers look forward to improvements in quality and increases in quantity of research in the near future, just as progress has been made in recent years. We hope that this book will be among the works in the field of MEMS and nanotechnology that will fuel the research on MEMS and nanotechnology.

Liwei Lin, University of California, Berkeley, USA

Contents

Fundamentals of Microsystem and Nanotechnology

Microsystem

Nanotechnology

Application Issues

Development and Prospects

Contributors

Zhi-Jian Li Tsinghua University, Beijing 100084, China
E-mail: LiZhJ@mail.tsinghua.edu.cn
Tian-Ling Ren Tsinghua University, Beijing 100084, China
E-mail: RenTL@tsinghua.edu.cn
Chih-Ming Ho Mechanical & Aerospace Engineering Department, University of California, Los Angeles, California 90095, USA
E-mail: chihming@ucla.edu
Yu-Chong Tai Electrical Engineering and Bioengineering Department, California Institute of Technology Pasadena, California, USA
E-mail: yctai@its.caltech.edu
Bingchu Cai Research Institute of Micro/Nano Science and Technology, Shanghai Jiao Tong University, No. 1954, Huashan Road, Shanghai 200030, China
E-mail: bccai@sjtu.edu.cn
Xudong Wang School of Materials Science and Engineering, Georgia Institute of Technology, Atlanta, GA 30332-0245, USA
E-mail: zhong.wang@mse.gatch.edu
Jun Zhou School of Materials Science and Engineering, Georgia Institute of Technology, Atlanta, GA 30332-0245, USA
Zhong Lin Wang School of Materials Science and Engineering, Georgia Institute of Technology, Atlanta, GA 30332-0245, USA
E-mail: zhong.wang@mse.gatch.edu
Aidi Zhao Hefei National Laboratory for Physical Sciences at Microscale, University of Science and Technology of China, Hefei, Anhui 230026, P. R. China
E-mail: adzhao@ustc.edu.cn
Hui Zhang Hefei National Laboratory for Physical Sciences at Microscale, University of Science and Technology of China, Hefei, Anhui 230026, P. R. China
J. G. Hou Hefei National Laboratory for Physical Sciences at Microscale, University of Science and Technology of China, Hefei, Anhui 230026, P. R. China
E-mail: jghou@ustc.edu.cn
Yu-Chong Tai Departments of Electrical Engineering and Bioengineering, California Institute of Technology Pasadena, California 91125, USA
E-mail: yctai@its.caltech.edu
Shanhong Xia State Key Laboratory of Transducer Technology Institute of Electronics, Chinese Academy of Sciences, No 19 Bei-Si-Huan West Road, Beijing 100190, China
E-mail: shxia@mail.ie.ac.cn

Deyong Chen State Key Laboratory of Transducer Technology Institute of Electronics, Chinese Academy of Sciences, No 19 Bei-Si-Huan West Road, Beijing 100190, China

Zhimei Qi State Key Laboratory of Transducer Technology Institute of Electronics, Chinese Academy of Sciences, No 19 Bei-Si-Huan West Road, Beijing 100190, China

Xiuli He State Key Laboratory of Transducer Technology Institute of Electronics, Chinese Academy of Sciences, No 19 Bei-Si-Huan West Road, Beijing 100190, China

Chunrong Peng State Key Laboratory of Transducer Technology Institute of Electronics, Chinese Academy of Sciences, No 19 Bei-Si-Huan West Road, Beijing 100190, China

Xianxiang Chen State Key Laboratory of Transducer Technology Institute of Electronics, Chinese Academy of Sciences, No 19 Bei-Si-Huan West Road, Beijing 100190, China

Chao Bian State Key Laboratory of Transducer Technology Institute of Electronics, Chinese Academy of Sciences, No 19 Bei-Si-Huan West Road, Beijing 100190, China

Lan Qu State Key Laboratory of Transducer Technology Institute of Electronics, Chinese Academy of Sciences, No 19 Bei-Si-Huan West Road, Beijing 100190, China

Jizhou Sun State Key Laboratory of Transducer Technology Institute of Electronics, Chinese Academy of Sciences, No 19 Bei-Si-Huan West Road, Beijing 100190, China

Yu-Chuan Su Department of Engineering and System Science, Hsinchu Tsing Hua University
E-mail: ycsu@ess.nthu.edu.tw

Liwei Lin Department of Mechanical Engineering, University of California, Berkeley, USA
E-mail: lwlin@me.berkeley.edu

Zhihong Li Institute of Microelectronics, Peking University, Beijing, China
E-mail: zhhli@ pku.edu.cn

Bo Liu Institute of Microelectronics, Peking University, Beijing, China

Wei Wang Institute of Microelectronics, Peking University, Beijing, China

Ming C. Wu University of California, Berkeley, EECS Department, 261M Cory Hall, Berkeley, CA 94720-1770, USA
E-mail: wu@eecs.berkeley.edu

Jui-che Tsai Graduate Institute of Photonics and Optoelectronics and Department of Electrical Engineering, Taiwan University
E-mail: jctsai@cc.ee.ntu.edu.tw

Wibool Piyawattanametha National Electronics and Computer Technology Center, Thailand

Pamela R. Patterson HRL Laboratories LLC, 3011 Malibu Canyon Road Malibu, CA 90265-4797, USA

Mu Chiao Department of Mechanical Engineering, University of British Columbia, Canada

Yu-Ting Cheng Electronics Department, Hsinchu Chiao Tung University

Yung-Chun Lee Department of Mechanical Engineering, Tainan Cheng Kung University
E-mail: yunglee@mail.ncku.edu.tw

Fei-Bin Hsiao Institute of Aeronautics and Astronautics, Tainan Cheng Kung University
E-mail: fbhsiao@mail.ncku.edu.tw

Yi Zhang Shanghai Institute of Aplied Physics, Chinese Academy of Sciences, Shanghai 201800, China
E-mail: yzhang@sinap.ac.cn

Jun Hu Shanghai Institute of Aplied Physics, Chinese Academy of Sciences, Shanghai 201800, China
Xudong Xiao The Chinese University of Hong Kong, Hong Kong, China
Ampere A. Tseng Department of Mechanical and Aerospace Engineering, Arizona State University, Tempe, Arizona 85287-6106, USA
E-mail: ampere.tseng@asu.edu
Zuliang Du Key Lab for Special Functional Materials of Ministry of Education, Henan University, Kaifeng, Henan 475004, China
Andrea Notargiacomo Physics Department Universita Roma TRE, Rome, Italy
Shyankay Jou Department of Materials Science and Engineering, Taiwan University of Science and Technology
Xinxin Li State Key Lab of Transducer Technology, Shanghai Institute of Microsystem and Information Technology, Chinese Academy of Sciences, China
E-mail: xxli@mail.sim.ac.cn
Wen H. Ko Pen-Tung Sah Research Center, Xiamen University, Xiamen, 361005, China EECS Department, Case Western Reserve University, Cleveland, Ohio, USA
E-mail: whk@cwru.edu
Zhaoying Zhou Department of Precision Instruments and Machanology, Tsinghua University, Beijing, 100084, China
E-mail: zhouzy@mail.tsinghua.edu.cn
Rong Zhu Department of Precision Instruments and Machanology, Tsinghua University, Beijing, 100084, China
Xu Fu Department of Precision Instruments and Machanology, Tsinghua University, Beijing, 100084, China
Ganghua Zhang Department of Precision Instruments and Machanology, Tsinghua University, Beijing, 100084, China
Weijie Yun Chief Executive Officer, Co-Founder Telegent Systems
E-mail: wyun@telegentsystems.com
Shih-Chia (Scott) Chang Smart Sensors and Integrated Microsystems, Department of Electrical & Computer Engineering, Wayne State University, 5050 Anthony Wayne Drive, Detroit, Michigan 48202
E-mail address: sc2chang@wayne.edu
Dafu Cui State Key Laboratory of Transducer Technology, Institute of Electronics, Chinese Academy of Sciences, Beijing, China
E-mail: dfcui@mail.ie.ac.cn
Chun-Wei Huang Department of Engineering Science, Tainan Cheng Kung University
Gwo-Bin Lee Department of Engineering Science, Tainan Cheng Kung University
E-mail: gwobin@mail.ncku.edu.tw
Stefan Haeberle HSG-IMIT. Institute for Micromachining and Information Technology, Wilhelm-Schickard-Straße 10, 78052 Villingen-Schwenningen, Germany
Daniel Mark HSG-IMIT. Institute for Micromachining and Information Technology,

Wilhelm-Schickard-Straße 10, 78052 Villingen-Schwenningen, Germany
Felix von Stetten HSG-IMIT. Institute for Micromachining and Information Technology, Wilhelm-Schickard-Straße 10, 78052 Villingen-Schwenningen, Germany
Laboratory for MEMS Applications, Department of Microsystems Engineering - IMTEK, University of Freiburg, Georges-Koehler-Allee 106, 79110, Freiburg, Germany
Roland Zengerle HSG-IMIT. Institute for Micromachining and Information Technology, Wilhelm-Schickard-Straße 10, 78052 Villingen-Schwenningen, Germany
Laboratory for MEMS Applications, Department of Microsystems Engineering - IMTEK, University of Freiburg, Georges-Koehler-Allee 106, 79110, Freiburg, Germany
E-mail: zengerle@imtek.de
Richard S. Muller University of California, Berkeley, Founding Director, Berkeley Sensor & Actuator Center (BSAC), IEEE/ASME Journal of Microelectromechanical Systems
E-mail: muller@eecs.berkeley.edu, r.muller@ieee.org
Wolfgang Menz IMTEK (Institute for Micro System Technology), University of Freiburg, Germany
E-mail: menz@imtek.uni-freiburg.de
Masayoshi ESASHI The World Premier International Research Center Initiative for Atom Molecule Materials, Tohoku University, Sendai, 980-8579, Japan
E-mail: Esashi@cc.mech.tohoku.ac.jp
Geoff Beardmore Myriad Technology, Shandon House off Noverton Avenue Prestbury, Cheltenham Glos GL52 5DB, UK E-mail: geoff@myriad-technology.com

Fundamentals of Microsystem and Nanotechnology

1 Information Electronics in the Nanotechnology Era

Zhi-Jian Li and Tian-Ling Ren

Tsinghua University, Beijing 100084, China
E-mail: LiZhJ@mail.tsinghua.edu.cn; RenTL@tsinghua.edu.cn

Abstract Information technology (IT) is entering the nanoelectronics era. Conventional CMOS (complementary metel oxide semiconductor) technology is approaching its performance limit. Though the minimum feature size of CMOS microelectronics is already in the range of nanometer, reduction of the feature size for achieving much higher ULSI (ultra-large scale integration) system performance and performance energy efficiency is still constantly required for satisfying the need of today's fast-paced IT development. The main directions of technological development in the new era include: (1) overcoming the technical barriers of CMOS scaling-down and pushing the technology forward as quickly as possible to reach its physical limit, (2) developing non-traditional silicon (Si) MOS and non-MOS binary new logic devices to break through the CMOS device performance limit, and (3) establishing and realize a new, non-traditional information processing model to greatly enhance the processing power and power-performance efficiency. In this article, first, the progress of the nanoscale CMOS technology is described and its physical limit discussed. Then, several promising non-CMOS nanoelectronic devices are introduced and the prospect of nanoelectronics based on these devices is profiled. Finally, as one of the prospective new models for information processing, quantum computation is introduced. Its physical realization methods and the energy requirement for the solid state quantum computer chip are briefly discussed.

Keywords Information processing, nanoscale CMOS, non-CMOS nano-electronics, quantum computation, and quantum comput

1.1 Introduction

The world strides in the nanotechnology era. The minimum feature size of CMOS microelectronics is already been in the range of nanometers. The even smaller feature size to achieve higher speed, lower power dissipation and larger density of integration is still the 'law' of information electronics development in the new era. The main directions of technological development of information electronics can be summed up as follows:

(1) Continuously overcome the technical barriers of CMOS scaling-down to achieve the maximum possible benefits, i.e., to extend Moore's Law as far as possible.

(2) Based on quantum physical effects, develop non-traditional Si MOS and non-MOS binary logic devices (nanoelectronic devices) to overcome the performance limit of CMOS and to obtain much faster, much more energy-efficient, and much more compact and reliable ULSI chips, i.e., to push Moore's Law to the 'post-Moore' stage.

(3) Change the basic model of traditional information processing, including: replacing the binary switch devices with more efficient functional devices and the classical von Neumann computation model with new, much more efficient computing models such as quantum computation, different bio-inspired information systems, etc.

In Section 1.2, a discussion of nanoscale CMOS device development and its scaling limit is presented. In Section 1.3, several types of new non-traditional CMOS binary switch devices—nanodevices—are introduced. In Section 1.4, the fundamental concept and realization methods of quantum information processing are discussed. Finally, a short conclusion is given.

1.2 Nano-CMOS Technology

1.2.1 Progress of CMOS Technology

At least for the next 10 to 15 years, traditional microelectronics based on CMOS technology will still be the mainstream of information electronics. However, at present, the technology has feature size in the range of nanometers. Although there is no difference in principle between nano-MOSFETs (metal-oxide-semiconductor Field-Effect Transistor) and traditional MOSFETs, the structure and the basic materials for both types of devices and their interconnects are likely to experience some important change, especially as the device size approaches its limit value. There are a series of different 'second-order' effects that need to be overcome for regular working of small MOSFETs. As the device size keeps getting smaller, the requirement becomes more difficult to be satisfied. Thus, for successive scaling in nanoscaled ULSI, i.e., in the course of continuously pushing Moore's Law [1, 2] forward, reduction of these secondary effects becomes a key problem.

R. H. Dennard was the first to propose a scaling-down principle for small-size MOSFETs in 1974[3], called constant electrical field scaling. If the longitudinal and transversal dimensions (L and W), the source and drain space charge width (W_S and W_D), and the voltages (V_G, V_D, V_T: gate, drain, and threshold voltages) are scaled down by a same factor of α, then the switching delay time τ_d is scaled down α times and switching power P_d, α^2 times, leading to the switching energy (device merit) $E_b(=\tau_d P_d)$ improvement by a factor of α^3. Meanwhile, the average electric field strength in the channel is kept constant. As the switch chip area is scaled down at the same rate of P_d reduction, α^2 times, it results in a constant chip power dissipation density. However, the device integration density (device number per unit chip area) is increased by a factor of α^2 at the same time. In practice, considering the restrictions of the 'second-order' effects for small-size MOSFETs, one has to modify the scaling rule somehow [4], but the scaling-down principle still describes the fast pace of the CMOS technology progress and serves as the foundation of the well-known Moore's Law (the CMOS chip integration density quadruples every three to four years from one generation to the next, with corresponding performance improvement. As a modern technology developing as fast as the Moore's Law described, CMOS microelectronics has been developing steadily for more than 40 years. Started in the beginning of 1990s, taking Moore's Law as reference, the US Semiconductor Industry Association (SIA) edited the National Technology Roadmap for Semiconductor (NTRS), which is now known as the International Technology Roadmap for Semiconductor (ITRS). ITRS is an important guide book of worldwide microelectronics development. It takes each three-year term as a development node and describes the recent and long-term prospects for Si-CMOS technology development, including advances in devices and ULSI technologies, characteristics, performance, application requirements, as well as new technical challenges.

1.2.2 The Second-Order Effects in Small-Size MOSFETs

When the MOSFET channel length becomes smaller and smaller, down to sub-micro level, even nanometers, some second-order effects, which are ignored in the long-channel MOSFET model (on which the Dennard's scaling principle is based), due to two-dimensional (2D) electric field distribution, thermodynamics, quantum mechanics effects, etc. become more and more important with regard to device characteristics and finally will restrict the scaling. The main second-order effects are summarized below[5]:

(1) Threshold voltage (absolute value of V_T) reduction with scaled-down channel length—short channel effect (SCE) As a result of SCE, the threshold voltage of a short-channel MOSFET depends greatly on its channel length. This makes ULSI manufacturability a serious problem, since the inevitable fabrication variations of channel length, ΔL, will lead to a variation of V_T both in a chip and among chips. Quantum mechanical analysis shows that SCE is enhanced when quantum effect

in a nanodevice is taken into account. SCE with and without considering quantum effect (as dependence of V_T on channel length L_g) is shown in Fig. 1.1[6].

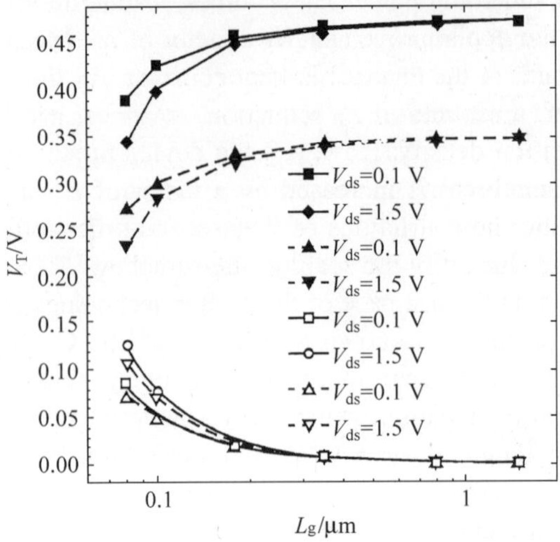

Figure 1.1 Short channel effect of MOSFETs[6]

Upper: NMOSFET, lower: PMOSFET; real line: without quantum mechanical effect; broken Line: with quantum mechanical effect

(2) Drain-induced barrier lowering (DIBL) The applied voltage between the source and the drain (V_{ds}) produces a drift electric field in the channel and widens the source and drain space charge regions. When the channel length L is very short, the electric field pattern there becomes two dimensionally distributed. Then, the drain voltage will produce an influence on the surface potential of the source p-n junction, lowering the energy barrier between the channel and the source, reducing the absolute value of V_T. This additional threshold voltage shift ΔV_T (absolute V_T reduction both of N and PMOSFETs) is V_{ds} dependent; the shorter the L and the higher the V_{ds} (NMOSFET), the stronger the DIBL effect. DIBL not only enhances ΔV_T (see Fig. 1.1 and compare curves with @V_{ds} = 0.1 V and @V_{ds} = 1.5 V) but also results in S factor degradation, device leakage current I_{off} increase, and even source-drain punch-through.

(3) Hot-Carrier Effects (HCE) With decrease of L, if the voltage has not been reduced accordingly, the electric field strength in the channel region, especially in the drain p-n junction space charge region, becomes so strong that drift carriers can have their average kinetic energy much higher than the equilibrium thermal energy K_BT and become hot carriers. At the Si/SiO_2 interface, part of the 'hot carriers' are possibly injected into the gate insulator both by tunneling through and jumping over the interface energy barrier. This process results in charge trapping in the gate insulator and interface state density increase. Both the above

effects lead to the drift of V_T with the increase of device working time and thus influence the long-term reliability of the device.

(4) Velocity saturation and velocity overshoot At low electric field strengths ($E \leqslant 10^3$ V·cm^{-1}), the carrier mobility μ is constant and the carrier drift velocity is proportional to the applied electric field strength *E,* i.e., $v_d = \mu E$. However, when the field strength is over a critical value, μ starts to decrease with *E*, and at last the v_d will reach a saturation value v_s (for electrons in (100) direction of Si, at room temperature, $v_s \sim 6\times10^6$ cm·s^{-1}[7]). Existence of velocity saturation makes the device with channel length *L* to have a delay time limit, τ_{min} (the minimum obtainable τ no matter how strong the applied *E*). Existence of τ_{min} is the main factor of performance limitation for each node of ULSI chips.

On the other hand, if *L* is decreased to less than the carrier mean free path, the carriers are hardly scattered during their drifting through the channel. Then, the carrier transport becomes ballistic and thus the restriction of v_s vanishes again.

(5) Channel impurity doping fluctuation When the device size comes into nanometer scale, the number of impurity atoms in the channel region of a MOSFET decreases dramatically, reaching the order of hundreds and even tens. No matter what kind of doping technology is adopted, the thermal fluctuation of doping concentration is not avoidable and in nanoscale case, and the fluctuation of channel doping concentration influences significantly on device's performance. Due to doping fluctuation, the impurity density varies distinctively from one location to another randomly on the same wafer, which results in the fluctuation of threshold voltages V_T ($\Delta V_T \cdot V_T^{-1}$) from the designed value both in a chip and among chips and thus seriously affects the ULSI manufacturability[8]. Quantum mechanical analysis indicates that the doping fluctuation effect is more serious than that considered only classically[9]. Figure 1.2 illustrates the different doping fluctuation effects on the surface potential at the interface for high doping (conventional MOSFETs) and low doping (nanoscale MOSFETs) cases.

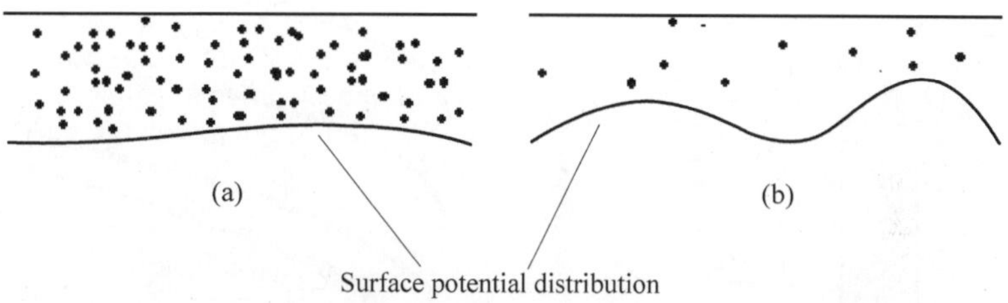

Figure 1.2 Fluctuation of surface potential for conventional and nanoscale MOSFETs caused by thermal fluctuation of channel doping: (a) high concentration, (b) low concentration

(6) Carrier tunneling through Si/SiO_2 interface energy barrier In Fig. 1.3(a), the schematic energy diagram of a MOS structure is presented. When the thickness

of the gate oxide is sufficiently thin (1 nanometer or so), the carriers (here, electrons of the NMOS) from the semiconductor can tunnel through the Si/SiO_2 interface to the poly-gate, forming the gate current. There are two possible mechanisms of electron tunneling. The first one is called indirect tunneling, by which electrons at the first tunnel across the interface barrier, and then drift through insulator layer and reach the gate. The second is called direct tunneling, in which electrons tunnel directly from the semiconductor to the gate. According to the simple Wentzel-Kramers-Brillouin (WKB) model for a rectangular energy barrier, the tunneling probability T can be expressed as:

$$T = \frac{\exp\left[-\frac{2}{\hbar}\int_{X_1}^{X_2}\sqrt{2m^*(V(x)-E)}\mathrm{d}x\right]}{1+\frac{1}{4}\exp\left[-\frac{2}{\hbar}\int_{X_1}^{X_2}\sqrt{2m^*(V(x)-E)}\mathrm{d}x\right]} \tag{1.1}$$

where $\hbar$ is the Dirac constant, m^* is the effective mass, X_2 and X_1 are two boundaries of the barrier, $V(x)$ and E are respectively the potential and electric field strength in it. Here, we see that T and thereby the gate current increase exponentially with decrease of gate oxide thickness t_{ox}. $(=X_2-X_1)$. For nano-MOSFETs, when the thickness of the gate oxide is reduced down to 1 nm or less, the gate tunneling current becomes an important part of the device off-state leakage current I_{off}. The contribution of the tunneling gate current with different t_{ox} is shown in Fig. 1.3(b) by I_g vs. V_g characteristics. Considering the exponential growth of I_{off} with decrease of t_{ox}, we can see that this effect is one of the most important factors to limit the device scaling. Quantum direct tunneling also occurs between the source and drain junctions and this should also be taken into account in calculating I_{off} for nano-MOSFETs.

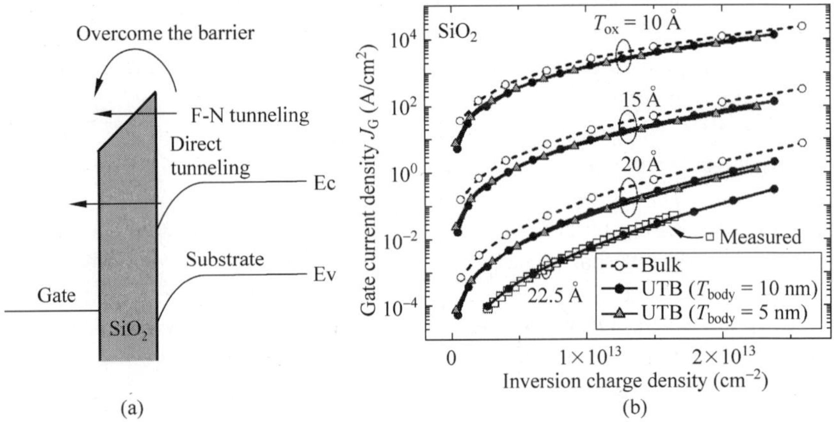

Figure 1.3 (a) Schematic energy diagram of electron tunneling in a MOS structure, (b) gate current in an ultrathin body devices

(7) Quantum Mechanical Effect (QME) on MOSFET Performance: Carrier transportation in a MOSFET's channel is restricted in the channel layer between two energy barriers of the Si/SiO_2 interface and substrate to the channel p-n junction. Since the thickness of the channel inversion layer is comparable with electron wave length, the transport behavior of channel electrons should be described as 2D electron gas (2DEG), not as that in three-dimensional (3D) solid classically. The energy density state function of 2DEG is quite different from that of the 3D (conventional) case: instead of parabolic, it is step-like. Besides, energy quantization elevates the conduction band edge E_C and lowers the valence band edge E_V, resulting in widening of the effective forbidden energy gap ΔE. On the other hand, from the quantum mechanical point of view, the channel carrier density at the interface must be zero. The density rises first and decays then when the depth increases toward the substrate p-n junction boundary, in spite of the classical theory, in which it has a maximum at the interface and monotonously decays to the junction. Taking the above-mentioned effects into account, we get a significant reduction of the channel carrier density by quantum mechanical calculation in comparison with the result of traditional classical calculation with the same V_{gs} and V_{ds}. Consequently, when QME is taken into account, the performance of the nano-MOSFET will be greatly degraded in comparison with what would be predicted classically. Moreover, as mentioned above, QME can greatly enhance many of the MOSFET's second-order effects, such as SCE and the doping fluctuation effect, and thus make the ULSI design and fabrication more difficult.

In addition to the above-listed second-order effects, there are others too, such as gate induced drain leakage (GIDL), which contributes to off-state current too, as well as parasitic resistance of MOSFET. These also need to be considered while designing useful nano-MOSFETs. The parasitic resistance of a MOSFET includes source and drain Ohmic contact resistance and sheet resistance of the source and drain regions. From the scaling principle, we can see that as the effective resistance of an intrinsic MOSFET is scaled down, the parasitic resistance is scaled up. Hence, the performance degradation caused by the parasitic resistance can be significant even in sub-micrometer MOSFETs. Evidently, this is also a serious and challenging problem for nano-MOSFETs.

Some of above mentioned second-order effects increase the off-state leakage current and thus the chip standing power. Others limit the performance improvement owing to successive scaling. In order to continuously scale down the ULSI feature size and get the benefits accordingly (i.e., to extend Moore's Law in the nanoera) at the device level, the key is to overcome or decrease these effects. It should be pointed out that these effects have complex internal correlations. For example, reduction of t_{ox} can enhance the gate-to-channel controllability and thus decrease SCE and the DIBL effect, but it intensifies the gate tunneling current at the same time. Therefore, compromise and trade-off are always necessary. If all the methods tried for achieving the device design that can meet the performance improvement, reasonable manufacturability, and reliability requirements with successive scaling fail, the scaling-down process will be terminated[10]. This means that Moore's Law can no longer be extended.

1.2.3 New Structures and Materials for Nano-MOSFETs

Researches on MOSFET devices always run ahead of the circuits and systems development. Nowadays, the minimum feature size of industrial ULSI is in range of 65 – 45 nm, but in laboratories, MOSFETs of minimum channel length below 10 nm with excellent performance have been reported. Obviously, they have been prepared for ULSI development during the period 2014 – 2018 or so, as predicted by ITRS.

Generally speaking, the goal of nano-MOSFET development is to achieve the expected performance enhancement by taking efforts to overcome the different second-order effects that occur during the scaling-down process. In fact, many effective improvements have been already made in sub-micrometer ULSIs for different purposes. This technique is called structural engineering or impurity engineering. Some examples are lightly doped drain (LDD), elevated drain and source, halo structure, δ-doped channel structure, and super retrograde channel doping. Some of them are still useful in nanoscale MOSFETs. New ideas have been focused mainly on innovative device geometrical structures and new MOS materials.

1.2.3.1 New Structures for Nano-MOSFETs

In order to reduce SEC, DIBL, and HCE, the above-mentioned impurity engineering techniques are applied to optimize the planar device structure of nano-MOSFETS to meet the manufacturability and performance upgrade requirement's[5].

For further performance improvement, especially when the channel length approaches its limiting value, in literatures, some non-conventional geometric structures have been proposed for the 'ultimate' nano-MOSFETs. These are briefly discussed below:

(1) Ultra thin body silicon on insulator (UTBSOI)[11] In comparison with conventional body CMOS, silicon-on-insulator (SOI) CMOS has smaller parasitic source and drain capacitance (source and drain are located on the SiO_2 film). Consequently, SOI CMOS technology is faster and more reliable than the conventional body CMOS. If the 'body' silicon (S) film of SOI is thicker than the space charge layer width under the channel and the (S) film is only partially depleted as MOSFET is in the 'on' state, then the SOI is called partially depleted (PDSOI). PDSOI has some harmful floating-body effects, such as latch-up and DIBL enhancement. With very thin (S) film, which is fully depleted in the MOSFET's 'on' state, the structure is called FDSOI and the floating-body effects can be avoided. Further investigations indicate that with FDSOI, one can also reduce the SCE and enhance the device driving power. Then, if the film is intrinsic Si and an appropriate metal (whose Fermi energy level is just located in the mid gap of Si) is used for the gate electrode, the doping fluctuation effect can also be prevented. This new MOSFET structure named ultra thin body SOI (UTBSOI) is

one of the most prospective structures of future nano-CMOSFETs. The key problems here are the gate material selection and the poor device thermal conduction.

(2) Double gate (DG)[12, 13], Finger gate[14], and Surrounding gate[15] MOSFETs As shown in Fig. 1.4(a), if the conventional single-gate of MOSFET is replaced by the double gate, or the finger gate (Fig. 1.4(c)), or even surrounding gate (Fig. 1.4(b)), we can see that with roughly the same chip area, the gate control power to the channel carriers will be enhanced by a factor of two or more, leading to great decrease of many secondary effects such as SCE and DIBL, and big improvement of device performance such as switching delay. At first glance, the new device structures appear to have no obvious advantage of device merit, $P_d\tau_d$. This is because together with the decrease of τ_d, the device power dissipation increases due to the increase of the driven current. However, since SCE and DIBL are reduced significantly with these new structures, one can expect to make useful devices with much smaller channel length than that of the conventional structures. The shorter the possible channel length of the ultimate CMOSFET is, the farther Moore's Law will be extended. The main problem here is the non-planar structure of the device, which makes the ULSI fabrication very complicated.

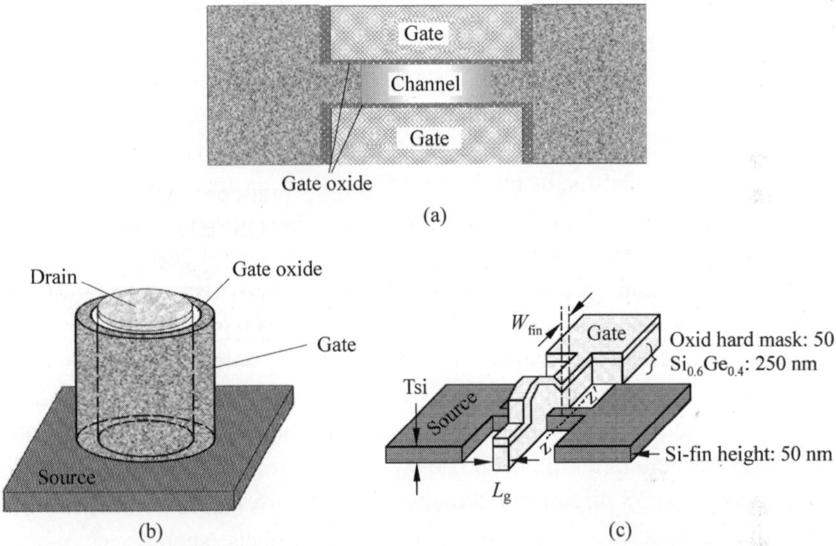

Figure 1.4 Schematic diagrams for some of the proposed new nano-MOSFET structures:[12–15] (a) double gate, (b) surrounding gate, (c) finger gate

(3) Grooved-gate (or elevated source and drain) MOSFETs This structure was proposed mainly for reduction of the sub-micrometer ULSI device parasitic resistance. The key technology is to elevate the source and drain region on the Si substrate a little higher than the channel plane so that for the channel, the S/D

junctions are still kept shallow (reduced by scaling) enough to maintain low SCE and DIBL effects, and the thicker Si layer of source and drain assures low S/D sheet resistance and leads to reduced resistance Ohmic contact.

1.2.3.2 New Materials for CMOS

Modern CMOS structure generally consists of the following materials: M-poly Si, O-SiO_2, S- (100) Si, and M-Al or Cu. With nano-CMOS, in order to extend Moore's Law further, in recent years, new materials have been widely investigated for replacements[16].

(1) High-K gate dielectrics and low-K insulating materials When the thickness of gate dielectrics of nano-MOSFETs is scaled down to several nanometers, even less than 1 nm, the tunneling gate current becomes so large that the ULSI off-state chip power, P_{off}, can be more than the value limited by chip heat dissipation ability and restricts further scaling. If the gate SiO_2 is replaced by a kind of high-K (with dielectric constant higher than that of SiO_2) dielectrics, one can make the layer thicker, which reduces the tunnel leakage distinctively without degradation on the controllability to the channel carriers. There are some conditions for these high-K materials, such as thermal-mechanical compatibility to the MOS system. To form low interface state density with silicon substrate, etc., SiON and HfO_2[17, 18] are now used practically in labs; others are under investigation.

In order to reduce the parasitic capacitance between devices and interconnects of ULSI, the conventional SiO_2 insulator layer is also expected to be replaced by other suitable low-K material. This would be discussed in Section 1.2.4.

(2) Strained-Si and GeSi substrate The channel carrier mobility is determined by carrier effective mass m^* in the substrate layer. Crystal strain can lead to energy band distortion, resulting in the effective mass change. For Si NMOSFETs, if m^* parallel to the direction of channel length becomes less, electron mobility will increase and the device driving power can be enhanced. Crystal strain can split the degeneracy of Si valance bands of light and heavy holes. If the light one is lifted up, then the light hole will dominate in channel conduction and the PMOSFET driving power can be increased. Experiments show that the existence of tensile strain is beneficial to NMOSFETs and compressive to PMOSFETs. The improvement of CMOS circuit performance by about 15% has been reported by the use of this technique [19].

The energy band structure of Ge_xSi_{1-x} changes from Si-like to Ge-like with the increase of the Ge percentage x. Since the carrier mobility of Ge is much larger than that of Si, it is expected that the CMOS ULSI performance would have a big improvement if Si substrate is replaced by an appropriated Ge_xSi_{1-x} film.

(3) Metal Gate For nano-MOSFETs, there is also a technical challenge to conventional poly-Si gate technology. The main reasons are: ① The doping impurity intensity in Si is limited by the saturated solid solubility, and the impurity (such

as boron in Si) concentration can be reduced significantly by impurity segregation at the poly-Si and SiO_2 interface. Therefore, decrease of the poly-Si gate sheet resistance by increasing the doping level is limited. Furthermore, as the gate oxide thickness is reduced to the level of nanometers, the high concentration boron in the poly gate can diffuse across the ultra thin insulator into the channel region and make it very difficult to control the PMOSFET V_T. ② Nano-MOSFETs generally require small value of V_T it is difficult to accurately adjust the Fermi level of poly-Si gate to suit low-valued V_T of both N and PMOSFETs. Metal electrical conductivity is much higher than any possibly doped poly-Si, and so replacement of poly-Si by metal layer as gate material is prospective. Furthermore, we can use metals with different work functions to satisfy the low V_T requirements separately for N and P MOS. Tungsten, titanium, tantalum, ruthenium, and their silicides as well as some high-conductive multilayer systems have been investigated extensively for this purpose. Some nitrides with high electrical conductivity have also been investigated as possible candidates[16]. For example, TiN not only has quite low resistivity but also has work function of 4.6 eV, which is suitable for gate material for 'near-intrinsic' N as well as PMOSFETs. In this case, the values of both N and PMOSFETs V_T can be scaled down to distinctively low levels, and as mentioned above, the harmful doping fluctuation effect might be avoided.

(4) New ohmic contact material system   Generally speaking, the sum of all parasitic resistances, including the *D*/*S* layer sheet resistance and the *D*/*S* contact resistance, should be less than one-tenth of the intrinsic device resistance. Since the *S* and *D* contact area is reduced to be very small in a nano-CMOS, the contact resistance can be a dominative factor to degrade the device performance[20]. Accepting new contact structures and using suitable new contact material systems are again the ways for solving this problem[21, 22].

1.2.4 High-Performance ULSI Interconnection

Interconnects form another important element of an electronic integrated system. For nanometer ULSI, interconnection plays an even more important role in determining ULSI chip performance[23, 24].

Resistance of an interconnect wire with length l and cross section A is given by

$$R = \rho \frac{l}{A} \tag{1.2}$$

The parasitic capacitance is

$$C = K_{\mathrm{i}} \in_0 \frac{A}{d_{\mathrm{i}}} \tag{1.3}$$

where ρ is the resistivity of the metal, K_{i} the relative permittivity of the dielectric layer, and d_{i} the equivalent thickness of the dielectrics. From Eq. (1.2) and Eq. (1.3), we see that resistance R is scaled up (when ρ is constant) linearly during scaling and the parasitic capacitance C (K_i is a constant) is scaled down linearly. Thus, by scaling, the RC delay of the interconnection will be kept constant, though the circuit 'intrinsic' delay is improved from one generation to the next. This means that the parasitic delay due to interconnection plays a more and more important role in determining nanoscaled ULSI circuit performance. Furthermore, the chip area and the longest effective length l_G of global interconnect of a ULSI chip (such as a CPU) increase much faster in every new generation than what is expected by normal scaling. Therefore, the RC delay due to global interconnect is scaling up practically. Hence the sheet resistance and RC delay problems are much more serious for chip global interconnections than for local interconnections. High interconnect resistance not only affects the circuit's speed but also produces a series of harmful effects such as power path voltage drop, signal cross talking, and additional power dissipation.

In order to overcome interconnect parasitic problems, a series of techniques have been adopted, which are discussed below. ① Multiple metal layer integration Up to nine interconnection layers are being used in modern advanced ULSI chips; ② New materials Use of metal of lower resistivity to replace conventional interconnection material, such as using Cu to replace Al; ③ Design and technology optimizations of metal-insulator system for different interconnect layers Thickness, width of leads and insulator layers, separation between metal and dielectric layers together with the plugs, and the contact technology should be carefully optimized; ④ Circuit design and package measures New circuit and system design strategies such as distributed power feeding, and synchronized and non-synchronized signal processing have been adopted to prevent the corresponding effects. Meanwhile, new package techniques such as flip chip and ball array package are used to reduce the global interconnect length.

In order to overcome the development bottleneck of ULSI interconnection, a series of new and revolutionary technologies have been suggested, such as: ① optical interconnection[25], ② RF interconnection[26], and ③ 3D integration[27, 28].

1.3 Non-CMOS Nanoelectronic Devices

Determined by basic device physics, CMOS feature size scaling down finally has its limitation. According to ITRS and as predicted by device physics investigation, it will occur by 2020, when the smallest physical channel length would reach several nanometers, electronic equivalent thickness of gate oxide, $T_{ox,equ}$ would be less than 1 nm, the minimum gate delay would be less than 10 ps, and the integration density would reach billions devices per chip. The room for CMOS microelectronics progress is not very large now, but the speed of progress is still very fast, and so the technical limit is likely to be reached soon. However, in spite of its rapid progress, modern electronics is still unable to satisfy the urgent of information processing such as high speed, low power dissipation, and high density integration. Starting from the last decade, people have been paying more attention toward developing new non-MOSFET devices. These devices, still working as binary switches but with different working mechanisms, are expected to have much better performance over that of ultimate CMOSFETS. Most of them work on the basis of quantum mechanical effects and generally in nanoscale dimension, and thus they are frequently called quantum devices or nanodevices. The aim is to overcome the limiting barrier of MOSFETs to obtain the continuing improvement of ULSI performances with the limited allowable chip power dissipation. The principles of these emerging devices are briefly introduced in this section.

1.3.1 Quantum-Resonant Tunneling Devices

In Fig. 1.5, the energy band diagram of a double-barrier single-well quantum system made of compound semiconductor layers (GaAs/AlAs/GaAs/AlAs/GaAs) and the corresponding electron tunneling probability energy spectra are demonstrated. The electron tunneling probability (here taken as transmission coefficient) is calculated according to the quantum mechanical principle[29].

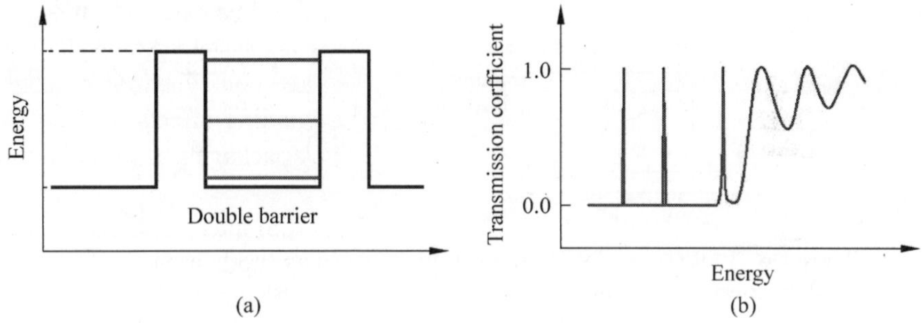

Figure 1.5[29] (a) energy band diagram of a single-well double-barrier quantum system, (b) quantum tunneling probability as function of energy (see color figure at the end of this book)

Quantum mechanics indicates that contrary to classical mechanics, when the energy barrier is thin enough (comparable to the electron wave length) and not very large in height, incident electrons with energy well below the barrier still have a probability to tunnel through it. The Fig. 1.5(b) shows that the transmission coefficient (TC) through the double barrier layer is quantized and the spectral lines broaden with the incident electron energy. Moreover, when the energy of the incident electron is near or even a little higher than the barrier height, the value of TC is not exactly equal to 1 as expected classically, but oscillates (see Fig. 1.5(b)) and finally approaches 1, showing the obvious wave character.

(1) Resonant tunneling diode (RTD) Figure 1.6(a) illustrates the structure of an RTD[30]. The energy band structure shown here is same as that of Fig. 1.5(a), but two Ohmic contacts are made on both barrier sides and current that can flow as a voltage drop is applied between the source and drain electrodes. As the left side (source) is biased negatively, the incidence electron energy increases, and with the bias increase, it gradually rises to match the first resonant level, leading to a rapid current increase. The current decreases quickly as the bias increases further because of the resonance disappearance. Thus, a peaked current versus voltage characteristic curve is produced as shown in Fig. 1.6(b). The existence of negative differential resistance (NDR) of the structure is used to form a type of new device, called RTD.

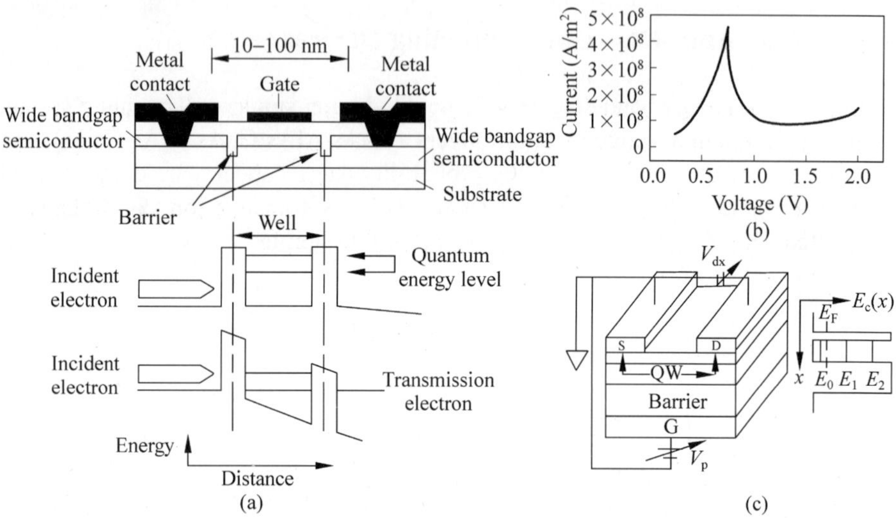

Figure 1.6[30] RTD and RTT: (a) RTD structure and its energy band diagram, (b) NDR Effect in RTD, and (c) Resonant tunneling transistor (RTT)

It is evident that by using NDR, one can form very fast two-level digital switches and also circuits for very high frequency oscillators. It is worthy to mention the important difference between RTDs and Esaki diodes: the tunneling effect of an Esaki diode is based on very high doping concentration of a p-n junction that leads to the increase of junction capacitance and thus restricts the device speed. Contrarily, the NDR of an RTD is mainly determined by the barrier widths and heights, which can be optimized by selection of system materials for the best device performance. The figure of merit of RTD as a binary switch is mainly determined by its peak to valley current ratio (PVR) and the device parasitic capacitance. RTDs made of Ⅲ–Ⅴ semiconductors with very high speed have already been used practically. However, silicon-based RTD requires further investigation to improve its PVR.

(2) Resonant tunneling transistor (RTT) RTD is a 2D device and there is no amplification during signal transmission. In order to get amplification, a third control electrode is added to form the RTT. The control gate electrode can be placed under the well layer (see Fig. 1.6(c)). The well potential (thus the resonant energy level in RTT) is controlled by applied voltage of the third (gate) electrode. Consequently, the drain to source current with definite S/D voltage is regulated by the gate voltage, forming a transistor.

(3) Monostable bistable logic element (MOBILE) Using RTD to realize some composite circuit functioning devices has been noticed by many researchers[31, 32]. For example, a single-well double-barrier structure controlled by two face-to-face gates can be regarded as a couple of RTTs connected in series. This unit performs as a SRAM cell. It is easy to understand that with such kind of functional devices, one can earn benefits in the chip area, delay time, as well as power reduction. Drawn in the center of Fig. 1.7(a) is a schematic diagram of two serially connected identical RTDs, one taken as the load and the other as the driver. Figures 1.7(a), (b), (c) illustrate the electrical $I \sim V$ characteristics and potential energy of this combined element versus the bias voltage for three different cases: $V_{bias} < 2Vp$,

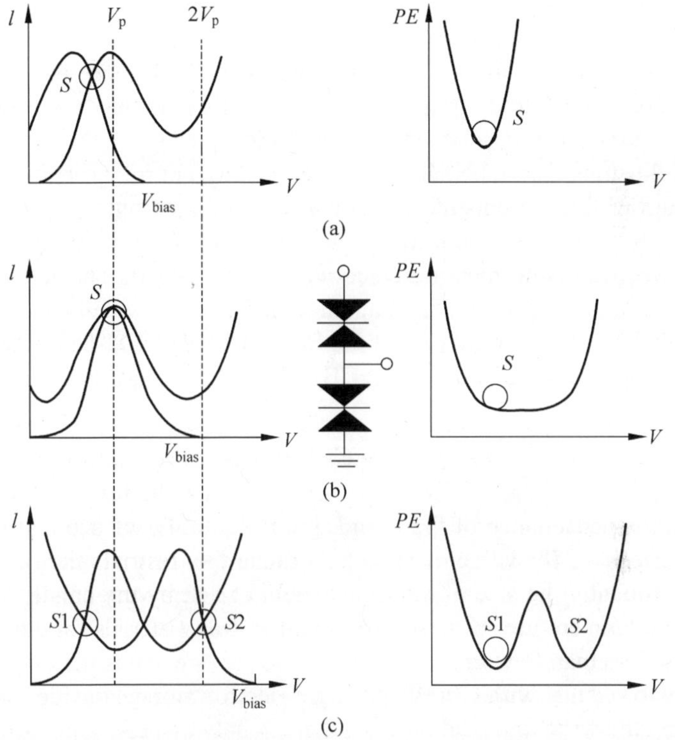

Figure 1.7[31–32] MOBILE, working principle: (a) $V_{bias} < 2V_p$—monostable, (b) $V_{bias} = 2Vp$—transition, (c) $V_{bias} > 2Vp$—bi-stable

$V_{bias} = 2Vp$, and $V_{bias} > 2Vp$. We see that these three cases correspond to three different states of the circuit: mono-stable (Fig. 1.7(a)), meta-monostable (transition state) (Fig. 1.7(b)), and bi-stable state (Fig. 1.7(c)). The structure so formed is called mono-bi-stable logic element (MOBILE). If we take the element of bi-stable state as a binary switch, but use the V_{bias} very near $2V_p$, then the barrier height of transition from '0' to '1' and vice versa, i.e., the switching energy, can be reduced to a small value limited by fundamental physics (such as thermal dynamics and quantum mechanics). MOBILE is quite a promising structure for the construction of binary switch circuits with critically small switching energy and high speed.

1.3.2 Single Electron Transistor

Given that an electrically isolated nanosize metal or semiconductor particle is placed on a semiconductor substrate, a so-called Coulomb Island is formed. As an 'artificial atom' (a quantum system), the Coulomb island is accompanied by an energy spectra. An energy barrier exists to resist electron entry into the energy well. When the electron energy is elevated enough, it can be injected into the well and it would get trapped at the lowest quantum energy level. However, when one electron is trapped, due to Coulomb repulsive force there is a tendency to repel the next new electrons from entering, or strictly speaking, the energy barrier height around the particle is raised. This effect is called Coulomb blockade[33−35]. Figure 1.8 illustrates the schematic energy band diagram for explaining the effect. The quantum well represents the electron affinity of the Coulomb island, and the two energy barriers are produced by the two dielectric thin layers, which are placed between the side metallic electrode and the island. The left part shows how an electron is trapped by tunneling through the barrier when the left electrode is negatively biased. The right part of the figure shows the raised barrier when an electron is trapped (Coulomb blockade (CB) effect). CB energy can be expressed as

$$W_C = \frac{1}{2}CV^2 = \frac{e^2}{2C} \tag{1.4}$$

where C is the capacitance of the island. From Eq. (1.4), we see that in order to let CB be effective, W_C value must be larger than the thermal energy K_BT. Thus, C and consequently the size of the island should be kept very small for practical use. At room temperature, C must be as small as 1 aF ($\sim 10^{-18}$F) and the diameter of the island less than few nm.

It is easy to see that with CB effect, single electron storage devices can be built. Since during the write and read process, there is only one electron concerned, the single electron transistor memory can work with high speed and low power dissipation. If a third electrode is added (see Fig. 1.9(a)) to change the well potential,

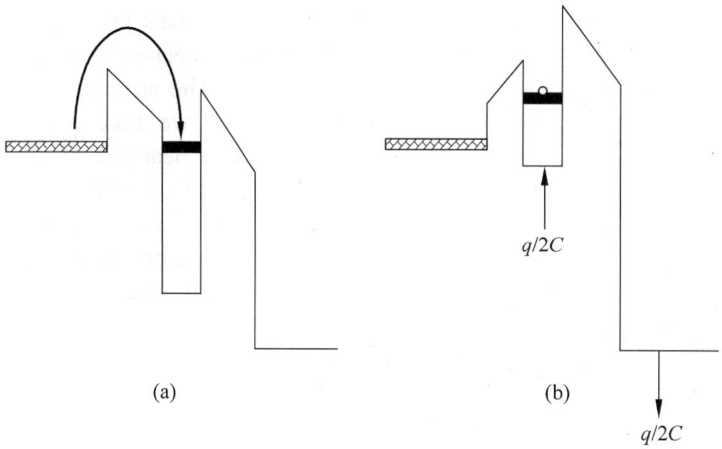

Figure 1.8 Coulomb blockade: (a) electron filling, (b) coulomb blockade

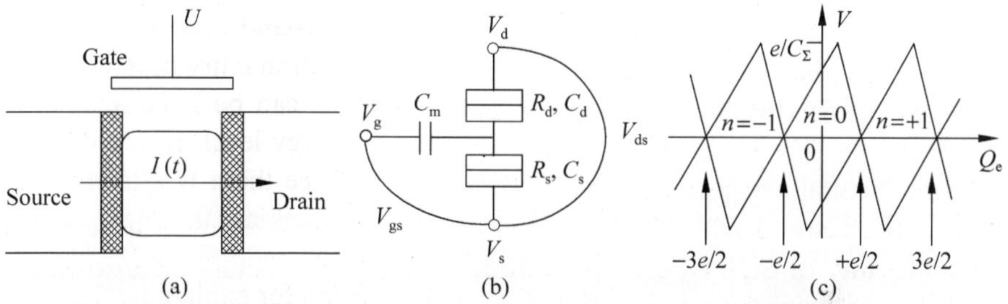

Figure 1.9 (a) Structure of a single electron transistor, (b) equivalent circuit, (c) the island voltage V vs. electric charge Q determined by both source and drain tunneling junction so that only some quantized (in e) charge can exist in coulomb island

then the transition of the electron from source to drain can be controlled and a kind of new transistor, called single electron transistor, is formed. Owing to the small device size, the integration density of ULSI based on single electron devices can obviously be much higher than that of conventional ULSI. Very small switching delay time and switching energy can also be expected in the case of single electron transistor based ULSIs. The delay time can be estimated by

$$\tau_{\mathrm{d}} = RC \tag{1.5}$$

where R is the equivalent resistance of tunneling and can be taken as:

$$R = \frac{h}{e^2} = 25.8\ \mathrm{K}\cdot\Omega \tag{1.6}$$

If we take C equal to 1 aF, then $\tau_{\mathrm{d}} \approx 2.6\times10^{-14}$ sec. Meanwhile, the minimum switching energy:

$$E_{\mathrm{b}} = P_{\mathrm{d}}\tau_{\mathrm{d}} = \left(I^2 R\right)\tau_{\mathrm{d}} = \frac{e^2}{\tau_{\mathrm{d}}} R \approx 6\times10^{-20}\ \mathrm{J} \tag{1.7}$$

In comparison with the corresponding ultimate conventional CMOS at room temperature ($\tau_{\mathrm{d}} \sim 1$ ps and $E_{\mathrm{b}} \sim 10^{-18}$ J), we see that the breakthrough is quite remarkable.

Figure 1.9(a) is a schematic diagram of single electron (or few electrons) transistor consisting of three electrodes, three dielectric layers, and a quantum dot in the middle. Two of the dielectric films are ultra thin (less than 1 nm), which serve as tunneling barrier layer of source and drain. The top dielectric layer with thickness of conventional gate oxide of nanodevices serves as the gate insulator. Figure 1.9(b) illustrates the equivalent circuit of the biased device, where C_{d} (C_{s}) is the capacitance of the tunnel junction together with the quantum dot (island), C_{m} the common gate capacitance, and R_{d} (R_{s}) are parasitic resistances. The two-touched rectangular symbol represents the tunneling junction.

Instead of electron drift in conventional MOSFET, the transportation in single electron transistor (SET) is performed by electron tunneling ('jumping') one after another from source to the island and then to drain, as shown in Fig. 1.9(c). Due to CB, the entrance of the next electron is forbidden before the former one is shifted out. Based on this mechanism, the so-called CB oscillation has been predicted and experimentally observed[35, 36].

A single electron RAM of megabits scale was reported[37] many years ago. The main difficulty of SET type ULSI realization is in manufacture: nanostructures fabrication and their integration. With larger island size, the device has to work at lower temperature. Many methods have been proposed for room temperature SETs fabrication[38]. A series of investigations on digital circuits based on SETs have been proposed in literatures[39, 40].

1.3.3 Carbon NanoTubes (CNT) Electronics

A single wall (SW) carbon nanotube[41] is a graphite sheet rolled in seamless nanocylinder of about 1 – 10 nm in diameter and several to hundred μm in length. The terminal ends of a CNT can be open or with semi-C_{60} sphere. Figure 1.10(a) illustrates the molecular structure of graphene, a 'planar graphite crystal'. A graphene sheet can be rolled into tubes with some definite axes, ($\boldsymbol{C}_h$), so that every carbon atom can be exactly bonded covalently with its four nearest neighbors, leading the tube structure to be seamless and in stable state. The condition for CNTs formation is:

$$\boldsymbol{C}_h = n\boldsymbol{a}_1 + m\boldsymbol{a}_2 \tag{1.8}$$

where $\boldsymbol{a}_1, \boldsymbol{a}_2$ are two basic cell vectors of graphene, and n and m are positive integers. Two types of CNT structures formed with different n and m are shown in Fig. 1.10(b): when n or m is 0, the structure is zigzag type; and when $n=m$, it is arm-chair type.

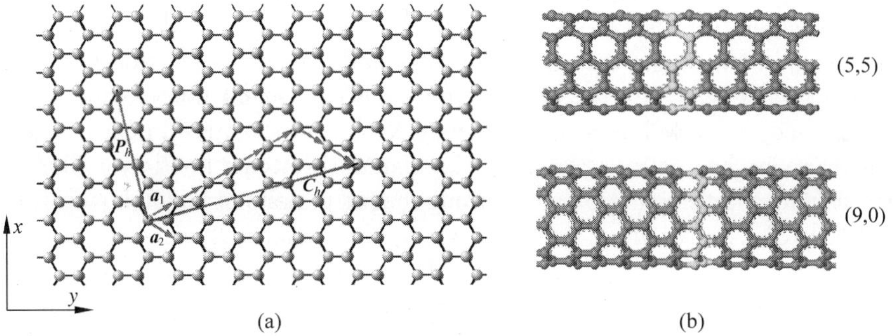

Figure 1.10[41] (a) Structure of graphene, (b) Two different CNT structures (see color figure at the end of this book)

With known crystal molecular structure, the energy band structure of CNT can be calculated[42]. Shown in Fig. 1.11 are energy diagrams with two typical CNT structures: (a) for $\boldsymbol{C}_h=(3,3)$ and (b) for $\boldsymbol{C}_h=(4,2)$. Since there is no energy gap in case (a), (3,3), the CNT is metal, while in case (b), an obvious forbidden band exists, thus the (4,2) CNT is a semiconductor. Moreover, as can be seen in the E versus k curve near the energy band edge (k: electron momentum vector in the tube axis direction), the dependence of E on k is nearly linear and the slope is rather sharp.

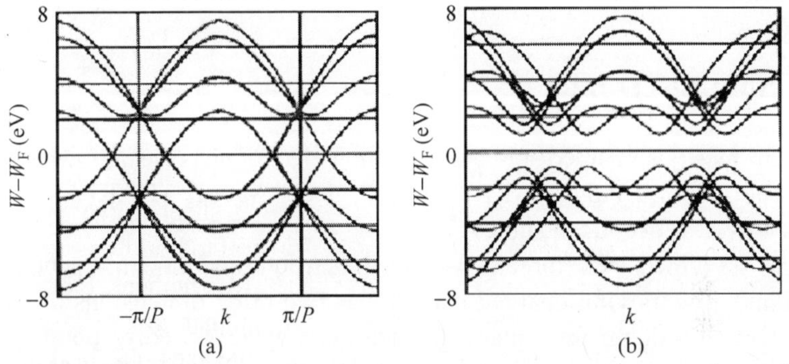

Figure 1.11 Typical energy diagram of two types of CNT[42]: (a) metal, (b) semiconductor

It indicates that electrons in a CNT may have large velocity independent of their thermal energy. Electronically, CNT is a kind of natural (nano) quantum-wire (1D system). Due to quantum confinement, the electron scattering probability is greatly reduced in comparison with those of the 2D and 3D cases. Hence, with CNT, one can expect to get much larger electron drift mobility and it can be even easier to achieve ballistic transportation.

Different CNT manufacturing methods have been reported[43, 44], including high voltage arc discharge, laser-ablation, and chemical vaporization deposition (CVD). High-energy carbon atoms are deposited on the surface of a cooled target with some transition metal elements, such as Ni or Co as catalyst. In early years, it was difficult to obtain single type CNTs (such as metal or semiconductor, multi-wall or single-wall). Now, it is possible to grow a CNT in definite orientations and on defined location, as well as semiconductor CNTs of N or P types. In 2001 [45], IBM researchers by alternative ablation of C_{60} and Ni forming a multilayer film, and then heating the film at 950℃ in a strong magnetic field, obtained a single-wall CNT (SWCNT) stick array with micrometer length and approximately the same diameter ($\phi \approx 50$ nm). Every stick consists of thousands of SWCNTs.

CNT has great potential for future applications to make various information processing devices, such as nanosensors and actuators, display devices, as well as digital switches and LSI interconnects. Thus, a new scientific field called carbon nanotube electronics[41] has been established.

CNTs are used for digital switching devices of integrated circuits. Besides the large carrier mobility that leads to great enhancement of the device trans-conductance and hence the circuit speed, CNTs have many other advantages such as high breakdown electric field strength (10^8 V/cm, much higher than that of Si) and higher thermal conductivity. The stronger gate control ability of carbon nanotube field effect transistor (CNTFET) over that of conventional CMOSFET is meaningful for reducing many second-order effects of CMOS and hence to overcome the speed limit. However, the integration of CNT devices onto useful LSI chips is still a very difficult problem today.

1.3.4 Spin Electronics

Spin electronics (also named spin transportation electronics) research, which started with a The Defense Advanced Research Projects Agency (DARPA) project in 1994, is now a well-noticed subject[46].

Besides six dimensions (three real-space dimensions and three momentum-space dimensions), any moving charged particle has two other dimensions of freedom: spin up and spin down. In a magnetic field, energy levels corresponding to the two differently oriented spins split, which makes electrons with different spins separable. Thus, we get a new freedom to control the electron movement by both electric and magnetic fields and to develop new storage and information processing devices.

(1) GMR and TMR Shown in Fig. 1.12(a) is a metal multilayer system consisting of ferromagnetic, non-ferromagnetic, and anti-ferromagnetic metallic thin films. To form this structure as a resistor, two types of electric contact structure

can be made: in the first, contact electrodes are placed on upper and bottom sides of the film system, while in the second, they are placed on the left and right sides. According to the current flow direction, perpendicular to or in parallel with the device plane, the device (resistor) is called giant magnetic resistance (GMR) of current perpendicular to plane (CPP) or current in plane (CIP) type. Magnetic resistance is defined as the ratio of device resistance change with the reversed magnetic field direction (perpendicular to the layer surface) to its original resistance, $\Delta R / R$. Figure 1.12(b) and Fig. 1.12(c) explain the mechanism of GMR[47]. When the magnetization direction of the bottom ferromagnetic layer is reversed by the outside magnetic field, that of the upper one (its magnetization direction is clamped by the antimagnetic layer) remains unchanged, and the electron spin directions of bottom and upper ferromagnetic (FM) films are altered from parallel to anti-parallel or vice versa. Figure 1.12(b) illustrates the energy band split by spin polarization and the corresponding electron populations. Transition of conducting electrons from one region to the other is free in the case of parallel spins (upper figure), but difficult in anti-parallel case. Figure 1.12(c) shows that considerable scattering occurs in spin anti-parallel case (upper) and less scattering in spin parallel case (lower). This mechanism leads to the big resistance difference of the two cases and thus to GMR effect.

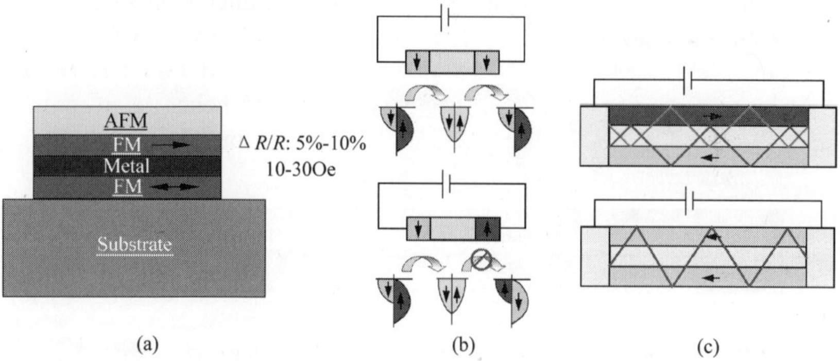

Figure 1.12 GMR[47]: (a) structure, (b) energy band structure and electron population, (c) high resistive and low resistive states (see color figure at the end of this book)

Conventional magnetic resistance was discovered in anisotropic semiconductor crystals, such as Ge and Si. It is rather small. The above-described magnetic resistance resulting from electron spins is as large as 5% – 10% has been observed and hence is named 'Giant Magnetic Resistance'. Used as magnetic sensors, GMRs[48] find applications in many fields, such as storage read header and earth magnetic field monitor. By replacing the middle non-magnetic conductor layer of the CPP GMR structure with an ultra-thin insulating film, we get a new type of device structure called tunnel magnetic resistance (TMR)[49] (see Fig. 1.13(a)). In TMR, the electrons of the bottom FM layer can transmit into the upper FM layer by quantum resonant tunneling when spins are in parallel and energy levels are in resonance, leading to a low resistance. The resistance is large when spins are anti-parallel. Obviously, the magnetic resistance of TMR can be much greater than that of the above-described GMR. In TMR experiments, a value of $\Delta R/R$ as large as 15% has been reported and theoretically even up to 50% is expected. In GMR and TMR, the FM to non-FM junction 'allows' only electrons with definite direction of spin polarization to pass through, resulting in a detectable signal, but does not allow the anti-parallel spin electrons to pass and result in any signal. Hence, this junction forms a kind of electron spin valve or spin filter.

(2) MRAM Since the polarization of ferromagnetic material as well as the polarization of conductive electron spins in it has hysteresis character, the electron spin signal can be stored in an FM film. The signals '0' and '1' presented by different directions of electron spin can be changed by altering the polarity of the outside magnetic field. Moreover, it is easy to detect the electron spin direction with a spin valve. Therefore, by the use of a structure like TMR, it is easy to construct a new type of RAM, named magnetic random access memory (MRAM). Figure 1.13(b) illustrates the schematic structure of an MRAM[49, 50]. As shown in the figure, the write process is performed by an electric current with two opposite directions for '0' or '1' signals and the spin valve detects the digit signal correspondingly. MRAM has advantages of high speed (both of write and read), low power dissipation, and possible high integration density. More importantly, the MRAM is nonvolatile.

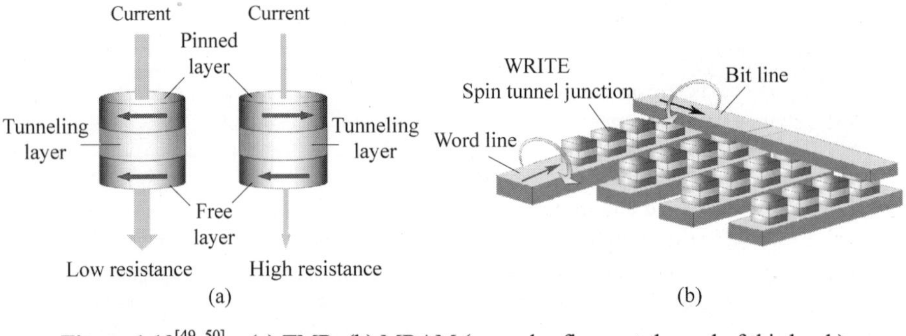

Figure 1.13[49, 50] (a) TMR, (b) MRAM (see color figure at the end of this book)

(3) Spin FET Figure 1.14(a) and (b) show the structure of an spin FET proposed by Datta and Das[51] in 1990. An engineered InAlAs/InGaAs film system forms a heterojunction structure, with a 2DEG layer (functioning as the conductive channel) on the InGaAs side of the interface. The schottky junction is taken as the gate electrode and the ferromagnetic metal/semiconductor junctions function as source and drain. The source junction injects spin polarized electrons into the channel, while the drain junction functions as a spin valve to detect the spin polarization of electrons from source junction. However, it will be shown that in

the system with the Rashba and Dresselhaus coupling effects, the interplay between these effects strongly suppresses the DP spin relaxation for spin helix state[52].

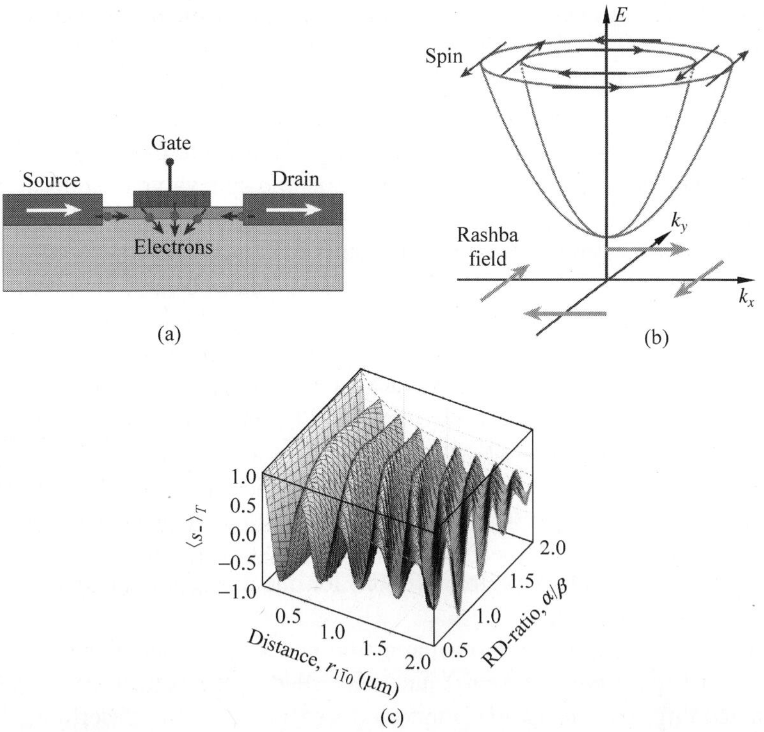

Figure 1.14[51,52] (a) The spin-FET conceived by Datta and Das is based on a semiconductor heterostructure. Electrons (red) injected from the source flow along the indium-arsenide channel (green) and are detected at the drain. The gate voltage produces an electric field in the growth direction of the heterostructure, which leads to a magnetic field known as the Rashba field. Since this field is perpendicular to both the electric field and the transport direction, the spin of the injected electron can precess. The gate voltage on the transistor controls the Rashba field, thereby modulating the current. (b) The energy of the electrons as a function of momentum, *k*. The Rashba field (green) splits the electrons in the conduction band into two sub-bands that are distinguished by the orientation of their spins. For a give field direction, the two spin-states have slightly different momenta. (c) Spin polarization component $\langle s_- \rangle_T$, with respect to source-drain distance r_{110}, and RD-ratio calculated at Eds = 3.0 kV/cm. (see color figure at the end of this book)

An SFET is a three-terminal device. Its drain current can be controlled not only by the electrical bias of each electrode, but also the magnetization direction of the drain and source electrode. From Fig. 1.14(c), we see that in an SFET, strong negative resistance may occur, which might be used for building high-speed switches. Moreover, since the magnetic polarization directions of both source and drain (spin-valve) can be changed by the polarity of the DC magnetic field, the device characteristics are programmable after its fabrication. This means with SFETs, the realization of programmable ULSI chips is principally possible.

Many years have passed since the suggestion by Datta and Das and considerable attention has been paid toward the development of SFETs. However, many theoretical and technical problems such as spin injection [53] and implementation technology still remain unresolved.

1.3.5 Superconductor Electronics

Superconductor electronics is strongly competitive to Si electronics especially in high-speed application areas. Due to the need for high-cost, low-temperature environment, the development of superconductor electronics once had slowed down in 80 s of last century in comparison with Si ICs. However, in recent two decades, because of Si microelectronics quickly approaching its performance limit, a lot of attention has been paid to this field again, especially to the superconducting quantum interference device (SQUID) and its applications[54, 55]. The use of SQUID to construct ultra-high speed (over that of Si limit) digital integrated circuits and to form very sensitive sensors is extraordinarily worthy of notice. Moreover, the QME of superconductor micro circuits has been found useful to form a kind of quantum bit (qubit) for quantum computation.

(1) Josephson Junction

By implementing a very thin insulator film between two superconductor layers, we can construct a type of tunnel junction called Josephson junction. A circuit loop containing one or serially connected two or more Josephson junctions is called Josephson loop.

According to Bardeen-Cooper-Schrieffer (BCS) theory, the charge carriers in a superconductor are Cooper pairs[56] of -2e charge. Each Cooper pair can be described by a planar quantum wave of

$$\psi(r,t)=|\psi|\exp[\mathrm{i}\varphi(r,t)] \tag{1.9}$$

where φ is the wave phase. The electric current transportation in a superconductor is realized by the propagation of Cooper pair waves. The phase drop at a Josephson junction is:

$$\phi=\varphi_1-\varphi_2 \tag{1.10}$$

where φ_1 and φ_2 are φs at each junction side. From the current continuity and Cooper pair wave property, it is easy to see that the current circulating in a Josephson loop without voltage drop $V=0$ is:

$$I=I_C\sin\phi_0 \tag{1.11}$$

where I_C is a specific current of the superconductor, over which the superconductor goes to its normal conduction state, and ϕ_0 is ϕ with $V=0$.

Equation (1.11) indicates that under the condition of superconduction, i.e., $T<T_C$ (T_C: Curie temperature), and the applied voltage $V=0$, a direct current of $I(-I_C \leqslant I \leqslant +I_C)$ can steadily circulate in a Josephson loop without any energy dissipation. This effect is called direct current Josephson Effect. When a definite voltage V is applied, the circulating current becomes alternative with frequency ω_j represented as:

$$I = I_C \sin \omega_j t \tag{1.12}$$

$$\omega_j \equiv 2\pi V / \Phi_0 \tag{1.13}$$

where Φ_0 is a universal constant called magnetic flux quantum and

$$\Phi_0 \equiv \frac{h}{2e} \tag{1.14}$$

This is called alternative current Josephson Effect. Furthermore, as the result of specific magnetic property (absolutely anti-magnetic) of the superconductor and the quantum mechanical property of the Cooper pair, it is easy to prove that the magnetic flux through any superconducting loop should be equal to:

$$\Phi = \left(n + \frac{1}{2}\right)\Phi_0 \tag{1.15}$$

$$\frac{\mathrm{d}\Phi}{\mathrm{d}t} = n\Phi_0 \quad (n=0, 1, 2, 3, \ldots) \tag{1.16}$$

where n is the quantum number.

Both direct and alternative current Josephson Effects are macroscopic in nature reflecting the microscopic interference property of Cooper pair waves.

(2) Superconductor Quantum Interference Device (SQUID)

A device based on the macroscopic interference effect of superconducting Josephson junction is called a superconductor quantum interference device (SQUID). SQUIDs are used in many fields: signal storage, sensor and digital logic circuit, etc[57]. Shown in Fig. 1.15(a) is the equivalent circuit of a SQUID with one Josephson junction, while (b) and (c) represent its direct voltage-ampere characteristics with and without hysteresis. In Fig. 1.15 (a), the conductance G(V) is introduced to reflect the existence of resistive conductance when the conductor is in its non-superconducting state ($I>I_C$). At $V=0$, $I=0$ or any of $I \leqslant I_C$, which is kept unchanged until $V=V_C$, because of no resistance of the superconductor. When V reaches a critical value of $V_C = \dfrac{\Delta}{e}$ (2Δ: Cooper pair separation energy), the conductor enters its normal resistive state and the $I{\sim}V$ characteristic starts to obey Ohm's law. When the applied voltage V drops from non-superconducting state ($I > I_C$), if the circuit damping is small, the current will descend to the original value as $V=0$, following the original voltage-ampere curve; if not, after descending to I_C, the current will remain unchanged ($=I_C$) with V until $V=0$. In the latter case, hysteresis of $I \sim V$ curve occurs, as shown in Fig. 1.15(b). Theory predicts that the condition of no hysteresis is the damping constant $\beta_C < 0.8$ with

$$\beta_C = 2eR^2 C I_C / \hbar \tag{1.17}$$

where C is the junction capacitance, and R is the resistance of the conductor in its normal state.

From the $I \sim V$ characteristic shown above, it is obvious that with SQUIDs, one can form both memories and digital logic devices.

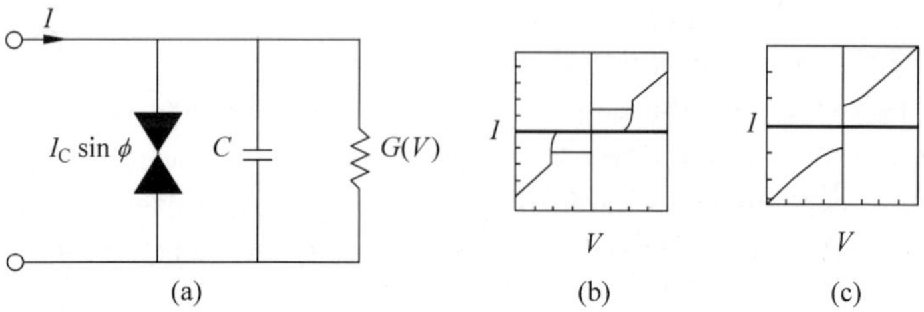

Figure 1.15 (a) equivalent circuit and (b, c) voltage-ampere characteristics of SQUID

Taking the junction area $\approx 10\ \mu m^2$, dielectric constant and film thickness of tunnel layer as 10 nm and 2 nm respectively, we have $C \approx 0.5$ pF. For an Nb/Al_2O_3/Nb system, the maximum current density Jcmax $\approx 1000\ A/cm^2$ and $2\Delta/e = 1.28$ mV. Thus, the resultant minimum reduced resistance $R_n \approx 13\ \Omega$ (from $I_{cmax} R_n = 2\Delta/e$). Therefore, in this 'intrinsic' case, $\beta_C > 0.8$ and in order to work in non-hysteresis regime, a smaller resistor of 6 Ω is shunted. As a result, the minimum delay time less than 1 ps is obtainable in logic circuits based on SQUID. Further reduction of junction area and usage of materials with larger Δ will make superconductor logic circuits with much higher speed possible. Since the minimum magnetic flux change on a superconductor circuit loop from one state to the other is one magnetic flux quantum, it is easy to estimate that the minimum switching energy based on SQUID is less then 2×10^{-19} J. Hence, in view of speed and energy, superconductor electronics is highly competitive to CMOS-based electronics.

(3) RSFQ

Different superconductor logic circuits have been developed and practically used. An Nb-based VLSI circuit working at 4.2 K with speed of 200 GHz has been reported. Circuits based on NbN can work at higher temperatures. With high T_c superconductor such as YBaCuO, circuits work at temperature of 20 K with integration of 100 gates have been published.

A big breakthrough in superconductor digital electronics is the invention of rapid single flux quantum (RSFQ) logic circuits[58]. The basic idea is to design the circuit parameters, such as self-inductance L of the Josephson loop and mutual inductance M between loops, together with the loop circulating currents so critically that the signal transmission deals only with the change of one single quantum flux in each circuit loop. As mentioned above, with such a design, the circuits can work with very small energy as well as very high speed. An RSFQ logic circuit with speed as high as 770 GHz has been demonstrated[59].

1.3.6 Molecular Electronics

There are two branches of molecular electronics research. One is referred to the film electronics, which involves developing organic molecular elements as devices to perform some circuit functions. Such devices are now used mainly in the area of panel display. The other branch refers to the direct use of single molecular electronic behavior to perform as digital electronic devices. A single organic molecule (or a few of the same molecules) connected by appropriate metal electrodes behaves as an electronic device, with its characteristics determined inherently by the molecular electronic structure. Functional circuits are then implemented with these molecular devices. When the metal (inorganic) is used for integration interconnects, the molecular electronics is called hybrid molecular electronics (HME). Otherwise, if molecular devices are integrated monolithically by self-assembly, then it is called monolithic molecular electronics (MME). The latter concept of molecular electronics was first carried out by Aviram and Ratner[60, 61]. They found that some single organic molecules connected appropriately with metallic electrodes can perform as a p-n junction: one side molecular group behaves as the donor, the other side behaves as the acceptor, and the middle insulation group behaves as the spacer. The size of molecules is generally in the range of nano or sub-nanometers. The electron transfer energy from one molecular site to its neighbors is about $1\ \text{eV} = 1.6 \times 10^{-19}$ J or so, and the corresponding transfer time is about 1 ps. The former is much below the limit value of the switching energy of a conventional CMOSFET at room temperature. The latter is about the same as that of the fastest ultimate MOSFET. Molecular electronic devices can work at room temperature and, quite differently from conventional small devices produced by the 'top-down' process, molecular electronic devices are structurally robust and perfect in nature.

The electrical conduction characteristics in an organic molecule is mainly determined by the electronic bonding structures: it is likely to be a good conductor if the whole molecular chain is bonded with parallel transversal π electrons; otherwise, if there exists any σ electron, perpendicular π electron, or any of insulation group interrupting the chain, it forms a semiconductor or insulator. For example, polyene and polybenzene are good conductors, while alkanes and tetra-methyl-substituted biphenyl are insulators. It is more important that many molecules intrinsically can perform certain functions just like specific circuits. The intrinsic function is determined by the molecular electronic structures. Some examples are shown in Fig. 1.16.

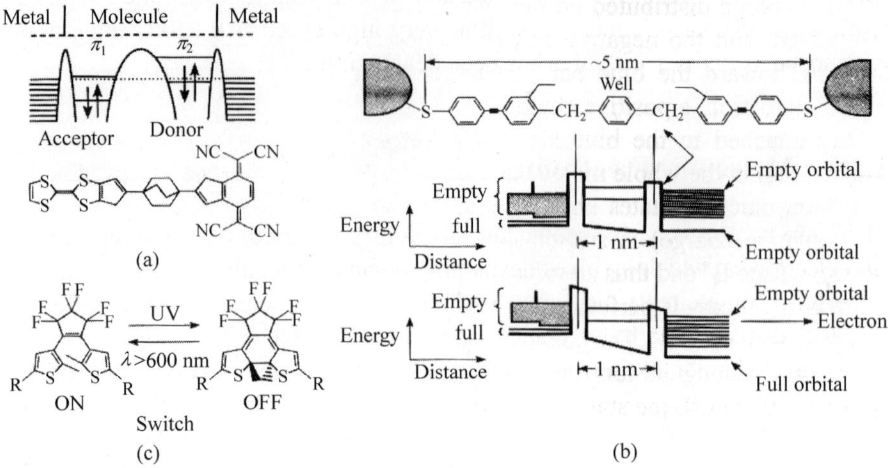

Figure 1.16 Structures and corresponding electronic functions: (a) a rectifier[62], (b) two quantum barrier, one quantum well RTD[63], (c) an optical switch[64]

Figure 1.16(a) illustrates a molecular rectifier proposed by Aviram and Ratner. In order to measure the electronic performance of a single molecule, a metal electrode is placed on its two sides. It is required that the Fermi level of the electrodes should match the free energy level of the outer bonding (π) electron of the molecule. On the right side, the free energy of the π electron is higher than metal Fermi level (E_F), and thus this part behaves as a donor of the device. On the contrary, the free energy of the left side is lower than E_F and it forms the acceptor. The central insulated group is the spacer[62]. The stick-like molecule shown in Fig. 1.16(b) has an energy band structure similar to that of an RTD[63], and thus produces the NDR effect beneficial to form high-speed switches. The molecule shown in Fig. 1.16(c) can be used as an optical switch[64]: when it is irradiated by UV, the structure takes a closed form, and when it is subsequently irradiated by light of wavelength $\lambda = 600$ nm, the structure returns to its open form and vice versa.

There are molecules whose structures can be used for information storage and to make memory devices. Theoretically, any molecular structure has two stable states and these states can be changed from one to another by a trigger signal. Then, the corresponding molecule can be used to form a two-digit (binary) storage element. For example, Rotaxane and Catenane are synthesized ultra-large molecules. Their structures satisfy the requirement of information storage[65]. Shown in Fig. 1.17 is a schematic diagram of Catenane structure for explaining the process of digital signal storage: there are two interlocked molecular loops in the big molecular structure, one is circular and the other is rectangular. The sign '+' at each angle of the rectangular loop indicates that these parts of molecule are charged positively. Although not shown in the figure, there would be the same quantity of negative charge distributed on the site of the circular loop to keep the molecule neutralized, and the negative charge on the circular loop site should be partly polarized toward the blue bar part to form a stable state of the structure A°. During oxidation, a positive charge ($-e^{-}$) is added to the molecule and at first it is mainly attached to the blue site of the tetrathiafulvalene (TTF) loop (orange circle), leading the whole molecule structure to state A^{+}. Since A^{+} is unstable, the TTF loop quickly rotates and the structure turns to B^{+}. As the applied voltage (i.e., positive charge) is subsequently removed, the B^{+} goes to another stable structural state B° and thus an information storage process is completed. In reverse, the rewrite process is performed by applying a negative voltage (charge -e) on the molecule with state B°. The positive charge of the tetracationic cyclophane structure (green gray rectangular loop) is reduced, B° changes to AB^{-}, and after the negative voltage is taken off, the state returns to A°.

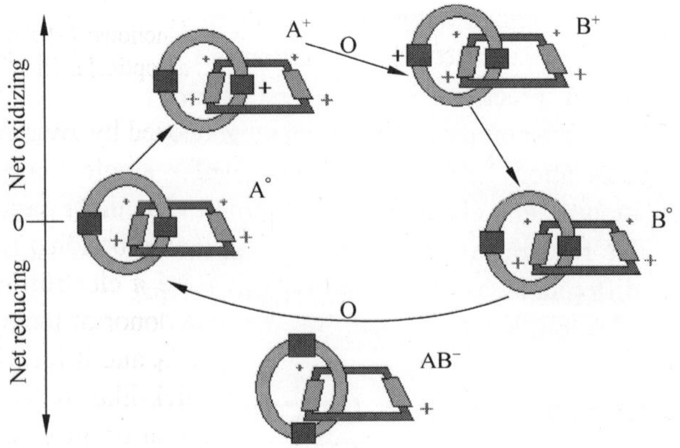

Figure 1.17 The write and rewrite process of binary information using catenane[65] (see color figure at the end of this book)

1.3.7 Nanoelectromechanical System (NEMS)

A micro electromechanical system (MEMS) integrates micro sensors and actuators (I/O devices) together with signal processing circuits and forms the 'real' system on chip (SoC) of intelligent information processing. NEMS refers to nano-electromechanical system[66, 67]. Here, 'from micro to nano' not only implies the great enhancement of the semi-classical size effects but also the appearance of many interesting quantum effects. In NEMS, one can not only use the much-enhanced sensitivity with ultra-small device size for sensors but also the various quantum effects for information processing. For example, when the size of a suspended beam is scaled to nanometers, its mechanical resonant frequency can reach tens, even hundreds of GHz and thus can be used to form new mechanical switches with very high switching speed for digital information processing. By reasonable estimation with this type of nanomechanical switches, switching energy as low as $\approx 10^{-19}$ J is obtainable. Another example: as the tip size of a micro probe is reduced to sub-nano scale, the electron tunneling current between the probe and the 'contacted' solid surface increases exponentially with the contact 'gap' between them. This provides the possibility of displaying microscopic solid surface morphology. It is well known that a series of display devices and instruments such as scanning tunneling microscopy (STM), atomic force microscope (AFM), and magnetic force microscope (MFM) have been developed based on such mechanisms. The great contribution of these devices for microscopic access of surface structural information is now well appreciated in various scientific and technological fields.

In fact, NEMS greatly widens the scope of sensor and actuator technologies. It opens many new fields of information processing. With NEMS, one can access structural information with space dimension in sub-nano scale, detect force at the atto-Newton level, distinguish between different molecules, displace atoms, etc. NEMS technology provides also tools for different QME investigations. A series of interesting physical effects are under investigation, such as Casimir force[68], quantization of heat transportation, charge quantization in electro-conductance[69], displacement quantization[70], interference of electron wave with mechanical nanobeam oscillation[71], and electric magnetic control of nanobeam extension and contraction[72]. The research results may indicate the new possibilities of using these effects for different areas of information processing.

1.4 Quantum Information Processing

Two basic supports for classical information processing are the von Neumann computing model and classical binary logic devices. It is well known that there are many problems that are difficult or impossible to be solved by using classical computers, especially when the computing time increases with the problem size much faster than that in any polynomial form. Besides, the practical information processing needs of different fields are growing so rapidly that the classical computing power required for microelectronic chips with even higher performance, more complex structure, and better processing performance with power efficiency seems to be endless. In order to change the situation, people are seeking new ways (new models) of information processing and expecting to achieve a breakthrough in the new era. Among the proposed prospective new system models are different 'bio-inspired' systems and quantum information processing. In this section, an introduction of the fundamental principles of quantum information processing is presented.

1.4.1 Basic Concept of Quantum Information Processing

In classical digital electronics, two basic states of a two-energy-level system are used to represent two digits: one (assumed as the lower energy state) as the digit '0' ('open') state and the other '1' ('closed') state. The system thus forms a classical digital two-bit (binary) switch with a switching energy to separate the two level. At any time, the switch can only be in one state, either '1' or '0'. In quantum information processing[73], a two-energy-level quantum system is used as the basic bit, called qubit (quantum bit). Due to the quantum mechanical property, a qubit can be not only in either of its two base states $|0\rangle$ or $|1\rangle$, but also in the superposition state $|\psi\rangle = a|0\rangle + b|1\rangle$, with $|a|^2 + |b|^2 = 1$ (a, b are complex numbers). For a two qubit system, $|\Psi\rangle$ can be in one of four base states: $|00\rangle$, $|11\rangle$, $|01\rangle$, $|10\rangle$ as well as in superposition state $a|00\rangle + b|01\rangle + c|10\rangle + d|11\rangle$ ($|a|^2 + |b|^2 + |c|^2 + |d|^2 = 1$). The qubit system carries not only the 'movement' information of classical particles, but also the quantum mechanical information: such as phase, coherence, superposition, and entanglement. An Nqubit quantum system, described by wave function $|\psi\rangle$, consists of n qubits in coherence. In quantum processing, information digits are encoded as a qubit state vector, same as that in a digital bit vector in classical processing. During the quantum information processing, the state vector $|\psi(t)\rangle$ evolves in Hilbert space. The change of $|\psi\rangle$ with time, which is the state evolution, is determined by Schrodinger Equation. Any one of the coherent quantum systems is naturally evolving according to the Schrodinger equation describing it, but in quantum information processing, the qubit system is controlled by a program (quantum algorithm) so that the quantum mechanical evolution runs along a defined path in the Hilbert space and leads the state $|\Psi\rangle$ from an initial state $|\psi(0)\rangle$ to the final state $|\psi(t_{\mathrm{f}})\rangle$. State $|\psi(t_{\mathrm{f}})\rangle$ represents the problem solution and is measured by a proper method (quantum measurement[74]). The practical solution is achieved by decoding $|\psi(t_{\mathrm{f}})\rangle$. Since the program is so edited that $|\psi(t_{\mathrm{f}})\rangle$ satisfies the original problem requirements, the goal of information processing is attained.

The Hamiltonian Operator used to describe the qubit system is Hermitian, and so the evolution of the nqubit system $|\boldsymbol{\psi}_n\rangle$ can be expressed by an $(\boldsymbol{n} \times \boldsymbol{n})$ unitary transformation matrix. This matrix can be decomposed into the vector product of $\boldsymbol{n}' \times \boldsymbol{n}'$ unitary transformation matrices, in which $\boldsymbol{n}'$ is smaller than $\boldsymbol{n}$. By continuing the decomposition process, finally we find that any transformation operator describing the qubit system evolution can be expressed as a vector production of $\mathbf{2} \times \mathbf{2}$ unitary transformations. These $\mathbf{2} \times \mathbf{2}$ unitary transformation operators are defined as different kind of quantum gates. Thus, just as in the classical case, quantum information processing can be performed by a series of gate (quantum gate) actions. It has been shown that, like the classical case, among all the possible different types of quantum gates, only two or three can be selected as the basic types and the action of other gates can be transformed into a combined action of them. Similar to classical binary information processing, quantum circuits are composed of a series of different quantum gates to perform different functions (quantum transformations). The combination of quantum circuits working together constructs a quantum processing system for proper purpose. In comparison with the classical one, the advantages of quantum information processing over the classical one are obvious:

(1) With the same n (number of bits and qubits), the dimension of the processing space (Hilbert space) in quantum processing is much larger than that of the classical case (2^n to n), resulting in exponential growth (2^{2^n} to 2^n) of storage volume and processing power with the same n.

(2) Due to coherence, operating one qubit simultaneously influences others and the whole quantum bit system, i.e., the quantum processing is inherently parallel, different from the serial processing as in the classical case.

(3) Quantum inherent characteristics such as entanglement, and quantum transportation can be used to greatly enhance the information processing power.

It has been shown that quantum processing is very powerful in solving different quantum simulation problems that are often difficult for classical computation due to the rapid growth of the computing time with the problem size. In 1994 and 1996, Shor[75, 76] proposed a quantum algorithm for factoring large integers and proved that such type of classically hard problems can be resolved easily by quantum computing, reducing the running time from O(expN) classically to $O(N^2 \ln N)$ quantum mechanically. Figure 1.18 shows the calculation computer time t versus the bit number N of the integer. Note that here the classical computer is proposed with 10^{15} operations per second (OPS), while the clock frequency used for an N qubit quantum computer is assumed to be only 100 MHz. In 1997, Grover[77] proposed an unsorted large database quantum search algorithm, which reduces the computing time from classical $O(N/2)$ to quantum mechanical $O\left(N^{\frac{1}{2}}\right)$. With these examples, we see that quantum information processing is indeed (at least in some application areas) much powerful than the classical processing and thus brings in a real breakthrough into the information technology.

Quantum processing must be performed in coherent state, that is the system decoherence time τ_Q must be $\geqslant nt_{op}$ where n is the number of quantum processing control steps and t_{op} the processing period of each step. Generally, the process is controlled with a specific algorithm, the quantum algorithm, and the result is measured with specific methods, known as quantum measurements. The appropriate initial state should be implemented at the start. Both the measurement and initial state making are accomplished with the help of a classical high-performance computer. Quantum system evolution (computing process) from any state $|\psi(t_1)\rangle$ to another state $|\psi(t_2)\rangle$ does not change the system's degree of freedom and thus the system entropy. Hence, the quantum evolution process is basically reversible. There is no explicit energy threshold for quantum gate control, and the quantum gate is noise-resistless. In order to archive fault-tolerant processing quantum, an error code correction technique is critically important in quantum computation[78, 79].

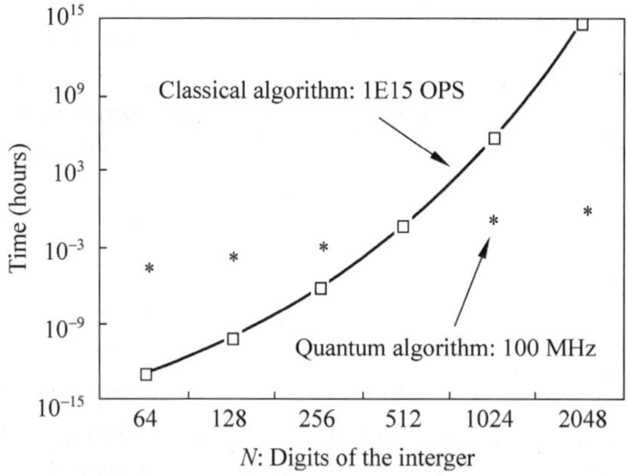

Figure 1.18 Computing time of integer factorization versus the integer digits N; a comparison of performances between classical and quantum mechanical computers (based on Shor's algorithm. The stars and squares represent results of quantum algorithm and classical algorithm, respectively)

1.4.2 Energy Analysis of Quantum Computers

Quantum system has a reversible evolution and does not change the system entropy. Thus, the internal energy of a qubit system remains constant during natural quantum mechanical evolution, i.e., the random quantum gate action requires no energy consumption. Practical quantum information processing requires the system to evolve along a definite path (defined by the quantum algorithm) and therefore error correction is necessary to be applied dealing with the noise-resistless quantum gates. Since during the error correction one needs to add the correct digits and delete the wrong ones, an inevitable change of entropy occurs. In other words, for fault-tolerant quantum processing, there exists system entropy change and energy consumption. An estimation of this energy gives a measure of the minimum energy needed to supply for a quantum computer of definite size. This energy is critically important for solid-state quantum computers, since the heat conduction of the solid chip finally will determine the dissipation power and thus the 'ultimate' computation power.

For fault-tolerant quantum computation, redundant bits (error correction code) are added to each 'calculation' qubit to form a 'logic qubit' and the gate operations run based on these logic bits. After any logic action, each code of the logic qubit is measured, the result assessed, and thereafter error digits replaced by the correct ones. During the error correction process, every error qubit is removed and a new, correct one added. Obviously, this is an irreversible process and there is system entropy change. As a result, a practical quantum computer requires energy supply. The quantity of entropy change is determined by the system noise level and the used error code correction technology. The theory of fault-tolerant quantum computation predicts that if the error probability ϵ can be kept lower than a critical value ϵ_c (estimated to be $10^{-5}-10^{-6}$)[73], then by use of error code correction technology, fault-tolerant quantum computation is always realizable for any large qubit systems. Based on this theory and assuming that the main noise is thermal, we can estimate the required power by the expression given by[80]

$$P = -nfK_B T \ln\left[\sqrt{\frac{3}{2}}\,\epsilon_c\right] \tag{1.18}$$

where n is the total number of qubits and $f=\tau_{op}^{-1}$ the processing signal frequency. In order to have fault-tolerant computing, i.e., to fulfill the condition $\epsilon_c \approx 10^{-5}-10^{-6}$, let us assume that the logic qubit number is S times the calculating qubit number N, i.e., the total qubit number n equals SN. For rough estimation, we assume $S=100$. Obviously, the relationship between the decoherence time τ_Q, and the time for one operation τ_{op} must satisfy:

$$\frac{t_{op}}{\tau_Q} \leqslant \epsilon_c \tag{1.19}$$

i.e.,

$$\tau_Q \geqslant \frac{t_{op}}{\epsilon_c} \tag{1.20}$$

Given $t_{op}=10^{-8}$ ($f=10^8$), $\epsilon=10^{-5}-10^{-6}$, the critical value of τ_Q should be about $10^{-3}-10^{-2}$ seconds. This requirement of decoherence time is relatively high and nowadays only nuclear spin and optical method-based systems can fulfill it. If τ_Q of the system is relatively small (for example, nowadays in solid state case, τ_Q is generally about 1 μs or less and is likely to reach 10 μs in the near future), τ_{op} must be reduced accordingly, otherwise a more advanced error code correction technology should be developed for increasing ϵ_c. Reduction of τ_{op}, i.e., increase of f will increase the quantum computing speed, but this requires more power consumption. In quantum computation, the classical computer is needed to do assistant tasks, such as qubits initialization, digits detection, and error code correction. Thus, if $\tau_Q=10^{-5}$, $\epsilon_c=10^{-5}$, the τ_{op} should be in the range of 10^{-10} seconds, which requires the assistant computer speed higher than 10^9 OPS. Therefore, the key problems to solve practically meaningful 'big' problems are getting higher τ_Q and realizing a solid-state quantum computer with a scale large enough.

Assume for case of $\tau_{op}=10^{-10}$, $\epsilon_c=10^{-5}$, $n=N_L=1\times10^6$ (as proposed in[80]). From Eq. (1.18), we can obtain a power of 483 μW, needed for a quantum computer chip capable of solving Shor's integer factorization problems with size up to 1 kb. Furthermore, if the chip area occupied by one qubit is assumed to be 1 um^2 (as proposed in[80]), then the area of the solid quantum chip equals 1×10^{-2} cm^2 and the dissipation power density of such a quantum chip should be 48.3 mW/cm^2 accordingly.

Another requirement for the minimum power dissipation comes from the condition of minimum control signal energy for obtaining ϵ_c. For simplicity, let us consider an electromagnetic wave with frequency ω' as the operating signal source. Since the operation signal pulse τ_{op} should be sharp enough in order to ensure the error probability is less than ϵ_c, ω' is required to satisfy the equation

$$(\omega'\tau_{op})^2 \geqslant \epsilon_c^{-1} \tag{1.21}$$

that is

$$\omega' \geqslant \frac{\epsilon^{-\frac{1}{2}}}{\tau_{op}} \tag{1.22}$$

On the other hand, for ensuring ϵ_c, the maximum fluctuation of the photon intensity should also be limited. At least,

$$n\hbar\omega'/\hbar\omega' = n \geqslant \epsilon_c^{-1} \tag{1.23}$$

where n is the number of controlling signal photons.

During each step of control, photons are focused on an area ($\approx Sd^2$) occupied by a logic calculating qubit and its logic qubits.

Summing up, the lowest power dissipation should be:

$$p_{d,min} = \frac{n\hbar\omega'}{Sd^2\,\tau_{op}} = \frac{\hbar\,\epsilon_c^{-3/2}}{Sd^2\times\tau_{op}^2} \tag{1.24}$$

given $\epsilon_c=10^{-5}$, $d=1$ μm, $S=100$, $\tau_{op}=10^{-10}$ s, $p_{d,min}$ equals about 13.2 W/cm^2.

If τ_Q is given, the minimum energy requirement for the quantum logical operations themselves should be:

$$p_{d,min} = \frac{\hbar\varepsilon^{-7/2}}{Sd^2\tau_Q^2} \tag{1.25}$$

given $\varepsilon=10^{-5}$, $d=1$ μm, $S=100$, $\tau_Q=10^{-5}$ s (corresponding to a τ_{op} of 10^{-10} s), $p_{d,min}$ equals about 13.2 W/cm^2. This is more rigorous than what is estimated above (48.3 mW/cm^2), but are still acceptable for good heat-conductive solid (such as silicon) chips. The above discussion indicates evidently that for fault-tolerant computation with larger n (signal intensity), the energy requirement from controlling is higher than that from resisting thermal noise. From Eq. (1.18), Eq. (1.24) and Eq. (1.25), smaller τ_{op} requires more chip power dissipation, while larger τ_Q requires less.

As mentioned above, with regard to the chip power dissipation, implementation of large-scale (as large as capable of performing 1 kb 'Shor factorization') solid-state quantum computer chips is practically feasible, though several technical and theoretical problems remain[80] ahead. Under some conditions, quantum computation can run adiabatically. With adiabatic quantum computation (AQC)[81, 82], the restriction of both decoherence time and power dissipation might be relaxed somehow.

1.4.3 Physical Realization of Quantum Computation

Physical realization is a key to quantum information processing. Selection of good physical qubits system carriers is most important. The conditions for being a good physical qubits system carrier are[83] listed below.

(1) Qubit must be robust, reliable, and easy to handle during quantum processing;

(2) Qubit system should have long enough decoherence time $\left(\tau_{\text{Q}} \geqslant \dfrac{t_{\text{op}}}{\epsilon_{\text{c}}}\right)$;

(3) Each of the system qubits is easy to access and to be set in the required initial state;

(4) Quantum measurement is possible and not difficult;

(5) System's qubit number is scalable, up to a necessary value.

A series of methods are proposed for quantum computation realization and many are still under intensive investigation. Among them are the following: nuclear magnetic resonance (NMR), trapped ion, optical and microwave guide, quantum dot, superconductor, impurity ion in silicon and full silicon. Due to the long decoherence time and existence of good experimental tools, the NMR method was developed earlier than the other methods[84, 85]. Details of NMR systems with qubit number as high as 7 to 9 have been published. Several quantum algorithms have been successfully verified on NMR quantum systems. However, further increase of the qubit number (scaling up) of the NMR system presents a big challenge. Together with other drawbacks, NMR is not likely to be a suitable method for practical quantum computer realization. From the scalability point of view, solid-state realization methods are more promising[86]. Among them, the superconductor quantum circuit based method is expected to be more prospective [87–90]. Several approaches are proposed for quantum processing with this method and different related topics are under intensive investigation. Since the carrier of quantum behavior for performing the quantum computation is the 'macroscopic' circuit instead of 'microscopic particles' as in other cases and the circuit system is fabricated with conventional modern microelectronic technology, the superconductor quantum computer inherently has the properties of easy scalability, more robustness, and good reliability. Furthermore, it is easy to integrate the quantum computing qubits with the high-speed assistant ICs by modern microelectronic technology to form the Quantum SoC.

1.5 Conclusion

IT is striding into the nanoelectronics era. Conventional CMOS technology is rapidly approaching its physical limit. Within the framework of CMOS technology, SoC progress takes place not only in the sense of widening its application fields but also of deepening its scientific research. New nanoelectronic devices based mainly on different QMEs are proposed and under intensive investigation. With these emerging devices, breakthroughs over some of the CMOS ULSI performance limitations (speed, power, and switching delay-power product) are expected, leading the electronics development to the stage of 'beyond the Moore'. Meanwhile, many new information processing system models and corresponding technologies have been suggested and are under intensive investigation too. The two main directions are based on quantum information processing and bio-information processing (or bio-inspired information processing). With these new information processing systems, a big progress step on the information processing power and performance-energy efficiency will appear. They may introduce in a new IT revolution very soon.

References

[1] Moore G. E., (1965), Cramming more circuits on chips, *Electron*, **19**: 114

[2] Moore G. E., (1975), Progress in digital electronics, *IEDM Tech. Dig.*, 11

[3] Dennard R. H., (1974), Design of ion implanted MOSFET with very small dimensions, *IEEE Solid State Circuits* **SC-9**: 256

[4] Taur Y., *et al.*, (1997), CMOS scaling into the nanometer regime, In: *Proc. IEEE*, **85**: 486

[5] Li Z. and R. Zhou, (2000), ULSI devices, Circuits and System Science Press

[6] Ma Y., (2001), The quantum mechanism effects and quantum tunneling in ULSI devices, Tsinghua Univ. Doctorial Dissertation

[7] Chen Z. and J. Wang, (1999), Basic material physics for semiconductor devices. Beijing: Science Press, 69

[8] Keyes R. W., (1975), The effect of randomness in distribution of impurity atoms of FET threshold, *Appl. Phys.*, **18**: 251

[9] Asenov A., *et al.*, (1999), Quantum mechanical enhancement of random dopant induced

threshold voltage fluctuations and lowering in sub 0.1 microns MOSFETs, *IEDM Tech. Dig.*, 535

[10] Keyes R. W., Physical limits in information processing, *Advances in Electronics and Electron Physics*, **70**: 154

[11] Toriumi A., *et al.*, (1995), Performance and reliability concerns of ultra-thin SOI and ultra-thin gate oxide MOSFETs, *IEDM Tech. Dig.*, 847

[12] Wong H. P., D. J. Frank, and P. M. Solomon, (1998), Device design consideration for double gate ground-plane and single gate ultra-thin SOI MOSFETs at 25 nm channel length generation, *IEDM Tech. Dig.*, 497

[13] Oh S-H., D. Monroe, J. M. Hergenrother, (2000), Analytic description of short channel effects in fully depleted double-gate and surrounding-gate MOSFETs. *IEEE Electron. Device Lett.*, **25**: 445

[14] Huang X., *et al.*, (1999), Sub 50-nm Fin-FET PMOS, *IEDM Tech. Dig.*, 67

[15] Auth C. P., J. D. Plummer, (1997), Scaling theory for cylindrical fully depleted surrounding gate MOSFETs, *IEEE Electron. Device Lett.*, **18**: 24

[16] Plummer J. D., (2001), Material and process limits in silicon VLSI technology, In *Proc. IEEE*, **89**: 240

[17] Roy P. K. and I. C. Kizilaili, (1998), Stacked high-k gate dielectric for gigascale integration MOS technology, *Appl. Phys. Lett.*, **72**: 2835

[18] Wilk G. D., R. M. Wallace, I. M. Mi. Anthony, (2000), Hafnium and zirconium silicates for advanced gate dielectrics, *J. Appl. Phys.*, **87**: 484

[19] Delhougne R., *et al.*, (2004), A simple and effective method for fabricating high performance strained silicon MOSFET devices, *J. Solid State Electronics*, **48**: 1307

[20] Ng K. K., W. T. Lynch, (1996), Analysis of gate voltage dependent series resistance of MOSFETs, *IEEE Trans. Electron Devices*, **33**: 965

[21] Osburn C. M., K. R. Bellur, (1998), Low parasitic resistance contacts for scaled ULSI devices, *Thin Solid Films*, **332**: 428

[22] Frank D. J., *et al.*, (2001), Device scaling limits of MOSFETs and their application dependencies, In *Proc. IEEE*, **89**: 259

[23] Havemann R. H., I. A. Hutchby, (2001), High performance interconnects: An integration overview, In *Proc. IEEE*, **89**: 586

[24] Miller D. A. B., (1999), On chip and chip to chip optical interconnects-status and prospects, In: *Interconnect technology beyond roadmap*, Saraswat KC Ed. SRC/SEMATECH/MARCO White Paper

[25] Miller D. A. B., (2000), Rationale and challenges for optical interconnects to electronic chips, In *Proc. IEEE*, **88**: 728

[26] Chang M. F., (1999), RF/wireless interconnect for enter- and intra- chip communications, In: *Interconnect technology beyond roadmap*, Saraswat KC Ed. SRC/SEMATECH/MARCO White Paper

[27] Krishnamoorthy A., *et al.*, (1995), 3D integration of modulators over active sub-micron CMOS circuits: 375 Mb/s t transimpedance receiver-transmitter circuit, *IEEE Photon. Technol. Lett.*, **7**: 1288

[28] Rahman A., D. Antoniadis, and A. Agarwal, Study of 3D integration of high performance

logic (1999), In: *Interconnect technology beyond roadmap,* Saraswat KC Ed. SRC/ SEMATECH/MARCO White Paper

[29] Chang L. L., L. Esaki, and R. Tsu, (1974), Resonant tunneling in semiconductor double barriers, *Appl. Phys. Lett.*, **24**: 593

[30] Jian P. S., *et al.*, (1998), Resonant tunneling diodes–models and properties, In *Proc. IEEE*, **86**: 641

[31] Mazumdler, *et al.*, (1998), Digital circuit applications of resonant tunneling diodes, In *Proc. IEEE*, **86**: 664

[32] Methews R. H., *et al.*, (1999), A new RTD-FET logic family, In *Proc. IEEE*, **87**: 596

[33] Likharev K. K., *et al.*, (1999), Singe electron devices and their applications, In *Proc. IEEE*, **87**: 606

[34] van Houten H., C. W. J. Beenaker, and A. A. A. Staring, Single Charge Tunneling, (1992), In: *Coulomb blockade oscillations in semiconductor nanostructures*, Grabert H, Devoret M. H., Eds. New York: Plenum, 167 – 216

[35] Beenakker C. W. J., (1991), Theory of coulomb-blockade oscillations in conductance of a quantum dot, *Phys. Rev. B*, **44**: 1646

[36] Ishikuro H., *et al.*, (1996), Coulomb blockade oscillations at room temperature in a Si quantum wire MOSFET fabricated by anisotropic etching on an SOI substrate, *Appl. Phys. Lett.*, **68**: 3585

[37] Yano K., *et al.*, (1998), A 128 MB, early prototype for gigascale single electron memories, *ICSSCC' 98 Dig. Tech. Papers*: 344

[38] Takahashi Y., *et al.*, (1995), A fabrication technique for single electron transistor operating in room temperature, *Electron Lett.*, **31**: 136

[39] Chen R. H., K. K. Likharev, (1998), Multiple-junction single electron transistors for digital applications, *Appl. Phys. Lett.*, **72**: 61

[40] Chen R. H., A. N. Korotkov, and K. K. Likharev, (1996), Single electron transistor logic, *Appl. Phys. Lett.*, **68**: 1954

[41] Avouris P., *et al.*, (2003), Carbon nano-tube electronics, In *Proc. IEEE*, **91**: 17

[42] Saito R., *et al.*, (1992), Electronic structure of chiral graphene tubules, *Appl. Phys. Lett.*, **60**: 2204

[43] Dresselhaus M. S., G. Dresselhaus, P. Avouris, eds., (2001), *Carbon nano-tubes synthesis, structure properties, and applications*, Springer

[44] Huang Z. P., *et al.*, (1998), Growth of highly oriented carbon nano-tubes by plasma-enhanced hot filament chemical vapor deposition, *Appl. Phys. Lett.*, **73**: 3854

[45] Ren Z. F., *et al.*, (1998), Synthesis of large arrays of well-aligned carbon nano-tube on glass, *Science*, **282**: 1105

[46] Johnson M., (2003), Overview of spin transport electronics in metals, In *Proc. IEEE*, **91**: 652

[47] Baibich, *et al.*, (1998), Giant magneto-resistance of (001)Fe/(001)Cr magnetic superlattices, *Phys. Rev. Lett.*, **61**: 2472

[48] Daughton J., (2003), Spin-dependent sensors, In: *Proc. IEEE*, **91**: 681

[49] Tehrani S., *et al.*, (2003), Magnetoresistive random access memory using magnetic tunneling junctions, In: *Proc. IEEE*, **91**: 703

[50] Tehrani S., *et al.*, (1999), High density sub-micron magneto-resistive random access memory, *J. Appl. Phys.*, **85**: 5822

[51] Datta A., B. Das, Electronic analog of electro-optic modulator, *Appl. Phys. Lett.*, **56**: 665

[52] Ting D. Z. Y., *et al.* (2003), Rashba effect resonant tunneling spin filter, In *Proc. IEEE*, **91**: 741

[53] Jonker B. T., (2003), Progress toward electrical injection of spin polarized electrons into semiconductors, In *Proc. IEEE*, **91**:727

[54] Hayakawa, *et al.*, Superconducting digital electronics, In *Proc. IEEE*, **92**: 1549

[55] Clark J., (1989), Principles and applications of SQUIDs, In *Proc. IEEE*, **77**: 1208

[56] Kittel C., (1979), In: *Introduction to Solid State Physics*. Translated by Yang S., *et al*, Beijing, China: Science Press, Chapter 12 407 – 430

[57] Hayakawa H., *et al.*, (2004), Superconducting digital electronics, In: *Proc. IEEE*, **92**: 1549

[58] Likharev K. K., V. K. Semenov, (1991), RSFQ logic/memory family: A new Josephson-junction technology for terahertz frequency digital systems, *IEEE Trans. Appl. Superconduct.*, **1**: 1

[59] Chen W., *et al.*, (1999), Rapid single flux quantum T-flip-flop operating up to 770 GHz, *IEEE Trans, Appl. Superconduct*, **9**: 3212

[60] Aviram A., eds., (1989), Molecular electronics: Science and technology. New York: United Engineering Trustees

[61] Aviram A., M. A. Ratner, Molecular rectifiers, *Chem. Phys. Lett.*, **29**: 277

[62] Reed M. A., *et al.*, (1997), Conductance of a molecular junction, *Science*, **278**: 252

[63] Chen J., *et al.*, (1999), Large on-off ratios and negative differential resistance in a molecular electronics device, *Science*, **286**: 1550

[64] Irie M., (1993), Light triggered molecular switch, *Mol. Cryst. Lig. Cryst.*, **227**: 263; and Irie M., *et al.*, (2002), A digital fluorescent molecular photo-switch, *Nature*, **420**: 759

[65] Collier C. P., *et al.* (2000), A catenae-based solid state electrically reconfigurable switch, *Science*, **289**: 1172

[66] Craighead H. G., (2000), Nano electromechanical systems, *Science*, **290**: 1532

[67] Dequesnes M., *et al*, (2002), Calculations of pull-in voltages for carbon nano-tube-based nano electromechanical switches. *Nanotechnology*, **13**: 120

[68] Chan H. B., *et al.*, (2001), Nonlinear micromechanical Casimier oscillator, *Phys. Rev. Lett.*, **87**: 211801

[69] Krommer H., *et al.*, (2000), Nano-mechanical oscillators operating as a charge detectors in nonlinear regime, *Europhys. Lett.*, **50**: 101

[70] Sapmaz S., *et al.*, (2003), Carbon-nano-tubes as a nano electro mechanical system. *Phys. Rev. B*, **67**: 235414

[71] Armour A. D., Blencowe M. P., (2001), Possibility of an electro-mechanical which-path interferometer, *Phys. Rev. B*, **64**: 035311

[72] Blencowe M. P., M. N. Wybourne, (2000), Quantum squeezing of mechanical motion for micron sized cantilevers. *Physical B*, **280**: 555

[73] Nielsen M. A., I. L. Chuang, eds., (2000), *Quantum Computation and Quantum Information.* Cambridge: Cambridge Univ. Press

[74] Legget J., (1980), Macroscopic quantum systems and the quantum measurement. *Prog.*

Theor., **Phys. Suppl**: 80 – 100

[75] Shor P. W., (1994), Algorithm for quantum computation: discrete logarithm and factoring, In: *Proc. annual symp. on foundations of computer science*, IEEE Press, Los Alamitos, CA, USA, 124 – 134

[76] Beckman D., *et al.*, (1996), Efficient networks for quantum factoring, *Phys. Rev. A*, **54**: 1304

[77] Grover L. K., (1997), Quantum mechanics helps in searching for a needle in a haystack, *Phys. Rev. Lett.*, **79**: 325 – 328

[78] Zanadi P. and M. Rasetti, (1997), Noiseless quantum codes, *Phys., Rev. Lett.*, **79**: 3306

[79] Shor P. W., (1996), Fault-tolerant quantum computation, In: *Proc. the 37th Conf. foundation of computer science*, Burlington, VT.

[80] Benacluche J. G. and L. B. Kish, (2005), Future directions in electronic computation and information procession, In: *Proc. IEEE*, **93**: 1858 – 1863

[81] Farhi E., *et al.*, (2001), A quantum adiabatic evolution algorithm applied to random instances of a NP-complete problem, *Science*, **292**: 472 – 476

[82] Amin M. H. S., *et al.*, Thermally assisted adiabatic quantum computation, *arXiv: cond-mat/0609332*, **1**: 13

[83] Divincenzo D. P., *et al.*, (2000), Universal quantum computation with exchange integration. *Nature*, **408**: 339

[84] Jones J. A. and M. Mosca, (1998), Implementation of a quantum algorithm on a nuclear magnetic resonance quantum computer, *J. Chem. Phys.*, **109**: 1648

[85] Vandersypen L. M. K., *et al.*, (2001), Experimental realization of Shor's algorithm using nuclear magnetic resonance, *Nature*, **414**: 883

[86] Ruda H. E. and B. B. Qiao, (2003), Modeling and prospects for solid state quantum computer, In *Proc. IEEE*, **91**: 1874

[87] Berggren K. K., (2004), Quantum computing with superconductors, In: *Proc. IEEE*, **92**: 1630

[88] Pashkin Y. A., *et al.*, (2003), Quantum oscillations in two coupled charge qubits, *Nature*, **421**: 823

[89] Chiorescu J., *et al.*, (2003), Coherent quantum dynamics of superconducting flux qubit, *Science*, **299**: 1869

[90] Orlando T. P., *et al.*, (2003), Flux-based superconducting qubits for quantum computation, *Physical C*, **299**: 1869

2 Micro/Nano Fluidics Mechanics and Transducers

Chih-Ming Ho[1] and Yu-Chong Tai[2]

[1] Mechanical & Aerospace Engineering Department, University of California, Los Angeles, California 90095, USA
E-mail: chihming@ucla.edu

[2] Electrical Engineering and Bioengineering Department, California Institute of Technology Pasadena, California, USA
E-mail: yctai@its.caltech.edu

Abstract In biochemical analyses, sample fluid volume in the nano or pico liter range is commonly encountered in various processes. For example, the preparation, mixing, separation, and concentration of cells and biomolecules in such small amount of fluids are very often needed in most analyses. From the science and technology point of view, efficient momentum and energy transfers of the desired fluid and particle motions in such small scales need sufficient comprehension of mechanics and MEMS (micro-electro-mechanical systems) transducers of similar length scales. Interestingly, MEMS/NEMS technologies do enable us to match the device and the fluid length scale for handling fluids in extremely small volume. This opens up a tremendous opportunity for research and development. In traditional fluid dynamics, the flow length scale is much larger than the molecular length scale. Continuum mechanics is the most common hypothesis used for flow research. In the case of micro/nano engineering systems, however, one may encounter regimes from continuum all the way down to molecule-dominated conditions. Therefore, in micro/nano fluidics, there are many new challenges that are very different from those in traditional fluidic systems. In this chapter, we discuss these special issues related to micro/nano fluidics and MEMS transducers in handling extremely small amount of fluids, including embedded particles.

Keywords Micro-electro-mechanical-systems (MEMS), nano sciences and technologies, sensors and actuators, microfluidics and nanofluidics, micro/Nano systems

2.1 Introduction

For most of the molecular medical diagnoses, the first step is often to collect cells from the embedded medium. When intracellular materials are involved, cells need to be lysed and reagents in liquid form are to be added in order to obtain a detection signal. In these processes, fluid serves as the medium to contain and transport cells, proteins, DNA/RNA, and particles from one location to another in the detection system. In the case where reactions need to take place, the molecules or probes in the reagents are required to be mixed with target cells or DNA/RNA. In other cases, we have to separate, purify and even concentrate the target molecules from the sample. These fluidic processes are generic in biochemical analyses in which the specificity, sensitivity and time required for accomplishing the processes are all key issues. The bulk fluid transport and the motion of the embedded molecules in the fluid play crucial roles in determining the processing time while the specificity and sensitivity are primarily decided by the sensor design.

In most cases, the length scale matching between the transducer and the phenomenon to be studied is a necessity for efficient couplings. These couplings, for examples, could be picking, placing and straining that involve both momentum and energy transfers. With the continuing improvement of the spatial resolution of transducers by MEMS/NEMS technology, nowadays it is possible to directly manipulate a single cell, which is only several microns in size. Kim, et al.[1] first demonstrated a micro mechanical griper that can hold a single euglena with a diameter of 7 microns. Recently, Kim's group[2] developed a pneumatic cell cage that can be operated in liquid mediums. A cell is the basic element of living organisms and cellular researches are always carried out in liquid environment. Therefore, fluidic processes in micro/nano configurations (i.e., in small size and in liquid) naturally emerge as a critical discipline in the biochemical field.

Micro/nano flows are very different from macro flows. Where continuum is commonly assumed. Molecular effects are only represented by physical constants such as viscosity. In macro flows, the inertia of fluid mass is usually much larger than the viscous force and hence the large Reynolds number. Most interesting phenomena are the manifestations of non-linear effects associated with the inertial forces. In micro devices, the typical Reynolds number is much less than one due to the small transverse length scale, which results in high velocity gradient and thus high viscous force. Low Reynolds flows and Stokes flows are linear in nature. However, linearity may not guarantee a simple solution, especially when the scale of the micro flows is not much larger than the sizes of macro-molecules such as DNA/RNA or protein. In other words, the basic hypothesis, i.e., continuum mechanics breaks down. Furthermore, due to the large surface to volume ratio in micro devices, these macromolecules could be quite close to the surface and their motions could be easily influenced by the surface potential, which leads to size effects that are not yet well understood. These intriguing molecular effects in microfluidics lead to a new direction for fundamental fluid mechanics research in addition to numerous applications in the biomedical engineering area. It is interesting to note that these features result only from the matching between molecular length scale and device length. Except in a few special nano/micro flow conditions, we have not observed the importance of individual molecular timescale because it is typically much smaller than the collective timescales of slow-moving micro flows. In other transport phenomena, such as in micro/nano heat transfer, the timescale effects could could be as important as the length scale effects[3].

Hydrodynamic pressure is the primary force field for driving the fluid in macro flows and is still frequently used in driving bulk fluid in MEMS. However, the pressure drop increases inversely with the second power of the transverse dimension and can be too large to be practical in micro/nano passages Electrokinetic (EK) force fields function efficiently near a surface (as of eletroosmotic (EO) force or dielectrophoretic (DEP) force) or in an electric potential field (as of electrophoretic force). Therefore, EK forces are commonly used in microfluidic systems. With proper design, the micro flow pattern driven by either hydrodynamic pressure or EK forces can directly manipulate the motion of molecules. Hence, molecule-manipulating nanotechnologies can be embedded in micro flows.

As a whole, microfluidics is important to understand the underlying physical mechanics of the molecule or bulk fluid motions in micro/nano configuration and to achieve efficient designs for facilitating the processes used in biomedical/chemical analyses. In this paper, the fundamental issues such as role of molecules in viscosity and the force fields for driving molecules are reviewed first. Then, the fluidic processes of directly manipulating biological objects and DNA by micro fluidics, sample concentration, mixing, separation, as well as molecular recognition for bio-detections are discussed.

2.2 Physical Constants

Physical constants are the links from molecular properties to the fluidic phenomena and usually govern the efficiency of the fluid/particle movements. Viscosity is a physical property derived under the hypothesis of continuum. It represents the tendency of a fluid to undergo deformation when subject to a shear stress. The deformation rate is determined by the inter-molecular force, which provides the force to balance the applied shear force. In fact, viscosity is a global fluid constant or a constant representing the propensity of a collection of fluid molecules to externally applied stress.

In the case of a pure liquid consisting of simple molecules, viscosity is considered to be an intrinsic property and its value is dependent on the temperature of the fluid alone. For more complex fluids, such as solutions of macromolecules, the viscosity may contain more than one variable. It generally shows a complex dependence on an additional number of parameters, such as type of solvent, or concentration, molecular weight, conformation, etc., of the solute. Nonetheless, even in these more complex cases, viscosity is ascribed to the intrinsic properties of the fluid itself[4].

When the length scale of the flow field approaches the size of the molecules of the liquid, the underlying normal assumption that the fluid can be described as a continuum is likely to be no longer valid. The 'intrinsic' viscosity shows a departure from typical values. When this happens, the concept of viscosity must be carefully reconsidered and reinterpreted as 'apparent' viscosity in continuum terms. This phenomenon is actually caused by 'molecular effects'. Experimental evidence of flows in a molecular size channel shows how dramatic the molecular effect is, as the size of the channel and the size of the molecules 'flowing' in it are comparable. For example, when the channel size is below 10 molecular diameters, in the order of a few nanometers, the fluid loses its liquid-like behavior and assumes solid-like characteristics[5]. The structure of the molecules in molecular size channels can change from a random order to a discrete number of ordered layers, with the 'apparent' viscosity as high as 10^5 times the 'regular' viscosity and the typical molecular timescale of the fluid 10^{10} times slower[6]. Figure 2.1 represents the results of a typical experiment where two parallel plates, separated by a few molecular layers of OMCTS (octamethylcyclotetrasiloxane), sliding with respect to each other, while the distance between the plates decreases with time (horizontal axis in Fig. 2.1). There are distinctive features of this sort of molecular flow: ① the frictional force increases almost in a stepwise fashion as the distance between the plates is reduced, and reaches a stable value when the separation consists of an integral number of molecular layers (1, 2, or 3); ② the saw-toothed behavior is due to a stick-slip motion of the plates coincident with the rearrangement of the molecular layers moving with respect to one another.

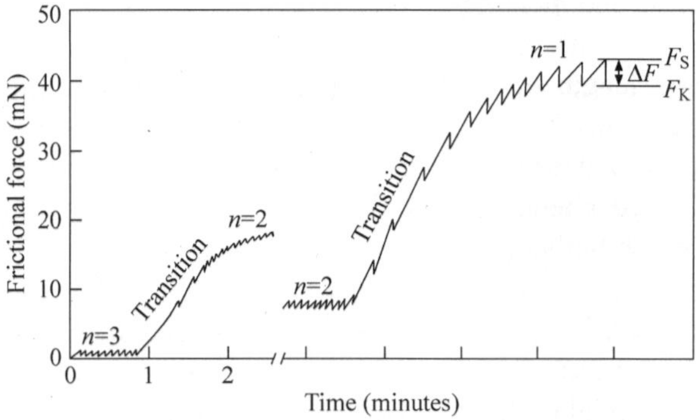

Figure 2.1 Friction force between two parallel plates

In the case of solutions of macromolecules, such as DNA, in most biological solutions, the contour length of DNA macromolecules can be about tens of microns and their persistence lengths in the order of 10 nm. The molecular effect can be apparent for much larger channels, a few microns or even larger, despite the fact that the solvent by itself behaves like a continuum, as its molecular size is 4 or 5 orders of magnitude smaller than the channel.

In the case of a dilute solution, the interaction between the macromolecules can be negligible. However, the interference of the DNA molecule with the wall can still be significant for channels of one micron or so. This 'wall effect' is likely to be predominant in MEMS devices due to the large surface to volume ratio. Again, this is due to the physicochemical interaction between fluid molecules and wall molecules. Interestingly, its extension is not necessarily confined to the first layer or the first few layers of molecules lying in contact with the wall, but can propagate across the whole flow field. For example, fluid molecules can then place (or structure) themselves at the wall in a different fashion depending on their hydrophilic or hydrophobic nature (or simply their surface energies). In the presence of shear flow, anomalous phenomena are observed for the case of a hydrophobic surface, and they are generally explained by the so-called 'wall slip'. Another example is the phenomenon of 'wall depletion' of polymer in a dilute polymer solution. The polymer concentration across the flow field presents a 'depleted sub-layer' at the wall[7]. Wall effects are the result of competing forces that create a different state of equilibrium within the fluid. In the latter case, for example, the electrostatic repulsive force caused by the wall competes with the osmotic force generated by the non-uniform distribution of solute in the bulk of the fluid. Hence, neither is the polymer concentration uniform nor is the polymer completely relegated to the center of the channel; instead, a finite concentration gradient forms across the channel. As in the case of the molecular effect, the wall effect is related to the ratio of two quantities. In the former case, it was the ratio of two characteristic lengths (molecular size versus channel size); in the latter, it is the ratio between surface forces and volume forces. In principle, surface forces scale with the second power of the characteristic length of the flow, while volume forces scale with the third power. Their ratio is inversely proportional to the characteristic length of the flow, so that when the ratio between volume forces and surface forces is small enough, body forces are negligible, and the behavior of the flow depends on the size. In general, it is reasonable to expect that surface-induced phenomena depend on some negative power of the flow characteristic length, although not necessarily equal to -1. Wall effects can also take place at much larger length scales of the flow than geometrical effects. For example, slips in both simple fluids and polymer solutions have been observed in tubes several millimeters in diameter. Unfortunately, not enough studies have been conducted to predict the behavior of such solutions in this size range and those studies performed to date are still far from being enough to provide a clear and consistent picture of the size effect. As a result, this offers a new area of research in the microfluidics field with both extreme scientific interest and important practical relevance.

In conclusion, the dependence of properties of the fluid on the flow scale has a great impact on the design and applications of MEMS. The hydraulic power required to perform a certain process is equal to the product of the total pressure drop sustained during the process and the flow rate. On the other hand, pressure drop and flow rate are related to each other by the value of the 'apparent' viscosity and, as such, they can be strongly affected by the size of the device. In a similar fashion, for applications where the control of flow rate is critical (e.g., drug delivery and, biomedical devices), the value of the 'apparent' viscosity pertaining to the size of the MEMS device must be known in order to correctly determine the actual amount of fluid being dispensed.

2.3 Fluidic Systems Based on Hydrodynamic Force

In a microfluidic system, hydrodynamic pressure can serve as a driving force for moving bulk fluids in devices with transverse dimension of 100 m or less. The hydrodynamic pressure is usually produced by a surface with positive displacement such as a piston and can provide an accurate re-producible flow rate. For example, a MEMS peristaltic pump is shown in Fig. 2.2[8]. This pump has a transverse dimension (i.e., thickness) of about 100 m and can pump up to 100 μL/min. On the other hand, the pressure drop increases inversely with the second power of the transverse dimension of the device. If the velocity is kept the same, a much less constraining condition than a constant flow rate, the pressure drop increases four orders of magnitude for devices with dimension of 1 micron. This is manifested by an even-smaller surface-micromachined pump in Fig. 2.3[9], which is a peristaltic pump with a transverse dimension of about 3 m and a normal pump rate about several 2 nL/min.

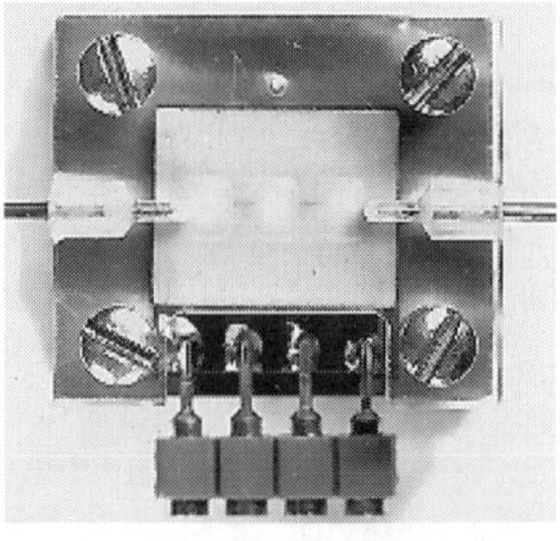

Figure 2.2 A Chip-assembled peristaltic pump[8] with a transverse dimension ~100 μm

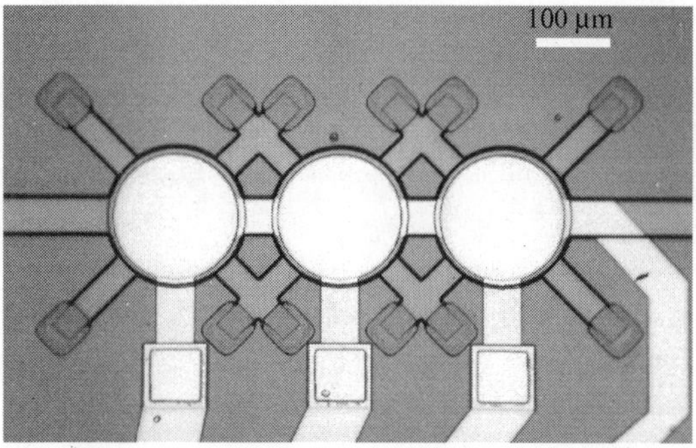

Figure 2.3 A surface-micromachined peristaltic pump[9] with a transverse dimension ~ 3 μm (see color figure at the end of this book)

2.4 Direct Manipulation of Biological Object by Hydrodynamic Field

Hydrodynamic drag plays an important role in the manipulation of biological objects. Manipulating particles with hydrodynamic force is naturally important because most biological elements exist naturally in a fluid medium. The order of magnitude of the hydrodynamic drag force can be estimated by using Stoke's law for a spherical object.

$$F_{\text{drag}} = 6\pi R\mu v$$

where R is the radius of the particles, μ is the viscosity of the fluid, and v is the velocity of the fluid medium. The force is linearly proportional to the size of the object ($F \sim R$). It is relatively stronger for smaller objects when compared to other volumetric forces ($F \sim R^3$), such as inertia or dielectrophoretic force.

2.4.1 Single Cell Manipulation

A hydrodynamic flow field can be used to transport different biological objects inside microfluidic channels or glass manipulators. We have developed processes for fabricating micromanipulators with different geometries from fused silica micro capillary tubing[10]. A sharpened injector and cell trapper with conical inner geometry can be fabricated by one-step etching processes. Figure 2.4 shows trapping of a live cell using a single-cell trapper. Adjusting the internal pressure of the glass cell trapper generates a flow field around the trapper. The hydrodynamic suction force produced on the target cell in the flow field is sufficient to drag the cell to the trapping site. The ability to trap a cell allows successful intracytoplasmic injection, where desired molecules are injected into the target cell[10].

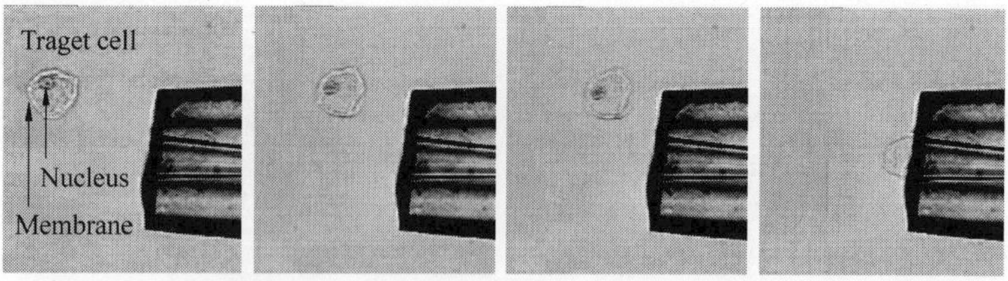

Figure 2.4 Capture of a cell (arrows) with a single-cell trapper (right) by flow entrainment. The images are separated by 1 s

2.4.2 DNA Manipulation

By proper microchannel design, hydrodynamic force is able to produce desired flow field, which can control the deformation of embedded macro molecules. When a DNA molecule experiences spatial velocity gradient, the differential hydrodynamic drag force along the molecule can deform the DNA far from the equilibrium conformation. Several groups[11 – 13] have reported the study of single DNA molecules under shear, velocity gradient in spanwise direction. Babcock, et al.[12,13] studied in detail the single DNA dynamics under shear generated between two parallel glass plates. Non-periodic fluctuations in extension and end-over-end tumbling were observed under steady shear. The rate of fluctuation and average extension increased as the shear rate increased.

Another way of stretching a DNA molecule is to use accelerating flow, whose velocity is increasing in the streamwise direction. We have designed a microfluidic device, which has three inlets and a converging section, for manipulating T2 DNAs[14]. The two side inlets and the converging section provide shear force to symmetrically accelerate the flow exiting from the center channel, similar to a cytometer but in micro scale. An accelerating flow along the streamwise direction was verified by micro particle image velocimetry and the stretching of DNA molecules was demonstrated. If the flow is stopped, the stretched DNA will coil back and allow measurement of the relaxation time. The relaxation time is governed by the force balance between DNA elasticity and hydrodynamic drag and can be measured. Perkins, et al.[15] used another technique to measure the relaxation of single λ DNA. One end of the DNA was chemically attached to a 1-μm-bead for anchoring with laser tweezers. Uniform flow was applied around the stationary bead; the DNA was stretched to its full extension due to hydrodynamic drag force. The relaxation was observed after the flow was stopped.

2.5 Electrokinetic Force Fields

As the dimension becomes smaller, hydrodynamic pressure can become inefficient for driving fluids inside microchannels. EK forces, on the other hand, are especially effective at small length scale. With the development of MEMS fabrication technology, the integration of micro or nanoscale electrodes in fluidic device is a relatively simple procedure. Therefore, EK forces are ideal for manipulating biological objects and performing fluidic operations. In general, many different EK forces can be used to manipulate the fluid and the embedded particles[16, 17]. For example, electrothermal flow and electroosmosis, as discussed in the following, can both generate bulk fluid flow in microfluidic channels. Electrowetting, which is an interfacial EK effect, allows movement of fluid droplets. In addition to these body forces that generate bulk fluid movement, there are also particle forces, such as electrophoresis and dielectrophoresis, in which the forces act only on the embedded particles.

2.5.1 Electrothermal Flow

Electrothermal flow arises from the temperature gradient in the medium generated by joule heating of the fluid. This temperature gradient induces local changes in the conductivity, permittivity, viscosity, and density of the solution. These gradients can generate forces, which act on the fluid[16]. For example, conductivity gradients produce free volume charge and Coulomb forces while a permittivity gradient produces dielectric forces. Ramos, et al.[17] have provided an order-of-magnitude estimation of the electrothermal flow. The power dissipation per volume is given by σE^2. In order to calculate the temperature rise, the energy equation has to be solved and the temperature rise, ΔT, can be approximated by

$$\Delta T \approx \frac{\sigma V_{\text{rms}}^2}{k} \tag{2.1}$$

where σ is the electrical conductivity, V_{rms} is the root mean square voltage, and k is the thermal conductivity. An analytical expression of the force generated is given for parallel electrodes. The order of magnitude of the force on the fluid can be estimated.

By properly designing the electrodes and microstructures, micro pumping based on electrothermal flow can be achieved. Electrothermal pumps have the advantage of being free of moving parts while only requiring a simple fabrication process. In addition, electrothermal flow can operate with an AC potential at high frequency, which prevents electrochemical dissociation of the fluid and accumulation of impurities on the electrode surface.

2.5.2 Electroosmosis

Electroosmosis describes the motion of an ionic fluid induced by an external DC potential applied along the stream. The electrical field exerts a net electrostatic force on the ions, which then drag the solvent along. Electroosmosis can occur due to the formation of an electrical double layer at the charged surfaces. The surface charge is balanced by counter ions in the medium. There is a layer of ions absorbed on the charged surface, called the Stern layer. The outer region, where ions are in rapid thermal motion, is called the diffuse electrical double layer that spans a distance in the order of the Debye length. If a potential is applied along the channel, the diffused electrical double layer will move due to the electrostatic force. Due to the cohesive nature of the hydrogen bonding of water molecules, the entire buffer solution is pulled. Therefore, the velocity profile is uniform across the channel. A solid surface in contact with a liquid experiences a surface charging mechanism through two possibilities:

(1) Surface molecules dissociate (protons leave the surface, which hence becomes negatively charged).

(2) Ions from the liquid bound to the surface.

The charged surface is then balanced by two populations of counterions, whose total charge equals the surface charge.

(1) Some ions transiently bound to the surface and form the Stern or Helmholtz layer.

(2) Some ions are in a rapid thermal motion close to the surface and form the diffused electric double layer.

The diffused electric double layer acts as a charged plate capacitor, whose equivalent plate separation is known as the Debye length, $1/\kappa$. It depends solely on the properties of the liquid and ranges from nm for high ionic concentration solutions to μm ($1/\kappa \approx 1$ μm for DI water). If a potential is applied along the channel, the diffused electric double layer will move due to electrostatic force. This means the fluid boundary layer is subject to a net force and moves, dragging along the rest of the fluid. The velocity profile is therefore constant across the channel.

2.5.3 AC Electroosmosis

AC electroosmosis is a recently identified EK phenomenon observed at frequency ranges below 1 MHz[17]. This observation has been reported for aggregation of yeast cells in interdigitated castellated electrodes. AC electroosmosis has an origin similar to DC electroosmosis, which exerts a force on the electrical double layer by a tangential electric field. Electric potential within the electrode causes charges to accumulate on the electrode surface, which changes the charge density near the surface and forms the electrical double layer. The process is called electrode polarization. The electrical double layer interacts with the tangential component of the electric field and generates a net force. The force acts on the double layer and cause fluid movement (Fig. 2.5). In the alternating electric field, the sign of charges in the electrical double layer changes with the applied electric field and the tangential component. Therefore, the direction of the driving force for the fluid remains the same in the alternative electric potential.

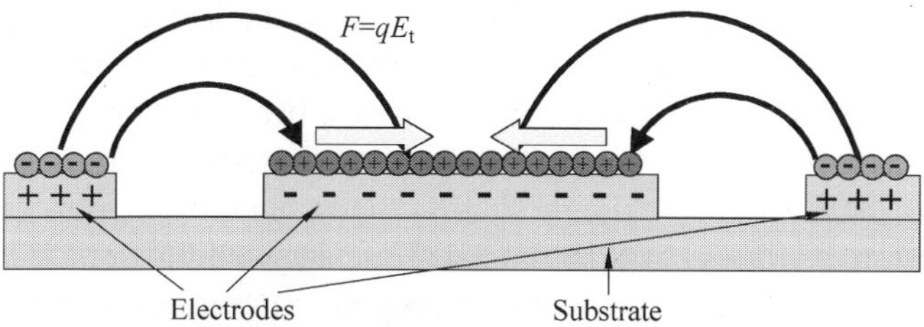

Figure 2.5 Principle of AC electroosmosis

Ramos, et al.[17] have modeled AC electroosmosis by considering the electrolyte and the electrical double layer as impedances in series. The model predicts the AC electroosmotic velocity v on parallel electrodes with small gap distance to be:

$$< v(r) >= \frac{1}{8} \frac{\varepsilon V_0^2 \Omega^2}{\mu r (1+\Omega^2)^2} \tag{2.2}$$

where ε is the permittivity of the electrolyte, V_0 is the potential applied to the electrodes, μ is the viscosity of the electrolyte, and r is the distance from the center of the electrode gap. The non-dimensional frequency Ω is given by

$$\Omega = \omega r \frac{\varepsilon}{\sigma} \frac{\pi}{2} \kappa \tag{2.3}$$

where ω is the angular frequency of the applied field, σ is the conductivity of the electrolyte, and κ is the reciprocal Debye length of the electrical double layer. A similar expression is also given by using linear electrical double layer analysis. The bulk fluid motion driven by the surface velocity can be calculated numerically.

Green, et al.[18] have performed detailed experimental measurements of the velocity on parallel electrodes. The AC electroosmotic flow velocity displays strong dependences on the applied frequency and the medium conductivity. The AC electroosmotic velocity is related to the charge density in the electrical double layer and the tangential electric field. At low frequency, the space charges can quickly respond to the electric field and most of the electric potential drops along the double layer. The tangential electric field is at a minimum at such frequencies and generates small AC electroosmotic velocities. At high frequencies, the net charge in the double layer is small and the impedance across the electrolyte dominates. Therefore, the AC electroosmotic velocity tends to be zero at high and low frequency and has a maximum at an intermediate frequency.

2.5.4 Electrowetting

Instead of driving the bulk fluid inside microchannels with mechanical or EK pumps, another approach is to perform fluidic operations in droplet-based digital fluidic circuits. It is envisioned that the entire biological analysis can be performed in digital fluidic circuits. This eliminates many problems, such as leakage and bounding, associated with channel-based micro fluidics. Digital fluidic circuits are made possible by the ability to manipulate fluid droplets (from pl to μl) with different mechanisms, such as thermocapillaries, dielectrophoresis, electrostatic force, voltage, or light mediated surface wetting.

Among those mechanisms, electrowetting on dielectric (EWOD) has been studied most extensively due to its low power consumption, high reversibility, and wide applicability to different fluids. In EWOD, a dielectric coating is used to cover the electrodes, eliminating the direct electrochemical interaction between the fluid and the electrode with a trade-off of higher driving voltage. Contact angles of liquid droplets on the electrode surface can be controlled by electric potential according to the Lippmann-Young equation

$$\cos\theta(V) - \cos\theta(0) = \frac{\varepsilon}{2\gamma_{\mathrm{LV}}t}V^2 \tag{2.4}$$

where $\theta(V)$ is the contact angle under electric potential V, γ_{LV} is the surface tension at the liquid-vapor interface, and ε and t are respectively the permittivity and thickness of the insulating layer. If AC voltage is applied, V is replaced by the root-mean-square voltage. Good agreement has been observed between the Lippmann-Young equation and the experimentally measured contact angles. The required driving voltage, therefore, can be minimized accordingly by using a thin layer of dielectric and a high permittivity material.

As the contact angle changes due to the applied voltage, the surface wettability changes. By applying a voltage at one end of the droplet to decrease the surface tension, a difference in force between the ends of the droplet can be created, which causes droplet motion. Different methods have been developed for driving droplets on a 2D space to realize the digital fluidic concept. Recently, Cho, et al. have demonstrated creation, transportation, cutting, and merging of fluid droplets. All these droplet operations can be done on a single chip. Mixing of fluorescence dye and separation of particles in digital fluidic chips has also been demonstrated.

2.5.5 Electrophoresis

The electrophoretic force is for moving a charged particle embedded in neutral medium. The particle of charge q subject to an external electric field E experiences an electrostatic force $F = qE$. An electrical field of 10^6 V/m (equivalent to 10 V over a 10 μm gap) yields a force of 1.6×10^{-13} N on a single charged particle. Thus, with a friction coefficient given by Stokes's law $f=6\pi\mu r$, where r is the particle radius and μ the medium viscosity, the particle has a velocity $v=\dfrac{q}{6\pi r\mu}E$. We should note that the viscosity, μ, might not be the nominal bulk viscosity for reasons discussed in the previous section. For micron-size particles in water, it yields velocities in the order of 20 μm/s. For a uniform electric field, the force is constant over distance, and does not depend on the properties of the particles, only its charge.

2.5.6 Dielectrophoresis

Dielectrophoresis (DEP) occurs when a polarizable particle is subjected to a diverging electric field. The induced dipole in the particle causes the particle to experience an unbalanced force. It is commonly used to generate relative displacement between the particles and the medium. The time average dielectrophoretic force is given by[19]

$$F_{\mathrm{DEP}}=2\pi R^3\varepsilon_m \operatorname{Re}\{K(\omega)\}\nabla|E_{\mathrm{rms}}|^2 \tag{2.5}$$

where R is the particle radius, E_{rms} is the root mean square electric field, ω is the angular field frequency, $\operatorname{Re}\{K(\omega)\}$ represents the real part of $K(\omega)$, and $K(\omega)$ is the Clausius-Mossotti factor at angular frequency ω. The Clausius-Mossotti factor is a measure of the effective polarizability of the particle in the medium and is given by

$$K(\omega)=\frac{\varepsilon_{\mathrm{p}}^*-\varepsilon_{\mathrm{m}}^*}{\varepsilon_{\mathrm{p}}^*+2\varepsilon_{\mathrm{m}}^*} \tag{2.6}$$

where $\varepsilon_{\mathrm{p,m}}^*$ are the complex permittivities of the particle and medium, respectively. If the polarizability of the particle is higher than the medium ($\operatorname{Re}\{K(\omega)\}>0$), the force is toward the high field strength region (positive DEP). In the other case ($\operatorname{Re}\{K(\omega)\}<0$), the force is toward the lower field region (negative DEP). For homogeneous particle and medium, the complex dielectric constant is given by

$$\varepsilon_{\mathrm{p,m}}^*=\varepsilon_{\mathrm{p,m}}+\frac{\sigma_{\mathrm{p,m}}}{\mathrm{j}\omega} \tag{2.7}$$

For a more general description, the complex permittivities of the particle and medium have to be replaced by the frequency-dependent values to account for different mechanisms of polarization[20–23]. For example, a cell consists of various materials and structures. Each material has very different electrical properties, leading to large interfacial polarizations at the boundaries between structures. Similarly, redistribution of the counterion cloud causes large polarization for charged molecules, such as protein and DNA.

Another effect of polarization is the stretching of the objects, such as cells or DNA molecules. This force may be used to stretch deformable objects such as cells or DNA. Figure 2.6 depicts the stretching and eventual lysing of a cabbage protoplast with dielectrophoretic force. Precise measurement of the mechanical properties of a cell provides useful information about its structural organization and physiological state. For example, the deformability of red blood cells can distinguish young cells from aged cells and can be directly applied in the diagnosis of many diseases, such as sickle cell anemia and elliptocytosis. It is interesting to understand the effect of individual components on the mechanical properties of the entire cell. In this study, we investigate the influence of the cytoskeletal actin on the viscoelastic properties of a cell. Actin-specific agents, including latrunculin A and jasplakinolide, are used to alter the organization of the cytoskeletal actin. Brassica oleracea protoplasts are treated with the drugs and deformed under an external electric potential. The relaxation processes of single protoplasts after electrodeformation are studied Fig. 2.6(a) and (b) show the stretching and relaxing of the cell. Figure 2.6(c) depicts the cell being broken by the electric field.

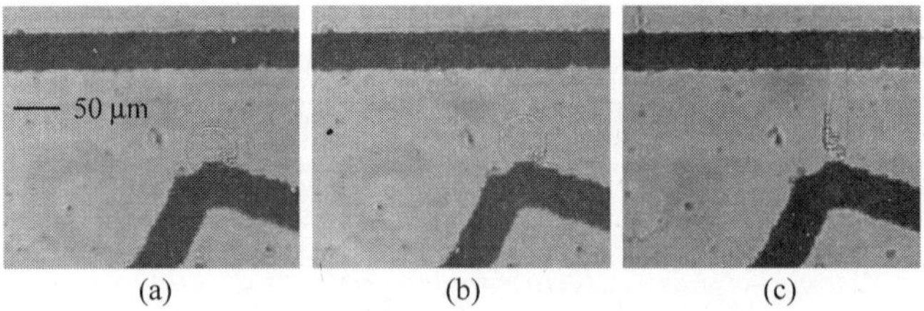

Figure 2.6 Stretch-and-relax experiment of a single brassica oleracea protoplast. (a) The protoplast is relaxed under no electric field. (b) It is deformed under dielectrophoretic force. (c) The cell membrane has ruptured under excessive high electric field

2.6 Microfluidic Processes for Bioanalyses

2.6.1 Sample Concentration

Extracting samples from quite diluted concentrate with a large amount of liquid or air is usually required. For example, centrifugal force is commonly used for enrich liquid concentrate samples on laboratory bench A centrifuge needs large rotation arm and high rotation frequency. Both requirements are difficult to meet in MEMS. For an MEMS-based bioanalysis system, on-chip sample concentration or enrichment is then a key interface between macro and micro worlds. In fact, most of the power consumption in the whole system could be at this step. Efficient micro concentration devices other than the centrifugal force-based approach needed. Various techniques have been developed for concentrating target samples in microfluidic chips, such as acoustic radiation pressure, microfabricated sieving filters, and evaporation-based concentration.

Among the others, membrane with perforations (filter) is a candidate for sample collection[24, 25] By passing liquid or air through the micromachined membrane as shown in Fig. 2.7[26], the target particle or biological agents can be collected. For the filtering of micron-sized particles, the membrane must be mechanically robust to withstand high pressure drop. In order to improve filter strength, a layer of Parylene C is conformally deposited on filters. The burst pressure of the filter increases up to 4.2 psi, which is four times more than that of an uncoated filter. With the configurations of 1 – 3 μm thickness and 4 – 12 μm hole size, data were collected from many filter designs with opening ratio ranging from 4% – 45%. Based on the collected data, we developed an empirical design rule for predicting the pressure drop[27,28]:

$$K = \frac{2\Delta P}{\rho U_{\text{in}}^2} = \beta^{-2}\left[3.5\frac{t}{d} + 3\right]\left[10\frac{\nu}{U_{\text{h}}d} + 0.22\right]$$

where U_{in} is the velocity in front of the filter, U_{h} the velocity through the hole of diameter of d, t the thickness, β the opening ratio, ρ the density of fluid, and ν the viscosity. Low pressure drop requires a high opening factor (ratio of hole area to total area), which allows a large amount of fluid passing through all the holes at low velocity.

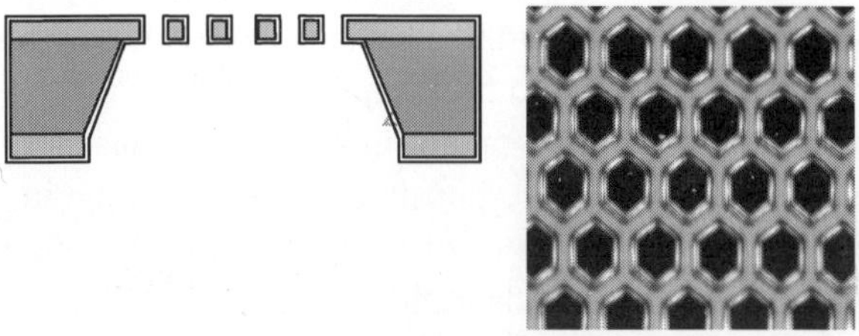

Figure 2.7 A MEMS particle filter[26]

After the particles are collected, the concentrated samples need to be transported into liquid phase for sample preparation. A dielectrophoretic force generated by electrodes deposited on top of the filter is used to move the particles[29,30]. Dielectrophoretic particle transportation was realized by using a 3-phase traveling voltage. In this system, the dielectrophoretic force enables particle transportation while adhesion forces, consisting of van der Waals forces, electro-static forces, image force, meniscus forces, and body forces resist against transportation. Based on different tests with various insulating materials and thickness, 90% particle transport efficiency has been achieved.

We have also developed a bioprocessor that exploits AC electroosmosis for concentrating bioparticles, such as cells and molecules. A combination of the AC electroosmotic flow and other EK forces are applied to concentrate bioparticles. The long-range bulk fluid flow transports the embedded particles to the region near the electrode surface, where other short-range EK forces trap the target cells and molecules. The advantage of AC electroosmosis is that only low applied voltage (a few volts) is required to generate the bulk fluid motion. The fluid flow can significantly increase the effective range of the bioprocessor while only small applied voltage is required. In addition, our device takes advantage of the hydrodynamic flow, which is effective for different sizes of objects, while maintaining the selectivity of EK forces to the targets through, for examples, size and electrical properties. A large variety of biological samples (from nanometer to micrometer range) can be concentrated on the same device by just changing the operating parameters. By optimizing the operating parameters, we have demonstrated concentration of various biological objects including *E.* coli bacteria, λ-phage DNA, and single-strand DNA fragments as small as 20 base pairs.

2.6.2 Mixing

In a variety of processes, such as cell lyses, polymerase chain reaction (PCR), and DNA hybridization, the mixing of particles, cells, and molecules inside the microfluidic devices determines the efficiency of the whole system. Effective mixing procedures can significantly reduce the time required for the entire process. In macro scale devices, turbulence is generated and increases the contact area of the two or more fluids. Complete mixing is then achieved by molecular diffusion. Typical liquid flow in microfluidic devices has very low Reynolds number. Molecular diffusion is responsible for the mixing in the absence of turbulence and requires a long time for accomplishing thorough mixing. Using force perturbations to generate folds in the micro mixing device can increase the total interfacial area and hence reduce the necessary diffusion length and the required mixing mixing.

In deterministic nonlinear dynamical systems, an unstable behavior, chaos, may happen[31]. A chaotic system is usually sensitive to its initial conditions. For example, two nearby particles with slightly different initial condition may separate far apart. The unpredictability of a chaotic flow system can serve as a practical way to improve the mixing problem. In low Reynolds number flow, the governing equations for the velocity field are linear in nature and therefore no chaos can be found. However, the equations of motion for fluid particle trajectories are generally not linear. Even rather simple, unsteady 2D flow fields can result in chaotic particle paths such as tendril-whorl flow and blinking vortex flow[32]. Stretching and folds help in increasing the contact area between species. The slow diffusion process completes the molecular mixing. If chaos is produced by properly imposed unsteadiness, the mixing among molecules is much more efficient than diffusion.

A chaos study in micro configurations has been carried out in a 3D serpentine microchannel[33] and in 2D unsteady flows[34,35]. Based on this concept, a two-stream fluid micro mixing device has been fabricated. We fabricated a microfluidic device consisting of a primary channel containing two parallel streams and several transverse channels[36]. Unsteady hydrodynamic perturbations are applied through the transverse channels for mixing the fluids in the two streams in the primary channel. When perturbations are operated at a certain frequency and amplitude range, chaos has been identified through numerical simulations. Efficient mixing has been observed in experiment. A parallel study on using DEP force to arrive at chaotic mixing is also in progress.

2.6.3 Separation

In bioanalyses, particles, cells, or molecules may need to be separated from one another. The separation process may be based on a certain physical-chemical property such as size, viscosity, diffusivity, charge, solubility, and density. Electrophoresis, chromatography, ultra filtration, filtration, sedimentation, extraction, and adsorption are among the most commonly employed separation techniques. The first three techniques provide the finest purification and are more effective in micro scale. For example, a MEMS ion-exchange liquid chromatography chip is shown in Fig. 2.8[37]. This device can handle a sample volume as small as 3 nL.

The nature of slow mixing in micro flow is a problem for enhancing the relative motion of molecules but can be used advantageously for separation process. An interesting example is a diffusion-based separation device[38,39], which separates particles based on their different diffusion coefficients and also relies on the non-mixing nature in a low Reynolds number fluid.

In many cases, ultra filtration is needed in biomedical applications[40]. For example, in the plasma fractionation process, the presence of even one unwanted particle, such as a virus, in the filtrate stream, could be catastrophic. An ultra filtration membrane used for size-based separation can be fabricated either by solvent-casting or ion track etching process. Recently, a number of micromachined filtration devices have been demonstrated by making either a one-structural layer process[26, 41] or a two-structural layer process[24, 40]. In a one-structural layer

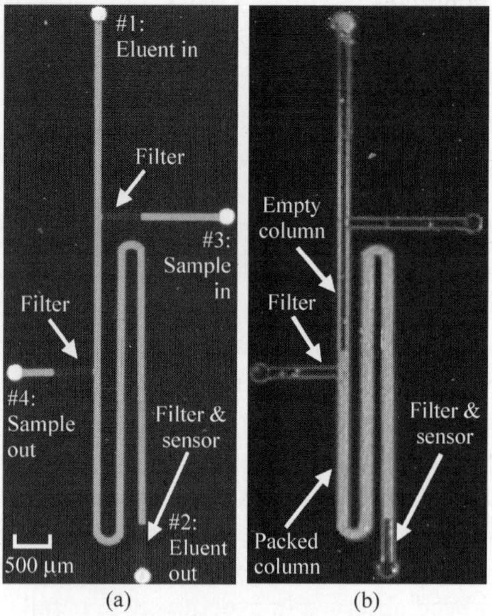

Figure 2.8 An ion-exchange liquid chromatography device with column length of 1 cm (see color figure at the end of this book)

process, the pores are directly made on a membrane layer and the pore size is determined by photolithography. In a two-structural layer process, since the nominal pore size is determined by the thickness of a sacrificial layer sandwiched between two structure layers, the pore size can be made much smaller to be about 50 nm[40].

Capillary electrophoresis (CE) is widely used in biological analysis[42, 43]. By applying MEMS fabrication technology, a sample injector and a separation capillary can be integrated in a simple cross-shape microchannel design. Both fast and efficient separation can be achieved by using short separation channels, high field strength, and a small volume sample plug. The efficiency of micro CE is comparable with that of the conventional CE but the analysis time is cut down to tens of seconds as compared to half an hour with the standard device[44]. By properly designing the separation channels or coupling CE with another separation technique, like chromatography, a number of 2D CE chips have been reported[45, 46], which can substantially increase the separation resolution. Recently, a capillary array electrophoresis chip was demonstrated to analyze 48 samples in a chip at the same time, which largely enhances the throughput of DNA sequencing[47].

2.6.4 Electrochemical DNA Detection

Although optical methods have higher sensitivity, enzyme-based electrochemical methods[48, 49] have important advantages such as low fabrication cost, ease of miniaturization, and automated detection. The principle of the enzyme-based electrochemical DNA detection is shown in Fig. 2.9.

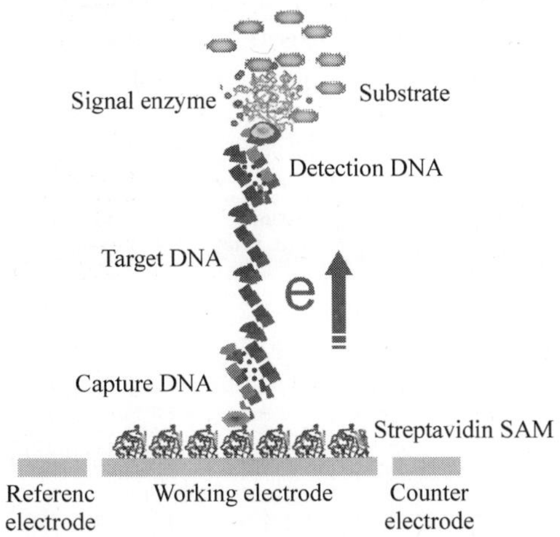

Figure 2.9 A schematic of electrochemical DNA detection (see color figure at the end of this book)

Two single-stand DNA probes are used with this sensor: a capture probe and a detection probe. These two probes recognize a specific sequence on the target DNA. Therefore, a hybrid will only form between the probe DNA and the target DNA. The hybrid is then immobilized through biotin-streptavidin binding onto the detection chip. Next, the unbound components are washed away. After loading the signaling enzyme onto the hybrid, the substrate is added and the enzymatic reaction may be detected amperometrically. Including the sample preparation, the detection can be completed in 45 minutes or less[50]. With this method, a sensitivity of one picomole can be obtained on a commercial electrochemical sensor (Fig. 2.10).

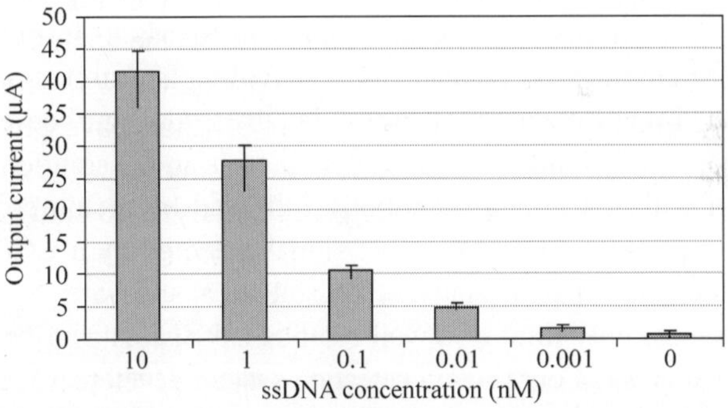

Figure 2.10 Detection result on commercial electrochemical sensor (AndCare)

The nanoscale self-assembled monolayer (SAM) on the surface of the sensor is a key factor to increase sensitivity by reducing noise[51]. By optimizing the sensor surface, a better performance has been demonstrated as shown in Fig. 2.11. As a result, a single cell can be detected without the need for a PCR. Furthermore, if a molecule beacon is used as the detection probe instead of linear single strand DNA, single nucleotide polymorphisms may be detected. This method may be leveraged to allow electrochemical protein detection.

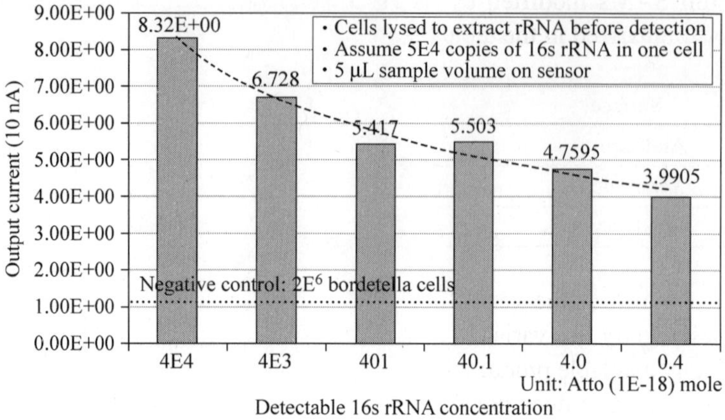

Figure 2.11 Detection result on gold sensor

2.6.5 Protein Detection

Another component of our biodetection system is an optical protein sensor targeted for human epidermal growth factor (EGF). Our goal is to develop a highly sensitive and reliable protein sensor that surpasses conventional protein assays by leveraging the sensitivity of fluorescence detection and noise minimization. EGF protein is the model protein used for detection since it is a potential biomarker for oral cancers. A glass surface is activated with SAMs to form the foundation for a consistent outermost monolayer of streptavidin. The streptavidin monolayer permits ordered immobilization of biotinylated capture antibodies. This active surface will specifically bind the EGF protein present in the solution. The captured EGF is labeled with a secondary antibody followed by a fluorescent molecule. Light excitation produces a fluorescence signal detected by a CCD camera. The fluorescence intensity image is analyzed by statistical software.

We used the sensitivity limit of a well-established ELISA assay as a benchmark to describe the progress of our protein detection system developed for a miniaturized system. However, the results are not consistent. Two problems are associated with the inconsistent data but both problems originate from surface issues. The first one is that the surface light intensity is not uniform. Reproducibility is the second issue. At present, positive identification of the presence of EGF protein has been demonstrated. Current efforts are focused on accurately quantifying the amount of protein.

In our efforts to improve the uniformity of the surface, we have researched the performance of three surfaces upon which to build a streptavidin monolayer. These include a commercially available streptavidin coated carbon paste surface (AndCare), streptavidin coated glass (Xenoprobe), and a gold surface with streptavidin SAMs modified by us. The values for the coefficient of variance (CV) are summarized in the table below.

Surface	CV
AndCare	8%–16%
Xenoprobe	6%–13%
SAMs on gold	10%–33%

These CVs reflect the variability within one sample surface. The Xenoprobe surface has slightly less variability than the AndCare surface. It is apparent that the commercially available products have smaller CVs than the gold surface indicating that the gold surface does not form uniform surfaces. It is likely that the results are due to the extra quality control measures the company performs on its products, in contrast to our limited control measures in our surface preparation protocol. This supports the theory that the surface properties of the sensor influence the uniformity of the surface and sensor performance.

The advantage of the carbon paste (AndCare) and streptavidin coated glass surface (Xenoprobe) are better surface uniformity, but they both have high noise values. This minimizes the signal to noise ratio. The noise characterization of the glass surface (Fig. 2.12) demonstrates that the major contribution to noise is non-specific binding. This result indicates that a surface that participates less in non-specific binding, such as gold, would be favorable. However, the CV results show that the SAM-forming protocol needs to be improved in order for us to use gold as the sensor surface. Most assays use a blocker to inhibit non-specific binding; however, we believe that if uniform and well-packed SAMs are formed, non-specific binding may be prevented without the use of a blocking protein.

The second problem we encountered before we were able to quantify protein with this sensor is the reproducibility. The goal is to not simply identify the presence of proteins on a one-time basis, but actually to have the ability to quantify the amount of protein present. For instance, in the case of EGF, it is always present in the saliva, but what may indicate diseased states is an elevated concentration of EGF in the saliva. We are currently in the process of identifying the source of the non-reproducibility, but it is speculated that the formation of uniform SAMs within samples and between samples will also improve the sensor reproducibility.

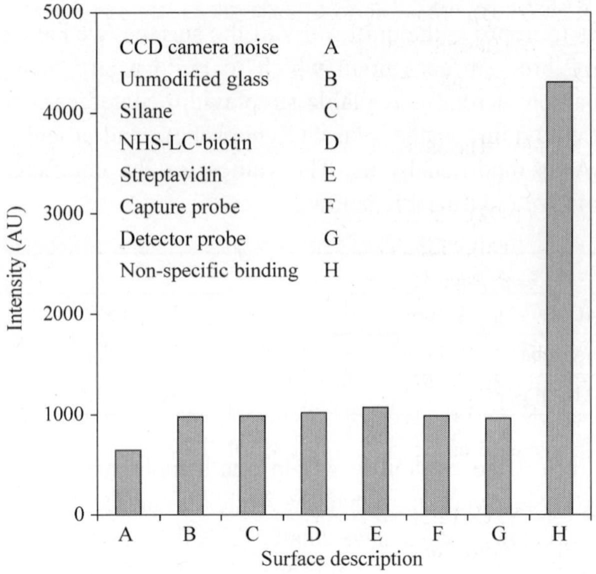

Figure 2.12 Noise analyses for EGF detection on a glass surface

2.7 Conclusions

Concentration, mixing, and separation of particles in fluids are common processes in industry. In biomedical fields, the encountered particles (e.g., DNA, proteins, and cells) are in the nanometer to micron range. Today, microfluidic processes can handle the particles down to molecular scales at high efficiency and, hence, have greatly advanced the biomedical diagnostic techniques.

Nevertheless, the molecular and size effects can influence transport properties of microflows in a significant way. Both the molecule-wall and molecule-molecule interactions are the basic mechanisms of the observed effects. Much still needs to be studied and research in nano/micro fluid flows will continue to discover intriguing new findings in both science and technology.

Acknowledgements

The authors would like to express their appreciation to the group of post-doctoral scholars and graduate students who have made this study possible.

References

[1] Kim C. J., A. P. Pisano, and R. S. Muller, (1992), *J. Microelectromechanical* Systems, **1**: 31

[2] Lu Y., C. J. Kim, (2003), "Micro-finger articulation by Pneumatic Parylene Balloons", in IEEE Transducer '03, Boston, 276 – 279

[3] Tien C. L., A. Majumdar, and F. M. Gerner, (1998), "Microscale Energy Transport", Taylor & Francis Pub

[4] Larson R. G., (1999), "The structure and rheology of Complex Fluids", Oxford University Press

[5] Israelachvili J. N., (1992), "Intermolecular and Surface Forces", Academic Press

[6] Gee M. L., et al., (1990), "Liquidlike to Solidlike Transitions of Molecularly Thin Films under Shear", *J. Chem. Phys.* **93**(3): 1895 – 1906

[7] Barnes H. A., (1995), "A Review of the Slip (Wall Depletion) of Polymer Solutions, Emulsions and Particle Suspensions in Viscometers: its Cause, Character, and Cure", *J. non-Newtonian Fluid Mech.,* **56**(3): 221 – 256

[8] Grosjean C., and Y. C. Tai, (1999), "A Thermopneumatic Peristaltic Micropump", 1999 International Conference on Solid-State Sensors and Actuators (Transducers '99), Sendai, Japan, June

[9] Xie J., J. Shih, and Y. C. Tai, (2003), "Integrated parylene electrostatic peristaltic pump", Proceedings, 2003 *Micro Total Analysis System (uTAS '03),* Squaw Valley, California, USA, Oct. 5 – 9, 865 – 869

[10] Wong P. K., U. Ulmanella, and C. M. Ho, "Fabrication Process of Microsurgical Tools for Single-Cell Trapping and Intracytoplasmic Injection", *J. Microelectromechanical Systems* (in press)

[11] LeDuc P., C. Haber, G. Bao, and D. Wirtz, (1999), "Dynamics of Individual Flexible Polymer in a Shear Flow", *Nature,* **399**: 564 – 566

[12] Smith D. E., H. P. Babcock, and S. Chu, (1999), "Single-polymer dynamics in steady shear flow", *Science*, **283**: 1724 – 1727

[13] Babcock H. P., D. E. Smith, J. S. Hur, E. S. G. Shaqfeh, and S. Chu, (2000), "Relating the microscopic and macroscopic response of a polymeric fluid in a shearing flow", *Physical Review Letters*, **85**(9): 2018 – 2021

[14] Wong P. K., Y. K. Lee, C. M. Ho, (2003), "Deformation of DNA molecules by hydrodynamic focusing", *Journal of Fluid Mechanics,* **497**: 55 – 65

[15] Perkins T. T., S. R. Quake, D. E. Smith, and S. Chu, (1994), "Relaxation of a single DNA molecule observed by optical microscopy", *Science,* **264**(5160): 822 – 826

[16] Wong P. K., T. H. Wang, J. H. Deval, C. M. Ho, "Electrokinetics in Micro Devices for Biotechnology Applications", *IEEE/ASME Transactions on Mechatronics* (in press)

[17] Ramos A., H. Morgan, N. G. Green, and A. Castellanos, (1998), "AC electrokinetics: a review of forces in microelectrode structures", *J. Phys D: Appl. Phys.*, **31**: 2338 – 2353

[18] Green N. G., and H. Morgan, (1998), "Separation of Submicrometer Particles Using a Combination of Dielectrophoretic and Electrohydrodynamic Forces", *J. Phys. D: Appl. Phys.* **3**: 1 25 – 30

[19] Pohl H. A., (1978), "Dielectrophoresis: the Behavior of Neutral Matter in Nonuniform

Electric Fields", Cambridge University Press

[20] Ramos A., H. Morgan, N. G. Green, and A. Castellanos, (1999), "The Role of Electrohydrodynamic Forces in the Dielectrophoretic Manipulation and Separation of Particles", *J. Electrostatics,* **47**: 71 – 81

[21] Schnelle T., T. Müller, G. Gradl, S. G. Shirley, and G. Fuhr, (2000), "Dielectrophoretic Manipulation of Suspended Submicron Particles", *Electrophoresis,* **21**: 66 – 73

[22] Hughes M. P., (2000), "AC Electrokinetics: Applications for Nanotechnology", *Nanotechnology,* **11**: 124 – 132

[23] Green N. G., and H. Morgan, "Dielectrophoretic separation of nano-particles", *J. Phys. D: Appl. Phys.* **30**: 41 – 84, (1997) **9**(2): 190 – 197, (2000)

[24] Kittilsland G., G. Steme, and B. Norden, (1990), "A Submicron Particle Filter in Silicon", *Sensors and Actuators A: Physical,* **23**: 904 – 907

[25] van Rijn C. J. M., M. van der Wekken, W. Hijdam, and M. C. Elwenpoek, (1997), "Deflection and Maximum Load of Microfiltration Membrane Sieves Made with Silicon Micromachining", 1997, *Journal of Microelectromechanical Systems,* **6**: 48 – 54

[26] Yang X., J. M. Yang, Y. C. Tai, and C. M. Ho, (1999), "Micromachined membrane particle filters", *Sensor and Actuators A; Physical,* **73**: 184 – 191

[27] Yang J. M., X. Yang, C. M. Ho, and Y. C. Tai, (1999), "Prediction of the Pressure Drop Through Micromachined Particle Filters", *Technical Proceedings of International Conference on Modeling and Simulation of Microsystems* (MSM '99), San Juan, Puerto Rico 546 – 549

[28] Hsiai T. K., J. M. Yang, X. Yang, S. K. Cho, Y. Chen, C. M. Ho, and Y. C. Tai, (2000), "Pressure Drops of Water Flow through Micromachined Particle Filters" submitted to ASME *Journal of Fluids Engineering*

[29] Lee S. W., J. M. Yang, Y. C. Tai, and C. M. Ho, (1999), "Electrostatically active microfilters for automated airborne particle collection", International Conference on Solid-State Sensors and Actuators (Transducers '99), Sendai, Japan

[30] Desai, S., W. Lee, and Y. C. Tai, (1999), "A MEMS electrostatic particle transportation system", *Sensors and Actuators A; Physical,* **73**: 37 – 44

[31] Lorenz E., (1963), "Deterministic nonperiodic flow", Journal of the Atmospheric Sciences, 20

[32] Ottino J. M., (1989), "The Kinematics of Mixing: Stretching, Chaos, and Transport", Cambridge University Press, New York

[33] Liu R. H., M. A. Stremler, K. V. Sharp, M. G. Olsen, J. G. Santiago, R. J. Adrian, H. Aref, and D. J. Beebe, (2000), "Passive Mixing in a Three-dimensional Serpentine Microchannel", *Journal of MEMS,* **9**(2): 190 – 197

[34] Volpert M., C. D. Meinhart, I. Mezic, and M. Dahelh, (1999), "An Actively Controlled Micromixer", Proc. of MEMS, ASME IMECE, Nashville, Tennessee, 483 – 487

[35] Lee Y. K., P. Tabeling, C. Shi, and C. M. Ho, (2000), "Characterization of a MEMS-Fabricated Mixing Device", Proc. of MEMS, ASME IMECE, Orlando, Florida, Nov

[36] Lee Y. K, J. Deval, P. Tabeling. and C. M. Ho, (2001), "Chaotic Mixing in Electrokinetically and Pressure Driven Micro Flows", Proceedings of the IEEE 14th Annual Workshop of Micro Electro Mechanical Systems (MEMS '01), Interlaken, Switzerland

[37] He Q., C. Pang, Y. C. Tai, and T. Lee, (2004), "Ion liquid chromatography on a chip with bead-packed parylene column", Proceedings, *The Seventeenth IEEE International Conference on Micro Electro Mechanical Systems (MEMS '04),* Maastricht, The Netherlands, Jan. 25 – 29, 212 – 215

[38] Weigl B. H., and P. Yager, (1999), "Microfluidic Diffusion-Based Separation and Detection", Science

[39] Brody J. P., and P. Yager, (1997), "Diffusion-based extraction in a microfabricated device", *Sensors and Actuators, A* **58**: 13 – 18

[40] Tu J. K., T. Huen, R. Szema, and M. Ferrari, (1999), "Filtration of sub-100 nm particles using a bulk-micromachined, direct-bonded silicon filter", *J. Biomedical Microdevices* **1**(2): 113 – 119

[41] van Rijn C., G. Veldhuis, and S. Kuiper, (1998), "Nanosieves with microsystem technology for microfiltration applications", *Nanotechnology* **9**: 343 – 345

[42] Effenhauser C. S., A. Manz, and H. M. Widmer, (1993), "Glass chips for high-speed capillary electrophoresis separations with submicrometer plate heights", *Anal. Chem.* **65**: 2637 – 2642

[43] Woolley A. T., and R. A. Mathies, (1995), "Ultra-high-speed DNA sequencing using capillary electrophoresis chips", *Anal. Chem.* **67**: 3676 – 3680

[44] Deyl Z., I. Miksik, and F. Tagliaro, (1998), "Advances in capillary electrophoresis", *Forensic Science International*, **92**: 89 – 124

[45] Burggraf N., A. Manz, E. Verpoorte, C. S. Effenhauser, H. M. Widmer, N. F. de Rooij, (1994), "A novel approach to ion separations in solution: synchronized cyclic capillary electrophoresis (SCCE)", *Sensors and Actuators*, **B20**(2 – 3): 103 – 110

[46] Becker H., K. Lowack, and A. Manz, (1998), "Planar quartz chips with submicron channels for two-dimensional capillary electrophoresis applications", *J. Micromech. Microeng.* **8**: 24 – 28

[47] Simpson P. C., A. T. Woolley, and R. A. Mathies, (1998), "Microfabrication technology for the production of capillary array electrophoresis chips", *J. of Biomedical Microdevices*, **1**(1): 7 – 26

[48] Ivnitski D., I. Abdel-Hamid, P. Atanasov, and E. Wilkins, (1999), "Biosensors for detection of pathogenic bacteria", *Biosensor and Bioelectronics,* **14**: 599 – 624

[49] Ivnitski D., I. Abdel-Hamid, P. Atanasov, E. Wilkins, and S. Stricker, (2000), "Application of Electrochemical Biosensors for Detection of Food Pathogenic Bacteria", *Electroanalysis*, **12**(5): 317 – 325

[50] Chen Y. F., J. M. Yang, J. J. Gau, C. M. Ho, and Y. C. Tai, (2000), "Microfluidic System for Biological Agent Detection", Proc. of *the 3rd International conference on the interaction of Art and Fluid Mechanics*, Zurich, Switzerland

[51] Gau J. J., E. H. Lan, B. Dunn, and C. M. Ho, (2000), "Enzyme-based electrochemical biosensor with DNA array chip", Proc. of *the fourth International Symposium on Micro Total Analysis Systems* (μTAS), Enschede, The Netherlands, **5**(14 – 18): 509 – 511

3 Material Issues for Microsystems

Bingchu Cai

Research Institute of Micro/Nano Science and Technology, Shanghai Jiao Tong University, No. 1954, Huashan Road, Shanghai 200030, China

E-mail: bccai@sjtu.edu.cn

Abstract For manufacturing a stable, reliable and durable microsystem, the designers must have the correct mechanical properties of materials which are used to prepare structural components before designing the Microsystems. It is well known that the mechanical properties of materials are not only depending on the materials composition, but also on its microstructure, manufacturing processes, and micro components size. Because the material's properties that could be found in handbook are for bulk materials which are prepared by standard producing processes (for example: rolling, forging). But the micro components in Microsystems are manufactured by the way quite different from the macro components with bulk materials (for example: CVD, Sputtering, Etching). Therefore, the microsystem designer can not use the materials properties listed in handbook to design micro components.

Due to above reasons, there is a serious challenge of materials issue to MEMS designer. It is hardly to make sure that what correct materials properties should he picked up. To find the data from handbook is incorrect, but he could not also find the suitable data from literatures based on the dimensions and preparation processes of micro component he designed. In such case, the designer should measure the materials properties for important microparts by himself before designing MEMS system.

Hereby, before the material's properties which are usually selected in Microsystems are introduced, this chapter will briefly descript the failure analysis of micro parts and the measuring methods of material's mechanical properties from the micro components.

Keywords Failure mechanism, Young's modulus, measuring technologies, structure materials, microtribological materials

3.1 Failure Mechanisms of Materials Used in Microsystems

Excessive plastic deformation and fracture are the main failure mechanisms of components used in macro systems. However, in microsystems, excessive plastic deformation will not occur since most of single and polycrystal of silicon, silicon nitride often used in microsystems are very brittle. Even though more ductile materials are used some times, excessive plastic deformation can be avoided through design. Thus, fracture is the most important failure mechanism of materials in microsystems. In addition to fracture, there is another failure mechanism of components operated in microsystems. It is named stiction. The micro components in MEMS device are so close that two moving components will be attracted to each other during operation or releasing of some micro component during the fabrication process due to various action forces. For example, stiction will take place between two driving electrodes in a comb finger static driver, resulting in a short circuit. Thereby, it is very important for the researcher in the field of microsystems to understand the failure mechanism of microcomponents used in a microsystem. Such failure can be eliminated through system design, material selection, microfabrication, and package processes to increase the stability and reliability of microsystems.

3.1.1 Fracture Mechanism

Fracture is mainly divided into two categories: plastic and brittle fracture. As mentioned before, excessive plastic deformation will not happen and hence plastic fracture will not occur in microsystems. Therefore, brittle fracture is the most possible mechanism. Brittle fracture is very dangerous because there is no any symptom before fracture bursts with. It is to be noted that the fracture is not only dependent on the nature of materials but also on the stress state applied and the environmental temperature. It is well known that the tensile stress and ultra low temperature will cause brittle fracture of materials. Cleavage fracture, fatigue fracture, and stress corrosion fracture are all classified under the brittle fracture category.

3.1.1.1 Brittle Fracture

The micro components in MEMS devices are usually made using single and polycrystal of silicon, silicon nitride, etc. If there are no crystal defects in single-crystal silicon (SCS), the theoretical fracture strength of silicon can be determined by the following equation:

$$\sigma_{\mathrm{cf}} = (E\gamma / a)^{1/2} \tag{3.1}$$

where E is the elastic modulus of single crystal silicon, and γ and a are the surface energy and the distance between two atoms in silicon respectively. However, the real fracture strength for SCS is far lower than its theoretical value, because the crystal defects inside the single crystal or the surface defects induced during microfabrications always exist. For such a case, the fracture strength of SCS will decrease dramatically. The famous Griffith equation provides an approach to calculate the fracture strength for brittle materials containing defects. The real fracture strength of Griffith equation is expressed as below:

$$\sigma_{\mathrm{cf}} = (2E\gamma/\pi C)^{1/2} \tag{3.2}$$

where C is the dimension of micro defects, such as micro crack. Comparing the above two equations, it is clearly shown that even the size of the crystal defect is only 5 times the distance between two atoms, the real fracture strength will decrease to 8 times the theoretical strength.

For designers of microsystems, it is difficult to use this equation to design microcomponents since the surface energy of the material is unknown. Moreover, this equation does not consider any plastic deformation ability, and so is not in agreement with the real case. The index for evaluating the ability of material to resist the brittle fracture is the fracture toughness K_{1c} in the macro engineering at present time.

What does K_{1c} indicate? K_{1c} is one of the mechanical properties of materials, just like yield strength and ductility. With the development of fracture mechanics, scientists recognized that there are defects or micro cracks existing in the materials or components. Under the applied stress, the micro crack will propagate, when it grows to certain crack length, the component will fracture suddenly. It was also found that for different materials, the ability to resist the crack growth or fracture is different. Later, the criterion $\sigma_{\mathrm{c}} = K_{1c}/Y(a)^{1/2}$, (where σ_{c} is the critical fracture stress, a is the crack length, and Y is a parameter determined by the geometry shape of sample and crack and also the manner of applied force and can be found in a handbook) was obtained under plane strain stress conditions. This means that when the total applied tensile stress (σ) is equal to or lager than $K_{1c}/Y(a)^{1/2}$, the component will break suddenly. Based on this equation, the designer can carry out safety designing. First, the micro crack length should be measured or estimated. Then, a material with known fracture toughness (K_{1c}) is selected and finally the maximum permitted applied stress can be calculated. Therefore, the geometry parameters of micro components can be determined.

3.1.1.2 Fatigue Fracture

It is estimated that more than 80% of the material failure of the moving components in macro engineering systems is due to fatigue. Therefore, the main effort in this area is to increase the fatigue strength (the stress level at which the fatigue failure occurs after a specified number of cycles) in order to increase the service life of the structure components. As macro components, many micro structure components in microsystems are working under alternative cycling loads, such as a typical microbeam in a comb finger driver, and hence fatigue failure will be the important factor limiting the long operation life of micro components.

To prolong the service time of micro components working under cycling loads, it is necessary to understand the mechanism of the formation and propagation of the fatigue crack. Based on this mechanism, the designers and the manufacturing engineers can take all approaches to prevent or prolong the formation, or to slow the propagation speed of micro fatigue crack.

For macro components, the source of micro fatigue crack is at the surface mostly, for example, surface defects and sharp corners. There are a few literatures dealing with fatigue crack formation and propagation of fatigue crack for components in microsystems. One reason for this is that there are not too many MEMS devices or microsystems that have been operated for a long service period. However, it is still true that the surface is the source of fatigue crack for micro components. Therefore, the surface quality of micro fabrication is extremely important for MEMS devices. Any surface defects left due to micro fabrication will be the source of fatigue cracks.

When the fatigue crack is formed, it will propagate under the cycle alternative load and then will suddenly break when the crack size propagates to a critical value, because the stress strength factor K_1 at tip of crack reaches the K_{1c} of the material at this moment.

Fatigue strength, fatigue life, and fatigue limit are usually used to characterize the fatigue properties of materials. Fatigue strength is defined as the stress level at which failure occurs after a specified number of cycles (usually 10^7 cycles). Fatigue life is defined as number of cycles to components failure at a particular stress amplitude. For macro components, some materials (low carbon steels) reach a fatigue limit (at 35%–65% of tensile strength) below which fatigue failure will not occur, regardless of the number of cycles. Others will fail at some number of cycles regardless of the stress amplitude (for example, aluminum). For micro components, there are no literatures that mention the idea of fatigue limit. Figure 3.1 shows the stress versus number of cycles curve of a 2 mm thick polycrystal silicon deposited by PECVD[1], which illustrates that there is no fatigue limit exists.

3.1.2 Stiction, Friction, and Wear

During the releasing processes of sacrifice layer in microfabrication process or in the service period of micro components, if the distance between the component and substrate or two micro components is close enough, and also the adhesive force between two surfaces is larger than the elastic resilience of the micro

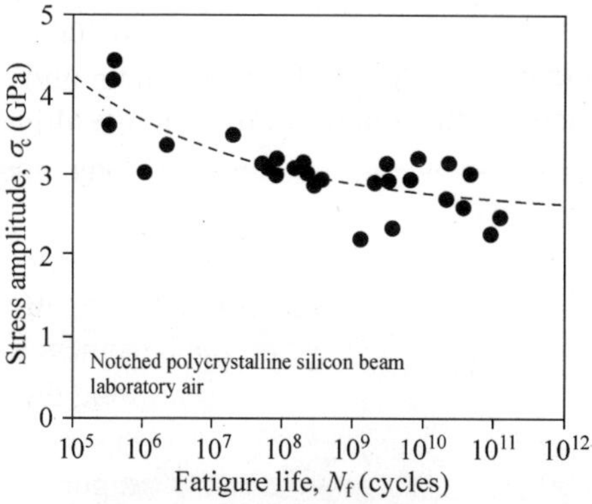

Figure 3.1 Stress versus number of cycles curve for polycrystal silicon

component, then the stiction phenomenon between the component and substrate or two components will occur, and the performance of the micro system will lose its function (failure). The detailed mechanism of stiction will be mentioned in the chapter on friction materials; friction and wear phenomenon are not discussed here.

3.1.3 Fractograph Analysis

Fractograph analysis plays an important role in determining the nature of material fracture. A search of the literatures on fractograph analysis of micro components revealed that very few articles exist. This is not because the fractograph method is not important for the fracture mechanism analysis of micro components, but because there are not many micro devices with moving components operating for a long period, or the failure mechanism is clearly due to designing issues or unsuitable fabrication processes.

It is very difficult to perform fractograph analysis for micro components by macro fractograph methods. Moreover, since the lens of optical microscope has short view depth, an electron microscope is the best choice for fractograph analysis of micro devices, especially a scanning electron microscope (SEM). For SEM method, the operation is easy, and the sample preparation is simple. The broken component can be directly used as the SEM sample in most cases. From SEM images, a lot of information, such as fracture route (transcrystal or intercrystal), crack source, and propagation path, can be obtained, and therefore the fracture mechanism can be deduced. Figure 3.2 gives the SEM image of fracture surface of square micropost made by an SU-8 resist[2]. From this image, it is clearly seen that the fracture path is not around the root of the micropost, where the serious stress condition is localized, but is in the side of the micropost, and there is a large hole at the fracture surface. Therefore, it can be deduced that the hole can be treated as a big crack, resulting in reducing the section area of the post, and when the K_1 value at the tip of crack reaches the K_{1c} of SU-8, the brittle fracture will occur suddenly. Based on this analysis, the following conclusion can be made: in order to increase the quality of the micropost, it is the manufacturing process of this post must be done very carefully, to prevent any micro contaminats from entering the SU-8 resist.

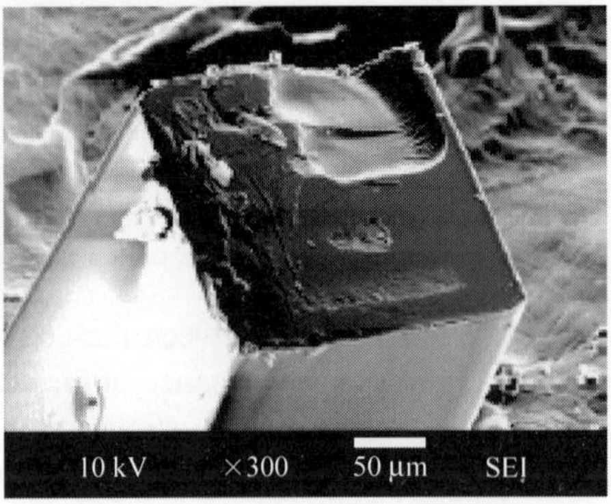

Figure 3.2 The fracture surface of micropost made of SU-8 resist

3.2 Methods for Measuring Mechanical Properties of Materials Used in Microsystems

As mentioned before, the properties of a material are controlled by its composition, preparation processes, and component dimension. Therefore, MEMS designers find it very hard to select the data regarding a material's mechanical properties from handbooks or literatures. In such cases, they have to measure the material's properties based on the fabrication process, component dimension themselves. This is because with further MEMS developments and the start of its commercialization, designers need correct and reliable data regarding a material's properties. Thus, the measuring methods for mechanical properties of MEMS materials such as Young's Modulus, tensile strength, and fatigue strength are introduced briefly. The evaluation of the variable methods will focus on the validity of the measuring method and the degree of ease for sample preparation and mounting and taking off, for alignment and loading, and for the measuring of force and displacement.

3.2.1 Micro Tensile Testing

This is a direct testing method of the Young's modulus, yielding, and tensile fracture strength for MEMS materials, but it has several disadvantages, such as difficulty in preparing the sample with a certain gauge length and in mounting and aligning the sample and precisely measuring the elongation. In order to overcome the sample mounting and alignment difficulty, literature[3] introduced a method to prepare the tensile testing sample by MEMS technology. The sample prepared using this method is shown in Fig. 3.3. It has a big connect ring at one end of the sample. During the sample mounting, the matching pin is inserted into the ring's inner hole to connect the sample and the moving stage of the set-up. When a force is applied, the sample can rotate slightly, and therefore the sample alignment can be completed automatically. Prof. Sharpe and his research group[4] at the John Hopkins University have developed a micro tensile testing set-up with the maximum loading ability of one pound. During a test when the force and displacement of the moving stage were recorded, the calculation of Young's modulus, yield strength, and finally the tensile fracture strength was found to be very straight forward.

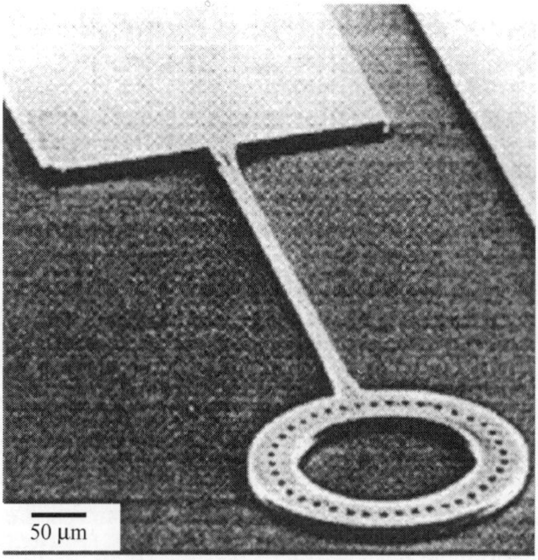

Figure 3.3 A SEM image of sample for direct tension test

In order to overcome the difficulty of mounting and aligning the sample, and to measure the elongation precisely, X. P. Li, et al.[5] used an on-chip tensile testing method. The detailed testing mechanism is shown in Fig. 3.4. The tensile test chip was made by the following procedure: First, a Cr/Cu seed layer was sputter-deposited on a silicon <100> wafer. Lithograph was done to pattern the resist where the sample of the material to be tested would be formed, and then the permalloy film with certain thickness was electroplated. The second step was to form the deep torsion bars by wet etching the silicon substrate from top, The last step was wet-etching the silicon wafer from the backside to form the torsion bars and load lever, as well as to release the film specimen.

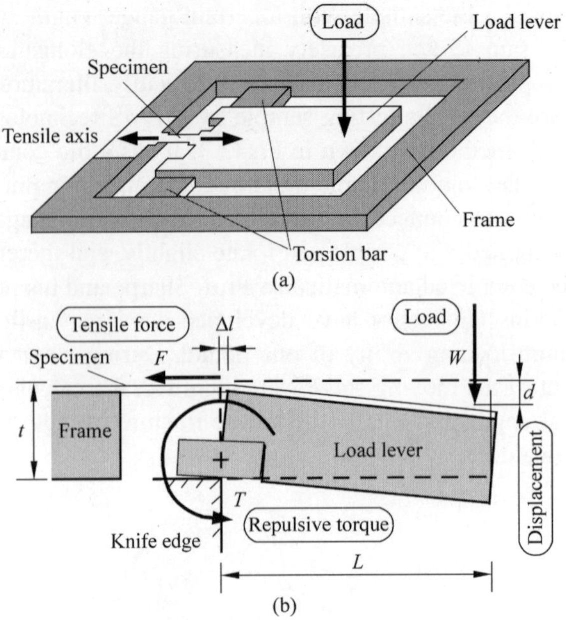

Figure 3.4 On-chip tensile testing method: (a) schematic on-chip tensile test chip; (b) testing mechanism

The loading mechanism of the 'on-chip' tensile method is schematized in Fig. 3.4(b). When an external load is applied to the load lever, there will be a moment balance on the load, W, the tensile force on the specimen, F, and the repulsive torque of the torsion bars, T, i.e.,

$$M(F)+T=M(W) \tag{3.3}$$

From this equation, it can be seen that the force F applied on the sample can be calculated from two curves of force-displacement. Therefore, the experiment was performed by making two force displacement curves, i.e., before and after the sample was fractured, as indicated by Fig. 3.5. Then, the final force F (obtained by subtracting the repulsive force from the loading curve shown in Fig. 3.5) and displacement curve of the tensile test can be drawn. From this curve, the Young's modulus, yield stress, and fracture strength of the testing material can be obtained. For a permalloy film dimension $100\times50\times5$ μm^3, its Young's modulus of 96.4 GPa was obtained by Li et al.[5].

The load and displacement are measured by the laser interference technique, since the load is applied by the spring force, which can be calculated if the elastic coefficient of spring is known. In addition to advantages mentioned above, this method can also test all the materials that can be deposited by physical and chemical deposition method. However, there is some limitation. For example, the testing sample thickness should be very thin relative to the load lever thickness; otherwise, there is additional toque applied on the sample.

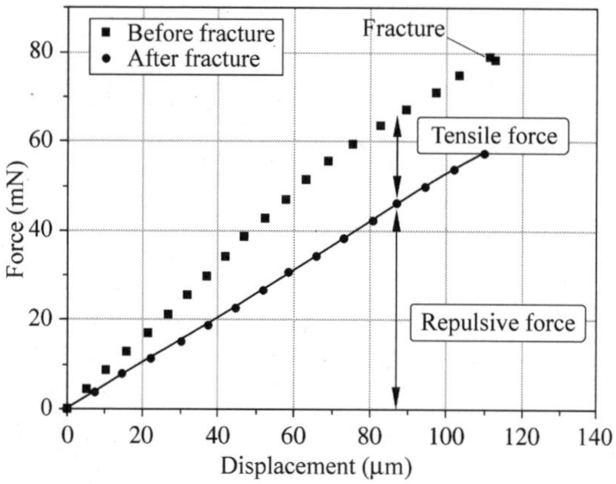

Figure 3.5 Force-displacement curves of loading position before and after the specimen fracture

3.2.2 Resonance Frequency Method

The Young's modulus of MEMS materials can be determined from the dynamic testing of a cantilever beam or other suspended structure. Peterson et al.[6] were the pioneers to perform this measurement. Figure 3.6(a) shows the set-up and the mechanism of the measurement The beam vibration was excited by a riable Frequency Oscilators with different frequencies, and the resonance frequency was measured by detecting the movement of the beam by using a reflect laser. Figure 3.6(b) depicts the vibration results for five silicon oxide beams of different lengths, giving the maximum vibration amplitude at different frequencies, whereby the resonance frequency f_r can be determined for different beams. Then, based on the relationship between the resonance frequency and its geometry ($f_r = 0.162t/L^2 \cdot (E/\rho)^{1/2}$) of the beam, the Young's modulus of the beam material can be calculated, where t and L are the beam thickness and length respectively, and ρ is the density. Li. X. X. et al.[7] tested the Young's modulus of a nanocantilever of SCS by the resonance frequency method, and showed the specimen dimension size effect of Young's modulus.

3.2.3 Bulge Test

Thin films are the main components of the micro structure or the functional part in microsystems. There are several experimental techniques by which the mechanical properties of thin films can be measured. Normally, these methods can be divided into two categories. The first category is based on measuring the mechanical properties of a composite structure. The thin film, the material property of which is required, was deposited on the substrate. Then, the mechanical

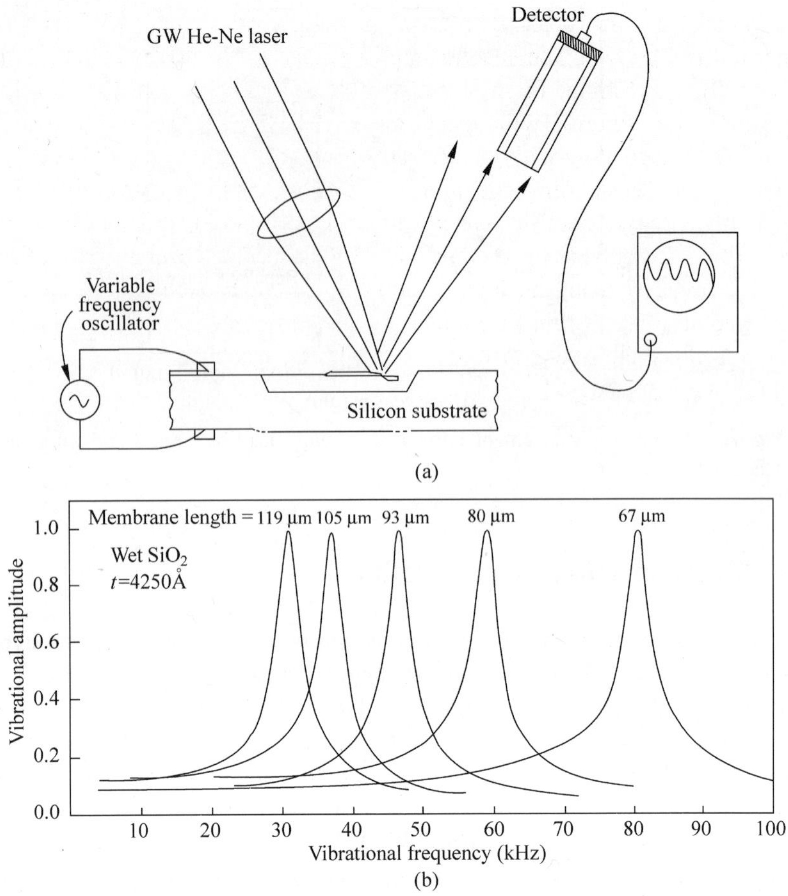

Figure 3.6 Cantilever resonance frequency method

properties of the composite structure were measured by nanoindentation or the substrate curvature technique. Therefore, the thin film's mechanical properties can be calculated if the mechanical properties of substrate are known. Another category is measuring the properties of freestanding thin films. In performing this bulge test, the freestanding film will bulge (deflect) when a uniform pressure is applied to. By measuring the pressure (*P*) and the deflection (*h*) at the center of the film, the plane stress and plane strain can be determined, and then the elastic, plastic, and time-dependent properties of the film can be obtained. Such a method has the advantage of simple sample preparation, and there is no sample alignment problem as in the case of direct tensile test. Xiang Y. et al.[8] introduced one kind of bulge testing method to measure the mechanical behavior of copper thin film through a set-up as shown in Fig. 3.7. The sample was prepared based on the following procedure: at first, the SiNx was deposited on the (100) Si substrate by PECVD, and then a layer of TaN and a very thin seed layer of Cu were sputter-deposited. Finally, the Cu layer with required thickness was electroplated and the protective layer of benzocyclobutene (BCB) was spin coated on the Cu layer. The second step in preparing the sample is to release the Cu layer from substrate. First, standard photolithography was used to define a long rectangular window (with aspect ratio 4∶1) on the SiNx layer coated on the backside of the substrate with the edges s of rectangular aligned with ⟨110⟩ of Si substrate. The freestanding rectangular Cu film could be created by using a potassium hydroxide solution based on wet etching, and obtained by removing the SiNx and TaN layers by Reactive Ion Etching (RIE), and stripping the BCB protective layer by using an organic solvent. This approach can be applied to a wide range of different thin film materials to measure their mechanical properties. Figure 3.8 shows the free Cu film prepared by the above method.

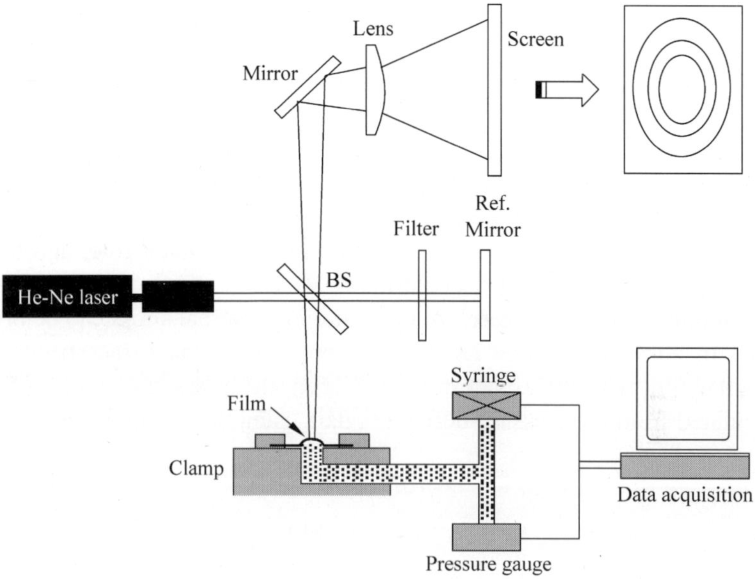

Figure 3.7 Schematic apparatus for bulge test

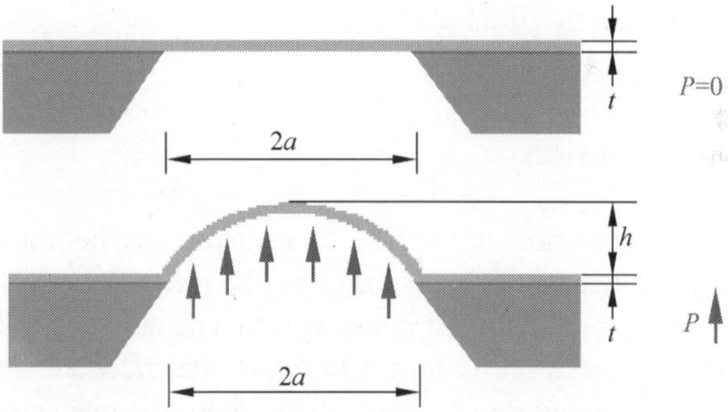

Figure 3.8 Schematic of the bulge test (see color figure at the end of the book)

The key technology for the bulge test is to measure the deflection of the center point of the film precisely. The measuring technique shown in Fig. 3.7 is in common use. A sample ready to be tested was fixed on the sample stage, and the pressure was applied by pumping de-ion water or gas (for example, nitrogen) into the cavity under the film. The deflection of the center point of the film was then measured by using a laser interferometer with a He-Ne laser source. Its measuring resolution is 0.3164 μm since the wavelength of He-Ne laser is 0.6318 μm. The experimental process can be controlled by a computer, and the pressure versus deflection curve can be recorded through a data acquisition system.

How do we obtain the mechanical properties of a thin film from the pressure deflection curve? The calculation formula is dependent on the specimen geometry. For the sample with square film, the following relationship between the pressure and deflection was derived by Maier-Schneider et al.[9]: $P = C_1 tho / a^2 + C_2 Eth^3 / a^4$ where C_1 and C_2 as a function of the material's Poisson ratio, when the Poisson ratio is 0.25, are determined by finite element simulation (FEM) as 3.45 and 2.48 respectively, t is the thickness of specimen, h the deflection of the film, $2a$ the edge length, σ s is the internal stress of the film, and E is the Young's modulus. The h will increase with the increase of $2a$. When h reaches a value high enough, the second term of the above equation will play a dominant role, and therefore the Young's modulus E can be determined If $2a$ is small, then the first term plays a dominant role, and therefore the material's internal stress can be obtained. In order to eliminate C_1 and C_2, Vlasaak and Nix[10] made the specimen as a rectangular film with the aspect ratio 4:1. Then, the stress and strain of film can be calculated from the pressure-deflection data using the simple formulae:

$$\begin{aligned} \sigma &= aP^2 / 2ht \\ \varepsilon &= \varepsilon_0 + 2h^2 / 3a^2 \end{aligned} \tag{3.4}$$

where ε is the strain and ε_0 is the residual strain. The material's Young's modulus can then be obtained from the stress versus strain curve. The mechanical properties of polyimide[11], polycrystal of silicon[12], silicon nitride[13], and silicon oxide[14] were measured by film bulge tests.

3.2.4 Nanoindentation

Nanoindentation test is another method to measure the hardness and Young's modulus of thin films deposited on a substrate. The measuring mechanism is based on pushing a small shaped diamond indenter into a sample and withdrawing it, at same time recording the force required to move the indenter and displacement (the intrusion depth of indenter into thin film). Then, the mechanical behavior of the thin film can be identified through the force versus displacement curve.

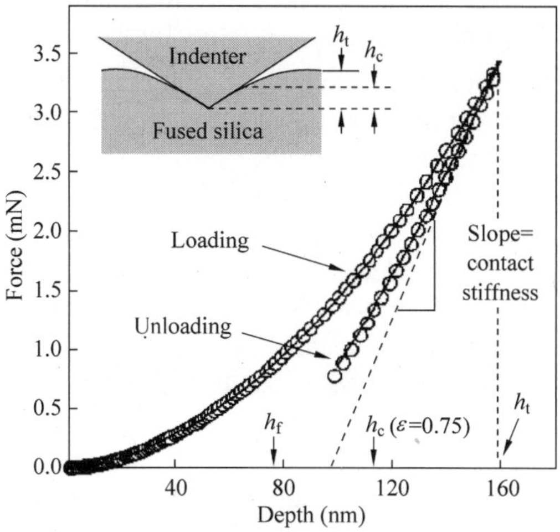

Figure 3.9 Load versus displacement curve

Johnny H. He.[15] described the nanoindentation test in the third chapter of his Ph. D. dissertation, but the pioneering efforts were taken by Oliver and Pharr[16]. Figure 3.9 shows a typical load versus displacement curve obtained from the bulk fused silica sample. From this figure, the maximum load F_m, the intrusion depth of the indenter h_t, and the residual depth h_f can be obtained. In order to calculate the hardness and Young's modulus, the contact depth h_c and contact area A_c should be calculated first, which can be given by following formulae:

$$h_c = h - \varepsilon F_m / S_m, \text{ and} \\ A_c = 24.5 h_c^2 \text{ [16]} \tag{3.5}$$

where S_m (contact stiffness) is defined as the maximum slope of the load-displacement curve, as the geometry constant (it equals 0.75 for Berkovitch indenter). Therefore, the maximum contact area can be calculated, and then the hardness of the thin film can be obtained from ($H=F_m/A_c$). The naturalized Young's modulus E_r is given by:

$$E_r = \sqrt{\pi} S_m / 2\beta\sqrt{A_c} \tag{3.6}$$

where β is equal to 1 usually. The thin film' Young's modulus E_f can be calculated by:

$$E_f = (1-\nu_f^2)/(1/E_r - (1-\nu_i^2)/E_i) \tag{3.7}$$

Here, E_i and ν_i are respectively the Young's modulus and Poisson ratio of the indenter, and ν_f is the Poisson ration of the thin film. It is to be noted that when the nanoindentation test is performed, the intrusion depth of the indenter should be less than one-tenth of the film thickness. Otherwise, the substrate will prevent correct measurement, especially when the thin film is very hard.

The nanoindentation test also can be used to study the super-elastic behavior of the thin film. The super-elastic behavior of a NiTi thin film shape memory alloy was investigated by our research group. Figure 3.10 depicts the maximum load and intrusion depth curve obtained by a nanoindentation test under different loads. From the figure, it can be seen that all loading curves are smooth, but the unloading curves have one 'terrace'. The width of the terrace is different for different applied loads; higher the load, wider the terrace. A 'terrace' means that when the applied load reduces to some value, the intrusion depth will decrease suddenly under constant load. The reason for this phenomenon is that the microstructure of the NiTi film is transferred from martensitic to austenitic since the austenite is stable thermodynamically, and that the stiffness of austenite is much high than martensite's for NiTi alloy. The reason for the increase in load leading to widening of the terrace is that higher load means higher stress applied on the NiTi film. More volume of NiTi film transformed from austenite to martensite is induced during the loading process. Therefore, more volume of NiTi film is transformed from martensite to austenite during the load releasing process, and the terrace is wider. In terms of the above reason, when the terrace on the force versus intrusion depth curve appears during the nanoindentation test, the material of the thin film is expected to have the super-elastic behavior.

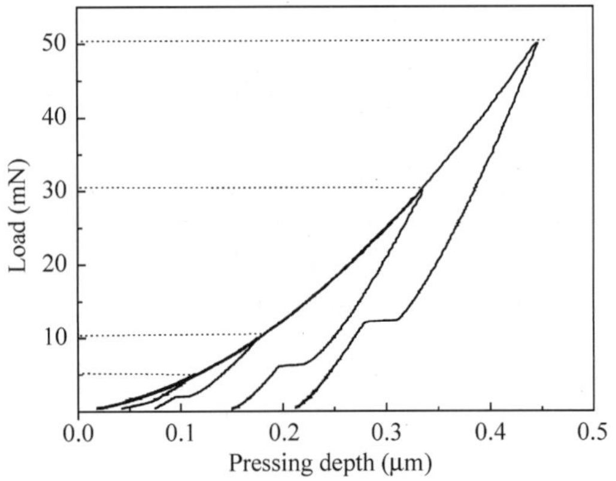

Figure 3.10 Loading and unloading curve of NiTi thin film

3.2.5 Beam Bending Test

This is the most popular way to measure the mechanical properties of materials to be used for micro/nano scale structures. When compared to the micro direct tensile test, the microbeam bending test needs only a small force to push the tip of the beam. It yields a displacement large enough to be measured by a optical microscope or laser interferometer and therefore, there are no specimen mounting and alignment problems. Moreover, the specimen can be much smaller than the tensile test. As a result, micro, even nano, mechanical effects can be evaluated. The sample preparation is easy. Either MEMS technology can be used or direct in situ measuring can be adopted. Furthermore, it is quite straightforward to enable calculation of the mechanical properties for simple beam. Figure 3.11 shows a schematic of a measuring mechanism[15], in which the cantilever beam has the length L with a point load F at its end. The curvature at any point of the beam is equal to the ds divided by dx at point x. For small deflection, the ds is closely equal to dx. Therefore,

$$\kappa = \mathrm{d}\theta / \mathrm{d}s \approx \mathrm{d}^2 y / \mathrm{d}x^2 = -M / EI = F\,(L - x) / EI^{[15]} \tag{3.8}$$

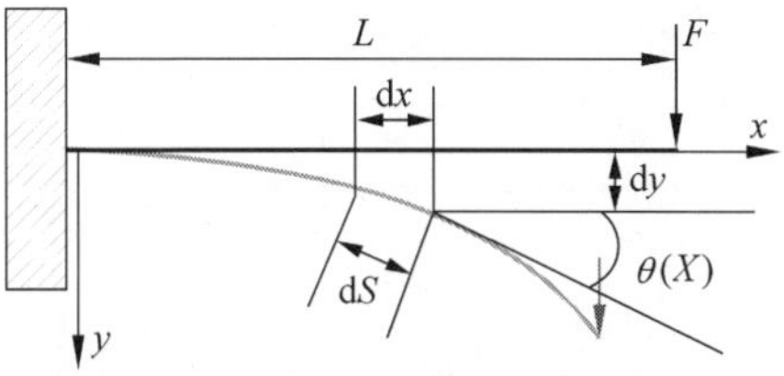

Figure 3.11 Schematic of micro beam bending test, (see color figure at the end of this book)

where I is the inertia moment of the beam ($=wt^3/12$), and w and t are the width and the thickness of the beam respectively. Assuming small deflection and integrating the above equation twice with the boundary condition $y=0$ and $\mathrm{d}y/\mathrm{d}x=0$ when $x=0$ and $x=L$, the following equation can be derived[17]:

$$y = FL / 2EI \cdot x^2 \cdot (1 - x / 3L) \tag{3.9}$$

If the loading point is at the end of the beam ($x=L$), therefore,

$$\begin{aligned} y_{\max} &= FL^3 / 3EI, \\ \text{and}\ E &= FL^3 / 3Iy_{\max}. \end{aligned} \tag{3.10}$$

If the specimen geometry and load applied are known, the deflection of the beam ($y_{\max}$) can be measured by experiment. Then, the inertia moment of the beam (I), and the Young's modulus of the beam material (E) can be calculated. The above calculation is only available to the simple beam (with long and narrow beam). Since the microbeam bending test has several advantages, the Young's modulus of SCS[18,19], silicon dioxide[20], gold[20], chromium[21], PECVD silicon nitride[22], and low pressure chemical deposition(LPCVD) silicon nitride[23] were measured using this method.

Even though the beam bending test has its merits, it is still not very suitable for factory laboratories. Dr. He[15] has developed a fast and inexpensive beam bending test by using a surface profilometer, which is owned by nearly all factory laboratories. Figure 3.12 illustrates the sample for this test, whose preparation processes are as follows. The thin film to be tested is deposited on the Si substrate, then the laser micromachining (or other dry, wet method depending on the materials) is used to etch and pattern the cantilever beam, and finally the beam is released through KOH wet etching. During the test, the cantilever is bended by the tip of the profilometer.

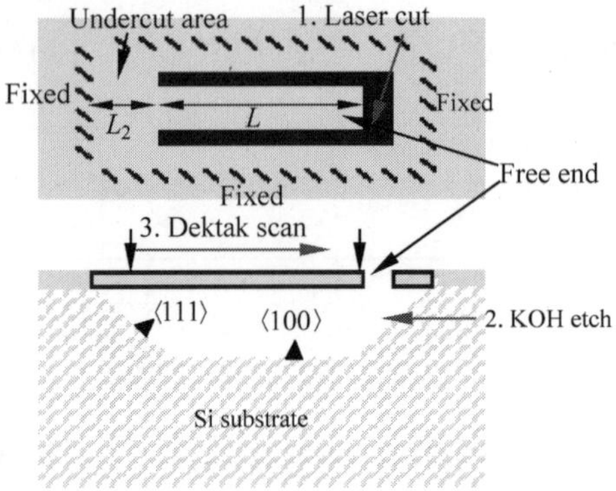

Figure 3.12 Sample preparation process flow of beam bending test[15], (see color figure at the end of this book)

Since the force applied on the tip of profilometer is constant, and the displacement is shown on the screen of the profiler, the sample geometry is known. Therefore, the Young's modulus of the thin film can be calculated from the above equation.

The beam bending test can also be used to measure the fracture strength of MEMS materials, if the deflection is large enough, and finally the beam is broken. For brittle materials, the calculation is straightforward. However, if the beam suffers large deformation during the test, the calculation of the fracture strength is not easy. The fracture strength in such a case was determined by Jones[24] and Wilson[19], who treated the data using analytical and numerical value solutions, respectively.

3.2.6 Test for Fatigue Characteristic and Fracture Toughness K_{1c} of MEMS Materials

With the great development in MEMS and NEMS techniques, the structure designer should consider the microstructure to be safe, reliable, and reasonable. The operation life of microsystems is required to be much longer in order to realize the commercialization of MEMS products. Therefore, micro system designers require data on the mechanical properties of the material such as fatigue limit and fracture toughness K_{1c}. As mentioned in the first part of this chapter, the fracture toughness K_{1c} is the materials constant, and it denotes the ability of the material to resist brittle fracture during service. However, it is very difficult to obtain the data of K_{1c} of MEMS/NEMS materials, and few paper introduce the measuring methods of K_{1c}.

The research group under the leadership of Professor Bhushan of Ohio University has estimated the nanoscale K_{1c} of silicon and silicon oxide tentatively. The details have been described in Dr. Sundararajan's dissertation[25] using an atomic force microscope (AFM). The steps of his method are outlined in Fig. 3.13. First, a crack of known geometry is introduced in the region of maximum tensile bending stress, i.e., on the top surface near the ends of the beam. This is achieved by generating a scratch with a high normal load across the width of the beam with a sharp diamond tip. The typical AFM 3D and 2D profile are shown in Fig. 3.13(b). Then the beam is bended through the AFM indenter until the beam is broken at the maximum stress concentration point of scratch. The load is recorded at the moment of beam break. The author assumed that the scratch tip acts as a crack tip, a bending stress will tend to open the crack in Mode I. In this case, the stress field around the crack can be described by K_1 (stress intens ity parameter for Mode I). Through simplification, the relationship between the fracture stress σ_f and the fracture toughness K_{1c} can be expressed by the following equation: $K_{1c}=\sigma_f(2\pi r)^{1/2}$, where r is the distance from the tip of the crack. However, the r cannot be taken as zero. Therefore, the r should be as close to the tip as possible. The author took r to be 1 to 4 times of the distance between the neighboring atoms in the crystal plane of (111), and so $r=0.4$ to 1.6 nm for

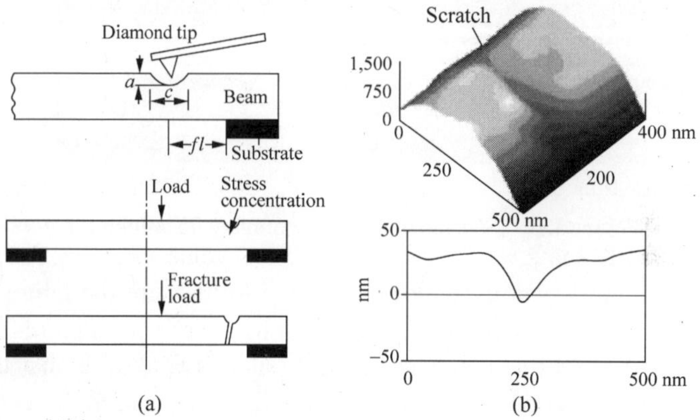

Figure 3.13 The method to generate a crack of known geometry and to measure the K_{1c} (see color figure at the end of this book)

silicon. Finally, based on the FEM analysis and the load recorded during the experiment (σ_f), K_{1c} can be calculated.

The fatigue property of MEMS materials becomes an important issue when long-term reliable operation is required for MEMS devices. However, the difficulty for designers is in finding or measuring the fatigue property. There are few papers you can find in literatures. One measuring method was introduced by C. L. Muhlstein et al.[26(a)]. The authors prepared a chip using MEMS technology as the testing sample. One part of the chip is used to measure the fatigue property as shown in Fig. 3.14. The notched cantilever beam sample is around 40 μm long, 19.5 μm wide, and 13 μm deep. It has a 1 μm root radius notch, which is attached to a large, perforated, plate-shaped mass. One side of the mass is integrated by the 'finger driver', and the other side by the capacitive sensor for motion. When the half-natural frequency with a sinusoidal voltage is applied on the comb driver, it will induce a resonant response of the mass piece, and result in the fatigue of the material at the notch of the sample with a symmetric tensile and compress load. The fatigue stress is controlled by the vibration amplitude, i.e., the applied driving voltage. During the test, the natural frequency decreases as fatigue damage accumulates, and eventually specimen failure occurs after a certain load cycle N_f. The applied voltage is changed and the experiment is repeated. Until enough $\sigma - N$ data are obtained. Finally, the $\sigma_a - N_f$ plot can be generated as shown in Fig. 3.1. Therefore, the fatigue property of the MEMS material can be extracted. The σ_a at the root of the notch under tensile and compress stress should be calculated by the FEM method.

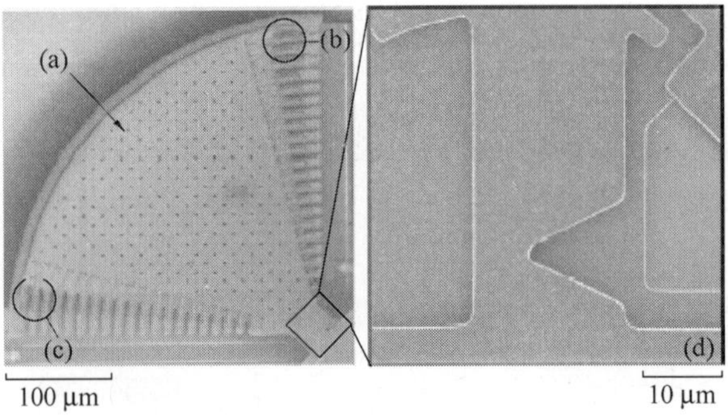

Figure 3.14 Specimen for fatigue property measurement

Dr. Sundararajan[25] also introduced a method to measure the fatigue property of the material with nanoscale size using an AFM instrument. Figure 3.15 shows a schematic of the test method. The principle of this method is that the load is applied by the diamond tip of the AFM, which is positioned at the center of the beam span. The amplitude of the applied stress is controlled by the diamond tip displacement, which is determined by the voltage applied to the piezocrystal. The one test run would end till the sample breaks after N cyclic vibrations. On changing the voltage (it means the σ changes), the second test run starts, and the whole test will finished until one set of $\sigma - N$ data is obtained.

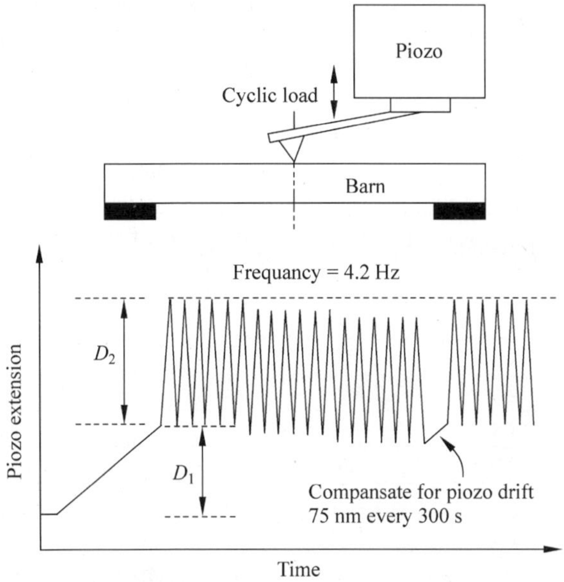

Figure 3.15 Testing method for fatigue property for nanostructure

3.3 Structure Materials for Microsystems

The criterion of material selection, as Petersen mentioned in his famous paper[27] is that four important issues of materials should be required: ① the material is inexpensive and the quality is easy to control; ② the fabrication processes and devices are based on thin film technologies; ③ the patterning of the film can be completed by lithography technology; and ④ the devices can be manufactured by batch production. Silicon becomes the important material for MEMS devices because it meets all four requirements.

3.3.1 Mechanical Properties of Silicon and Silicides

The designers of microsystems must certainly take into account the mechanical properties of MEMS materials. Table 3.1[27] presents a comparative list of the mechanical characteristics of silicon and other materials.

From this list, it can be seen that the Young's modulus of silicon has a value approaching that of stainless steel. A silicon single crystal has a tensile yield strength at least three times higher than that of a stainless steel wire. Therefore, its specific strength is nine times that of stainless steel, since its density is only one-third that of steel. From this point of view, silicon is an excellent structure material for MEMS devices. However, it should be pointed out that silicon is a kind of brittle material. Hence, the stress concentration in the components, induced in manufacturing processes at the corner, or any defect cannot be relaxed through plastic deformation. Therefore, silicon is very sensitive to defects whether at the surface or inside the components, especially with regard to the fatigue property

Table 3.1 Mechanical properties of various materials

Material	Yield strength (GPa)	Knoop hardness (kg/mm^2)	Young's modulus (10^2 GPa)	Density (g/cm^3)	Thermal expansion (10^{-6}/℃)
Diamond	53	7,000	10.35	3.5	1.0
SiC	21	2,480	7.0	3.2	3.3
Si_3N_4	14	3,486	3.85	3.1	0.8
SiO_2 fiber	8.4	820	0.73	2.5	0.55
Si	7.0	850	1.9	2.3	2.33
Steel	4.2	1,500	2.1	7.9	12
Stainless steel	2.1	660	2.0	7.9	17.3

to surface defects. The microstructure will break during service or even during the chip-level manufacturing process, if the structure designing or fabrication processes are not effective. Therefore, single-crystal silicon (SCS) is intrinsically very strong, but the apparent strength of a silicon-based component or device will depend on its geometries, and micro or bulk defects. Thus, the general rules to keep in mind during the manufacture of devices are listed below[27]:

(1) In order to minimize the stress concentration, the silicon should maintain the lowest bulk, surface, and edge crystallographic defects.

(2) All mechanical processing such as sawing, grinding, scribing, and polishing should be minimized or eliminated, since these processes will cause edge and surface imperfections that could result in the chipping of edges and/or internal strains, subsequently leading to breakage. Many micro components should be separated from the wafer by etching rather than by cutting.

(3) If the conventional sawing or other mechanical operations are necessary, the affected surface and edges should be etched afterward to remove the highly damaged regions.

(4) Since many of the structures in a microsystem are patterned by anisotropic etching, sharp edges or corner will be formed. This geometry can also result in stress accumulation or concentration, thereby accelerating the damage of the structure. Therefore, to round such sharp corners or edges, a subsequent isotropic etch or other smoothing methods are required.

(5) Tough, hard, corrosive-resistant, thin film coatings such as CVD SiC or

Si_3N_4 should be applied to prevent direct mechanical contact to silicon itself, especially in applications involving high stress or abrasion.

(6) During the microfabrication of the silicon mechanics, low-temperature processing techniques are very important, while high-temperature cycling invariably results in high stress within the wafer due to the different thermal expiation coefficients of various doped or deposited layers. Low-temperature processing will alleviate such thermal mismatch stress, which otherwise might lead to breakage or chipping under severe mechanical conditions.

(7) The nucleation of fatigue cracks always occurs at stressed surfaces. The rate of fatigue depends strongly on surface preparation, morphology, and defect density. One way of increasing the fatigue life is to decrease the surface defects and roughness through chemical polishing. Another way is to deposit a film, such as Si_3N_4, on the silicon surface that tends to be under tension. This film would impart a compressive stress on the silicon surface, resulting in the decrease of the tensile fatigue stress.

The requirements to be met for the thin film materials.

Thin film materials have been widely applied in microsystems, for example, a single or polycrystal silicon thin film is used as a structure material; an SiO_2 film is used as masking, insulating, and sacrificial material; and a Si_3N_4 film is used as a masking or surface passive material. This section does not discuss the deposition methods or the relationship between the preparation method and the film properties. It focuses on the main requirements to be met by thin film materials used in microsystems, which are listed below.

(1) Good adhcsivc force to the substrate materials, preventing the thin film peeling off or delamination;

(2) Keeping the internal residual stress as low as possible, to prevent the structure distortion, warp, and even rupture;

(3) Suitable mechanical properties, to meet the requirement of designing;

(4) Low density of pinhole, and good chemical stability.

Whether or not the above requirements can be met depends not only on the thin film materials, but also on the deposition processing and substrate materials.

Reducing the Residual Stress:

For the purpose of reducing the residual stress existing in micro components, the mechanism of inducing the residual stress should be understood first. Residual stress exists between the thin film and the substrate or between two thin films after the manufacturing processes. It is comprised of extrinsic (or thermal stress) and intrinsic stresses. Thermal stress is formed between two neighboring layers with different thermal expansion coefficient after a thermal process. It can be expressed by:

$$\sigma = E(\sigma) = E(\alpha_f - \alpha_s)(T_d - T_r)/(1-\nu) \tag{3.11}$$

where E is the Young's Modulus of the thin film, and α_f and α_s are the thermal expansion coefficient of the thin film and substrate, respectively. T_d is the deposition temperature of the thin film (or the annealing temperature) and T_r is the room temperature. From this equation, it can be seen that for reducing the thermal stress the T_d should be reduced and two-layer materials with closing thermal expiation coefficient only should be selected. Intrinsic stress is formed due to atomic mismatch at the layer border or crystal defects inside of thin film. It can be released by suitable annealing treatment.

3.3.1.1 Young's Modulus of Silicon and Silicides

Silicon and silicides have widely been used in the electronic industry, where the physical properties of materials are important. As the material are used to form the structure of MEMS the mechanical properties of the materials are much more important than the physical. Data regarding the Young's modulus of silicon and silicides can be obtained from literatures, but when the designers select the data, they should pay attention to whether the data in the literature concerning the sample's size and fabrication processing are the same or closer to those of the systems they have designed.

(1) Young's modulus of single crystal of silicon (SCS)

Single and polycrystal silicon are popularly used as structure materials in MEMS. Many literatures that provide the data on the Young's modulus of SCS, as indicated in Table 3.2 from microstructure. Here, it should be noted that SCS has the anisotropy of Young's modulus and therefore, the data given in Table 3.2 gives the Young's modulus of SCS along a certain crystal direction. Moreover, when the designers use the data, they should pay attention to the source of the data. The microstructure of SCS is made of bulk SCS by using the top-down method. Therefore, the Young's modulus of MEMS SCS should be equal to the Young's modulus of bulk SCS, if there are no serious defects on the surface of the microstructure after microfabrication, since most authors believe that the Young's modulus of SCS[25,28] has no size effect (larger than some critical value, such as 40 nm). The data given by

Table 3.2 SCS Young's modulus in (GPa)

	⟨100⟩	⟨110⟩	⟨111⟩	
Brantley[29]	130.2	168.9	187.5	Based on ultrasonic bulk silicon
Greenwood[30]	129.5	168.0	186.5	Numerical calculation
Wilson, et al.[19]	120.0	168.0	—	FEM simulation
Sato[31]	138+/–11	155+/–15	180+/20	Tensile test on a test chip by vertical loading
Schweitz[32]	142+/–9	—	—	Tensile test in SEM chamber
Yi, et al.[33]	—	169.2+/–3.5	—	Uniaxial tensile test by PZT actuator

The Young's modulus data obtained by Brandtley and Greenwood are close to the actual data and are correct, since they are obtained through measurement of bulk SCS and numerical calculation, respectively. The other data shown in the table show some errors due to sample mounting, alignment problems, etc.

(2) Young's modulus of polycrystal of silicon

Polycrystal silicon is mostly used as a structural material in microsystems except SCS, especially, in microfabrication processing of surface micromachining. It can be also used as a masking material for SiO_2 sacrificial layer. The polysilicon used in MEMS usually exists in the form of a thin film, which is deposited by CVD. Different microstructures of polysilicon, such as polycrystal, amorphous, and α-Si can be obtained using different deposition processes. Therefore, the mechanical properties, including the Young's modulus are dependent on the deposition processes. Table 3.3 gives the data of the Young's modulus and fracture strength of polycrystal silicon with different sample size and measuring methods. Designers of MEMS can choose the Young's modulus of polysilicon (between 130 – 170 GPa) based on the sample size and deposition process. In order to eliminate the problems of different custom deposition methods, four research groups (UC Berkeley, CIT, John Hopkins University, and Failure Analysis Associations (FAA)) measured the same specimen source (provided by MEMS center of North Carolina State University) of polysilicon with their individual measuring instruments, the results of which are listed in Table 3.4[36].

Table 3.3 Young's modulus and fracture strength of polycrystal silicon

	Sample width and thickness (μm)	Young's modulus and fracture strength (GPa)	Measuring Method
Chasiotis, et al.[34]	50.0/1.9	132	Sample holding by electrostatic method, displacement measurement by AFM
Greek et al.[3]	10/10	167/1.25	Force measurement by strain gauge, displacement measuring by optical coding
Sharpe et al .[4]	600/3.5	168/1.21	Sample holding by glue, displacement measuring by interferometer
Tsuchiya, et al.[35]	2~5/2	/2.5	Sample holding by electrostatic method, displacement measuring by interferometer

(3) Young's modulus of silicides

Young's Modulus of Silicon Nitrides[15]: In order to reduce the residual stress of the film, most researchers use the silicon-rich SiN[37], the reason is mentioned above, but the Young's modulus of SiN layer is strongly dependent on the deposition processes, i.e., temperature, chemical vapor ratio, and pressure. Levy et al.[38] investigated the dependence of Young's modulus on the deposition

Table 3.4 Measurement results for polycrystal of silicon by different organizations

Description	UCB	CalTech	FAA	Hopkins	Hopkins
Loading type	Bending	Tensile	Bending	Tensile	Tensile
Polycrystal of silicon thickness (μm)	1.9	1.9	2.0	1.5	3.5
Number of samples tested	90	3	12	19	14
Young's modulus (GPa)	174±20	132	137±5	136±14	142±25
Fracture strength (GPa)	2.8±0.5		2.7±0.2	1.3±0.2	1.3±0.1

temperature of LPCVD silicon nitride. It was found that the value of Young's modulus increased from 130 – 185 GPa when the deposition temperature was increased from 650℃ – 900℃. Above 800℃, the modulus is saturated at 185 GPa. The chemical vapors used were $C_6N_{19}N_3Si$ and NH_3 in the volume ratio 2:1, which resulted in a silicon-rich nitride thin film.

The Young's modulus of LPCVD silicon-rich nitride is given in Table 3.5, which shows that the value of silicon-rich SiN is dispersed between 138 Gpa and 290 GPa. Surely, this discrepancy is due to different deposition processes and testing methods.

Table 3.5 The effect of testing method on Young's modulus of LPCVD SiN

	Young's Modulus (GPa)	Testing Method
Bromley[39]	138	Bulge Test
Tabata[12]	290	Bulge Test
Vlassak&Nix[10]	222	Bulge Test
Vlassak&Nix[10]	216	Nanoindentation
Drummond[40]	150/195/260	AFM
Zhang[23]	203	Bridge-nanoindentation

Young's Modulus of SiO_2: The preparation methods of SiO_2 film are normally thermal oxidation, LPCVD, and PECVD, but there is a film thickness limit (less than 2 μm) for thermal oxidation. The Young's modulus of the fused bulk SiO_2 (Quartz) is 73 GPa[27, 41]. Professor Bhushan's research group[25] measured the Young's modulus of single crystal of SiO_2 with a nanoscale beam formed by thermal oxidation. The 13 samples were tested, the results of which are given in Fig. 3.16. The figure shows that the average Young's modulus of SiO_2 is scattered in the range of (85±13) GPa. The authors believe that the scatter in the value may be due to the differences in orientation of the beam with respect to the trench and the loading being a little off the center of the beam span. The average value is higher than the bulk value, due to the 20% error of uncertainty for this measuring and calculation method. Therefore, the Young's modulus of SiO_2 with nanoscale sample size should theoretically be equal to the bulk value of 73 GPa, and it did not show size effect in the range of 200 – 700 nm.

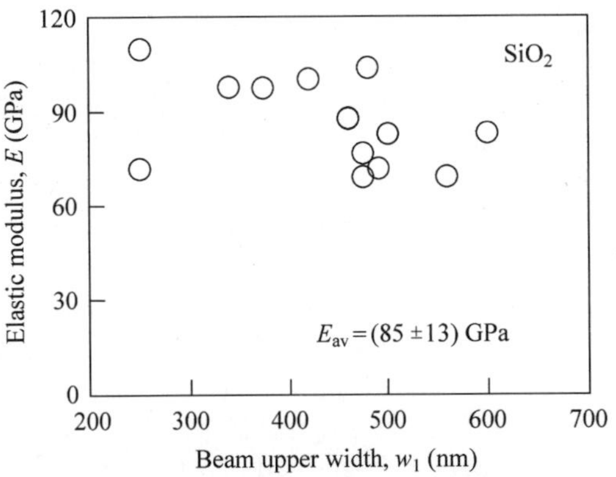

Figure 3.16 Young's Modulus of SiO_2 with nanoscale sample

3.3.1.2 Fracture Strength and Fracture Toughness of Silicon and Silicides

Since these materials are brittle, therefore, the fracture strength and fracture toughness of witch is one of the most important materials properties for the Microsystems designers. Several authors have reported their measuring results and it has been found that the sample preparing, chemical etching solution, crystal orientation, and testing methods have a major effect on the fracture strength of single crystal silicon. Figure 3.17 shows that chemical etching solutions have a strong effect on the fracture strength of SCS with ⟨110⟩ orientation[33]. Tsuchiya at al.[35] reported that the fracture strength of polysilicon decreases with the increase of the sample length.

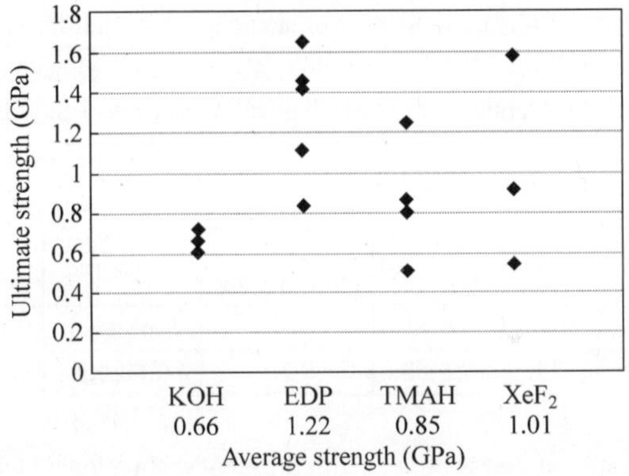

Figure 3.17 Chemical etching solutions have a major effect on scs's fracture strength

The possible reason could be that the probability of the surface defects will increase with the increase in sample length. Four different research groups[36] have measured the fracture strength of polysilicon using the same sample with different testing methods. The results are listed in Table 3.4.

Professor Bhushan's group[25] has measured the fracture strength and fracture toughness of Si and SiO_2 using the AFM method (bending of nanobeam). The experimental results are shown in Fig. 3.18 and Table 3.6. The fracture toughness of the SCS nanobeam is close to the value listed in Table 3.7, reported by Ericson et al.[42], but its fracture strength is two times of the values of the bulk or micro size of SCS. This group believed that the fracture toughness of a material is independent of sample size, and the fracture strength of a material has the size effect. The present author has the same idea, because the surface area of the nanobeam is much less than the value of micro beam or bulk materials. Therefore, the probability of surface defects for the nanoscale sample is much less than for big size samples. When the fracture toughness is measured, it is assumed that the sample already has a microcrack inside, and so the sample size has very small effect on the fracture toughness.

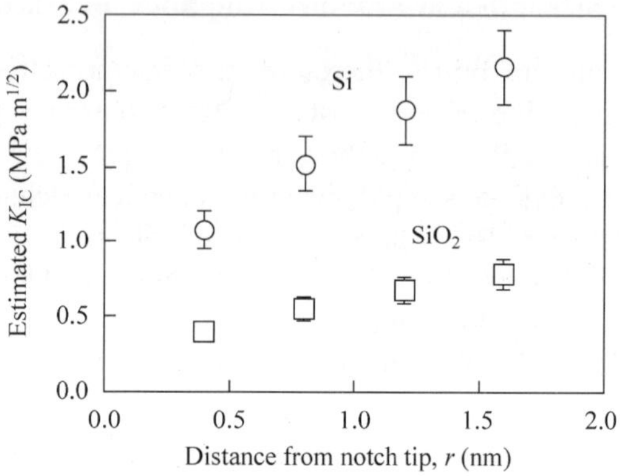

Figure 3.18 Fracture toughness of si and sio_2 taking different r values

Table 3.6 Comparison of mechanical properties of Si with SiO_2

Sample	Young's Modulus E (GPa)		Bending Strength σ_b (GPa)		Fracture Toughness K_{1c} (MPa $m^{1/2}$)		
	Measured	Bulk	Measured	Reported (Micro Size)	Measured	Reported (Micro Size)	Bulk
Si	182±11	169	18±3	10	1.67±0.4	0.6–1.65	0.9
SiO_2	83±13	73	7.6±2	2	0.6±0.2	0.5–0.9	

Table 3.7 Fracture toughness of SCS with different orientation and that of polysilicon

Orientation of SCS	K_{1c} (MPa $m^{1/2}$)
⟨111⟩	0.83–0.95
⟨100⟩	0.91
⟨110⟩	0.94
Polysilicon	0.94

3.3.1.3 Fatigue Property of Silicon

The long-term stability of a microsystem is one of the most important requirements before it comes into mass production. For microdevices or components, such as comb finger drivers and resonant microbeams under the cyclic loading condition, the materials selected to construct them must have good fatigue property. Silicon is the commonly used material for these devices. Therefore, it is necessary to understand the fatigue property of silicon.

Silicon is a typical brittle material, whose dislocation movement is hardly observed at low temperature. Bulk silicon has not been found to be susceptible to environmentally induced cracking in moisture or water. Therefore, most people consider that silicon has no fatigue problem. Indeed, there has been no evidence of bulk silicon being susceptible to fatigue failure. However, a thin film with microscale thickness does have premature failure due to cyclic loading at room temperature. In order to prolong the fatigue life and increase the fatigue strength, it should work out the fatigue failure mechanism of silicon thin film. Muhlstein etc.[26b] have made a good academic study in this issue. They have thoroughly studied the fatigue process of a polysilicon thin film of thickness of 2 microns prepared by a standard process from MCNC/Cronos MUMPS. The fatigue test and the sample are mentioned in Fig. 3.14. During the test, the notched cantilever beam specimen is subjected to a fully symmetric sinusoidal stress at 40 kHz. After certain cycles, the specimen was examined by a high-resolution Transmit Electron Microscopy (TEM). Based on the experimental results, they made the following conclusions:

(1) A native SiO_2 oxide layer with around 30 nm thick at the surface of polysilicon was revealed by the high-voltage TEM. However, during fatigue cycling, this layer was thickened by a factor of three roughly in the immediate vicinity of the notch root. As high resolution IR measurements revealed that the temperature of the notch did not exceed 1 K above ambient temperature, such enhanced notch root oxidation is considered to be primarily mechanically induced.

(2) After certain cycles, the high-voltage TEM revealed the presence of stable cracks about tens of nanometers in length within the enhanced oxide layer. Such subcritical crack growth is reasoned to occur by moisture-induced stress corrosion cracking in the amorphous SiO_2.

(3) The change of the microcrack length was measured by resonant frequency method. It was found to be consistent with the progressive evolution of the damage in terms of oxide formation and subcritical cracking of the oxide. Fracture mechanics-based calculation revealed that the crack size did not exceed 50 nm, comparable with the value observed by the high-voltage TEM. This implies that the entire process of fatigue crack initiation, subcritical cracking, and the onset of catastrophic failure, are wholly within the native oxide layer.

(4) The fatigue failure of the thin film polysilicon is ascribed to a 'surface

reaction layer' mechanism, involving mechanically induced oxide thickening and stress corrosion cracking of the resulting oxide film. Since the thickness of the specimen is so thin, the stress strength factor at the tip of the notch root may reach the K_{1c} value of the polysilicon, and so fatigue failure will occur.

(5) The 'surface reaction layer' mechanism is also applicable to bulk silicon although in comparison with thin film, its effect will be negligible. This is because the critical crack size for bulk silicon is much larger than the native oxide thickness. This means that the stress strength factor at the tip of the notch root will never reach the K_{1c} value of polysilicon, and so the catastrophic fatigue failure will not occur. The full fatigue processes for polysilicon thin film are shown in Fig. 3.19.

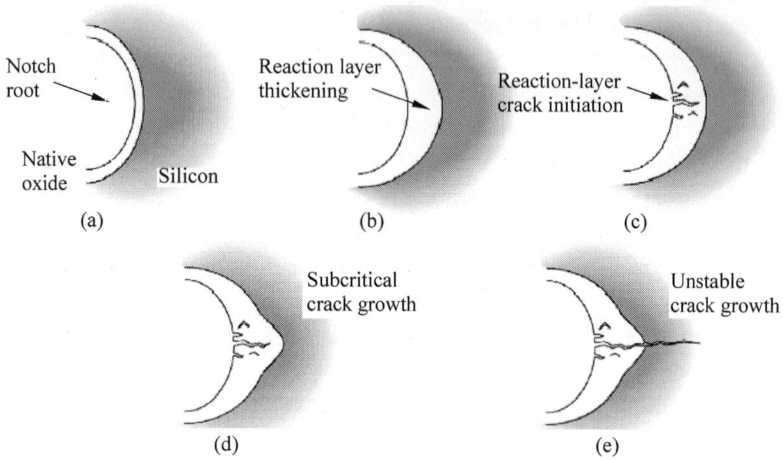

Figure 3.19 Schematic of the reaction layer fatigue mechanism of polysilicon thin film[26b]

(6) The susceptibility of the polysilicon thin film to fatigue failure under high cycle fatigue loading can be suppressed through the use of alkene-based monolayer coatings, which bond directly to the hydrogen-terminated silicon surface, inhibit the formation of the oxide, and further act to prevent the ingress of both moisture and oxygen.

Generally speaking, fatigue failure will not occur for bulk silicon, but for a thin film of silicon, it will. The reaction layer mechanism can be used to explain the fatigue failure of thin film silicon. Through the use of alkene-based monolayer coating, the fatigue failure of thin film silicon can be suppressed. Figure 3.1 indicates that the fatigue strength of silicon film is 2.6 GPa under 100 G cycles. Professor Bhushan et al.[25] measured the fatigue properties of nanoscale silicon and SiO_2 using the AFM method. Figure 3.20 gives their fatigue strength under low cycle numbers.

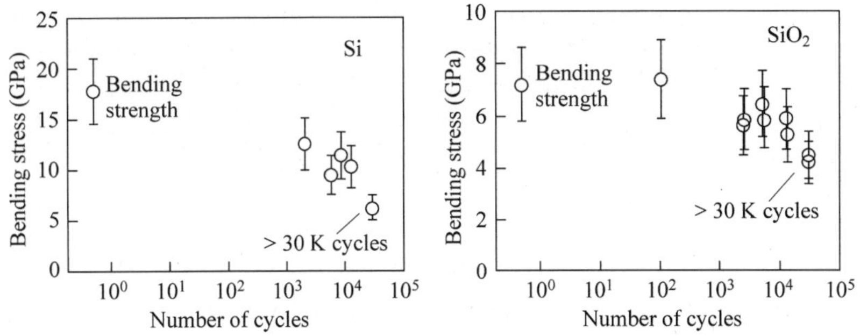

Figure 3.20 Fatigue strength of nanoscale silicon and SiO_2 under low cycle loading

3.3.2 Parylene's Properties and Its Applications

In 1982, Petersen made a description in his paper of 'Silicon as a Mechanical Material'[27] that the polymer parylene thin film deposited by CVD has shown no pinhole, low porosity, passivating film and exceptional point, edge, and hole coverage capability, and can be used to coat and passivate implantable biomedical sensors and electronic instrumentation. In the recent 10 years, the authors, especially, CalTech's research group under the leadership of professor Yu-Chang Tai have conducted several studies on the properties of parylene and its application in MEMS[43]. Since then, the parylene thin films are being used not only as a decoration film for microdevices and components, but also as structure, sensing, driving, and low K dielectric materials in MEMS.

3.3.2.1 Properties of Parylene

Parylene is the generic name for members of a unique family of thermoplastic polymer that can be deposited by using the dimer of para-xylyene through CVD. There are three commercialized parylenes in the market: parylene *N*, *C*, and *D*. Parylene *N* is poly-para-xylylene, a completely linear and highly crystalline polymer. Parylene *C* is basically parylene *N* with a chlorine atom replacing one of the aromatic hydrogens. Parylene *D* is similar to parylene *C* but with two aromatic hydrogens being replaced by chlorine atoms. Parylene *C* is used mostly in MEMS.

The typical physical and mechanical properties of parylene are listed in Table 3.8[43]. It is to be noted that parylene has very low Young's modulus (2 – 5 GPa) and good plasticity. An elongation of more than 200% makes parylene *C* a perfect membrane material for large deflection applications. Moreover, parylene has low dielectric constant and high dielectric strength, and is therefore one kind of RF MEMS material.

A comparison of critical process temperature of parylene with other MEMS materials is given in Table 3.9. The table shows that parylene has very low CVD

Table 3.8 Typical properties of parylene

Property	Parylene *N*	Parylene *C*	Parylene *D*
Dielectric Strength(V/μm)	>200	>200	>200
Dielectric Constant	2.6	3.1	2.8
Young's Modulus (GPa)	2–5	2–5	2–5
Yield Strength (MPa)	42	55	62
Elongation (%)	20–250	200	10
Density (g/cm^3)	1.12	1.29	1.42
Index of Refraction (℃)	1.66	1.64	1.67
Melting Point (℃)	420	290	380
Glass Transition Point (℃)	>300	240	240
Thermal Coefficient of Expansion (℃)	6.9×10^{-5}	3.8×10^{-5}	3.8×10^{-5}
Specific Heat (At 20℃, in Cal/g℃)	0.20	0.17	/
Thermal Conductivity (At 20℃, in Cal/cm℃)	3.0×10^{-4}	2.0×10^{-4}	/

deposition temperature, and therefore its MEMS processes are compatible with the later CMOS processes. Moreover, its CVD deposition is fully conformal. This is the main reason that parylene is considered a good MEMS material. However, compared to silicon and silicides, parylene has high thermal expansion coefficient. Therefore, when the multilayers of parylene with silicon or silicides are formed, the misfit of thermal coefficient of different layers is large. Therefore, all the thermal process temperatures should be strictly limited (including the baking temperature of the lithography resist) to be lower than 160℃, which would prevent higher internal thermal stress. Another point to be noted is that the glass transit temperature of parylene is only 150℃ – 240℃. Thus, MEMS processes with higher process temperatures are limited, because the high process temperature will induce high thermal stress. when this stress reaches the yield stress of parylene (55 MPa)[44], it will result in the serious distortion of micro components made by parylene.

Table 3.9 Critical process temperature for MEMS materials

Material	Temperature (℃)
LPCVD nitride	800
LPCVD doped polysilicon	650
LPCVD amorphous silicon	590
LPCVDLTO/PSG	450
Annealing of PSG (for densification)	950
Annealing of Polysilicon (for reducing stress)	1050
Parylene	Room temperature

3.3.2.2 CVD Deposition Process of Parylene Film[43]

The deposition process of parylene consist of three steps, i.e., vaporization of solid dimer, pyrolysis of dimer, and polymerization of monomers at room temperature. Before deposition of parylene, the substrate should be cleaned by the following steps: ① dipping in the solution (500 ml of di-ionic water, 500 ml IPA, and 5 ml A-174) for 20 – 30 minutes; ② dipping in the IPA solution for 1 – 2 minutes; and ③ spinning dry and baking for 5 minutes at 50℃ – 60℃. After this, the substrate can be moved into the deposition chamber. The equipment supplied in the market, such as PDS 2060 made by SCS, is shown in Fig. 3.21. Inside the deposition unit, a cold trap at approximately –70℃ is used to collect the unreacted monomers before they enter the mechanical pump to pollute the atmosphere and equipment. The details of the deposition processes are given below.

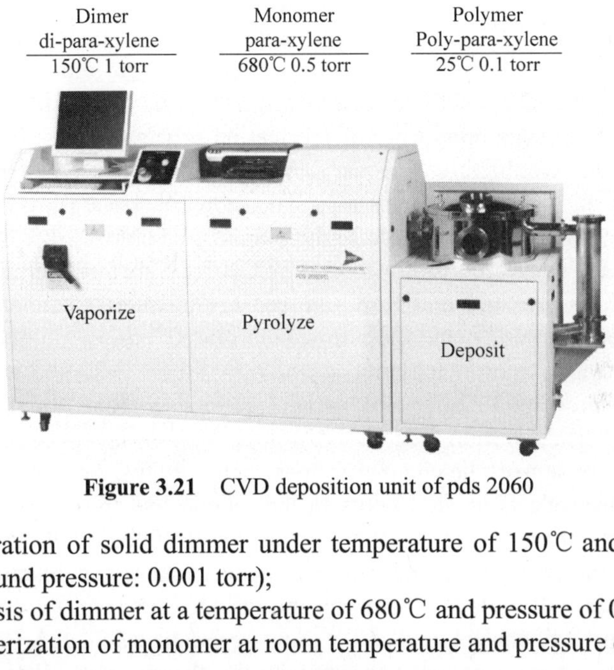

Figure 3.21 CVD deposition unit of pds 2060

① Evaporation of solid dimmer under temperature of 150℃ and pressure of 1.0 torr (ground pressure: 0.001 torr);

② Pyrolysis of dimmer at a temperature of 680℃ and pressure of 0.5 torr; and

③ Polymerization of monomer at room temperature and pressure of 0.1 torr.

3.3.2.3 Patterning of the Parylene Film[43]

Since parylene deposition is conformal, the lift-off process to pattern the parylene is difficult. Therefore, O_2 plasma etching with a photoresist as the mask is used in most cases. The key issue of parylene pattering is to select the mask material. The most important criterion for selecting a mask material is the adhesion force between the mask and parylene material. The photoresist is a kind of good mask material because it is a polymer like parylene, and therefore it possible to achieve good adhesion between the two. In order to enhance the adhesion between the parylene film and the substrates, A-174 is the adhesion promoter suggested by the equipment manufacturer. It has been experimentally shown that a short O_2 plasma treatment between successive parylene depositions can enhance the adhesion between the different parylene layers. It has also been found that the plasma also helps to improve the adhesion between photoresister and parylene.

3.3.2.4 Parylene Film's Application in Microsystems

Since parylene film can be deposited conformally at room temperature by CVD, and etched by O_2 plasma; these processes are compatible with later CMOS processes; moreover, the parylene film is stable chemically, insulating highly, compatible with bio-organisms, and has low Young's modulus and high elongation, therefore, parylene materials used as MEMS materials have been studied widely, especially in microfluidic systems, such as chemical analysis and biomedical systems.

The total integration of a microfluidic system has been a long-sought goal, since such a system usually consists of a micro structural component (such as pipe and valve), an actuator (like pump), and a sensor (to control flow rate). The most efficient way to realize total integration is to use the same material to manufacture the micro components, sensors, and actuators. If different materials are used, then the incompatibility of fabrication processes must be met and the total integration would fail. The parylene films can be used to make pumps, check valves, and mass flow controllers. Therefore, parylene films can be used to fulfill the total integration of microfluidic system on a chip.

Professor Tai's research group in CALTECH have manufactured many micro devices, such as pressure and flow rate sensors in micro channels[45,46], check valves[47], creep pumps[43], and mass flow controllers[48] using multilayer parylene/ photoresist surface micromachining technology. Figure 3.22 shows a capacitive pressure sensor (Fig. 3.22(a)) and parallel plate capacitive dielectric constant sensor of chemical solution (Fig. 3.22(b)) made by four layers of parylene films. For the pressure sensor, the channel is constructed by two top layers of parylene. The upper electrode is located between the second and third layer of parylene. The bottom electrode is fixed on the substrate and covered by the fourth parylene layer. When the pressure in the channel changes, the upper electrode with the parylene layers will deflect. Therefore, the distance between the two electrodes of the capacitor will change, and so the pressure can be calculated. In Fig. 3.22(b), the capacitance of the capacitor changes with the change in the dielectric constant of the liquid, and therefore the dielectric constant of the liquid can be measured.

The main properties required of check valves of microfluidic systems are: low opening pressure, low membrane-induced flow resistance, small reverse leakage, and large operational reverse pressure. Since parylene possesses low Young's modulus, if the check valve is made of parylene, it will have low opening pressure. Moreover, because the membrane cap has large displacement, the distance between the cap and valve seat is large. Therefore, the resistance to fluid flow in the valve is low and the pressure loss of fluid is also low. Figure 3.23 shows the schematic and micro image of the check valve made by parylene[47].

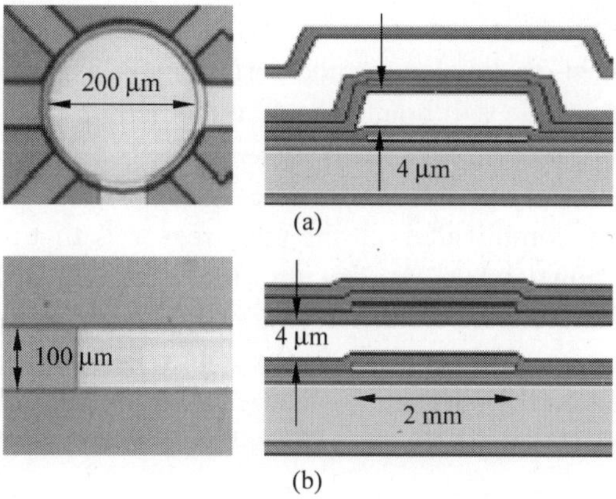

Figure 3.22 A capacitive pressure sensor (see color figure at the end of this book)

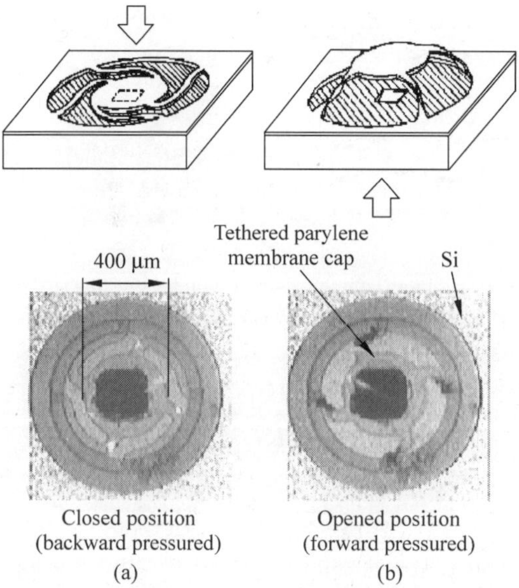

Figure 3.23 Tethered Parylene Plate Check Valve (see color figure at the end of this book)

Prof. Tai presented a four-parylene-layer surface micromachining technology for making an electrostatic peristaltic micropump[43]. As shown in Fig. 3.24, three electrostatic actuators drive continuously in turn to perform the pump function. As mentioned, for the pressure sensor by four-parylene layer, in this pump, CVD parylene is used as the structural material, while the normal photoresist is the sacrificial layer and Cr/Au, the electrode. This versatile process enables a peristaltic pump design, in which the electrical field does not exist inside the fluid. For this pump, the pull-in voltage is 150 V for a 200 μm diameter membrane. In order to study the parylene film used as the electrostatic driving material, Yao T.J. et al.[49]

studied the charging characteristic of parylene when it used as a dielectric material and its effect on the electrostatic performance. The results show that the closed actuating electrode will bounce back to the natural position (free standing position) when the driving electrical field is higher than 0.56 MV/cm, the electrostatic actuator stops its function. The reason for such a 'bouncing back' phenomenon is very complicated but the main reason is that the air between the electrodes breaks down when the driving electrical field is higher than some critical value. In addition, the charge retention capability of parylene dielectrics was investigated by Yao T. J. et al[49]. It was found that the decay of the positive charge accumulated on the parylene dielectric material is closely related with the temperature. Figure 3.25 indicates the effect of temperature on the charge holding capacity of parylene dielectrics.

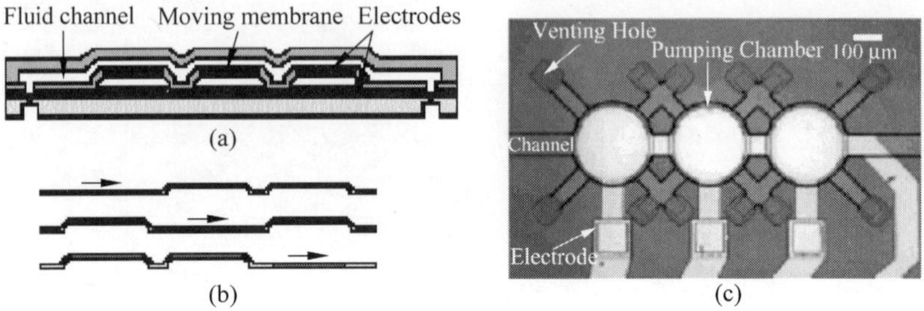

Figure 3.24 Electrostatic driven peristaltic pump by four-parylene-layer technology

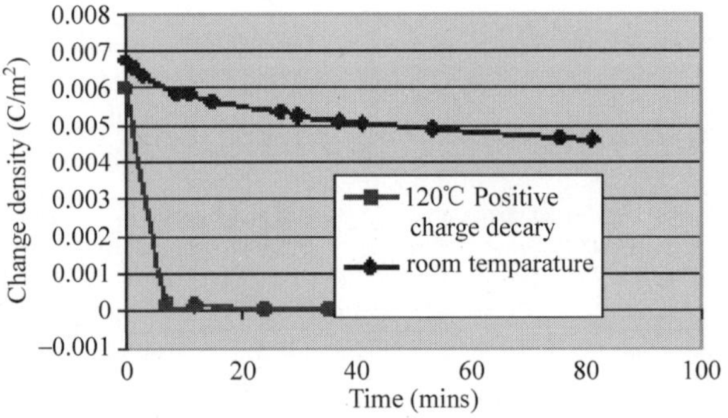

Figure 3.25 Positive charge decays at room temperature and 120℃ (see color figure at the end of this book)

In the microfludic system, the mass flow rate controller is an important component. It is composed of a controllable micro valve and flow sensor. Professor Tai's group[48] developed a new type of mass flow controller using integrated multilayer parylene/photoresist surface micromachining technology. The upper part shown in Fig. 3.26 is the schematic of the controller, and the lower part is the fabricated one. From the figure, it can be seen that the main structure of the device consists of four layers of parylene film. The micro valve is constituted by the round parylene membrane, which is actuated electrostatically. All the electrodes are enveloped by the parylene layers. When the electrical field is applied to the electrode, the rounded parylene membrane moves down until it makes contact with the valve seat. The same four-layered parylene film can be used as the main structure of a thermal flow sensor. However, in order to meet the requirement of thermal flow sensor, the Cr/Au electrode encapsulated in the parylene film is patterned. During operation, the signal from the thermal flow sensor is compared with a given value. After data treatment, the new signal will be fed back to the controllable valve that actuates the voltage both in voltage amplitude or pulse width mode, to realize the closed-loop feedback control of the flow rate.

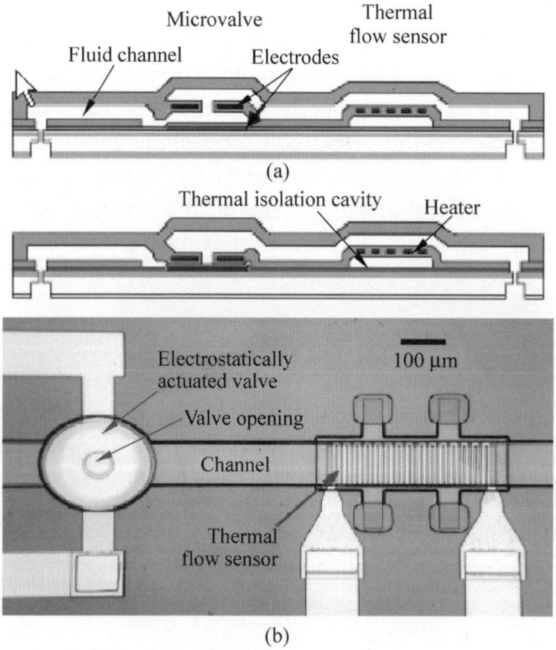

Figure 3.26 Integrated micro mass flow controller (see color figure at the end of this book)

3.4 Materials for Microtribological Application

3.4.1 Self-Assembled Monolayer (SAM) Film

In the first section, it was mentioned that the main failure mechanisms of microsystem are brittle fracture, fatigue fracture, and stiction. Friction and wear of micro devices with two components in contact with each other and having relative movement have a great effect on their operating life and reliability. The friction is related with the stiction to a great degree, while wear is related with friction.

In order to solve the stiction problem, the stiction mechanism should be understood first. Professor Bhushan has clearly described the mechanism of stiction, measuring methods, and relief approaches[50]. The mechanisms that cause stiction are: the electrostatic force (valence bonds, ionic bonds, metallic bonds, hydrogen bonds, or bonds between surface charge), van der Waals force, or the capillary force (coming from the surface tension of the condensed liquid and the meniscus force if the microdevices operate in wet air). The capillary force has the biggest effect on the stiction of micro devices. There are two approaches to reduce this force: one is surface chemical modification and the other is introducing a roughness or bump on the surface to reduce the contact area. An author treated the Si surface by using HF or NH_4F in order to change the Si surface from hydrophilic to hydrophobic. However, the effect could be maintained only for a few days, because the hydrogen terminations on the Si surface are metastable. There are several literatures dealing with surface chemical modification to reduce stiction, while many scientists agree that the most promising approach is SAM technology.

3.4.1.1 Thiol-Based SAMs Film

The structure of the monolayer film is composed of three parts: head groups, spacer chains, and terminal groups. The head group has the chemical reaction with the substrate surface and forms a SAM with the high order spacer chain. The surface energy of the SAM film depends on the property of terminal groups. The types of terminal and head groups, the spacer chain orientation, and stacking property have an effect on the mechanical properties of the SAM film, and therefore on its friction and wear properties.

Two kinds of SAM films have been mainly studied: Thiol- and silane- based (Si-O-Si). Thiol-based SAM films have been widely investigated since their self-assembly processes are easy, and as they have good stability, order degree, and density. Its self-assembly process is as follows: the substrate is first dipped into the chemical solution in which the sulfide is contained; next, the sulfides will then adhere to the substrate quickly, and the contact angle will reach the limited value and the thickness will reach 80% – 90% of the maximum value. The next step is the surface reorganizing process, which will take several hours. Liu at al.[51] have studied the micro/nano tribological properties of five thiol-based SAM films, having Alkylthiol and Biphenyl spacer with different terminal and head groups. They are:

① Hexadecane thiol (HDT); ② 16-mercaptohexadecanoic acid thiol (MHA); ③ 4, 4'-dihydroxybiphenyl (DHBp); ④ 1,1'-biphenyl-4-thiol (BPT); ⑤ 1,1'-biphenyl-4-thiol (BPTC) cross-linked through irradiation of 50 eV electrons.

HDT and MHA have the same head group and spacer chain, but their terminal groups are –CH_3 and –COOH, respectively. BOT and DHBp have the same spacer chain, while the head group and terminal group for DHBp are –OH and –CH, respectively, they are –SH and –CH for BPT. The tribological properties of these SAM films on the Si (111) and Au (111) surface are measured by using a commercial AFM. The testing results show that HDT has the lowest adhesive and friction force due to their low work function of adhesion of CH_3-terminal group and high compliance long carbon chain. The adhesive forces vary linearly with the work of adhesion of SAM layer. The friction forces of SAM layer are closely related with the mechanical properties of the spacer chain. In order to explain the frictional magnitude difference among various SAM layers, the author presented the molecular spring model. DHBp has the best wear resistance, which can be influenced by interface bond strength, the molecular structure of the spacers, and the substrate hardness. The authors suggested that SAM layers, which combine the DHBp and HDT molecular structures, when deposited directly on hydrogenated Si (111), may have optimized tribological performance. Compared to organic silane-based SAMs, thiol-based SAM layers have low thermal stability[52]. When the temperature is higher than 60℃, defects are induced due to the distortion of terminal groups and the thermal de-adhesion will occur.

3.4.1.2 Silane-Based SAM Film

Srinivasan et al.[53] have investigated the effect of two type of silane-based SAM films (OTS (octadecyltrichlorosilane) and FDTS (1H,1H,2H,2H-perfluorodecyltrichlorosilane) on the stiction of polisilicon MEMS, while such stictions are release-related and are in use. Due to the hydrophobicity of these coatings, the water capillary forces responsible for the release-related stiction are eliminated, for example, the SAM-coated cantilever beam of thickness 2 μm, 2 μm above the substrate, and up to 2 mm in length emerges dry and free standing when removed from the final water rinse. The effects of SAM coatings on the stiction were studied using arrays of cantilever beams with different lengths structure made with a polysilicon of 3 nm rms roughness gave apparent works of adhesion of 30 and 8 $\mu J/m^2$ for OTS and FDTS SAM coatings, respectively, in comparison to 56 mJ/m^2 for standard oxide-coated structure. The results show that the apparent work of adhesion for FDTS-coated polysilicon cantilever beams is approximately four orders of magnitude lower than that of standard oxide coating and three times less than that of OTS. With regard to thermal stability, both SAM coatings can withstand heat treatment for 5 minutes at 450℃ in an N^2 ambient. In air, the OTS film begins to degrade at 150℃ while FDTS remains stable up to 400℃. Good thermal stability of the SAM coating makes the SAM coating process compatible with the MEMS package process.

Ahmed et al.[54] have studied the microtribological properties of SAMs of OTS and FDTS on the oxide-terminated Si(100) using a self-made microfriction tester.

The experimental results show that the friction coefficient of Si(100) coated by SAMs is 15 times less than the one without SAM coatings. Moreover, no wear phenomenon was found during the test.

It is to be noted that a Silane-based SAM film has a disadvantage. The quality of the SAM film is very sensitive to its forming process parameters, such as temperature and water content.

3.4.2 Extra-Thin Hard Film

3.4.2.1 Extra-Thin Diamond-Like Carbon (DLC)

Wear is another microtribological property that has a major effect on the reliability of the microsystem. SAM films coated on the microstructure surface can only reduce the friction coefficient and relieve or eliminate the stiction phenomenon, but do not improve the wear resistance of the microstructure. In order to increase the resistance of wear resistance, coating a film with thin, hard, chemically stable and well bonded to the microstructure, would be an efficient approach. Till now, hard amorphous carbon coatings, referred to as diamond-like carbon (DLC), are considered effective wear-resistant coatings for MEMS. The mechanical and tribological properties of DLC films are dependent on the structure of the films. For normal DLC, its microstructures are composed of most amorphous or quasi-amorphous carbon, in addition to some diamond (sp^3), graphite (sp^2,) and unknown micro/nano crystals. The hardness of DLC films is controlled by the content of sp^3. The detailed microstructures of DLC films depend on the deposition method of DLC. Sundararajan S. et al.[25] investigated four deposition methods of DLC and their effect on the mechanical properties of films. These methods are: filtered cathodic arc (FCA), ion beam (IB), RF-biased electron cyclotron resonance plasma chemical vapor deposition (ECR-CVD), and RF sputtering deposition. Table 3.10 lists the effect of different deposition methods

Table 3.10 Effect of different deposition techniques on mechanical properties of DLC film of thickness 100 nm

Deposition technique	Hardness (GPa)	Young's modulus (GPa)	Fracture toughness K_{1c} ($MPam^{1/2}$)
FCA	24	280	11.8
IB	19	140	4.9
ECR-CVD	22	180	6.4
SP	15	140	2.8
Bare Si (100)	11	165	0.95

on the mechanical properties of DLC films. It can be seen that the DLC films deposited by FCA, IB, and ECR-CVD have good mechanical properties to be used as wear-resistant coatings. Bhusan B. [55] reported that the thickness of DLC can be controlled as thin as 3 nm, and films with 5 nm thickness can prevent the wear of the microstructure.

3.4.2.2 Ultra Thin Al_2O_3 Coating for Micro Structure with High Aspect Ratio

Extra-thin DLC films deposited by the four above-mentioned methods are hard to coat on a microstructure with high aspect ratio. T. M. Mayer et al.[56] demonstrated that thin, conformal, wear-resistant coatings can be applied to Si surface micromachining structures by atomic-layer deposition (ALD). They obtained 10 nm thick films of Al_2O_3 by using a binary reaction sequence with precursors of trimethyl aluminum and water. Deposition is carried out in a viscous reactor at 1 torr and 168℃, with N_2 as a carrier gas. Cross-sectional TEM analysis shows that the film uniformity is within 5% on the MEMS device structure with aspect ratio ranges from 10 to >100. The nature of the film is amorphous stoichiometric Al_2O_3, which has very high hardness, chemical and thermal stability, and is one of the potential materials to be used for wear-resistant coatings of microstructures with high aspect ratio.

(1) Closure: future prospect of materials for microsystems

Developing new MEMS materials through bulk and surface micromachining technologies

Silicon and silicides can be microfabricated through mature bulk and surface micromachining technologies. Therefore, they are being widely used in most microsystems at present, even though in some MEMS, they cannot meet all the requirements which are needed for the MEMS products.

Parylene is one of the potential materials for MEMS devices, Although it can be used to make micro sensors, actuators, and also structural materials, it cannot be used for all MEMS materials. For example, in some MEMS devices, anodic bonding technology (at 400℃) is required, since parylene's glass transition point is 160℃. Every material has its dual properties, That means it might be a very good choice for some microdevices, but not a good one for some others. Therefore, an urgent task for all material scientists working in the field of microsystems is to develop new MEMS materials, especially microstructure materials.

One of the necessary requirements for an MEMS structure material is that it can be micro fabricated by bulk or surface micromachining technologies. Today, there exist several thousands of materials. Therefore, developing new MEMS materials involves developing new bulk and surface micromachining technologies for these existing materials. Aimi M. F.[57] has reported that the Department of Materials, and Mechanical and Environmental Engineering at UCSB of USA has developed a metal anisotropic reactive ion etching with oxidation (MARIO) technology, which is used to carry out high aspect ratio bulk micromachining of titanium foil, ranging from 10 – 500 μm. The bulk micromachining titanium structures are generally free of residual stresses and are preferred when large, rigid, flat, and/or high force actuation is desired. Of course, this is only an example used to develop new MEMS materials. Present need is to develop various such technologies to micro-fabricate other nonsilicon organic and inorganic materials, to provide a choice of more materials to the microsystem designers.

(2) More NanoMaterials to be Used in Microsystems

Nanomaterials have unique mechanical, electronic, magnetic, optical, and chemical properties. The use of novel nanomaterials in microsystems will lead to revolutionary changes in the functionality and reliability of microsystems. It is well known that the recording density of a hard disk drive increases rapidly when multilayer nanomaterials, resulting in GMR effect, are used in the read head. When the cross-section area of a silicon piezoresistor wire is reduced to the range of 50 nm×50 nm, the longitudinal piezoresistance coefficient of the silicon wire will increase by 60%. The sensitivity of the sensors is greatly increased when a silicon wire with the size less than the above critical value is used as the sensing material. Many SAM layers decorated on sensing structure will make the sensor have specific functionality. The mstnews 2004-04 issue contained a review article on the applications and challenges of nano- and micromaterials for microsystems. The article mentioned that organic semiconductors, high-purity single-wall carbon nanotubes, various nanoparticles, biomoleculars, and polymers for nanoprinting are expected to be the novel nano functional and structure materials used in future microsystems.

References

[1] Muhistein C. L., E. A. Stach, and R. O. Ritchie, (2002), Mechanism of fatigue in micro-scale films of polycrystalline silicon for microelectromechanical systems, *Applied Phys. Lett.*, **80**(9): 1532 – 1534

[2] Khoo H. S., K. K. Liu, and F. G. Tseng, (2003), Mechanical strength and interfacial failure analysis of cantilevered SU-8 microposts, *J. of Micromech. Microeng.*, **13**: 822 – 831

[3] Greek. S. and S. Johansson, (1997), Tensile testing of thin film microstructure, Proc. SPIE, **3224**: 344 – 351

[4] Sharpe W. N., B. Jr. Yuan, and A. Edwarde, (1997), new technique for measuring the mechanical properties of thin film, J. of Microelectromechanical System, **6**(3): 193 – 199

[5] Li X. P., G. F. Ding, T. Ando, M. Shilkida, and K. Sato, (2007), Micromechanical characterization of electroplated permalloy films for MEMS, Microsystem Technology, **14**: 131 – 134

[6] Peterson K. E., and C. R. Guarnieri, (1979), Young's modulus measurements of thin films using micromechanics, *J. of Appl. Phys.*, **50**(11): 6761 – 6766

[7] Li X. X. et al., (2003), Ultrathin single crystalline silicon cantilever resonators: Fabrication technology and significant specimen size effect on Young's modulus, *Appl. Phys. Letters*, **83**(15): 3081 – 3083

[8] Xiang Y., X. Chen, and J. J. Vlassak, (2002), The mechanical properties of electroplated Cu thin films measured by means of the Bulge test technique, *Mat. Res. Symp. Proc.* **695**: L4.9.1 – L4.9.5
[9] Schneider D., J. Maibach, and E. Obermeier, (1995), New analytical solution for the load-deflection of square membranes, *J. of Microelectromechanical Systems*, **4**(4): 238 – 241
[10] Vlassak J. J., and W. D. Nix, (1992), New bulge test technique for the determination of Young's modulus and Poisson's ratio of thin film, *J. of Materials Research*, **7**(12): 3242 – 3249
[11] Allen M. G., and S. D. Senturia, (1987), Microfabricated structures for the measurement of adhesion and mechanical properties of polymer films, Proceedings of the ACS, 1987, Denver, CO, USA
[12] Tabata O. et al., (1989), Mechanical property measurements of thin films using load-deflection of composite rectangular membranes, *Sensors and Actuators* **20**(1 – 2): 135 – 141
[13] Ziebart V. at al., (1998), Mechanical properties of thin film from the load deflection of long clamed plates, *J. of Microelectromechanical systems*, **7**(3): 320 – 328
[14] Gad-el-Hak M., 2002 MEMS Handbook
[15] He. J. H., Ph.D. Thesis, 2004, Cambridge University
[16] Oliver W. C. and G. M. Pharr, (1992), Improved technique for determining hardness and elastic modulus using load and displacement sensing indentation experiments, *J. Materials Research*, **7**(6): 1564 – 1580
[17] Senturia S. D., (2001), Microsystem Design, Kluwer Academic Publishers
[18] Wilson C. J., A. Ormeggi, and M. Narbutovskih, (1996), Fracture testing of silicon microcantilever beams, *J. of Appl. Phys.*, **75**(5): 2386 – 2393
[19] Wilson C. J., P. A. Beck, (1996), Fracture testing of bulk silicon microcantilever beams subjected to a sideload. *J. of Microelectromechanical Systems*, **3**(5): 142 – 150
[20] Weihs T. P., et al., (1988), Mechanical deflection of cantilever microbeams: A new technique for testing the mechanical properties of thin film, *J. of Materials Research*, **3**(5): 931 – 942
[21] Nilsson S. G., E. L. Sarwe, and L. Montelius, (2003), Fabrication and mechanical characterization of ultrashort nanocantilevers, *Appl. Phys. Letters*, **83**(5): 990 – 992
[22] Denhoff M. W., (2003), A measurement of Young's modulus and residual stress in MEMS bridge using a surface profiler, *J. of Micromechanics and Microengineering*, **5**: 686 – 692
[23] Zhang T. -Y. et al., (2000), Microbridge testing of silicon nitride thin films deposited on silicon wafers, *Acta Materialia*, **48**(11): 2843 – 2857
[24] Jones P. F., G. C. Johnson, and R. T. Howe, (1996), Micromechanical structures for fracture testing of brittle thin films, Proc. MEMS DSC-Volume 59, Atlanta, GA, November, 325 – 330
[25] Sundararajan S., Ph.D. thesis, 2001, Ohio State University
[26] Muhlstein C. L., S. B. Brown, and R. O. Ritchie, (a) High cycle fatigue and durability of polycrystalline silicon films in ambient air, Sensors and Actuators A, 2001, **94**: 177 – 188 (b) A reactive-layer mechanism for the delayed failure of micro-scale polycrystalline silicon structural films subjected to high-cycle fatigue loading, Acta Materialia, 50, 2002, 3579 – 3595

[27] Petersen K. E., (1982), Silicon as a mechanical material, *Proc. of the* IEEE, **70**(5): 420 – 457

[28] Jadaan O. M., et al., (2002), Probabilistic Weibull behavior and mechanical properties of MEMS brittle materials, *J. of Materials Science*, **38**(20): 4087 – 4113

[29] Brantley W. A., (1993), Calculated elastic constants for stress problems associated with semiconductor devices, *J. of Appl. Physc.*, **44**(1): 534 – 535

[30] Greenwood J. C., (1998), Silicon in mechanical sensors, *J. of Physics E: Scientific Instruments*, **21**(12): 1114 – 1128

[31] Sato K., et al., (1998), Tensile testing of silicon film having different crystallographic orientations carried out on a silicon chip, *Sensors and Actuators*, **70**(1 – 2): 148 – 152

[32] Schweitz J. A., and F. Ericson, (1994), Evaluation of mechanical materials properties by means of surface micromachined structures, *Sensors and Actuators, A: Physical*, **74**(1 – 3): 126 – 133

[33] Yi T., et al., (2000), Microscale material testing of single crystalline silicon: Process effects on surface morphology and tensile strength, Sensors and Actuators A, *Physical*, **83**(1): 172 – 178

[34] Chasiotis I. and W. Knauss, (1998), Mechanical properties of thin polysilicon films by means of probe microscopy, *Proc. of* SPIE, **3512**: 66 – 75

[35] Tsuchiya T., O. Tabato, et al., (1998), Specimen size effect on tensile strength of surface micromachined polycrystalline silicon thin film, *J. of Micromechanical Syst.*, **7**: 106 – 113

[36] Sharpe W., S. Brown, at el., (1998), Round-robin tests for modulus and strength of polysilicon, Proc. Microelectromechanical Structure for Materials Research, 1998(518), Materials Research Society Spring Meeting, San Francisco, CA, **4**: 57 – 65

[37] Madou M. J., (1997), Fundamentals of Microfabrication, **2**: 53 – 87

[38] Levy R. A., et al., (1996), Low pressure chemical vapor deposition of silicon nitride using the environmentally friendly tris(dimethylamino)silane pressure, *J. of Materials Research*, **11**(6): 1483 – 1488

[39] Bromley E. I., et al., (1983), Technology for the determination of stress in thin films, Proc. of the Int. Symp. on Electron, Ion, and Photon Beams, **1**(4): 1364 – 1366

[40] Drummond C. J., and T. J. Senden, (1995), Characterization of the mechanical properties of thin film cantilever with the atomic force microscope, Materials Science Forum, **189 – 190**: 107 – 114

[41] Bhushan B., and B. K. Gupta, (1991), Handbook of tribology, Materials coatings and surface treatments, Reprint edition, 1991, Krieger, Malabar FL

[42] Ericson F., et al., (1998), Hardness and fracture toughness of semiconducting materials studied by indentation and erosion techniques, Materials Science and Engineering, A, **105 – 106**: 131 – 141

[43] Tai Y. C., Parylene MEMS: Material technologies and applications, Proc .of the 20th Sensor Symposium on Sensors, Micromachines, and Applied Systems, 2003, July 23 – 24, Tokyo, Japan, 1 – 8

[44] Harder T. H., et al., (2002), Residual stress in thin film parylene, Proceedings, The Fifteenth IEEE International Conference on Micro Electro Mechanical Systems, Las Vegas, USA, 2002, 435 – 438

[45] Shih J., et al., (2003), Surface micromachined and integrated capacitive sensors for microfluidic applications, Technical Digest, The 12th International Conference on Solid-State Sensors, Actuators, and Microsystems (Transducers '03), Boston, USA, 2003, 388 – 391

[46] Meng E., et al., (2003), A parylene MEMS flow sensing array, Technical Digest, The 12th International Conference on Solid-State Sensors, Actuators and Microsystems (Transducers '03), Boston, USA, 2003, 686 – 689

[47] Wang X. Q., et al., (1999), A parylene micro check valve, Proceedings, IEEE 12th International Micro Electro Mechanical Systems Conference (MEMS '99), Orlando, Florida, Jan. 1999, 177 – 182

[48] Xie J., et al., (2003), Integrated surface micromachined mass flow controller, Proceedings, The Sixteenth IEEE International Conference on Micro Electro Mechanical Systems (MEMS '03), Kyoto, Japan, Jan. 2003, 20 – 23

[49] Yao T. J., et al., (2002), Dielectric charging effects on parylene electrostatic actuators, Proceedings, The Fifteenth IEEE International Conference on Micro Electro Mechanical Systems (MEMS '02), Las Vegas, USA., 2002, 614 – 617

[50] Bhushan B., (2003), Adhesion and stiction: Mechanisms, measurement techniques, and methods for reduction, *J. of Vac. Sci. Technol.*, **21**(6): 2262 – 2295

[51] Liu H., and B. Bhushan, (2002), Investigation of nanotribological properties of self-assembled monolayers with alkyl and biphenyl spacer chains, *Ultramicroscopy*, **91**: 185 – 202

[52] Delamarche E., at al., (1994), Thermal stability of self-assembled monolayers, *Langmuirr*, **10**: 4103 – 4108

[53] Srinivasan U., et al., (1998), Alkyltrichlorosilane-based self-assembled monolayer film for stiction reduction in silicon micromachines, *J. Microelectromechanical Systems*, **7**(2): 252 – 260

[54] Ahmed S. I., et al., (1999), Microtribological properties of self-assembled monolayers, www.iavf.de/pdf/deutsch, 1999, 1 – 8

[55] Bhushan B., (1999), Chemical, mechanical, and tribological characterization of ultra-thin and hard amorphous carbon coating as thin as 3.5 nm: Recent developments, *Diamond and Related Materials*, **8**: 1985 – 2015

[56] Mayer T. M., et al., (2003), Atomic-layer deposition of wear-resistant coatings for microelectromechanical devices, *Applied Phys. Letters*, **82**(17): 2883 – 2885

[57] Aimi M. F., et al., (2004), High-aspect-ratio bulk micromachining of titanium, *Nature Materials*, **3**: 103 – 105

4 Nanopiezotronics and Nanogenerators

Xudong Wang, Jun Zhou, and Zhong Lin Wang

School of Materials Science and Engineering, Georgia Institute of Technology, Atlanta, GA 30332-0245, USA

E-mail: zhong.wang@mse.gatch.edu

Abstract Today's nanoelectronics rely on the transport of charge carriers under the driving of externally applied voltage to perform specific functionality, such as transistors and diodes. Recently, Piezotronics was introduced as a new field in nanoelectronics[1,2]. It utilizes the coupled piezoelectric and semiconducting property of nanowires (NWs) and nanobelts (NBs) for designing and fabricating electronic devices such as transistors and diodes. Piezoelectricity is a coupling between a material's mechanical and electrical behavior. When a piezoelectric crystal is mechanically deformed, the positive- and negative-charge centers are displaced with respect to each other. Therefore, while the overall crystal remains electrically neutral, the difference in charge center displacements results in an electric polarization within the crystal. Electric polarization resulting from mechanical deformation is perceived as piezoelectricity. Once the piezoelectric materials are also semiconductors, such as ZnO, their electronic characteristic can be affected by the piezoelectric potential. This phenomenon becomes more obvious when the crystal size is in nanometer regime and so it is also called nano-Piezotronics. It is anticipated to have a wide range of applications in electromechanical coupled sensors and devices, nanoscale energy conversion for self-powered nanosystems, and harvesting/recycling of energy from environment.

In this chapter, ZnO, as a typical and widely studied piezotronic material, is reviewed in detail from the origin of its piezoelectric property to the novel nanodevices made from piezotronic ZnO NWs.

Keywords ZnO nanowire, nanogenerator, piezopotential, piezotronics

4.1 Piezotronic Property of ZnO Nanowires

4.1.1 Crystal Structure of ZnO

Zinc oxide has a Wurtzite hexagonal structure (space group P63mc) with lattice parameters $a = 0.3296$, and $c = 0.52065$ nm. The structure of ZnO can be simply described as a number of alternating planes composed of O^{2-} and Zn^{2+} ions, stacked alternatively along the c-axis (Fig. 4.1(a)). The oppositely charged ions produce positively charged Zn-(0001) and negatively charged O-(000$\bar{1}$) polar surfaces, resulting in a normal dipole moment and spontaneous polarization along the c-axis. Such spontaneous polarization leads to the self-assembly of novel nanostructures like nanorings and nanosprings, which are driven by the minimization of electrostatic energy coming from the ionic charges on the polar surfaces. Inside the crystal, O^{2-} and Zn^{2+} ions are tetrahedrally coordinated, which results in a non-central symmetric structure. The lack of a center of symmetry, combined with large electromechanical coupling, results in strong piezoelectric and pyroelectric properties and the consequent use of ZnO in actuators[3], piezoelectric sensors[4,5], piezoelectric diodes,[6] and nanogenerators (NGs)[7]. To illustrate the piezoelectric effect, consider a zinc atom with positive charge that is surrounded tetrahedrally by negatively charged oxygen anions (Fig. 4.1(b)). Strong piezoelectric effect can be observed along ZnO [0001] crystal direction. Once the {0001} is the biggest surface of a ZnO nanobelt, the effective piezoelectric coefficient d_{33} has been measured 14 pm/V, which is larger than that of the bulk (0001) ZnO, 9.93 pm/V[8].

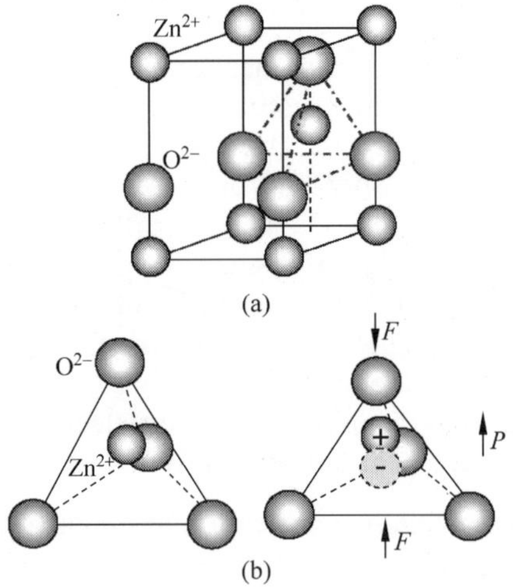

Figure 4.1 (a) Wurtzite structure model of ZnO. (b) The tetrahedral coordination of Zn-O and the corresponding Polarization of ions under stress (see color figure at the end of this book)

4.1.2 Piezoelectricity of ZnO Nanowire

A ZnO NW is a beam-like structure that always grows along its [0001] direction and exhibits a hexagonal cross-section[9]. When such a NW is laterally bent, a positive voltage can be created on the tensile side surface; while a negative voltage shows on the compressive side. On the basis of a static model calculation for a case in which the force is uniformly applied to the NW along its length, and without considering the conductivity of ZnO, the piezoelectric potential at the surface can be calculated as follows[10]. We assume that all the external forces are surface forces with no body force acting on the wire; therefore,

$$\nabla \cdot \boldsymbol{\sigma} = 0 \tag{4.1}$$

where $\boldsymbol{\sigma}$ is the stress tensor, which is related to strain ε, electric field E, and electric displacement D by the following constitutive equations:

$$\begin{cases} \sigma_p = c_{pq}\varepsilon_q - e_{kp}E_k \\ D_i = e_{iq}\varepsilon_q - \kappa_{ik}E_k \end{cases} \tag{4.2}$$

Here c_{pq} is the linear elastic constant, e_{kp} is the linear piezoelectric coefficient, and κ_{ik} is the dielectric constant. In our calculation, we only need to consider the direct piezoelectric effect, and the converse piezoelectric effect can be neglected. Under an approximation of ignoring the electric conductivity of ZnO, the following Gauss equation is satisfied:

$$\nabla \cdot \vec{D} = 0 \tag{4.3}$$

With Eqs. (4.1) – (4.3) and the geometrical compatibility equations, the electric field generated by the NW can be calculated when a proper boundary condition is given. Under a simplified condition, where we assume that the nanowire has a cylindrical shape with a uniform cross-section of diameter $2a$ and length l, the maximum potential at the surface of the NW is given by the following equation:

$$\varphi_{\max}^{(T,C)} = \pm \frac{3}{4(\kappa_0 + \kappa_\perp)}[e_{33} - 2(1+\nu)e_{15} - 2\nu e_{31}]\frac{a^3}{l^3}v_{\max} \tag{4.4}$$

where φ is the electric potential; κ_0 and $\kappa_\perp$ are the dielectric constants of the vacuum and ZnO crystal along its c-plane, respectively; e_{33}, e_{15}, and e_{31} are the linear piezoelectric coefficients; ν is the Poisson ratio; and $v_{\max}$ is the maximum deflection at the NW's tip. This equation clearly shows that the electrostatic potential is directly related to the aspect ratio of the NW instead of its dimensionality.

In our model, the bottom of the NW is assumed to be affixed on a well-grounded substrate. We assume that the nanowire is subjected to a force uniformly distributed on one of its four lateral sides. The mechanical property of ZnO is $E = 129.0$ GPa and $\nu = 0.349$; the relative dielectric constants are $\kappa_\perp^r = 7.77$ and $\kappa_\parallel^r = 8.91$ for bulk ZnO; and the piezoelectric constants are $e_{31} = -0.51$ C/m^2, $e_{33} = 1.22$ C/m^2, and $e_{15} = -0.45$ C/m^2. For a typical NW that was grown through the vapor-liquid-solid (VLS) process[11], the diameter is $d=50$ nm, length is $l=600$ nm. When it is bent 145 nm to the right by an 80 nm lateral force, ±0.3 V piezoelectric potential can be induced on the two side surfaces, as shown in Fig. 4.2(b), the calculated potential distribution across the NW cross section. Figure 4.2(a) depicts the potential distribution along the bent NW generated by finite element calculation using the above equation. Calculation also shows that the piezoelectric potential in the NW almost does not depend on the z-coordination along the NW. Under this situation, the NW is approximately like a 'parallel plate capacitor'. Similar results have been found on NWs with different geometry. For a larger size NW with $d=300$ nm and length $l=2$ μm[12], the surface piezoelectric potential can reach ±0.6 V, when it is deflected by a 1,000 nN force. This numerical calculation shows that the maximum piezoelectric potential that can be generated at the NW surface is directly proportional to the lateral displacement of the NW and inversely proportional to the length-to-diameter aspect ratio of the NW.

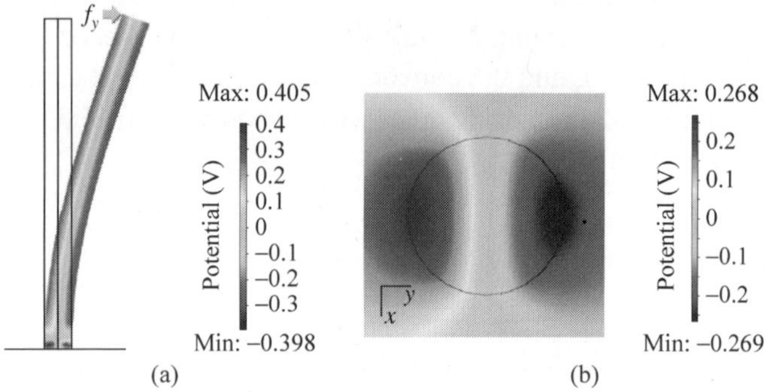

Figure 4.2 Potential distribution for a ZnO nanowire with $d=50$ nm, $l=600$ nm at a lateral bending force of 80 nN. (a) and (b) are side and cross-sectional (at $z=300$ nm) output of the piezoelectric potential in the NW given by finite element calculation (see color figure at the end of this book)

The voltages at the stretched and compressed sides of the NW can be experimentally detected by using a metal micro-needle to contact each side of the NW while it is bending[13]. An experimental design to measure the voltage and current output by a PFW is shown in Fig. 4.3(a). All of the experiments were carried out at room temperature and normal atmosphere pressure. A NW was placed on the edge of a Si substrate, with one end fixed to the substrate, which was electrically grounded, and the other end was left free. A tungsten needle coated with 0 – 2 μm thick Au was connected to an external measurement circuit. The needle was placed at one side of the NW, and Ar gas was blown from the other side along a direction perpendicular to the orientation of the needle. When a periodic gas flow pulse was applied to a ZnO NW, the wire was vibrating and a corresponding periodic negative voltage output Fig. 4.3(b) was detected by connecting the surface of the compressed side of the NW with an external measurement circuit. The largest voltage output detected here was –25 mV. Correspondingly, a periodic positive voltage output (Fig. 4.3(c)) was detected at the stretched side of the NW by using the Au-coated needle when the ZnO wire was periodically pushed by this needle.

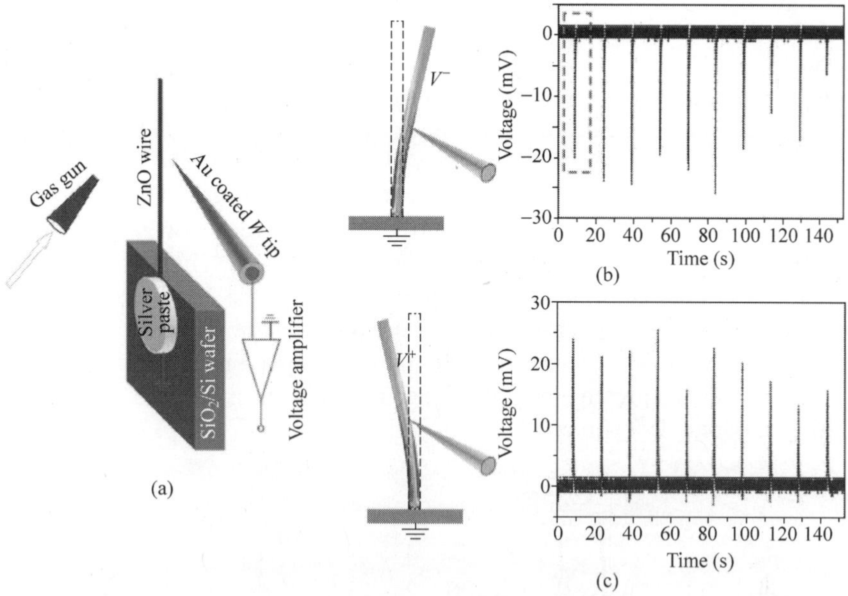

Figure 4.3 (a) Schematic experimental set-up for detecting the surface potential. (b) By placing a metal tip at the right-hand side and blowing Ar pulses at the left-hand side, negative voltage peaks of 0 – 25 mV were observed once the pulse was on. (c) By quickly pushing and releasing the wire at the right-hand side by a metal tip, a positive voltage peak of 0 – 25 mV was observed for each cycle of the deflection (see color figure at the end of this book)

The measured voltage signal in our experiment is much lower than that predicted by the static calculation. The following reasons may account for this difference. First, the contact resistance can be very large as a result of the small contact area between the ZnO wire and Au-coated tungsten tip. Therefore, the voltage created by the piezoelectric effect of the ZnO wire is largely consumed at the contact because of the contact resistance, and only a small portion is received as the output. Second, the capacitance of the measurement system could be much larger than the capacitance of the ZnO NW. The large system capacitance consumes most of the charges produced by the ZnO NW and results in a low voltage output. More importantly, the finite conductivity of ZnO may greatly reduce the magnitude of the piezoelectric potential, which is not included in theoretical calculation. Beyond the static model, the dynamic discharge process has to be considered as well.

4.1.3 Combination of Piezoelectric and Semiconducting Properties

Unlike other traditional piezoelectric materials, ZnO is also a semiconductor material. It has a direct wide band gap of 3.37 eV with a large excitation binding energy (60 meV). Typical ZnO NWs are n-type semiconductors that result from oxygen vacancies and/or zinc interstitials. The carrier density of ZnO NWs is in the range of $10^{15} - 10^{16}$ cm^{-3} mostly, depending on the fabrication conditions. However, the carrier density can also be altered by experimental circumstances, for example, UV light illumination[14]. Figure 4.4 shows the UV response of the vertically aligned ZnO NWs and the underlying ZnO thin film by connecting two electrodes at the two ends of the film, as shown in the inset. By applying a constant voltage V_0, the transport current was monitored when the UV was turned on or off. The conductance of the film responded rapidly to UV and reached saturation after ~300 s. However, the current decayed very slowly after the UV was turned off, possibly due to the following reason. The UV light can effectively create electron-hole pairs in ZnO and greatly increase the carrier density. After turning off the UV, the electrons and holes would recombine and thus decrease the conductivity. However, some carriers may be trapped in the surface/vacancy states in ZnO, which greatly delayed the electron-hole recombination rate, possibly resulting in a long decay in conductivity.

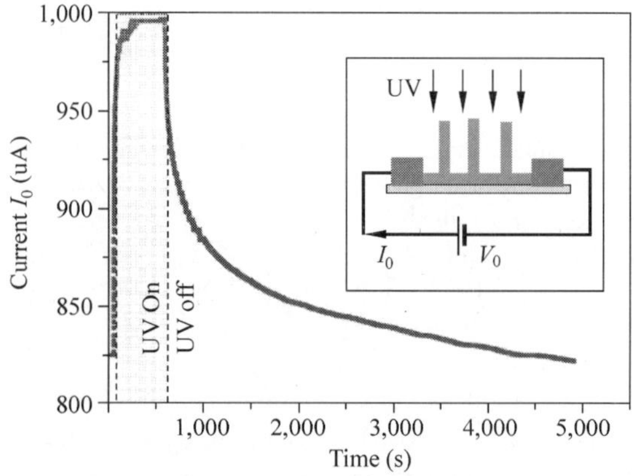

Figure 4.4 Response of the current transported through a thin ZnO film with NWs on top when it is subjected to UV illumination. The inset is the measurement set-up (see color figure at the end of this book)

Combination of the piezoelectric and semiconducting properties of ZnO NWs leads to a new concept in nanoelectronics—piezotronics. In general, the transport property in semiconducting ZnO NWs can be controlled by its piezoelectricity. On the other hand, the piezoelectricity can be rectified and released by the semiconducting property. This establishes the basis for several novel piezotronic nanodevices for sensing and energy harvesting.

For example, field-effect transistors (FETs) based on nanowires/nanotubes are one of the most studied nanodevices. A typical NW FET is composed of a semiconducting NW that is connected by two electrodes at the ends and placed on a silicon substrate covered by a thin layer of gate oxide. A third electrode is built between the NW and the gate oxide (Fig. 4.5(a)). The electric signal output from the drain electrode of the NW is controlled by a gate voltage applied between the gate and the NW. An NW-based sensor is a source-drain structured NW FET without a gate. Thus, a large portion of the NW is exposed to the environment. The mechanism of NW sensors for sensing gases, biomolecules, or even viruses relies on the creation of a charge depletion zone in the semiconductor NW by the surface-adsorbed sensing targets[15].

By connecting a ZnO NW across two electrodes that can apply a bending force to the NW, the electric field created by piezoelectricity across the bent NW serves as the gate for controlling the electric current flowing through the NW (Fig. 4.5(b)). Once deformed by an external force *F*, a piezoelectric potential is built across the bent NW, and some free electrons in the n-type ZnO NW may be trapped at the surface of the positive side and become non-movable charges, thus lowering the effective carrier density in the NW. On the other hand, even though the positive-potential side could be partially neutralized by the trapped electrons, the negative potential side remains unchanged. The free electrons will be repelled away by the negative potential and leave a charge depletion zone around the compressed side surface. Consequently, the width of the conducting channel in the ZnO NW becomes smaller and smaller while the depletion region becomes larger and larger with the increase of the NW bending. Therefore, the role played by the piezoelectric-induced field across the width of the NW is analogous to the case of applying a gate voltage across the width of the ZnO NW as for a typical NW FET. The process shown in Fig. 4.2(b) gives a good example of the transport property of a ZnO NW modified by its piezoelectricity. Therefore, it is called piezoelectric FET (PE-FET)[16].

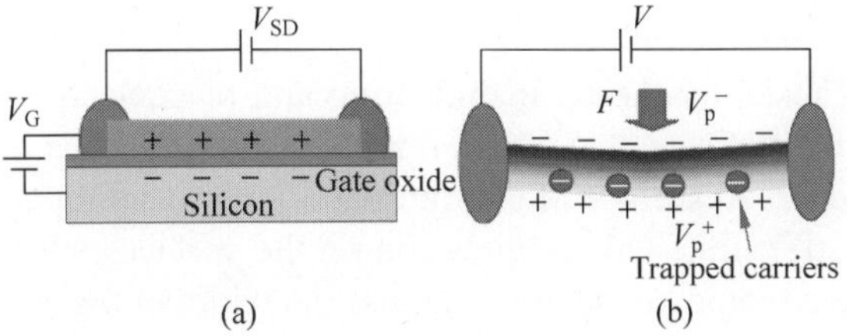

Figure 4.5 (a) Schematics of conventional field-effect transistors (FETs) using a single nanowire/nanobelt. (b) The principle of the piezoelectric field-effect transistor (PE-FET) (see color figure at the end of this book)

In the next two sections of this chapter, piezotronic nanodevices will be reviewed as nanosensors and mechanical energy harvesting nanosystems.

4.2 Piezotronics Nanodevices from ZnO Nanowires

The interaction between the piezoelectric and semiconducting properties demonstrated a novel operation concept of FETs–the PE-FET. Based on this concept, several important prototype devices, such as force and pressure sensors, mechanical electrical triggers, and strain sensors have been demonstrated.

4.2.1 PE-FET and Force Sensor

As described previously, PE-FET is an alternative design of an NW FET without using the gate electrode. By connecting a ZnO NW across two electrodes that can apply a bending force to the NW, the electric field created by piezoelectricity across the bent NW serves as the gate for controlling the electric current flowing through the NW. The PE-FET is a new type of FET, which can be turned on/off by applying a mechanical force. As a result, it has the potential to be used as a force sensor for measuring forces in the nanonewton range or even smaller.

In the experiment, a ZnO NW was suspended between the source and drain electrodes, which were Ohmic contacts to the NW. Under the observation in a scanning electron microscope (SEM), the ZnO NW was bent by precisely moving the source electrodes close to the drain electrode. Then, the electron beam of the SEM was turned off and the current-voltage ($I\sim V$) characteristic was measured by sweeping the voltage from –5 – 5 V. This is to eliminate the effect from the electron beam in the SEM. After the measurement, the electron beam was turned back on again and the NW was bent further by moving the SEM stage in situ under direct imaging. The bending of the NW was recorded. Following such a procedure, a sequential measurement was carried out. Five $I\sim V$ curves were recorded Figs. 4.6(a) – (e) show the five different bending curvatures of the ZnO NW and Fig. 4.6(f) shows the corresponding $I\sim V$ curves. It was clearly observed that the current dropped significantly with the increase of bending, indicating the decrease in conductance with the increase in strain.

The possible mechanisms of the bending induced conductance change are believed to be caused by the semiconducting and piezoelectric dual property of ZnO. We have recently seen that a bent ZnO NW can produce a positively charged and negatively charged surface at the outer and inner bending arc surfaces of the NW due to the stretching and compression on the surfaces, respectively. Thus, a small electric field would be generated across the width of the ZnO NW, as shown in the cross-section image of the NW in Fig. 4.7(a). Upon the build-up of the electric field, two possible effects can be proposed to explain the reduction of the NW's conductance: carrier trapping effect and the creation of a charge depletion zone.

When the piezo-potential appears across the bent NW, some free electrons in the n-type ZnO NW may be trapped at the positive side surface (outer arc surface) and become non-movable charges, thus lowering the carrier density in the NW

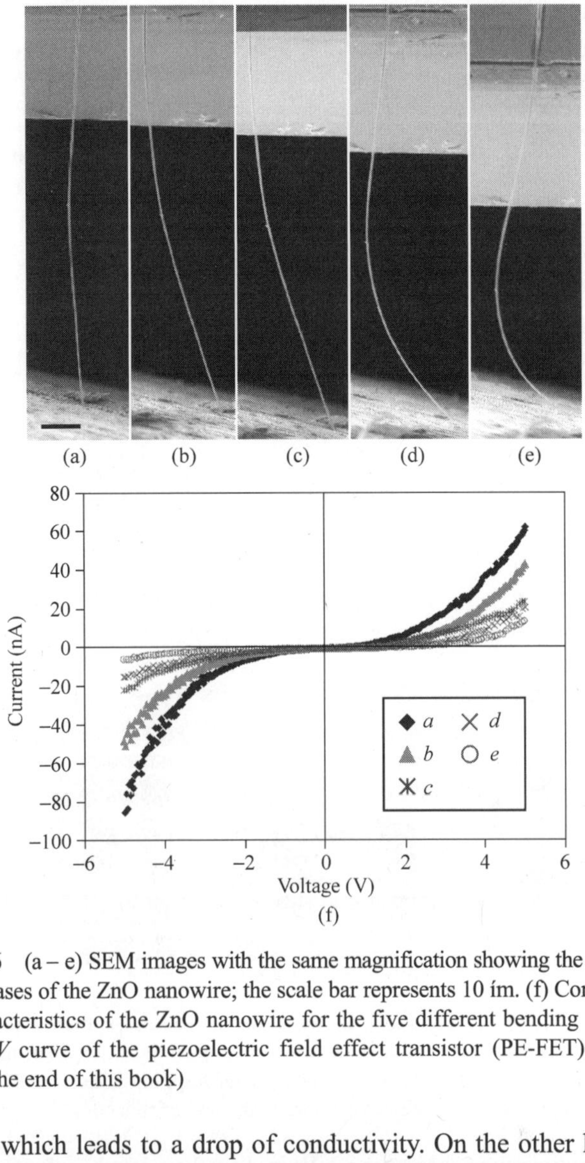

Figure 4.6 (a – e) SEM images with the same magnification showing the five typical bending cases of the ZnO nanowire; the scale bar represents 10 ím. (f) Corresponding $I\sim V$ characteristics of the ZnO nanowire for the five different bending cases. This is the $I\sim V$ curve of the piezoelectric field effect transistor (PE-FET) (see color figure at the end of this book)

(Fig. 4.7(b)), which leads to a drop of conductivity. On the other hand, even the positive-potential side could be partially neutralized by the trapped electrons, the negative potential remains unchanged. Hence, the piezo-induced electric field is retained across the width of the NW. This situation is similar to the case of applying a gate voltage across the width of the ZnO NW as the operation of a typical NW FET. The free electrons will be repelled away by the negative potential and leave a charge depletion zone around the compressed side, as shown in Fig. 4.7(c). Consequently, the conducting channel in the ZnO NW becomes smaller and smaller, while the depletion region becomes larger and larger with the increase in the NW bending. The two effects presented in Fig. 4.7(b) and Fig. 4.7(c) could be the main reasons responsible for a dramatic drop in the conductance of the ZnO NW with the increase in the bending. The maximum width that the depletion zone can develop is up to the strain-free plane (close to the central axis of the NW) with consideration of the piezoelectric field, which naturally sets an upper limit to the effect contributed by the depletion charges. The structure shown in Fig. 4.7 is the working principle of a FET except that the gate voltage is produced by piezoelectric effect. Therefore, the single ZnO across two Ohmic contacts is a piezoelectric-field effect transistor (PE-FET).

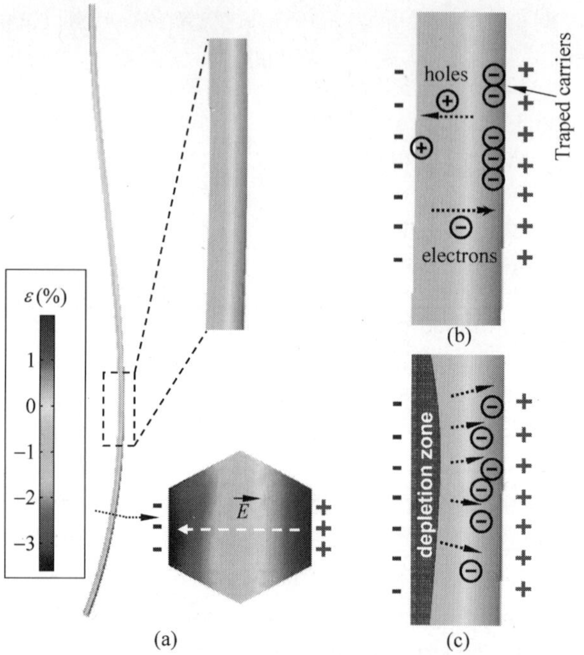

Figure 4.7 Schematic diagrams showing the mechanisms responsible for the conductance change. (a) A finite element simulation of the strain distribution along the ZnO nanowire when it is bent. (b) The carrier trapping effect. (c) The creation of a charge depletion zone (see color figure at the end of this book)

Since the bending curvature of the NW is directly related to the force applied to it, a simple P-FET force/pressure sensor is realized. The important step for calibrating the force/pressure sensor is how to quantitatively determine the force applied to the NW. As shown schematically in the inset in Fig. 4.8, when the NW is pressed vertically, under small deflection angle approximation, the NW is deflected mainly due to the transverse force F_y, and the bending shape of the NW is given by[17]

$$\frac{d^2y}{dx^2}=\frac{F_y\cdot(L-x)}{YI} \tag{4.5}$$

where Y is the bending modulus; I is the momentum of inertia; and L is the total length of the NW. The shape of the bent NW is

$$y = \frac{F_y}{YI}\left(\frac{1}{2}Lx^2 - \frac{1}{6}x^3\right) \tag{4.6}$$

At the tip of the NW ($x = L$), the maximum deflection of the NW is

$$y_{\mathrm{m}} = \frac{F_y L^3}{3YI} \quad \text{or} \quad F_y = \frac{3YIy_{\mathrm{m}}}{L^3} \tag{4.7}$$

The bending modulus of ZnO NWs has been measured to be 109 GPa according to our previous data[18] and I was calculated to be $6.62 \times 10^{-28}\ \mathrm{m}^4$ for this particular NW. y_{m} was measured from the SEM images. Since the SEM image is a projection of the 3-D structure, in order to obtain an accurate measurement, the bending curve should be parallel to the projecting screen. Considering this effect, the tungsten needle surface was tilted 15° to the right-hand side and the initial bending was achieved by lateral moving of the NW instead of directly pushing downward. After parallel bending of the NW, the stage was then pushed downward to further bending the nanowires. Since the nonlinear $I \sim V$ characteristics, the conductance was determined by the current measured at a constant 5 V potential. The total force versus conductance is shown plotted in Fig. 4.8. At small bending, the decrease of conductance was almost linear to the bending force.

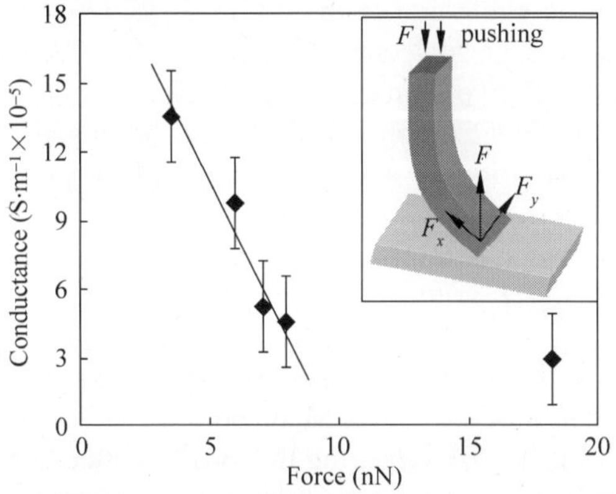

Figure 4.8 A plot showing the relationship between the ZnO nanowire conductance as PE-FET and the deflection force derived from the experimental data, demonstrating a nanoforce or nanopressure sensor using a single nanowire. Inset is the schematic of the deflected NW

With the increase of bending at higher transverse force (17 nN), the dropping tendency of the conductance was reduced. This can also be understood from the two processes illustrated in Fig. 4.7. At the beginning of bending, both contributions from the carrier trapping effect and the depletion zone increased with the bending curvature, thus producing a quick drop in the conductance. However, unlike the normal gate-controlled FETs, there was a positive potential on the outer side of the NW, which increased simultaneously with the negative potential at the inner side during the bending. The depletion region cannot extend beyond the neutral plane of the NW to the positive potential side. Thus, when the NW was bent to a significant degree, the piezoelectric field could not increase the size of the charge depletion zone, hence, it cannot reduce the size of the conduction channel.

It must be pointed out that the calculation in Eqs. (4.6) and (4.7) are for an NW that is subject to a small bending. Non-linear effect has to be included if the degree of bending is large. This may cause significant change in the calibration of the measured force at larger applied forces. For practical application as force sensors, the measurements are recommended to be carried out under small deflections. For the data shown in Fig. 4.8, the first four data points are most reliable for calibrating the sensor performance.

4.2.2 Chemical/Humidity Nanosensors

The coupling effect of piezoelectric and semiconducting properties of ZnO has also been used as a new type of chemical/humidity sensors. The prototype device was based on a single-side coated ZnO NB functionalized with multilayers of polymers[19]. Upon exposure to high humidity vapors, the polymers swell and produce an asymmetric strain across the ZnO NB. In return, the deformation of the ZnO NB produces a piezoelectric field across the NB, which serves as the gate for controlling the flow of current along the NB.

Polymers for functionalization of NB are anionically charged poly*N*-isopropylacrylamide (PNIPAM) and poly(diallyldimethylammonium chloride) (PDADMAC). PNIPAM is the most well-known temperature-sensitive polymer in aqueous solution, which exhibits a lower critical solution temperature (LCST) of around 32 ℃ [20]. The volume change ratio of a cross-linked PNIPAM corresponding to its hydration and dehydration transition can go up to 20[21]. The device was fabricated through a layer-by-layer self-assembly process by immersing ZnO NB in a dilute PDADMAC solution followed by an anionically charged PNIPAM solution.. By repeating this process alternatively, multilayers of polymer with controlled layer numbers were assembled on the ZnO NB surface. This multilayer functionalization configuration is schematically shown in Fig. 4.9(a), in which the green dots represent the cationically charged PDADMAC and the orange dots represent the anionically charged PNIPAM.

PNIPAM and PDADMAC are both very sensitive to environment humidity changes, which introduces surface strain on the NB. As shown in Fig. 4.9(b), these polymers are closely packed before vapor exposure. Upon exposure to water vapor, these polymers undergo a hydration process. As a result, the volumes of these polymers are increased in a significant ratio. Since the polymers are coated only at one side of the ZnO NB, the swelling of polymers then generates an asymmetric tensile stress at the contact surface with the ZnO NB. Consequently, the ZnO NB bends, resulting in an asymmetric strain across the thickness of the NB. As discussed in the previous section, a bent ZnO NB could produce a piezoelectric potential across the NB due to the strain-induced piezoelectric effect. With the stretch and compression effects of a deformed ZnO NB, a positively charged surface and a negatively charged surface are produced at the outer and inner bending surfaces of the ZnO NB, respectively. Consequently, a piezoelectric field is built across the ZnO NB Fig. 4.9(c). These ionic charges are immobile on the ZnO NB surface without releasing the strain. Such piezoelectric potential could act as a gate voltage to control the conductivity of the NB channel as presented in the PE-FET mechanism. When the sample is dehydrated in dry air, the strain is released and the ZnO NB returns to its original shape.

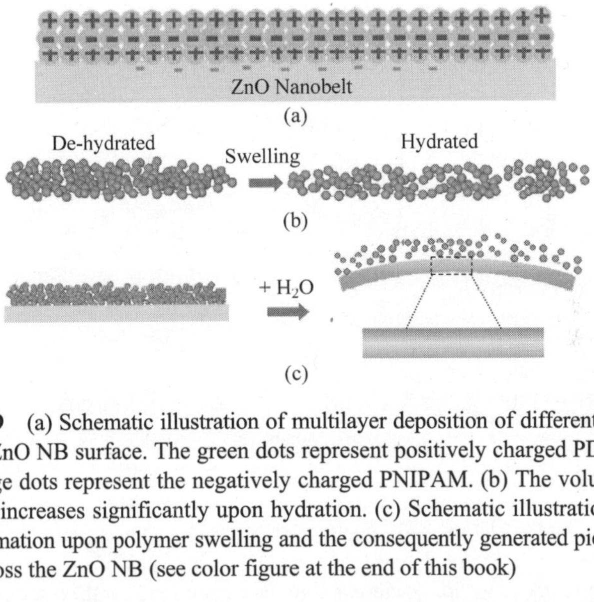

Figure 4.9 (a) Schematic illustration of multilayer deposition of different polymers onto the ZnO NB surface. The green dots represent positively charged PDADMAC. The orange dots represent the negatively charged PNIPAM. (b) The volume of the polymers increases significantly upon hydration. (c) Schematic illustration of ZnO NB deformation upon polymer swelling and the consequently generated piezoelectric fields across the ZnO NB (see color figure at the end of this book)

To apply this concept as a chemical/humidity sensor, the ZnO NBs could be further treated using focused ion beam microscopy to deposit Pt to secure the contacts before polymer functionalization. Figure 4.10(a) depicts the $I\sim V$ characteristics of PNIPAM functionalized samples upon exposure to 85% RH water vapor (black line) and 12% RH water vapor (red curve). This current response to vapor on and off states can be repeated for many cycles and the detection limit could be very accurate according to the strong and steady response to the 12% RH water vapor in the experiment.

To explore the origin of the reduced current upon vapor exposure, we carried out a series of experiments based on different functional materials on the devices.

As shown in Fig. 4.10(b), the current flowing through the uncoated ZnO NB (black) increased from 0.005 – 0.055 μA upon 85% water vapor exposure. We suggest that upon vapor exposure, the pre-adsorbed oxygen that caused the conductivity decrease was replaced by the ionic species, which might have resulted in an increase in conductivity. Similar current increase was observed when the conducting channel contains only multilayers of polymers (Fig. 4.10(b)–red). This is due to the ion mobility increase in the dehydrated multiple polymers. Current responses of the multilayer polymers without a ZnO NB or with a ZnO NB only but without polymer are opposite to the response of polymer functionalized ZnO NBs. These experiments prove that neither ZnO NB nor multilayer polymers could produce the decreased current response upon exposure to vapor. Therefore, the decreased current response arises from the mechanism of PE-FET relying on the self-contraction/expansion of the polymer, which builds up a strain in the piezoelectric NB and induces a potential drop across the NB that serves as the gate voltage for controlling the current flowing through the NB.

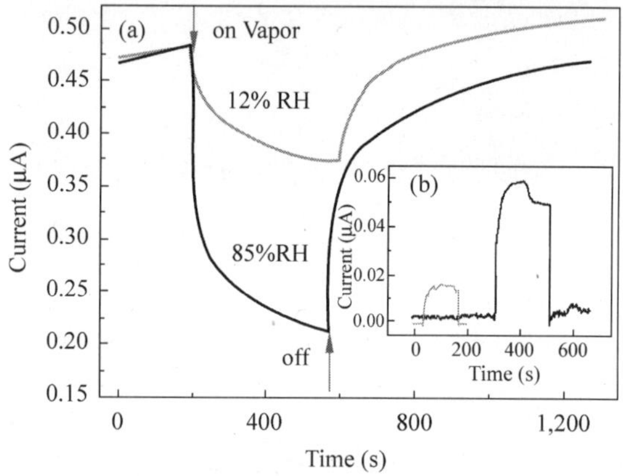

Figure 4.10 (a) IV responses of the PNIPAM polymer functionalized devices upon exposure to 85% (black curve) and 12% (red curve) relative humidities. (b) Current response of an uncoated ZnO NB upon exposure to 85% relative humidity (black) and the polymer (red), showing that neither of them individually is responsible for the reduction of current in (a) (see color figure at the end of this book)

4.2.3 Mechanical-Electrical Strain Sensors

Based on a single ZnO piezoelectric NW, an alternative design of a fully packaged strain sensor device was developed. The strain sensor was fabricated by bonding a ZnO PFW laterally on a polystyrene (PS) substrate[22]. The $I \sim V$ behavior of the device was modulated by strain due to the change in the Schottky barrier height (SBH). The combined effects from strain-induced band structure change and piezoelectricity result in the change of SBH.

The schematic of the strain sensor device is shown in Fig. 4.11(a). The ZnO wires used in this device have diameters of 2 – 6 μm and lengths of several hundred micrometers to several millimeters. The same principle and methodology apply to NWs. A ZnO NW was placed on the PS substrate by using a probe station under optical microscopy. Silver paste was applied at both ends of the ZnO NW to fix its two ends tightly on the substrate. The silver paste was also used as source and drain electrodes. A thin layer of polydimethylsiloxane (PDMS) was used to package the device. The thickness of the PDMS layer is much thinner than the thickness of the PS substrate. The PDMS thin layer not only enhances the adhesion of the silver paste to the PS substrate, but also prevents the ZnO wire from contamination or corrosion. After annealing at 80℃ for 12 hours, a flexible, optically transparent, and well-packaged strain sensor device was fabricated. Figure 4.11(b) shows an optical image of the strain sensor device, indicating that a smooth ZnO wire was placed on the substrate with two ends fixed.

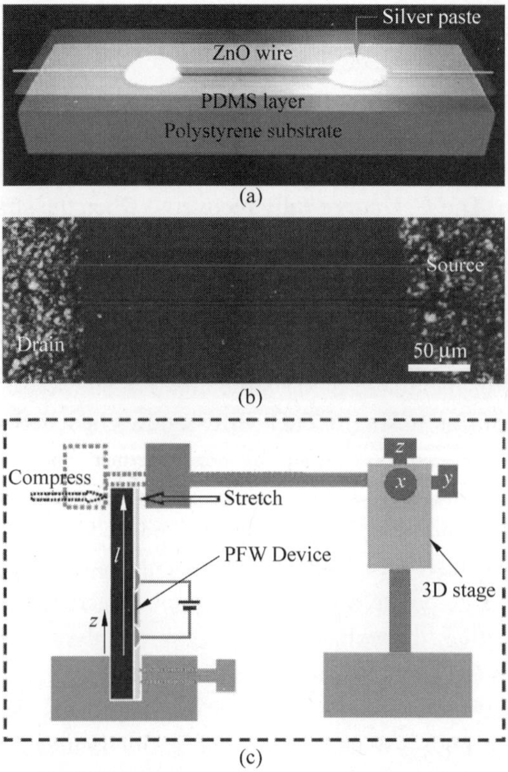

Figure 4.11 (a) Schematic of a single ZnO PFW-based strain sensor device. (b) Optical image of a strain sensor device. (c) Schematic of the measurement system to characterize the performance of the sensor device. (see color figure at the end of this book)

The characterization of the $I\sim V$ behavior of the sensor device with strain was carried out in atmosphere at room temperature, and the measuring system is schematically shown in Fig. 4.11(c). One end of the device was affixed on a sample holder that was fixed tightly on an optical air table, with another end free to be bent. An *x-y-z* mechanical stage with movement resolution of 1 μm was used to bend the free end of the sensor device to produce a compressive or tensile strain. Meanwhile, a continuous triangle-sweeping voltage was applied through the ZnO wire to measure its $I\sim V$ characteristics during deformation. To study the stability and response of the sensor devices, a resonator with controlled frequency and amplitude was used to periodically bend the sensor device.

The original $I\sim V$ characteristic of the sensor device was first measured. The nonlinear $I\sim V$ characteristics are commonly observed in measuring semiconductor devices[23]. Generally, the nonlinearity is caused by the Schottky barriers formed between the semiconductor and the metal electrodes in the semiconductor device, and the shape of the $I\sim V$ curve depends on the heights of the Schottky barriers formed at the source and drain due to different interface properties[24]. In this study, we focused only on the devices that have Schottky contacts at the two ends of the NW, but with distinctly different barrier heights. The $I\sim V$ curve shape is quite asymmetric. Typical $I\sim V$ characteristics under various strains are shown in Fig. 4.12(a). The $I\sim V$ curves shift upward with tension strain and downward with compressive strain. The $I\sim V$ curve fully recovered when the strain was relieved.

The $I\sim V$ curve shown in Fig. 4.12(a) clearly demonstrates that there were Schottky barriers present at the contacts but with distinctly different barrier heights. The presence of a Schottky barrier at the metal/semiconductor interface plays a crucial role in determining the electrical transport property of the metal-semiconductor-metal (M-S-M) structure. As shown in Fig. 4.12(b), our device is considered as a single ZnO wire sandwiched between two opposite Schottky barriers. We assume that the barrier height at the drain side φ_d (eV) is significantly higher than that at the source side. At a fixed bias voltage V, the voltage drop occurs mainly at the reversely biased Schottky barrier according to the measurement by in situ scanning surface potential microscopy[25]. In our case, when a relatively large positive voltage V is applied across the drain and source with the drain positive, the voltage drop occurs mainly at the reversely biased Schottky barrier φ_s (eV) at the source side, and it is denoted by V_s. Here, we assume $V_S \approx V$. With consideration that our measurements were made at room temperature and the ZnO NW had a low doping, the dominant transport property at the barrier is thermionic emission and diffusion, while the contribution made by tunneling can be ignored. Thus, as inspired by the shape of the $\ln I\sim V$ curve in Fig. 4.2(b) and according to the classic thermionic emission-diffusion theory (for $V \gg 3\,kT/q \sim 77$ mV) for a reversal bias voltage V and at temperature T, the

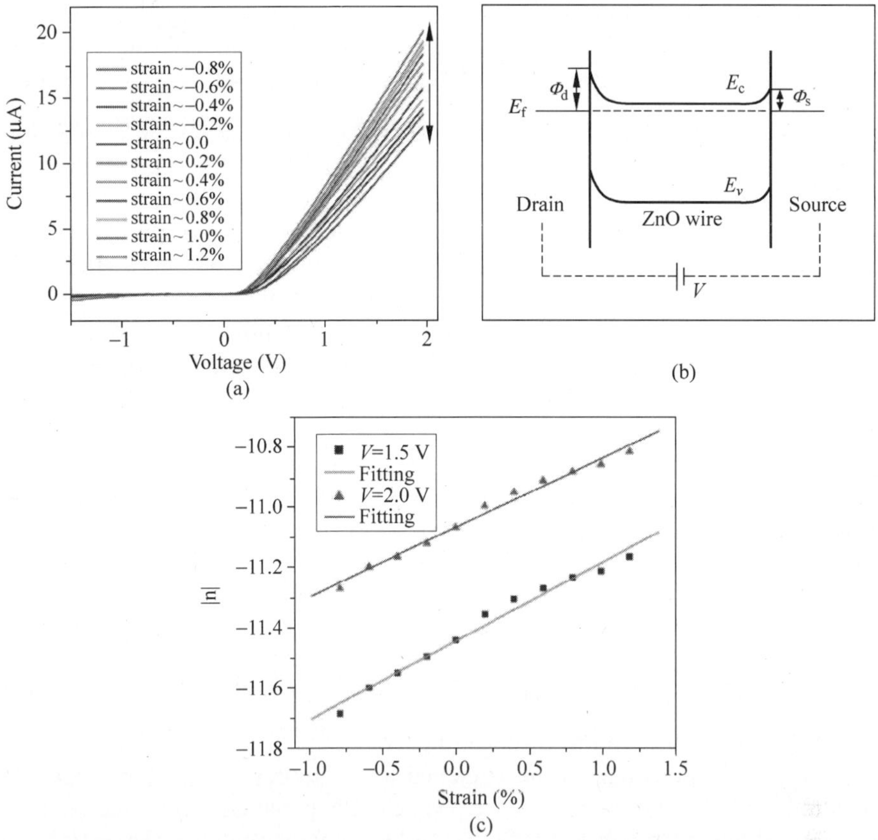

Figure 4.12 (a) Typical $I \sim V$ characteristics of the sensor at different strain. (b) Energy band diagram illustrates the asymmetric Schottky barrier heights at the source and drain contacts of a NW, where the offset by the applied drain-source voltage V was not included, for easy discussion. (c) Logarithm plot of the current (in unit of ampere) at fixed bias of $V = 1.5$ V and 2.0 V as a function of strain (see color figure at the end of this book)

current through the reversely biased Schottky barrier φ_s is given by:

$$I = SA^{**}T^2 \exp\left(-\frac{\varphi_s}{kT}\right)\exp\left(\frac{\sqrt[4]{q^7 N_D (V + V_{bi} - kT/q)/(8\pi^2 \varepsilon_s^3)}}{kT}\right) \tag{4.8}$$

where S is the area of the source Schottky barrier, A^{**} is the effective Richardson constant, q is the electron charge, k is the Boltzmann constant, N_D is the donor impurity density, V_{bi} is the build in potential at the barrier, and ε_s is the permittivity of ZnO.

By assuming that S, A^{**}, T, and N_D are independent of strain for small deformation[26], φ_s can, in principle, be derived from the logarithm of the current

($\ln I \sim V$) plot. Subsequently, the change of SBH can be determined by:

$$\ln[I(\varepsilon_{zz})/I(0)] = -\Delta\varphi_s / kT \tag{4.9}$$

where $I(\varepsilon_{zz})$ and $I(0)$ are the current measured through the NW at a fixed bias with strain and without being strained, respectively. In reality, $V_s < V$; thus, the calculated $\Delta\varphi_s$ value may be slightly affected by the choice of V, but the linear dependence of $\Delta\varphi_s$ on the strain will not be affected much. Figure 4.12(c) shows the change of $\ln I$ at fixed bias of V. 1.5 V and 2.0 V as a function of strain. The change of $\ln I$ varies approximately linearly with the applied strain.

In conclusion, the sensor devices have excellent stability, fast response, and high gauge factor of up to 1,250. The $I \sim V$ characterization of the device is modulated by the change of SBH, which has a linear relationship with strain. The underlying mechanism for the change of SBH is attributed to the combination of strain-induced band structure change and piezoelectric effect. The strain sensor developed here based on a flexible substrate has application in strain and stress measurements in cell biology, biomedical sciences, MEMS devices, structure monitoring, and even earthquake monitoring.

4.3 ZnO Nanowire Nanogenerators

It is clear that the bending of a piezotronic ZnO NW can generate positive and negative electric potential on the stretched and compressed sides, respectively. By introducing a Schottky barrier, the piezoelectric potential can be accumulated and released while the polarity of the Schottky barrier is switched. This forms the basis of a NG that is able to convert small mechanical energy, such as vibration, wind blowing, pressure variation, or water flow into electricity. In this section, the basic concept and development of several types of NGs are introduced.

4.3.1 Single Nanowire Nanogenerator

The existence of piezoelectric potential in a bent ZnO NW was first demonstrated by atomic force microscopy (AFM). These charges can be accumulated and then released when a Schottky contact is introduced between the charged ZnO surfaces and the contacting electrode. As discussed in the first section, across the width of the NW at the top end, the piezoelectric potential between V_s^- and V_s^+ is distributed from the compressed surface to the stretched surface. In experimental design, a Pt coated Si AFM tip was used to deflect the ZnO NW and connect it to the external circuit. The contact between Pt and ZnO was Schottky type, which dominates the entire transport process. In the first step, the AFM conductive tip that induces the deformation is in contact with the stretched surface of positive potential V_s^+ (Fig. 4.13(a)). Since the Pt metal tip has a potential of nearly zero,

$V_m = 0$, the metal tip-ZnO interface is negatively biased for $\Delta V = V_m - V_s^+ < 0$. With consideration the n-type semiconductor characteristic of the as-synthesized ZnO NWs, the Pt metal-ZnO semiconductor (M-S) interface in this case is a reversely biased Schottky diode (Fig. 4.13(a)), resulting in little current flowing across the interface. In the second step, when the AFM tip is in contact with the compressed side of the NW (Fig. 4.3(b)), the metal-ZnO interface is positively biased for $\Delta V = V_L = V_m - V_s^- > 0$. The M-S interface in this case is a positively biased Schottky diode, resulting in a sudden increase in the output electric current, e.g., a sharp increase in output voltage V_L (positive). The current is the result of ΔV-driven flow of electrons from the semiconductor ZnO NW to the metal tip. The flow of the free electrons from the loop through the NW to the tip will neutralize the ionic charges distributed in the volume of the NW and thus reduce the magnitude of the potential V_s^- and V_s^+. Therefore, the output voltage V_L starts to drop and reaches zero until all of the ionic charges in the NW are fully neutralized.

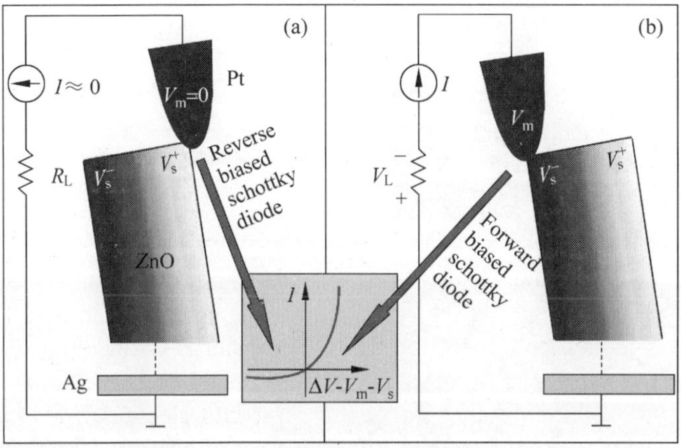

Figure 4.13 Schematic diagram showing the metal-semiconductor contacts between the AFM tip and the ZnO N with reverse (a) and forward (b) biased Schottky rectifying behavior. (see color figure at the end of this book)

This proposed mechanism has been clearly observed when the Pt coated AFM tip scans over a long ZnO wire that is large enough to be seen under an optical microscope[27]. As shown in Fig. 4.14(a), one end of the ZnO wire was affixed on an intrinsic silicon substrate by silver paste, while the other end was left free. The wire was laid on the substrate but kept at a small distance from the substrate to eliminate the friction with the substrate except at the affixed side. This wire was deflected and measured simultaneously in AFM contact mode under a constant normal force of 5 nN between the tip and sample surface. The output voltage across an outside load of resistance $R_L = 500\ \mathrm{M\Omega}$ was continuously monitored during the scan. The topography image directly captured whether the tip passed over the belt or not because it is a representation of the normal height received by the cantilever. When the tip pushed the wire but did not go over and across it, as judged by the flat output signal in the topography image (Fig. 4.14(b)), no voltage output was produced, indicating that the stretched side produced no piezoelectric discharge event. Once the tip went over the wire and in touch with the compressed side, as indicated by a peak in the topography image, a sharp voltage output peak is observed (Fig. 4.14(c)). By analyzing the positions of the peaks observed in the

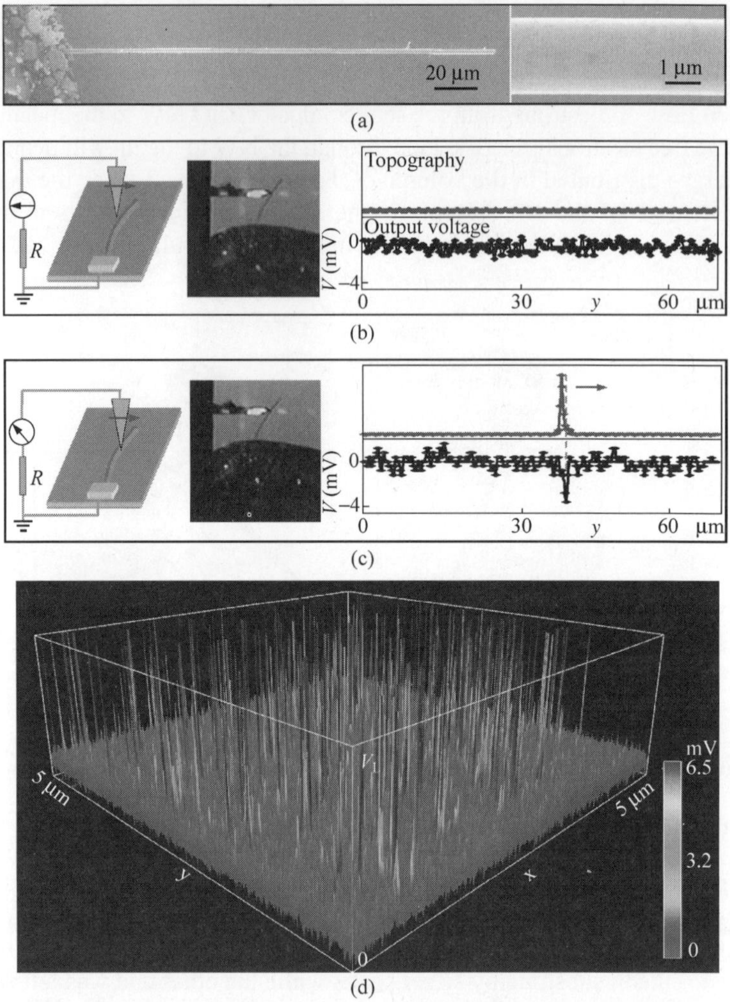

Figure 4.14 In situ observation of the process for converting mechanical energy into electric energy by a piezoelectric ZnO wire. (a) SEM images of a ZnO wire with one end affixed on a silicon substrate. (b, c) Two characteristic snapshots and the corresponding topography (red curve) and output voltage (blue curve) images when the tip is scanned across the middle section of the wire. The schematic illustration of the experimental condition is shown at the left hand side, with the scanning direction of the tip indicated by an arrowhead. (d) Output voltage image map of ZnO NW arrays when they are deformed by a conductive AFM scanning (see color figure at the end of this book)

topography image and the output voltage image, we noticed that the discharge occurred after the tip nearly finishing acrossing the wire. This clearly indicates that the compressed side is responsible for producing the negative piezoelectric discharge voltage.

A similar scanning process has also been applied on vertically aligned ZnO NW arrays and many sharp output voltage peaks have been observed[7]. The aligned ZnO NWs with an average height of ~1 μm were grown on GaN substrate, which was connected to an external load through silver paste. In the AFM contact mode, a constant normal force was maintained between the tip and the sample surface. The tip scanned over the top of the vertically aligned ZnO NWs, which were thus bent and then released. Meanwhile, the corresponding output voltages across the load were recorded. In the output voltage image shown in Fig. 4.14(d), many sharp output voltage peaks (like discharge peaks) have been observed, which are typically about 4 – 50 times higher than the noise level and most of the voltage peaks were ~ 6 – 9 mV in magnitude.

4.3.2 Direct Current Nanogenerator

Although the AFM-based approach has explored the principle and potential of the nanogenerator, for technological applications, we must make an innovative design to drastically improve the performance of the nanogenerator in the following aspects. First, we must eliminate the use of AFM for mechanical deformation of the NWs so that the power generation can be achieved by an adaptable, mobile, and cost-effective approach over a larger scale. Second, all of the NWs are required to generate electricity simultaneously and continuously, thereby enabing all the electricity to be effectively collected and output. Finally, the energy to be converted into electricity has to be provided in a form of wave/vibration from the environment, so the nanogenerator can operate 'independently' and wirelessly.

In addressing these challenges, we have developed an innovative approach by using ultrasonic waves to drive the motion of the NWs, leading to the production of a continuous current[28]. The prototype of such a nanogenerator is schematically shown in Fig. 4.15(a). An array of aligned ZnO NWs was covered by a zigzag Si electrode coated with Pt, which created a Schottky contact at the interface with ZnO. The NWs were grown on sapphire substrates covered with a thin layer of ZnO film (Fig. 4.6(b))[29], which served as a common electrode for directly connecting the NWs with an external circuit. The density of the NWs was ~10 mm^2, and the height and diameter were ~1.0 mm and ~40 nm, respectively. The top electrode was composed of parallel zigzag trenches fabricated on a (001) orientated Si wafer[30] and coated with a thin layer of Pt (200 nm in thickness) (Fig. 4.15(c)). The electrode was placed above the NW arrays with a precise spacing control. The assembled device was sealed at the edges to prevent the penetration of liquid. A cross-sectional image of the packaged NW arrays is shown in Fig. 4.15(d); it displays a 'lip/teeth' relationship between the NWs and the electrode. Some NWs are in direct contact with the top electrode, but some are located between the teeth of the electrode. The inclined NWs in the SEM image were primarily caused by the cross-sectioning of the packaged device.

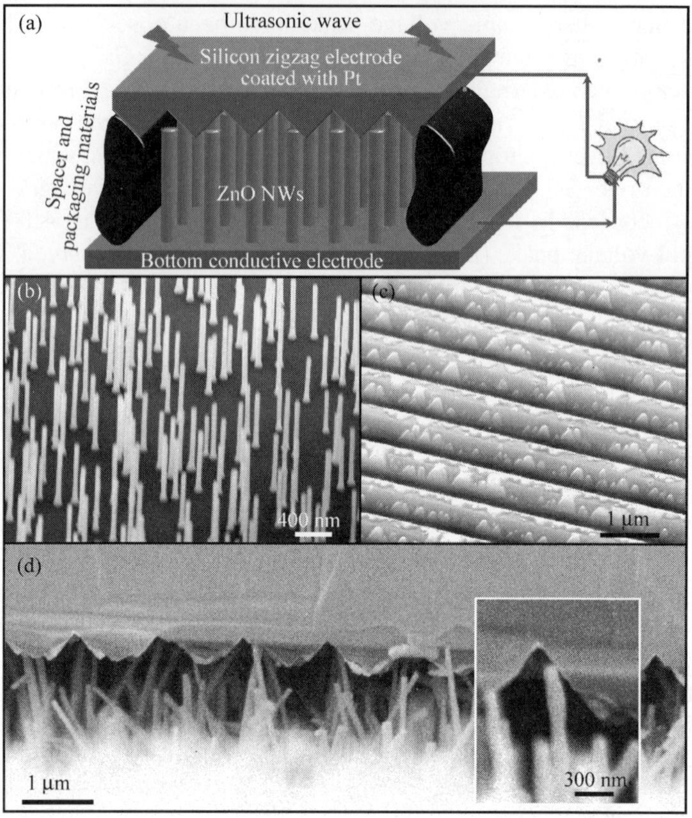

Figure 4.15 Nanogenerators driven by an ultrasonic wave. (a) Schematic diagram showing the design and structure of the nanogenerator. (b) Low-density aligned ZnO NWs grown on a GaN substrate. (c) Zigzag trenched electrode coated with Pt. (d) Cross-sectional SEM image of the nanogenerator; Inset: A typical NW that is forced by the electrode to bend (see color figure at the end of this book)

In this design, the zigzag trenches on the top electrode act as an array of aligned AFM tips. Figures 4.16(a) – (c) show four possible configurations of contact between a NW and the zigzag electrode. When subject to the excitation of an ultrasonic wave, the zigzag electrode can move down and push the NW, which leads to lateral deflection of NWⅠ. This, in turn, creates a strain field across the width of NWⅠ, with the NW's outer surface being in tensile strain and its inner surface in compressive strain. The inversion of strain across the NW results in an inversion of piezoelectric field E_z along the NW, which

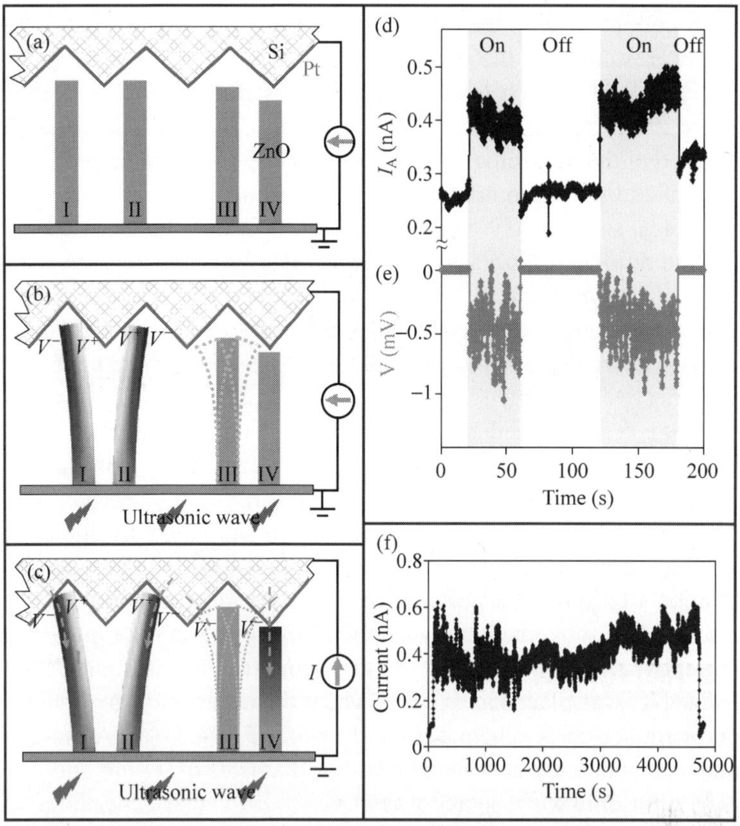

Figure 4.16 (a to c) The mechanism of the nanogenerator driven by an ultrasonic wave. (d, e) Current and voltage measured on the nanogenerator, respectively, when the ultrasonic wave was turned on and off. (f) Continuous current output of the nanogenerator for an extended period of time (see color figure at the end of this book)

produces a piezoelectric-potential inversion from V^- (negative) to V^+ (positive) across the NW (Fig. 4.16(b)). When the electrode makes contact with the stretched surface of the NW, which has a positive piezoelectric potential, the Pt metal–ZnO semiconductor interface is a reversely biased Schottky barrier, resulting in little current flowing across the interface. This is the process of creating, separating, preserving, and accumulating charges. With further pushing by the electrode, the bent NWⅠ will reach the other side of the adjacent tooth of the zigzag electrode (Fig. 4.16(c)). In such a case, the electrode is also in contact with the compressed side of the NW, where the metal/semiconductor interface is a forward-biased Schottky barrier, resulting in a sudden increase in the output electric current flowing from the top electrode into the NW. This is the discharge process. Analogous to the situation described for NWⅠ, the same processes apply to the charge output from NWⅡ. NWⅢ is chosen to elaborate on the vibration/resonance induced by an ultrasonic wave. When the compressive side of NWⅢ is in contact with the electrode, the same discharge process as that for NWⅠ occurs, resulting in the flow of current from the electrode into the NW (Fig. 4.16(c)) NWⅣ, which is short in height, is forced (without bending) into compressive strain by the electrode. In such a case, the piezoelectric voltage can also be created at the top of the NW. Thus, it contributes to the electricity output.

The current and voltage outputs of the nanogenerator are shown in Fig. 4.16(d) and Fig. 4.16(e), respectively, with the ultrasonic wave being turned on and off regularly. A jump of ~0.15 nA was observed when the ultrasonic wave was turned on, and the current immediately fell back to the baseline once the ultrasonic wave was turned off. Correspondingly, the voltage signal exhibited a similar on and off trend but with a negative output of ~ –0.5 mV. The size of the nanogenerator is ~2 mm^2 in effective substrate surface area. The number of NWs that were actively contributing to the observed output current is estimated to be 250 – 1,000 in the current experimental design. The nanogenerator worked continuously for an extended period of time of beyond 1 h (Fig. 4.16(f)).

The DC NG prototype has been improved for operation in liquid[31]. In this design, the nanogenerator core was completely packaged by a polymer to prevent the infiltration of fluid. The polymer also has certain flexibility to remain the freedom of relative movement between the ZnO NWs and the top electrode. The output current was increased by 20 – 30 times and reached as high as 35 nA when a 2 mm^2 size NG was placed at a region where the ultrasonic waves were focused. The experiment set-up is schematically shown in Fig. 4.17(a). A bio-compatible fluid was filled into a glass container with a diameter of 11 cm and a height of 9.5 cm. The ultrasonic wave source was placed at the center beneath the container. Once the ultrasonic wave was excited inside the container, it was reflected by the container's wall and the water surface. As a result, the wave intensity was enhanced in a certain region inside the fluid. An NG was placed inside the fluid and held by a clap that can be freely moved in any direction to trace the enhanced ultrasonic wave, while the output current was continuously monitored. First, the NG was placed at the center region above the water surface and the ultrasonic wave was kept on. The corresponding current signal is shown in Fig. 4.17(b). Then the NG was slowly moved into the fluid along the z direction (depth direction) and a jump in current for ~1 nA was immediately detected once the NG touched water surface. When the NG reached ~3.3 cm below the water surface, the current quickly jumped to ~20 nA. The output can be kept at such a high level as long as the NG stays at this depth. After a 15-second steady high output, the NG was moved further down and the current dropped back to the 1 – 2 nA level. When it reached the bottom of the container, the NG was pulled upward to the water surface. The same 20 – 25 nA high current output was observed again once the NG reached a depth of 3.3 cm. The current signal dropped back to its baseline after the NG was pulled out of water. This model successfully showed the feasibility of NG operation inside a bio-fluid and set a solid foundation for self-powering implantable and wireless devices and systems.

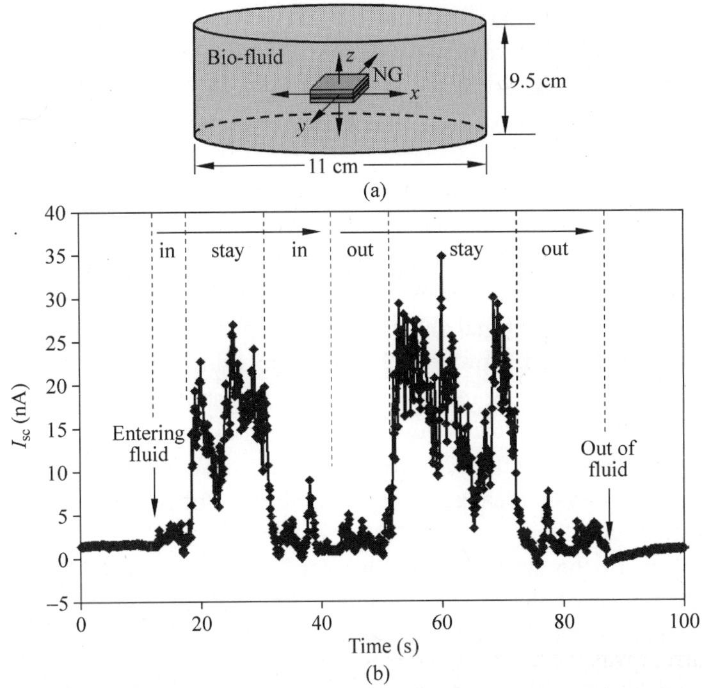

Figure 4.17 Enhanced output power by seeking the strong local intensity of the ultrasonic waves. (a) Schematic of the NG's position and moving directions inside a biofluid. (b) Short-circuit current signal measured during the movement of NG along the z direction (from water surface to the bottom and then back to the surface) (see color figure at the end of this book)

Nevertheless, the voltage/current output is still rather low for applying the NG as a practical power source. In combination with the existing knowledge on the relationship between the morphology of ZnO NW arrays and the performance of an NG, we summarize the key factors that are important to boost the voltage output as follows:

(1) Increase the number of active NWs for participating in electricity generation. This is crucial in determining the voltage output performance. There are two possible approaches to increase the active NWs. One is to utilize ZnO NW arrays with uniform size, especially uniform in length. The other approach is to pattern the NW arrays according to the dimension and shape of the top electrode. An increase in output voltage will be accompanied with a simultaneous increase in output current.

(2) Increase the charges generated by individual NWs during the deflection process. This may be possible by increasing the magnitude of the external excitation, because the magnitude of the generated voltage is proportional to the deflection of the NW.

(3) Increase the total charge output by a NW to the external load. This requires

a great decrease in the contact resistance between the metal electrode and the NW. From experimental measurements, the sum of the contact resistance and inner resistance of the NW was estimated to be ~35 MΩ. This large resistance dissipates a large voltage at the contact. It is thus essential to reduce the contact resistance to receive larger output voltage.

(4) Optimize the electric conductivity of the ZnO NW. Our previous study[32] has indicated the relationship between the carrier density and the performance of the NG. A too high conductivity destroys the Schottky contact at the interface, while a too low conductivity consumes too much voltage. It is expected that by tuning the carrier density to an optimal value, both the current and the voltage outputs can be significantly increased. However, the optimum value of the conductivity needs to be modeled while keeping in mind the charge transport dynamics.

(5) Decrease the capacitance between individual NWs and the top electrode, as well as the system capacitance. The size of the electrodes can make a large contribution to the system capacitance. The other factor is the capacitance of the measurement circuit.

Being aware of the above factors, we carefully chose ZnO NW arrays with minimum variance of the average length. This is to maximize the number of NWs that would contribute to the power generation process while minimizing the parasitic capacitance that could bring down the voltage output. Both the current and the voltage outputs exhibit high levels for this type of NG, with a current of ~500 nA (Fig. 4.18(a)) and voltage of ~10 mV (Fig. 4.18(b))[33]. A power generation density of ~83 nW/cm^2 is reported, which shows a great potential to power nanosensors[34].

Developing a DC NG is a significant progress from the AFM-operated model. It has achieved the following practical goals. First, it replaced the use of an expensive and sophisticated AFM by ultrasonic wave/vibration for inducing the elastic deformation and vibration of the NWs, and demonstrated a cost-effective prototype technology for fabricating the NG. Second, it integrated an array of 'tips' into a zigzag electrode for simultaneous creating, collecting, and outputting the electricity generated by many NWs, establishing the principle for scale-up of the NG technology. Finally, it achieved a continuous and fairly stable DC output.

4.3.3 Flexible Nanogenerator and Power Fiber

NW NGs built on hard substrates have been demonstrated for harvesting local mechanical energy produced by high-frequency ultrasonic waves. To harvest the energy from vibration or disturbance originating from footsteps, heartbeats, ambient noise, and air flow, it is important to explore innovative technologies that work at low frequencies (such as 10 Hz) and that are based on flexible soft materials. We

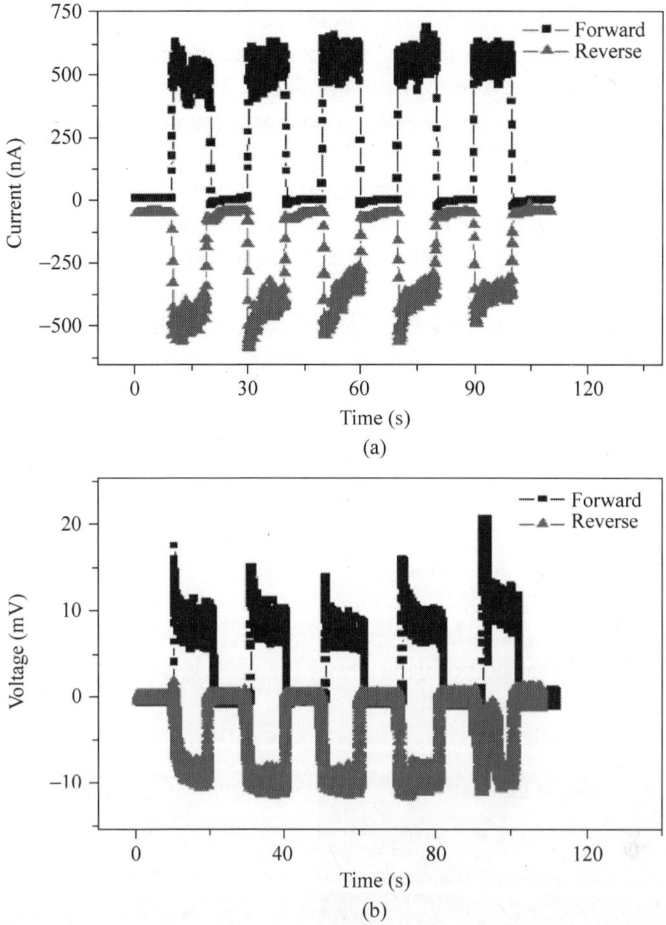

Figure 4.18 Performance of a high-output NG when periodically excited by an ultrasonic wave. (a) Closed circuit current output and (b) open circuit voltage output measured at forward polarity (dark line) and reversed polarity (red line) connection with the measurement system (see color figure at the end of this book)

developed a simple, low-cost approach that converts low-frequency vibration or friction energy into electricity using piezoelectric zinc oxide NWs grown radially around textile fibers[35].

We designed a double-fiber model system to demonstrate the power generation ability of the ZnO NW-covered fibers (Fig. 4.19(a)). Two fibers, one coated with a 300-nm-thick gold layer and the other as-grown, were entangled to form the core for power generation. The relative brushing between the two fibers was simulated by pulling/releasing the string using an external rotor with a controlled frequency. In this design, the gold-coated ZnO NWs acted as an array of scanning metal tips that deflected the ZnO NWs rooted at the other fiber. The coupled piezoelectric and semiconducting property resulted in a process of charge creation and accumulation, and charge release. The gold coating completely covered the ZnO NWs and formed a continuous layer along the entire fiber. Once the two fibers were firmly entangled together, some of the gold-coated NWs penetrated slightly into the spaces between the uncoated NWs rooted at the other fiber, as shown by the interface image in Fig. 4.19(b). Thus, when there was a relative sliding/deflection between them, the bending of the uncoated ZnO NWs produced a piezoelectric potential across their width, and the Au-coated nanowires acted as the 'zigzag' electrode (as for a DC NG) for collecting and transporting the charges.

The short-circuit current (I_{sc}) and open-circuit voltage (V_{oc}) were measured to characterize the performance of the fiber NGs. The pulling and releasing of the gold-coated fiber was accomplished by a motor at a controlled frequency. The resulting electric signals detected at 80 rpm. are shown in Fig. 4.19(c) and Fig. 4.19(d). Current pulses ~5 pA were detected at each pulling-releasing cycle (Fig. 4.19(c)), and the amplitude of the voltage signal in this case was ~1 – 3 mV (Fig. 4.19 (d)).

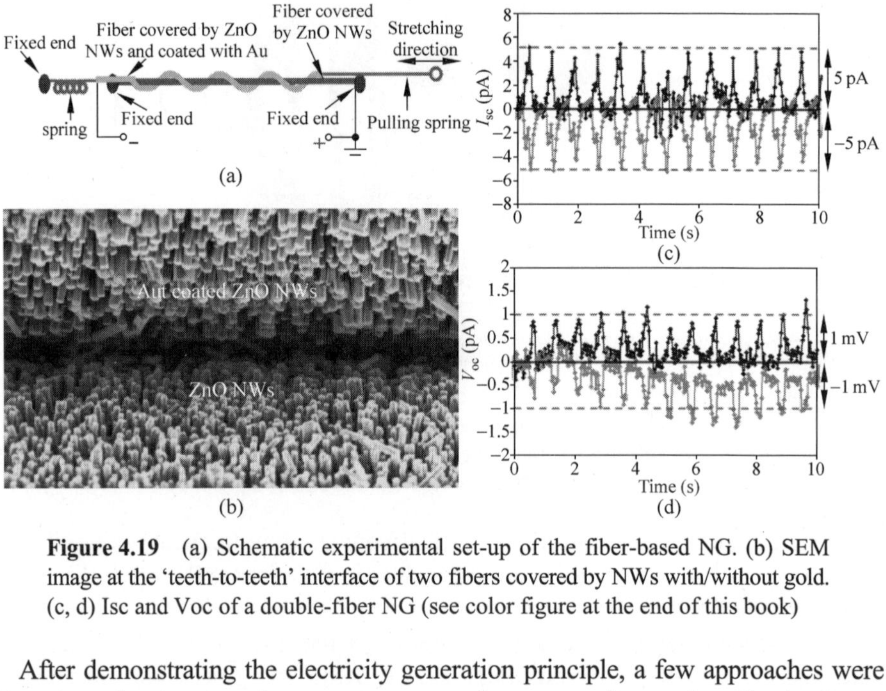

Figure 4.19 (a) Schematic experimental set-up of the fiber-based NG. (b) SEM image at the 'teeth-to-teeth' interface of two fibers covered by NWs with/without gold. (c, d) Isc and Voc of a double-fiber NG (see color figure at the end of this book)

After demonstrating the electricity generation principle, a few approaches were investigated to increase the output power and prototype integration. To simulate a practical fabric made of yarn, a single yarn made of 6 fibers was tested. Three fibers were covered with NWs and coated with Au, and three were covered with NWs. All of the gold-coated fibers were movable in the testing (Fig. 4.20(b)). At a motor speed of 80 rpm., an average current of ~0.2 nA was achieved (Fig. 4.20(a)), which is ~30 – 50 times larger than the output signal from a single-fiber NG. This is due to the substantially increased surface contact area among the fibers. The width of each pulse was broadened, apparently due to the unsynchronized movement and a relative delay in outputting the current among the fibers.

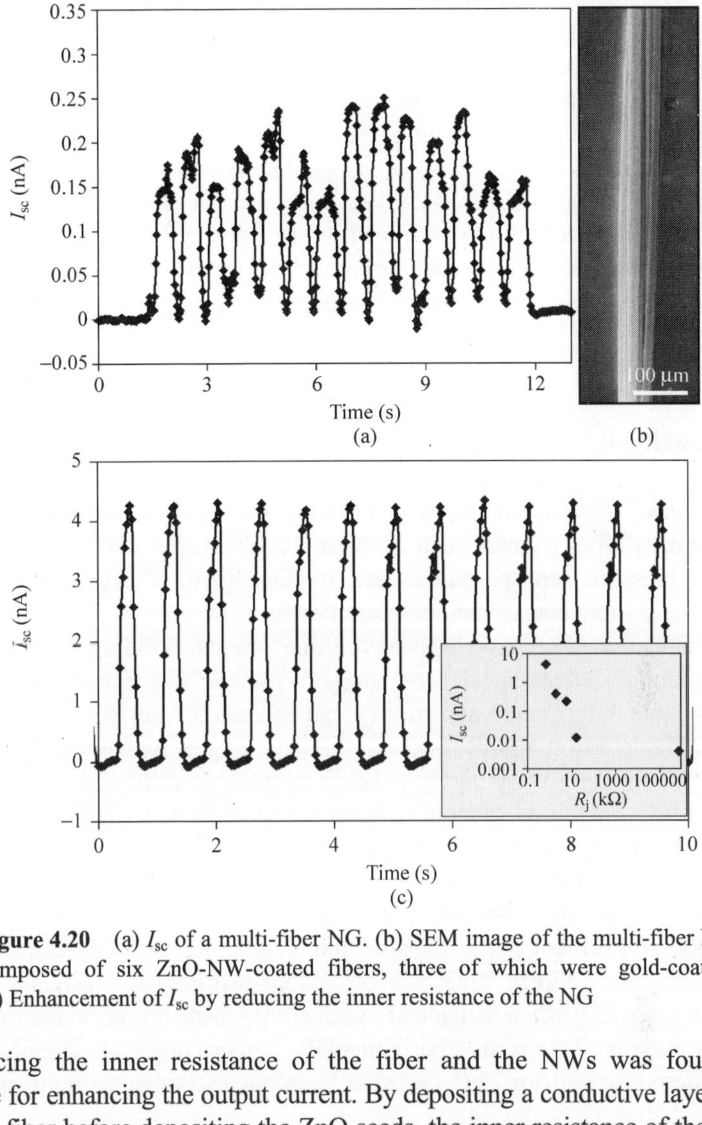

Figure 4.20 (a) I_{sc} of a multi-fiber NG. (b) SEM image of the multi-fiber NG composed of six ZnO-NW-coated fibers, three of which were gold-coated. (c) Enhancement of I_{sc} by reducing the inner resistance of the NG

Reducing the inner resistance of the fiber and the NWs was found to be effective for enhancing the output current. By depositing a conductive layer directly onto the fiber before depositing the ZnO seeds, the inner resistance of the NG was reduced from ~1 kΩ – ~1 GΩ. Thus, the output current I_{sc} of a double-fiber NG was increased from ~4 pA to ~4 nA (Fig. 4.20(c)). The current I_{sc} is approximately inversely proportional to the inner resistance of the NG (inset in Fig. 4.20(c)). This study shows an effective approach for increasing the output current.

The textile-fiber-based NG has demonstrated the following innovative advances in comparison to DC NGs. First, using ZnO NWs grown on fibers, it is possible to fabricate flexible, foldable, wearable, and robust power sources in any shape (such as a 'power shirt'). Second, the output electricity can be dramatically enhanced by using a bundle of fibers as a yarn, which is the basic unit for fabrics. The optimum output power density from textile fabrics can be estimated on the basis of the data we have reported, and an output density of 20 – 80 mW per square meter of fabric is expected. Third, the NG operates at low frequency, in the range of conventional mechanical vibration, footsteps, and heartbeats, greatly expanding the application range of NGs. Last, as the ZnO nanowire arrays were grown using chemical synthesis at 80℃ on a curved substrate, we believe that our method would be applicable for growth on any substrate. Thus, the fields in which the NGs can be applied and integrated may be greatly expanded. This study establishes a methodology for scavenging light-wind energy and body-movement energy by using fabrics.

4.4 Outlook

Based on the semiconducting and piezoelectric coupled properties, several important prototype devices, such as NGs, PE-FETs, piezoelectric diodes, and piezoforce/pressure sensors, have been demonstrated. These devices are the fundamental components of nanopiezotronics.

Piezotronics based on NWs/NBs as the fundamental building blocks have the following unique advantages: First, the NW-based NGs can be subjected to extremely large deformation and so they can be used for flexible electronics as a flexible/foldable power source. Second, the large degree of deformation that can be withstood by the NWs is likely to result in a larger volume density of power output. Third, ZnO is a biocompatible and biosafe material[36]. It has great potential as an implantable power source within the human body. Fourth, the flexibility of the polymer substrate used for growing ZnO NWs/NBs makes it feasible to accommodate the flexibility of human muscles so that the mechanical energy (body movement or muscle stretching) in the human body can be used to generate electricity. Fifth, ZnO NW/NB nanogenerators can directly produce current as a result of their enhanced conductivity with the presence of oxygen vacancies. Finally, ZnO is an environmentally 'green'. material. The phenomena we have demonstrated for ZnO can also be applied to other wurtzite-structured materials, such as GaN and ZnS.

The future in nanotechnology research lies in the area from single devices, arrays of devices with multifunctionality, and integrated nanosystems. It is important to find various approaches that are feasible for harvesting energy and recycling energy from the environment to self-power a nanosystem so that it can operate wirelessly, remotely, and independently with a sustainable energy supply.

It is also important to develop zero-power sensors that respond to a change in the environment. The principle demonstrated for the piezoelectric NG could be the foundation for self-powered nanosystems. It also has the potential to harvest/ recycle energy from the environment and/or recycle energy that is wasted, such as the energy when walking.

Piezoelectric FETs and diodes are outstanding examples of devices made by using piezoelectric NWs and NBs. Based on the electromechanical coupled properties of the nanostructures, novel and unique applications are likely to be explored in areas of sensors, actuators, switches, and MEMS.

Acknowledgements

This study was supported by DOE BES, NSF, DARPA, and NASA. We thank the contributions from our group members Dr. Jinhui Song, Dr. Yong Qin, Dr. Jin Liu, Dr. Rusen Yang, Yifan Gao, Peng Fei, Dr. Puxian Gao, Dr. Jr-Hau He, Dr. Changshi Lao, Dr. Yi-Feng Lin, and Wenjie Mai.

References

[1] Wang Z. L., (2007), *Nanopiezotronics Adv. Mater.*, **19**: 889 – 892

[2] Wang Z. L., (2007), The New Field of Nanopiezotronics, *Materials Today*, **10**: 20 – 28

[3] Buchine B., W. L. Hughes, F. L. Degertekin, et al., (2006), Bulk Acoustic Resonator Based on Piezoelectric ZnO Belts, *Nano. Lett.*, **6**: 1155 – 1159

[4] Wang X. D., J. Zhou, J. H. Song, et al., (2006), Piezoelectric Field Effect Transistor and Nanoforce Sensor Based on a Single ZnO Nanowire, *Nano. Lett.*, **6**: 2768 – 2772

[5] Lao C. S., Q. Kuang, Z. L. Wang, et al., (2007), Polymer Functionalized Piezoelectric-FET as Humidity/Chemical Nanosensors, *Appl. Phys. Lett.*, **90**: 262107

[6] He J. H., C. L. Hsin, J. Liu, et al., (2007), Piezoelectric Gated Diode of a Single ZnO Nanowire, *Adv. Mater.*, **19**: 781 – 784

[7] Wang Z. L., J. H. Song, (2006), Piezoelectric Nanogenerators Based on Zinc Oxide Nanowire Arrays, *Science*, **312**: 242 – 246

[8] Zhao M. H., Z. L. Wang, S. X. Mao, (2004) Piezoelectric Characterization on Individual Zinc Oxide Nanobelt under Piezoresponse Force Microscope. *Nano Lett.*, **4**: 587 – 590

[9] Wang X. D., C. J. Summers, Z. L. Wang, (2004), Large-Scale Hexagonal-Patterned Growth of Aligned ZnO Nanorods for Nano-Optoelectronics and Nanosensor Arrays, *Nano. Lett.*, **4**: 423 – 426

[10] Gao Y. F., Z. L. Wang, (2007), Electrostatic Potential in a Bent Piezoelectric Nanowire, The Fundamental Theory of Nanogenerator and Nanopiezotronics, *Nano. Lett.*, **7**: 2499 – 2505

[11] Wang X. D., J. H. Song, P. Li, et al., (2005), Growth of Uniformly Aligned ZnO

Nanowire Heterojunction Arrays on GaN, AlN, and Al0.5Ga0.5N Substrates. *J. Am. Chem. Soc.*, **127**: 7920 – 7923

[12] Gao P. X., J. H. Song, J. Liu, et al., (2007), Nanowire Nanogenerators on Plastic Substrates as Flexible Power Source, *Adv. Mater.*, **19**: 67 – 72

[13] Zhou J., P. Fei, Y. F. Gao, Y. D. Gu, J. Liu, G. Bao, and Z. L. Wang, (2008), Mechanical-Electrical Triggers and Sensors Using Piezoelectric Microwires/Nanowires, *Nano. Letters*, online

[14] Liu J., P. Fei, J. H. Song, X. D. Wang, C. S. Lao, R. Tummala, and Z. L. Wang, (2008), Carrier Density and Schottky Barrier on the Performance of DC Nanogenerator, *Nano. Lett.*, **8**: 328 – 332

[15] Zheng G. F., F. Patolsky, Y. Cui, W. U. Wang, and C. M. Lieber, (2005), Multiplexed electrical detection of cancer markers with nanowire sensor arrays, *Nat. Biotechnol.*, **23**: 1294 – 1301

[16] Wang X. D., J. Zhou, J. H. Song, et al., (2006), Piezoelectric Field Effect Transistor and Nanoforce Sensor Based on a Single ZnO Nanowire, *Nano. Lett.*, **6**: 2768 – 2772

[17] Song J. H., X. D. Wang, E. Riedo, Z. L. Wang, (2005), Elastic property of vertically aligned nanowires, *Nano. Lett.*, **5**:1954 – 1958

[18] Zhou J., C. S. Lao, P. X. Gao, W. J. Mai, W. L. Hughes, N. S. Xu, and Z. L. Wang, (2006), Nanowires as pictogram balance at workplace atmosphere, *Solid State Comm.*, **139**: 222 – 226

[19] Lao C. S., Q. Kuang, Z. L. Wang, M. C. Park, and Y. Deng, (2007), Polymer functionalized piezoelectric-FET as humidity/chemical nanosensors, *Appl. Phys. Lett.*, **90**: 262107

[20] Schild H. G., (1992), Poly(N-isopropylacrylamide)-Experiment, Theory and Application. *Prog. Polym. Sci.*, **17**: 163 – 249

[21] Shi S. H., L. J. Liu, (2006), Microwave-assisted preparation of temperature sensitive poly(N-isopropylacrylamide) hydrogels in poly(ethylene oxide)-600, *J. Appl. Polym. Sci.*, **102**: 4177 – 4184

[22] Zhou J., Y. D. Gu, P. Fei, W. J. Mai, Y. F. Gao, R. S. Yang, G. Bao, and Z. L. Wang, (2008), Flexible Piezotronic Strain Sensor. *Nano Lett.*, **8**(9): 3035 – 3040

[23] Zhang Z. Y., C. H. Jin, X. L. Liang, Q. Chen, L. M. Peng, (2006), Current-voltage characteristics and parameter retrieval of semiconducting nanowires, *Appl. Phys. Lett.*, **88**: 073102

[24] Freeouf J. L., J. M. Woodall, (1981), Schottky barriers: An effective work function model, *Appl. Phys. Lett.*, **39**: 727 – 729

[25] Fan Z. Y., J. G. Lu, (2005), Electrical properties of ZnO nanowire-field effect transistors charaterized with scanning probes, *Appl. Phys. Lett.*, **86**: 032111

[26] Liu Y., Z. Kauser, P. P. Ruden, Z. Hassan, Y. C. Lee, S. S. Ng, F. K. Yam, (2006), Effect of hydrostatic pressure on the barrier height of Ni Schottky contacts on n-AlGaN, *Appl. Phys. Lett.*, **88**: 022109

[27] Song J. H., J. Zhou, Z. L. Wang, (2006), Piezoelectric and Semiconducting Coupled Power Generating Process of a Single ZnO Belt/Wire, A Technology for Harvesting Electricity from the Environment, *Nano. Lett.*, **6**: 1656 – 1662

[28] Wang X. D., J. H. Song, J. Liu, et al., (2007), Direct Current Nanogenerator Driven by

Ultrasonic Wave, *Science*, **316**: 102 – 105

[29] Wang X. D., J. H. Song, C. J. Summers, et al., (2006), Density-Controlled Growth of Aligned ZnO Nanowires Sharing a Common Contact: A Simple, Low-Cost, and Mask-Free Technique for Large-Scale Applications, *J. Phys. Chem.*, **B 110**: 7720 – 7724

[30] Frühauf J., S. Krönert, (2005), Wet Etching of Silicon Gratings with Triangular Profiles, *Microsyst. Technol.*, **11**: 1287 – 1291

[31] Wang X. D., J. Liu, J. H. Song, and Z. L. Wang, (2007), Integrated Nanogenerators in Biofluid, *Nano. Lett.*, **7**: 2475 – 2479

[32] Liu J., P. Fei, J. H. Song, X. D. Wang, C. S. Lao, R. Tummala, and Z. L. Wang, (2008), Carrier Density and Schottky Barrier on the Performance of DC Nanogenerator, *Nano. Lett.*, **8**: 328 – 332

[33] Liu J., P. Fei, J. Zhou, R. Tummala, and Z. L. Wang, (2008), Toward high output-power nanogenerator, *Appl. Phys. Lett.*, **92**: 173105

[34] Yu C., Q. Hao, S. Saha, L. Shi, X. Y. Kong, and Z. L. Wang, (2005), Integration of metal oxide nanobelts, *Appl. Phys. Lett.*, **86**: 063101

[35] Qin Y., X. D. Wang, and Z. L. Wang, (2008), Microfiber–nanowire hybrid structure for energy scavenging, *Nature*, **451**: 809 – 813

[36] Zhou J., N. S. Xu, Z. L. Wang, (2006), Dissolving behavior and stability of ZnO wires in biofluids: A study on biodegradability and bioacompatibility of ZnO nanostructures, *Adv. Mater.*, **18**: 2432 – 2435

5 Electron Transport in Single Molecules and Nanostructures

Aidi Zhao, Hui Zhang, and J. G. Hou

Hefei National Laboratory for Physical Sciences at Microscale, University of Science and Technology of China, Hefei, Anhui 230026, P. R. China
E-mail: adzhao@ustc.edu.cn; jghou@ustc.edu.cn

Abstract Electron transport in nanoscale materials has attracted much attention with the fast development of the nanofabrication and scanning probe techniques in the past years. Quantum effects such as electron tunneling and quantum confinement effect have become predominant in nanostructures, leading to a diversity of novel transport phenomena. In particular, single electron tunneling (SET) effect, rectifying effect, negative differential resistance (NDR) effect, Kondo effect, and some novel mechanisms responsible for these effects were revealed in the electron transport properties of single atoms, molecules, and nanoparticles. These effects and mechanisms are found to result from the discrete energy levels and localized molecular orbitals in the nanostructures. Recent developments of the measurement techniques and progresses of the studies on electron transport in single molecules and related nanostructures are reviewed in this chapter.

Keywords Electron transport, single molecule, quantum dot, scanning tunneling microscopy, Kondo effect, inelastic electron tunneling

5.1 Electron Transport in Nanoscale Junctions

The first step toward the measurement of electron transport in a single molecule or a nanostructure (denoted by *C* in Fig. 5.1) is to create a nanojunction consisting of two metallic electrodes (denoted by *A* and *B* in Fig. 5.1) separated by a nanoscale gap. In the simplest case (Fig. 5.1(a)), *C* is well connected to both *A* and *B* without a contact barrier. A typical example of such a contact is a molecule covalently bonded to an electrode. If *C* is well connected to one electrode and weakly coupled with the other, it forms a single barrier tunnel junction (SBTJ) (Fig. 5.1(b)). If *C* is weakly coupled with both *A* and *B*, then it forms a double barrier tunnel junction (DBTJ), as shown in Fig. 5.1(c).

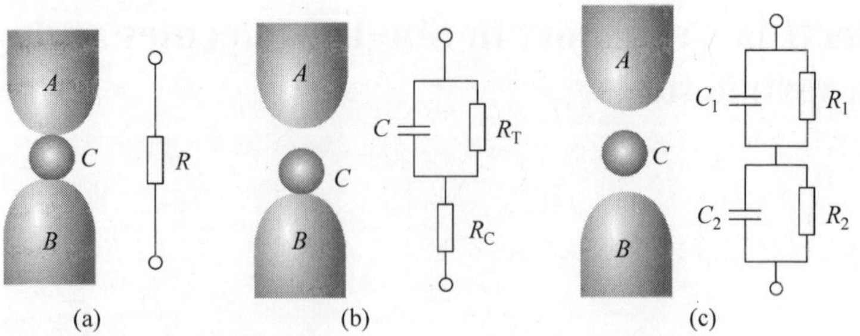

Figure 5.1 Schematics of nanojunctions and their equivalent circuits. (a) direct contact, (b) SBTJ, (c) DBTJ

The formation of a nanometer-sized gap can be realized by two methods based on scanning probe microscopy (SPM) technique and electron-beam lithography technique respectively (Fig. 5.2). The SPM technique, especially the scanning tunneling microscopy (STM)[1,2], is a unique and powerful tool for studying the atomic-scale configuration of nanostructures because it possesses the highest spatial resolution (lateral resolution of 0.1 nm and vertical resolution of 0.01 nm) and flexibility among all microscopy techniques. The STM technique can also be combined with scanning tunneling spectroscopy (STS) to probe the local transport property and local electron states of a scanned point with a typical energy resolution of 1meV. A scanning tunneling microscope itself serves as a two-terminal nano-junction with a typical separation of about 1 nm between the tip and the substrate. The electron-beam lithography technique allows fabrication of narrow metallic nanowires on an insulating oxide substrate. The wires can be broken into two electrodes with a tiny gap of only a few nanometers by means of an electromigration process[3] or a mechanically controllable break junction (MCBJ) technique[4]. Figure 5.3 shows a nanojucntion fabricated by the electromigration technique. The generation of the nanogap can be verified by monitoring the conductance of the nanowire (Fig. 5.3(c)). A schematic view of the MCBJ technique and a scanning electron micrograph image of the produced nanojunction are shown in Fig. 5.4.

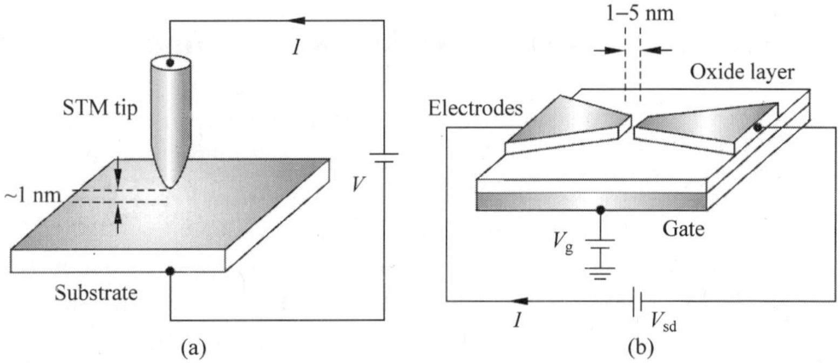

Figure 5.2 Schematics for the junctions formed by SPM technique (a) and electron-beam lithography technique (b)

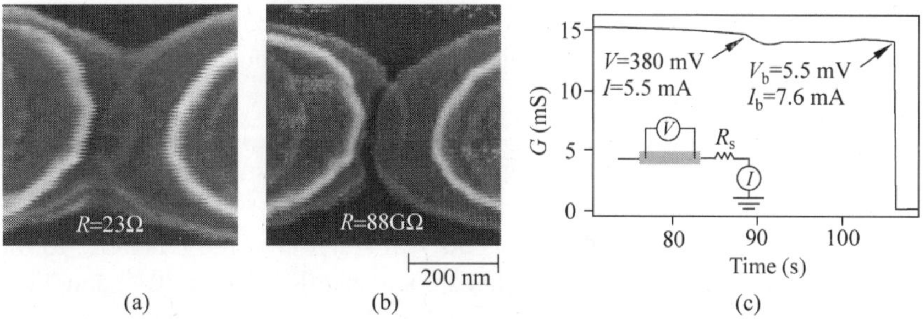

Figure 5.3 Field-emission scanning electron micrographs of a representative gold nanowire (a) before and (b) after the breaking procedure. (c) Representative conductance trace obtained during a nanowire breaking procedure. The conductance is measured in a four-probe configuration schematically shown in the inset. Reprinted with permission from Ref.[3], copyright 1999, American Institute of Physics

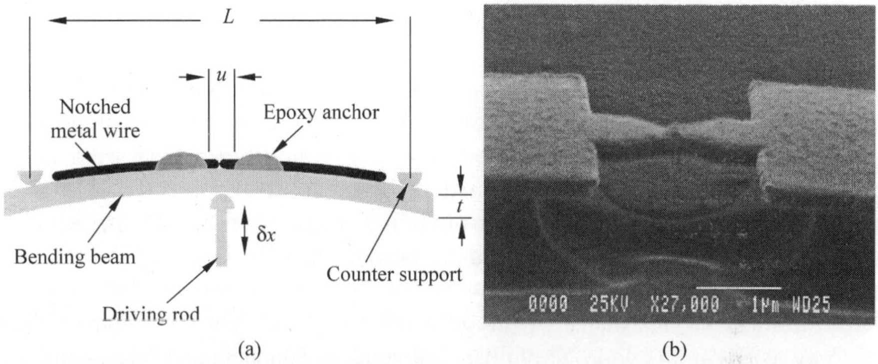

Figure 5.4 Left panel: Schematic of the MCBJ set-up. A notched metallic wire is anchored at two points to a bending beam. When the driving rod bends the beam, the suspended region elongates and the nanoscale gap may be produced. Right panel: SEM picture of the junction after break operation. Reprinted with permission from Ref. [4], copyright 1996, American Institute of Physics

5.2 Conductance Measurement

5.2.1 Landauer Formula and Quantized Conductance

The electron transport through a 1D conductor can be described by the Landauer formula developed by Landauer in 1957[5]. In this picture presented by Landauer, the conductor is treated as a barrier with an electron transmission T at the Fermi energy (E_F). The single channel Landauer formula is given as:

$$G = \frac{2e^2}{h} T . \tag{5.1}$$

where h is the Planck's constant and e is the electron charge. With an ideal channel with transmission $T=1$, we get the fundamental conductance, also called conductance quantum $G_0 = 2e^2/h$, corresponding to a resistance of about 12.9 kΩ.

According to the Landauer formula, quantized conductance should be observed for nanostructures with a single conducting channel. This was confirmed in the two-terminal point contact experiments 30 years later after the Landauer formula was derived[6, 7]. The Landauer formula can be generalized to multi-channel cases. It has been well accepted and widely used to describe the electron transport in various nanostructures. In the formalism, the conductance of a nanostructure is determined only by the number of 1D channels available for electron transport, and by the transmission of each channel of the nanostructure.

5.2.2 Conductance of a Single Atom

Among all techniques, the scanning probe microscopes have a powerful ability to measure the conductance of a single atom or molecule because the vertical position of the tip can be precisely controlled. The first conductance measurement on the single atomic level was performed by Pascual, et al. in 1993[8]. In their experiment, a gold tip in a scanning tunneling microscope (STM) was used to mechanically contact a gold surface to produce a gold mound. They found quantized current flowing between the tip and the substrate, indicating a quantization of the resistance of the gold point contact. When the contact area was only a few atoms wide, they observed steps in conductance only of integer numbers of the conductance quantum G_0. It has been confirmed that a single noble-metal atom (Au[9], or Ag or Cu[10]) can provide a conducting channel with nearly one conductance quantum. A further study showed that while simple metals like Au exhibit almost constant conductance plateaus, Al and Pb show inclined plateaus with positive and negative slopes[11].

5.2.3 Conductance of a Single Molecule

To be able to measure the conductance of a single given molecule is the basic step of future molecular electronics. Molecules have much more complex geometric and electronic structures than single atoms. Electron transport in single molecules has been proven to show different behaviors than in single atoms. A long-standing challenge is to create a molecule junction in which the molecule is well connected to both electrodes. In 1997, M. A. Reed, et al.[12] successfully measured the conductance of a molecular junction using an MCBJ system with benzene-1,4-dithiol molecules self-assembled onto the gold electrodes. Although the measured $I \sim V$ curves showed a nearly symmetric behavior near the Fermi level, the experiment demonstrated the ability of studying conductance of molecules at the molecular level, even for single molecules. In the following years, a facile method to form a well-defined molecular junction using SPM techniques[13,14] was developed, enabling the unambiguous measurement of single molecule conductance. In 2003, Xu and Tao[14] developed the STM break junction method to measure the resistance of single molecules covalently connected to two gold electrodes. They created individual molecular junctions by repeatedly moving a gold STM tip into and out of contact with a gold substrate in a solution containing the sample molecules. Conductance trace of the junction showed quantum steps near multiples of G_0 for gold atomic contact and a series of conductance steps for the sample molecules in the solution (Fig. 5.5). These steps are attributed to the formation of the stable molecular junction between the tip and the substrate electrodes. The resistances for single 4,4' bipyridine and *N*-alkanedithiol molecules near zero bias were determined from the conductance histograms. Moreover, they found that the resistance for *N*-alkanedithiol is approximately given by a decay

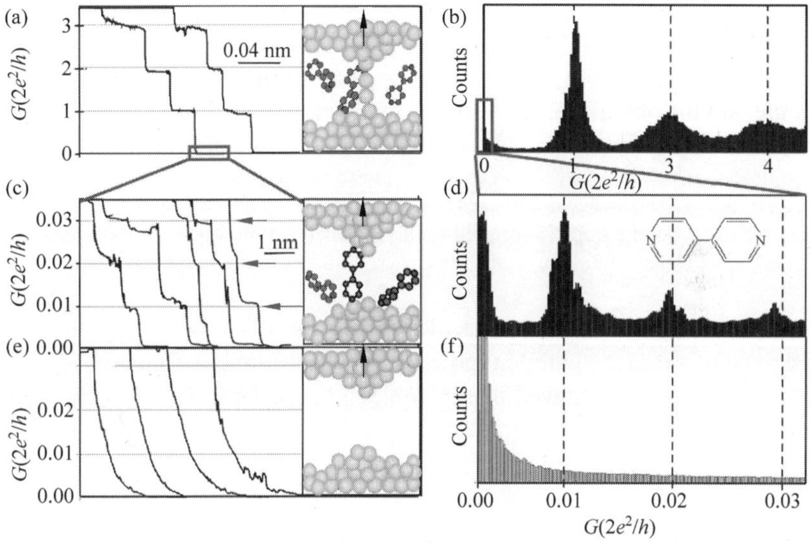

Figure 5.5 (a) conductance of a gold contact formed between a gold STM tip and a gold substrate decreases in quantum steps near multiples of G_0 as the tip is pulled away from the substrate; (b) a corresponding conductance histogram constructed from 1,000 conductance curves as shown in (a); (c) when the contact shown in (a) is completely broken, a new series of conductance steps appears if 4,4' bipyridine molecules are present in the solution. The steps are due to the formation of the stable molecular junction between the tip and the substrate electrodes; (d) a conductance histogram obtained from 1,000 measurements as shown in (c); (e) −(f) in the absence of molecules, no such steps or peaks are observed within the same conductance range. From Ref. [14]. Reprinted with permission from American Association for the Advancement of Science (AAAS) (see color figure at the end of this book)

function $A_{\exp}(\beta_N N)$, where $A \sim 1.3h/2e^2$, N is the number of carbon atoms in the alkane chain, and β_N is the tunneling decay constant determined by the electronic coupling strength along the molecule. Such a decaying behavior of the conductance was also found for other long chain molecules. Figure 5.6 shows the length dependence of conductance G for saturated chains (alkanes and peptides) and conjugated molecules (carotenoids)[15].

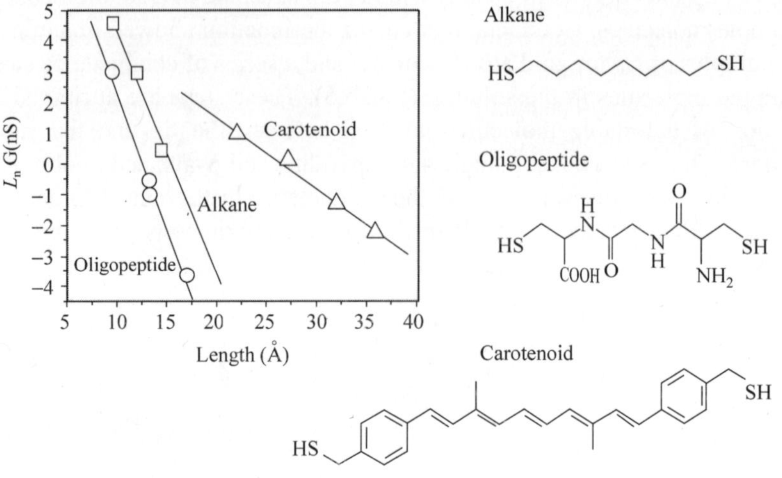

Figure 5.6 The conductance in each system decreases exponentially with the length but with a different slope. Reprinted with permission from Macmillan Publishers Ltd: Nature Nanotechnology (Ref. [15]), copyright 2006

Hydrogen is the simplest molecule consisting of only two protons. The conductance of a single hydrogen molecule was measured by Smit, et al.[16] using an MCBJ. Their results showed that in contrast to results from organic molecules, the bridge has a nearly perfect conductance of one quantum unit, indicating that a single H_2 molecule can provide a perfect quantum conducting channel like noble metal atoms.

5.3 Single Barrier Tunnel Junction and Resonant Tunneling

5.3.1 Electron Tunneling in STM

As a direct result of the wave properties of electrons, electron tunneling is a quantum mechanical phenomenon by which electrons can penetrate through a potential barrier that they would not be able to cross according to classical mechanics. Electron tunneling becomes predominant in electron transport through a nanoscale junction. The electron transmission from one electrode to another depends on the applied bias voltage and the height and width of the barrier. To interpret the electron transport properties of an actual system like STM containing electrodes with complex 3D geometric structures, effective theoretical approaches are needed. Bardeen perturbation method[17], especially the modified Bardeen approximation (MBA) method[18], provides an analytical expression of tunneling current. As a feasible approximation of the MBA method, the Tersoff-Hamann method[19, 20] assumes that tip states are of constant s-type orbital, i.e., the ideal electronic structure. The tunneling current can be simply expressed as a proportional relationship with the local density of states (LDOS) of the tip,

$$I \propto \int_0^{eV} \mathrm{LDOS_s}(E)\mathrm{d}E \,, \tag{5.2}$$

If the LDOS of the tip is treated as a constant at different biases voltages (V), the differential conductance is proportional to the LDOS of the sample,

$$\frac{\mathrm{d}I}{\mathrm{d}V} \propto \mathrm{LDOS_s}(E)\,. \tag{5.3}$$

This relationship is now widely used in STM studies for interpreting the current-voltage ($I \sim V$) and differential conductance ($\mathrm{d}I/\mathrm{d}V$) tunneling spectra.

5.3.2 Scanning Tunneling Spectroscopy of Single Molecules

If the molecule in a two-terminal junction is strongly bonded to one electrode and weakly bonded to another, then a SBTJ is formed. In this case, the molecule is chemically or covalently bonded to the electrode, and the Fermi energy level of the molecule is usually tied to the Fermi level (E_F) of the substrate and the LDOS of the molecule is strongly disturbed by the molecule-substrate interaction.

A typical SBTJ system is a chemisorbed molecule investigated with STM (Fig. 5.7). According to STM theory, the $\mathrm{d}I/\mathrm{d}V$ should be proportional to the LDOS of the sample at a given applied bias voltage. The resonant tunneling through an energy level of the molecule should induce a resonance in the $\mathrm{d}I/\mathrm{d}V$ spectra. For example, single C_{60} molecules are covalently bonded to the underlying silicon atoms when adsorbed on a silicon surface[21,22]. There are three different adsorption sites for the C_{60} molecules on the Si(111)-7×7 surface (denoted by *A*, *B*, and *C* in Fig. 5.8). It is well known that the C_{60} molecule has a fivefold-degenerate highest occupied molecular orbital (HOMO) and a threefold-degenerate lowest unoccupied molecular orbital (LUMO), separated by an energy gap of about 1.7 eV. However, the conductance spectra measured over the adsorbed C_{60}

molecules showed much reduced HOMO-LUMO gap of 1.4, 0.8, and 1.3 eV for *A*, *B*, and *C* types, respectively. The electronic states of the chemisorbed C_{60} are shifted and broadened due to the covalent interactions of the carbon cages of the molecules with the dangling bonds of the silicon surface atoms.

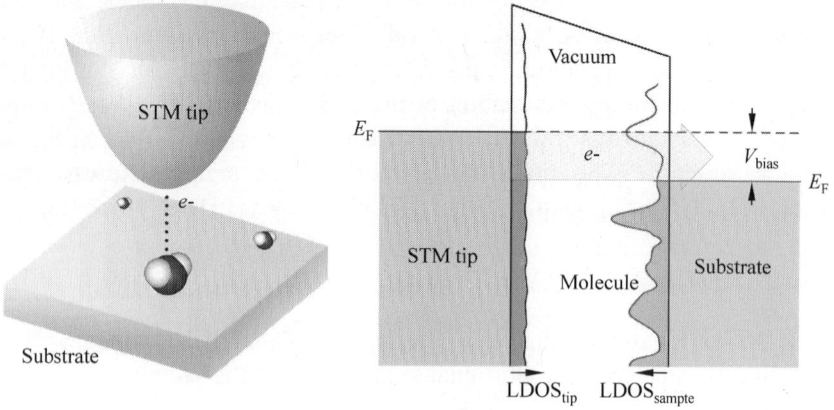

(a) (b)

Figure 5.7 (a) Schematic view of single molecules chemisorbed on a substrate detected with an STM tip. (b) Schematic diagram of the STM tip with a constant DOS to probe the single adsorbed molecule with a featured DOS. The Fermi level of the adsorbed molecule is on the same energy of E_F of the substrate upon adsorption (see color figure at the end of this book)

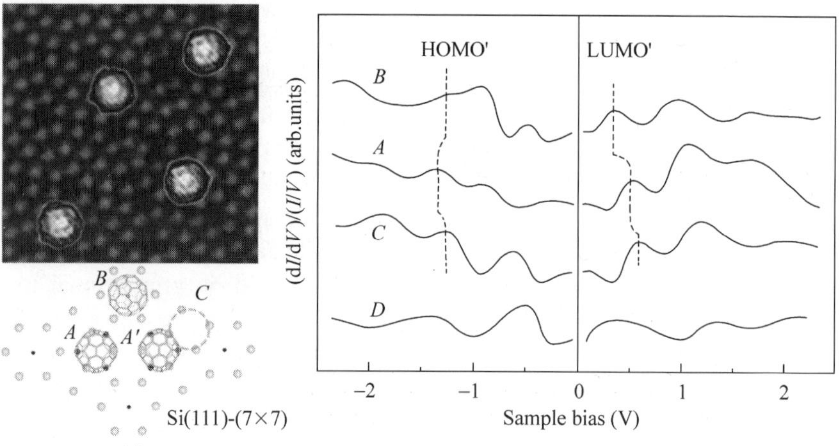

(a) (b)

Figure 5.8 (a) STM image of individual C_{60} molecules adsorbed on a Si(111)-7×7 surface (upper) and the three adsorption sites. (b) d*I*/d*V* spectra measured over the three types of molecules and on a bare silicon surface (*D*) (see color figure at the end of this book)

5.4 Double Barrier Tunnel Junction and Single Electron Phenomena

5.4.1 Single Electron Phenomena

In a DBTJ formed by two electrodes and a zero-dimensional nanomaterial between them (Fig. 5.9), the central nanoisland is isolated from the electrodes by an insulating gap and usually called a Coulomb island. It can be a semiconductor quantum dot or a metallic nanocluster. One fascinating phenomenon of these nanoscale tunneling junction systems is the single charge tunneling (SCT), also called SET, in which current transfers from one electrode to another through the island can be controlled by single charges[23]. The equivalent circuit of such a system is shown in Fig. 5.9(b).

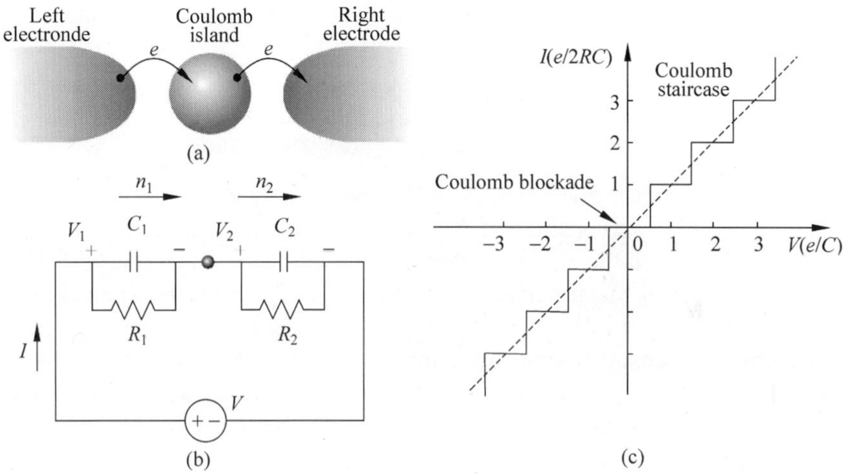

Figure 5.9 (a) schematic of a quantum dot in DBTJ; (b) an equivalent circuit diagram of the DBTJ; (c) $I\sim V$ characteristic of the quantum dot showing Coulomb blockade and Coulomb staircases

When an electron is to be transferreOd from the source electrode to the Coulomb island in a DBTJ, it must overcome the Coulomb charging energy $E_C = e^2/2C$, where C is the capacitance of the Coulomb island (in the simplest case, $C_1 = C_2 = C$).

In order to get large enough E_C that would be comparable to thermal energy (k_BT is ~26 meV at 298 K, and ~ 0.4 meV at 5 K), the size of the Coulomb island should be reduced correspondingly down to the nanometer scale. Assuming negligible small thermal fluctuation, electrons cannot tunnel into the island unless enough bias ($V_{bias} > e^2/2C$) is applied to the two electrodes. In the $I\sim V$

characteristic, it will cause a zero-current Coulomb gap at low bias voltages, which is called Coulomb blockade (CB). This phenomenon also occurs when the Coulomb island loses one electron (the electron tunnels from the island to the drain at negative biases). With the bias continuously increased, the first electron is able to tunnel from source to drain through the island, and then two, three, and more electrons, leading to current steps in the $I \sim V$ characteristic (Fig. 5.9(c)), which is called Coulomb staircase.

5.4.2 The Atomic-Like State in Nanocrystal Quantum Dots

For a DBTJ system, one of the important quantum effects is the quantized energy levels in the electronic structure of the isolated nanoparticles. If the nanoparticles are crystalline in structure and small enough, such an electronic structure with discrete energy levels will affect the single-electron tunneling effect (especially at low temperatures) significantly. For a metal or semiconductor nanoparticle, the interval of its discrete energy level can be estimated by the following formula with free electron approximation:

$$\delta E = \frac{1}{g(E_{\mathrm{F}})v} = \frac{2\hbar^2\pi^2}{vm(3\pi^2\rho)^{1/3}} \tag{5.4}$$

In this formula, v is the volume, m is the effective electron mass, and ρ is the electron density. If we consider an Al nanoparticle with a diameter of 1 nm, then the $\delta E \approx 0.15$ eV, and the charging energy is about 0.2 eV. Therefore, the discrete energy interval of a metal particle with the scale of 1 nm approximately equals the charging energy. Both the discrete energy level effect and the single electron phenomenon are observable at low temperatures. For those metal nanoparticles with larger size, the interval of energy levels will decrease with increasing size. It is not easy to observe discrete electronic levels even at sufficiently low temperatures. This situation changes for those semiconductor nanoparticles. Since their effective electron mass and electronic density are much smaller than those of the metal nanoparticles with the same volume, their discrete energy level effect is much more predominant. Such semiconductor nanoparticles have been predicted to have atomic-like electronic wavefunctions, such as s and p characters. These nanoparticles are known as the quantum dots or 'artificial atoms'[24].

The prediction was examined by later STM experiments. Banin, et al.[25] studied the transport properties of single InAs nanocrystals using low temperature STM/STS. In their study, the nanocrystal quantum dots were linked to the gold substrate by hexane thiol molecules, which served as an insulating barrier. They clearly identified the atomic-like electronic states with s and p characters in the measured tunneling spectrum (Fig. 5.10). These states are manifested in the dI/dV spectrum as degenerate two- and six-fold single-electron-charging peaks respectively, as shown in Fig. 5.10(b), in which E_{c} is the single-electron charging energy, E_{g} is

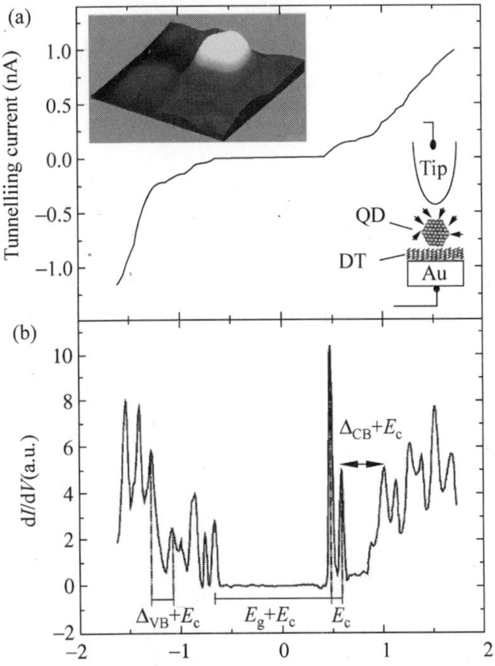

Figure 5.10 (a) STM topographic image of an InAs quantum dot and the tunneling $I \sim V$ characteristic, exhibiting single-electron tunneling effects. A schematic of the STM-based DBTJ system is also shown; (b) The tunneling conductance spectrum, dI/dV. Reprinted with permission from Macmillan Publishers Ltd: Nature (Ref.[25]), copyright 1999 (see color figure at the end of this book)

the band gap of the nanocrystal, and Δ_{VB} and Δ_{CB} are the spacings between levels in the valence and conduction bands, respectively.

5.4.3 SET in 3D Nanocluster and the Quantum Size Effect

For metal nanoclusters, the discrete energy level arising from the quantum size effect could be observed in clusters with smaller sizes than semiconductor ones. Wang, et al.[26] studied the current-voltage characteristics of a series of heptanethiol-stabilized gold particles with narrowly distributed core sizes ranging from ~1.8 – 15 nm using STM/STS. These nanoparticles were synthesized and deposited on alkanethiol SAM on top of a gold surface to form DBTJ systems within an STM framework. The results showed that while equidistant staircases originating from the CB effect are observed for large particles (> ~ 4.6 nm), irregular staircases are observed for small particles (nominal size of 1.8 nm). The latter indicates that both the CB effect and discrete quantum energy levels contribute to the $I \sim V$ spectra. Furthermore, they found that the single-electron tunneling behavior can be tuned either by varying the gold particle size or by adjusting the tip-particle distance. A schematic of the DBTJ system and a comparison between the conductance characteristics of nanoparticles with nominal sizes of 9.4 nm and 1.8 nm are shown in Fig. 5.11.

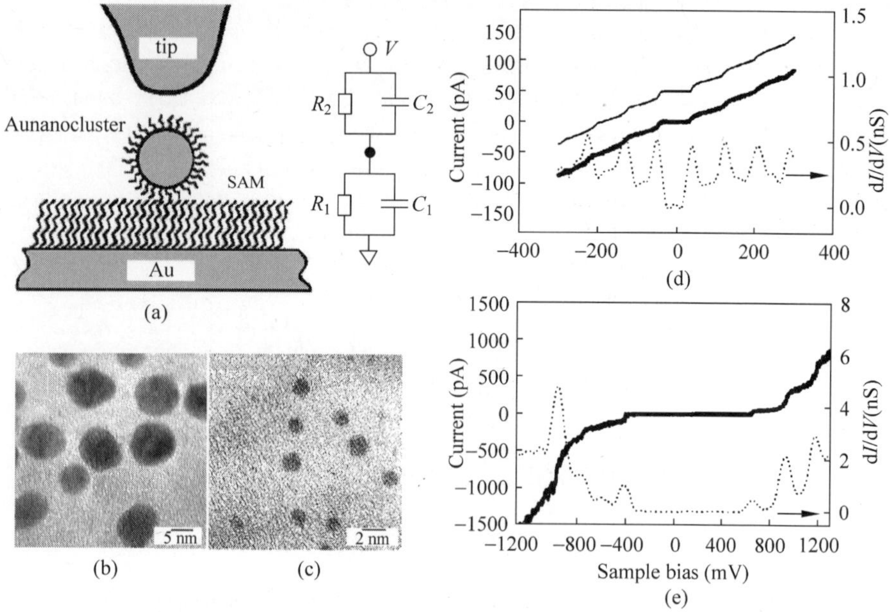

Figure 5.11 (a) A schematic of the DBTJ formed by an STM tip, a ligand-stabilized gold particle, and a Au substrate; (b) and (c) HREM images of ligand-stabilized gold particles with core sizes of 9.4 nm and 1.8 nm in diameter; (d), (e) Typical $I \sim V$ curves (thick solid line) and their digital differential conductance (dotted lines) taken from different samples with nominal particle sizes of 1.8 nm and 9.4 nm, respectively

For ultrasmall crystalline Pd nanoparticles, their $I \sim V$ characteristics exhibit fine features caused by their discreteness of energy states[27, 28]. It was found that the peak widths as well as the intrapeak spacings in differential conductance $\mathrm{d}I/\mathrm{d}V$ spectra increase as the size of Pd nanoparticles decreases. These size-dependent behaviors of the peak width and the intrapeak spacing were attributed to the clustered electronic structures around the Fermi level due to certain size-dependent dynamic effects.

5.4.4 SET in 2D Nanoclusters and Nonclassical Capacitance

With rapid developments of fabrication techniques, sizes of electronic devices are gradually approaching the nanometer scale, where many classical concepts and results might no longer be applicable and quantum corrections must be made. Capacitance is one of them. In addition to the geometry and dielectric constant, which are sufficient to determine the capacitance at the macroscale or microscale, the capacitance of a nanostructure can be affected by quantum effects[29]. Theoretical studies have shown the capacitance quantum corrections to come mainly from the finite DOS of the nanosized electrodes, the finite screening length to the electron-electron interaction, and quantum tunneling. However, it is a challenge to study the quantum effect of capacitance of a nanojunction because of the lack of a suitable nanojunction system for accurate measurements in the past. It was found that a 2D metal nanoparticle in a DBTJ may serve as an ideal system for this study. Hou, et al.[30] made the first experimental effort to investigate the capacitance behavior of a nanojunction formed by an STM tip and a nanosized 2D metal cluster (3 – 5 nm in diameter). By measuring the capacitance of this nanojunction as a function of tip-cluster separation d in a DBTJ geometry (via the CB effect), they found that as d decreases, the measured capacitance first increases, as would be anticipated by the classical theory (Fig. 5.12). Below a critical separation d_c, however, the capacitance starts to decrease, a clearly nonclassical behavior. This nonmonotonic behavior indicates that the capacitance at the nanoscale can no longer be described by the classical theory but requires quantum corrections. When the quantum corrections are included, the capacitance can be expressed approximately as:

$$C \approx \frac{R}{\frac{1}{C_0}+\frac{1}{D_{\mathrm{I}}}+\frac{1}{D_{\mathrm{II}}}}$$

where R is the electron reflection probability of the nanojunction, C_0 is the classical contribution based on geometry, and D_i ($i=$ Ⅰ, Ⅱ) is the scattering local partial density of states in the electrodes.

Besides the nonclassical behavior in the capacitance, the 2D Au nanoclusters show anisotropic behaviors in the $I \sim V$ characteristics[31]. By studying the size dependence of the Coulomb blockade and staircase, it was found that the measured zero conductance gap as a function of cluster size is in excellent agreement with an anisotropic model, in which the 2D Au island is treated as metallic in the planar direction but nonmetallic in the normal direction.

5.4.5 Suppression of Quantum Confinement Effects in Amorphous Metal Nanoparticles

In the past decades, a number of studies concerning the electronic properties of nanoparticles have been focused on the correlations between the properties and the size, shape, and composition of crystalline ones. However, it is well known that the amorphous solids have distinct transport properties from the crystalline ones. This raised the question of what is the fundamental impact of disorders on the properties of nanoscale systems. By synthesizing size-selectable ligand-passivated

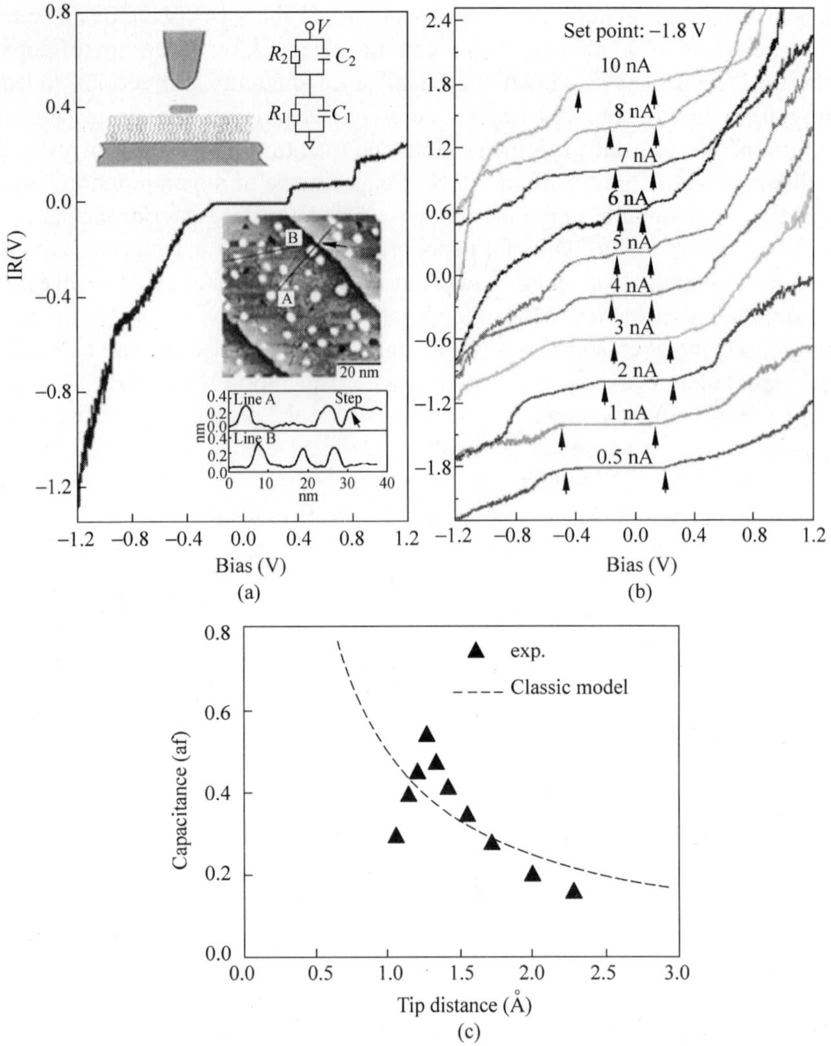

Figure 5.12 (a) a typical $I\sim V$ curve showing clearly the Coulomb blockade and Coulomb staircases. Inserts show the schematic of the DBTJ system consisting of a 2D nanoparticle and a typical STM image, (b) a series of $I\sim V$ curves taken at 5 K for a 4 nm Au cluster at different set point tunneling current. The CB width is indicated by arrows for each $I\sim V$ curve. The curves are shifted vertically for clarity, (c) the deduced capacitance C of the tip-cluster nanojunction as a function of tip-cluster separation d (see color figure at the end of this book)

crystalline (*c*-Pd) and amorphous (*a*-Pd) Pd nanoparticles (< 4 nm) and verifying their transport properties by STM/STS at 5 K, Hou, et al.[28] revealed the suppression of quantum confinement effects by disorder in the amorphous Pd nanoparticles. The $I\sim V$ curves of both these two types of nanoparticles exhibit clear CB and Coulomb staircases (Fig. 5.13). However, size-dependent multipeak

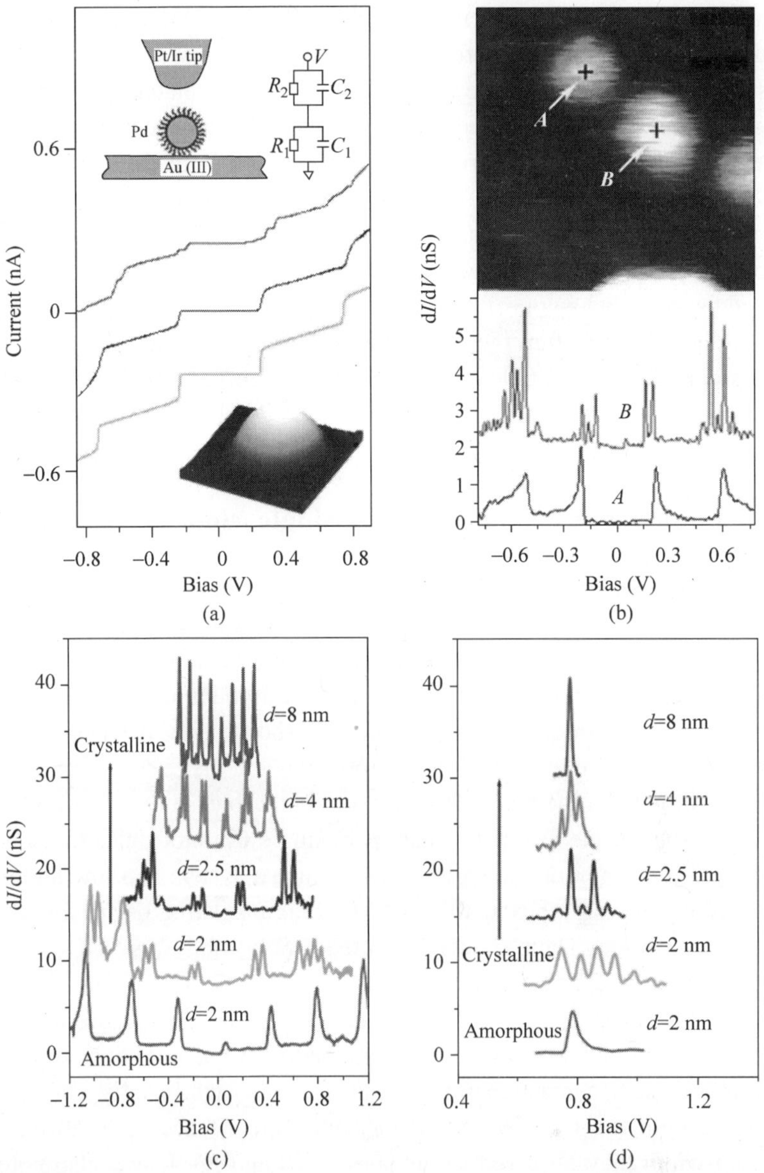

Figure 5.13 (a) curves 1 and 2 are typical $I \sim V$ curves for *c*-Pd and *a*-Pd particles, each about 2 nm in diameter. Curve 3 is a fitting curve using the orthodox theory by assuming the DOS is a constant. The top inset is a schematic of the STM DBTJ. The bottom inset is a $6 \times 6\ \text{nm}^2$ STM image, showing a Pd nanoparticle; (b) up panel: An STM image showing an *a*-Pd particle A and a *c*-Pd particle B; Down panel: d*I*/d*V* spectra acquired on particle A and particle B, respectively; (c) d*I*/d*V* spectra of *c*-Pd particles and an *a*-Pd particle. For clarity, curves are shifted vertically; (d) comparison of fine spectral features of the second CB steps for various particle size. Peaks are shifted in voltage coordinate (see color figure at the end of this book)

spectral features in the differential conductance curves are observed for the crystalline Pd particles but not for the amorphous ones. With careful theoretical analysis, they found that these spectral features are related to the quantized electronic states in the crystalline Pd particle and the suppression of the quantum confinement effect in the amorphous particle arises from the reduction of the degeneracy of the eigenstates and the level broadening due to the reduced lifetime of the electronic states. This research indicates that reducing the size alone is insufficient to push a system into its quantum regime. Disorder extends the semiclassical behavior of the metallic particle into a regime that would otherwise be fully quantum mechanical in an ordered system. The degree of the atomic order of a nanoparticle plays an equally important role in determining its quantum or classical nature.

5.4.6 Single Electron Tunneling in Single Molecules

Sphere molecules like C_{60} fullerenes can be trapped in a DBTJ and also show a single-electron tunneling effect. The $I\sim V$ characteristics of the C_{60} molecule in a single molecule transistor made by electromigration technique did show a CB behavior[32] (Fig. 5.14). However, real space investigation of the coupling of C_{60} molecules to the electrodes is inaccessable with their set-up. A recent STM study implies that both the single-electron phenomenon and the resonant tunneling into the frontier orbitals of the molecules play important roles in the electron transport. Li, et al.[33] studied the electron transport in single C_{60} molecules in a DBTJ by employing STM. They measured the STS of such a system at a low temperature of 78 K by employing a hexanethiol SAM as the insulating barrier between C_{60} and a gold substrate. Their results exhibited a noticeably large HOMO-LUMO gap of ~2.8 eV (see Fig. 5.15), which is about 1 eV larger than the intrinsic HOMO-LUMO gap (E_g) of ~1.7 eV. Since the size of a C_{60} molecule is about 7 Å, much smaller than other metal or semiconductor quantum dots, the charging energy E_C of such a nanojunction, about 1 eV, is significantly enough to be comparable with the E_g of a neutral C_{60} molecule. Hence, they attributed the larger gap width they observed to the sum of E_g and E_C. It was also noted that their differential tunneling spectra showed clearly fine peaks at the positions of HOMO and LUMO energy regions. The three peaks in the positive bias region and five peaks in the negative bias region were well attributed to the degenerate splitting of threefold degenerate LUMO and fivefold degenerate HOMO levels, respectively. The reason for the orbital degeneracy was considered to be the strong local electrical field and the Jahn-Teller effect.

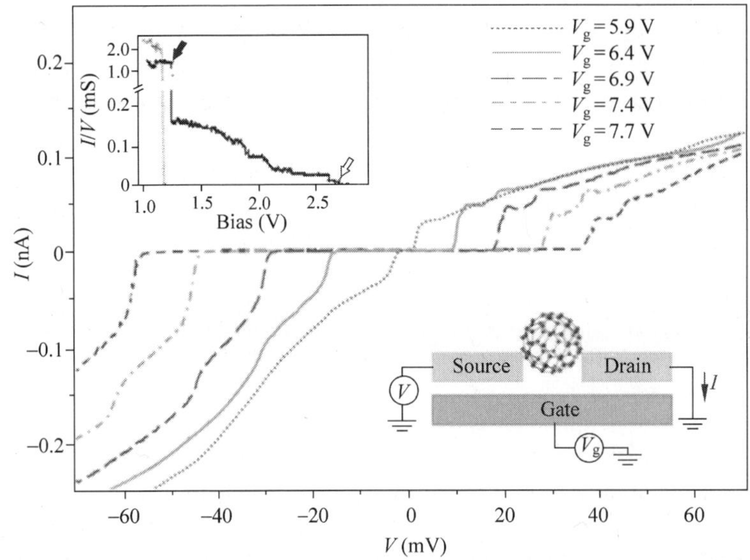

Figure 5.14 $I\sim V$ curves obtained from a single-C_{60} transistor at $T=1.5$ K. Five $I\sim V$ curves taken at different gate voltages are shown. Upper inset: A large bias was applied between the electrodes while the current through the connected electrode was monitored (black solid curve). Lower inset shows an idealized diagram of a single C_{60} transistor formed by the electromigration method. Reprinted with permission from Macmillan Publishers Ltd: Nature (Ref.[32]), copyright 2000 (see color figure at the end of this book)

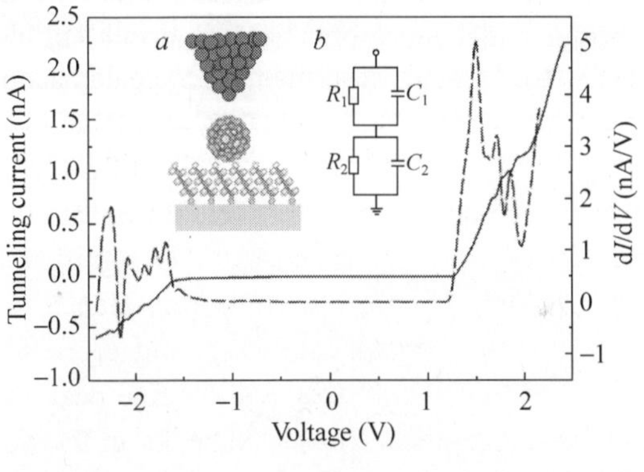

Figure 5.15 Scanning tunneling spectroscopy of a single C_{60} molecule in a DBTJ system. Dashed line is the dI/dV curve; solid line is the $I\sim V$ characteristic curve. (a and b) represent schematics of the DBTJ system and the corresponding equivalent circuit diagram (see color figure at the end of this book)

5.5 Rectifying Effect in Single Molecules

5.5.1 Aviram-Ratner Mechanism for a Single Molecule Rectifier

Rectifying is one of the most important effects in electric and electron transport. Rectification of electrical current was first discovered one hundred years ago in vacuum tube diodes. The simplest condensed matter rectifier is a semiconductor p-n junction. Realizing rectifying effect with a new kind of materials is the first step toward practical electronics when it is considered to be an electronic building block. Among all alternative proposals, the most promising and fascinating concept is to realize all functions of modern electronics by employing a single molecule consisting of several functional groups, namely, molecular electronics. The first concept of molecular electronics was proposed in 1974 by Arich Aviram and Mark Ratner[34]. They suggested a prototype of a single molecular rectifier based on the use of a single organic molecule. The A-R (Aviram-Ratner) type molecular rectifier consists of an electron donor part and an electron acceptor part, separated by a sigma-bonded tunneling bridge, i.e., a *D-σ-A* structure. However, it is a long-standing challenge to fabricate a device in which only a single organic molecule is connected by two electrodes, due to the limit of experimental techniques. This situation changed in the late 1990s when researchers were able to measure the conductance of a unimolecular monolayer or even a single molecule[12]. Metzger, et al.[35] reported direct evidence of rectification induced by intramolecular tunneling in a single-molecular level AR-type Langmuir-Blodgett (LB) monolayer of molecule γ-(*n*-hexadecyl)quinolinum tricyanoquinodimethanide, $C_{16}H_{33}Q$-3CNQ. Compared to the *D-σ-A* structure in the original AR mechanism, this molecule possesses a slight modified *T-D-π-A* structure, where the σ bridge is replaced by a π bridge and T represents the hexadecyl 'tail' needed to help form good LB films (Fig. 5.16). In their experiment, both macroscopic and nanoscopic *I~V* measurements revealed asymmetries in the electrical conductivity through the LB multilayers and even monolayers, demonstrating the feasibility of AR mechanism for realizing a single molecular level rectifier.

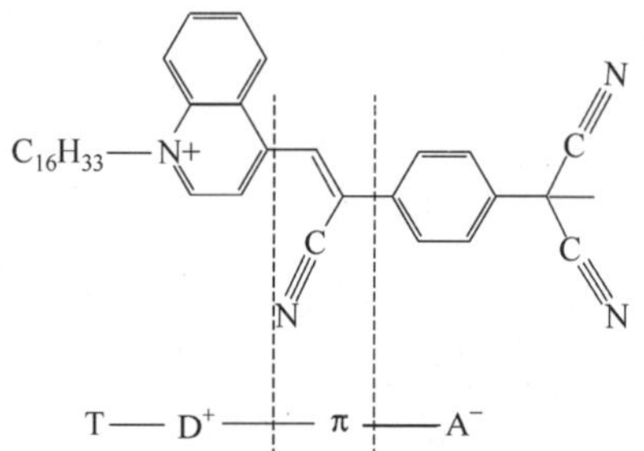

Figure 5.16 Structure sketch of the polar zwitterionic ground-state of a $C_{16}H_{33}Q$-3CNQ molecule

5.5.2 Single Molecule Rectifier with AR Mechanism

However, in the above molecule and other previously studied molecules with *D-σ-A* or *D-π-A* structure, there were long alkyl or alkanethiolate tails connected to electrodes. Thus, the rectifying effect observed in such molecules was doubted by other researchers. In general, a conjugated molecule is more conductive than a saturated molecule of the same length. Hence, in a system of *D-σ-A* or *D-π-A* tailored with alkyl chains, the main voltage is expected to drop over the tailored chains, but only by a small fraction over the *D-σ-A* or *D-π-A* group itself, which causes a small shift of the energy levels between the *D* and the *A* part. In such a situation, the mechanism of the rectification may be different from the original model of AR rectifiers. This requires insight into the conduction mechanism of AR rectifiers based on analyzing the electron transport through molecular orbitals and, thus, requires an investigation at a single molecular scale.

Wang, et al.[36] presented the electron transport of chemisorbed pyridyl aza(60) fulleroid molecules, abbreviated as C_{60}NPy, which is based on the *D-σ-A* architecture, at a single molecular scale using STM (Fig. 5.17). The C_{60} moiety participates as an electron acceptor (*A*), the pyridine moiety bonded to the Au substrate as an electron donor (*D*), and the single methylene (–CH_2–) bridge as a σ-bridge. A rectifying effect was observed in the current-voltage characteristics. The positive onset voltage is 0.5 V, and the negative onset voltage is –1.7 V. Theoretical calculation shows that the HOMO and the LUMO are well localized either on the Py moiety (donor) or on the C_{60} moiety (acceptor), indicating that the σ-bridge decouples the LUMO and the HOMO of the donor and the acceptor,

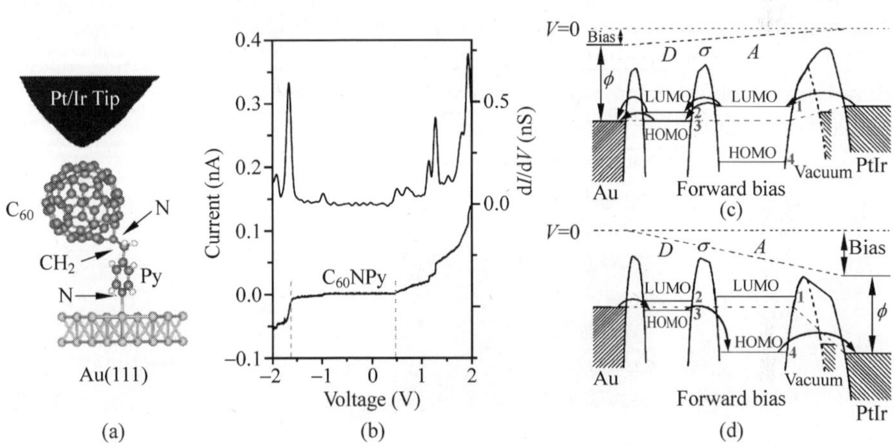

Figure 5.17 (a) Schematic drawing of the model of the C_{60}NPy on Au(111) surface. (b) *I-V* curve and its numerical d*I*/d*V* spectrum for C_{60}NPy measured at 5 K taken at a sample bias voltage of 2.0 V and a set-point current of 0.2 nA. (c), (d) Schematic drawings of the electron transport in C_{60}NPy for (c) forward bias and (d) reverse bias. The vacuum barriers in dashed lines denote the barriers at a higher feedback current (see color figure at the end of this book)

respectively. This structure agrees well with the unimolecular rectifying model proposed by Aviram and Ratner, without a long chain tail connected to the electrode. By directly comparing the experimental conductance peaks and the calculated density of states of the C_{60}NPy, they found that the observed rectification could be attributed to the asymmetric positioning of the LUMOs and the HOMOs of both sides of the acceptor and the donor of the C_{60}NPy molecules with respect to the Fermi level of the electrodes.

5.5.3 Single $C_{59}N$ Molecule as a Rectifier

As mentioned above, the most widely designed and experimentally synthesized molecular rectifiers are based on the *A-R* proposal. Recently, an alternative mechanism was suggested and demonstrated, where a single electroactive unit is positioned asymmetrically with respect to the electrodes, and the HOMO and LUMO are positioned asymmetrically with respect to the Fermi level. In 2005, Zhao, et al.[37] reported a new kind of experimental realization of molecular rectifier, which is based on a single azafullerene $C_{59}N$ molecule in a DBTJ via the SET effect. They observed obvious rectifying effects in the $I \sim V$ characteristics of a $C_{59}N$ molecule adsorbed on a SAM on Au(111). The positive onset voltage is about 0.5 – 0.7 V, while the negative onset voltage is about 1.6 – 1.8 V in Fig. 5.18. Theoretical analyses show that the half-occupied HOMO and the asymmetric shift of the Fermi level when the molecule is charged (i.e., the HOMO-LUMO gaps of $C_{59}N^+$ and $C_{59}N^-$ are distinctly different) are responsible for the molecular rectification. This study expanded the application field of the SET devices. It also demonstrated that the transport properties of a single molecule can be dramatically changed by chemical doping at the single atom level, indicating a possible method for designing and realizing novel single molecule devices with specific properties.

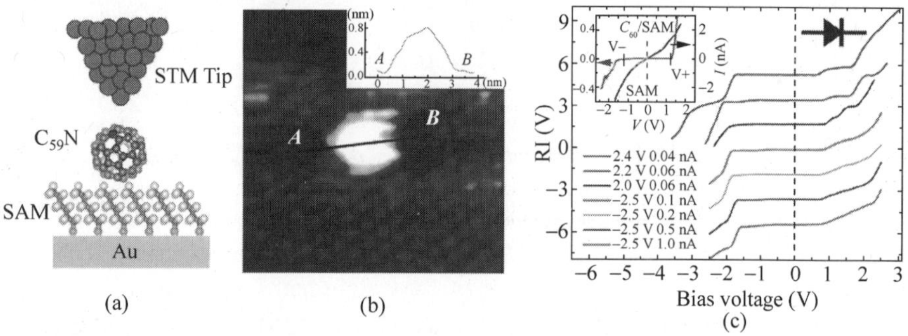

Figure 5.18 (a) the diagram of the experimental system. (b) the STM image of an isolated $C_{59}N$ adsorbed on thiol SAM at 5 K. Inset shows line profile along the line AB. (c) a set of $I \sim V$ curves for individual $C_{59}N$ molecules measured at 5 K and at various setting parameters. The inset shows the $I \sim V$ curves for the SAM substrate and individual C_{60} for comparison (see color figure at the end of this book)

5.6 NDR Effect

5.6.1 Resonant Tunneling and NDR Effect in Nanostructures

The NDR effect refers to a negative differential resistance in the transport property (i.e., a valley appears in the $I\sim V$ spectrum) of a device or a junction. In the 1970s, with development of the techniques of solid thin film epitaxial growth, for example, molecular beam epitaxy (MBE), it became possible to fabricate thin film semiconductor heterostructures with a thickness of few atomic layers and low impurity concentration. For example, in the layered structure of GaAs/Al_xGa_{1-x}As/GaAs, the precision-doped AlxGa_{1-x}As layers serve as 2D barriers. Tsu and Esaki[38] in IBM predicted theoretically that in a semiconductor double barrier or multi barrier superlattice structure, the NDR behavior may arise in the $I\sim V$ characteristics due to the resonant tunneling effect of the electron transport through the quantum mechanically confined system. This NDR effect was confirmed by a subsequent experiment[39]. The NDR effect in a DBTJ can be well understood by considering a confined structure with discrete energy levels (quantum well) located between two tunneling barriers, as shown in Fig. 5.19. When the Fermi level of both sides of the DBTJ are on the same level without applying a bias voltage, the system is in equilibrium state and there is no current flowing through the system. The current is greatly enhanced when the potential of the resonant state E_1 matches the Fermi level of the left electron reservoir, which leads to resonant tunneling through the DBTJ and hence the NDR effect. This effect has potential application in nanometer-size RTD, which can be used in high-frequency nanoscale electronic devices.

The NDR effect was found in the electric transport of a single layered molecular system with an amazing peak-to-valley ratio of 1030 : 1, where a two-step reduction process that modifies the charge transport through the molecule was proposed for the NDR mechanism[40]. However, due to the lack of single molecular level investigation, the real mechanism remains in doubt. It was found theoretically that a nanoscale tunneling system with sharp LDOS features can result in an NDR effect with a different mechanism. In 1986, Lang[41, 42] studied the electron tunneling between two parallel plane electrodes with one adatom adsorbed on each surface. In this system, the LDOS of both electrodes are strongly localized in a small energy window (as a result of the single atom adsorption). From the Bardeen perturbation theory[17], the tunneling current between the two electrodes can be calculated approximately by the convolution of the LDOS of the two single-atom electrodes at low biases. It is possible to induce an NDR effect in the tunneling spectra due to the greatly enhanced tunneling current flow when the energies of the two sharp LDOS peaks match (Fig. 5.20).

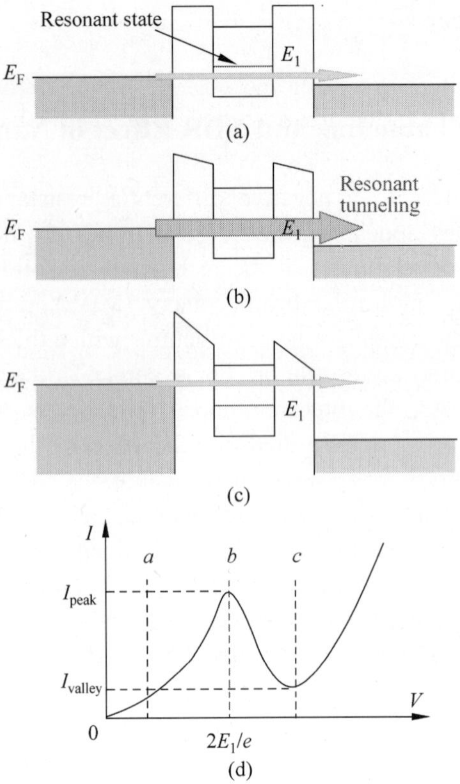

Figure 5.19 Schematic energy diagram (a, b, c) of the NDR effect in a DBTJ. (d) Schematic $I \sim V$ characteristics (see color figure at the end of this book)

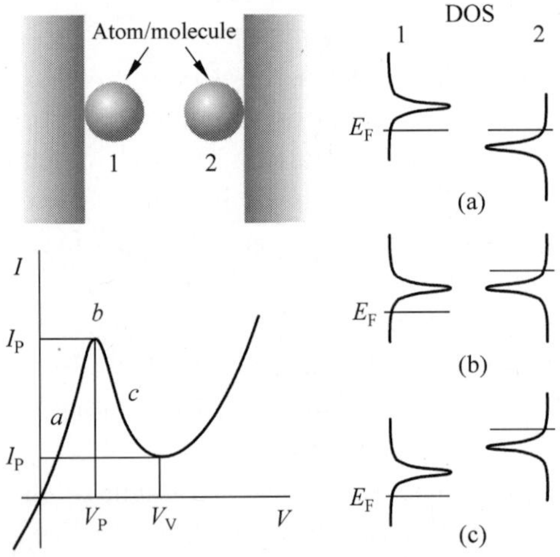

Figure 5.20 Schematic diagram for the NDR effect generated by the resonant tunneling between two atoms/molecules with narrow LDOS features

5.6.2 NDR Effect Involving Two C_{60} Molecules

Although it is possible to control and observe single atoms or molecules with adequately narrow LDOS features adsorbed on an atomically plane surface using newly developed microscopy, e.g., STM, it is still not easy to obtain such sharp LDOS in a chemical adsorption system because of considerable hybridization of the electronic states and broadening effect of the LDOS upon adsorption. The interaction of the adsorbate with the substrate can be weakened by introducing a buffer layer or barrier between them. On the other hand, the narrow LDOS features of the tip are usually realized by 'sharpening' the tip apex by attaching adatoms. However, the structure of such 'sharpened tip' and the associated LDOS are uncontrollable and unstable. Zeng, et al.[43] demonstrated the realization of the NDR molecular device involving two C_{60} molecules in a DBTJ system, one adsorbed on the Pt-Ir tip and the other physically adsorbed on the hexanethiol SAM (Fig. 5.21). Such controllable tunneling structure and the associated known electronic states ensure the stability and reproducibility of the NDR device. In this study, they picked up a C_{60} molecule using the tip to form a stable sharpened apex, and measured the $I\sim V$ curves over another C_{60} molecule. The NDR effect was found in the characteristics of this architecture, which can be well attributed to the narrow LDOS feature of the C_{60} molecule.

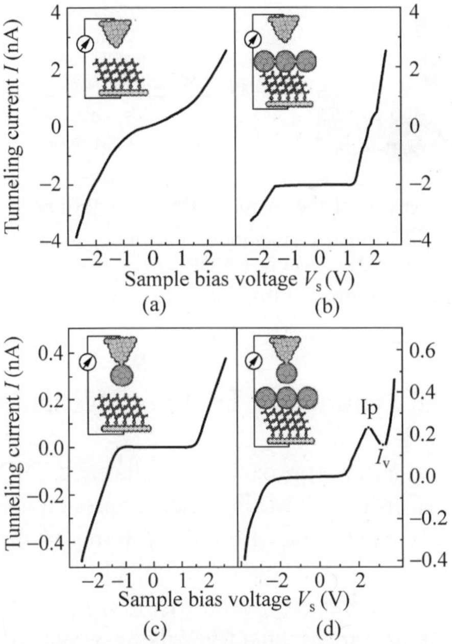

Figure 5.21 $I\sim V$ curves obtained from four kinds of tunneling configurations, as shown in the insets. (a), (b), (c), and (d) correspond to bare Pt-Ir tip over thiols, bare Pt-Ir tip over C_{60}, C_{60}-modified tip over thiols, and C_{60}-modified tip over C_{60}, respectively. Clear NDR effect was found in (d)

5.6.3 NDR Effect Involving Two Metal Nanoparticles

Similar to C_{60} molecules with sharp LDOS features, metal nanoparticles with discrete energy levels can also be involved in a vertically coupled system to exhibit NDR effect (Fig. 5.22). Wang, et al.[44] carefully used a tip in a STM to pick up a Pd nanoparticle from a substrate and imaged the nearby area to find another Pd nanoparticle. The $I \sim V$ characteristics over the particles were measured. The schematics of the manipulation and two coupled nanoparticles in series in a STM-DBTJ are depicted in Fig. 5.22. The mechanism of the observed NDR effect can be understood in a similar manner to that observed in the system with C_{60} molecules by the same theory.

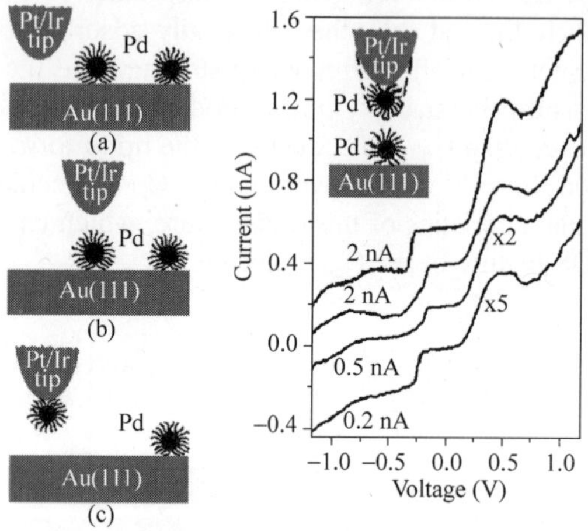

Figure 5.22 A schematic of the manipulation of a Pd nanoparticle by STM tip and the formation of a vertically coupled system with two Pd nanoparticles. Right panel: typical $I \sim V$ curves showing clear NDR effect measured over a Pd crystalline nanoparticle with another particle adsorbed on the tip

5.6.4 Local Orbital Symmetry Matching Mechanism for NDR Effect

Chen, et al.[45] presented a new approach for realizing an NDR effect simply with a nonatomic sharp or even flat STM tip. Their approach is based on the concept of local orbital symmetry matching of the apex atoms of the electrode terminals. In this case, NDR always appears at a well-defined bias where a spatially localized orbital component in a broad energy band of the tip matches the symmetry of a molecular orbital. This occurs irrespective of the actual physical shapes of the tips, in stark contrast to the conventional mechanisms reported before. In this study, they investigated the tip dependence of the $I \sim V$ characteristics of a single cobalt phthalocyanines (CoPc) molecule adsorbed on a Au substrate by a joint experimental and theoretical scanning tunneling microscope study. For two different metal tips used, Ni and W, a very strong NDR behavior with I_{max} at about −0.9 V was only found with Ni tips and showed no dependence on the geometrical shape of the tip (Fig. 5.23). Theoretical calculations demonstrated that the unexpected NDR effect differed from previous mechanisms and originated from the strong resonant tunneling between the d*xz*(*yz*) orbitals of both Ni tip apex and Co atom due to the local orbital symmetry matching. The significance of this study is that it showed that even for a continued energy band without a narrow LDOS feature, one can still take advantage of its spatial discreteness to control the electron transport through the device. The new mechanism they found emphasizes the spatial resonance and local symmetry matching of the electronic bands in different parts of the device, rather than the actual geometrical shape of the electrodes. It can thus simplify the design of electrodes in molecular devices.

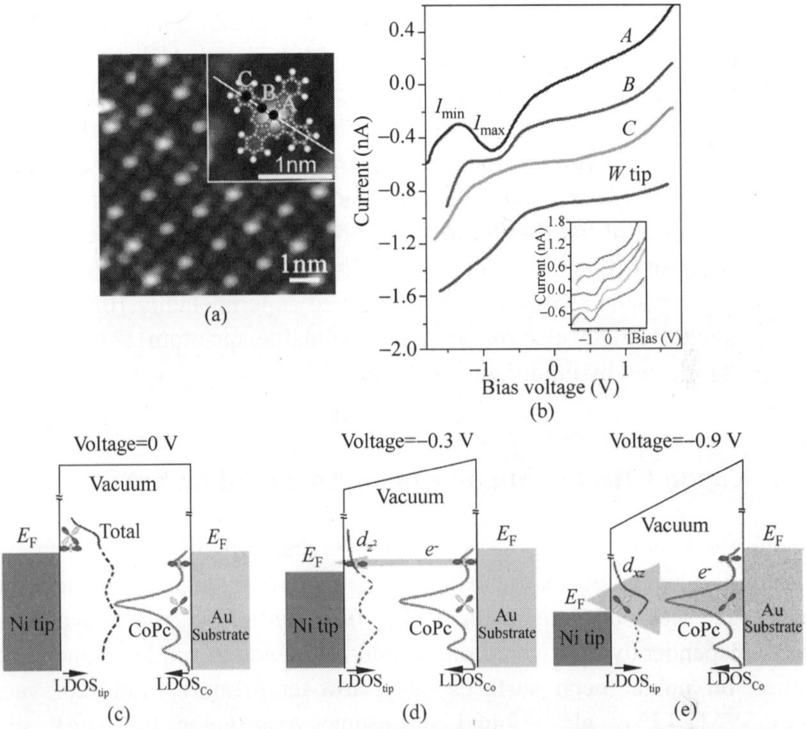

Figure 5.23 (a) An STM image of CoPc monolayer on a Au(111) surface. The inset in (a) is a magnified molecule image with a superimposed CoPc ball-stick sketch. (b) *I*~*V* curves measured with the Ni tip over sites *A*, *B*, and *C* (marked in the inset of (a)), and with the *W* tip over site *A*. The inset in (b) shows results of five different Ni tips over site A. (c−e) The *d* orbitals of the Ni tip, (c) at the zero bias, not matching any of the Co orbitals, hence no current; (d) at −0.3 eV, interacting with the d_{z^2} orbitals of the Co atom, generating weak tunneling current; (e) at −0.9 V, matching the $d_{xz(yz)}$ orbitals of the Co atom, resulting in the strong NDR effect (see color figure at the end of this book)

5.7 Kondo Effect

5.7.1 Kondo Effect Revisited on the Nanoscale

Interactions between individual localized spins and conduction electrons in a metallic host can give rise to a subtle phenomenon known as the Kondo effect[46]. This effect was first discovered as a resistance minimum when measuring the temperature dependence of resistance of magnetic dilute alloys at low temperatures and then named after the Japanese scientist J. Kondo who gave the first theoretical explanation for it in 1964[47].

With the development of the capability of studying the transport properties of nanoscale matters in which electrons are strongly localized and quantum effects are predominant, the Kondo effect attracted much attention again in both theoretical and experimental aspects from the late 1980s. Glazman, et al.[48] and Ng, et al.[49] predicted in 1988 that the Kondo effect will manifest as a strong resonance in a quantum dot or similar systems if an odd number of electrons is accommodated in the dot. The dot then has a localized spin that is expected to couple with the electron seas of the source and drain electrodes, resulting in a Kondo effect. A direct consequence of the Kondo effect is a resonance pinned at the Fermi level in the local density of states, which is usually called the Kondo resonance. The presence of the Kondo resonance was confirmed experimentally 10 years later in a semiconductor single electron transistor (tunable quantum dot with a gate electrode) fabricated by lithography technique[50].

5.7.2 Kondo Effect in Single Atoms Adsorbed on Surfaces

Although the Kondo effect originates from the scattering of conduction electron spins at individual magnetic impurities, investigation of single magnetic impurity in real space was not achived for a long time until 1998, when two research groups independently discovered the Kondo resonance in single magnetic atoms adsorbed on noble metal surfaces using low-temperature ultra-high vacuum (UHV) STM. Li, et al.[51] found antiresonance at E_F in the dI/dV spectra measured over single Ce atoms on a Ag surface. Madhavan, et al.[52] found an asymmetric resonance at E_F in the dI/dV spectra of single Co atoms on a Au surface (Fig. 5.24). Both of the groups interpreted the resonance as a Kondo effect associated with the Fano resonance. In the following years, the Kondo effect has been found in various magnetic atoms adsorbed on a number of different substrates[53, 54].

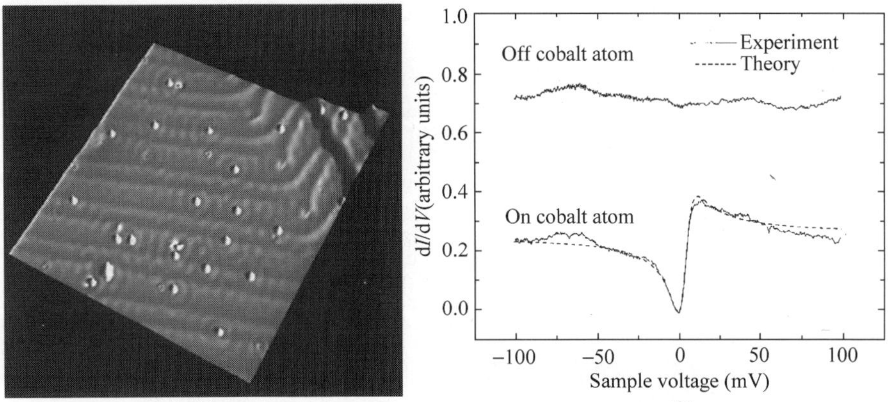

(a) (b)

Figure 5.24 (a) STM topographic image (400 Å by 400 Å) of individual Co atoms adsorbed on a Au(111) surface. (b) A pair of d*I*/d*V* spectra taken with the STM tip held over a single Co atom and over the nearby bare Au surface. The feature identified as a Kondo effect associated with Fano resonance appears over the Co atom. From Ref. [52]. Reprinted with permission from AAAS

5.7.3 Kondo Effect in Single Magnetic Molecules

Molecules can serve as good templates for carrying single spin centers, for example, coordination complexes enclosing single or few magnetic atoms. These molecules are promising in future spin-related nanoelectronics due to their flexibility and variety in structure. In 2002, two independent groups found clear evidences of the Kondo effect in single-molecule transistors. Park, et al.[55] fabricated single atom transistors by incorporating two related molecules containing a Co ion bonded to polypyridyl ligands, $(Co(tpy\text{-}(CH_2)_5\text{-}SH)_2)^{2+}$ and $(Co(tpy\text{-}SH)_2)^{2+}$. The electron transport in the former molecule showed single-electron phenomenon similar to single electron transistors studied previously. However, the $I \sim V$ spectra of the latter molecule showed a clear Kondo resonance, which was examined by observing the split in strong magnetic fields (Fig. 5.25). Liang, et al.[56] also found clear evidence of the Kondo resonance in a single divanadium molecule transistor. In these studies, the Kondo effect and the charge and spin states of the single molecule transistors can be tuned by varying the gate voltages.

Zhao, et al.[57] demonstrated a new approach to control the spin state and the Kondo effect of a single molecule by directly changing the molecular structure. They showed that the Kondo effect of the Co ion in a single CoPc molecule adsorbed on Au surfaces can be controlled by cutting away the outer hydrogen atoms of the molecule. For a CoPc molecule, a magnetic Co^{2+} ion is embedded in its center, but the magnetism disappears when the molecule is adsorbed onto the Au surface due to the electronic interactions between the Co ion and the substrate. The nonmagnetic behavior was verified both from experimental d*I*/d*V* spectroscopy and from theoretical calculations. However, they found that by

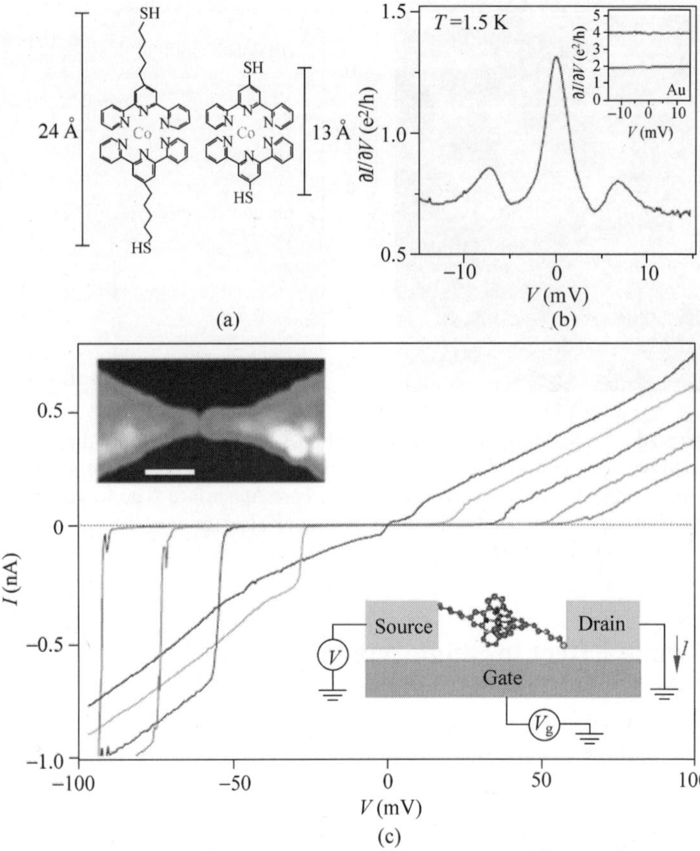

Figure 5.25 (a) Structure of $(Co(tpy\text{-}(CH_2)_5\text{-}SH)_2)^{2+}$ and $(Co(tpy\text{-}SH)_2)^{2+}$. (b) Differential conductance of a $(Co(tpy\text{-}SH)_2)^{2+}$ device at 1.5 K showing a Kondo peak. The inset shows dI/dV plots for bare gold point contacts for comparison. (c) $I \sim V$ curves of a $(Co(tpy\text{-}(CH2)_5\text{-}SH)_2)^{2+}$ single-molecule transistor at different gate voltages showing a Coulomb blockade behavior. Upper inset: A topographic atomic force microscope image of the electrodes with a gap (scale bar, 100 nm). Lower inset, a schematic diagram of the device. Reprinted with permission from Macmillan Publishers Ltd: Nature (Ref. [55]), copyright 2002 (see color figure at the end of this book)

cutting away eight hydrogen atoms from the molecule with high-energy tunneling electrons emitted from a STM tip, both the electronic and geometric structures of the molecule changed remarkably (Fig. 5.26). The molecule was arched away from the surface and all the four lobes disappeared in a topographic image, indicating a strong chemical bonding of the highly-reactive benzene ring to the Au surface. In this fully-dehydrogenated CoPc (*d*-CoPc) molecule, a strong resonance was found at E_F arising in the dI/dV spectroscopy; however, the original d_{z^2} orbital-induced resonant state located at −150 mV in a pristine CoPc molecule completely disappeared. This zero-bias resonance was attributed to the Kondo effect associated with Fano resonance by careful theoretical analysis.

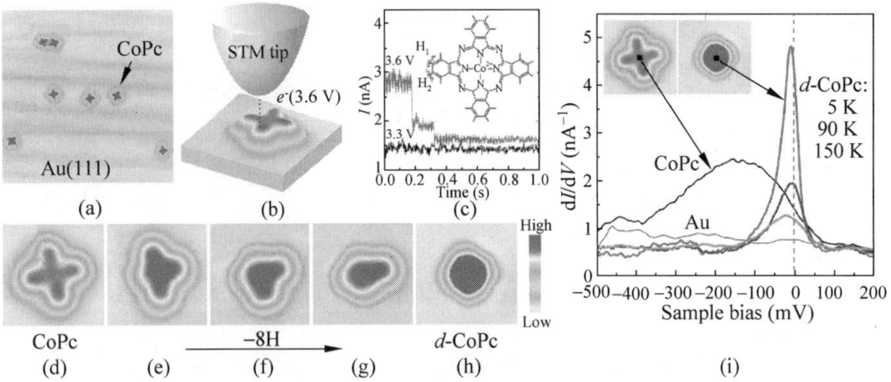

Figure 5.26 (a) individual CoPc molecules adsorbed on Au(111) surface. (b) diagram of the dehydrogenation induced by the tunneling electrons. (c) current traces during two different voltage pulses on the brink of one lobe. Inset shows the molecular structure of CoPc and the two hydrogen atoms to be pruned off in each one lobe. (d) – (h) STM images of a single CoPc molecule during each step of the dehydrogenation process, from (d) an intact CoPc to (h) a d-CoPc. The color scale represents apparent heights, ranging from 0 Å (low) to 2.7 Å (high). (i) dI/dV spectra measured directly over center Co atoms of *d*-CoPc showing strong Kondo resonances near the Fermi level. Two spectra for CoPc and bare Au surface are presented for comparison (see color figure at the end of this book)

5.8 Inelastic Electron Tunneling Spectroscopy (IETS)

5.8.1 IETS of Single Molecules

Inelastic electron tunneling spectroscopy (IETS) is an ultra-sensitive technique for detecting molecular vibration spectra or other inelastic scattering effect. The first IETS measurement was demonstrated by Jaklevic and Lambe in the late 1960s[58, 59] for single-layer molecules buried in a metal-oxide interface of a metal-oxide-metal SBTJ. The principle of this technique for detecting molecular vibration spectra is quite simple: electrons tunneling through the junction with energies exceeding the energy of a certain vibrational mode of the buried molecules are able to excite this mode, and an inelastic channel in conductance is thus opened. The enhancement of the conductance of the junction can be characterized as an abrupt step in the dI/dV spectra and as a sharp peak in the d^2I/dV^2 spectra (Fig. 5.27). This technique is particularly useful for chemical identification because vibrational modes are the fingerprint of a given molecule. A few years after the invention of STM, Binnig, et al.[60] first discussed the possibility of IETS based on an STM and found there is no obstacle in principle for an STM to perform IETS measurement even at the single molecular level. However, experimental realization is not easy because it requires extreme mechanical stability during measurement. The challenging task was accomplished by Ho, et al.[61] in 1998 when they obtained the first single-molecule vibrational spectroscopy for acetylene molecules adsorbed on a Cu(100) surface by using a homemade UHV–STM working at 8 K. The IETS spectra they obtained from the acetylene molecules showed clear peaks at 358 meV for C_2H_2 and 266 meV for C_2D_2, which were identified as the ν(C–H) and ν(C–D) stretch mode respectively.

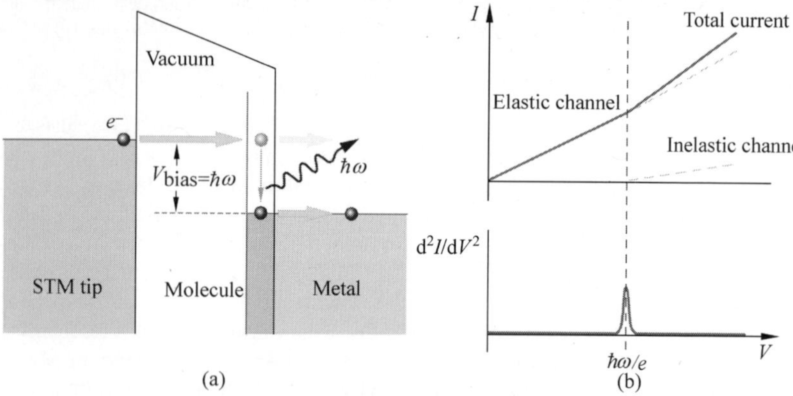

Figure 5.27 (a) Schematic energy diagram of IETS. (b) I–V and d^2I/dV^2 characteristics of IETS (see color figure at the end of this book)

5.8.2 Spin-Flip Spectroscopy of Single Magnetic Atoms

To manipulate the flip of a single spin is of great scientific merit because of its potential applications in future single-spin-based quantum information processing and quantum computation. IETS provides the ability to detect the spin flips driven by inelastic electron scattering. In 2004, A. J. Heinrich, et al.[62] demonstrated the first measurement of sin-flip spectroscopy of single magnetic Mn atoms adsorbed on Al_2O_3 thin films on a NiAl(110) substrate employing a homemade UHV high-magnetic field STM working at 0.6 K. In the d^2I/dV^2 spectra measured over the Mn atoms, they found that at $B = 0.7$ T, the conductance near the Fermi level is reduced by ~ 20%, showing symmetric steps at an energy of ~ 0.8 meV. These conductance steps gradually shifted toward E_F with decreasing B, and vanished at $B = 0$. The steps showed clear evidence that a spin-flip inelastic tunneling channel was opened at high magnetic fields. By measuring the shift of the spin-flip conductance step with magnetic field, they discovered the Zeeman energy of the Mn atoms and thus found out the corresponding g factor, ~1.88 (Fig. 5.28). It is worthy to note that Al_2O_3 thin films on which Mn atoms were deposited served as an insulator to preserve the intrinsic spin properties of individual Mn atoms. For those Mn atoms directly adsorbed on the NiAl surface,

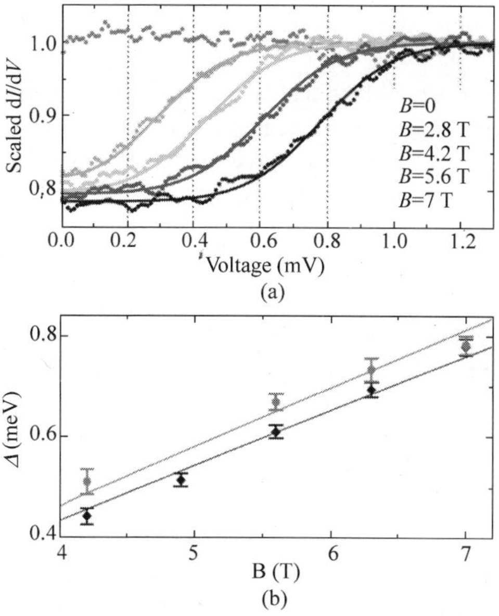

Figure 5.28 (a) conductance spectra (points) for an isolated Mn atom on oxide at different magnetic fields. (b) magnetic field dependence of the Zeeman energy Δ. Black points are extracted from the fits in (a), and red points were taken on a Mn atom near the edge of an oxide patch. Linear fits (black and red lines) constrained to $\Delta=0$ at $B=0$ yield g values of 1.88 and 2.01, respectively. From Ref. [62]. Reprinted with permission from AAAS (see color figure at the end of this book)

no spin-flip steps can be observed. This is to say, a DBTJ system is needed for detecting the spin-flip spectroscopy; otherwise, the spin of individual magnetic impurities might be strongly disturbed by the atom-substrate interaction. They also found that the Mn atom located within 1 nm of the edge of an oxide patch showed a significantly different g value (red points) of ~2.01, indicating that the spin-flip properties are extremely sensitive to the local environment of the magnetic atom (Fig. 5.28(b)). It is expected that the spin-flip process of single magnetic molecules, for example, metallophthalocyanine molecules, may also be manipulated in a similar manner. This study highlighted the possibility of information storage and processing by employing the spin degree of freedom at the single molecular level.

Acknowledgements

This study was supported by the National Basic Research Program of China (Grant No. 2006CB922001), and by the National Natural Science Foundation of China. We also acknowledge support from the Chinese Academy of Sciences and the University of Science and Technology of China.

References

[1] Binnig G., H. Rohrer, Ch. Gerber, and E. Weibel, (1982), Surface Studies by Scanning Tunneling Microscopy, *Phys. Rev. Lett.*, **49**: 57 – 61

[2] Binnig G., H. Rohrer, Ch. Gerber, and E. Weibel, (1982), Tunneling through a controllable vacuum gap, *Appl. Phys. Lett.*, **40**: 178 – 180

[3] Park H., A. K. L. Lim, A. P. Alivisatos, J. W. Park, and P. L. McEuen, (1999), Fabrication of metallic electrodes with nanometer separation by electromigration, *Appl. Phys. Lett.*, **75**: 301 – 303

[4] Van Ruitenbeek J. M., A. Alvarez, I. Piñeyro, C., Grahmann P. Joyez, M. H. Devoret, D. Esteve, and C. Urbina, (1995), Adjustable nanofabricated atomic size contacts, *Rev. Sci. Instrum.*, **67**: 108 – 111

[5] Landauer R., (1957), Spatial variation of currents and fields due to localized scatterers in metallic conduction, *IBM J. Res. Dev.*, **1**: 223 – 231

[6] Van Wees B. J., H. Van Houten, C. W. J. Beenakker, J. G. Williamson, L. P. Kouwenhoven, and D. Van der Marel, (1988), Quantized conductance of point contacts in a two-dimensional electron gas, *Phys. Rev. Lett.*, **60**: 848 – 850

[7] Wharam D. A., T. J. Thornton, R. Newbury, M. Pepper, H. Ahmed, J. E. F. Frost, D. G. Hasko, D. C. Peacock, D. A. Ritchie, and G. A. C. Jones, (1988), One-dimensional transport and the quantization of the ballistic resistance, *J. Phys.*, C **21**: L209 – L214

[8] Pascual J. I., J. Mendéz, J. Gomez-Herreró, A. M. Baró, N. García, V. T. Binh, (1993), Quantum contact in gold nanostructures by scanning tunneling microscopy, *Phys. Rev. Lett.*, **71**: 1852 – 1855

[9] Kröger J., H. Jensen, R. Berndt, (2007), Conductance of tip–surface and tip—atom junctions on Au(111) explored by a scanning tunneling microscope, *New J. Phys.*, **9**:153:1 – 9

[10] Limot L., J. Kröger, R. Berndt, A. Garcia-Lekue, and W. A. Hofer, (2005), Atom Transfer and Single-Adatom Contacts, *Phys. Rev. Lett.*, **94**:126102-1 – 126102-4

[11] Cuevas J. C., A. Levy Yeyati, A. Martín-Rodero, G. Rubio Bollinger, C. Untiedt, and N. Agraït, (1998), Evolution of Conducting Channels in Metallic Atomic Contacts under Elastic Deformation, *Phys. Rev. Lett.*, **81**: 2990 – 2993

[12] Reed M. A., C. Zhou, C. J. Muller, T. P. Burgin, J. M. Tour, (1997), Conductance of a molecular junction, *Science*, **278**: 252 – 254

[13] Cui X. D., A. Primak, X. Zarate, J. Tomfohr, O. F. Sankey, A. L. Moore, T. A. Moore, D. Gust, G. Harris, S. M. Lindsay, (2001), Reproducible Measurement of Single-Molecule Conductivity. *Science*, **294**: 571 – 574

[14] Xu B. and N. J. Tao, (2003), Measurement of Single-Molecule Resistance by Repeated Formation of Molecular Junctions, *Science*, **301**: 1221 – 1223

[15] Tao N. J., (2006), Electron transport in molecular junctions, *Nature Nanotechnology*, **1**: 173 – 181

[16] Smit R. H. M., Y. Noat, C. Untiedt, N. D. Lang, M. C. van Hemert, and J. M. van Ruitenbeek, (2002), Measurement of the conductance of a hydrogen molecule, *Nature*, **419**: 906 – 909

[17] Bardeen J., (1961) Tunneling from a Many-Particle Point of View, *Phys. Rev. Lett.*, **6**: 57 – 59

[18] Chen C. J., (1993), Introduction to Scanning Tunneling Microscopy, Oxford University Press

[19] Tersoff J. and D. R. Hamann, (1983), Theory and Application for the Scanning Tunneling Microscope, *Phys. Rev. Lett.*, **50**: 1998 – 2001

[20] Tersoff J. and D. R. Hamann, (1985), Theory of the scanning tunneling microscope, *Phys. Rev.*, *B* **31**: 805 – 813

[21] Hou J. G., J. L. Yang, H. Q. Wang, Q. X. Li, C. G. Zeng, H. Lin, and B. Wang, (1999), Identifying Molecular Orientation of Individual C_{60} on a *Si*(111)-(7 × 7) Surface, *Phys. Rev. Lett.*, **83**: 3001 – 3004

[22] Wang H. Q., C. G. Zeng, Q. X. Li, B. Wang, J. L. Yang, J. G. Hou, Q. S. Zhu, (1999), Scanning tunneling spectroscopy of individual C_{60} molecules adsorbed on Si(111)-7 × 7 surface, *Surf. Sci.*, **442**: L1024 – L1028

[23] Grabert H. and M. H. Devoret, (1992) Single Charge Tunneling: Coulomb Blockade Phenomena in Nanostructures (NATO Science Series: B), Plenum, New York

[24] Brus L. E. (1984), Electron-electron and electron-hole interactions in small semiconductor crystallites: The size dependence of the lowest excited electronic state. *J. Chem. Phys.*, **80**: 4403 – 4407

[25] Banin U., Y. W. Cao, D. Katz, and O. Millo, (1999), Identification of atomic-like electronic states in indium arsenide nanocrystal quantum dots, *Nature*, **400**: 542 – 544

[26] Wang B., H. Q. Wang, H. X. Li, C. G. Zeng, J. G. Hou, and X. D. Xiao, (2000), Tunable single-electron tunneling behavior of ligand-stabilized gold particles on self-assembled monolayers, *Phys. Rev.*, B **63**: 035403-1 – 035403-7

[27] Wang B., K. D. Wang, W. Lu, J. L. Yang, J. G. Hou, (2004), Size-dependent tunneling differential conductance spectra of crystalline Pd nanoparticles, *Phys. Rev.*, B **70**: 205411-1 – 205411-6

[28] Hou J. G., B. Wang, J. L. Yang, K. D. Wang, W. Lu, Z. Y. Li, H. Q. Wang, D. M. Chen, and Q. S. Zhu, (2003), Disorder and Suppression of Quantum Confinement Effects in Pd Nanoparticles, *Phys. Rev. Lett.*, **90**: 246803-1 – 246803-4

[29] Büttiker M., (1993), Capacitance, admittance, and rectification properties of small conductors, *J. Phys. Condens. Matter*, **5**: 9361 – 9378

[30] Hou J. G., B. Wang, J. L. Yang, X. R. Wang, H. Q. Wang, Q. S. Zhu, and X. D. Xiao (2001), Nonclassical Behavior in the Capacitance of a Nanojunction, *Phys. Rev. Lett.*, **86**: 5321 – 5324

[31] Wang B., X. D. Xiao, X. X. Huang, P. Sheng, and J. G. Hou, (2000), Single-electron tunneling study of two-dimensional gold clusters, *Appl. Phys. Lett.*, **77**: 1179 – 1181

[32] Park H., J. Park, A. K. L. Lim, E. H. Anderson, A. P. Alivisatos, and P. L. McEuen, (2000), Nanomechanical oscillations in a single-C_{60} transistor, *Nature*, **407**: 57 – 60

[33] Li B., C. G. Zeng, J. Zhao, J. L. Yang, J. G. Hou, and Q. S. Zhu, (2006), Single-electron tunneling spectroscopy of single C_{60} in double-barrier tunnel junction, *J. Chem. Phys.*, **124**: 064709-1 – 064709-11

[34] Aviram A., M. A. Ratner, (1974), Molecular Rectifiers, *Chem. Phys. Lett.*, **29**: 277 – 283

[35] Metzger R. M., B. Chen, U. Höpfner, M. V. Lakshmikantham, D. Vuillaume, T. Kawai, X. Wu, H. Tachibana, T. V. Hughes, H. Sakurai, et al., (1997), Unimolecular Electrical

Rectification in Hexadecylquinolinium Tricyanoquinodimethanide, *J. Am. Chem. Soc.*, **119**:10455 – 10466

[36] Wang B., Y. S. Zhou, X. L. Ding, K. D. Wang, X. P. Wang, J. L. Yang, and J. G. Hou, (2006), Conduction Mechanism of Aviram-Ratner Rectifiers with Single Pyridine-σ-C_{60} Oligomers, *J. Phys. Chem., B* **110**:24505 – 24512

[37] Zhao J., C. Zeng, X. Cheng, K. Wang, G. Wang, J. Yang, J. G. Hou, and Q. Zhu, (2005), Single $C_{59}N$ molecule as a Rectifier, *Phys. Rev. Lett.*, **95**: 045502-1 – 045502-4

[38] Tsu R. and L. Esaki, (1973), Tunneling in a finite superlattice, *Appl. Phys. Lett.*, **22**: 562 – 564

[39] Soller T. C. L. G., W. D. Goodhue, P. E. Tannenwald, C. D. Parker, and D. D. Peck, (1983), Resonant tunneling through quantum wells at frequencies up to 2.5 THz, *Appl. Phys. Lett.*, **43**: 588 – 590

[40] Chen J., M. A. Reed, A. M. Rawlett, J. M. Tour, (1999), Large On-Off Ratios and Negative Differential Resistance in a Molecular Electronic Device, *Science*, **286**: 1550 – 1552

[41] Lang N. D., (1986), Spectroscopy of single atoms in the scanning tunneling microscope, *Phys. Rev.*, B **34**: 5947 – 5976

[42] Lang N. D., (1997), Negative differential resistance at atomic contacts, *Phys. Rev.*, B **55**: 9364 – 9366

[43] Zeng C. G., H. Q. Wang, B. Wang, J. l. Yang, and J. G. Hou, (2000), Negative differential-resistance device involving two C_{60} molecules, *Appl. Phys. Lett.*, **77**: 3595 – 3597

[44] Wang B., K. D. Wang, W. Lu, H. Q. Wang, Z. Y. Li, J. L. Yang, and J. G. Hou, (2003), Effects of discrete energy levels on single-electron tunneling in coupled metal particles, *Appl. Phys. Lett.*, **82**: 3767 – 3769

[45] Chen L., Z. P. Hu, A. D. Zhao, B. Wang, Y. Luo, J. L. Yang, and J. G. Hou (2007), Mechanism for negative differential resistance in molecular electronic devices: local orbital symmetry matching, *Phys. Rev. Lett.*, **99**: 146803-1 – 146803-4

[46] Hewson A. C., (1993), The Kondo Problem to Heavy Fermions, Cambridge Univ. Press, Cambridge

[47] Kondo J., (1964), Resistance minimum in dilute magnetic alloys, *Prog. Theor. Phys.*, **32**: 37 – 49

[48] Glazman L. I. and M. E. Raikh, (1988), Resonant Kondo transparency of a barrier with quasilocal impurity states, *JETP Lett.*, **47**: 452 – 455

[49] Ng T. K. and P. A. Lee, (1988), On-site Coulomb repulsion and resonant tunneling, *Phys. Rev. Lett.*, **61**: 1768 – 1771

[50] Goldhaber-Gordon D., H. Shtrikman, D. Mahalu, D. Abusch-Magder, U. Meirav, and M. A. Kastner, (1998), Kondo effect in a single-electron transistor, *Nature*, **391**: 156 – 159

[51] Li J., W. D. Schneider, R. Berndt, and B. Delley, (1998), Kondo Scattering Observed at a Single Magnetic Impurity, *Phys. Rev. Lett.*, **80**: 2893 – 2896

[52] Madhavan V., W. Chen, T. Jamneala, M. F. Crommie, and N. S. Wingreen, (1998), Tunneling into a Single Magnetic Atom: Spectroscopic Evidence of the Kondo Resonance, *Science*, **280**: 567 – 569

[53] Jamneala T., V. Madhavan, W. Chen, and M. F. Crommie, (2000), Scanning tunneling

spectroscopy of transition-metal impurities at the surface of gold, *Phys. Rev.*, *B* **61**: 9990 – 9993

[54] Knorr N., M. A. Schneider, L. Diekhöner, P. Wahl, and K. Kern, (2002), Kondo Effect of Single Co Adatoms on Cu Surfaces, *Phys. Rev. Lett.*, **88**: 096804-1 – 096804-4

[55] Park J., A. N. Pasupathy, J. I. Goldsmith, C. Chang, Y. Yaish, J. R. Petta, M. Rinkoski, J. P. Sethna, H. D. Abruña, P. L. McEuen, and D. C. Ralph, (2002), Coulomb blockade and the Kondo effect in single-atom transistors, *Nature*, **417**: 722 – 725

[56] Liang Wenjie, M. P. Shores, M. Bockrath, J. R. Long, and H. K. Park, (2002), Kondo resonance in a single-molecule transistor, *Nature*, **417**: 725 – 729

[57] Zhao A. D., Q. X. Li, L. Chen, H. J. Xiang, W. H. Wang, S. Pan, B. Wang, X. D. Xiao, J. L. Yang, J. G. Hou, et al., (2005), Controlling the Kondo Effect of an Adsorbed Magnetic Ion Through Its Chemical Bonding, *Science*, **309**:1542 – 1544

[58] Jaklevic R. C. and J. Lambe, (1966), Molecular Vibration Spectra by Electron Tunneling, *Phys. Rev. Lett.*, **17**: 1139 – 1140

[59] Lambe J. and R. C. Jaklevic, (1968), Molecular Vibration Spectra by Inelastic Electron Tunneling, *Phys. Rev.*, **165**: 821 – 832

[60] Binnig G., N. Garcia, and H. Rohrer (1985), Conductivity sensitivity of inelastic scanning tunneling microscopy, *Phys. Rev.*, B **32**: 1336 – 1338

[61] Stipe B. C., M. A. Rezaei, and W. Ho, (1998), Single-Molecule Vibrational Spectroscopy and Microscopy, *Science*, **280**: 1732 – 1735

[62] Heinrich A. J., J. A. Gupta, C. P. Lutz, D. M. Eigler, (2004), Single-Atom Spin-Flip Spectroscopy, *Science*, **306**: 466 – 469

Microsystem

6 Introduction to MEMS

Yu-Chong Tai

Departments of Electrical Engineering and Bioengineering, California Institute of Technology Pasadena, California 91125, USA
E-mail: yctai@its.caltech.edu

Abstract The first research on MEMS can be traced all the way back to the 50's[1]. In the 80's, there was a burst of MEMS using semiconductor materials. In the 90's, MEMS was formally an emerging technology. Today, MEMS has grown to be a big field with hectic international competition on many commercial applications. Without doubt, MEMS is already ubiquitous, but various new MEMS devices are continuing to show up. There is no end in sight as we continue to see MEMS branch into new fields and applications. At the same time, though, there is still much to do with both science and technology issues because of its 'multidisciplinary' and 'system' nature. MEMS is becoming more exciting than ever considering its bright long-term prospects going into BioMEMS and NEMS. There is no doubt that MEMS will be a key factor for bridging our world into nanotcchnology. The best day for MEMS is yet to come with a continuous drive to make our life smaller, cheaper, and better.

Keywords Micro-electro-mechanical systems, microsystems, MEMS technologies, sensors and actuators

6.1 What is MEMS

MEMS is the acronym for micro eletcro mechanical system. This acronym was first used in the late 80's in USA, but the exercise of MEMS technologies can be traced all the way back to the 50's[1]. It is worth noting that MEMS is not the only name used to represent the field. Today, people continue to use names such as microsystems (MS), microdynamics, micromachines, microrobots, etc. for MEMS. From the technological point of view, these names are basically the same, and researchers have no problems in going to the same conferences or meetings to share knowledge with each others.

There's no doubt that for the last twenty years or so, the MEMS field has grown to be a big, international, high-tech field. Although not yet conclusive, a general consensus does exist (as in Fig. 6.1) that we can define MEMS to be a functional unit that contains electrical and/or mechanical 'components' with characteristic sizes ranging from 100 nm to 1 mm. Devices ranging from 1 – 100 nm (sometimes this upper bound may be 30 nm or 300 nm) are officially included in 'nanotechnology' field according to many US national funding agencies such as NSF, NIH and DARPA. Devices made of components larger than 1 mm can be categorized into macro or meso domain. In other words, a device is a MEMS device as long as at least one component in the device has a characteristic size in the 0.1 – 1,000 μm range in either of the *x*, *y* or *z* dimension. Of course, not everyone completely agrees, and, for example, some people simply limit the overall size of a MEMS device to be less than 1 cm^3. The important thing, however, is that MEMS devices, when compared to conventional devices, should have one or more of the following distinct features of miniaturization: multiple components, complex functions, system integration, and the ability of mass production. In other words, miniaturization or smaller size is not the only emphasis; performance and quantity are also important. One should not miniaturize just for the sake of miniaturization. MEMS devices are expected to be smaller, cheaper, and better.

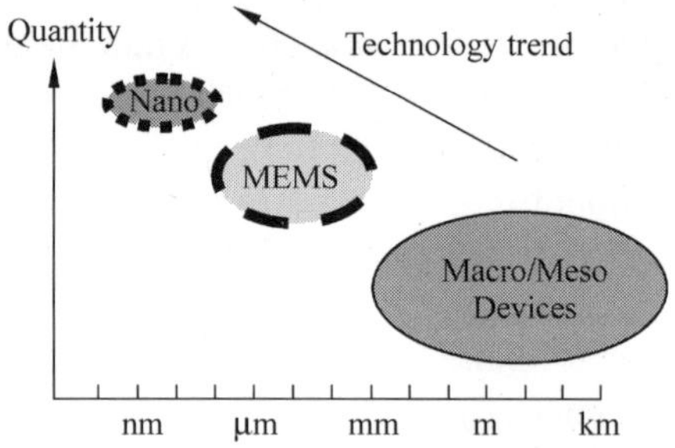

Figure 6.1 The size ranges for various devices and the technology trend (see color figure at the end of this book)

Lastly, one can understand from Fig. 6.1 that if nanotechnology indeed will be the technology of the future, MEMS then is the technology for today and the near future. As evidence, the name of nano electro mechanical system (NEMS) is getting more popular nowadays to represent devices of MEMS nature but in the nano domain. There's no doubt that MEMS plays an extremely important role in bridging macro-world to nanoworld. The maturity of MEMS technology may prove to be indispensable for nanotechnology. It is believed that combining MEMS technology and nanotechnology will give us a brighter future than nanotechnology alone will.

6.2 MEMS Technology

Obviously, the great interest is to build useful MEMS devices. Making devices, however, requires technology. Although there are a lot of important MEMS science issues as well, a major portion of the past R&D effort has been on the development of MEMS technology. In addition, knowing MEMS technology helps understanding the MEMS history. Therefore, we'll discuss MEMS technology here.

6.2.1 Strong Ties to Semiconductor Technology

The core MEMS technology is still based largely on the semiconductor industry. As the interest in MEMS commercialization is growing, the competition in development of MEMS technology is also on. The materials and techniques used in MEMS technology are constantly expanding. Some processes are essentially identical to their semiconductor industry analogs; however, other processes have been adapted to suit specific needs. As time goes on, the underlying focus of a semiconductor process *v.* a MEMS process can be drastically different to the extent that frequently it is very difficult to integrate both electronics and MEMS on the same piece of real estate. Microfabricated semiconductor devices are contained mainly within the top few microns of the substrate material. MEMS devices may require the entire substrate thickness, utilize both sides of the substrate, or even require bonding multiple substrates together. Over the years, the spectrum of processes considered to be part of the MEMS technology has expanded greatly. Traditional techniques are still very popular, but are now equipped by a host of newer ones.

6.2.2 Fundamental MEMS Techniques

Although MEMS has its roots in semiconductor (i.e., mainly silicon) technology, alternative substrates such as metal, glass/quartz, ceramics, plastic, and silicone rubber are also gaining in popularity. Driving factors for this change are the desire to move towards producing devices that are cheaper, biocompatible and easier to fabricate from both the process standpoint and when considering the required infrastructure to do so. Even so, most devices are still fabricated in silicon because of its availability and well-known material properties[2]. Silicon-based devices are also attractive in that there is a possibility of integrating silicon electronics next to MEMS devices on the same substrate.

The MEMS toolbox consists of a set of processes that is based in silicon microfabrication techniques. The key process steps include silicon planar technology, bulk micromachining, surface micromachining, LIGA, wafer bonding, and other special techniques. A majority of devices are still fabricated using some combination of these techniques. Silicon planar technology is the base for silicon semiconductor industry and its information is largely available[3, 4], so it is beyond the scope of this paper. Also because detailed 'MEMS Fabrication' will be discussed in this book, only a very brief description of the MEMS technologies is given here as an introduction.

6.2.2.1 Bulk Micromachining

Bulk micromachining uses wet (e.g., chemicals and solvents) or dry (e.g., plasma and gas) to selectively etch a substrate, typically with the help of masking layers, to form 3D micromechanical structures. In other words, it is defined as the fabrication of 3D mechanical structures from a substrate. Although there are many choices of substrate material and methods of material removal, historically, single-crystalline silicon has been used as the major substrate material, which usually is selectively removed by chemical etching, either isotropically or anisotropically, depending on the selection of etching chemicals[2,5].

Mixtures with different ratios of hydrofluoric acid, nitric acid, and acetic acid (HNA) have been the most common aqueous chemicals for silicon isotropic etching[2, 6–8], while xenon difluoride (XeF_2)[9] and bromine trifluoride (BrF_3)[10] have been used for silicon isotropic dry etching. Isotropic bulk etching is illustrated in Fig. 6.2(a). On the other hand, aqueous solutions, such as potassium hydroxide (KOH)[11–14], ethylene diamine pyrocatechol (EDP)[15, 16], tetramethylammonium hydroxide (TMAH)[17, 18], and ammonium hydroxide (NH_4OH)[19], have been employed for anisotropic silicon etching. Interestingly, the etching anisotropy exhibited in these chemical-etching processes is due to different chemical reaction rates of certain crystal planes of silicon. The etching rates are much faster for silicon in the $\langle 100 \rangle$ and $\langle 110 \rangle$ silicon crystallographic directions than in the $\langle 111 \rangle$ direction. This allows mechanical components to be designed as microstructures naturally bounded by $\langle 111 \rangle$ crystalline planes as illustrated in Figs. 6.2(b) and (c). Moreover, the etching rate can be decreased by heavily doping boron into silicon[14, 20] as well as electrochemically biasing a silicon p-n junction[21]. This adds an additional way of etching control besides the concentration and temperature of the etching solution. Anisotropic etching has been applied to fabricate many MEMS devices and structures such as pressure sensors, ink-jet nozzles, accelerometers, neural probes and wells, microgimbals and suspension for hard disk drives, flow sensors, fluidic filters and mixers, micro pumps, and air-jet nozzles, etc.

In addition to chemical etching, plasma-enhanced etching such as plasma etching[22], reactive ion etching (RIE)[23], and deep reactive ion etching (DRIE), illustrated in Fig. 6.2(d)[24, 25], have also been widely applied to bulk silicon etching. It should be pointed out that many other techniques like silicon fusion bonding[26], silicon-to-glass anodic bonding[27], electrode discharge machining (EDM)[28, 29], and laser machining[30], are often used with silicon bulk micromachining as well.

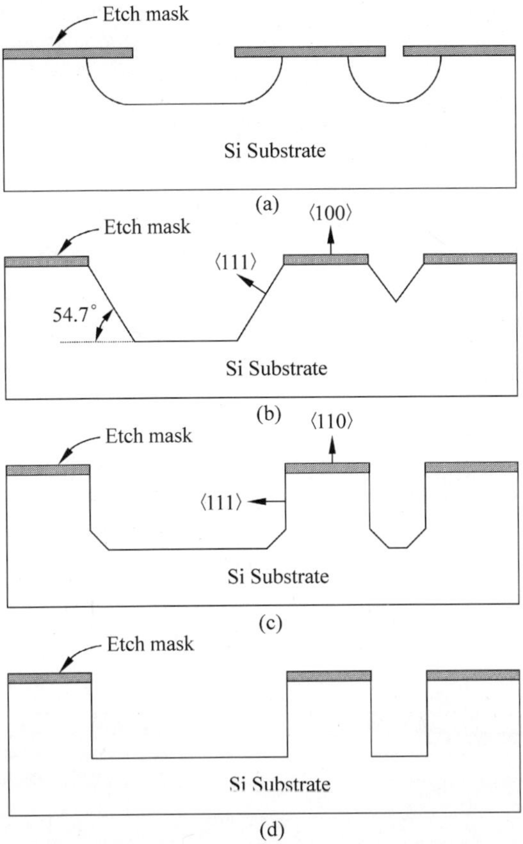

Figure 6.2 Bulk micromachining technology: (a) isotropic etching, (b) silicon anisotropic etching on ⟨100⟩ surface, (c) silicon anisotropic etching on ⟨110⟩ surface, (d) deep reactive ion etching (DRIE)

6.2.2.2 Surface Micromachining

Surface micromachining is the carving of layers put down sequentially on the substrate by using selective etching of sacrificial thin films to form free-standing or even completely released thin-film microstructures[31]. Comparatively, surface micromachining emphasizes the fabrication of microstructures on top of the substrate surface. The substrate only provides mechanical support, and can be made up of silicon, quartz, glass, and even metal. In surface micromachining, a series of thin film depositions and patterning steps are performed to form microstructures using various standard methods similar to IC fabrication.

As illustrated in Fig. 6.3, selective etching is often performed to remove certain sacrificial layers and free other structural layers by taking advantage of high etching selectivity of the sacrificial layers and structural layers. The end products will be free-standing microstructures, with sizes determined by the film patterning technique. In a way, the concept of surface micromachining is extremely simple.

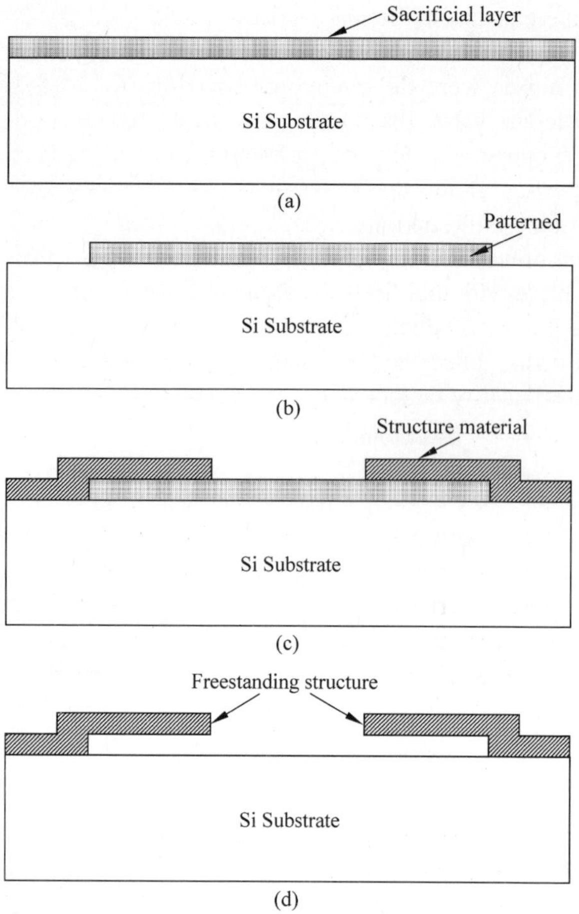

Figure 6.3 The major processing steps of surface micromachining technology: (a) sacrificial layer deposition, (b) sacrificial layer patterning, (c) structural material deposition and patterning, (d) sacrificial layer etching

That is, one only needs to have the combination of an inert substrate, structural material, sacrificial material, and a selective etching method (for the sacrificial material). The reality of practicing surface micromachining, however, is by no means trivial. The main issues reside in the control of the mechanical properties (such as stress and rigidity) of the free-standing materials and the prevention of their degradation. Nevertheless, there's no lack of effort to do surface micromachining. Technologically, it is of no surprise that the first surface micromachining used metals as the main materials because of their easy availability[1]. Various metals can also be used together with photoresists[32]. It was not until the 80's that the surface micromachining technique using semiconductor thin films was largely explored. For example, if hydrofluoric (HF) acid was chosen as the selective etchant, oxides like silicon dioxide and phosphor silicate glass (PSG) were popular sacrificial materials, and polycrystalline silicon and low stress silicon nitride were the commonly used structural materials[33-39]. Other sacrificial materials were also explored, such as, aluminum[40], polysilicon[41], polymer[42-44], copper[45], etc. The main limitations of surface micromachining are the thicknesses of the deposited films and their mechanical quality. Time considerations and build up of internal stresses typically limit deposited films to several microns of thickness. Large inertial masses and high out-of-plane stiffness are difficult to achieve with thin films. Reduction of parasitic coupling, both electrical and magnetic, between structures requires an increase in the overall footprint of the device. Finally, since the deposited films are typically polycrystalline, the high mechanical quality factors achieved in bulk single-crystal silicon beams are not matched in surface micromachined structures.

6.2.2.3 LIGA

LIGA was initially developed in 1982 for the fabrication of micron-sized separation nozzles for nuclear power production applications in Germany[46]. The name is actually derived from the German acronym for 'X-ray lithographie galvanoformung abformung', which means X-ray lithography, electrodeposition, and molding. In a typical LIGA process, a thick X-ray resist is exposed and used as a mold for electroplating. This newly formed metal mold can then be used to injection mold plastic parts or more plastic molds. High-aspect-ratio and smooth-wall structures ranging from microns to millimeters in height with high resolution (< 0.2 μm) can be formed in this manner. An assortment of devices such as accelerometers[47], optical couplings[48], and microfluidic devices[49] have been fabricated using LIGA. While the capability of producing three-dimensional structures using LIGA is attractive, LIGA is a costly process due to the synchrotron source required for X-ray exposure and X-ray masks. Thus, less expensive means of producing the same results are being investigated.

6.2.2.4 Wafer Bonding

Wafer bonding is a convenient means of permanently joining wafers together and circumventing the wafer thickness limitation on devices. It also gives a means to create multi-level devices by combining wafers processed using bulk or surface micromachining or even adding electronics. Other applications of wafer bonding are device packaging and hermetic sealing. Historically, glass-to-metal bonding had been investigated as early as 1969[50]. Today, the three most common forms of bonding are fusion bonding (e.g., silicon-to-silicon)[26, 51, 52], anodic bonding (e.g., silicon-to-glass)[27, 53-55], and eutectic bonding (e.g., silicon-to-gold)[56]. When considering wafer bonding, one should thoroughly understand the bonding requirements before choosing the bonding method in terms of temperatures, pressures, strengths, electric fields, hermeticity, etc.

6.2.2.5 Other MEMS Technologies

Adding to the wealth of variety in the MEMS processing toolbox also include a number of non-conventional micromachining techniques that have been developed over the years. The desire to create truly three-dimensional structures has led to the development of micro EDM[28, 29, 57, 58], laser micromachining[30, 59], and 3D stereolithography[60, 61]. With the ever-increasing demand for biocompatible devices, plastics are becoming more popular as techniques to process them are more readily available. Injection molding[62, 63] and compression molding/hot embossing[64, 65] can be used to fabricate inexpensive plastic parts quickly and in high volume. Another inexpensive and fast process is the 'soft lithography'[66, 67] of compliant silicone rubber structures. This technique has become particularly popular in the microfluidics field. As always, man looks back to nature for inspiration; self assembly[68] hopes to bring micromachining to a new level by taking advantage of naturally occurring biological and chemical processes to assemble useful devices and structures.

6.3 A Brief History of MEMS

The time is right to learn about MEMS history after knowing MEMS technologies. First of all, the beginning of MEMS still has not being ascertained. For example, some believe that MEMS started in the 80's because temporally earlier events happened quite independently, and the establishment of the MEMS field was really based on the works in the 80's. However, there's no doubt that there were many technological developments that should not be ignored. The purpose of this paper is to provide a brief but complete view of MEMS. Accordingly, the timeline shown in Fig. 6.4 spans more than 5 decades and the major milestones include historical events, paper publications, technological disclosures, device announcement and formal creation of MEMS subfields.

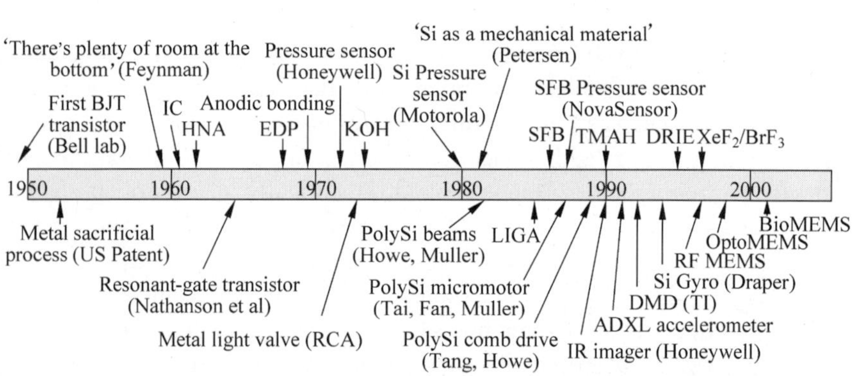

Figure 6.4 The timeline of the major events in MEMS history

6.3.1 The Beginning of Electronic Miniaturization

Historically, MEMS technologies mainly originated from semiconductor technology; so we can start with the birth of semiconductor device. In 1947, Bell Labs researchers (i.e., Shockley, Bardeen and Brattain) made an amazing invention: the point-contact bipolar junction transistor. Since then, tremendous investment on semiconductor technologies produced better transistors, integrated circuits, microprocessors, CPU's, etc. In other words, over the course of the intervening 50 years, the 'electronic miniaturization' has made possible the current Information Age. Today, transistors have been refined and improved to the point where the size of a single device can be expressed as easily in atomic radii as in conventional metric units. A complex, yet straightforward system of laying down layer upon layer of material, each patterned into specific shapes for a certain function is now utilized by hundreds of foundries that produce numerous components every year. The resulting silicon infrastructure has made possible thousands of new enterprises and areas of scientific research, which also includes the MEMS technology.

6.3.2 The Beginning of Mechanical Miniaturization

Following the success of electronic miniaturization naturally was the mechanical miniaturization. The earliest (surface) micromachining work that the author can trace is from a US patent (No. 2,749,598) filed as early as 1952[1]. As in Fig. 6.5, it showed a method of making free-standing electrostatic shutters using a sacrificial etching of metals. All techniques described were microfabrication processes and the finished shutter devices were clearly MEMS.

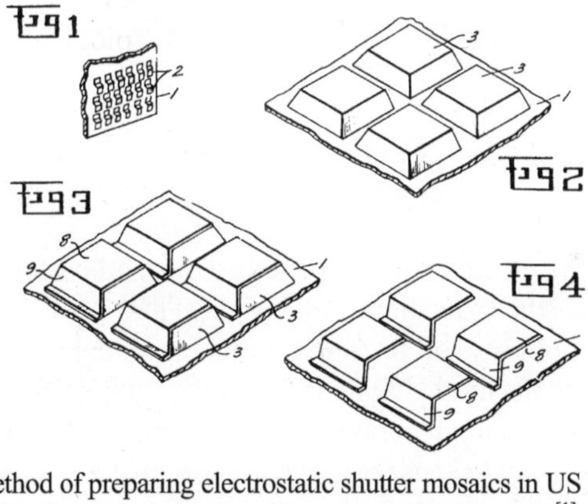

Figure 6.5 Method of preparing electrostatic shutter mosaics in US Patent 2,749,598. This patent was filed on Feb. 1, 1952 and issued on June 12, 1956[1]

This 1956 patent could arguably be an important start of MEMS, but unfortunately it apparently did not raise much interest from the public. Instead, the most notable historical events relating to mechanical miniaturization was perhaps when Richard Feynman challenged the scientific community to explore the realm down to atomic regime in 1959[69]. Foreseeing the miniaturization trend and need arising in semiconductor devices, Richard Feynman (1918 – 1988 Physicist, 1965 Nobelist) proposed that scientists and engineers should strive for a similar reduction in the size of mechanical components. He first presented his ideas in a speech to the American Physics Society, 'There's plenty of room at the bottom.' Feynman pointed out the void in research done on 'manipulating and controlling things on a small scale.' He explained to scientists that this field 'might tell us much of great interest about the strange phenomena that occur in complex situations… a lot of new things that would happen that represent completely new opportunities for design' and that 'it would have an enormous number of technical applications.' In order to properly explore this field and be able to construct small machines, it would be necessary to design a new set of infinitesimal machines that not only require scaling but also redesign. Ironically, modern equipment used to construct semiconductor and MEMS devices is by no means infinitesimal but there is hope in self-assembly and nanotechnology that these tiny machines can be realized. He then issued a challenge to anyone willing to take on the task. He offered a prize of $1,000 to 'the first guy who can take the information on the page of a book and put it on an area 1/25,000 smaller in linear scale in such manner that it can be read by an electron microscope' and a second $1,000 to 'the first guy who makes an operating electric motor—a rotating electric motor which can be controlled from the outside and, not counting the lead-in wires, is only 1/64 inch cube.' With this challenge, Feynman hoped to spur a new area of research and the development of new fabrication technologies. A year after the gauntlet was thrown down, William McLellan claimed the prize for the motor using conventional machining techniques. While technically the winner, Mr McLellan readily admits that his approach was not necessarily in the spirit of the contest. It wasn't until several decades later, in 1988, that an electric micro motor fabricated with truly new processing technology was finally realized[70, 71]. During the intervening time, the field of micromachining was born, stagnated, and then given new life.

After Feynman's challenge, a group of scientists published a paper on a device they called a 'resonant gate transistor'[32] in 1967. As shown in Fig. 6.6, this transistor had a free-standing gold beam as a gate, an air gap as the dielectric, and a standard source/drain/channel structure from the substrate. It was made by using nickel as the sacrificial material. This novel structure aimed to reproduce the functionality of its semiconductor counterpart in a mechanical, rather than electronic fashion. More importantly, the team that conceived this device realized that the same technology used to integrated circuits could be used to fabricate very small-scale sensors and actuators. Like their electronic brethren, micromachined devices attracted limited attention in their initial years and save for a few publications, went largely unnoticed. Recent developments and substantial commercial investment has shown that the technology was simply ahead of its time.

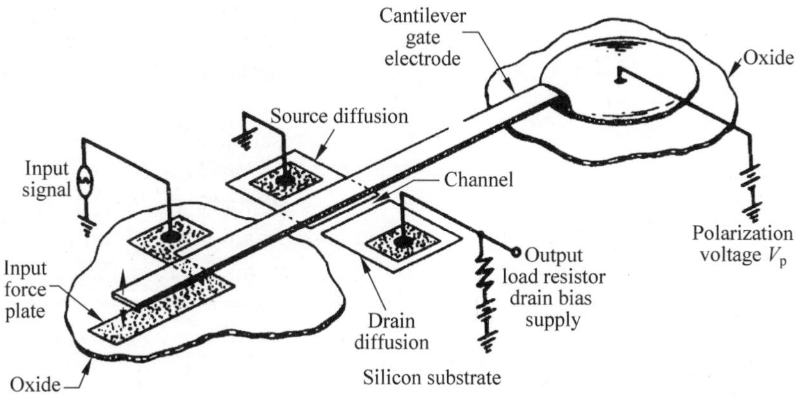

Figure 6.6 The first resonant-gate transistor made by surface micromachining using metals

During the 60's and 70's, however, many silicon etching (i.e., bulk micromachining) technologies including HNA, EDP and hydroxide-based etchants were developed. Along the way, many MEMS devices (per today's standard) such as the optical imager, metal light valve (i.e., earlier version of digital mirror), field-emission array, RF switches, low-parasitics discrete components, etc, were explored[72]. Moreover, probably the most quoted paper in MEMS, 'Silicon as a mechanical material,' was published in 1982[2] with a thorough review of silicon bulk micromachining and MEMS devices such as inkjet nozzle, light modulators, gas chromatography device, chip-sized optical bench, thermal print head, etc. Interestingly, however, many people believe that the MEMS effort in this period was actually sustained by the success of miniature silicon pressure sensors[73].

Then, a resurgence of interest in MEMS devices arose in the 80's that has since led to a burgeoning new field of research and industrial development. Beginning primarily in universities, including UC Berkeley and MIT, MEMS researchers explored new ways of using semiconductor materials for micromechanical devices (such as free-standing beams, joints, motors and comb drives) and the new crop of devices focused on the study of basic science and fundamental operation of microscopic machines. The common thread amongst all of these works was the use of 'surface micromachining' based on microelectronic fabrication processes to produce the various devices. For example, Figure 6.7 shows various 'first' polysilicon MEMS devices that were demonstrated in the 80's including beams[74], sliders[38], gears, micro springs, comb drives[36], and micro motors[71].

It was this time around late 80's, the name MEMS was first officially used in USA. In the 90's, MEMS programs in most major universities and large companies explored many interesting micro sensors and actuators that could be fabricated alongside with integrated circuits. Among all, ink jet printer heads, integrated accelerometers and digital mirrors were the most known ones.

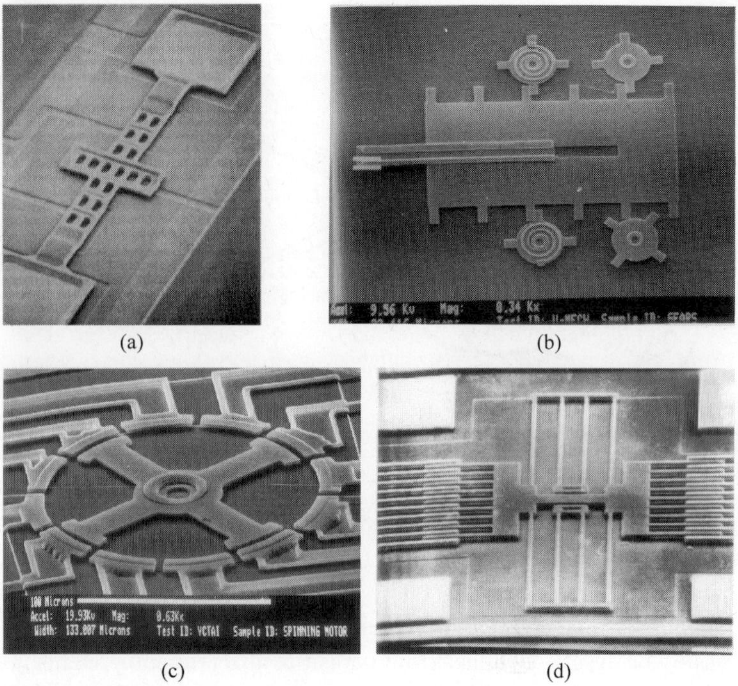

Figure 6.7 Various first surface-micromachined polysilicon MEMS devices: (a) a polysilicon clamp-clamp beam gas sensor[74], (b) a slider-gear-spring micromechanical combination[38], (c) an electrostatic micro motor[71], (d) a linear comb-drive resonator[36]

The key to these MEMS products is their minimal size, weight, and low end-user complexity. Additionally, MEMS technology promises to deliver these devices at very low cost, with very high reliability, and with in-package 'intelligence.' Today, the MEMS field is bigger than ever, and is still growing with unprecedented numbers of MEMS journals and conferences/meetings. It is interesting to point out that the MEMS field has also branched into many sub-fields like optical MEMS, RF MEMS, BioMEMS, etc., and each of these sub-fields has developed its own community. No doubt, MEMS is already ubiquitous in all fields of science and engineering, and the future is even brighter considering its unlimited potential going into nanodomain for the 21st century.

6.3.3 MEMS Applications and Prospects

The economist Norman Poire first pointed out that on average, it takes about 28 years for a new technology to gain wide acceptance, which can then fuel a rapid growth lasting an additional 56 years[75]. If we accept that MEMS was started in the mid-80's, we then are still in the early stage but ready to gain wide acceptance as shown in Fig. 6.8.

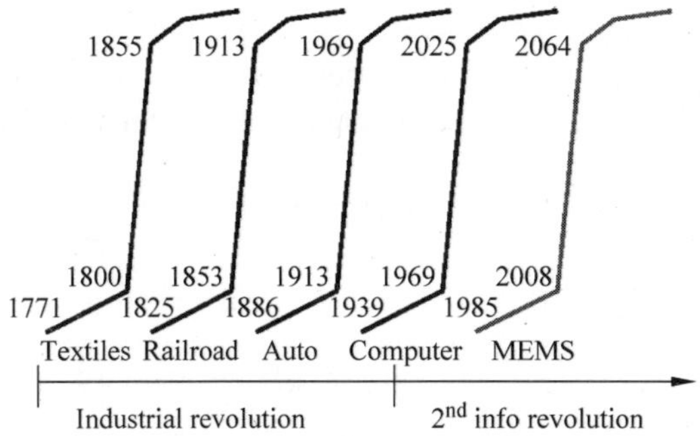

Figure 6.8 Historical technology revolutions and evolutions

In fact, it is very true that we are seeing the impact of MEMS on the society in which we live. MEMS products have a growing commercial presence. Undoubtedly, the pressure sensor and airbag-deployment accelerometers in our cars; the ink jet heads in our printers; and the digital mirror displays in the digital light processing (DLP) in our movie theaters are the most popular and prevalent products to date. With the increasing interest in national security, BioMEMS systems are being explored as a means to warn us of dangerous biological agents. They are also being heavily explored in their ability to aid in chemical and biological assays. MEMS are miniaturized, less expensive versions of their macro world analogs that perform as well as or better. This technology has matured to a point where the transition from pure research to commercial products can be made.

Consistently, many have forecasted a continuous, rapid growing, and profitable MEMS market with the primary areas of interest being data storage, displays, automotive applications, telecommunications, environmental monitoring, and medical/biochemical applications. According to the MEMS Industry Group[76], we should already have 5 MEMS devices per person today in the US, while the number was only 1.6 in 2003. Also, in 2000, the MEMS industry was estimated to be worth \$2 – \$5 billion only and is around \$10 billion today. We continue to see strong development with at least more than 20% growth per year.

6.4 Future of MEMS

6.4.1 'Multidiscipline' and 'System' as the Key Words

It is increasingly important that as the MEMS progresses, it is obvious that MEMS applications are moving towards system-level functions. By nature, MEMS is a multidisciplinary field; therefore, MEMS has to fuse various different fields to work properly. Technically, MEMS likely has to deal with complex issues such as originated from solids, fluids, electronics, control, reliability, self calibration, etc.

In other words, disciplines that are constantly needed include electrical engineering, mechanical engineering, material sciences, physics, optics, chemistry, biology, and so on. Moreover, there are numerous fundamental science and technology issues that need to be studied. To name a few, they can include solid mechanics (e.g., material properties, elastic constants, intrinsic and extrinsic stresses), fluid mechanics[77] (e.g., Knudsen effect, damping, fluid-wall interaction, and viscosity), heat transfer (e.g., conduction, convection, and quantum transport), tribology (e.g., fatigue, fracture, wear, and lubrication), surface chemistry (e.g., surface reliability, molecular coating, and self-assembly coating), surface forces (e.g., surface tension and surface charges), etc. These issues are often intertwined with each other in both the micro and nanodomains.

With the multidisciplinary and complex issues in mind, one should not underestimate the time and effort needed to develop working MEMS systems[73]. This is also evident from existing successful commercial MEMS devices. For example, although it took TI about 10 years to develop its version, the famous digital mirror display concept actually has a >40 years of history. Another example is the inkjet MEMS, which took about 20 years of development by Xerox and HP. In addition, there are devices like the MEMS relays still facing difficult reliability issues (e.g., reliability) that prevent them from being practical. It is important for MEMS researchers to realize both the pros and cons before miniaturization. Other challenges may originate from commercial profitability and sustainability. MEMS engineers also have to realize the economic values of their MEMS devices. Some MEMS devices may not have a big enough market size to make them practical. In many cases, MEMS product sustainability would require high unit price (>$100/unit) for low-volume (<10,000 units/year) production, while better sustainability can have lower price (<$10/unit) for large volume (>1 M units/year) production. Obviously, the broad market demand continues to be an important economic factor for successful MEMS development.

6.4.2 Promising Future Directions

MEMS is still one of few shining fields in the engineering world as the international competition in MEMS continues. The question is, 'What are the promising directions for MEMS?' The following may provide some good starts and they include Optical MEMS (e.g., display, optical fiber communication, and optical-bench-on-a-chip), RF MEMS (e.g., filters, capacitors, inductors, switches, and tunables), Inertial MEMS (e.g., accelerometers, gyroscopes, and navigational devices), Data-storage MEMS (e.g., hard-drive motor and SPM memory), Microfluidicis and Bio MEMS (e.g., μTAS, drug delivery, genomics, proteomics, bio detection, and water/food safety), and Composite CAD (e.g., multi-domain simulation, and system design). The readers can find more clues from various MEMS-related conferences such as the IEEE Transducers, IEEE MEMS

Conference, IEEE NEMS Conference, and μTAS. There are also books[78-82] for valuable information. In fact, MEMS devices are already part of our daily life. For examples, there are the TI's DLP in high-definition TV, various sensors in automobiles, accelerometers in Wii and iPhone and RF-MEMS in wireless communication. More excitingly, more new devices are also coming such as gyroscopes and magnetic sensors. After all, the prediction of MEMS advancement in Fig. 6.8 will likely be a reality.

Finally, one can not ignore the natural evolution from 'M'EMS to 'N'EMS. This is partly due to the evolution in nanoelectronics as many nanotechnologies (such as nanolithography and nanomaterials) are becoming available, and partly due to performance advantages going into nanodomain (such as quantum effects and single-molecule sensor sensitivity). Again, though, the fundamental soundness and maturity of MEMS will likely be the key to transition from MEMS to NEMS.

6.5 Conclusions

MEMS has a long history of development and MEMS is already ubiquitous in our life. There still is the hectic international competition on various commercial applications and there is no end in sight as we continue to see MEMS branch into new fields and applications. But, one should not ignore the importance of many science and technology issues because of its 'multidisciplinary' and 'system' nature. Finally, MEMS is becoming more exciting than ever, considering its bright long-term prospects going into BioMEMS and NEMS. MEMS will be a key factor to bridge our world into nanotechnology. The best day for MEMS is yet to come with continuous drive to make our life smaller, cheaper and better.

Acknowledgements

The authors would like to acknowledge all the people in MEMS field who collectively made the history of MEMS.

References

[1] Method of preparing electrostatic shutter mosaics, (1956), US Patent 2,749,598

[2] Petersen K. E., (1982), "Silicon as a mechanical material," *Proceeding of the IEEE*, **5**: 420 – 457, May

[3] Wolf S., and R. N. Tauber, *Silicon Processing for the VLSI Era*, Volume 1-3, Lattice Press

[4] Chang C. Y. and S. M. Sze, (1996), "ULSI Technology," McGraw-Hill Book Co

[5] Kovacs G. T. A., N. I. Maluf, and K. E. Petersen, (1998) "Bulk Micromachining of Silicon," *Proc IEEE*, **86**(8): 1536 – 1551

[6] Robbins H. and B. Schwartz, (1959) "Chemical etching of silicon, Ⅱ. The system HF, HNO_3, $HC_2H_3O_2$," *J. Electrochem. Soc.*, **106**: 505

[7] Schwartz B. and H. Robbins, (1976), "Chemical etching of silicon, Ⅵ. Etching technology," *J. Electrochem. Soc.*, **123**: 1903

[8] Williams K. R. and R. S. Muller, (1996), "Etch rate for micromachining process," *J. Microelectromech. Syst.*, **5**(4): 256 – 269

[9] Winters H. F. and J. W. Coburn, (1979), "The etching of silicon with XeF_2 vapor," *Appl. Phys. Lett.*, **34**(1): 70 – 73

[10] Wang X. Q., X. Yang, K. Walsh, and Y.C Tai, (1997), "Gas Phase Silicon Etching with Bromine Trifluoride," *Proceedings, Transducer*, 97

[11] Price J. B., (1973), "Anisotropic etching of silicon with potassium hydroxide-water-isopropyl alcohol," in *Semiconductor Silicon*, H. R. Huff and R. R. Burgess, Eds. Princeton, NJ: Electrochemical Society, 1973: 339

[12] Bean K. E., (1978), "Anisotropic etching of silicon," *IEEE Trans. Electron Devices*, **ED-25**: 1185 – 1193

[13] Seidel H., L. Csepregi, A. Heuberger, et al., (1990), "Anisotropic etching of crystalline silicon in alkaline-solutions. 1. Orientation dependence and behavior of passivation layers," *J Electrochem Soc.*, **137**(11): 3612 – 3626

[14] Seidel H., L. Csepregi, A. Heuberger, et al., (1990), "Anisotropic etching of crystalline silicon in alkaline-solutions. 2. Influence of dopants," *J Electrochem Soc.*, **137**(11): 3626 – 3632

[15] Finne R. M. and D. L. Klein, (1967), "A water-amine-complexing agent system for etching silicon," *J Electrochem Soc.*, **114**(11): 965

[16] Moser D., (1993), "CMOS flowsensors," Doctoral dissertation, Swiss Federal Institute of Technology, Zurich, Switzerland

[17] Tabata O., R. Asahi, H. Funabash, K. Shimaoka, and S. Sugiyama, (1992), "Anisotropic etching of silicon in TMAH solutions," *Sensors and Actuators A*, **34**(1): 51 – 57

[18] Merlos A., M. Acero, M. H. Bao, J. Bausells, and J. Esteve, (1993), "TMAH/IPA anisotropic etching characteristics," *Sensors and Actuators*, **A37** – **38**: 737 – 743

[19] Schnakenberg U., W. Benecke, and B. Lochel, (1990), "NH_4OH-based etchants for silicon micromachining," *Sensors and Actuators*, **A23**(1 – 3): 1031 – 1035

[20] Raley N. F., Y. Sugiyama, and T. Van Duzer, (1984), "(100) silicon etching rate dependence on boron concentration in ethylenediamine pyrocatechol water solutions," *J Electrochem Soc.*, **131**(11): 161 – 171

[21] Jackson T. N., M. A. Tischler, and K. D. Wise, (1981), "An electrochemical p-n junction etch-stop for the formation of silicon microstructure," *IEEE Electron Device Letters*, **EDL-2**(2): 44 – 45

[22] Coburn J. W. and H. F. Winters, (1979), "Plasma etching—A discussion of mechanisms," *J. Vac. Sci. Technology.*, **16**(2): 391 – 403

[23] Schwartz G. C. and P. M. Schaible, (1979), "Reactive ion etching of silicon," *J. Vac. Sci. Technol.*, **16**(2): 410 – 413

[24] Murakami K., Y. Wakabayashi, K. Minami, and M. Esashi, (1993), "Cryogenic dry etching for high aspect ratio microstructures," in *Proc. IEEE MEMS Conf.*, Fort Lauderdale, FL., 65 – 70

[25] Klaassen E. H., K. Petersen, J. M. Noworolski, et al., (1995), "Silicon fusion bonding and deep reactive ion etching: A new technology for microstructures," *in Dig. Tech. Papers transducers'95/Eurosensors IX*, Stockholm, Sweden, June 25 – 29, **1**: 556 – 559

[26] Barth P. W., (1990), "Silicon fusion bonding for fabrication of sensors, actuators and microstructures," *Sensors and Actuators A*, **23**(1 – 3): 919 – 926

[27] Rogers T. and J. Kowal, (1995), "Selection of glass, anodic bonding conditions and material compatibility for silicon-glass capacitive sensors," *Sensors and Actuators*, A **46**(1 – 3): 113 – 120

[28] Reynaerts D., P. H. Heeren, and H. Van Brussel, (1997), "Microstructuring of silicon by electro-discharge machining (EDM)—part I: theory," *Sensors & Actuators*, A **60**(1 – 3): 212 – 218

[29] Heeren P. H., D. Reynaerts, H. Van Brussel, C. Beuret, O. Larsson, and A. Bertholds, (1997), "Microstructuring of silicon by electro-discharge machining (EDM)—part Ⅱ: applications," *Sensors & Actuators*, A **61** (1 – 3): 379 – 386

[30] Bloomish T. M. and D. J. Ehrlich, "Laser Stereo Micromachining at one-half million cubic micrometers per second, " *Solid-state Sensors and Actuators Workshop, Technical Digest*, June 13 – 16, Hilton Head, NC, 142 – 144

[31] Gabriel K., J. Jarvis, and W. Trimmer, (1988), "Small Machines, Large Opportunities: A report on the emerging field of microdynamics,"

[32] Nathanson H. C., W. E. Newell, R. A. Wickstrom, and J. R. Davis, Jr., (1967), "The Resonant Gate Transistor," *IEEE Transactions on Electron Devices*, **ED-14**(3): 117 – 133

[33] Tai Y. C. and R. S. Muller, (1987), "Lightly doped polysilicon bridge as an anemometer," *Tech. Digest, Transducers '87*, 4th Int. Conf. On Solid-state Sensors and Actuators, Tokyo, Japan, 360 – 363

[34] Chen P., R. S. Muller, T. Shiosaki, and R. M. White, (1979), "Silicon cantilever beam accelerometer utilizing a PI-FET capacitive transducer," *IEEE Trans. Electron Devices*, **ED-26**: 1857

[35] Fan L. S., Y. C. Tai, and R. S. Muller, (1988), "IC-processed electrostatic micromotor," *Technical Digest,* IEEE International Electron Device Meeting (IEDM), 666 – 669

[36] Tang W. C., T. C. H. Nguyen, and R.T. How, (1989), "Laterally driven for polysilicon resonate microstructures," *Sensor and Actuators*, **20**: 25 – 32

[37] Bustillo J. M., R. T. Howe and R. S. Muller, (1998), "Surface micromachining for microelectromechanical systems," *Proceedings of IEEE*, **86**(8): 1552 – 1574

[38] Fan L. S., Y. C. Tai, and R. S. Muller, (1988), "Integrated movable micromechanical structures for sensors and actuators," *IEEE Trans. Electron Devices*, **ED-35**: 724 – 730

[39] Liu J. Q., Y. C. Tai, J. Lee, K. C. Pong, Y. Zohar, and C. M. Ho, (1993), "In Situ Monitoring and Universal Modelling of Sacrificial PSG Etching Using Hydrofluoric Acid," *Proceedings, IEEE Micro Electro Mechanical Systems Workshop (MEMS '93)*, Fort Lauderdale, FL, 71 – 76, Feb. 7 – 10, 1993

[40] Schmidt M. A., R. T. Howe, S. D. Senturia, and J. H. Haritonidis, (1998), "Design and

Calibration of a Microfabricated Floating-Element Shear-Stress Sensor," *IEEE Transactions on Electron Devices*, **35**(6): 750 – 757

[41] Tabata O., H. Funabashi, K. Shimaoka, R. Asahi, and S. Sugiyama, (1991), "Surface micromachining using polysilicon sacrificial layer", *the Second International Symposium on Micromachine and Human Science*, 1991, Japan

[42] Frazier A. B. and M. G. Allen, (1992), "High Aspect Ratio Electroplated Microstructures Using a Photosensitive Polyimide Process," *Proceedings of IEEE MEMS 92*, February 87 – 92

[43] Storment C., D. Borkholder, V. Westerlind, J. Suh, N. Maluf, and G. Kovacs, (1994), "Dry-released process for aluminum electrostatic actuators," *Technical Digest, Solid-state Sensor and actuator Workshop*, Hilton Head Island, 1994, 95 – 98

[44] Man P., D. Jones and C. Mastrangelo, (1997), "Microfluidic Plastic Capillaries on Silicon Substrates: A new inexpensive technology for bio analysis chips," *Proceedings, IEEE MEMS Meeting*, Nagoya, Japan, 1997, 311 – 316

[45] Tsao T. R., T. Y. Hsu, and Y. C. Tai, (1996), "Copper Sacrificial Layer Technology for use in Surface Micromachining," *SCCAVS Micromachining Workshop* Ⅲ, September 1996

[46] Becker E. W., W. Ehrfeld, D. Munchmeyer, H. Betz, A. Heuberger, S. Pongratz, W. Glashauser, H. J. Michel, and V. R. Siemens, (1982), "Production of Separation Nozzle Systems for Uranium Enrichment by Combination of X-Ray Lithography and Galvanoplastics. *Naturwissenschaften*," **69**: 520 – 523

[47] Strohrmann M., P. Bley, O. Fromhein, and J. Mohr, (1994), "Acceleration Sensor with Integrated Compensation of Temperature Effects Fabricated by the LIGA Process," *Sensors and Actuators*, A **42**(1 – 3): 426 – 429

[48] Rogner A., W. Ehrfled, D. Münchmeyer, P. Bley, C. Burbaum, and J. Mohr, (1991), "LIGA-based flexible microstructures for fiber chip coupling," *Journal of Micromechanics and Microengineering*, **1**(3): 167 – 170

[49] Schomburg W. K., J. Vollmer, B. Büstgens, J. Fahrenberg, H. Hein, and W. Menz, (1994), "Microfluidic components in LIGA technique," Journal of Micromechanics and Microengineering, **4**(4): 186 – 191

[50] Wallis G. and D. I. Pomerantz, (1969), "Field Assisted Glass-Metal Sealing," *Journal of Applied Physics*, **40**(10): 3946 – 3949

[51] Harendt C., W. Appel, H. G. Graf, B. Höfflinger, and E. Penteker, (1991), "Wafer fusion bonding and its application to silicon-on-insulator fabrication," *Journal of Micromechanics and Microengineering*, **1**(3): 145 – 151

[52] Harendt C., H. G. Graf, B. Höfflinger, and E. Penteker, (1992), "Silicon fusion bonding and its characterization," *Journal of Micromechanics and Microengineering*, **2**(3): 113 – 116

[53] Hanneborg A., M. Nese, and P. Øhlckers, (1991), "Silicon-to-silicon anodic bonding with a borosilicate glass layer," *Journal of Micromechanics and Microengineering*, **1**(3): 139 – 144

[54] Cozma A. and B. Puers, (1995), "Characterization of the electrostatic bonding of silicon and Pyrex glass," *Journal of Micromechanics and Microengineering*, **5**(2): 98 – 102

[55] Obermeier E., (1995), "Anodic Wafer Bonding," *Electrochemical Society Proceedings*, **95-7**: 212 – 220

[56] Ko W. H., J. T. Suminto, and G. J. Yeh, (1985), "Bonding Techniques for Microsensors, in Micromachining and Micropackaging of Transducers," C.D. Fung, P.W. Cheung, W.H. Ko, and D.G. Fleming, Editors, Elsevier Science Publishing Company Inc. 41 – 61

[57] Masaki T., K. Kawata, and T. Masuzawa, (1990), "Micro Electro-Discharge Machining and its Applications," in MEMS '90, Napa Valley, CA, 21 – 26

[58] Takahata K., S. Aoki, and T. Sato, (1997), "Fine Surface Finishing Method for 3-Dimensional Micro Structures," *IEICE Transactions on Electronics*, **E80C**(2): 291 – 296

[59] Müllenborn M., H. Dirac, J. W. Petersen, and S. Bouwstra, (1996), "Fast three-dimensional laser micromachining of silicone for Microsystems," *Sensors and Actuators*, A **52**(1 – 3): 121 – 125

[60] Ikuta K. and K. Hirowatari, (1993), "Real Three Dimensional Micro Fabrication Using Stereo Lithography and Metal Molding," in MEMS '93, Fort Lauderdale, FL, 42 – 47

[61] Ikuta K., K. Hirowatari, and T. Ogata, (1994), "Three Dimensional Micro Integrated Fluid Systems (MIFS) Fabricated By Stereo Lithography," in MEMS '94, Oiso, Japan, 1 – 6

[62] Larsson O., O. Öhman, Å. Billman, L. Lundbladh, C. Lindell, and G. Palmskog, "Silicon Based Replication Technology of 3D-Microstructures by Conventional CD-Injection Molding Techniques," in Transducers '97, Chicago, IL, 1415 – 1418

[63] Despa M. S., K. W. Kelly, and J. R. Collier, "Injection molding of polymeric LIGA HARMs," *Microsystem Technologies*, **6**(2): 60 – 66

[64] Becker H. and U. Heim, (2000), "Hot embossing as a method for the fabrication of polymer high aspect ratio structures," *Sensors & Actuators*, **A 83**(1-3): 130 – 135

[65] Heckele M., W. Bacher, and K. D. Müller, (1998), "Hot embossing - The molding technique for plastic microstructures," *Microsystem Technologies*, **4**(3): 122 – 124

[66] Xia Y. N., and G. M. Whitesides, (1998), "Soft lithography," *Annual Review of Materials Science*, **28**: 153 – 184

[67] Qin D., Y. Xia, J. A. Rogers, R. J. Jackman, X. M. Zhao, and G. M. Whitesides, (1998), "Microfabrication, Microstructures and Microsystems," *Topics in Current Chemistry*, **194**(5369): 1 – 20

[68] Whitesides G. M., J. P. Mathias, and C. T. Seto, (1991), "Molecular Self-Assembly and Nanochemistry: A Chemical Strategy for the Synthesis of Nanostructures," *Science*, **254**: 1312 – 1319

[69] Feynman R., (1992), "There's plenty of room at the bottom," reprinted in *J. Microelectromechanical Systems*, **1**(1): 60 – 66

[70] Fan L. S., Y. C. Tai, and R. S. Muller, (1998), "IC-processed Electrostatic Micromotors," Tech. digest, IEEE International Electron Device Meeting (IEDM'88), San Francisco, CA, 666 – 669, Dec. 11 – 14, 1988

[71] Tai Y. C. and R. S. Muller, (1989), "IC-processed electrostatic synchronous micromotors," *Sensors and Actuators*, **20**: 49 – 55

[72] Nathanson H. C. and J. Guldberg, (1975), "Topologically structured thin films in semiconductor devices operation," *Physics of Thin Films*, Vol. 8, New York, Academic Press

[73] Bryzek J., K. Petersen, J. Mallon, L. Christel, and F. Pourahmadi, (1990), "Silicon sensors and microstructures," NovaSensor

[74] Howe R. T. and R. S. Muller, (1984), "Resonant polysilicon microbridge with integrated NMOS detection circuitry, "*Extended Abstract*, Vol. 84-2, ECS Meeting, New Orleans, LA, 892 – 893

[75] Milunovich S. and J. Roy, (2001), "The Next Smaller Thing—an introduction to nanotechnology," Technical Report, Merril Lynch, Sept. 4, 2001

[76] MEMS Industry Group, (2001), "MEMS Industry Group Annual Report 2001," MEMS Industry Group, Pittsburg, PA, 2001

[77] Ho C. M. and Y. C. Tai, (1998), "Micro Electro Mechanical systems (MEMS) and Fluid Flows," *Annual Review of Fluid Mechanics*, **30**: 579 – 612

[78] Muller R., R. Howe, S. Senturia, R. Smith, and R. White, "*Microsensors*" (1991), IEEE Press, New York

[79] Ljubisa Ristic, (1994), "*Sensor Technology and Devices*," Artech House, Inc., Boston

[80] Sze S. M., (1994), "*Semiconductor Sensors*," John Wiley & Sons, Inc., New York

[81] Madou M., (1997), "*Fundamentals of Microfabrication*," CRC Press, New York

[82] Kovacs G., (1998), "*Micromachined Transducers Source Book*," McGraw Hill

7 Microelectromechanical Sensors

Shanhong Xia, Deyong Chen, Zhimei Qi, Xiuli He, Chunrong Peng, Xianxiang Chen, Chao Bian, Lan Qu and Jizhou Sun

State Key Laboratory of Transducer Technology Institute of Electronics, Chinese Academy of Sciences, No 19 Bei-Si-Huan West Road, Beijing 100190, China

E-mail: shxia@mail.ie.ac.cn

Abstract Microelectromechanical sensors are miniature sensors made by micro fabrication technique, with typical characterization dimensions between nanometer and millimeter range. Micro sensors have attracted great attention because of their many merits and wide applications. They have experienced several significant stages in the last few decades, along with tremendous progress in fabrication technologies. The main advantages of microsensors are their capability of batch fabrication, low cost, small size, light weight, low power consumption, and ease for integration. In this chapter, the development of physical, chemical and biological microsensors are described, and the principles, fabrication techniques, properties and applications of several microsensors are presented.

Keywords Micro, sensor, fabrication, application

7.1 Introduction

Sensors are devices that can sense certain quantities or substances (e.g., physical quantities, chemical or biological substances) that cannot be directly or accurately detected by our human senses, and convert the detected signal into a form (e.g., electrical, optical) that can be recognized by human beings. Micro electromechanical sensors are miniature sensors made by micro fabrication techniques, with typical characterization dimensions between nanometer and millimeter range. The main advantages of micro electromechanical sensors are their capability of batch fabrication, low cost, small size, light weight, low power consumption, and ease for integration.

Sensors are classified in different ways. Classification according to the quantities measured is most common, as listed in Table 7.1, where sensors are classified into physical, chemical, and biological sensors depending on the nature of input stimuli. Classification according to sensing principles is also often used, for example, piezoelectric sensors, optical fiber sensors, and so on.

Micro sensors have experienced several significant development stages in the last few decades, along with tremendous progress in fabrication technologies[1–5]. The first semiconductor micro pressure sensor was created in 1950s. Following the invention of a series of batch fabrication techniques, micro sensors paced into industry and brought a fast growing market. The development stages of a few widely used micro sensors are listed in Table 7.2.

Table 7.1 Types of micro sensors

Types of signal		Measurands
Physical	Mechanical	Acceleration, force, pressure, strain, flow, etc.
	Electric	Charge, electric field, etc.
	Magnetic	Magnetic field, magnetic flux, etc.
	Acoustic	Wave amplitude, surface acoustic wave, etc.
	Optical	Wave amplitude, image, etc.
	Radiation	Energy, intensity, etc.
	Thermal	Temperature, flux, etc.
	Others	
Chemical	Gas	Toxic gases, flammable gases, explosive gases, etc.
	Ion	pH, H+, metallic ions, etc.
	Humidity	Moisture, etc.
	Water pollution parameter	Dissolved oxygen, COD, BOD, etc.
	Others	
Biological	Enzyme	Glucose, lactic acid, cholesterol, acetone body, etc.
	Immuno	Protein (e.g., IgG, AFP), virus (e.g., HIV), etc.
	Microbial	Bacteria (e.g., salmonella, coliform), etc.
	Others	

Table 7.2 Development stages of several micro sensors
(Source: Roger Grace Associates and Northwest Technology Ventures)

Product	Discovery	Evolution	Cost Reduction	Full Commercialization
Pressure sensors	1954 – 1960	1960 – 1975	1975 – 1990	1990
Accelerometers	1974 – 1985	1985 – 1990	1990 – 1998	1998
Gyroscopes	1982 – 1990	1990 – 1996	1996 – 2004	2004
Bio/chemical sensors	1980 – 1994	1994 – 2000	2000 – 2005	2005

Developments in nanotechnology are greatly augmenting the current research of MEMS sensors. A large number of endeavors concern nanostructures and nanomaterials combining with MEMS technology, biotechnology, and microelectronics to improve the properties of micro sensors. Related new technologies such as Lab-on-Chip, micro Total Analysis System (μTAS) and wireless sensor networks are also developing rapidly. The trend of MEMS sensors is anticipated as high sensitivity, fast response, system integration, multi-function, and intelligence.

Several micro sensors, including physical, chemical, and biological sensors have been presented in this chapter. The operation principles, fabrication techniques, properties, and applications of these sensors are also described.

7.1.1 Physical Sensors

In MEMS physical sensors, a certain physical parameter of the ambient environment can affect characteristics of the micromechanical transducer in such a manner that this change can be measured using electronic, optical, or other means; MEMS actuators do the exact opposite.

The most important sensing mechanisms for physical sensors include piezoresistivity, piezoelectricity, variable capacitance, optical, and resonant sensing techniques. Sensing based on measurement of change in resistance has strong dependence on temperature that must be compensated for with external electronics. Capacitive sensing relies on an external physical parameter changing either the spacing or the relative dielectric constant between the two plates of a capacitor. This has very low power consumption and relative stability with temperature. A resonant sensor is designed such that the resonator's natural frequency is a function of the measurand. Resonant sensors exhibit excellent performances of higher resolution compared with piezoresistive and capacitive techniques.

The main actuation methods are electrostatic, piezoelectric, thermal, and magnetic. Electrostatic actuation relies on the attractive force between two conductive plates or elements carrying opposite charges. Piezoelectric actuation generates mechanical force or deformation through the reverse piezoelectric effect. Thermal actuation based on thermal expansion effect consumes more power than electrostatic or piezoelectric actuation, but can provide actuation forces on the order of hundreds of millinewtons or higher. The electromagnetic and magnetic effects are generally recognized to produce larger forces at larger air gaps compared to the electrostatic methods.

7.1.2 Chemical Sensors

Chemical sensors are devices consisting of a suitable transducer (such as electrochemical, optical, or mass) with chemically selective layers and a signal processor. They are capable of continuously recognizing concentrations of chemical constituents in liquids or gases and converting this information in real-time to an electrical or optical signal.

There exist many different types of chemical sensors. According to the substances to detect, there are toxic gas sensors, flammable gas sensors, explosive gas sensors, metallic ion sensors, water pollution monitoring sensors, and so on. According to the features of signals or sensing element, there are metal-oxide semiconductor gas sensors, fiber optic sensors, electrochemical sensors, and so on. A pH-testing paper strip may be the simplest chemical sensor, and the commercial pH meter is perhaps the most common electrochemical sensor. The need to identify multi-analytes simultaneously has led to the development of array-based sensors.

Chemical sensors have widespread applications in medical diagnostics, environmental pollution monitoring, security control, quality and process control, and so on. For practical applications, chemical sensors are desired to be sensitive, selective, stable, reliable, and quickly responsive. Micro-electro-mechanical-system (MEMS) technique has been successfully applied to chemical sensor fabrications, offering advantages of small size, low power consumption, and capable of multi-sensor integration. The interactive chemically selective material is considered as the primary part of a sensor, and has attracted much research attention. Recent developments of nanostructure functional materials such as nanotubes, nanowires, nanoparticles and nano porous structures significantly improve the properties of the chemically selective layers of chemical sensors.

7.1.3 Biological Sensors

A biosensor usually consists of three parts: the sensitive biological element (enzymes, antibodies, nucleic acids, tissue, organelles, cell receptors, etc.), the transducer that transforms the signal resulting from the biological interaction into another signal (i.e., electrical signal), and associated signal processors.

Research and development in biosensors is an interdisciplinary field spanning life sciences and information technology. The first biosensor was reported in 1962 by Clark[6] in the form of enzyme electrode. It was based on the selectivity of enzymes to different substrates, and enzyme was immobilized on traditional ion-selective electrodes. Widespread studies of biosensors were carried out from the 1980s, and kept expanding rapidly in the following years.

There are three so-called 'generations' of biosensors: first generation biosensors, where the product of the reaction diffuses spontaneously to the transducer and causes the electrical response; second generation biosensors, which involve specific mediators between the reaction and the transducer in order to generate improved response; and third generation biosensors. where the reaction itself produces the response signal and no product or mediator is needed.

The key part of a biosensor is the transducer. During the detection process of a biosensor, it makes use of a physical change accompanying the biological reaction. Depending on the nature of the transducers and the transduced parameters, there are different types of biosensors in the analytical field, for example: potentiometric biosensors, based on changes in the distribution of charges causing an electrical potential to be produced; amperometric biosensors, based on movement of electrons produced in a redox reaction; optical biosensors, based on light output during the reaction or a light absorbance difference between the reactants and products; other biosensors, such as piezoelectric, thermometric, and magnetic biosensors.

The key issues for a biosensor to be valuable in application are the accurate recognition of a target molecule, availability of a suitable biological recognition element, and the potential to become a cheap, portable, and easy-handling device. There are various potential applications of biosensors, for example, medical health related detection, environmental monitoring, food quality appraisal, and so on.

7.2 Resonant Mechanical Sensors

A block diagram of a typical resonant sensor is shown in Fig. 7.1. The key component is the resonator, which is a mechanical structure designed to vibrate at a particular resonant frequency. The measurand typically alters the stiffness, mass, or shape of the resonator, hence causing a change in its resonant frequency. The other components of a resonant sensor are the vibration drive and detection mechanisms. The drive mechanism excites the vibrations in the structure while the detection mechanism senses these vibrations. For silicon micromachined resonators, electrostatic, electromagnetic or thermal excitation mechanisms, and capacitive, electromagnetic, piezoresistive detection mechanisms are commonly used. The frequency of the detected vibration forms the output of the sensor and this signal is also fed back to the drive mechanism via an amplifier maintaining the structure at resonance over the entire measurand range. Sensing by frequency shift is of high accuracy, high stability, and immune to electromagnetic interference.

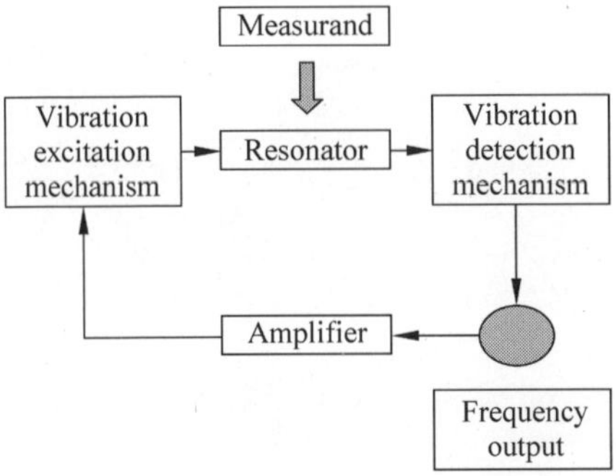

Figure 7.1 A block diagram of a typical resonant sensor

In mechanical sensing applications, the most common mechanism for coupling the resonator to the measurand is to apply a strain across the structure by mounting the resonator in a suitable location on a specifically designed sensing structure that deflects due to the application of the measurand. The applied strain effectively increases the stiffness of the resonator, resulting in an increase in its natural frequency. Based on this principle, many mechanical sensors, such as force sensors, pressure sensors, accelerometers and flow sensors, etc., have been developed.

7.2.1 Resonant Pressure Sensors

Resonant pressure sensors typically use a resonating mechanical structure as a strain gauge to sense the deflection of the pressure-sensitive diaphragm. The earliest MEMS resonant pressure sensor was developed by Greenwood[7, 8] and later commercialized by Druck. A schematic of the sensor is shown in Fig. 7.2. The two rectangular plates are made to oscillate in see-saw fashion, restrained by the v-shaped ligatures which attach them to the two supporting piers. Application of air pressure to the underside of the diaphragm causes the piers to move upwards and apart, increasing the tension in the ligatures and raising the frequency of oscillation. A small link joins adjacent ends of the plates to ensure that the structure has a single antiphase resonance. The resonator and diaphragm are fabricated using the boron etch stop technique. The resonator is driven electrostatically and its vibrations are detected capacitively via metal electrodes on the support chip. A vacuum is trapped around the resonator by mounting the support chip on a glass stem and sealing the end of the stem while in vacuum. The assembly is then mounted by the stem, which provides some measure of isolation from packaging stresses. The resonator has a Q-factor of 40,000, and the sensor has a resolution of 10 ppm and total error of less than 100 ppm.

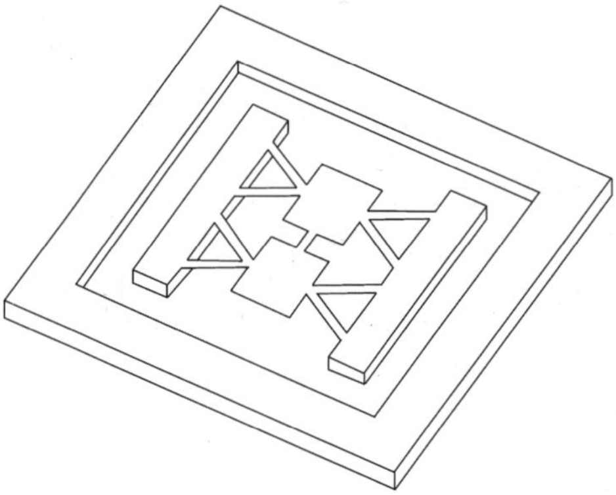

Figure 7.2 Schematic of the pressure sensor

Another successfully commercialized device was developed by the Yokogawa Electric Corporation[9,10]. This consists of two resonators located on a diaphragm, the differential output of which provides the sensor reading. The resonators are driven electromagnetically by placing the device in a magnetic field and running an alternating current through the structure. The pressure sensor arrangement is shown in Fig. 7.3. The fabrication process associated with this device is particularly impressive. The beams are vacuum encapsulated at wafer level using a series of epitaxial depositions, selective etches, and finally annealing in nitrogen, which drives the trapped gases left by the sealing process through the cavity walls or into the silicon. This leaves a final cavity pressure of below 1 mTorr, and the resonator possesses a Q-factor of more than 50,000.

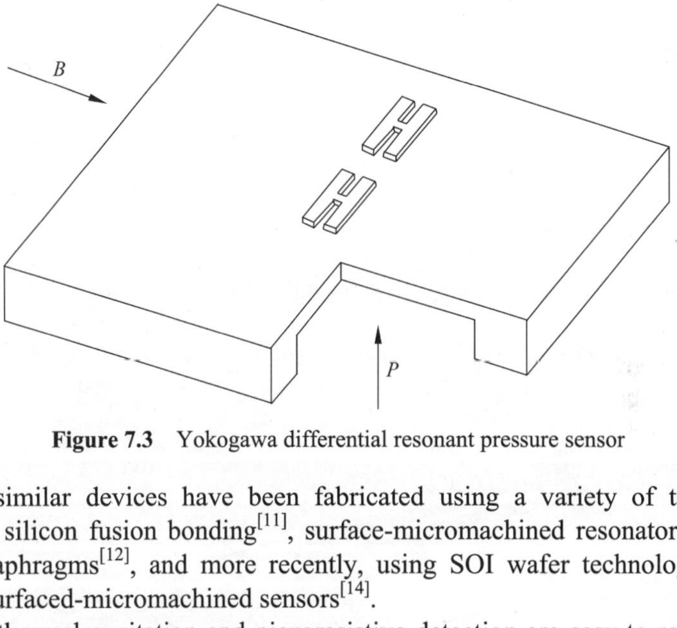

Figure 7.3 Yokogawa differential resonant pressure sensor

Other similar devices have been fabricated using a variety of techniques including silicon fusion bonding[11], surface-micromachined resonators on bulk etches diaphragms[12], and more recently, using SOI wafer technology[13] and entirely surfaced-micromachined sensors[14].

Electrothermal excitation and piezoresistive detection are easy to realize, and have proved to be feasible for the thin and long structures, such as beams and cantilevers[15-18]. D. Chen et al.[15-17] describe a resonant pressure sensor with thick silicon-rich silicon nitride as a mechanical resonator, whose resonant frequency is changed by axial stress induced by applied pressure. Without silicon-silicon directly bonding, the sensor element is formed in one piece from single crystal silicon, using porous silicon as a sacrificial layer. Figure 7.4 illustrates the resonant pressure sensor with a novel structure[17]. The vibrating element in this case is a silicon nitride beam mounted above a silicon diaphragm. The beam forms a bridge clamped at both ends. Application of pressure p to the silicon diaphragm causes bending of the diaphragm, inducing an axial stress in the fully clamped beam $\sigma_p \propto p$ (which is, to a first order approximation, linearly proportional to the applied pressure). The upper part is 10 μm thick silicon nitride film, deposited on a silicon substrate. A deep cavity is etched into the front side of the wafer by removing the sacrificial porous silicon layer, leaving a doubly clamped SiN beam supported by two rectangular piers in the center. The pressure diaphragm is formed by wet etching from the backside of the silicon wafer. Figure 7.5 is the schematic of the beam resonator. A thin film platinum heater is fabricated on the center of the beam and a platinum detector on one end of the beam. The beam can be excited to resonance by applying an AC voltage on the heater, and the piezoresistive property of platinum thin film will send electrical signals to detection circuit.

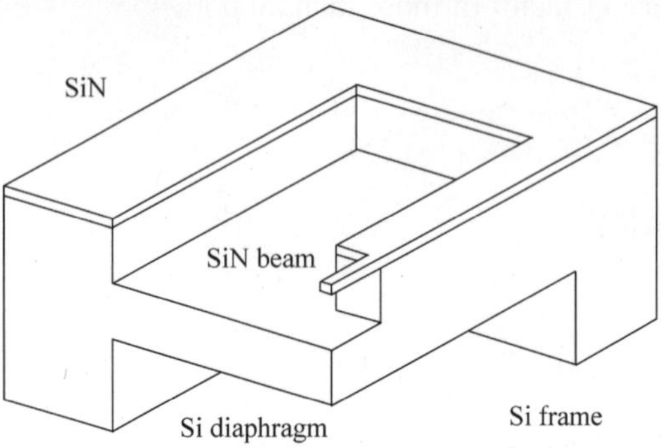

Figure 7.4 Schematic of one quadrant of the entire pressure sensor structure

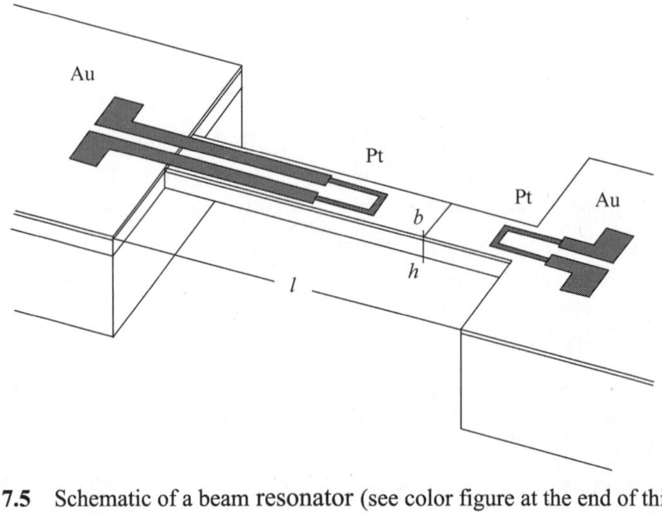

Figure 7.5 Schematic of a beam resonator (see color figure at the end of this book)

Using commercial FEA software, computer simulation is done on the characteristics of the resonator and the pressure sensitivity for several silicon/silicon nitride beam structures. Resonant pressure sensors are fabricated by IC process and MEMS technology, bonded to a stress isolating mechanical structure, and sealed into an evacuated package. Figure 7.6 shows the SEM photograph of the SiN beam released by porous silicon sacrificial layer technique. Both an open-loop and a close-loop measuring system are established for detecting vibration of the resonant beams and the response of the resonant frequency at different applied pressure loads, based on special lock-in amplification technology. These systems measure relationships of resonant frequencies with excitation conditions, applied pressures, and environmental temperatures for several structures.

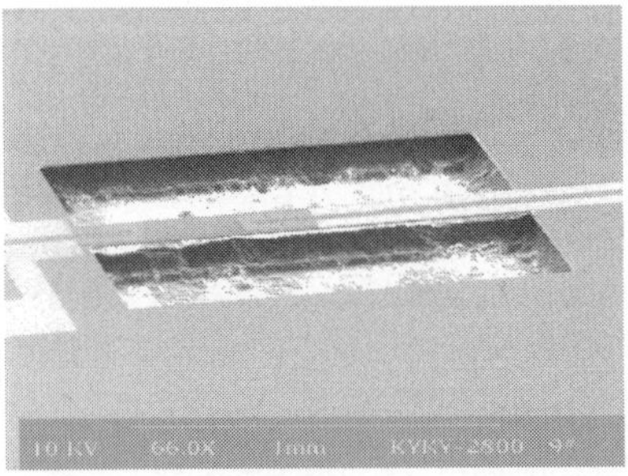

Figure 7.6 SEM photograph of a SiN beam resonator (see color figure at the end of this book)

Correction of temperature drift of the sensor has to be calculated in order to achieve sufficient accuracy. From the previous results, the measured frequency is a function of applied pressure and temperature, which can be written as $f(p,T) = f_1(p) + f_2(T)$. $f_1(p)$ is a real value of resonance frequency related to applied pressure, $f_2(T)$ is an addition frequency caused by temperature drift. Hence, $f_1(p) = f(p,T) - f_2(T)$, which means that the real temperature-independent resonance frequency can be calculated by subtracting temperature drift frequency from the measured frequency. Here a linear interpolation method is employed to calculate the temperature drift frequency at any temperature, using a set of calibration data. Figure 7.7 gives a relative error distribution of resonance frequency

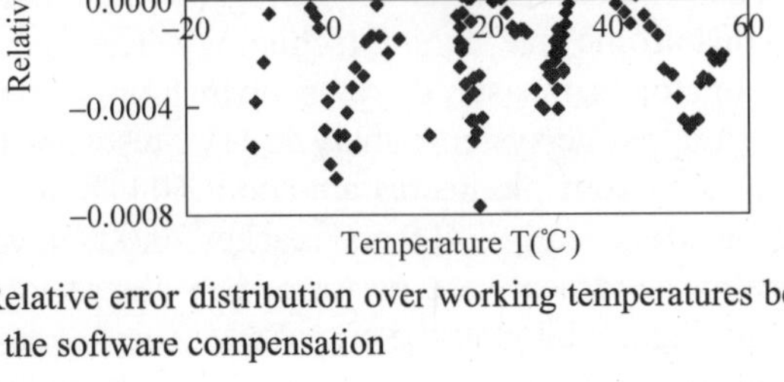

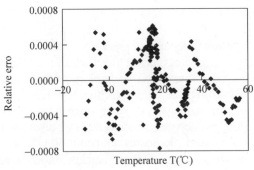

Figure 7.7 Relative error distribution over working temperatures between −10℃ and 60℃ after the software compensation

of a sample device after the software compensation described above. The relative errors of frequencies are now reduced to below 0.16% from 15% within the temperature range used.

Silicon nitride beam resonant pressure sensors with complete packages have been made successfully. The quality factor Q values are about 2,000 in air and rise to ~40,000 in vacuum. The full scale of the pressure sensor is between 100 – 600 kPa, the sensitivities are from 20 – 200 Hz/kPa for different structure. The new type peninsula design exhibits sensitivity at least 10 times higher than the rectangular cavity design[16]. There is a satisfactory agreement between simulation and experimental results.

Based on their earlier work, D. Chen, J. Wang, et al. [19, 20] propose an electromagnetically excited resonant pressure sensor using bulk micromachining processes, which are different from that of the Yokogawa Electric Corporation[9, 10], and LPCVD silicon rich silicon nitride[19] or boron diffused silicon[20] other than poly silicon are chosen as the resonant beam. Figure 7.8(a) is the schematic diagram of the new resonant pressure sensor. The sensor is temperature-compensated by adding a pair of additional pressure sensitive beams on both sides of the central resonant beam supported by two piers. These three beams are clamped at both ends with one in the center of the pressure diaphragm and the other two symmetrically distributed at both sides. To enhance quality factor of the resonator, a triple-beam resonator has been covered in this design. Actually, the triple beam consists of four identical beams with the central two beams coupled through a link, and they are joined together via decoupling zone. The differential mode (in which the vibrating direction of two outer beams is opposite to the vibrating direction of the central beam) is desired and it can be tuned in closed-loop operation by a self-oscillating circuit. The central beam and either of the side ones are electromagnetically driven into vibration when in work. The two vibrating beams have identical sizes, and are expected to have equal resonant frequencies at zero pressure loads. When a pressure is applied on the diaphragm, the central beam induces an axial tensile stress which increases the resonant frequency, while the side one, an axial compressive stress leading to decrease of the resonant frequency. The applied pressure is then measured by working out the difference of the two resonant frequencies. Because the measurement is based on the frequency difference, if there is ambient temperature influence, the frequency drift induced on both beams will be the same. The frequency difference will be unchanged, guaranteeing a temperature independent pressure sensing.

Figure 7.8(b) shows a photograph of the pressure sensor fabricated by the standard bulk-silicon micromachining technology, which combines ICP deep etching and KOH anisotropic wet etching technology. The frequency response of the triple-beam resonator is measured by an open loop scanning method with help of the HP3562A dynamic systems analyzer. The resonant frequencies of the differential mode of the two triple-beams are about 50 kHz in air at atmospheric pressure, and the Q factor is nearly 1,400 and reaches 20,000 in vacuum (~0.1 Pa).

Static sensitivity measurements are performed in closed loop operation by a self-oscillating circuit. Figure 7.9 plots the output frequency versus applied pressure.

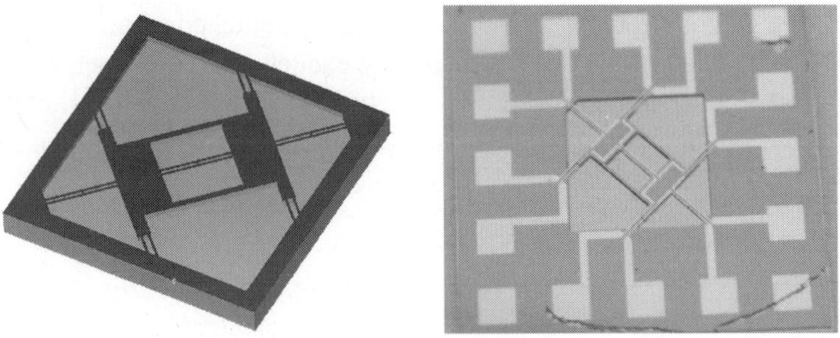

(a) (b)

Figure 7.8 Schematic (a) and photograph (b) of an electromagnetically excited resonant pressure sensor (see color figure at the end of this book)

With increase of applied pressure loads, f_2, relating to vibration of a side beam, goes down linearly corresponding to a Δf_r of 8% at full scale pressure (100 kPa). f_1, which is related to vibration of the central beam, goes up linearly corresponding to a Δf_r of 22% at full scale pressure. Working on differential mode, i.e., choosing the frequency difference of the two beams as output, the differential output ($f_1 - f_2$) sensitivity of this sensor is about 0.155 kHz/kPa over the range 0 – 100 kPa with improved sensitivity and linearity.

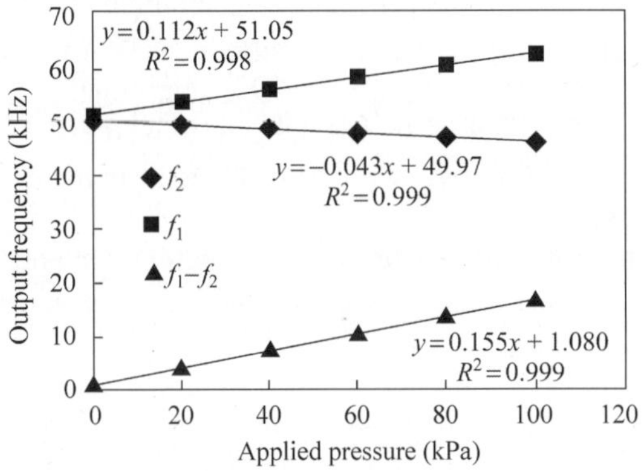

Figure 7.9 Measured static sensitivity of a pressure sensor

7.2.2 Resonant Accelerometers

Resonant sensors have many advantages over the conventional type, such as high resolution, wide dynamic range, and quasi-digital nature of the output signal. For resonant silicon accelerometers, cantilever-supported structures with two hinges suspending the proof mass and a load sensitive silicon beam clamped between the bulk and the mass are often used to measure an out-of-plane acceleration[19]. Figure 7.10 shows the schematic of the sensor. It consists of a proof mass suspended by two hinges and one central triple beam. A second matched triple beam is located in the stiff bulk. The beam is electrothermally excited into resonance and detected piezoresistively. The fabrication process includes an electrochemical etch stop at a double diffusion, permitting the fabrication of membranes with different thickness. The scale factor of the device is 200 Hz/g at a beam resonant frequency of 90 kHz.

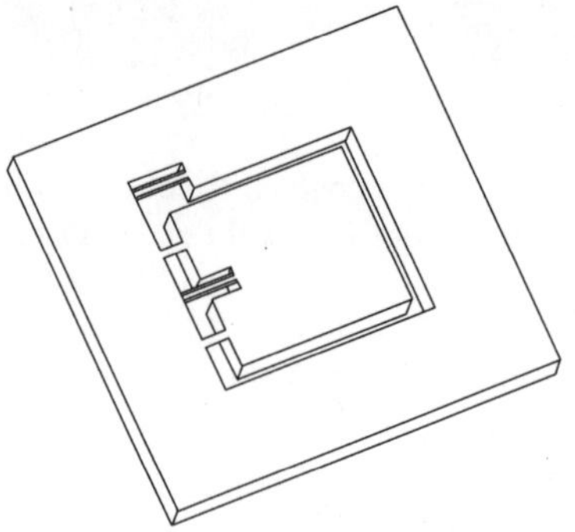

Figure 7.10 schematic of the resonant silicon accelerometer in bulk micromachining technology

Another microleverage force amplifying mechanism is involved to realize an in-plane acceleration measurement through a DETF (double ended tuning fork) resonator. Roessig et al.[22] designed a polysilicon surface micromachined DETF resonant accelerometer and achieved a 45 Hz/g scale factor using a single stage microlever. Seshia et al.[23] and Jia et al.[24] improved the lever structure and fabricated DETF accelerometers with a 17 Hz/g scalefactor and a 27.3 Hz/g scalefactor, respectively.

To enhance scale factor of the resonant accelerometer and to improve other performance such as cross sensitivity of insensitive input acceleration, linearity, temperature stability, etc., D. Chen et al.[25] propose a resonant microbeam accelerometer of a novel highly symmetric structure based on the same force amplifying mechanism as a resonant beam pressure sensor. The schematic diagram of the new resonant silicon accelerometer is shown in Fig. 7.11. The sensor consists of a proof mass, four supporting beams, four anchors and two vibrating beams, each of which is clamped via two supporting beams. The resonant beams are excited electrostatically and sensed capacitively by plate electrodes located at the two sides of each beam. The two vibrating beams have almost identical sizes, and are expected to have nearly equal resonant frequencies at zero acceleration loads. When an in-plane acceleration is applied along y direction, one resonant beam induces an axial tensile stress, which increases the resonant frequency, and the other one, an axial compressive stress leading decrease of the resonant frequency. The output resonant frequency is taken as subtracted value between output frequencies in each resonator. Differential frequency output scheme between two resonators has advantages of a good linearity, high signal-to-noise ratio (SNR) compared with single frequency output. Since the measurement is based on the frequency difference, if there is ambient temperature influence, the frequency drift induced on both beams will be the same. The frequency difference will be unchanged, guaranteeing a temperature independent acceleration sensing. On the other hand, the sum of the two resonant frequencies approximately keeps unchanged under different accelerated loads for two perfectly matched resonant beams, and is only a function of temperature, which can be calibrated as temperature signal output for more precise temperature compensation.

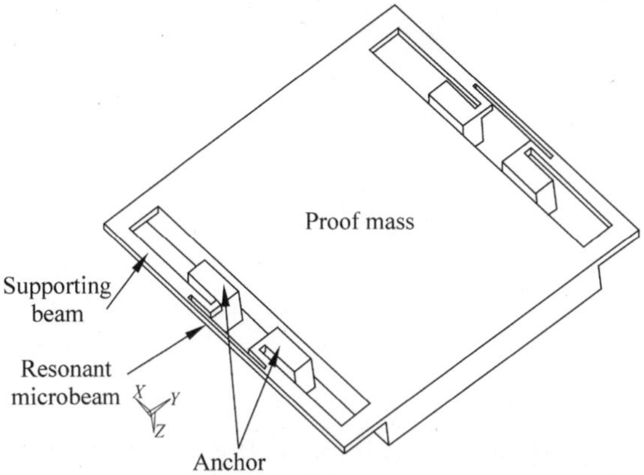

Figure 7.11 Schematic drawing of a differential resonant silicon accelerometer with a novel highly symmetric structures

By FEA simulation, one can get scale factors of each sensitive direction. SF(y) is about 7.9 kHz/g, SF(x) is about 0.4 Hz/g, and SF(z) is about 1.8 Hz/g. The cross axis sensitivities of x and z axis are 50 ppm and 220 ppm, respectively. Figure 7.12 is the resonant frequency shifts of the two modals due to applied acceleration over the full-scale operating range. As applied acceleration changes from –2g – 2g, f_2 goes down with a negative slope of –3,981 Hz/g and f_1 goes up with a positive slope of 3,985.1 Hz/g, resulting in much better linear output of $f_1 - f_2$ and a total scale factor of 7,966.1 Hz/g over the ±2 g full scale.

Simulation results reveal that the novel structure increases the scale factor of the resonant accelerometer, and improves other perfrmance such as cross axis sensitivity of insensitive input acceleration, linearity, temperature stability, etc.

7.2.3 Resonant Gas Flow Sensors

In order to escape from danger, insects have the ability to detect low velocity gas flows by using wind receptors in their tails[26, 27]. Biomimetic microsensors derived from this kind of mechanoreceptors based on piezoresistive[28–31] or capacitive[32] detection have been under focus. In order to enhance its resolution to measure low velocity gas and make it more immune to environmental noise, J. Chen and D. Chen et al.[33] propose a novel microsensor based on resonant principle including cantilever-based thin film and DETF (double-ended tuning fork).

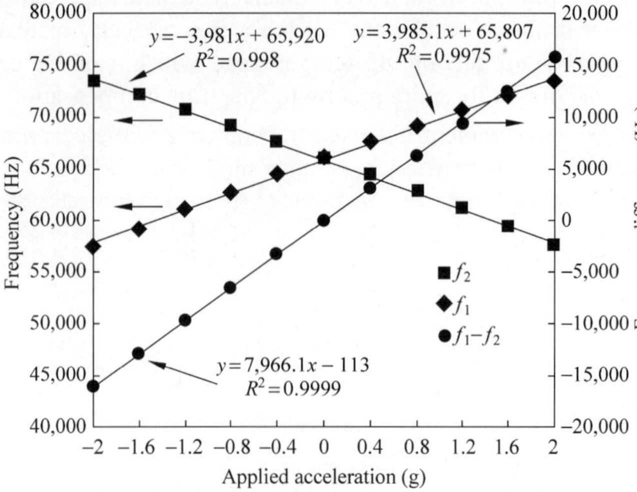

Figure 7.12 FEA model results for a ±2 g device. A base frequency of 65,000 Hz and an acceleration sensitivity of nearly 3,980 Hz/g from each microbeam, resulting in linear output and a total scale factor of 7,966.1 Hz/g over the ±2 g full scale

The novel resonant microsensor is shown in Fig. 7.13, which includes cantilever-based thin film that is treated as infinite long beam to sense gas flow and double-ended tuning fork (DETF) as the resonator. This design is based on the assumption that when gas flow ranges in low Reynolds number, drag force, which is the function of gas velocity can be dominant compared to other forces in micro-size[27]. The main principle is that when gas flow exists in *Y* direction, passing around cantilever-based thin film, the drag force which is the function of velocity of gas flow would bend cantilever-based thin film. The deflection of the thin film would bend DETF and modify its intrinsic frequency.

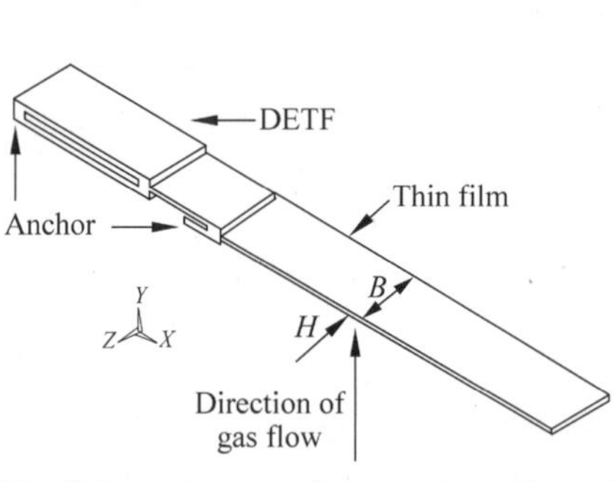

Figure 7.13 Schematic view of resonant gas flow microsensor

Fluid-structural coupled analysis is conducted to find the relationship between velocity of gas flow and frequency shift of this microsensor. The result of FEA simulation shows that when Reynolds number is below 1, a linear relationship exists between input and output of this micro sensor, and its sensitivity is 1.6 Hz/cm/s.

7.3 Silicon Based Electrostatic Field Sensors

Electrostatic field measurement has been the subject of much research over the past half century[34]. Measurements have been made both near the ground and at altitude in the study of weather phenomena such as lightning storms[35]. In industrial applications, the electrostatic voltmeters and fieldmeters are widely applied in most electrostatic discharge sensitive electronic manufacturing processes to evaluate electrostatic charges or electrostatic fields.

Electrostatic field sensors (EFS) of many different types may be found in use today. The rotating covering type has become the instrument of choice in much of atmospheric science and electric power systems, while the vibrating reed type is used in the probe heads of non-contacting voltmeters and fieldmeters[34]. A vibrating wire field mill was reported in atmospheric experiments[34].

Although numerous devices have been developed, all currently used electrostatic field sensors are difficult to integrate with other systems. Their application is further limited because of their relatively high cost and power dissipation.

Recently, more attention has been paid to micromachined electrostatic field sensors due to their small sizes, low cost, and low power dissipation advantages over traditional EFS. Therefore, some electrostatic field sensors based on MEMS technology have been developed. In 1991, C. H. Hsu and R. S. Muller developed a micromechanical electrostatic voltmeter[36]. Mark N. Horenstein et al.. developed a micro-aperture electrostatic field mill[34] in 2001. An integrated electrostatic field sensor with a resolution of 630 V/m was demonstrated at U. C. Berkeley[37] in 2003. A high performance resonant micromechanical electrostatic field sensor with a resolution of better than 100 V/m was demonstrated in 2006[38]. Thermal actuators have firstly been employed to drive the shutter of EFS with smaller voltages[39]. A vertical vibration micromachined EFS with a thermal actuator was developed at Institute of Electronics of Chinese Academy of Sciences[40]. Currently, there are mainly three kinds of micromechanical electrostatic field sensors. They are comb-driven resonant EFS, thermally-driven lateral vibration MEFS, and thermally-driven vertical vibration EFS.

The sensing principle, structure design and measurement of micromechanical electrostatic field sensors will be introduced in the following sections.

7.3.1 Sensing Principle

The operation principle of micromechanical electrostatic field sensors is shown in Fig. 7.14. The EFS uses moving, grounded shielding electrodes that are used to shield and expose sensing electrodes. Therefore, when a normal electric field $\boldsymbol{E}$ is present, an amount of charge Q_i is induced on the sensing electrodes. According to Gauss' law, the amount of the charge is proportional to the exposed area A_e[37]:

$$Q_i = \varepsilon_0 \mid E \mid A_e \tag{7.1}$$

When the shielding electrodes (or shuttle) move periodically, there is an effective area A_e exposed to the electric field E, which generates a current i_e, given by:

$$i_e = \frac{dQ_i}{dt} = \varepsilon_0 \mid E \mid \frac{dA_e}{dt} \tag{7.2}$$

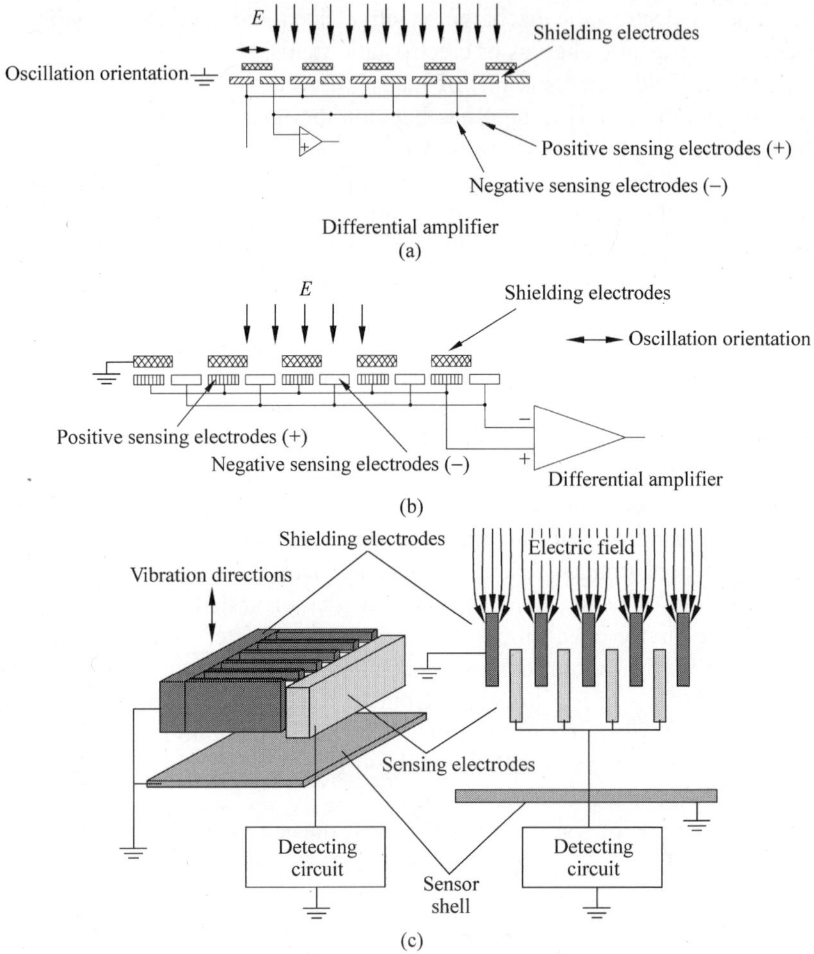

Figure 7.14 The sensing principle of the EFS(a) electrostatic comb-driven lateral vibration type; (b) thermally driven lateral vibration type (c) thermally driven vertical vibration type

In order to improve the signal-to-noise ratio (SNR) and minimize the feed-through noise, the structures are designed by using differential drive and differential sense. As the shielding electrodes oscillate back and forth, they cover the sensing surface of either the positive sensing electrodes or negative sensing electrodes, causing a differential current that is converted to a differential voltage by the differential transresistance amplifier, and then amplified by a gain stage.

7.3.2 Structure of MEMS EFS

A schematic view of a electrostatic comb-driven EFS is shown in Fig. 7.15(a). The micromechanical structure consists of four groups of comb drives, a grounded shielding electrode, sensing electrodes, and suspension folded beam. The shielding electrode is supported by two sets of thin folded beams that are connected to the grounded plane at two anchor points. Besides differential detection, differential driving is also utilized to minimize the noise and to improve the SNR of the EFS[34, 36, 37]. A common DC bias voltage and antisymmetric AC sine waveforms are applied to drive the grounded shielding electrode on either side of the structure. The driving voltages are $V_1 = V_d - V_a \sin(\omega_a t)$ on one pair of the comb drive and $V_2 = V_d + V_a \sin(\omega_a t)$ on the other pair of comb drive, where V_d is the DC bias, V_a is the AC signal amplitude, and ω_a is the actuation frequency. The corresponding net electrostatic force excited in the driving direction is[37]:

$$F_x(t) = 2\frac{\partial C}{\partial x} V_d V_a \sin(\omega_a t) \tag{7.3}$$

where C is the total comb capacitance.

For maximum sensitivity to electric field E, the MEMS electrostatic field sensor was designed to operate at its resonant frequency[38, 41].

Different from the electrostatic comb-driven type EFS, the thermally driven lateral vibration EFS uses a cascaded bent beam thermal driver other than the electrostatic comb driver to drive the grounded shielding electrodes into vibration as shown in Fig. 7.15(b). Two differential square wave drives of +V and –V were applied on the driving pads. As reported by Gianchandani Y. B. and Que L., et al.[42–44], the bent beam thermal driver has the advantage of low driving voltage, large driving force and displacement, compact structure, easy to integrate with the other structure and compatible with the PolyMUMPs process, etc.

For the thermally driven vertical vibration EFS, a U-shaped thermal actuator can provide vertical actuation[45], as shown in Fig. 7.15(c). The actuator consists of two layers (bottom layer and top layer) fixed on four anchors. When voltage is applied to anchor 1 and anchor 2, and the other two anchors are grounded, the current goes only through the bottom layer. The bottom layer is Joule heated and expanded, and then the temperature difference between bottom layer and top layer causes the dip of the actuator to deflect upwards. With periodic voltage U and –U, the actuator vibrates up and down periodically.

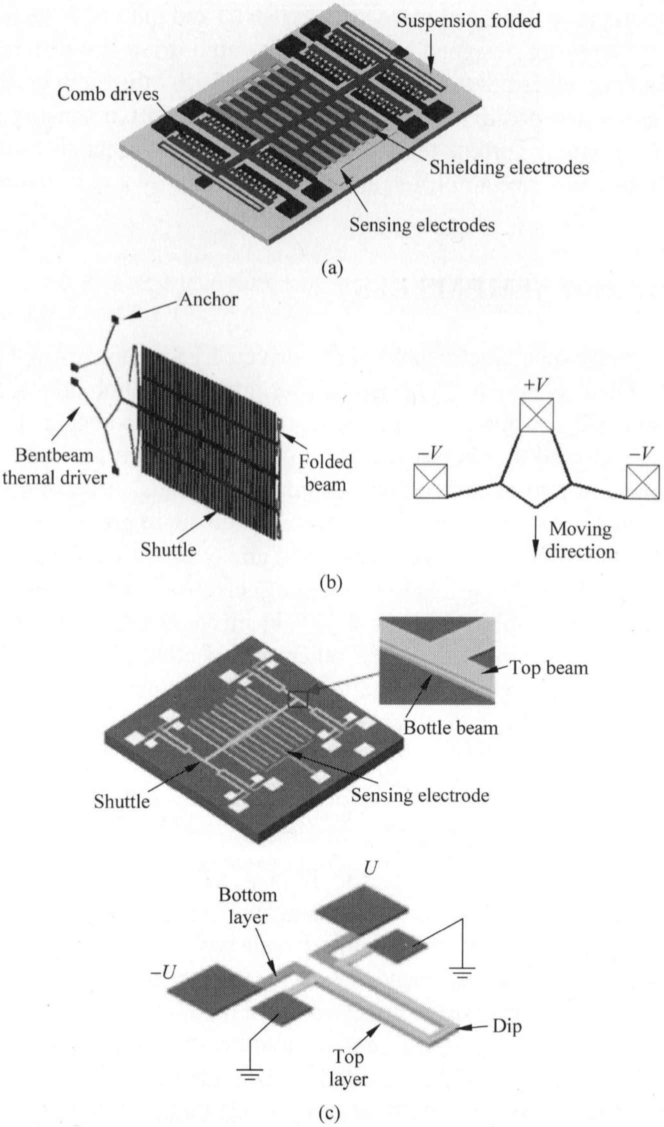

Figure 7.15 The schematic structure of the EFS (a) electrostatic comb-driven lateral vibration type (b) thermally driven lateral vibration type (c) thermally driven vertical vibration type (see color figure at the end of this book)

The electrostatic comb–driven resonant micromechanical EFS based on the PolyMUMPs process[46] has been demonstrated by Chunrong Peng et al.[38, 41], which is shown in Figs. 7.16(a). (b) and (c) show the thermally driven lateral vibration micromechanical EFS developed by Xianxiang Chen et al.[39] and the thermally driven vertical vibration micromechanical EFS developed by Chao Ye et al.[40] respectively.

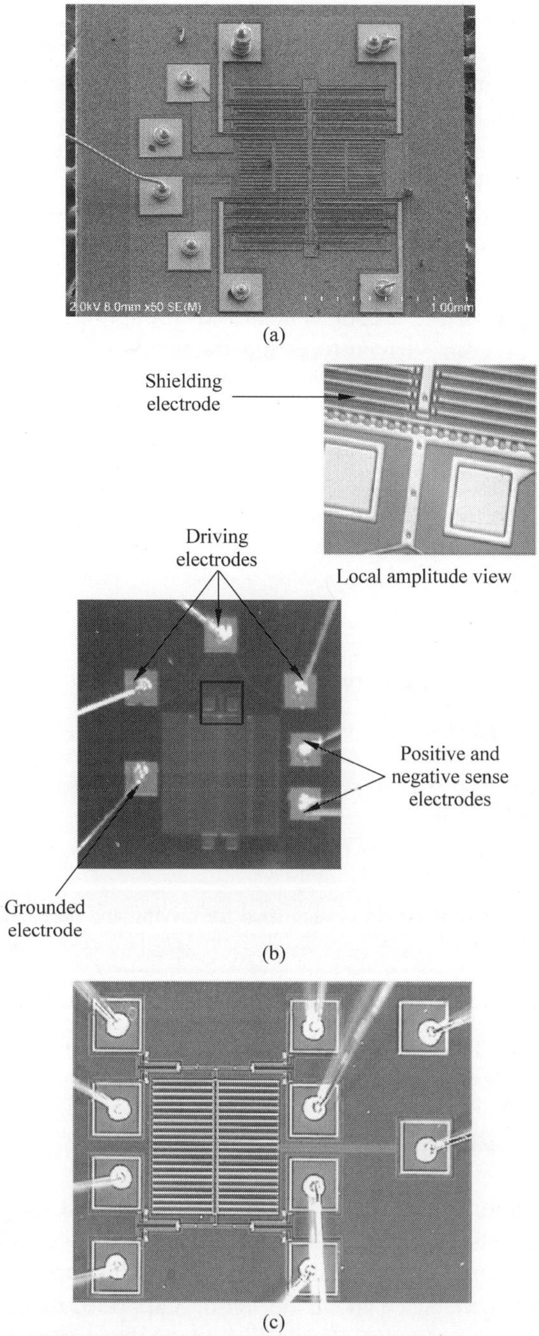

Figure 7.16 Photographs of micromechanical EFS based on PolyMUMPs. (a) electrostatic comb-driven lateral vibration type (b) thermally driven lateral vibration type (c) thermally driven vertical vibration type

7.3.3 Electronics and Noise

A general block diagram of electronics for micromechanical EFS is shown in Fig. 7.17. The induced current is firstly converted to an alternating voltage by the transresistance amplifier (i.e., current-to-voltage converter), and then synchronously demodulated by a lock-in amplifier or a phase-sensitive demodulator referenced to the signal at twice the drive waveform frequency. Using synchronous- detection-based system, the fundamental frequency output of the EFS can be largely reduced, and the signal-to-noise ratio (SNR) is improved. Ultimately, the electric field response output of the sensor is achieved through a low pass filter (LPF). For the electrostatic comb-driven type, the frequency of the reference signal of the lock in amplifier or the demodulator is the same as the fundamenl frequency of the driving signal. But for the thermally driven type, the sensor produces an output signal with a component at twice the motional frequency. Detecting this second-harmonic signal with a narrow-band amplifier allows the feed-through signal at the drive frequency to be largely rejected.

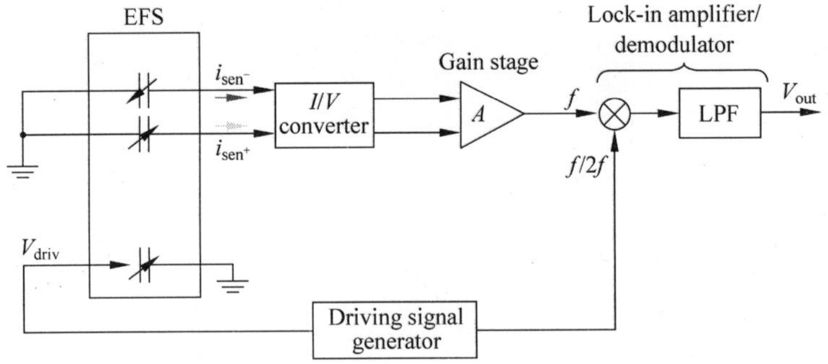

Figure 7.17 Electronic circuit system used for driving and processing the signal from the EFS

For current-to-voltage converter, the amplifiers with low bias current, low offset voltage, and low noise are selected to minimize the feed-through and noise.

7.3.4 Testing and Characteristic

The calibration equipment must be first constructed to test the EFS. In general, the equipment consists of two test electrodes (upper test electrode and lower test electrode) just like a parallel plate capacitor[37–40]. The upper test electrode can be positioned at a known space above the sensor and biased to an arbitrary voltage to generate a uniform electrostatic field normal to the sensor chip.

A linear range of voltages are applied to the upper test electrode to produce a variable external electric field for testing the response properties of the sensor.

As shown in Fig. 7.18(a), results of the electrostatic comb-driven EFS testing

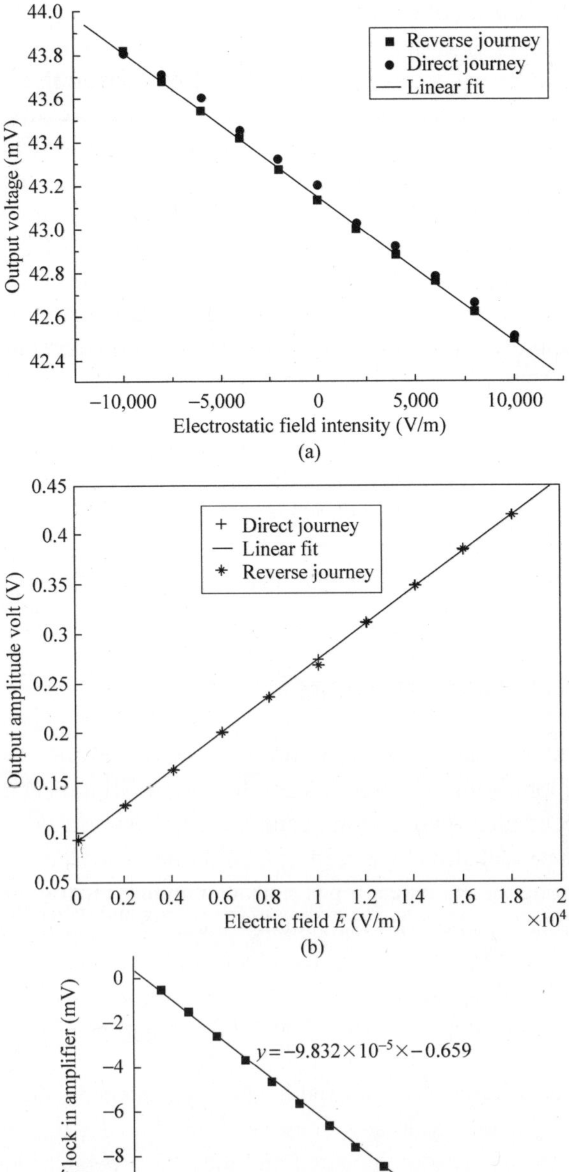

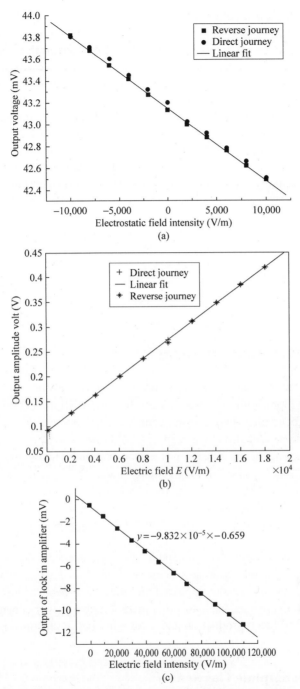

Figure 7.18 The measurement results of the EFS (a) electrostatic comb-driven lateral vibration type (b) thermally driven lateral vibration type (c) thermally driven vertical vibration type

show that in a measurement range of 0 – 10 kV/m, a nonlinearity of 1.8% (end-point-straight-line) is achieved. The drift of the EFS is less than 100 V/m within a few hours. We have also achieved an uncertainty of 4.62% for measurement data. The feed-through at output of the sensor is less than 10 mV. An external electric field less than 200 V/m in strength can be distinguished with the EFS, which is the best figure for a MEMS-based electric field sensor.

The detection results for the thermally driven lateral vibration EFS are shown in Fig. 7.18(b). A 20 kHz square wave with upper voltage of 2 volts and lower voltage of 0 volt is applied on the upper drive pad of the thermal driver. A 20 kHz square wave with upper voltage of 0 volt and lower voltage of –2 volts is applied on the two bottom drive pads of the thermal driver. An external electric field less than 241 V/m in strength can be distinguished with the EFS. Its output drift is less than 300 V/m within a few hours.

Figure 7.18(c) shows the testing results of the thermally driven vertical vibration EFS. The sensor was driven by the offset sine driving signal U and –U with frequency 209 Hz, and peak-to-peak value of U was 0.6 V. The sensor responded to the external electrostatic field linearly, and the nonlinearity was 4%. The sensor also achieved a resolution of 200 V/m in the experiments.

7.4 MEMS Based Microgas Sensor

Gas sensors have been extensively used in industrial process control and environmental monitoring. Gas sensors can be classified into conductometric gas sensors, electrochemical gas sensors, catalytic combustion gas sensors, infrared gas sensors, mass sensitive gas sensors, and others based on the response mechanism. Among all the types of gas sensors, conductometric gas sensors based on semiconducting metal oxides are actually one of the most investigated groups due to the advantages such as simplicity, low cost, fast response, high sensitivity, and large number of detectable gases.

Most metal oxide gas sensors work at about 300℃ or even higher temperatures. The power consumption of traditional metal oxide gas sensors is about 0.5 – 1.0 W. It is too high to meet some needs of hand-held equipments. Low power consumption is expected with metal oxide gas sensors. With the development of MEMS technology, micro gas sensors appeared and they have been widely investigated because of the advantages, such as miniaturization, low power consumption, ease of integration and batch production, etc. over other bulky sensors.

7.4.1 Microhotplate Gas Sensor

The silicon based microgas sensor was first reported by Q. Wu et al. at the 4th international meeting on chemical sensors (IMCS)[47]. Since then, silicon process technology has improved and a number of designs have been reported for gas sensors.

The silicon based micro hotplate (MHP) is a common structure. The two widely used types of micro hotplates are the front-side etched micro-bridge[48, 49] and back-side etched diaphragm[50–52] Figure 7.19 and Figure 7.20 show the schematic graphs of the two types of micro hotplates respectively. The former structure with the polysilicon resistive heater was usually fabricated by surface micromachining techniques. It shows high mechanical strength and is compatible with CMOS technology. But there is generally a long term drift of electrical resistance occurring at high temperatures[53]. The latter structure with the platinum resistive heater was usually fabricated by bulk micromachining techniques. Investigations have shown that platinum-based micro-heaters are more robust than polysilicon resistive heaters. The micro hotplate with diaphragm structure shows low power consumption, but more endeavors need to be done to increase its mechanical stability.

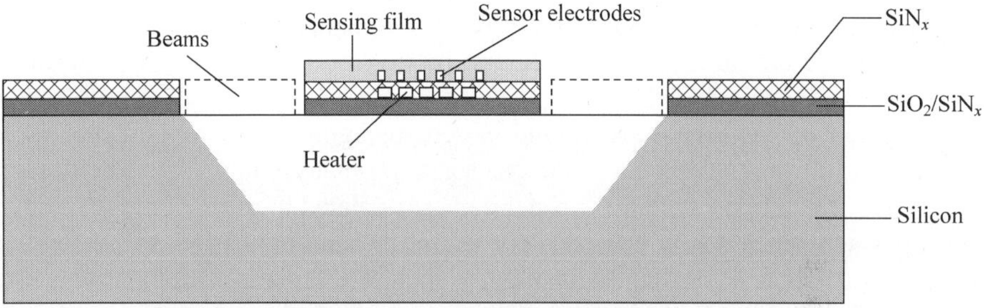

Figure 7.19 Schematic graph of micro-bridge hotplate gas sensor

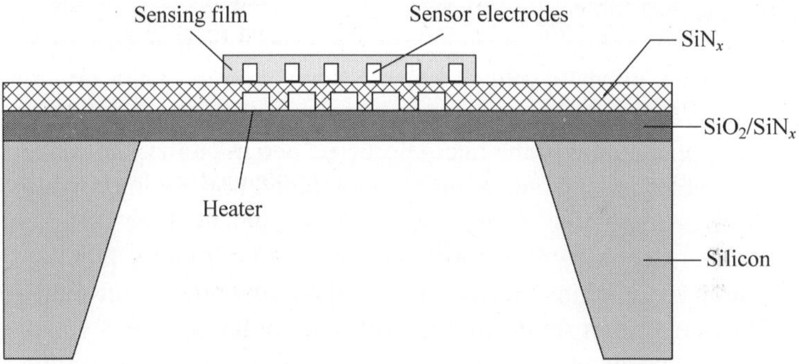

Figure 7.20 Schematic graph of diaphragm micro hotplate gas sensor

Xiuli He et al.[54] reported the typical steps for microhotplate sensor fabrication: ① 0.8 μm thick SiO_2 was prepared on n-type ⟨100⟩ silicon wafer with dry and wet oxidation successively. ② 1 μm thick Si_3N_4 was deposited using LPCVD (low pressure chemical vapor deposition) method. ③ Pt heater and the temperature sensors were sputtered and figured by lift-off method. ④ The low stress SiON film, 1 μm thick, was deposited as the insulating layer using PECVD (plasma enhanced chemical vapor deposition). ⑤ The interdigitating electrode was prepared on the SiON layer by sputtering. ⑥ The window was formed through the backside etching of silicon with KOH solution. The dimension of the device is 3 mm × 3 mm and the size of the hotplate is 1.4 mm × 1.4 mm. The working area (where the heater and interdigitating electrodes are located) is 0.72 mm × 0.72 mm. The power consumption to maintain the operating temperature of 300℃ is about 75 mW and the operating temperature can be modulated in several micro seconds from room temperature to 500℃.

7.4.2 Microgas Sensor Array

Most metal oxide gas sensors have poor selectivity to a given gas. For example, a SnO_2-based ethanol gas sensor may be interfered by gasoline, perfume and water vapor, etc. The selectivity of metal oxide gas sensors can be improved by optimizing the operating temperature and modifying the surface characteristics of the sensing materials, but the problem is essentially not solved. With the development of gas sensor arrays and pattern recognition techniques, electronic nose (E-nose) has replaced the single gas sensor in many fields[55–57]. The volume and power consumption of an E-nose are mainly related to those of sensor arrays. Microgas sensor arrays, which are very useful in hand-held E-noses, are widely investigated because of their advantages such as miniaturization, low power consumption, and batch production[58, 59].

More efforts have been made on microgas sensor arrays to fabricate more sensors on one device and realize the monolithic integration of microgas sensors and circuitry. Yaowu Mo et al. fabricated the 2 × 4 metal oxide gas sensor array on a 2 mm × 4 mm silicon chip[60]. Seung-Chul Ha et al. prepared 16 polymer/carbon black gas sensors on a 30 mm × 14 mm silicon chip[61]. High-integration was reported by NIST that there were 340 sensors on a silicon chip with the area of 40 mm^2[49]. Full integration of the microelectronic and micromechanical components on one chip enables on-chip signal amplification and notably improves the overall sensor performance. C.Hagleitner et al.[62] incorporated three different sensors (mass-sensitive, capacitive and calorimetric) and the circuitry (analog-to-digital converters and an on-chip interface to transmit the data to off-chip recording units) to fabricate a smart single-chip microsensor system to detect volatile organic compounds. M. Afridi et al.[63] designed and fabricated a monolithic MEMS-based gas sensor with the pre-CMOS processing, and the sensor showed high sensitivity to 100 ppm carbon monoxide. Bin Guo et al.[64] prepared a monolithic 4 × 4 tin oxide gas sensor array together with on-chip multiplexing and differential read-out circuitry with post-CMOS processing. The sensor array showed good sensing properties to ethanol, methane, hydrogen, and carbon monoxide.

Figure 7.21 shows the pictures of 2×2 microsensor array fabricated at State Key Lab of Transducer Technology, IECAS. The array includes single membrane and multi membrane respectively. It can be seen from Fig. 7.22 that power consumption to maintain the operating temperature of 300℃ is about 30 mW per sensor. Figure 7.23 shows the encapsulated microgas sensor array.

Front side   Back side (multi membrane)   Back side (single membrane)

Figure 7.21 The picture of the microgas sensor array

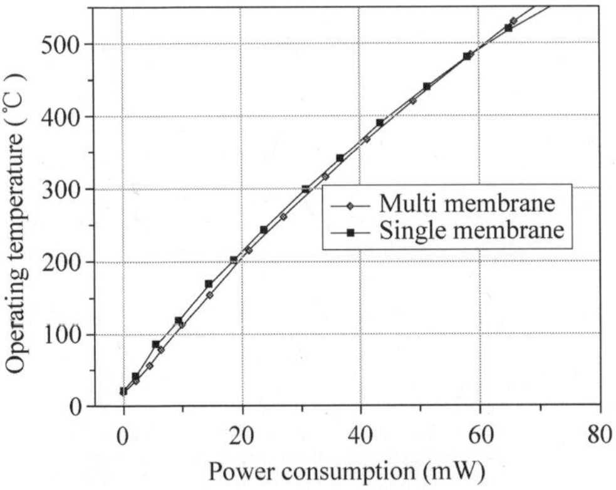

Figure 7.22 The relation between power consumption and operating temperature

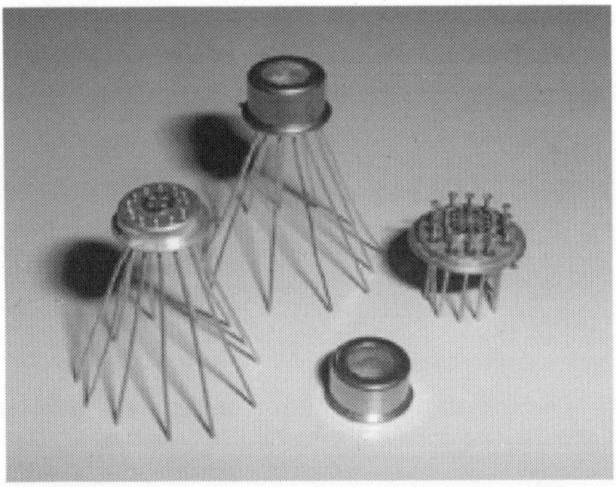

Figure 7.23 Encapsulated microgas sensor array (see color figure at the end of this book)

7.4.3 Nanofiber Based Gas Sensing Materials

Metal oxides, especially tin dioxide, were applied as the primary gas sensing materials. In order to improve the gas sensing performance, many researches are focused on nanostructured metal oxides[65–67]. Currently, one-dimensional nanostructured metal oxide with high surface to volume ratio attracts special attention. Considerable efforts have been made to fabricate metal oxide nanowires, nanobelts, nanorods, and nanofibers via thermal oxidation, thermal evaporation, self-catalytic growth, molten salt synthesis, and electrospinning. As a novel preparation process of one-dimensional nanomaterial, electrospinning is a cost-effective route to generate ultra-thin fibers by electrostatic stretching[68].

Figure 7.24 is the basic setup for electrospinning. In a typical electrospinning process, a solution droplet under the needle tip is highly electrified by a strong electric field and the induced charges are distributed over the surface. As a result, the droplet experiences two major types of electrostatic forces: an electrostatic repulsion between the surface charges and a Coulombic force exerted by the external electric field. Under these electrostatic interactions, the droplet is distorted into a conical object commonly known as Taylor cone. When the intensity of electric field reaches a critical value, the electrostatic forces overcome the surface tension of the solution and an electrified jet is produced. The jet is subsequently stretched by the electric field force to form a continuous and thin fiber.

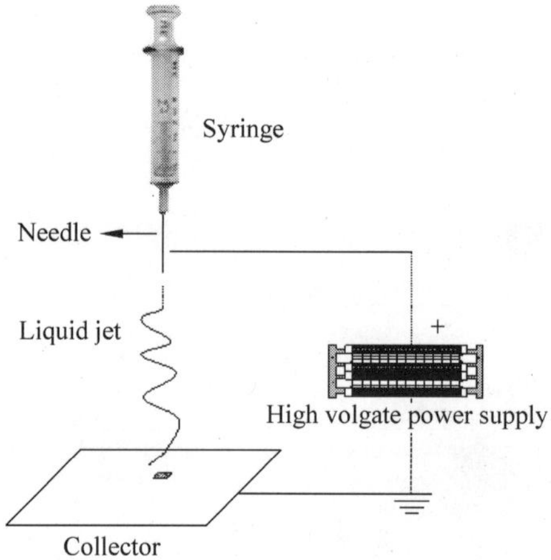

Figure 7.24 The schematic illustration of the setup for electrospinning

Early work on electrospinning mainly dealt with conventional organic polymers with high molecular weights. In recent years, functional ceramic fibers, such as CuO, SnO_2, TiO_2, ZnO[69–72], were also prepared by electrospinning of the polymer solutions incorporated metal precursors and annealing.

The electrospun fibers with a high surface to volume ratio offer potential applications in gas sensors. Researches on the gas sensing properties of organic electrospun materials can be found in some literature[73, 74]. For inorganic electrospun materials, the electrospun TiO_2 nanofiber mats exhibited exceptional sensitivity to NO_2 with a detection limit below 1 ppb[75] and the electrospun WO_3 nanofibers had a high sensitivity to ammonia with a wide range of concentrations[76]. However, research on the gas sensing properties of inorganic electrospun materials is far from being satisfied.

Yang Zhang et al.[77] reported a kind of micro gas sensor based on SnO_2 nanofibers fabricated with electrospinning PVA/$SnCl_4 \cdot 5H_2O$ composites on a micro hotplate. The certain amount of $SnCl_4 \cdot 5H_2O$ was added in the 6 wt % PVA (Mw = 80,000 g/mol) aqueous solution. The electrode-to-collector distance was settled as 5 mm and the applied voltage was 5 kV. The electrospun fibers were dried for 24 hours at 100℃ to ensure that the solvents were vaporized completely. Subsequently, the fibers were annealed in air at 700℃ for 4 hours.

Figure 7.25 shows the SEM and TEM images of the SnO_2 fibers. The fibers with several hundred micrometers in length are randomly distributed on the substrate and intercross with each other to form porous fiber networks. The diameter of the fibre is about 50 nm and the size of the SnO_2 particle is about several nanometers. The porosity of the fibres provides a high surface to volume ratio and large surface accessibility for the interaction between SnO_2 and ethanol. Figure 7.26 shows the response/recovery curves of the sensor to ethanol in the range of 0.01 – 5,000 ppm at 330℃. The sensor exhibits a large response to 10 ppm ethanol (4.5), low detection limit (<10 ppb), fast response/recovery (<14 s), and good reproducibility. The results show that the electrospun SnO_2 nanofibers can be used as novel gas sensing material.

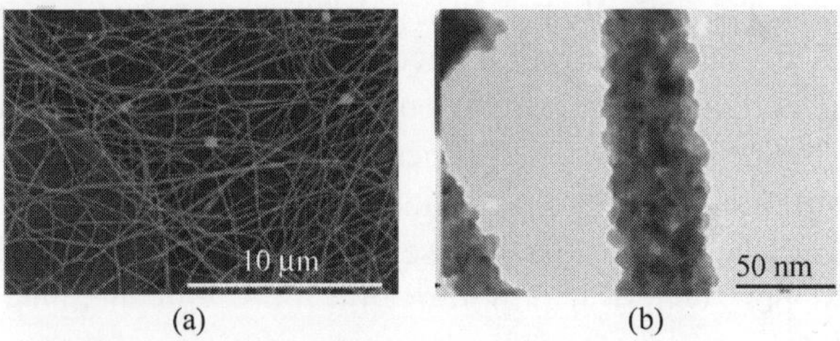

(a) (b)

Figure 7.25 (a) SEM and (b) TEM images of the fibers

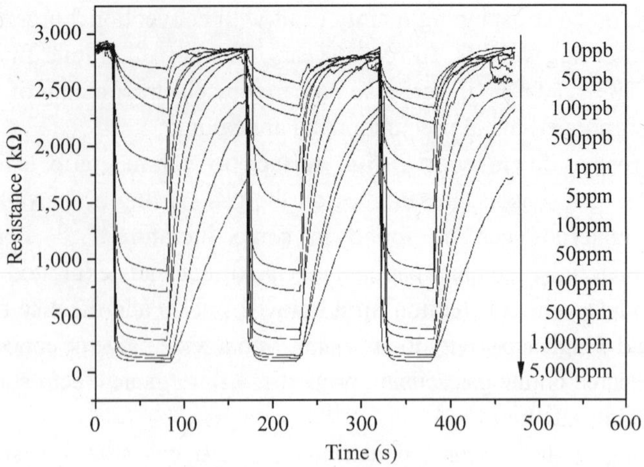

Figure 7.26 Response/recovery curves of the sensor to ethanol in the range of 0.01 – 5,000 ppm at 330℃

7.5 Waveguide-Based Nanoporous Thin-Film Sensors for Chemical, Biological and Gas Detection

Nanoporous materials have currently attracted considerable attention due to their distinctive properties and potential applications in the fields of optics, catalysis, sorption, separation, lithium battery, solar cell, and chemical/biochemical sensors[78, 79]. Of a large variety of nanoporous materials, nanoporous thin films of SiO_2, TiO_2, and Al_2O_3 are most popular with material scientists because they are readily fabricated in simple and low-cost processes from the corresponding raw materials easily available. Nanoporous SiO_2, TiO_2, and Al_2O_3 thin films are optically transparent, chemically robust, and thermally stable. They possess a high surface area and a low refractive index relative to the corresponding bulk materials. The narrow pore-size distribution and the uniform pore arrangements render such nanoporous thin films homogenous in subwavelength scale, thereby making them capable of either guiding light or serving as the cladding layer of optical waveguides[80, 93–95]. Large internal surface areas of nanoporous SiO_2, TiO_2, and Al_2O_3 thin films allow for accommodating a great number of external molecules, which could lead to a high sensitivity and a low detection limit for the chemical and biological sensors fabricated with the nanoporous thin films. Moreover, careful control of the pore size of nanoporous SiO_2, TiO_2, and Al_2O_3 thin films could make the sensors size-selective to biomolecules. It is feasible to functionalize the pore wall of nanoporous thin films with chemical and biological molecules, which is very useful for improving selectivity of the sensors.

Nanoporous SiO_2, TiO_2, and Al_2O_3 thin films are usually fabricated by three techniques. The first technique is sol-gel surfactant templating chemistry that can be used to prepare ordered mesoporous thin films with the pore sizes ranging from 2 nm to 50 nm. The second technique is direct coating of the colloidal solutions on the substrates to produce random nanoparticle films with interparticle spaces as the nano-sized irregular pores. The third method consists of two steps: first, anodizing semiconductive silicon or metallic substrates to create nanoporous layers on the substrates, and subsequently heating the substrates in air to oxidize the pore wall of the layers into the corresponding oxides. The first two methods are flexible, allowing for fabricating nanoporous thin films of pure and doped oxides on a variety of substrates. The last method requires the substrates to be conductive and generally limits the nanoporous layers to the undoped materials. However, the recent advances in anodizing methods allow for fabricating nanoporous thin films on the insulating substrates covered with conductive layers[80, 81]. Nanoporous thin films can have different nanostructures, depending on the synthetic methods used. Figure 7.27 shows microscopic images of four nanoporous materials: (a) sol-gel block copolymer (P123) templated mesoporous SiO_2 thin film with a 2-dimensional (d) hexagonal mesostructure, (b) sol-gel ionic surfactant templated mesoporous SiO_2 layer with a 3D cubic mesostructure, (c) anodized alumina film with the open-pore structure, and (d) TiO_2 nanoparticle film with irregular nanopores. Images (a) and (b) were taken by transmission electron microscopy (TEM), and images (c) and (d) were taken by scanning electron microscopy (SEM). Except the 2D hexagonal mesostructure shown in the image (a), the other three nanostructures are favorable for rapid molecular diffusion with in the mesoporous thin films.

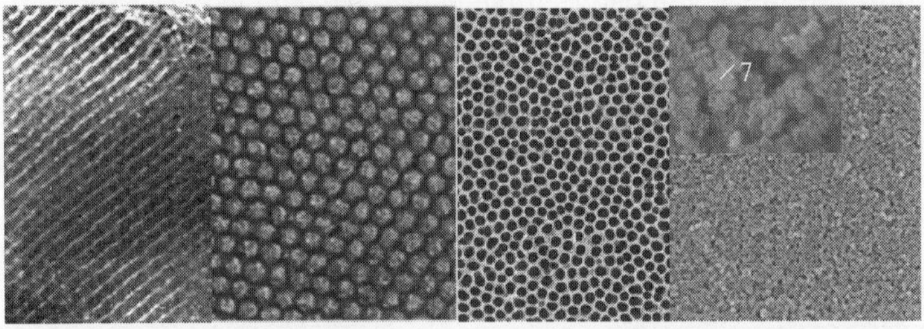

(a) (b) (c) (d)

Figure 7.27 Microscopic images of four nanoporous materials (a) TEM-hexagonal SiO_2; (b) TEM-cubic SiO_2; (c) SEM- anodized Al_2O_3; (d) SEM-colloidal TiO_2 layer

Chemical, biological, gas and humidity sensors based on nanoporous SiO_2, TiO_2, and Al_2O_3 thin films have been developed by use of different measuring methods, including surface acoustic wave (SAW) transduction[82], quartz crystal microbalance (QCM) transduction[83], surface photovoltage (SPV) measurement[79], electrical conductometry[82, 89], optical absorptiometry[90], fluorimetry and interferometry[84–87]. Since nanoporous thin films are compatible with optical waveguides, we are interested in waveguide-based nanoporous thin-film sensors.

Waveguide-based sensors have several intrinsic advantages such as high sensitivity, strong resistance to electromagnetic interference, good safety due to the inability to yield electric spark, and good capability for remote detection in harsh and dangerous environments with the help of fiber coupling and communication. There are two factors to significantly affect sensitivity of waveguide-based sensors. One factor is the depth of interaction between the guided wave and the analyte molecules, and another factor is the interaction pathlength. Conventional waveguide-based sensors prepared with dense and crack-free thin films permit the analyte molecules to interact with only the sensor surface, thereby limiting the interaction depth to the monomolecular adlayer thickness (several angstroms to a few nanometers), making the sensitivity per unit interaction pathlength small. For high sensitivity, the interaction pathlength of conventional waveguide-based sensors has to be increased, consequently leading to an increase in size of the sensor device. With use of nanoporous thin films, the waveguide-based sensors would overcome this shortcoming. This is so because the nanoporous thin films as the sensing layer of waveguide-based sensors can extend the interaction depth from a monomolecular adlayer thickness to the thickness of nanoporous films (hundreds of nanometers to a few micrometers), thereby enabling the sensitivity per unit interaction pathlength to be greatly increased. On the basis of the same reason, it is also effective to enhance the sensitivity of surface plasmon resonance (SPR) sensors by using the nanoporous thin films to cover the gold (or silver) layers deposited on the prism surface[96]. To help understand the interaction-depth extension induced by the nanoporous thin films, Figs. 7.28 and 7.29 schematically illustrate the comparisons between the SPR sensors uncovered and covered with the nanoporous thin films, and between the dense-waveguide-based and nanoporous-waveguide-based sensors.

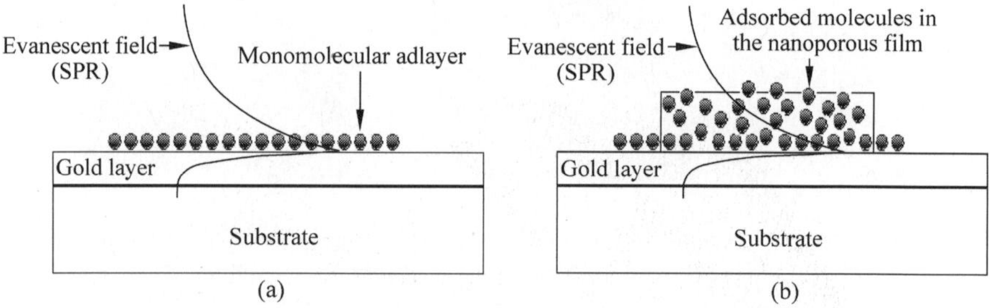

Figure 7.28 Schematic diagram for explaining the nanoporous layer induced extension of the interaction depth of the SPR sensor (a) conventional SPR; (b) SPR with the top layer of a nanoporous film

We recently developed a novel waveguide-based nanoporous thin-film sensor that operates with single-beam polarimetric interferometry (PI)[88]. The PI sensor was used for detection of trace ammonia gas at room temperature, and it was prepared by using the sol-gel triblock copolymer templating technique to fabricate

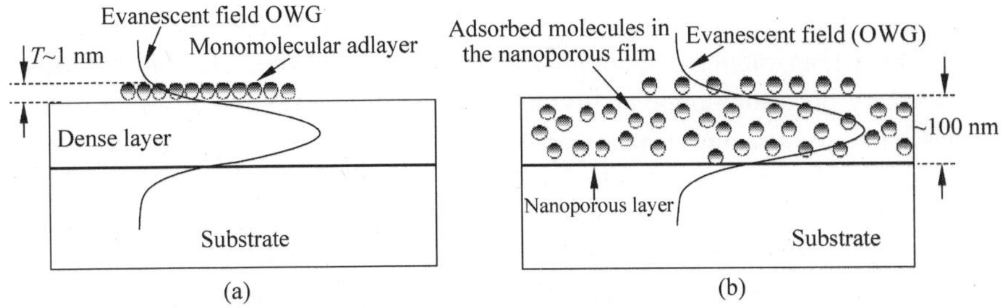

Figure 7.29 Comparison between the dense-waveguide-based and the nanoporous-waveguide-based sensors (a) dense waveguide (b) nanoporous waveguide

the phosphor-doped mesoporous TiO_2 thin films on the multilayer-layer region of the planar composite waveguides. The sol-gel process for fabricating mesoporous TiO_2 thin films was described in detail in a previous work[88]. The triblock copolymer template used was Pluronic P123. The dry sol-gel thin films were calcined at 350℃ in air for 5 hours to remove the P123 template from the films. Incorporation of phosphor into the TiO_2 thin films was aimed at suppressing the pore collapse during calcination. The spectroscopic ellipsometry measurements indicate that the mesoporous TiO_2 films are typically 60 nm thick with a refractive index of $n \approx 1.59$ at a wavelength of $\lambda = 633$ nm. Figure 7.30 shows atomic force microscope (AFM) image of the mesoporous TiO_2 thin film. The open pores with a uniform distribution on the film surface are clearly seen from the AFM image. Such open-pore mesoporous TiO_2 thin films would facilitate the rapid diffusion of gaseous molecules within the films and therefore could expedite

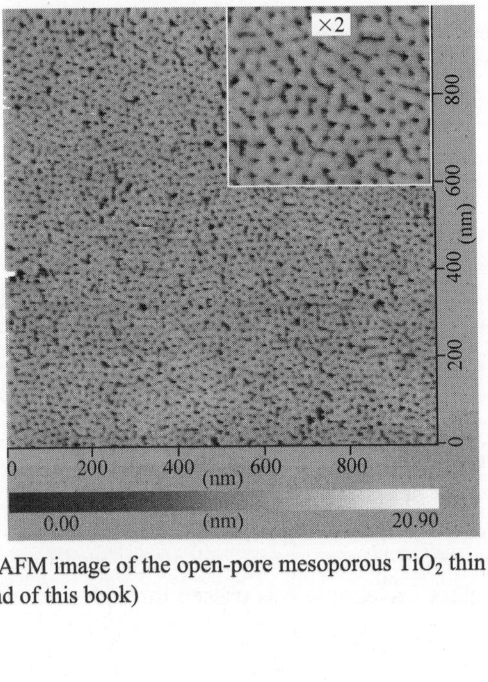

Figure 7.30 AFM image of the open-pore mesoporous TiO_2 thin film (see color figure at the end of this book)

the response and recovery of the PI sensor. In addition, the AFM image suggests the lack of a long-range order degree of the pore arrangement, which was also confirmed by both low-angle X-ray diffractometry (XRD) and TEM techniques (the XRD pattern and the TEM image not shown).

The so-called planar composite waveguide is a single-mode tin-diffused glass slab waveguide locally covered with a sputtered TiO_2 thin film[92]. The TiO_2 thin film was tapered by mounting a mask in front of the substrate during sputtering for adiabatic transition of the guided mode between the uncovered and covered regions of the glass waveguide, based on the tapered velocity coupling theory. The sputtered TiO_2 thin film with the two 1-mm-long tapers is 18 nm thick and 12 mm wide. Its refractive index was measured as $n \approx 2.30$ at $\lambda = 633$ nm, being much higher than that of the mesoporous TiO_2 layer. The single-beam PI sensor was constructed with the planar composite waveguides and the prism-coupling method as shown in Fig. 7.31.

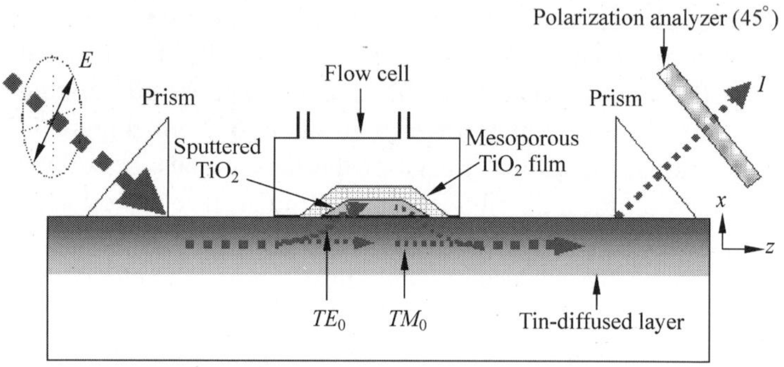

Figure 7.31 Single-beam PI sensor constructed with the planar composite waveguides (see color figure at the end of this book)

Qi developed the single-beam PI sensor based on planar composite waveguides in 1999 when he was pursuing his doctoral degree in Yokohama National University, Japan[92]. It is a simple and inexpensive yet extremely sensitive optical transducer whose sensitivity to refractive index is 100 times greater than that of conventional SPR sensors. The basic principle of the PI sensor is that the zero-order transverse electric (TE_0) and magnetic (TM_0) modes simultaneously excited in the polarization-insensitive glass waveguide, with a linearly polarized laser beam under the prism-coupling condition, undergo spatial separation in the waveguide region covered with the tapered thin TiO_2 film due to differences in the cut-off thickness between the TE_0 and TM_0 modes. Lift-up of the TE_0 mode leads to a very strong evanescent field relative to the TM_0 mode. Therefore, the TE_0 mode serves as the active beam and the TM_0 mode as the reference. With the second TiO_2 taper, both the TE_0 and TM_0 modes recombine as they return from the film-covered waveguide region into the uncovered region. The light beam coupled out of the glass waveguide was passed through a 45° polarization analyzer for the interference between the TE and TM components to occur. The interference signal was detected with a silicon photodiode detector in front of which a pinhole was mounted. The interference signal can be expressed by Eq. (7.4) and the difference in the integral phase between the TE_0 and TM_0 modes can be written as Eq. (7.5).

$$I = I_0(1 + \gamma \cos \phi) \tag{7.4}$$

$$\phi = \frac{2\pi}{\lambda} \int_0^L (N_{TE} - N_{TM}) dz \tag{7.5}$$

where γ is the fringe contrast, ϕ is the integral-phase difference, λ is wavelength in vacuum, L is the width of the tapered layer of TiO_2 along the mode-propagating direction z, and N_{TE} and N_{TM} are effective refractive indexes for the TE_0 and TM_0 modes. The PI sensor with an uncovered composite waveguide was demonstrated to have a refractive-index sensitivity of $\Delta n = 5\times10^{-6}$ for $\Delta\phi = 1°$ (see Fig. 7.32).

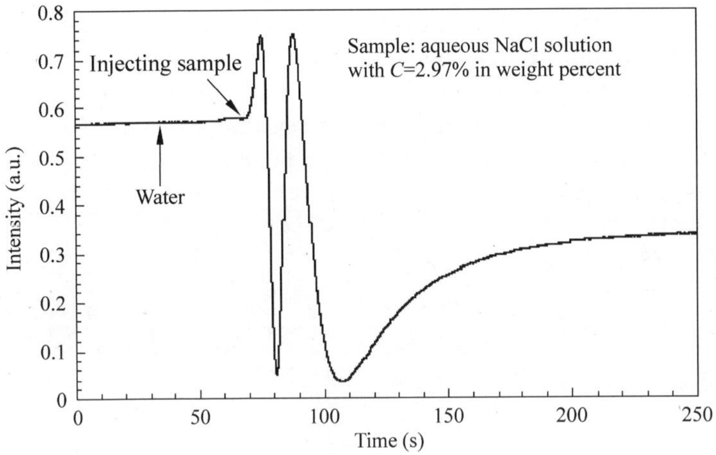

Figure 7.32 Interference pattern of the PI sensor measured with the aqueous NaCl solution to replace the deionized water on the tapered TiO_2 layer of the planar composite waveguide

Adsorption of gaseous molecules within the pores of the thin film would lead to an increase in the film index of refraction when the top layer of the planar composite waveguide is a mesoporous TiO_2 thin film, according to the Bruggeman approximation that can be expressed by Eq. (7.6)[97]. Consequently, the molecular adsorption within the mesoporous thin film would cause N_{TE} and N_{TM} to change. However, ΔN_{TE} is always larger than ΔN_{TM} because, with the TE_0 mode, the optical power fraction in the mesoporous thin film is greater than that with the TM_0 mode. Therefore, the signal of the PI sensor changes with the amount of the analyte molecules adsorbed within the mesoporous thin film.

$$f_1 \frac{n_1^2 - n^2}{n_1^2 + 2n^2} + f_2 \frac{n_2^2 - n^2}{n_2^2 + 2n^2} + f_3 \frac{n_3^2 - n^2}{n_3^2 + 2n^2} = 0 \tag{7.6}$$

where f_1, f_2, and f_3 are volume fractions of the TiO_2, the pores, and the adsorbed gas-phase analyte, respectively, and n_1, n_2, and n_3 are refractive indexes of the above three components.

The gas-sensing properties of the PI sensor with the sensing layer of a 60-nm-thick open-pore mesoporous TiO_2 thin film were investigated by use of the dry gas-flow system. Switching between the target gas and pure nitrogen make the flow rate stable during each measurement. Figures 7.33 – 7.35 show the experimental results. The findings demonstrate that the PI sensor is reversibly responsive to ammonia gas at room temperature, the response and recovery times are less than 90 seconds, and the detection limit is less than 99 ppb of ammonia gas. In contrast with the sensitivity to ammonia, the PI sensor is almost not responsive to benzene vapor. Insensitivity of the PI sensor to nitrogen dioxide was also observed (the response to NO_2 not shown). From the point of view of the dipole-dipole interaction between the gas-phase analyte and the mesoporous TiO_2 layer, the good selectivity of the PI sensor to ammonia among the three gases could be attributed to a large permanent dipole moment of NH_3 molecules (1.47 D) relative to those of NO_2 (0.3 D) and C_6H_6 (0 D). We did not investigate the influence of humidity to the ammonia sensitivity of the PI sensor, but the presence of water molecules adsorbed within the mesoporous TiO_2 thin film was confirmed by mass spectroscopy.

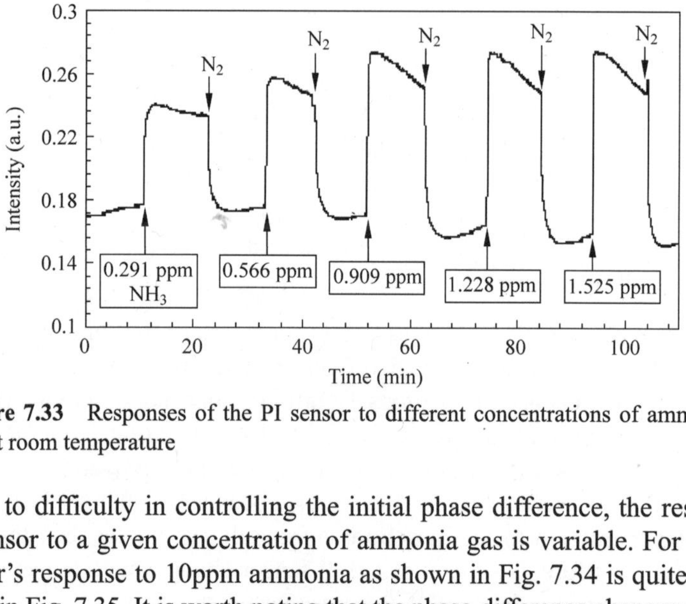

Figure 7.33 Responses of the PI sensor to different concentrations of ammonia gas at room temperature

Owing to difficulty in controlling the initial phase difference, the response of the PI sensor to a given concentration of ammonia gas is variable. For example, the sensor's response to 10ppm ammonia as shown in Fig. 7.34 is quite different from that in Fig. 7.35. It is worth noting that the phase-difference changes measured at the two times should be identical with each other despite the different responses of the PI sensor. For a desirable response to a small concentration of ammonia, the signal of the PI sensor should be in the quasi-linear segment of the cosine curve, which can be realized by using a quarter-wave plate to adjust the initial phase difference.

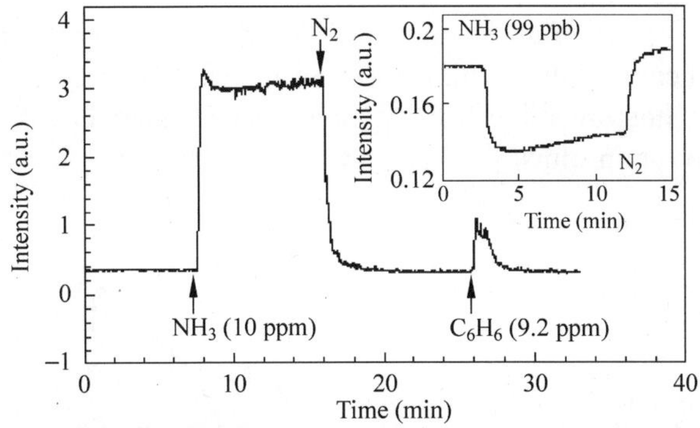

Figure 7.34 Comparison between the response of the PI sensor to ammonia gas and that to benzene vapor (the benzene exposure led to a pulse change of the signal; not a stable change as detected for the ammonia exposure). Insert reveals that the sensor's detection limit for ammonia gas is below 99 ppm

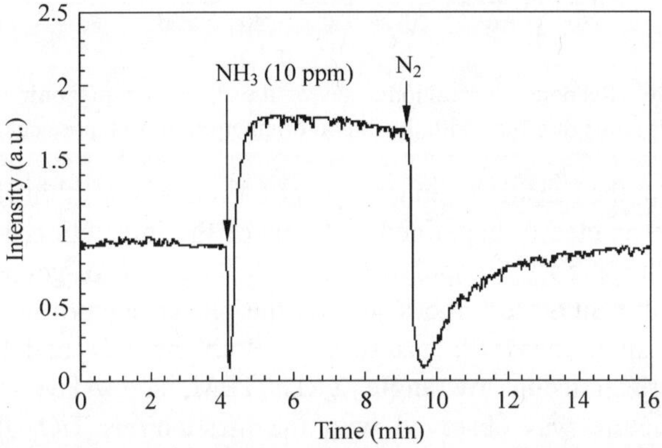

Figure 7.35 Response of the PI sensor upon exposure to 10 ppm of ammonia gas

As mentioned above, the PI sensor exhibits rapid response and recovery to ammonia gas, attributable to the open-pore structure of the mesoporous TiO_2 sensing layer. For comparison, we fabricated the sol-gel mesoporous silica thin films on the planar composite waveguides and then investigated the gas-sensing properties of the resulting PI sensor[87]. Combination of the low-angle XRD pattern and the TEM image (see Fig. 7.27(a)) of the mesoporous silica thin films indicates that the pore channels in the film are arranged into a 2D hexagonal structure with the orientation being parallel to the substrate. This means that the gaseous molecules are accessible to the mesoporous silica thin film by lateral diffusion. Figure 7.36 shows the response at room temperature to 2.1 ppm ammonia of the PI sensor coated with the mesoporous silica layer. Upon exposure to ammonia, the sensor signal slowly changes with time. Switching the ammonia gas to pure nitrogen did not lead to a fast and complete recovery of the sensor signal. It is evident that the lateral diffusion of ammonia molecules in the pore channels of the silica film is too slow. The findings suggest that the sol-gel mesoporous silica thin films with the 2D hexagonal mesostructure and the lateral orientation are not favorable sensing layers as compared with the open-pore mesoporous TiO_2 thin films.

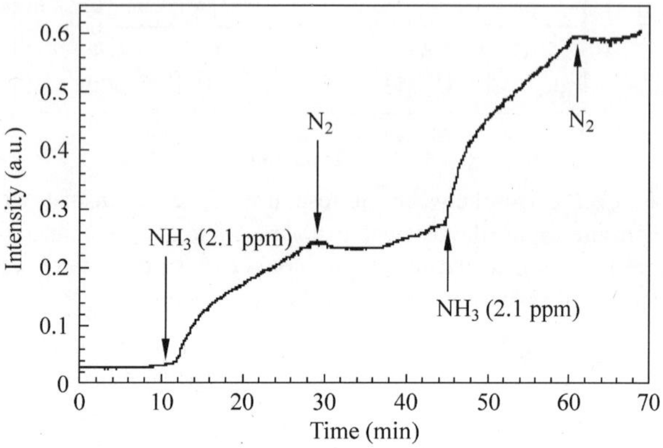

Figure 7.36 Response to ammonia gas of the PI sensor containing an ordered mesoporous silica thin film with the lateral orientation of mesopore channels

In conclusion, the sensitivity enhancement for nanoporous thin-film evanescent-wave sensors was clearly explained in terms of the interaction-depth extension. By using the Pluronic P123 copolymer template, the two sol-gel mesoporous thin films of TiO_2 and SiO_2 were fabricated on the planar composite waveguides for application as single-beam PI gas sensors. Both the TiO_2 and SiO_2 thin films were characterized using low-angle XRD, TEM, and AFM techniques. The open-pore structure was observed with the mesoporous TiO_2 thin films. The mesoporous SiO_2 thin films contain long-range ordered 2D hexagonal mesostructure and lateral orientation of pore channels. The PI sensors with mesoporous TiO_2 thin films are sensitive to low concentration of ammonia gas at room temperature, and the sensor's response and recovery are fast. However, the PI sensor with the mesoporous SiO_2 thin film yielded a too slow response upon exposure to ammonia gas. The comparison between the two PI sensors suggests that for chemical, biological and gas sensor applications of nanoporous thin films, the behavior of the resulting sensor is closely related to the nanoporous structure of the sensing layer.

7.6 Electrochemical Reaction Based Biochemical Sensors

Biosensors and chemical sensors are simply known as biochemical sensors. The biochemical sensors hold an important portion in the domain of sensors. Potentiometric biochemical sensors and amperometric biochemical sensors are both based on electrochemical reactions of the transducers.

With the development of micro/nano fabrication technology, biochemical sensors can be integrated with electronics on single silicon chips, which are readily associated with concepts such as robustness, mass production, high yields, and low manufacturing costs. Other considerations such as low power, high speed, small dimensions, and portability, being of great value especially in the field of medical healthcare, are also motivations for developing biochemical sensors based on micro/nano fabrication technology. All these factors made possible the integration of extremely small sensors with signal-processing circuits and performing sensing in chemical, biochemical, and biomedical industries.

7.6.1 Ion-Sensitive Field Effect Transistor (ISFET) pH Sensors

The potentiometric biochemical sensors normally have a working electrode and a reference electrode. They enable the detection of analytes at levels previously only achievable by high performance liquid chromatography (HPLC) and liquid chromatography/mass spectrometry (LC/MS), without rigorous sample preparation. The response signal is produced by electrochemical and physical changes in the sensitive layer due to reactions occurring at the surface of the sensor. Such changes can be attributed to ionic strength, pH, hydration, and sometimes redox reactions.

ISFET is a typical potentiometric biochemical sensor. In the past two decades, CMOS VLSI technology has played an important role for the realization of modern electronic systems. With the advantages of small size, reliability, rapid time response, compatibility with standard CMOS fabrication technologies, and on-chip signal processing, ISFET-based transducers are being increasingly used in physiological data acquisition and environment monitoring. ISFET is a MOS based device, and it is analogous to a metal oxide field-effect transistor (MOSFET) except for the metal gate that is replaced by the electrolyte and a reference electrode; so the most straightforward approach for such micro-systems compatible integration is CMOS technology. Such integrated systems (also called system on a chip, SOC) offer the potential for a full-scale biological and clinical analysis on a single chip.

Discrete ISFET sensors have had a long history of development since their first announcement in 1970[101]. As shown in Fig. 7.37, an ISFET is based on the charge adsorption at the ion/solid interface between the sensing layer, which contains hydroxyl groups and the electrolyte, from which hydroxyls may accept or donate protons. In this process, a double-layer capacitance is created with a potential drop, which influences the threshold voltage of the transistor depending on the value of H^+ protons activity. Therefore, it combines the operational principles of low-output impedance MOSFET and ion-sensitive ion-selective electrode (ISE)[102, 103]. ISFETs are not restricted to use only as $[H^+]$ sensors, as other ions can be detected if additional sensitive films are deposited over the inorganic membrane and in contact with the liquid. Compared with traditional ISE, ISFET has the advantages of robustness, integration, small size, short response time, high sensitivity, mass production, high yields and low manufacturing costs, etc., and it has been used in chemical, biochemical, and biomedical industries.

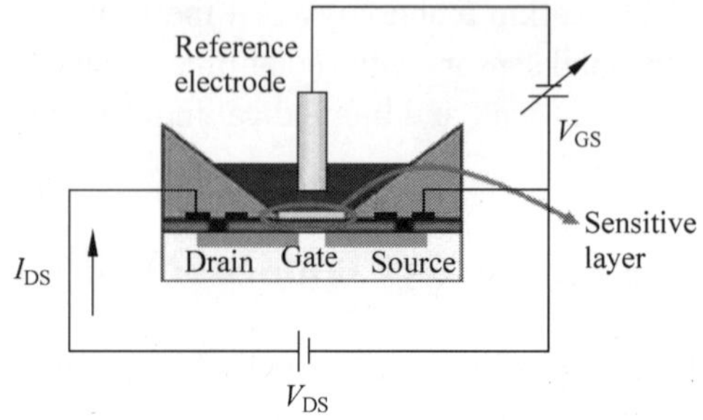

Figure 7.37 Schematic diagram of an ISFET (see color figure at the end of this book)

To achieve accurate measuring, the differential measuring method with a working electrode and a reference electrode is desired. Most of the conventional reference electrodes are not suitable for integration due to their large size and short lifetime. Developing a reference electrode that can be integrated with ISFET in one chip with the same electric characteristics as ISFET is the current trend.

An ISFET-based CMOS micro-system for pH measurement has been reported[104]. The chip consists of a constant current source and differential ISFET/reference FET (REFET) operational trans-conductance amplifier (OTA). The devices are designed and fabricated using an unmodified standard CMOS process. All signal acquisition and readout circuitry is implemented on-chip using standard library components. Figure 7.38 shows the cross section of the differential pH sensor system schematically. The sensor includes two FETs, which are the ISFET and the REFET. For compatibility with the standard CMOS techniques, an extended-gate ISFET structure was designed, which was different from conventional MOSFET-based open gate ISFET. To achieve pH measurement by a differential method, ion-sensitive membrane and ion-insensitive membrane were deposited onto gate areas of the ISFET and the REFET, respectively.

An ISFET-based integrated pH sensor chip with the size of 2 mm×2.5 mm was developed for pH measurement. The chip consisted of two FETs and relative signal processing circuits, which were designed and fabricated using a commercial standard CMOS process. Because they were fabricated by the same process, the ISFET, the REFET, and their signal processing circuit could be integrated together in the same chip. After that, post CMOS process flow was conducted in our laboratory to fabricate the ISFET and REFET, and the sensor chip was encapsulated. Figure 7.39(a) is the photograph of the chip and Fig. 7.39(b) is the schematic diagram of the encapsulation.

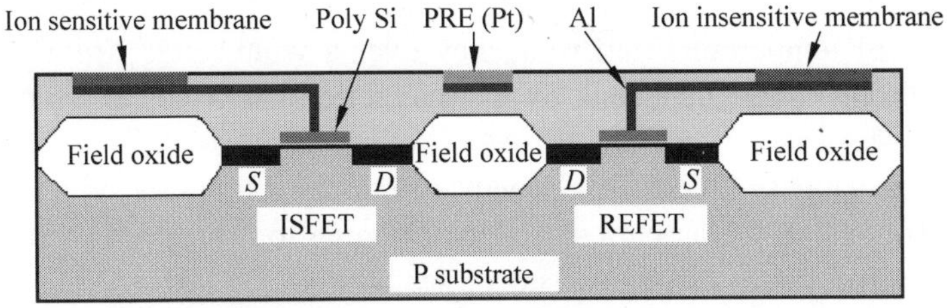

Figure 7.38 Schematic diagram of the differential pH sensor (see color figure at the end of this book)

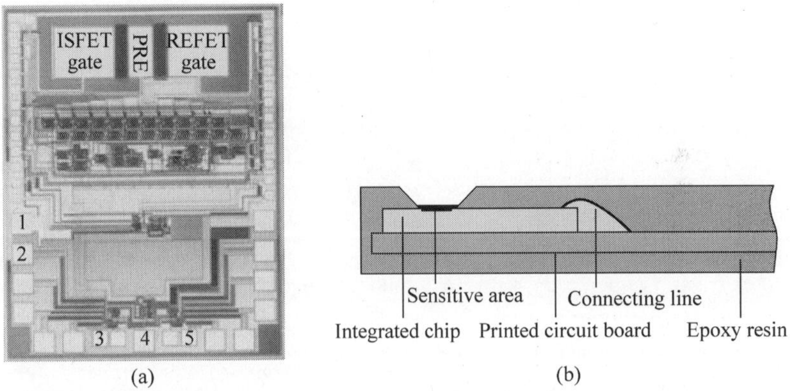

Figure 7.39 (a) Photograph of the chip and (b) schematic diagram of the encapsulated chip (see color figure at the end of this book)

During measurement, the gate voltage of an ISFET was directly proportional to the change of pH, represented by a change in the threshold voltage of the ISFET. The OTA provided a constant bias current I_{DS} and a constant voltage V_{DS} for ISFET/REFET to operate in the linear region. The gate voltage of the ISFET/REFET was measured through the OTA derived buffers.

Different kinds of materials such as Ta_2O_5, polypyrrole (PPy) and polytetrafluoroethylene (PTFE) were applied to construct the ion-sensitive membrane and the ion-insensitive membrane.

Ta_2O_5 has been studied as the pH-sensitive material and PTFE (Poly-Tetrafluoro-Ethylene, Teflon) as the pH-insensitive material[105]. Because of its good chemical stability, insolubility in solution, stability, and fast response time over a wide pH range, even at harsh environments, Ta_2O_5 can provide a suitable alternative to unstable insulator materials like SiNx and SiO_2 membranes. The choice of the electrically identical material for REFET was very restricted, which made it challenging to develop a REFET. In this case, a PTFE 'ion-unblocking' membrane was deposited to construct the REFET. PTFE has good insensitivity to pH variation, chemical stability, insulating ability, and dielectric strength, which is essentially independent of temperature and frequency over a wide range. Both Ta_2O_5 and PTFE membranes were deposited by RF magnetron sputtering and patterned by lift-off process.

The sensor using Ta_2O_5 and PTFE membranes proves to be sensitive, linear, and has low drift. Due to the on-chip signal conditioning for improved signal-to-noise ratio, the micro system exhibits a superb sensitivity of 53.67 mV/pH within the pH range of 4.01 to 12.45 and an enhanced linearity (as shown in Fig. 7.40).

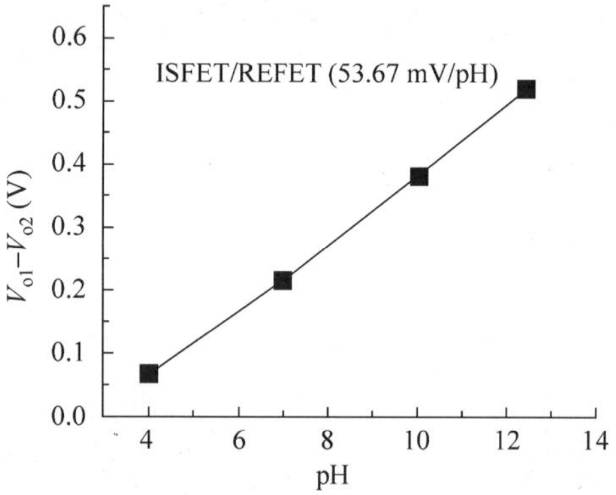

Figure 7.40 Sensitivity of ISFET (see color figure at the end of this book)

Polypyrrole (PPy) has been studied as the material used for both the pH-sensitive and pH-insensitive film. As a kind of conducting polymer, PPy can be obtained by the way of electrochemical polyermization. It was reported that the thickness of PPy membrane had great effect on the potentiometric response and linear range, and had strong effect on the response time and stability[106]. PPy membrane was grown on the gate of ISFETs by cyclic voltammetry. A high sensitivity of 53 mV/pH was achieved within the pH range from 1 to 12, the response time was less than 0.1 second, and time drift was less than 1 mV/h. In the differential measuring mode, the ISFET pH sensor system achieved a sensitivity of 21 mV/pH to pH, and very small response to Na^+ and K^+ (as shown in Fig.7.41).

The two examples show that integrated pH-ISFET micro system can be fabricated using standard CMOS technology.

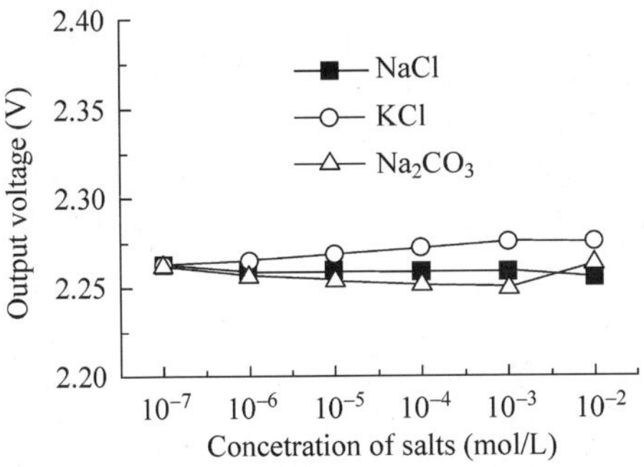

Figure 7.41 Selectivity of the pH-ISFET to Na^+ and K^+

7.6.2 Hemoglobin Biosensors Based on ISFET

Recently, biosensors based on microelectronics and MEMS techniques have received considerable attention. ISFET biosensors can achieve rapid and label-free detection of a wide range of chemical and biological species. Further more, since ISFET biosensors can be fabricated by the standard CMOS process, they could be reduced in size and mass-produced. They are known as one of the most important miniaturized biosensors[107]. Micro potentiometric hemoglobin (Hb) and henoglobin-A1c (HbA1c) immunosensors based on ISFETs have great potential to become portable devices and help for personal monitoring of diabetes.

For potentiometric biosensors, the general preparation procedure involves the immobilization of bioactive entities (antibodies and the like) onto electrochemical transducer surfaces. With the electrode miniaturization, the technique of depositing different biocompatible films on miniaturized electrodes and easy control of film characteristics are of great importance. Gold nanoparticles (AuNPs) have raised growing interest due to their unique size-dependant properties. They have been intensively studied in bioreagents immobilization via the large specific interface area, desirable biocompatibility, and high surface free energy of nanosized particles.

HbA1c is a kind of minor hemoglobin formed by a non-enzymatic reaction of glucose with the amino-terminal valine of the Hb β-chain[108]. The HbA1c level reflects the blood glucose concentration of the previous 2 – 3 months. Therefore, clinical methods for the determination of HbA1c has become an established procedure in the diagnosis and monitoring of diabetes[100]. HbA1c is measured as a relative content of total Hb with the clinical range 5% – 20%, and 4% – 6% is estimated as the normal value for a healthy adult. A miniaturized device which can carry out inexpensive and portable HbA1c and Hb analysis is highly desired.

A micro potentiometric Hb/HbA1c immunosensor based on ISFETs was reported[108]. A simple and direct procedure was developed to form PPy-AuNPs composite film, with the electrochemical growth of AuNPs in PPy. Based on this method, the antibody immobilization onto micro gold electrodes was enhanced.

The sensor consisted of a MEMS fabricated micro electrode and an integrated ISFET chip. The ISFET chip contained two ISFETs, two reference FETs (REFET), and the signal read-out circuits. The integrated ISFET chip containing two n-channel FETs were fabricated using a commercial CMOS process[111]. Two gold working electrodes, two gold reference electrodes, and a platinum pseudo reference electrode (PRE) were designed to construct the micro electrode, as shown in Fig. 7.42. The working electrodes and the reference electrodes were connected to the gates of the FETs, working as floating gate of FET. The working electrodes were connected to ISFET, and the reference electrodes were connected to REFET.

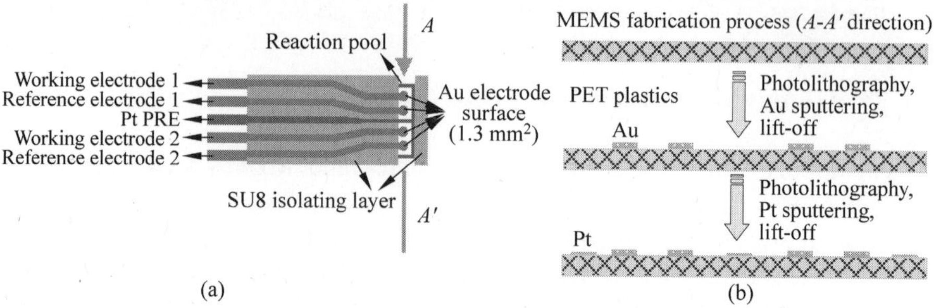

Figure 7.42 Schematic diagrams of (a) the electrode chip of the immunosensor and (b) the MEMS fabrication process (see color figure at the end of this book)

PPy-AuNPs composite and pure PPy were respectively deposited on the working electrodes and the reference electrodes. Immobilization of immunoactive entities and inactivated entities were carried out on the working electrode and the reference electrode respectively, so as to achieve differential measurement. Based on immobilization of Hb antibody or HbA1c antibody on the PPy-AuNPs, a hemoglobin/hemoglobin-A1c immunosensor was constructed. The PRE was used as the reference electrode and counter electrode during the electrode preparation and potentiometric measurement. An SU-8 micro reaction pool was designed to enclose the reaction solutions.

The antibody immobilization strategy employed the electrochemical synthesis of PPy-gold chloride acid ($HAuCl_4$) composite on gold electrode surface, the electrochemical reduction of $HAuCl_4$ into AuNPs, and the adsorption of antibodies to this composite film, as illustrated in Fig. 7.43.

This sensor carried out rapid measurement of Hb and HbA1c. For Hb measurement, a linear dose-response behavior between 60 μg/ml and 180 μg/ml was obtained, with a sensitivity of 0.099 mV μg^{-1} ml. For HbA1c measurement, 10 μl of HbA1c solutions with concentrations of 4 – 15 μg/ml were measured. The differential output voltage response to successive additions of HbA1c antigen solutions were displayed in Fig. 7.44. A linear dose-response behavior between 4 and 15 μg/ml was obtained with a sensitivity of 1.8 mV μg^{-1} ml. The response time was less than 1 minute.

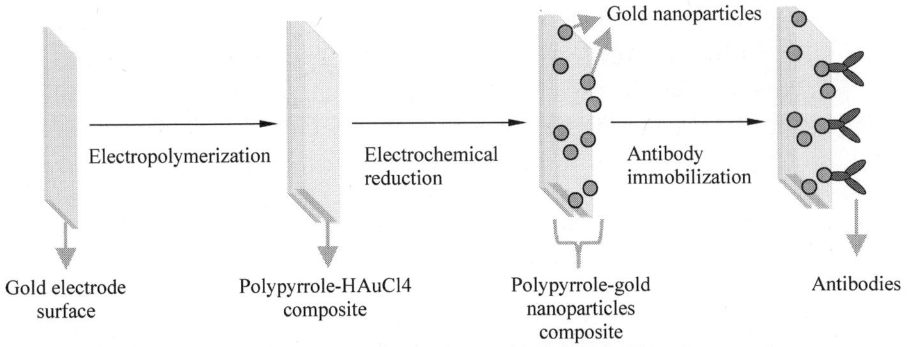

Figure 7.43 Schematic diagrams of the electrochemical synthesis of PPy-AuNPs composite and the antibody immobilization strategy (see color figure at the end of this book)

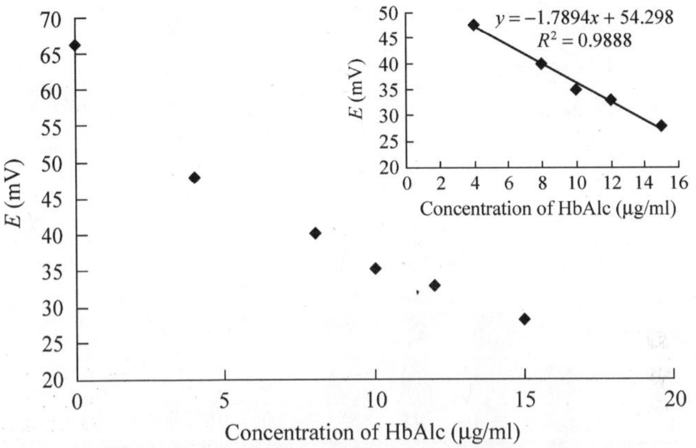

Figure 7.44 ISFETs differential voltage response of the hemoglobin-A1c immunosensor to successive injections of 0, 4, 8, 10, 12 μg/ml and 15 μg/ml HbA1c solution in PBS (pH 7.4). Reported voltages were taken 60 seconds after HbA1c injection. The inset is the calibration curve with HbA1c concentrations of 4 – 15 μg/ml

The surface morphologies study of PPy-AuNPs electrodes were conducted by scanning electron microscopy (SEM). Figure 7.45(a) displays the electrode surface morphologies of PPy-$HAuCl_4$ film, and Figure 7.45(b) shows the PPy-AuNPs composite film. The image of PPy-$HAuCl_4$ composite shows a rough structure on the gold electrode with no nanoparticles in sight (Fig. 7.45(a)). The morphologies of PPy are typical.

By contrast, after the electrochemical voltage bias treatment, the synthesized PPy-AuNPs composite shows a rough PPy structure with AuNPs in it (Fig. 7.45(b)). The AuNPs (small white dots in the image) in sight have uniform distribution, which is different from the report that metal nanoparticles tend to congregate into large nanostructures at the surface of PPy film[112]. This can be attributed to the method used for the formation of AuNPs. During the PPy-AuNPs electrode preparation procedure, $AuCl_4^-$ were uniformly distributed in the PPy film by the electropolymerization process of PPy-$HAuCl_4$ composite. Similarly, the AuNPs were entrapped and uniformly distributed in the PPy film, since they were formed by electrochemical reduction from the Au (III) in the form of $AuCl_4^-$.

The size distribution of AuNPs approximates to Gauss distribution, as shown in Fig. 7.45(c). The average size of AuNPs is 12.8 nm, when the PPy-AuNPs composite films were formed with a PPy/$HAuCl_4$ ratio of 100:1.

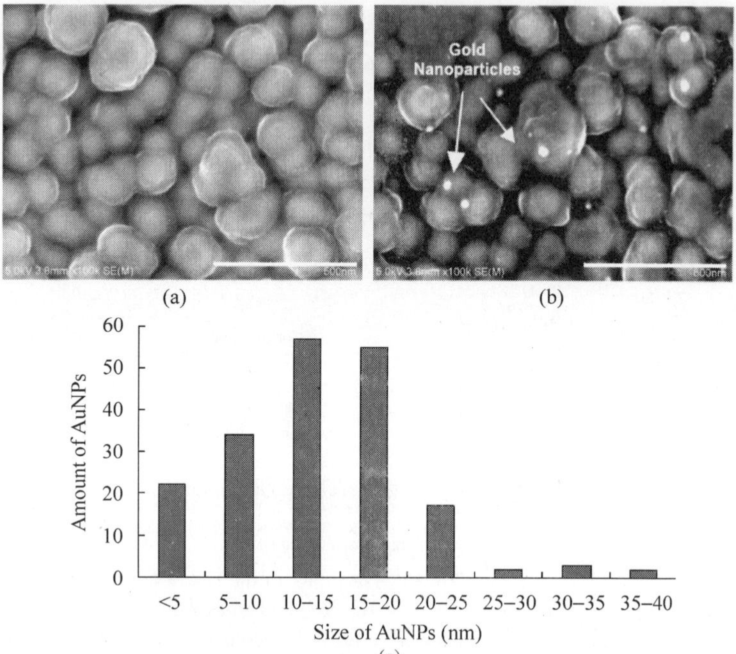

(c)

Figure 7.45 Field emission scanning electron micrographic (FE-SEM) images of gold electrodes coated with (a) electropolymerized PPy-$HAuCl_4$ composite, (b) PPy-AuNPs composite formed by a negative voltage bias, and (c) a size distribution curve of the AuNPs. In (a) and (b), the scale bars indicate 500 nm

The employment of gold nanoparticles in PPy film enlarges effective surface area of the polymeric film. It also allows the proteins to be more strongly adsorbed in large quantity with well-retained bioactivity, compared to the flat metal surface and the PPy film. With the AuNPs and the PPy film structure which has a rough surface with many gaps and pores, more space can be provided for protein molecules (antibodies and the like) to become immobilized on the electrochemically synthesized PPy-AuNPs composite.

7.6.3 Amperometric Immunosensors

The amperometric sensors usually have three electrodes, i.e. a working electrode, a counter electrode and a reference electrode. The target analyte is involved in the reaction that takes place on the working electrode surface. The current that flows through the working electrode is proportional to the analyte concentration, and the ions produced there create a potential which is subtracted from that of the reference electrode to give a signal. We can either measure the current at a fixed potential, or the potential can be measured at zero current.

Nowadays, more and more electrochemical sensors have been widely applied for biomedical detection. As an important type of these sensors, the electrochemically-based immunosensors are valuable analytical tools for monitoring of the antibodies or antigens. Requirements for an ideal immunosensor include high specificity and high sensitivity using a protocol that can be completed in a relatively short time. Tremendous research effort has been put into the development of such analytical devices[113−115]. Among many methods developed for this purpose, the amperometric biosensor utilizing the high specificity of antigen-antibody bond and the amplified response produced by enzyme-substrate reaction is especially promising because of its simplicity and high sensitivity[116−119]. Moreover, the amperometric immunosensors that can be miniaturized and automated offer significant advantages over current technology, especially if detection is needed in the field. Therefore it has gained great interest since later 1990s. Various amperometric immunosensors with different electrodes such as gold, carbon, glass and carbon have been reported[120−122].

With MEMS and microelectronic technology, a micro amperometric immunosensor consisting of an 'Au/Pt/Pt' microelectrode system integrated with SU-8 micro pools was fabricated on silicon wafer (Fig. 7.46)[123]. Both the working electrode (WE) and counter electrode (CE) are inside the micro reaction pool. The sensitive area of the WE is 1mm^2 within the confine of the micro sensitive

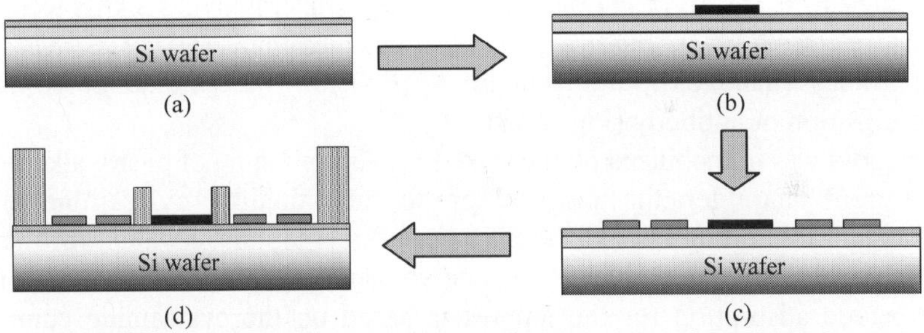

Figure 7.46 Illustrations of the fabrication process of the microelectrode

(a) Deposoting SiO_2 (300 nm), Si_3N_4 (200 nm) on Si wafer; (b) Patterning, depositing Au (300 nm) and lifting off; (c) Patterning, depositing Pt (300 nm) and lifting off; (d) Double exposure and single development of SU-8 photoresist pool. The final fabricated sensor chips are shown in Fig. 7.47, which are much smaller than conventional amperometric immunosensors and need only a few micro liters of the reagents for electrode modification and sensor measurement. Microelectrode amperometric immunosensors based on the micro/nano fabrication technology show attractive advantages, such as miniaturization, compatibility with CMOS techniques, easy to be designed into micro arrays, and enable relatively rapid, reliable and inexpensive field-analyses. The fabrication process is fully compatible with CMOS integrated circuit manufacturing processes.

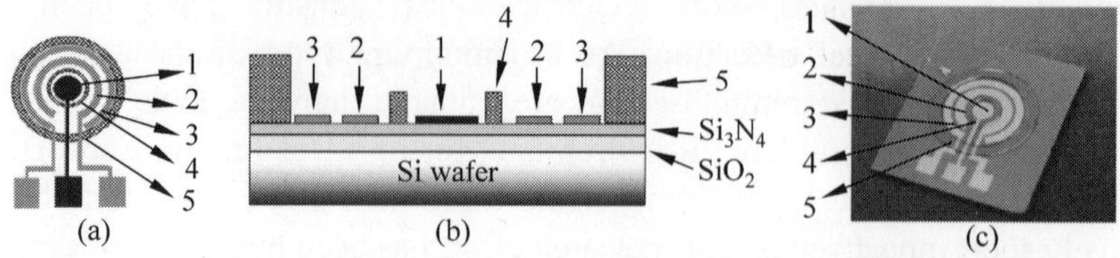

1. Working electrode (Au); 2. Counter electrode (Pt); 3. Reference electrode (Pt); 4. Immuno-reaction pool (SU-8); 5. Electrochemical reaction pool (SU-8).

Figure 7.47 Structural design of the microelectrode (a) top view; (b) cross section view; (c) Photograph of the micro immunosensor (8 mm× 8 mm) (see color figure at the end of this book)

The crucial step for biosensors is to immobilize bimolecular on the sensor transducers. Recent years have witnessed increasing attention being paid to using of nanoparticles for development of electrochemical immunosensors[124, 125], genosensors[126] and third-generation biosensors[127]. Gold nanoparticles (nanogold) have been intensively studied in bioreagents immobilization via the large specific interface area; desirable biocompatibility and high surface free energy of nanosized particles[128–132]. It turned out that sensors using nanoparticles in the immobilization approach showed high sensitivity, reproducibility, and long-term stability.

For example, a novel antibody immobilization strategy was investigated by combining the nanogold and mixed self-assembled monolayers (SAMs) technologies[133]. In 'Au/Pt/Pt' microelectrode system, employing SAMs technique, the Au electrode was modified by 1, 6-hexanedithiol (HDT) SAMs, gold nanoparticles (nanogold) and protein A (PA) for the orientation-controlled immobilization of antibody (Fig. 7.48).

Nanogold was immobilized on the mixed SAMs consisting of binary alkanethiols of different chain lengths and end group functionality, cysteamine and 1, 6-hexanedithiol, through two different types of interactions: covalent for the thiol and electrostatic for the amines. As is known, nanogold binds covalently to thiols. Electrostatic adsorption for the amines is based on the cysteamine containing $-NH_3^+$ group to absorb the negative-charged nanogold by way of the opposite-charged adsorption technique. Subsequently, antibody was immobilized to nanogold by thiols bound covalently and amines adsorbed electrostatically. Mandal et al. have proved the possibility of using amine functionality to bind ligands to the

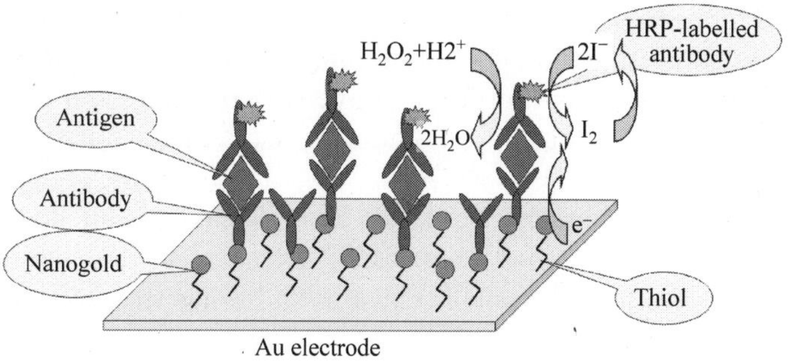

Figure 7.48 Antibody immobilization strategy: using nanogold and PA for the orientation-controlled immobilization of antibody with mixed SAMs technologies (see color figure at the end of this book)

surface of nanogold[134]. It was found that amine binding is as strong as thiol binding. The advantages of mixed SAMs, attractive physico-chemical characteristics of nanogold, specificity of the antibody-antigen reaction, amplification effect of enzyme catalysis, and the microelectronic amperometric immunosensors can be used to detect trace amounts of immunoactive entities such as α-fetoprotein (AFP), a widely used tumor marker for the diagnosis of patients with germ cell tumors and hepatocellular carcinoma. The performance of the proposed immunosensors in AFP quantification was determined by measuring their current response to a range of AFP concentrations under optimal analytical conditions (Fig. 7.49).

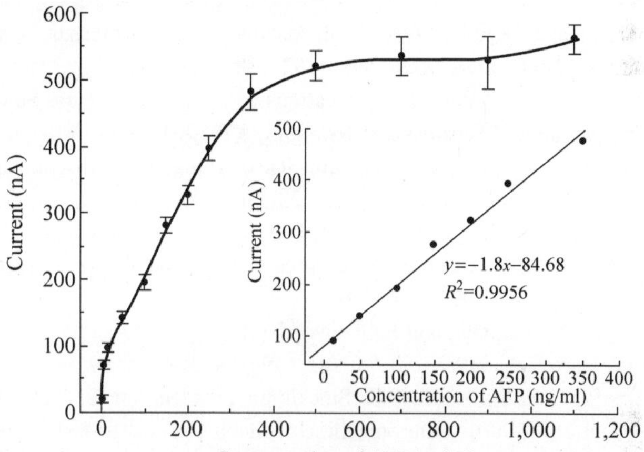

Figure 7.49 Calibration curve of the current response v. concentration of AFP with the immunosensor under optimal conditions. Inset shows linear calibration curves

The sensitivity and linear range of the current response for the detection of AFP were enhanced, as a result of the enlargement in specific interface area and reduction in steric hindrance, which was brought about by using binary alkanethiols of different chain lengths and end group functionality. Moreover, high stability of nanogold formed on the mixed SAMs assembled on the gold electrode makes it easier to immobilize antibodies and keep efficient activity retention of loading immunoreactants, which can further improve the sensitivity and linear range of the immunosensor. This kind of the immunosensors are also easily regenerated and reused.

The amperometric immunosensor in the example has been applied to AFP as a model system. Recently it has been readily extended toward the detection of other clinically or environmentally interested biospecies, such as IgG and Salmonella typhimurium[135].

References

[1] Sze S. M., (1994) *Semiconductor Sensors*, John Wiley & Sons, Inc

[2] Ristic L., (1994) Sensor Technology and Devices, Artech House

[3] Frank R., (1996) Understanding Smart Sensors, Artech House

[4] Gopel W., J. Hesse, and J. N. Zemel, (1995) Sensors, A Comprehensive Survey, Volume 8, Micro- and Nanosensor Technology/Trends in Sensor markets

[5] Gardner W. J., V. K. Varadan, and O. O. Awadelkarim, (2001) Microsensors, MEMS, and Smart Devices, John Wiley & Sons, Inc

[6] Clark, L. C., Jnr. C. Lyons, (1962) Electrode systems for continuous monitoring in cardiovascular surgery. *Ann NY Acad. Sci.*, **102**, 29 – 45

[7] Greenwood, J. C., (1984) "Etched silicon vibrating sensor," *J. Phy. E. Sci. Instrum.*, **17**: 650 – 652

[8] Greeenwood, J., and T. Wray, (1993) "High Accuracy Pressure Measurement with a Silicon Resonant Sensor," *Sensors and Actuators A*, **37** – **38**: 82 – 85

[9] Harada, K., et al., (1990) "Various Applications of Resonant Pressure Sensor Chip Based on 3-D Micromachining," *Sensors and Actuators*, **A73**: 261 – 266

[10] Ikeda, K., et al., (1990) "Silicon Pressure Sensor Integrates Resonant Strain Gauge on Diaphragm," *Sensors and Actuators*, **A21** – **23**: 146 – 150

[11] Petersen, K., et al., (1991) "Resonant Beam Pressure Sensor Fabricated with Silicon Fusion Bonding," *Proc. 6th Intl. Conf. on Solid State Sensors and Actuators (Transducers '91)*, San Francisco, CA, June 1991, 664 – 667

[12] Welham, C. J., J. W. Gardner, and J. Greewood, (1995) "A Laterally Driven Micromachined Resonant Pressure Sensor," *Proc. 8th Int. Conf. on Solid State Sensors and Actuators (Transducers '95) and Eurosensors IX*, Stockholm, Sweden, June 25 – 29, 586 – 589

[13] Beeby S. P., et al., (2000) "Micromachined Silicon Resonant Strain Gauges Fabricated Using SOI Wafer Technology," *IEEE J. Microelectromechanical Systems*, **9**(1): 104 – 111

[14] Melvås, P., E. Kälvesten, and G. Stemme, (2001) "A Surface Micromachined Resonant Beam Pressure Sensor," *IEEE J. Microelectromechanical Systems*, **10**(4): 498 – 502

[15] Chen D., D. Cui, et. al., (2001) "Thermally excited SiN beam resonant pressure sensor," *Proceedings of SPIE*, Vol. 4408, 2001, 548 – 554

[16] Chen D., D. Cui, et. al., (2001) "SiN beam resonant pressure sensors using sacrificial porous silicon," *Proceedings of The International MEMS Workshop 2001, 4 – 6 July, 2001, Singapore*, 673 – 677

[17] Chen D., D. Cui, et. al., (2002) "SiN beam resonant pressure sensors with a novel structure," *Sensors, 2002. Proceedings of IEEE*, **2**: 994 – 997

[18] Cui Z., D. Chen, S. Xia, (2002) "Modelling and Experiment of a Silicon Resonant Pressure Sensor," *Analog Integrated Circuits and Signal Processing*, **32**: 29 – 35

[19] Chen D., D. Chen, et. al., (2009) "Design and modeling of an electromagnetically excited silicon nitride beam resonant pressure sensor," Proceedings of IEEE NEMS 2009

[20] Wang J., D. Chen, et al., (2008) "A novel method to eliminate the co-channel interference of micro-machined diffused silicon," Sensors, 2008 IEEE, 395 – 398

[21] Burrer C., J. Esteve, (1995) "A novel resonant silicon accelerometer in bulk-micromaching technology," *Sensors and Actuators,* **A46 – 47**: 185 – 189

[22] Roessig T., R. Howe, A. Pisano, et al., (1997) "Surface-micromachined resonant accelerometer," Proc. Ninth International Conference on Solid-State Sensors and Actuators, Transducers'97, 859 – 862

[23] Seshia A., M. Palaniapan, T. Roessig, et. al., (2002) "A vacuum packaged surface micromachined resonant accelerometer," *Journal of Microelectro Mechanical Systems*, **11**(6): 784 – 793

[24] Jia Y., Y. Hao, R. Zhang, (2005) "Bulk based resonant accelerometer," *Chinese Journal of Semiconductors*, **26**(2): 281 – 286

[25] Chen D., J. Chen, et. al., (2006) "Design and modeling of a novel resonant silicon accelerometer," Proceedings of 2006 Asia-Pacific Conference of Transducers and Micro-NanoTechnology (APCOT2006), 25 – 28, June, 2006, Singapore

[26] Joseph Y., et al, (2005) "A Review of Biological, Biomimetic and Miniature Force Sensing for Microflight. Intelligent Robots and Systems," 2005 IEEE/RSJ International Conference, 2 – 6 Aug. 2005, 3939 – 3946

[27] Lee M. H., H. R. Nicholls, (1999) "Tactile sensing for mechatronics—a state of the art survey," *Mechatronics,* **9**: 1 – 33

[28] Ozaki Y., T. Ohyama, T. Yasuda, and I. Shimoyama. (2000) "A gas flow sensor modeled on wind receptor hairs of insects," Proc.MEMS 2000 (Miyazaki, Japan), 531 – 537

[29] Chen J., Z. Fan, J. Zou, J. Enpl, and C. Liu, (2003) "Two dimensional micromachined flow sensor array for fluid mechanics studies," *Journal of Aerospace Engineering*, **16**(2): 85 – 97

[30] Fan Z., J. Chen, J. Zou, D. Bullen, C. Liu, F. Delcomyn, (2002) "Design and fabrication of artificial lateral-line flow sensors," *J. Micromech. Microeng*, **12**: 655 – 661

[31] Zhang H., E. So, (2002) "Hybrid resistive tactile sensing," *IEEE Trans. Syst. Man Cybernet*, **B32**: 57 – 65

[32] van Baar J., M. Rijkstru, R. Wiegerink, T. Lammerink, R. de Boer, and G. Krijnen, (2005) "Arrays of cricket-inspired sensory hairs with capacitive motion detection," Micro Electro Mechanical Systems, 2005, MEMS 2005, 18th IEEE International Conference on 30 Jan-3 Feb. 2005, 646 – 649

[33] Chen J., D. Chen, J. Wang, (2006) "Research on Resonant Low-Velocity Gas Flow Micro-sensor Based on Trichoid Sensillum of Insects", 5th IEEE Conference on Sensors, 2006, 1065 – 1069

[34] Horenstein M. N., P. R. Stone, (2001) "A micro-aperture electrostatic field mill based on MEMS technology," *Journal of Electrostatics*, **51 – 52**: 515 – 521

[35] Harold K., et al, (2002) "On the Measurement of Stationary Electric Fields in Air," IEEE Conference on Precision Electromagnetic Measurements, 524 – 525

[36] Hsu C. H., and R. S. Muller, (1991) "Micromechanical electrostatic voltmeter," IEEE International conference on Transducer '91, 659 – 662

[37] Riehl P. S., K. L. Scott, R. S. Muller, R. T. Howe, J. A. Yasaitis, (2003) "Electrostatic Charge and Field Sensors Based on Micromechanical Resonators," *Journal of Microelectromechanical System*, **12**(5): 577 – 589

[38] Peng C. R., X. X. Chen, C. Ye, H. Tao, G. P. Cui, Q. Bai, S. F. Chen, and S. H. Xia, (2006) "Design and Testing of a Micromechanical Resonant Electrostatic Field Sensor," *Journal of Micromechanics and Microengineering,* **16**: 914 – 919

[39] Chen X., C. Peng, H. Tao, C. Ye, Q. Bai, S. Chen, and S. Xia, (2006) "Thermally driven microelectrostatic fieldmeter," *Journal of Sensors and Actuators A*, **132**(2): 677 – 682

[40] Ye C., C. R.Peng, X. X. Chen, S. H. Xia, (2006) "A micromachined Electrostatic Field Sensor with Vertical thermal actuation," IEEE SENSOR 2006 Conference, 1419 – 1421

[41] Peng C., X. Chen, Q. Bai, L. Luo, and S. Xia, (2006) "A novel high performance micromechanical resonant electrostatic field sensor used in atmospheric electric field detection," Proceedings of the 19th IEEE Micro Electro Mechanical Systems Conference, MEMS 2006, Istanbul, Turkey, January 2006, 698 – 701

[42] Gianchandani Y. B., K. Najafi, (1996) "Bent-Beam Strain Sensors," *Journal of Microelectromechanical Systems*, **5**: 52 – 58

[43] Que L., J. S. Park, and Y. B. Gianchandani, (1999) "Bent-beam electro-thermal actuators for high force applications," *Proc. IEEE Conf. on Micro Electro Mechanical Systems, Orlando, Florida, America, Jan. 1999*, 31 – 36

[44] Que L., J. S. Park, Y. B. Gianchandani, (2001) "Bent-Beam Electrothermal Actuators—Part I: Single Beam and Cascaded Devices," *Journal of Microelctromechanical Systems,* **10**: 247 – 254

[45] Yan D., A. Khajepour, and R. Mansour, (1955) "Design and modeling of a MEMS bidrectional vertical thermal," *Phil. Trans. Roy. Soc. London*, **A247**: 529 – 551

[46] David K., C. Allen, and M. Ramaswamy, et al., PolyMUMPs Design Handbook, Rev. 10.0, http://www.memscap.com

[47] Qinghai W., K. M. Lee, and C. C. Liu, (1992) "Development of chemical sensors using microfabrication and micromaching techniques," The fourth international meeting on chemical sensors, Tokyo, 2 – 5

[48] Fung S. K. H., Z. Tang, P. C. H. Chan, J. K. O. Sin, P. W. Cheung, (1996) "Thermal analysis and design of a micro-hotplate for integrated gas sensor applications," *Sensors and Actuators A*, **54**: 482 – 467

[49] Semancik S., R. E. Cacicchi, M. C. Wheller, et al., (2001) "Microplate platforms for chemical sensor research," *Sensors and Actuators B*, **77**: 579 – 591

[50] Udrea L., J. W. Gardner, (1996) "Design of a silicon mircosensor array device for gas analysis," Microelectronics Journal, **27**: 449 – 457

[51] Lee D. D., W. Y. Chung, M. S. Choi, et al., (1996) "Low-power micro gas sensor," *Sensors and Actuators B*, **33**: 147 – 150

[52] Hellmich W., G. Muller, C. B. Braunmuhl, et al., (1997) "Field-effect-induced gas sensitivity changes in metal oxides," *Sensors and Actuators B*, **43**: 132 – 139

[53] Courbat J., D. Briand, N. F. de Rooij, (2007) "Reliability improvement of suspended platinum-based, micro-heating elements," *Sensors and Actuators A,* **142**: 284 – 291

[54] HE X. L., J. P. LI, X. G. GAO, W. Li, (2003) "NO_2 sensing characteristics of WO_3 thin film microgas sensor," *Sensors and Actuators B*, **93**: 463 – 467

[55] Gardner J. W., P. N. Bartlet, (1999) "Electronic Noses Principles and Applications," London: Oxford University Press

[56] Gardner J. W., P. N. Bartlett, (1994) "A brief history of electronic noses," *Sensors and Actuators B*, **18 – 19**: 211 – 220

[57] Snopok B. A., I. V. Knuglenko, (2002) "Multisensor systems for chemical analysis: state-of-the-art in electronic nose technology and new trends in machine olfaction," *Solid Films*, **418**: 21 – 41

[58] Zee F., J. W. Judy, (2001) "Micromachined polymer-based chemical gas sensor array," *Sensors and Actuators B*, **72**: 120 – 128

[59] Hong H. K., H. W. Shin, H. S. Park, et al., (1996) "Gas identification using micro gas sensors array and neural-network pattern recognition," *Sensors and Actuators B*, **33**: 68 – 71

[60] Mo Y. W., Y. Okawa, M. Tajima, et al., (2001) "Micro-machined gas sensor array based on metal film micro-heater," *Sensors and Actuators B*, **79**: 175 – 181

[61] S. C. Ha., Y. Yang, Y. S. Kim, S. H. Kim, Y. J. Kim, S. M. Cho, (2005) "Environmental temperature-independent gas sensor array based on polymer composite," *Sensors and Actuators B*, **108**: 258 – 264

[62] Hagleitner C., A. Hierlemann, D. Lange, et al., (2001) "Smart single-chip gas sensor microsystem," *Nature*, **414**(15): 293 – 296

[63] Afridi M., A. Hefner, D. Berning, C. Ellenwood, A. Varma, B. Jacob, S. Semancik, (2004) "MEMS-based embedded sensor virtual components for system-on-a-chip (SoC)," *Solid-State Electronics*, **48**: 1777 – 1781

[64] Guo B., A. Bermak, P. C. H. Chan, G. Z. Yan, (2007) "A monolithic integrated 4×4 tin oxide gas sensor array with on-chip multiplexing and differential readout circuits," *Solid-State Electronics*, **51**(1): 69 – 76

[65] Comini E., G. Faglia, G. Sberveglieri, D. Calestani, L. Zanotti, M. Zha, (2005) "Tin oxide nanobelts electrical and sensing properties," *Sensors and Actuators B*, **111 – 112**: 2 – 6

[66] Xu C. N., J. Tamaki, N. Miura, and N. Yamazoe, (1991) "Grain size effects on gas sensitivity of porous SnO_2-based elements," *Sensors and Actuators B*, **3**: 147 – 155

[67] Yamazoe N., (1991) "New Approaches for improving semiconductor gas sensors," *Sensors and Actuators B*, **5**: 7 – 19

[68] Lyons J., K. Jim, (2004) "Electrospinning: Past, Present & Future," *Textile World*, **154**(8): 46 – 48

[69] Guan H., C. Shao, B. Chen, et al., (2003) "A novel method for making CuO superfine fibres via an electrospinning technique," *Inorganic Chemistry Communications*, **6**: 1409 – 1411

[70] Li D., Y. Xia, (2004) "Electrospinning of nanofibers: reinventing the wheel," *Advanced Materials*, **16**(14): 1151 – 1170

[71] Dharmaraj N., C. H. Kim, K. W. Kim, H. Y. Kim, E. K. Suh, (2006) "Spectral studies of SnO_2 nanofibers prepared by electrospinning method," *Spectrochim. Acta A*, **64**: 136 – 140

[72] Yang X. H., C. L. Shao, H. Y. Guan, X. L. Li, J. Gong, (2004) "Preparation and

characterization of ZnO nanofibers by using electrospun PVA/zinc acetate composite fiber as precursor," *Inorg. Chem. Commun.*, **7**: 176 – 178

[73] Liu H. Q., J. Kameoka, D. A. Czaplewski, H. G. Craighead, (2004) "Polymeric nanowire chemical sensor," *Nano Lett.*, **4**: 671 – 675

[74] Kessick R., G. Tepper, (2006) "Electrospun polymer composite fiber arrays for the detection and identification of volatile organic compounds," *Sens. Actuators B*, **117**: 205 – 210

[75] Kim I. D., A. Rothschild, B. H. Lee, D. Y. Kim, S. M. Jo, H. L. Tuller, (2006) "Ultra-sensitive chemiresistors based on electrospun TiO_2 nanofibers," *Nano Lett.*, **6**: 2009 – 2013

[76] Wang G., Y. Ji, X. R. Huang, X. Q.Yang, P. I. Gouma, M. Dudley, (2006) "Fabrication and characterization of polycrystalline WO_3 nanofibers and their application for ammonia sensing," *J. Phys. Chem. B*, **110**: 23777 – 23782

[77] Zhang Y., X. L. He, J. P. Li, Z. J. Miao, F. Huang, (2008) "Fabrication and ethanol-sensing properties of micro gas sensor based on electrospun SnO_2 nanofibers," *Sensors and Actuators B*, **132**: 67 – 73

[78] Palaniappan A., X. Su, F. Tay, (2006) "Functionalized mesoporous silica films for gas sensing applications," *J. Electroceramics,* **16**: 503 – 505

[79] Yamada T., H. Zhou, H. Uchida, M. Tomita, Y. Ueno, I. Honma, K. Asai, T. Katsube, (2002) "Application of a cubic-like mesoporous silica film to a surface photovoltage gas sensing system, " *Micropor. Mespor. Mater*, **54**: 269 – 276

[80] Lau K. H. A., L. S. Tan, K. Tamada, M. S. Sander, W. Knoll, (2004) "Highly Sensitive Detection of Processes Occurring Inside Nanoporous Anodic Alumina Templates: A Waveguide Optical Study," *J. Phys. Chem. B,* **108**: 10812 – 10818

[81] Lazarowich R. J., P. Taborek, B. Y. Yoo, N. V. Myung, (2007) "Fabrication of porous alumina on quartz crystal microbalances," *J. Appl. Phys.,* **101**: 104909 (1 – 7)

[82] Varghese O. K., D. Gong, W. R. Dreschel, K. G. Ong, C. A. Grimes, (2003) "Ammonia detection using nanoporous alumina resistive and surface acoustic wave sensors," *Sens. Actuators B*, **94**: 27 – 35

[83] Palaniappan A., X. Li, F. Tay, J. Li, X. Su, (2006) "Cyclodextrin functionalized mesoporous silica films on quartz crystal microbalance for enhanced gas sensing," *Sens. Actuators B,* **119**: 220 – 226

[84] Lin V. S. Y., K. Motesharei, K. S. Dancil, M. J. Sailor, M. R. Ghadiri, (1997) "A Porous silicon-based optical interferometric biosensor, " *Science,* **278**: 840 – 843

[85] Gao J., T. Gao, M. J. Sailor, (2000) "Porous-silicon vapor sensor based on laser interferometry," *Appl. Phys. Lett.*, **77**: 901 – 903

[86] Qi Z. M., I. Honma, H. Zhou, (2007) "Nanoporous leaky waveguide based chemical and biological sensors with broadband spectroscopy," *Appl. Phys. Lett.* **90**: 011102 (1 – 3)

[87] Qi Z. M., I. Honma, H. Zhou, (2006) "Ordered-mesoporous-silica-thin-film-based chemical gas sensor with integrated optical polarimetric interferometry," *Appl. Phys. Lett.,* **88**: 053503 (1 – 3)

[88] Qi Z. M., I. Honma, H. Zhou, (2006) "Chemical gas sensosr application of open-pore mesoporous thin films based on integrated optical polarimetric interferometry," *Anal. Chem.*, **78**: 1034 – 1041

[89] Teoh L. G., I. M. Hung, J. Shieh, W. H. Lai, M. H. Hon, (2003) "High sensitivity semiconductor NO_2 gas sensor based on mesoporous WO_3 thin film," *Electrochemical*

and Solid-State Lett., **6**: G108 – G111
[90] Fiorilli S., B. Onida, D. Macquarrie, E. Garrone, (2004) "Mesoporous SBA-15 silica impregnated with reichard's dye: a material optically responding to NH_3," *Sens. Actuators B*, **100**: 103 – 106
[91] Gong J., W. Fei, S. Seal, Q. Chen, (2004) "Nanocrystalline Mesoporous SMO thin films prepared by sol-gel process for MEMS based hydrogen sensor," *Proc. of SPIE*, **5346**: 48 – 55
[92] Qi Z. M., K. Itoh, M. Murabayashi, H. Yanagi, (2000) "A composite optical waveguide-based polarimetric interferometer for chemical and biological sensing applications," *J. Lightwave Technol.*, **18**: 1106 – 1110
[93] Qi Z. M., I. Honma, H. Zhou, (2006) "Fabrication of ordered mesoporous thin films for optical waveguiding and interferometric chemical sensing," *J. Phys. Chem. B*, **110**: 11590 – 11594
[94] Qi Z. M., M. Wei, I. Honma, H. Zhou, (2006) "Sensitive slab optical waveguides composed of mesoporous metal-oxide thin films on the tin-diffused layers of float glass substrates," *J. Appl. Phys.*, **100**: 083102 (1 – 7)
[95] Miller L. M., M. I. Tejedor, B. P. Nelson, M. A. Anderson, (1999) "Mesoporous Metal Oxide Semiconductor-Clad Waveguides," *J. Phys. Chem. B*, **103**: 8490 – 8492
[96] Oh S., J. Moon, T. Kang, S. Hong, J. Yi, (2006) "Enhancement of surface plasmon resonance (SPR) signals using organic functionalized mesoporous silica on a gold film," *Sens. Actuators B*, **114**: 1096 – 1099
[97] Alvarez-Herrero A., R. L. Heredero, E. Bernabeu, D. Levy, (2001) "Adsorption of water on porous Vycor glass studied by ellipsometry," *Appl. Opt.* **40**: 527 – 532
[98] Compiled by A. D. McNaught and A. Wilkinson, IUPAC. (1997) *Compendium of Chemical Terminology*, 2nd ed. (the "Gold Book"), Blackwell Scientific Publications, Oxford
[99] Clark, L. C. Jnr. (1962) *Ann. NY Acad. Sci.* **102**: 29 – 45
[100] Turner, A. P. F. (1991), (1992), (1993), (1995) "Advances in Biosensors", I; II; Suppl. I; III, JAI Press, London, UK
[101] Bergveld P., "Development of an ion-sensitive solid state device for neurophysiological measurements," *IEEE Trans. Bio-Med. Eng. BME-17*, (1970): 70–71
[102] Martinoia S., G. Massobrio, (2000) "A behavioral macromodel of the ISFET in SPICE," *Sens. Actuators B*, **62**: 182 – 189
[103] Mundt C. W., H. T Nagle, (2000) "Applications of SPICE for modeling miniaturized biomedical sensor systems," *IEEE Trans. Biomed. Eng. BME*, **47**: 149 – 154
[104] Sun H. G., J. H. Han, J. B. Wei, S. H. Xia, (2005) "A pH-ISFET Based Micro Sensor System on Chip," *China Mechanical Engineering*, **16**(z1), 176 – 178 (in Chinese)
[105] Wang Z. M., H. G. Sun, J. H. Han, H. G. Yang, S. H. Xia, (2006) "A Novel Fully Integrated Chip System With Ptfe-refet," Asia-Pacific Conference of Transducers and Micro-Nano Technology (APCOT)
[106] Wang Z. M., J. H. Han, Z. X. Ren, C. Bian, S. H. Xia, (2007) "Characteristics of the PPY Material as pH Sensitive Membrane," *Proceedings of the 2nd IEEE International Conference on Nano/Micro Engineered and Molecular Systems*, Jan. 16 – 19, 2007, *Bangkok, Thailand*
[107] Liu Y., A. G. Erdman, T. H. Cui, (2007) *Sens. Actuators A: Phys.*, **136**(2): 540 – 545

[108] Qu L., S. H. Xia, C. Bian, J. Z Sun, J. H. Han, (2008) "A Micro Potentiometric Hemoglobin Immunosensor Based On Electropolymerized Polypyrrole-Gold Nanoparticles Composite, *Biosensors & Bioelectronics*," doi: 10.1016/j.bios.2008.07.077

[109] Bunn H. F., D. N. Haney, S. Kamin, K. H. Gabbay, P. M. Gallop, (1976) *J. Clin. Invest.* **57**: 1652 – 1659

[110] McDonald J. M., J. E. Davis, (1979) *Hum. Pathol.* **10**: 279 – 291

[111] Wei J. B., H. G. Yang, H. G. Sun, Z. J. Lin, S. H. Xia, (2006) *Rare Metal Mat. Eng. 35(suppl.3)*, 443 – 446

[112] Li Y., G. Q. Shi, (2005) *J. Phys. Chem. B* **109**(50): 23787 – 23793

[113] Xue M., T. Haruyama, E. Kobatake, M. Aizawa, (1996) *Sens. Actuators B* **36**: 458

[114] Jie M., C. Y. Ming, D. Jing, L. S. Cheng, L. H. Na, F. Jun, C. Y. Xiang, (1999) *Electrochem. Commun.* **1**: 425

[115] Zhang L., R. Yuan, X. Huang, Y. Chai, S. Cao, (2004) *Electrochem. Commun.* **6**: 1222

[116] Yu H., F. Yan, Z. Dai, H. Ju, (2004) *Anal. Biochem.* **331**: 98

[117] Dai Z., F. Yan, J. Chen, H. Ju, (2003) *Anal. Chem.* **75**: 5429

[118] Ionescu R. E., C. Gondran, L. A. Gheber, S. Cosnier, R. S. Marks, (2004) *Anal.Chem.* **76**: 6808

[119] Danilowicz C., J. M. Manrique, (1999) *Electrochem. Commun.* **1**: 22

[120] Darain F., Park S., Shim Y. B., (2003) *Biosensors and Bioelectronics*, **18**(5/6): 773

[121] Li J., Xiao L. T., Zeng G. M., et al., (2003) *Analytica Chimica Acta*, **494**(1/2): 177

[122] Fernández-Sánchez C., González-Garciá M. B., Costa-Garciá A., (2000) *Biosensors and Bioelectronics [J]*, **14**(12): 917

[123] Bian C., S. H. Xia, Y. Y. Xu, S. F. Chen, Z. Cui, "A micro amperometric immunosensor based on two electrochemical layers for immobilizing antibody," *The 4th IEEE Conference On Sensors Proceedings*, USA, 416 – 419

[124] Tang D., R. Yuan, Y. Chai, J. Dai, X. Zhong, Y. Liu, (2004) *Bioelectrochemistry*, **65**: 15

[125] Xu W., S. Xu, X. Ji, B. Song, H. Yuan, L. Ma, Y. Bai, (2005) *Colloids Surf. B: Biointerfaces,* **40**: 169

[126] Ren C., Y. Song, Z. Li, G. Zhu, (2005) *Anal. Bioanal. Chem.,* **381**: 1179

[127] Wang L., E. Wang, (2004) *Electrochem. Commun.,* **6**: 225

[128] Tang D. P., R. Yuan, Y. Q. Chai, X. Zhong, Y. Liu, J. Y. Dai, (2004) *Biochem.Eng. J.,* **22**: 43

[129] Xu S. Y., X. Z. Han, (2004) *Biosens. Bioelectron.*, **19**: 1117

[130] Zhang C., Z. Y. Zhang, B. B. Yu, J. J. Shi, X. R. Zhang, (2002) *Anal. Chem.,* **74**: 96

[131] Thanh N. T. K., Z. Kosenzweig, (2002) *Anal. Chem.,* **74**: 1624

[132] Lei C. X., F. C. Gong, G. L. Shen, R. Q. Yu, (2003) *Sens. Actuators B,* **96**: 582

[133] Xu Y. Y., C. Bian, S. F. Chen, S. H. Xia, (2006) "A microelectronic technology based amperometric immunosensor for α-fetoprotein using mixed self-assembled monolayers and gold nanoparticles," *Analytica Chimica Acta*, **561**(1 – 2): 48 – 54

[134] Mandal S., S. Phadtare, M. Sasiry, (2005) *Curr. Appl. Phys.,* **5**: 118

[135] Sun J. L., S. H. Xia, C. Bian, L. Qu, "A new method based on electropolymerizing Staphylococcal Protein A to immobilize antibody in micro amperometric immunosensor," *Advanced Material Research*, in press

8 MEMS Design

Yu-Chuan Su[1] and Liwei Lin[2]

[1] Department of Engineering and System Science, Hsinchu Tsing Hua University
E-mail: ycsu@ess.nthu.edu.tw

[2] Department of Mechanical Engineering, University of California, Berkeley, USA
E-mail: lwlin@me.berkeley.edu

Abstract Microelectromechanical systems (MEMS) involve both electronic and mechanical elements that may perform sensing, actuation, and other functions such as signal transduction, processing, control and communication. These systems have been evolving from simple function-specific devices to elaborate systems with complicated microstructures and integrative circuitry with the help of modern design tools and advanced manufacturing capabilities. Various engineering issues and problems including functionality, performance, integration, packaging, reliability, cost, etc. must be systematically and thoroughly considered for constructing these new generation microsystems. This chapter presents an overview on the design process with which engineers formulate plans for the realization of MEMS devices and systems, taking advantages of fundamental sciences on device physics, computer aided design (CAD) tools, as well as state-of-art fabrication libraries and manufacturing experiences. A short introduction to MEMS design is covered in Section 8.1. Section 8.2 addresses CAD tools for MEMS, including the current available software and research directions in this area. Design issues in the two most common micromachining processes, bulk-micromachining and surface-micromachining processes, have been discussed in Sections 8.3 and 8.4 with design examples. Finally, we conclude the chapter with summary and future trends in Section 8.5.

Keywords Design process, design for production, computer-aided design, drug delivery system, pressure sensor, finite element analysis

8.1 Introduction

Powered by tremendous efforts and innovation in development of the technology and explorations of its applications in all aspects, the field of microelectromechanical systems (MEMS) has been growing at a promising pace over the last few decades. MEMS generally refers to miniature devices and systems that may have integrated electronic and mechanical components for sensing or actuation for various engineering applications. These tiny devices and systems have been applied to various applications, especially for automotive, medical, consumer, communication, aerospace, and other industries[1-7]. These micro devices and systems offer advantages over their conventional counterparts, including significant reduction in size, dramatic improvement in performance, new functions that could not be otherwise realized, integrated functionalities, and great reduction in cost. Because of the tremendous promise, MEMS technology has generated a significant amount of interest in both academic and industrial research communities as well as commercial markets.

MEMS design generally means the design of small devices and systems of mechanical and electronic nature at the micrometer scale. However, in contrast to the advanced integrated circuitry designs in the field of microelectronics, MEMS typically uses simple and well-known electronics in its system architecture. As such, this chapter will concentrate on designs other than the microelectronics where more valuable features of MEMS are coming from at the current stage. The design process basically follows the general engineering flow chart as outlined in Fig. 8.1. It begins with a need and a decision to do something about it. In contrast to scientific or mathematical problems, practical design problems have neither clear definitions nor unique answers[8]. Furthermore, design problems are usually subject to certain constraints. Therefore, it is critical to clearly quantify the problems and apply necessary constraints to these problems at the very early stage of the design process. Problems are further divided into concrete tasks after the clarification and definition steps. Afterward, the main task is to apply scientific and engineering knowledge to solve the technical problems, and then to optimize

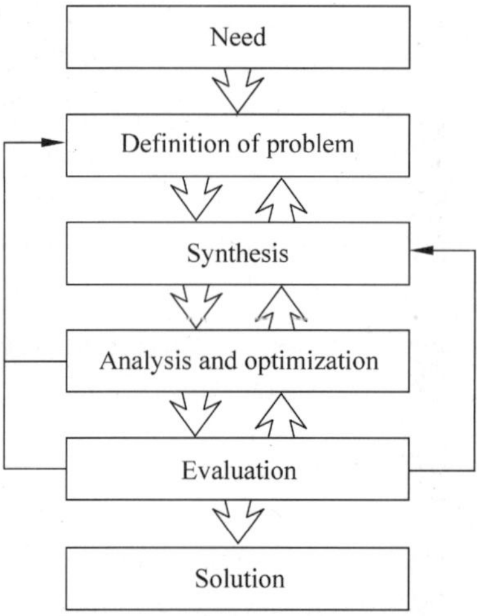

Figure 8.1 General engineering design process

these solutions within the requirements and constraints set by material, technological, economic, legal, environmental, and other considerations[9]. During the process, potential solutions, constraints, and even the definition of the problems must be refined repeatedly in order to achieve optimal design result. After several iterations, the process ends with a solution that satisfies the need with best performance and lowest cost.

When solving the technical problems, many different approaches are employed. For designers, up-to-date technological data, which can be found in technical journals and patent files, provide a wealth of important information. For example, existing designs can provide a most useful survey of known solution possibilities. In addition to literature review, designers often seek and discover solutions for difficult problems by intuition—that is, solutions come to them in a flash after a period of search and reflection[10]. These solutions suddenly appear as conscious thoughts and often their origins are difficult to trace. Once potential solutions are obtained, designers must then analyze whether the device conceptions, as implemented in specific technologies, will actually perform as desired. Furthermore, the analysis results provide insight into the problems and facilitate the improvement of designs. At this stage, designers employ mathematical models to predict the performance of potential designs and optimize these designs based on their predicted performance. Modeling and analysis do not replace the creative thinking needed to conceive product ideas that will have impact, but they support the entire design process[2].

In addition to performance characteristics, fabrication related issues must also be considered while evaluating and improving a potential design solution. Design for production, which means designing for the minimization of production cost and time while maintaining the required quality of the product, is critical for the development of any engineering design, especially for MEMS products. Because of the limited availability of standard fabrication processes for MEMS, in many cases, designers must create realistic fabrication processes for the desired devices or systems. As a result, the design of the manufacturing process itself could be the most challenging task in the overall MEMS design process. The problems are dramatically simplified if the product can be fitted into a foundry-based process. However, depending on the nature and complexity of the design, majority of MEMS products must be fabricated by a custom process. During the fabrication process, the designer needs to be familiar with process details such as material incompatibilities, chemical etchants, stress free thin-film, mechanical and material properties that are appropriate for the design. This is undoubtedly a task that requires a great deal of process knowledge, and it is a major time consuming step of the design process for MEMS.

While some market surveys for MEMS products have calculated $10 billion dollars or more per year, the current and projected market is widespread and segmented[11]. In order to be profitable, fixed costs associated with developing and maintaining repeatable fabrication processes, as well as the costs associated with design, analysis, and evaluation, must be shared by several or perhaps many different MEMS products. The per-chip costs can be effectively minimized by amortizing the costs of developing multiple market segments or niches, thereby allowing the MEMS technology to penetrate a broad scope of market segments and applications. Significant design flexibility, system integration, well-characterized processes, and a full suite of design, analysis, and evaluation tools are required to achieve efficient and profitable access to the segmented MEMS markets. Recognizing the variety of MEMS fabrication processes and the difficulty to address the design issues for each of them, this chapter will focus discussions on the available CAD tools, bulk-micromachining process together with a plastic molding sequence, surface-micromachining process based on a foundry service, and a practical design, fabrication and packaging example in the sections ahead.

8.2 MEMS Design Tools

Efficient MEMS development requires flexible and integrated design, analysis, and evaluation tools. Many research entities and software companies have developed design tools for MEMS[12−15], each with its unique set of strengths and weaknesses. Table 8.1 lists some of the major companies and research institutes

Table 8.1 Currently available MEMS design tools

Software	Developer	Category
Coventorware[16]	Coventor, Inc.	Integrated design environment
IntelliSuite[17]	IntelliSense Software Corp	Integrated design environment
MEMSCAP[18]	MEMSCAP, Inc.	Integrated design environment
MEMX[19]	MEMX Incorporated	Integrated design environment
PhoeniX[20]	PhoeniX BV	Integrated design environment
NODAS[21]	Carnegie Mellon University	Nodal Simulation
SUGAR[22]	U.C. Berkeley	Nodal Simulation
ANSYS[23]	ANSYS, Inc.	Multi-Physics Simulation
ABAQUS[24]	ABAQUS, Inc.	Multi-Physics Simulation
FEMLAB[25]	COMSOL, Inc.	Multi-Physics Simulation
CFDRC[26]	CFD Research Corporation	Fluidic Simulation
FLOW-3D[27]	Flow Science, Inc.	Fluidic Simulation
HFSS[28]	Ansoft Corporation	Electromagnetic Simulation
ACES[29]	U.I. Urbana-Champaign	Process Simulation
SIMODE[30]	TU Chemnitz	Process Simulation
L-Edit Pro[31]	Tanner Research, Inc.	Layout Design
LinkCAD[32]	Bay Technology	Layout Conversion

that are developing MEMS design tools. In general, design issues at the microscale may differ greatly from those encountered in the macroscale. For example, effects caused by electrostatic attraction, surface tensions, Van der Walls forces, and others can be more significant than inertia and gravity. Therefore, design and analysis tools developed for macroscale devices are inadequate in most cases for MEMS devices.

Although MEMS devices and systems are generally fabricated using lithography-based planar technologies developed for the integrated circuit (IC) industry, the three-dimensional geometric shape of MEMS and diversified device working principles implies that the required design tools are very different from those used by IC designers. It is therefore necessary to develop MEMS-specific, and sometimes, application-specific design tools. In general, MEMS engineers need basic tools, such as computer-aided design (CAD) framework, layout design, solid modeling, analysis, optimization, and fabrication simulation tools, to facilitate their design tasks.

8.2.1 CAD Framework

A CAD framework for MEMS supports representation and analysis in multiple energy domains (electrical, mechanical, thermal, radiant, chemical, magnetic, acoustic, and fluidic) with coupling between them. With proper definition and system configuration, design can be performed effectively and accurately by either novice or expert designers under the CAD framework. The basic function of the CAD framework is the layout tool.

The characteristics of MEMS devices, which typically are constructed layer by layer, are mainly determined by the geometry of all these structure layers. The layer geometry of each patterning step in the fabrication of MEMS devices is defined by a 2D mask, which is fabricated from layout drawing. For simple MEMS design, designers can employ standard IC layout tools that typically support Manhattan rectangles to design geometry and generate output file in special format for mask making. However, MEMS layouts usually include complicated shapes such as circles and polygons that are difficult to construct using standard layout programs. Furthermore, MEMS devices usually require special features, such as etch holes and geometrically varied arrays, to perform releasing and testing functions. For example, large complex layouts may need thousands of etch holes placed. It will be tedious for designers to manually place these etch holes. Currently, layout tools that can perform MEMS-specific functions to facilitate the design process are available on the market. These tools can draw planar features and are easy to use. Some of them have the capability to include processing files and show the cross sectional view of the layout based on the specific micromachining processes. Alternatively, one can use the common CAD layout tools such as

AutoCAD to design the microstructures but translation software is needed to convert the AutoCAD files to IC readable formats such as GDSII or CIF (Caltech Intermediate Format) for mask making machines to make manufacturing masks.

MEMS devices are three-dimensional structures in nature although they are typically manufactured layer-by-layer with planar lithography processes. It is difficult and time-consuming (at least for most engineers) to design complex 3D structures with only separated layer geometry. The employment of 3D CAD tools in MEMS design can significantly simplify the synthesis step and help integrate various design tools. For example, engineers can start the design process directly from building the 3D models of the MEMS devices, and then generate layout drawing automatically by slicing the 3D models into layered geometries. The 3D models can also be used to analyze the performance of the MEMS devices and optimize the design afterwards. Several MEMS design software allow output format to be compatible with some of the powerful 3D design tools such as AutoCAD or SolidWorks and 3D models can be easily established in those software.

8.2.2 Analysis, Optimization and Fabrication Tools

Analysis of MEMS devices and systems is intended to provide designers with the ability to ensure that the designs will meet functional and performance requirements of the specific application. For example, if a mechanical microstructure is involved, a powerful analysis tool is the finite element analysis that is commonly used in mechanical and civil engineering for structural analyses. Certain kinds of finite element analysis programs can be applied to MEMS devices as long as a good understanding of device and microscale physics are taken into account and scaling and unit conversion is performed correctly. Typically, stress/strain, dynamic, thermal, electromagnetic, and fluidic analyses are applied in MEMS design processes to help search the optimal scheme.

Another important issue for the MEMS designers is material characterization such as Young's modulus, stress, and slight changes in geometry from layout. Because of the diversity and lack of standards in microfabrication, the performance of MEMS devices may vary significantly even with exactly the same geometrical design. The characteristics of the fabrication facilities and processes employed to manufacture MEMS devices must be considered in order to predict the performance correctly. The data is usually obtained by creating geometrically varied arrays of a test device such that material properties may be extracted from the varied dependencies. The process-dependent material properties can be collected and fed into analysis modules to assure the accuracy of the results.

The design of fabrication processes for MEMS devices and systems requires a working knowledge of semiconductor thin film processing, along with a knowledge of materials and processes and a great deal of ingenuity. Some commercial VLSI processes require as many as 500 – 700 process steps, and a comparable degree of fabrication complexity occurs in the fabrication of three-dimensional MEMS structures using planar processes. To overcome this obstacle, process simulation tools are developed to help designers evaluate the fabrication steps in constructing MEMS devices[33 – 38]. Tools for simulating the etching and deposition processes of various etchants and thin films are currently available.

8.3 Bulk-Micromachining Based MEMS Design

In bulk micromachining, features are sculptured in the substrate materials[39]. This technology started early, and has been the foundation of many micromachined devices, starting from micro pressure sensors to micro mirrors. In the early 1980s, Kurt Peterson's seminal paper, 'Silicon as a Mechanical Material', summarized some of the most important bulk-micromachined devices before 1980[40]. Today, many etching methods are available for bulk processing of silicon and other materials employed in MEMS fabrication[41]. The early foundation of bulk-micromachining comes from silicon crystallography. Every silicon atom in the tetrahedral structure has four nearest neighbors by covalent bonds similar to a diamond structure as shown in Fig. 8.2. Silicon substrate can be etched either by isotropic etching or anisotropic etching depending on the etching chemicals. Isotropic etching has the same etching rate in all crystallographic directions[42 – 45] while anisotropic etching has different etching rates in crystallographic directions with $\langle 110\rangle > \langle 100\rangle > \langle 111\rangle$ surfaces[46, 47]. As a result, the anisotropic etching processes can easily fabricate v-grooves or inverted pyramids with 54.74° angles with the planar surface. Figures 8.3, 8.4 illustrated the typical etching results from isotropic and anisotropic etching processes, respectively.

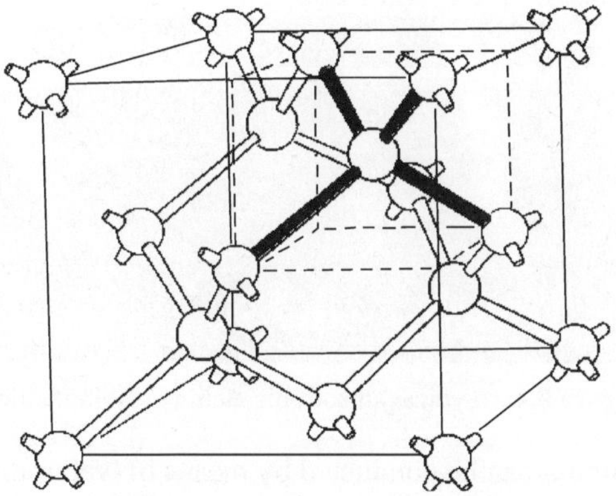

Figure 8.2 Silicon crystallography

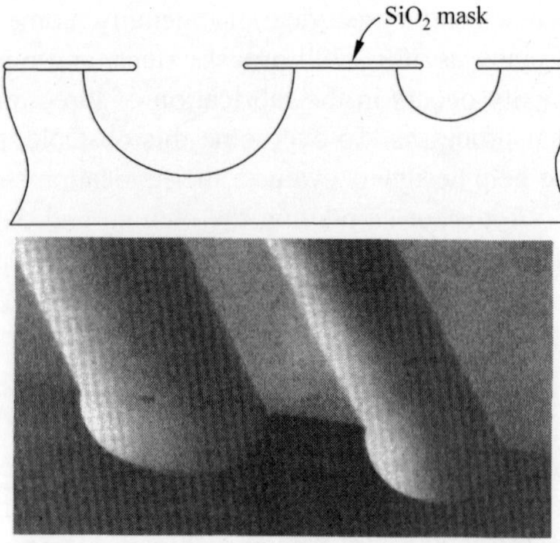

Figure 8.3 Typical isotropic etching result of silicon

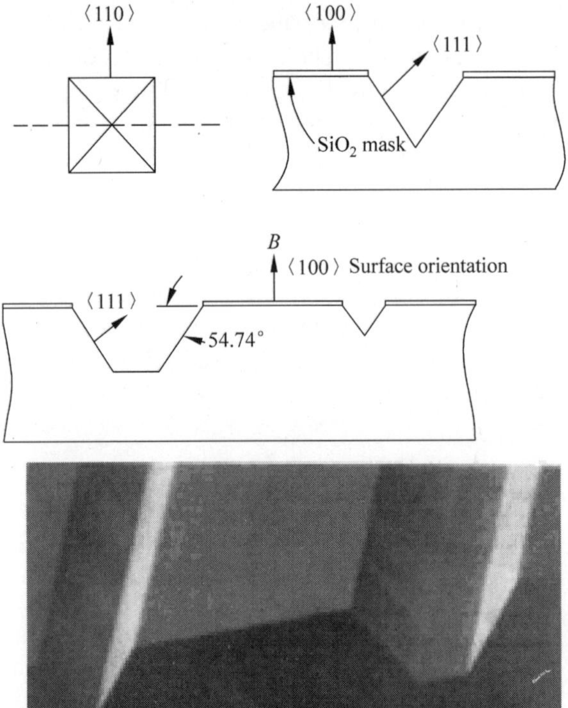

Figure 8.4 Typical anisotropic etching result of silicon

Bulk-micromachining can be conducted by means of wet or dry etching processes. Wet and dry etchants are selected on the basis of a large number of characteristics, including selectivity to etch masks, exposed metallization and other materials, availability of etch-stop methods, etch rate, degree of surface roughness created, safety, and others. Some of the other non-standard bulk-micromachining processes include laser/KOH micromachining[48], bias and/or illumination-assisted silicon etching[49] for micro-porous silicon[50], electrochemical etch-stop[51], deep reactive ion etching process[52], dissolved-wafer process[53], SCREAM[54] and HEXIL processes[55]. The construction of plastic microfluidic drug delivery system using a bulk-machined silicon substrate in a micro polymeric manufacturing process is exemplified in this section to illustrate the general bulk-micromachining design process.

A schematic diagram of a micro drug delivery system is illustrated in Fig. 8.5[56]. The system is composed of two major parts: an osmotic microactuator at the bottom and a cover at the top, including a drug storage reservoir, a delivery microfluidic channel and a delivery port. Induced by the concentration difference across the semipermeable membrane at the bottom of the osmotic microactuator, water from aqueous environment is drawn through the semipermeable membrane into the chamber filled with osmotic driving agent to power the drug delivery system. By virtue of the incompressibility of water, the top actuating membrane, which is hundreds of times more flexible than the bottom semipermeable membrane, expands to drive and release the liquid drug stored in the reservoir.

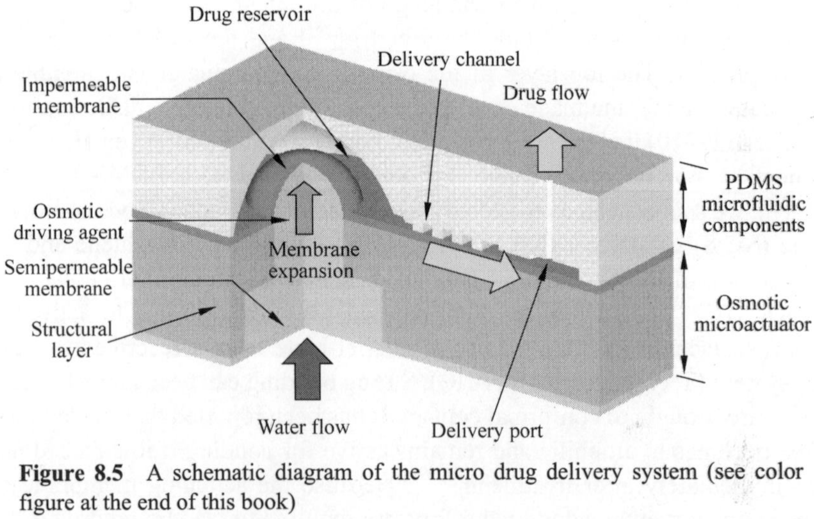

Figure 8.5 A schematic diagram of the micro drug delivery system (see color figure at the end of this book)

Figure 8.6 shows the fabrication process of the micro drug delivery system. A layer of 100 μm thick negative photoresist (MicroChem SU-8 100) is spin-coated and patterned on top of a clean silicon wafer to create a mold for microfluidic components in the following polymer casting process as shown in Fig. 8.6(a). Placing a droplet of SU-8 on top of the designated spot naturally forms the dome-shape mold of drug reservoir as shown in Fig. 8.6(b). Because of its high viscosity, the SU-8 dome can be more than 1 mm tall and the actual height can be controlled by temperature. After the SU-8 mold is fully UV cured, it is placed in a desiccator under vacuum for 2 hours with a vial containing a few drops of tridecafluoro-1,1,2,2-tetrahydrooctyl-1-trichlorosilane to silanize the surfaces[57]. Silanization of the mold facilitates the removal of the polymeric replica after casting. Figure 8.7 shows the SEM micrograph of the SU-8 mold where the drug reservoir is 1.8 mm in diameter and 800 μm in height. A mixture of 10:1 PDMS pre-polymer and curing agent (Dow-Corning Sylgard 184) is stirred thoroughly and then degassed under vacuum. The pre-polymer and curing agent mixture is then poured onto the mold, degassed, and cured for 1 hour at 75℃ as shown in Fig. 8.6(c). Before the PDMS is fully cured, a needle is inserted to form a delivery port (for flow rate measurement, not shown in the figure). After it is thoroughly cured, this PDMS replica is then peeled off from the mold and the needle is removed. Figure 8.8 is the molded PDMS replica containing microfluidic channel with a one-cent coin. Because PDMS is permeable to vapor, a 15 μm thick barrier film (DuPont Mylar M45) is added on back of the replica as shown in Fig. 8.6(d) to prevent liquid in the reservoir from evaporating and diffusing into outside environment. Native PDMS has low surface energy and cannot form strong enough bonding with Mylar. To prepare surfaces to achieve reliable bonding, both PDMS and Mylar surfaces are treated by oxygen plasma. These treated surfaces finally form strong bonding. The major challenge of the integration process of a micro osmotic actuator (process details described in[58]) and the PDMS replica is the bonding process. The top layer of the osmotic micro-actuator is a flexible and impermeable membrane made of vinylidene chloride and acrylonitrile copolymer (Dow Saran F-310) that cannot form strong bonding with PDMS even after plasma treatment[57]. For polymers cannot be directly bonded with PDMS by plasma treatment, we spin coat an intermediate layer to facilitate bonding. Styrene-isoprene-styrene (S-I-S) copolymer (KRATON D-1193) is dissolved in toluene and spin-coated on top of the Saran membrane to form a 30 μm thick intermediate layer. Both KRATON and PDMS are then exposed to oxygen plasma to activate the bonding surfaces (Fig. 8.6(e)) using a parallel-plate reactor reactive ion etching (RIE) system (Technics series 800-IIC). Strong bonding can be achieved once two surfaces are brought to conformal contact. It has been reported that treated PDMS surface becomes hydrophilic and remains active for bonding if it is placed under liquid immediately after treatment[57, 59]. Because the actuating membrane only moves in one direction, additional efforts are required to feed liquid drug into the drug reservoir and microfluidic channel. For aqueous drugs, since both treated surfaces are hydrophilic and the appearance of liquid around the bonding interface will not disturb the bonding process, liquid drug can fill microfluidic channel spontaneously and be encapsulated by employing the plasma-activated bonding process (Fig. 8.6(f)). The extra liquid drug in the gap between two bonding surfaces will eventually evaporate and strong bonding will be achieved once two surfaces are in contact. The cross-sectional view of the assembled micro drug delivery system is shown in Fig. 8.9 where the thickness of the PDMS layer is 1.5 mm.

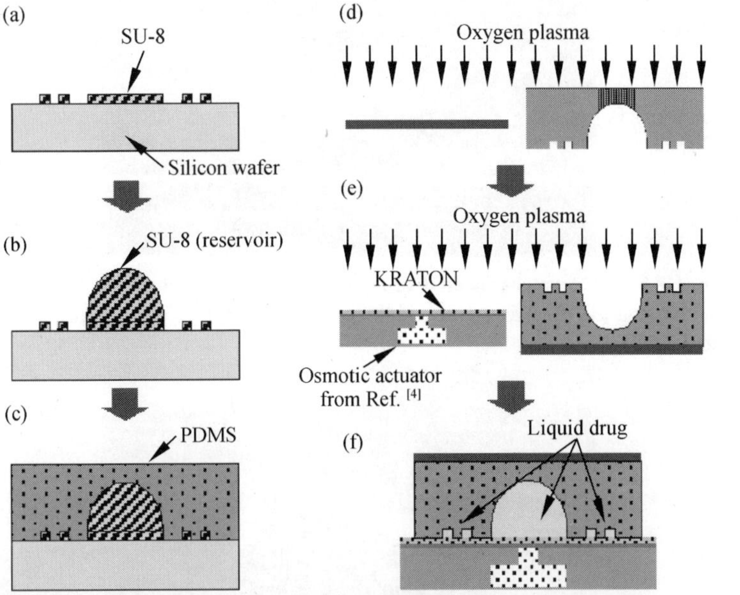

Figure 8.6 Fabrication process of the micro drug delivery system (see color figure at the end of this book)

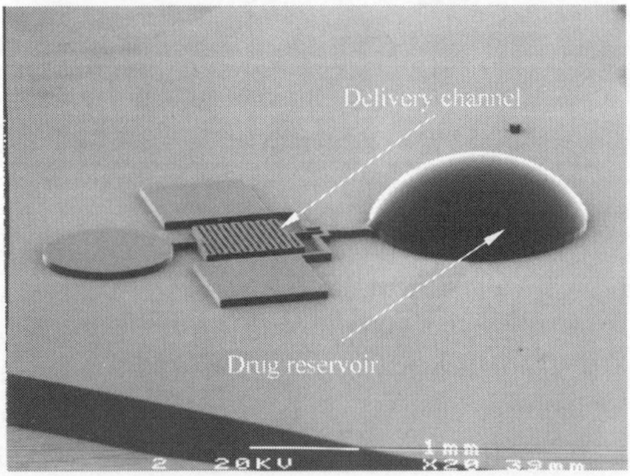

Figure 8.7 SEM micrograph of SU-8 mold for PDMS casting (step (b) in Fig. 8.6)

The length and cross-sectional area of the delivery channel are chosen to make sure that: ① the diffusive flow rate of exiting drug is much lower than the convective flow rate of exiting drug such that the total drug delivery rate will keep consistent and dominated by the osmosis reaction; ② the diffusive flow rate of entering fluid is much lower than the convective flow rate of exiting drug such that

Figure 8.8 The water-powered drug delivery system pictured with a one-cent coin showing the drug reservoir and drug delivery port (see color figure at the end of this book)

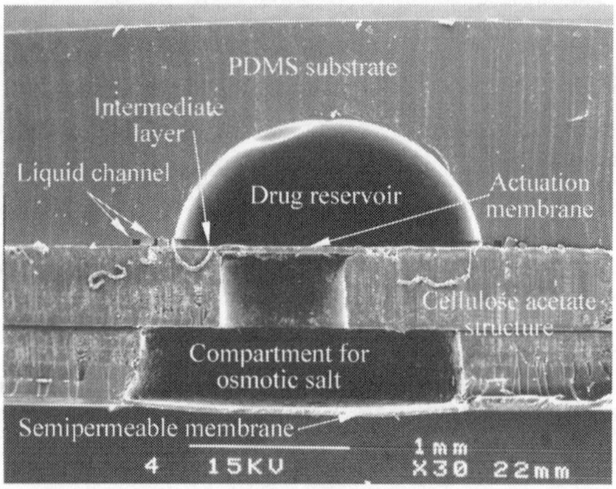

Figure 8.9 Cross-sectional SEM micrograph of the assembled microdrug delivery system

contamination, destabilizing, and diluting is minimized. To verify the prototype design, the following real values are used: $L = 1$ cm, $Q_c = 0.2$ μl/hr, $D_d = 2\times10^{-10}$ m^2/s, $\mu = 500$ centipoise, $w = 30$ μm, $h = 100$ μm, and $A = 30$ μm$\times$100 μm. The theoretical calculation indicates that $I_c = 0.00108$ and $\Delta P = 873$ Pa. Even though the flow resistance across the delivery channel is high (~10^{16} kg/m^{4}s), the resulted pressure drop is negligible compared to the driving pressure provided by the micro osmotic actuator, which can be as high as 25 MPa if sodium chloride is chosen as the driving agent. Furthermore, the convective flow rate is much larger than the diffusive flow rate as required by the micro osmotic drug delivery system.

Diffusive and convective flows need to be considered simultaneously to estimate the overall drug and contaminant flow rates across the microfluidic channel. Assuming they are steady flows with no accumulation and generation along the channel, the overall drug and contaminant flow rates, Q_d and Q_e, respectively, through any cross section are constants as shown in Fig. 8.10, and can be approximated as follows:

$$Q_d = -D_d A \frac{dC_d}{dx} + C_d Q_c \tag{8.1}$$

$$Q_e = D_e A \frac{dC_e}{dx} - C_e Q_c \tag{8.2}$$

where D_e is the diffusivity of contaminant along the channel and C_e is the concentration of contaminant. The concentrations C_d and C_e are functions of the distance from reservoir, x, as follows:

$$C_d(x) = \frac{C_d(0)}{1 - e^{-Q_c L / D_d A}} (1 - e^{-Q_c (L-x) / D_d A}) \tag{8.3}$$

$$C_e(x) = \frac{C_e(L)}{1 - e^{-Q_c L / D_e A}} (e^{-Q_c (L-x) / D_e A} - e^{-Q_c L / D_e A}) \tag{8.4}$$

where $C_d(0)$ is the concentration of drug inside the reservoir, $C_e(L)$ is the concentration of contaminant in the environment, and $C_d(L)$ and $C_e(0)$ are assumed to be ignorable. By plugging Eq. (8.3) into Eq. (8.4) into Eqs. (8.1) and (8.2), respectively, the overall flow rate Q_d and Q_e are derived as:

$$Q_d = \frac{C_d(0)}{1 - e^{-Q_c L / D_d A}} Q_c \tag{8.5}$$

$$Q_e = \frac{C_e(L)}{1 - e^{-Q_c L / D_e A}} Q_c e^{-Q_c L / D_e A} \tag{8.6}$$

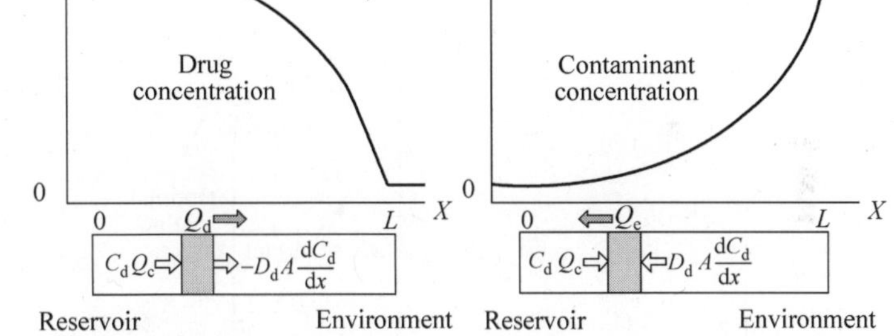

Figure 8.10 Schematic diagram of diffusive and convective flows through a cross section along the channel

It is observed in these equations that as long as the area/length (A/L) ratio is minimized, the diffusive flow of drug and the overall flow of contaminant will be low, and therefore potential flow fluctuation, contamination, destabilizing and diluting can be minimized.

Although channels with small area A and large length L are preferred, extremely small A and large L will cause significant pressure drop if highly viscous drugs such as suspensions are to be delivered. Considering a suspension with viscosity (μ) equal to 50,000 centipoise being driven through the same microchannel with the same flow rate as in the previous example, the pressure drop ΔP in this case increases to 87 kPa while I_c remains around 0.001. While designing microfluidic channel for transporting high viscosity drugs, constraints applied and diffusive flow, as well as pressure drop must be minimized simultaneously. Another performance index that includes both factors can be defined as:

$$I_s = I_c \Delta P \propto \frac{D_d \mu}{A} \tag{8.7}$$

where I_s defines the efficiency regarding both diffusion and pressure issues and lower values indicate higher efficiency. As indicated in Eq. (8.7), channel length L is not included and cross-sectional area A is the only geometrical parameter left to be used to rove overall performance. Figure 8.11 shows the design constraints, upper bounds of L, A, L/A^2 and lower bounds A and L/A, and resulted feasible area for parameter L and A. According to the performance index I_s, the optimal combinations of L and A are located on the boundary with maximum A. Considering the previous case with highly viscous drugs, a larger cross-sectional area should be used while area/length ratio remains the same to reduce the pressure drop, while keeping the same low diffusive/convective ratio.

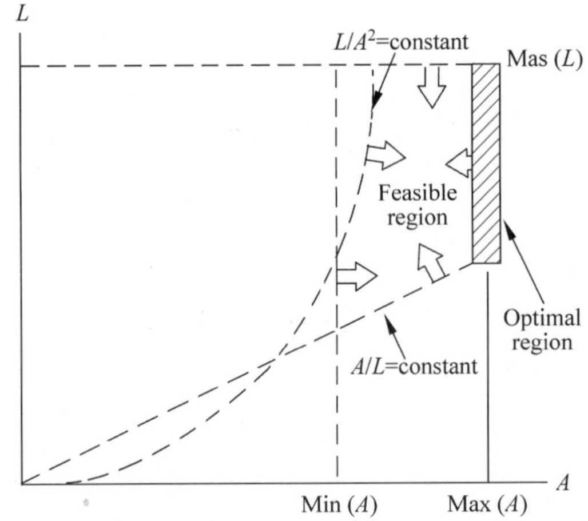

Figure 8.11 Constraints and feasible region of geometric parameters L and A

8.4 Surface-Micromachining Based MEMS Design

The early surface-micromachining process dated back to the late 1950s when researchers at Bell Lab developed a 'beam lead' process, and later in mid-1960s when a resonant gate transistor was demonstrated at the Westinghouse Research Lab[60]. Surface-micromachined structures are fabricated by selective etching of multiple layers of deposited and patterned thin film, and the simplified key process steps are illustrated in Fig. 8.12. A typical process will have the deposition of 'sacrificial layer.' The patterning and etching process on the sacrificial layer can follow to define anchor areas. A 'structure' layer is then deposited, patterned and etched to define the lateral dimensions of the microstructure. Finally, the sacrificial layer is etched away and freestanding structures are released.

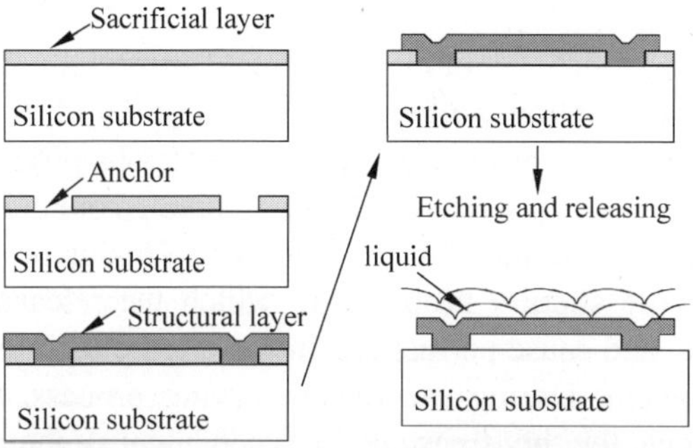

Figure 8.12 Key steps in a surface micromachining process

In the early work at the Westinghouse Research Lab, metallic material was used as the structural layer and its mechanical property suffered during the operation due to aging and fatigue such that the resonant frequency drifted over time. The project was abandoned until the early 1980s when researchers at UC-Berkeley started to use polysilicon, that has been the gate material in MOSFET, as the structural material, by when there was extensive infrastructure and knowledge of its electrical properties as a function of deposition conditions and post-deposition thermal cycles. For example, polysilicon microbridge and cantilever were demonstrated[61] and later the integration with NMOS was accomplished in a possible vapor gas sensing application[62].

Many material systems have been chosen to make surface-micromachined structures, and Table 8.2 summarizes the existing material systems that have been used to make surface micromachined structures. Among these material systems, the most popular one is to use polysilicon as the structural layer and silicon dioxide as the sacrificial layer. For example, the MUMPs[63] provides a 3-polysilicon-layer process and the SUMMIT[64] provides a 5-polysilicon-layer process. There are several issues to be addressed for these standard surface-micromachined processes.

Table 8.2 Structural, sacrificial materials and etchants in surface-micromachining processes

Structural material	Sacrificial material	Etchant
Polysilicon	Silicon dioxide	HF
Polysilicon	Aluminum	Al etchant
Silicon dioxide	Polysilicon	EDP
Silicon nitride	Polysilicon	KOH or EDP
Polyimide	Aluminum	Al etchant
Tungsten	Silicon dioxide	HF
Metals	Polymers	Solvents

First, the fabrication processes could be different, such as deposition temperature, pressure, gas concentration, flow rate, doping/annealing processes, etchant exposure, and anti-stiction coating, which will affect the properties of the thin film. Second, the polysilicon microstructure could be different in texture, grain size, surface roughness, dopant segregation, and grain boundaries. Third, the end result could cause different mechanical properties between different process runs or within the same substrate in residual strain[65], strain gradient, Young's modulus, fracture strength, and material damping. Fourth, one of the major problems in surface-micromachining is the stiction problem, in which the released structure could stick to the substrate and cause permanent failure. Figure 8.13 illustrates the origin of the stiction problem. During the release drying process, the final layer of liquid could pull down the tiny freestanding mechanical structure to the substrate, and chemical bond may form at the interface to cause the structure to stick to the substrate[66]. Several methodologies have been developed to solve this problem, and the most successful one is to use the 'super-cirtical-CO_2-drying' method that has been used in the field of biology for many years to address this problem. Other effective methods include the use of anti-stiction coating by ways of SAM (self-assembled-monolayer)[67] to protect both process-related and operation-related stiction problems.

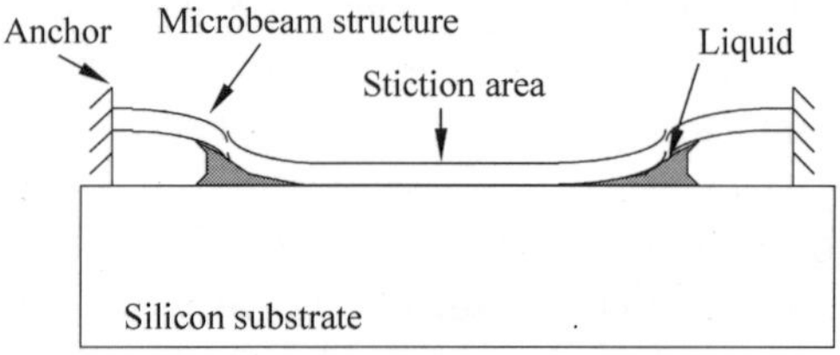

Figure 8.13 The origin of the stiction problem for surface-micromachined structures

There have been many important surface-micromachined structures that could be adopted as design examples, such as the early vertically-driven clamped-clamped beam resonators[62], movable micro mechanisms with pin-joints[68], IC-processed motors[69], laterally-driven electro-static comb resonators[70], micro hinge structures[71], thermal actuators, and arrays[72]. Furthermore, there are a few very successful commercial products out of the surface-micromachining technologies, including the accelerometers for air-bag applications (such as the products by Analog Devices Inc. and Motorola Inc.) and digital-light-processors for display applications by Texas Instrument Inc. The successful demonstrations of these devices provide designers the foundations to follow for new device designs.

The most effective way for a beginner to learn about the MEMS process and design, is probably to use the foundry service and follow their design rules. For example, the MUMPs process provides very extensive design guidelines on the internet[18] and one can follow the process to design their devices. There is also a very extensive library called 'CaMEL' or consolidated micromechanical element library in the same website that stores many design examples and tools. First, the 'non-parameterized library' has stored many successful designs that have been fabricated by the standard surface-micromachining process, such as linear comb resonators, gear train with slider, pad, stepping and wobble motors, accelerometer, tong and a micro hand. The 'parameterized library' has a set of generators that allow users to create micro mechanical elements in a quick and easy manner and allow them to specify the dimensions of the devices such as linear comb resonators and rotary side drive motors. Another document for the MUMPs process has very extensive design rules. These design rules are conservative based on the fabrication capabilities at the foundry service. Designers are welcome to over-rule these design results at their own expenses.

The following example is a surface-micromachining based pressure sensor from design, fabrication to test, but it does not follow the standard surface-micromachining process, and its process will also be briefly introduced[73]. Both square- and circular-shape diaphragms have been designed, fabricated, and characterized. These pressure sensors are constructed with surface-micromachined diaphragms by a micromachining process that uses LPCVD sealing to create vacuum cavities. The process starts with cleaning the wafer. A thin layer, 0.15 m, of LPCVD silicon nitride is then deposited. The cavity area is defined by a first mask via dry etching process to etch into the silicon of 1 m in depth. The wafer then goes through a thermal oxidation process to create about 2 μm thick silicon dioxide at the cavity area and to construct a flat surface, as illustrated in Fig. 8.14(a). LPCVD oxide of 0.5 m is then deposited to form the etch channels. These etch channels are defined by dry etching with a second mask. It is followed by a 1 μm LPCVD polysilicon deposition, etch holes patterning (mask 3), and dry etching, as shown in Fig. 8.14(b). The oxide in the etch channels and the cavity are now cleared by concentrated hydrofluoric acid (HF) etching. The second layer of polysilicon with 1 μm in thickness is then deposited by a second LPCVD polysilicon deposition step, which seals the etch holes and channels and creates a vacuum environment inside the cavity. The cross-sectional view at the end of this step is shown in Fig. 8.14(c). The piezoresistive resistors are then constructed by

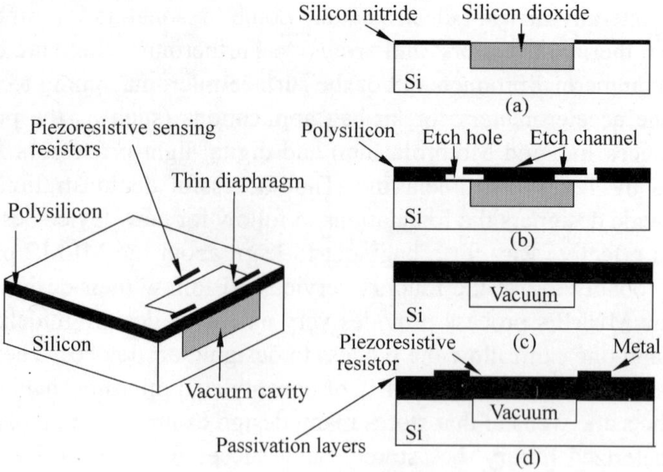

Figure 8.14 The fabrication process of a surface-micromachined diaphragm pressure sensor

using a fourth mask on top of the diaphragm made of undoped-polysilicon. Boron is implanted at an energy of 25 keV and a dose of 10^{15} cm^{-2}. An LPCVD oxide passivation layer is deposited with contact holes opened by using the fifth mask. Aluminum deposition and patterning (mask 6) are then followed to finish the process, as shown in Fig. 8.14(d). Figure 8.15 is an optical micrograph of a fabricated pressure sensor. The size of the square diaphragm is 100 μm in width. There are eight etch channels around the diaphragm as access channels to remove the sacrificial oxide inside the cavity. Aluminum metal pads can be clearly identified in this figure. Circular-shape diaphragms have also been fabricated with various sizes. Conventional theories of solid mechanics have been investigated in order to determine the optimal design of the sensing resistors, including position, orientation

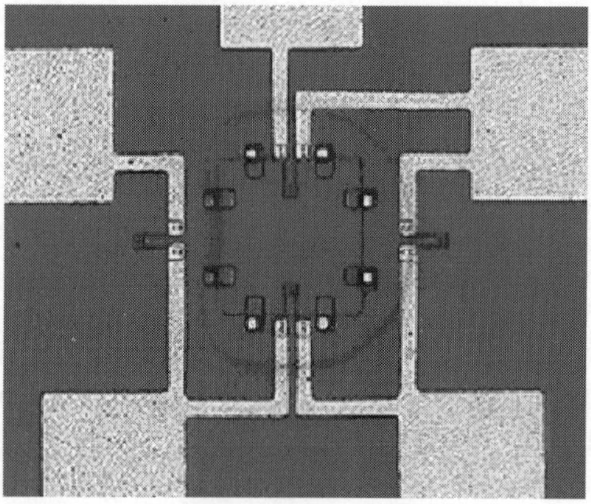

Figure 8.15 Optical photo of a fabricated pressure sensor (see color figure at the end of this book)

and length. These pressure sensors are designed to be operated in the small deflection regions since linear response is desired. For simplicity, we only discuss the case of the circular diaphragm while the discussion of the square diaphragm can be found in the original paper. When a circular plate is under a uniform pressure, q, governing equation can be derived in terms of the cylindrical coordinate system. The deflection function is derived as:

$$w = \frac{qr^4}{64D} + \frac{C_1 r^2}{4} + C_2 \log\frac{r}{a} + C_3 \tag{8.8}$$

where r is the radial coordinate in the cylindrical coordinate system; a is the radius; D is the flexural rigidity of the diaphragm; C_1, C_2, C_3 are the constants to be determined by the boundary conditions of the diaphragm. For micro diaphragms with clamped boundary, the radial and circumferential strain can be derived from Eq. (8.8) as:

$$\varepsilon_r = -\frac{3qa^2(1-\nu^2)}{8Eh^2}\left(1-3\left(\frac{r}{a}\right)^2\right) \tag{8.9}$$

$$\varepsilon_\theta = -\frac{3qa^2(1-\nu^2)}{8Eh^2}\left(1-\left(\frac{r}{a}\right)^2\right) \tag{8.10}$$

E is the Young's modulus, ν is Poisson's ratio, and h is the thickness of the diaphragm, respectively. Based on these analyses, Fig. 8.16 shows the strain distributions of a circular diaphragm (100 μm in diameter, 2 μm in thickness) that is under a uniform pressure of 100 Psi. Only half of the diaphragm is plotted due to symmetry. It is observed that the radial strain goes from compressive state (at the center) to the tensile state (at the edge). The circumferential strain is all the way compressive and the maximum value is at the center of the diaphragm. It can be concluded that radial strain at the edge of the diaphragm has a higher value than

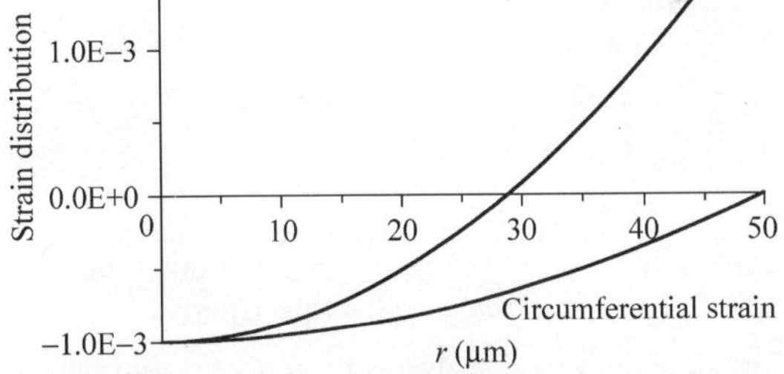

Figure 8.16 Radial and circumferential strain on a circular diaphragm of 100 μm in diameter and 2 μm in thickness under 100 Psi

other positions. The next step is to determine the geometry of the resistor including length and shape for optimal sensitivity. In order to maximize the piezoresistivity, line shape resistors are designed for detecting strain changes parallel to the direction of the input current. These line shape resistors are placed at the edges of the circular diaphragm to gain maximum sensitivity. Since misalignment is unavoidable during the fabrication process, the sensing resistors are designed to have a non-effective portion of 2 μm outside of the diaphragm. In order to match the desired impedance and to fully utilize the most sensitive regions on the diaphragms, resistor will be covered by metal in the manufacturing process such that they are considered as the non-effective parts. Only the effective parts of the sensor that are inside the diaphragm will be active during the pressure measurements. According the Wheastone bridge configuration, the output voltage is derived as:

$$V_{\text{out}} = \frac{\Delta R_{\text{eff}}}{2(R_{\text{eff}} + NR) + \Delta R_{\text{eff}}} V_{\text{in}} \tag{8.11}$$

where NR is the magnitude of the non-effective resistance, R_{eff} is the value of the effective resistance, and ΔR_{eff} is the change of the effective resistance due to outside pressure. It can be derived as:

$$\frac{\Delta R_{\text{eff}}}{R_{\text{eff}}} = \frac{1}{l} \int_{L}^{L-l} \frac{\Delta R}{R} \mathrm{d}x \tag{8.12}$$

where l is the length of the effective resistor, L is the radius of the diaphragm. The optimal length of the effective resistor can be calculated by using the above derivations. Figure 8.17 shows the simulation result of a 100 μm in diameter, 2 μm in thickness, circular-shape diaphragm. It is observed that the diaphragm has an optical output when the effective resistor length is about 12 μm. Increasing or

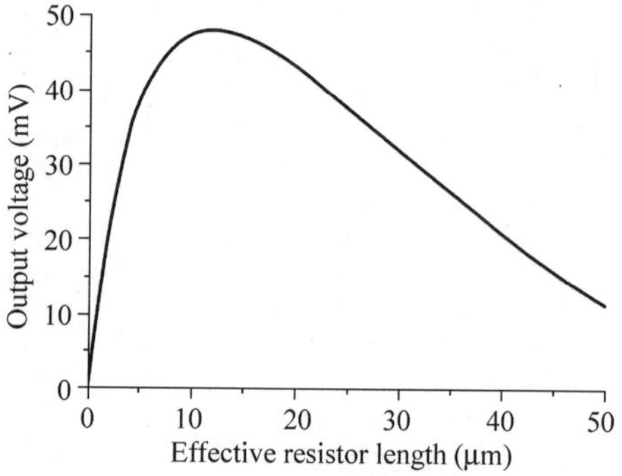

Figure 8.17 Design optimization analysis of effective resistor length on a circular diaphragm

decreasing this length will reduce the output voltage. The performance of devices made of the thin polysilicon deprograms is illustrated in Fig. 8.18. The measured sensitivity is 0.15 mV/V/Psi with a maximum linearity error of ±0.1% FSS (Full Scale Span) at room temperature. The sensitivity increases as the temperature decreases because the piezoresistivity changes with temperature. However, the linearity remains excellent at different temperatures as shown. The temperature range of −40℃ – 120℃ fits well for automobile applications. In a short summary, this device demonstrates the design, fabrication, and testing of a surface-micromachined diaphragm pressure sensor.

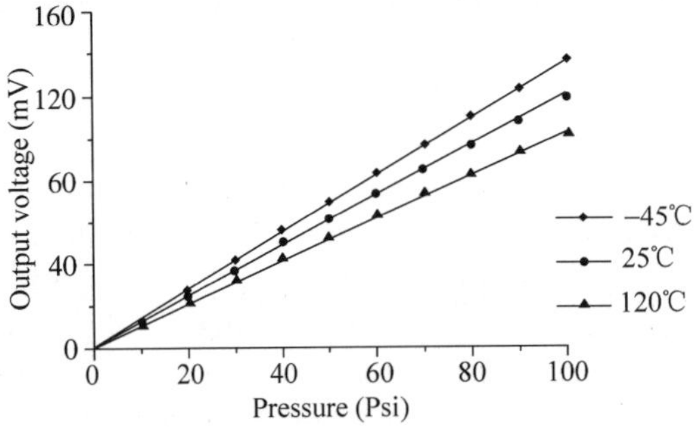

Figure 8.18 Testing results of the MEMS pressure sensor at different temperature

8.5 Future Trends and Summary

Although there have been many remarkable and revolutionary advances made in MEMS design and fabrication during the past decade, the need for more efficient design approaches remains. At present, each new MEMS development is still expensive and time consuming. MEMS fabrication processes have matured rapidly, but they are still many and varied. The experience of the VLSI research community in evolving design methodologies and fabrication processes should provide useful guidance[74]. Over the last few decades, the microelectronics industry, which MEMS derived from, has undergone unprecedented growth. Research activities in both industry and academia have led to the rapid introduction of advanced semiconductor process technology, hierarchically structured design methodologies, automated design tools, simulation models, and rapid prototyping techniques. One key to the rapid success of the VLSI development effort was the early definition of a clean digital interface that separated design efforts at increasingly high levels of abstraction from the growing complexities of the fabrication processes. This allowed the designer to focus on process-independent design tools and methodologies that are available to research and academic community for rapid prototyping of VLSI chips.

Although there is no clean separation between design and fabrication in MEMS development at present, and significant differences between VLSI design and MEMS design clearly exist, sufficient parallels also exist to strongly encourage research on structured design methods for MEMS. While the challenges in developing structured design methods for MEMS that preserve the clean separation are significant, the benefits of such methods will greatly enhance advances in MEMS. Developing structured design methods for MEMS holds the promise to significantly reduce the costs and time to create new devices and systems, and increase the complexity and robustness of devices and systems that can be designed. Three areas currently in use in VLSI design have been identified as common elements for structured MEMS design: languages for interchange of data among designers and between designers and fabricators; libraries for storing previously successful MEMS device designs for reuse; and simulation of desired functions and fabrication processes. Each of these has played a crucial role in the development of design methodologies for VLSI, and building on those prior VLSI developments will form the basis for a clean separation between design and fabrication of MEMS, and will provide the greatest leverage from an investment in research resources. Advances in these three areas will provide the foundation for automatic synthesis of MEMS, perhaps by compiling a schematic or language describing desired function into a set of masks and processing information to fabricate a device or system that will robustly exhibit the desired function. The long-range objective is to enable a MEMS designer to specify a desired micro-mechanical function (e.g., a mechanical spring with particular characteristics), and have a system automatically generate the information (mask-layout, and other fabrication instructions) to create the shape that exhibits the desired function. This approach will mean that MEMS designers will be able to concentrate on the desired function of the device, rather than the details of its physical manifestation.

In summary, MEMS devices and systems involve both electronic and mechanical elements that perform sensing, actuation, and other functions. These systems are steadily moving from simple function-specific devices of the past to more elaborate systems with complicated structures. Various engineering issues including integration, performance, packaging, reliability, and others must be thoroughly considered to construct these powerful systems. Significant design flexibility, system integration, well characterized processes, and a full suite of design, analysis, and evaluation tools are required in order to achieve efficient and profitable access to the segmented MEMS markets.

References

[1] Kovacs G. T. A., (1998) *Micromachined Transducers Sourcebook*, WCB/McGraw-Hill

[2] Senturia S. D., (2001) *Microsystem Design*, Kluwer Academic Publishers

[3] Maluf N, (1999) An Introduction to Microelectromechanical Systems Engineering, Artech House
[4] Trimmer W, (1997) Micromechanics and MEMS: Classic and Seminal Papers to 1990, IEEE Press
[5] Nguyen N. T., and S. T. Wereley, (2002) Fundamentals and Applications of Microfluidic, Artech House
[6] Manz A. and H. Becker, (1999) Microsystem Technology in Chemistry and Life Sciences, Springer Verlag
[7] Menz W., J. Mohr, and O. Paul, (2001) Microsystem technology, Wiley-VCH
[8] Shigley J. E., and C. R. Mischke, (2001) Mechanical Engineering Design, McGraw-Hill
[9] Pahl G., and W. Beitz, (1996) Engineering Design, Springer
[10] French M., (1999) Conceptual Design for Engineers, Springer
[11] System Planning, (1999) "Microelectromechanical Systems (MEMS), An SPC Market Study"
[12] Senturia S. D., R. Harris, B. Johnson, S. Kim, K. Nabors, M Shulman, and J. White, (1992) "A computer-aided design system for microelectromechanical systems," *Journal of Microelectromechanical Systems*, **1**(1): 3 – 13
[13] Mukherjee T., G. K. Fedder and R. D. Blanton, (1999) "Hierarchical Design and Test of Integrated Microsystems," *IEEE Design and Test*, **16**(4): 18 – 27
[14] Clark J. V., D. Bindel, W. Kao, E. Zhu, A. Kuo, N. Zhou, J. Nie, J. Demmel, Z. Bai, S. Govindjee, K. S. J. Pister, M. Gu, and A. Agogino, (2002) "Addressing the Needs of Complex MEMS Design," *Proceedings of IEEE Micro Electro Mechanical Systems Conference*, 204 – 209
[15] Sandmaier H., H. L. Offereins, and B. Folkmer, (1993) "CAD tools for micromcchanics," *Journal of Micromechanics and Microengineering*, **3**(3): 103 – 106
[16] Coventorware, Coventor, Inc., http://www.coventor.com/coventorware/
[17] IntelliSuite, IntelliSense Software Corp., http://www.intellisensesoftware.com/products.html
[18] MEMSCAP, MEMSCAP, Inc., http://www.memscap.com/products-cad.html
[19] MEMX, MEMX Incorporated, http://www.memx.com/design_tools.htm
[20] PhoeniX, PhoeniX BV, http://www.phoenixbv.com/index.html
[21] NODAS, Carnegie Mellon University, http://www.ece.cmu.edu/~mems/projects/memsyn/nodasv1_4/index.shtml
[22] SUGAR, U. C. Berkeley, http://www-bsac.eecs.berkeley.edu/cadtools/sugar
[23] ANSYS, ANSYS, Inc., http://www.ansys.com/
[24] ABAQUS, ABAQUS, Inc., http://www.hks.com/
[25] FEMLAB, COMSOL, Inc., http://www.comsol.com/
[26] CFDRC, CFD Research Corporation, http://www.cfdrc.com/
[27] FLOW-3D, Flow Science, Inc., http://www.flow3d.com/
[28] HFSS, Ansoft Corporation, http://www.ansoft.com/products/hf/hfss/
[29] ACES, U.I. Urbana-Champaign, http://mass.micro.uiuc.edu/research/completed/aces/
[30] SIMODE, TU Chemnitz, http://www.infotech.tu-chemnitz.de/~wetel/simode.htm
[31] L-Edit Pro, Tanner Research, Inc., http://www.tanner.com/EDA/products/ledit/default.htm
[32] LinkCAD, Bay Technology, http://www.linkcad.com/site/linkcad

[33] Fruhauf J., K. Trautman, J. Witting, and D. Zeilke, (1993) "A Simulation tool for orientation dependent etching," *Journal of Micromechanics and Microengineering,* **3**: 113 – 115

[34] Asaumi K., Y. Iriye, and K. Sato, (1997) "Anisotropic-etching process simulation system MICROCAD analyzing complete 3D etching profiles of single crystal silicon," *Proceedings of IEEE Micro Electro Mechanical Systems Conference*, 412 – 417

[35] Zhu Z., and C. Liu, (2000) "Micromachining Process Simulation Using a Continuous Cellular Automata Method," *Journal of Microelectromechanical Systems*, **9**(2): 252 – 261

[36] Fujinaga M., and N. Kotani, (1997) "3-D topography simulator (3-D MULSS) based on a physical description of material topography," *IEEE Transaction on Electron Devices*, **44**: 226 – 238

[37] Hubbard T. J., and E. K. Antonsson, (1994) "Emergent faces in crystal etching," *Journal of Microelectromechanical Systems*, **3**(1): 19 – 28

[38] Tellier C. R., and S. Durand, (1997) "Micromachining of (hhl) silicon structures: Experiments and 3D simulation of etched shapes," *Sensors Actuators A*, **A60**: 168 – 175

[39] Madou M. J., (1997) Fundamentals of Microfabrication, CRC Press

[40] Petersen, K. E. (1982) "Silicon as a Mechanical Material," *Proceedings of the IEEE*, **70**: 420 – 457

[41] Kovacs G. T. A., N. I. Maluf, and K. E. Petersen, (1998) "Bulk Micromachining of Silicon," *Proceedings of the IEEE*, **86**: 1536 – 1551

[42] Robbins H. R., and B. Schwartz, (1959) "Chemical Etching of Silicon—I," *J. Electrochem, Soc.*, **106**(6): 505 – 508

[43] Robbins H. R., and B. Schwartz, (1960) "Chemical Etching of Silicon—II," *J. Electrochem. Soc.*, **107**(2): 108 – 111

[44] Schwartz B., and H. R. Robbins, (1961) "Chemical etching of silicon—III," *J. Electrochem. Soc.*, **108**(4): 365 – 372

[45] Schwartz B., and H. R. Robbins, (1976) "Chemical etching of silicon—IV," *J. Electrochem. Soc.*, **123**(12): 1903 – 1909

[46] Seidel H., L. Csepregi, A. Heuberger, and H. Baumgartel, (1990) "Anisotropic Etching of Crystalline Silicon in Alkaline Solution—Part I," *J. Electrochem. Soc.*, **137**(11): 3612 – 3626

[47] Seidel H., L. Csepregi, A. Heuberger, and H. Baumgartel, (1990) "Anisotropic Etching of Crystalline Silicon in Alkaline Solution—Part II," *J. Electrochem. Soc.*, **137**(11): 3626 – 3632

[48] Schumacher et al., (1994) "Mit Laser und Kalilauge," *Technische Rundschau*, **86**: 20 – 23

[49] Lehmann and Foll, (1990) "Formation Mechanism and Properties of Electrochemically Etched Trenches in n-Type Silicon," *J. Electrochem. Soc.*, **137**: 653 – 659

[50] Lehmann, (1993) "The Physics of Macropore Formation in Low Doped n-Type Silicon," *J. Electrochem. Soc.*, **140**: 2836 – 2843

[51] Kloeck et al., (1989) "Study of Electrochemical Etch-Stop for High-Precision Thickness Control of Silicon Membranes," *IEEE Trans. Electron Devices*, **36**: 663 – 669

[52] http://www.mems-exchange.org/catalog/deep_rie/

[53] Gianchandani Y., and K. Najafi, (1992) "A Bulk Silicon Dissolved Wafer Process for Microelectromechanical Devices," *IEEE/ASME J. Micro Electro Mechanical Systems*, **1**(2): 77 – 85

[54] Shaw and MacDonald, (1996) "Integrating SCREAM Micromachined Devices with Integrated Circuits," *MEMS Workshop*, 44 – 48

[55] Keller and Ferrari, (1994) "Milli-Scale Polysilicon Structures," 1994 Solid-State Sensors and Actuators Workshop, 312 – 137

[56] Su Y. C., and L. Lin, (2004) "A Water-Powered Micro Drug Delivery System," *IEEE/ASME Journal of Microelectromechanical Systems*, **13**: 75 – 82

[57] Duffy D. C., J. C. McDonald, O. J. A. Schueller, and G. M. Whitesides, (1998) "Rapid Prototyping of Microfluidic Systems in Poly(dimethylsiloxane)", *Anal. Chem.*, **70**: 4974 – 4984

[58] Su Y. C., L. Lin, and A. P. Pisano, (2002) "A Water-Powered Osmotic Microacutator," *IEEE/ASME Journal of Microelectromechanical Systems*, **11**: 736 – 742

[59] Jo B. H., L. M. V. Lerberghe, K. M. Motsegood, and D. J. Beebe, (2002) "Three-Dimensional Micro-Channel Fabrication in Polydimethyl-siloxane (PDMS) Elastomer," *IEEE Journal of MEMS*, **9**: 76 – 81

[60] Nathanson et al., (1965) "A Resonant Gate Transistor with High-Q Bandpass Properties," *Appl. Phys. Lett.*, **7**(4) 84 – 86

[61] Howe R. T., and R. S. Muller, (1983) "Polycrystalline silicon micromechanical beams," *J. of the Electrochemical Society*, **130**: 1420 – 1423

[62] Howe R. T., and R. S. Muller, (1986) "Resonant-microbridge vapor sensor," *IEEE Trans. on Electron Devices*, **ED-33**: 499 – 506

[63] http://www.memscap.com/memsrus/crmumps.html

[64] http://www.mdl.sandia.gov/mstc/technologies/micromachines/tech-info/technologies/summit5.html

[65] Lin L., A. P. Pisano, and R. T. Howe, (1997) "A Micro Strain Gauge with Mechanical Amplifier," *IEEE/ASME Journal of Microelectromechanical Systems*, **6**: 313 – 321

[66] Mastrangelo C. H., and C. Hsu, (1993) "Mechanical Stability and Adhesion of Microstructures under Capillary Forces," *IEEE/ASME J. of Microelectromechanical Systems*, **2**: 44 – 55

[67] Maboudian R., (1998) *Surf. Sci. Rep.* **30**: 207 – 269

[68] Fan L. S., Y. C. Tai, and R. S. Muller, (1988) "Integrated Movable Micromechanical Structures for Sensors and Actuators," *IEEE Trans. on Electron Devices*, **ED-35**: 724 – 730

[69] Fan L. S., Y. C. Tai, and R. S. Muller, (1989) "IC-processed electrostatic micromotors," *Sensors and Actuators*, **20**: 41 – 48

[70] Tang W. C., T. C. H. Nguyen, M. W. Judy, and R. T. Howe, (1990) "Electrostatic-Comb Drive of Lateral Polysilicon Resonators," *Sensors and Actuators A*, **21**(1 – 3): 328 – 331

[71] Pister K. S. J., M. Judy, S. Burgett, and S. Fearing, (1992) "Microfabricated Hinges," *Sensors and Actuators*, **33**(3): 249 – 256

[72] Comtois J. H., and M. Victor, (1997) "Applications for surface-micromachined polysilicon thermal actuators and arrays," *Sensors and Actuators A*, **58**(1): 19 – 25

[73] Lin L., H. C. Chu, and Y. W. Lu, (1999) "A Simulation Program for the Sensitivity and Linearity of Piezoresistive Pressure Sensors," *IEEE/ASME Journal of Microelectromechanical Systems*, **8**: 514 – 522

[74] Antonsson E. K., (1995) "Structured Design Methods for MEMS," NSF Sponsored Workshop on Structured Design Methods for MEM

9 MEMS Processing and Fabrication Techniques and Technology—Silicon-Based Micromachining

Zhihong Li, Bo Liu, and Wei Wang

Institute of Microelectronics, Peking University, Beijing, China
E-mail: zhhli@ pku.edu.cn

Abstract The silicon-based micromachining technology, which is originated from the silicon IC (integrated circuits) technology, is the mainstream technology for MEMS fabrication, and the most MEMS products on market are manufactured with this technology. The silicon-based micromachining technologies can be divided into two categories: surface micromachining technology and bulk micromachining technology. Instead of introducing detailed individual techniques, this chapter will focus on utilizing and combining different processes to achieve different device fabrication and meet different requirements. For surface micromachining, isolation, metallization and monolithic integration are specially emphasized; while for bulk micromachining, we discuss more details on different sets of processes after a brief introduction of individual processes, such as DRIE and bonding.

Keywords Surface micromachining, bulk micromachining, DRIE, bonding, integration

The silicon-based micromachining technology was originated from the silicon microelectronics technology[1], taking its advantages of inexpensive cost, high precision, mass production, maturity and powerful capability. More importantly, as reported in K. Petersen's classic literature, 'Silicon as a Mechanical Material'[2], the silicon, in conjunction with its conventional role as an electronic material, is also a high-strength and high-reliability mechanical material. Besides, MEM (micro-electromechanical) devices fabricated with the silicon-based micromachining technology are more suitable to be integrated with the circuitry monolithically and form a microsystem on chip, which has more functionality than either MEM devices or ICs (integrated circuits) solely. Therefore, the silicon-based micromachining technology is the mainstream technology for MEMS fabrication[3], and most MEMS products on market are manufactured with this technology[4, 5] Contrast with 'pure' microelectronic fabrication technology, the silicon-based micromachining technology has its own features as follows:

(1) All structures in ICs are fixed on a substrate, whereas the structures in MEMS are normally suspended and/or movable, and therefore, have to be released with special processes.

(2) In the IC field, people normally only care about the electrical properties of materials. Different materials play different roles such as interconnection, insulation, active regions, and so on. In the field of MEMS, however, the devices have various functionalities. Not only the electrical properties of materials, but also mechanical, optical, magnetic, and even biological properties need to be concerned according to specific applications. Therefore quite more materials are employed in MEMS than in IC.

(3) Integrated circuit fabrication adopts the thin film technology. Its basic structure is two-dimensional with the thickness of each layer not very large. On the contrary, many MEMS structures are 3D (three-dimensional) or quasi-3D. In order to improve the device performance, sometimes very thick structures are preferred. Some special micromachining processes, which may not be compatible with IC fabrication, have to be adopted. Therefore, some MEMS structures can not be integrated in IC.

In accordance with different machining methods, normally the silicon- based micromachining technologies can be divided into two categories: surface micromachining technology and bulk micromachining technology. Each has its own characteristics respectively, but the boundary between them is not always clear. Sometimes these two technologies can be employed together. In both technologies, unique techniques and processes unlike the traditional IC technology are involved. In surface micromachining technology, sacrificial layer etching[6, 7], anti-stiction release[8], and residual stress control technologies[9, 10] are additional to the IC process flow; while in bulk micromachining technology, deep reactive ion etching (DRIE)[11, 12], anisotropic wet etching[13, 14] and bonding[15] technologies are specially developed for the fabrication of complex 3D structures. A lot of books and articles have already reviewed these techniques. Readers who are interested in these techniques can refer to relevant literature. This chapter will not focus on detailed individual techniques, but on utilizing and combine different processes to achieve different device fabrication and meet different requirements.

9.1 Surface Micromachining Technology

9.1.1 Introduction

The surface micromachining technology generally refers to the sacrificial layer technology, a technological process in which suspended microstructures are obtained through deposition of different layers on the substrate surface with subsequent selective etching. Developed on the basis of planar IC processing technology, it has many similar characteristics of IC technology, such as batch process, low cost, and high precision. Furthermore, it is compatible with IC technology, and requires minimum unconventional equipment besides IC processing one, which enables the monolithic integration of MEMS and IC. However, there are also some disadvantages. For example, only 2D or quasi-3D structures, not real 3D ones, can be obtained by this technology; its structural layer is so thin, usually only a few microns, that it is not suitable for processing high-precision MEMS devices; the structural layer is usually made of polysilicon, silicon nitride and some metal, of which the mechanical properties are inferior to those of single crystal silicon.

This technological process dated back to 1965, when it was applied to the resonant gate transistor reported by H. C. Nathanson[16]. However, this technology did not receive real attentions and mass applications until its application in an electrostatic micro-motor developed at UC Berkeley[17]. Later, with this technology, Analog Devices, Inc. (ADI) produced a commercial integrated accelerometer, which extremely promoted its development. Figure 9.1 shows the process sequence of a typical double-polysilicon surface micromachining, in which the first layer of polysilicon is used as the bottom electrode (Poly0) that is not released, and the second layer is the structural layer (Poly1). The detailed steps are as follows:

(1) The silicon dioxide and silicon nitride layers are successively deposited on the substrate silicon wafer as an insulation layer. Then a heavily-doped polysilicon (Poly0) layer, which is typically 3,000 Å in thickness, is formed and etched to make the bottom electrode and interconnection (Fig. 9.1(a)).

(2) The phosphosilicate glass (PSG) deposited with LPCVD (low pressure chemical vapor deposition) is used as a sacrificial layer. Contrasting with updoped silicon dioxide, it has higher etching rate in hydrofluoric acid (HF), which is better for releasing. In addition, it can also be used as the doping source for polysilicon. Its typical thickness is 2 μm. In order to make bumps on the following polysilicon structure to avoid stiction, a little pit (Fig. 9.1(b)), which is 0.3 μm in depth, is made through lithography and etching. (See the following section.)

(3) The anchor, which is used as the fixed support for the movable structure, is formed through lithography and PSG etching (Fig. 9.1(c)).

(4) The polysilicon layer is deposited as the structural material, the thickness of which is typically 2 μm (Fig. 9.1(d)). Through different methods of structure doping, its resistance can be decreased.

(5) The polysilicon is etched to form the mechanical structure (Fig. 9.1(e))

(6) The sacrificial layer is etched away by hydrofluoric acid (HF) to release the structural layer. After drying, the final structure can be obtained.

Figure 9.2 shows a micro resonator fabricated with this technology[18].

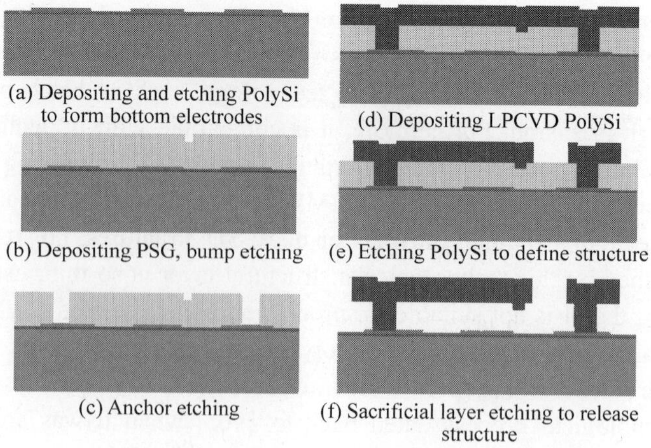

(a) Depositing and etching PolySi to form bottom electrodes
(b) Depositing PSG, bump etching
(c) Anchor etching
(d) Depositing LPCVD PolySi
(e) Etching PolySi to define structure
(f) Sacrificial layer etching to release structure

Figure 9.1 The basic process sequence of silicon surface sacrificial layer technology (see color figure at the end of this book)

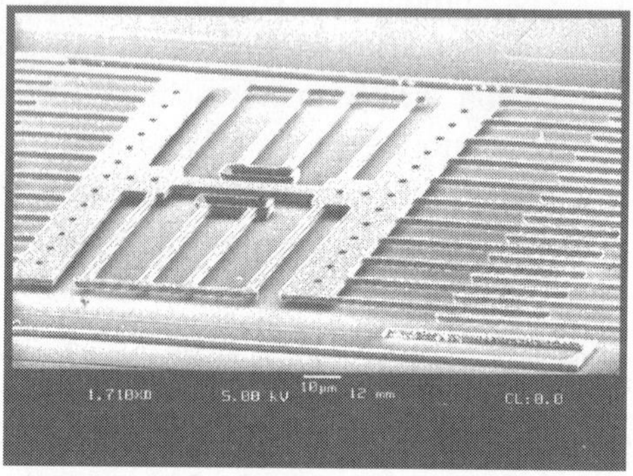

Figure 9.2 The SEM picture of a microresonator fabricated at Peking University through basic silicon surface sacrificial layer technology

The major issues in the surface micromachining technology that should be addressed are stiction and residual stress control, which are studied in lots of references[8–10] and will not be discussed here.

9.1.2 Standard Surface Micromachining Technology and Multilayer Polysilicon

The surface micromachining based on polysilicon is widely used for manufacturing a variety of MEMS devices and has become one of the mainstream micromachining technologies. Consequently, many micro/nanofabrication foundries offer it to users as a standard process. The most famous example is the multi-user MEMS Technology (MUMPs—Multi-User MEMS Processes) launched by MCNC in the

1990s[19, 20]. This technology has the most important feature that it can realize multi-user's devices on the same silicon wafer. The first introduced standard process is the polysilicon surface sacrificial layer micromachining (PolyMUMPs)[20, 79], in which three polysilicon layers and two sacrificial layers are included. By using this technology, MEMS devices, such as accelerometers and micromotors, can be integrated with circuits.

The SUMMiT (Sandia Ultra-planar, Multi-level MEMS Technology)[21] developed by Sandia National Laboratories in the United States represents the standard surface micromachining technology of the highest level. Owing to the adoption of CMP technique, each layer of it is extremely flat, so that a multilayer plane structure can be realized. The current polysilicon has reached to five layers. Structures of typical processed devices are shown in Fig. 9.3[22].

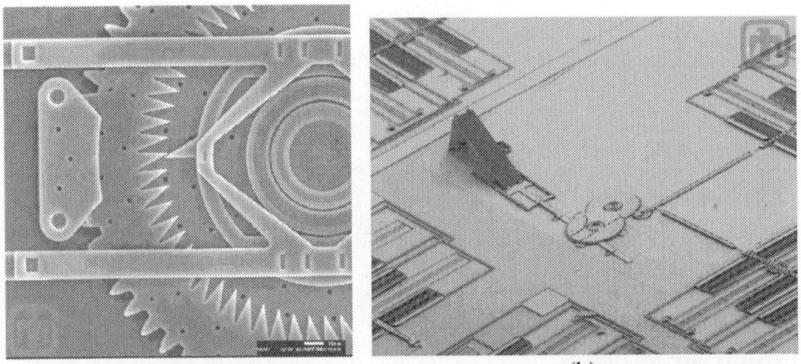

(a) (b)

Figure 9.3 Micro Pictures of structures of typical devices processed through extremely flat multilayer technology—summit, at Sandia national laboratories in the United States. (a) The Micromachine wedge Stepper Motor. (b) Micro torque coverter (transmission) and positionable micro mirror[21, 22] (© Sandia National Lab)

9.1.3 Metallization

In surface micromachining, thin films of polysilicon are normally doped and conductive[23, 24]. In applications such as RF MEMS[25–34], however, the resistivity of polysilicon is still too high, even with very heavy doping (~mΩ–·cm at a concentration of 10^{20} cm^{-3})[35]. In fact, low parasitic series resistance is required for most MEMS devices to reduce RC delay and improve dynamic performance. Using metal to replace polysilicon may solve the problem, but the mechanical performance of metal materials that can be used in MEMS is much inferior to that of polysilicon. In addition, some new processes incompatible with CMOS have to be used in metal micromachining. Another method is to cover the polysilicon film with a layer of metal, such as Al, Cu, or Au, in order to lower the resistance. The poor mechanical performance of the metal layer and mismatch will also degrade the performance of the microstructures. Metals must be deposited onto the silicon structures through evaporation or sputtering. However, the bimorph metal/silicon structures tend to warp due to thermal expansion mismatch (see Fig. 9.4[30]).

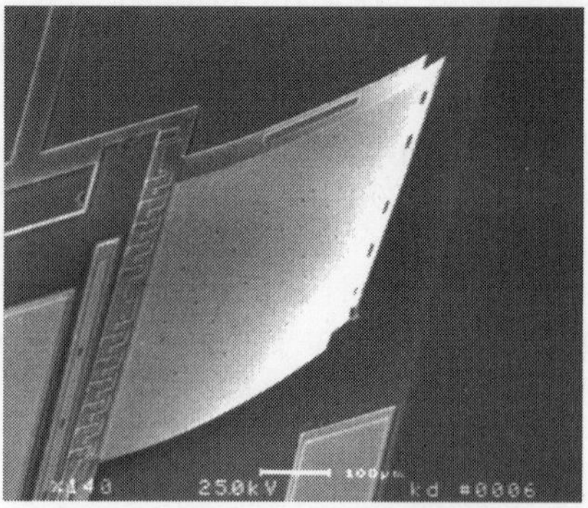

Figure 9.4 SEM image of a hinged membrane bent due to thermal expansion mismatch between 0.5 μm of gold and 2 μm of polysilicon before annealing[30] (© 2000 IEEE)

Besides, in some applications such as lateral microswitch, low-contact resistance is needed. The contact performance of polysilicon-to-polysilicon is very poor, since a layer of native silicon dioxide is always grown on the surface of polysilicon. It is very difficult to form a metal layer on the sidewall of the polysilicon microstructure.

9.1.3.1 Silicide

Metal silicide has been used in the VLSI technology for decades to reduce the series resistance for gates and local interconnects, as well as the contact resistance at source and drain areas[36–43]. Metal silicide has merits for VLSI, such as low resistivity (tens μΩ·cm), low contact resistivity, capability of self-aligned formation through selective etching, and so on. Besides, metal silicides have crystal structures, and are good elastic material rather than plastic materials like most metals. Therefore, silicides have been employed in microstructure fabrication, especially in surface micromachining[44].

For the double-polysilicon surface micromachining mentioned previously, silicide can be used for both polysilicon layers, but requirements in the two layers are different. The grounded polysilicon layer mainly serves as the electrical interconnect material and undergoes a high temperature process when the structural polysilicon is annealed to reduce the residual stress. Therefore, low resistance and high thermal stability of silicide is the most important index. For the structural polysilicon, the silicide should have a low residual stress and can endure HF etching during the removal of the sacrificial layer. If the basic process sequence is used, then the silicide on Poly0 is also under the attack of the HF solution. However, the layer can be protected from HF attack by a minor modification in the process sequence. A process flow using silicide is shown in Fig. 9.5. In the process, after study of different metals, cobalt (Co) was chosen to form silicide on Poly0, because $CoSi_2$ has high thermal stability and low resistivity; while platinum (Pt) was chosen for Poly1, because PtSi has high etching resistance in HF solution. In the process, a layer of Si_3N_4 was used to protect the silicide on Poly0 from HF etching. The detailed process is as follows (shown in Fig. 9.5):

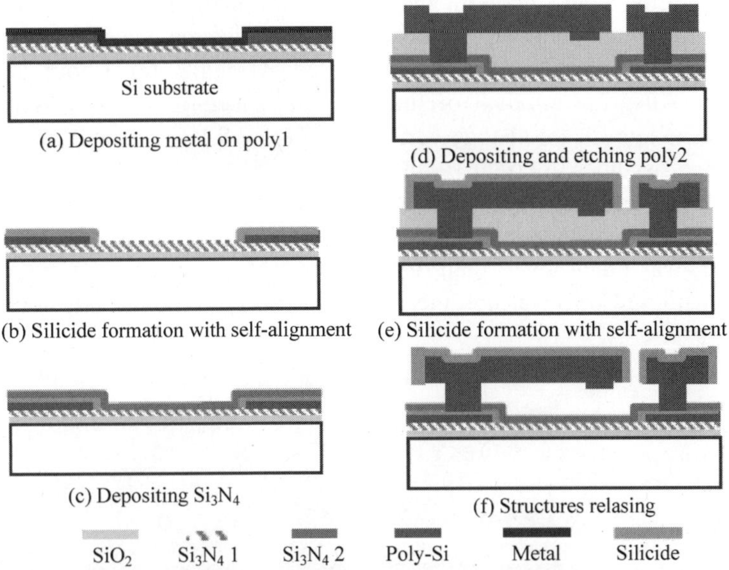

Figure 9.5 Surface micromachining process flow using silicide on both Poly0 and Poly1[44] (see color figure at the end of this book)

(1) After Poly0 is deposited and patterned, a 300 Å thick Co is deposited on the top.

(2) After deposition of 300 Å Co, the wafer is treated by rapid thermal annealing (RTA) at 600℃ in N_2 ambience. Silicide is formed on the surface of polysilicon, but not on oxide. In this case, Co silicide is not entirely yet $CoSi_2$ but a mixture of Co_2Si, CoSi and $CoSi_2$. By using $HCl:H_2O_2$ [30%] solution with volume ratio of 3:1, unreacted Co is removed selectively, whereas silicide is not etched. The samples are treated by another RTA at 900℃ for 20 s in N_2 ambient, when the silicide is completely changed to $CoSi_2$. The thickness of $CoSi_2$ will be about 1,050 Å, since the ratio of Co to $CoSi_2$ is about 3.52:1[36].

(3) A 2,200 Å-thick LPCVD Si_3N_4 film is deposited to protect the silicide from etching during the removal of the sacrificial layer.

(4) Similar to the basic surface micromachining process, Poly1 is deposited and patterned after the sacrificial layer is deposited and etched. The difference is that the Si_3N_4 should be etched away during anchor window etching.

(5) A layer of Pt is deposited on the surface. Then, the silicide, PtSi, is selectively formed on the surface of polysilicon through a similar process as $CoSi_2$ is formed.

The selective etching solution is aqua regia, and the temperature of RTA is 900℃.

(6) The wafer is immersed in saturated hydrofluoric acid (HF) for 7 min to remove the sacrificial PSG layer, and the structures are released.

Some test structures were fabricated for characterization. For Poly0, the sheet resistance was about 200 Ω/sq before Co deposition. After $CoSi_2$ formation, the sheet resistance was significantly decreased to 1.8 to 2.0 Ω/sq. As mentioned above, thermal stability is an important index, since the structural polysilicon will be annealed at high temperature for a long time to reduce the residual stress. To test the thermal stability, a sample was annealed at 1000℃ for 1 hour after PSG deposition. After the removal of the PSG, the sheet resistance was measured again, and no significant change was found. Figure 9.6 shows a structure to test the series resistance of Poly0 (with/without $CoSi_2$) and the contact resistance between Poly1 and Poly0 (with/without $CoSi_2$). Figure 9.7 shows $I \sim V$ curves of the test structure, which indicates that series and contact resistance for the structure with $CoSi_2$ was much lower than that without $CoSi_2$. Besides, the curve for the structure without $CoSi_2$ was nonlinear, which means the contact was not ohmic.

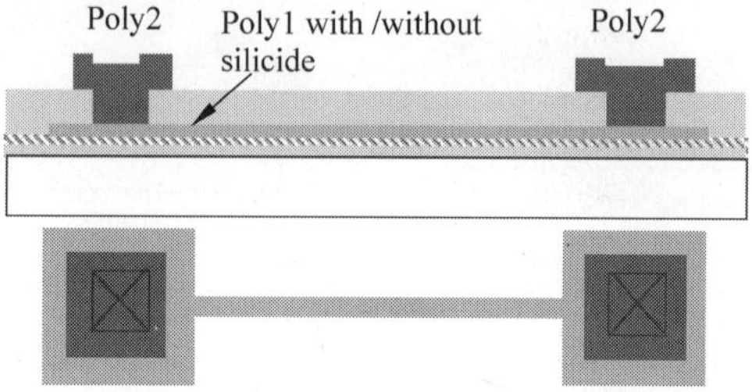

Figure 9.6 Structure to test series resistance of Poly0 (with/without $CoSi_2$) and contact resistance between Poly1 and Poly0 (with/without $CoSi_2$)[44] (see color figure at the end of this book)

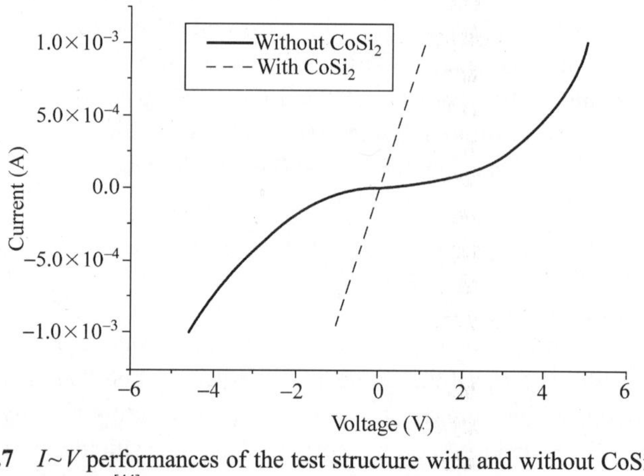

Figure 9.7 $I \sim V$ performances of the test structure with and without $CoSi_2$ on the grounded polysilicon[44]

For Poly1, the sheet resistance was about 60 Ω/sq before Pt deposition. After PtSi was formed, the sheet resistance was decreased to 2.5 Ω/sq. After treatment in saturated HF solution for 7 min, the sheet resistance of PtSi covered on the Poly1 film was increased to 3.0 Ω/sq, which showed that PtSi was slightly dissolved in saturated HF solution. However, the sheet resistance was still much lower than that of the structural polysilicon film without PtSi. A serious problem is that the PtSi film, like other silicides, has significant tensile stress on polysilicon. The measured stress on the PtSi film formed from the 400 Å-thick Pt layer was about 2.1×10^9 Pa. Such large stress could cause a freestanding structure warped and the PtSi layer delaminated from the polysilicon (Fig. 9.8). A simple method to reduce the stress is to use a thinner PtSi film. Therefore, we deposited 200 Å instead of 400 Å. Though the method would double the series resistance, the resistance was still decreased significantly compared to that without silicide. After release, no crack or delamination in the Pt film was found (Fig. 9.9). However, for a long beam, there was still a little warpage. The measured stress was about 1.5×10^9 Pa. Therefore, the method is still not good enough for a structure with high performance requirements, though it is acceptable for some applications.

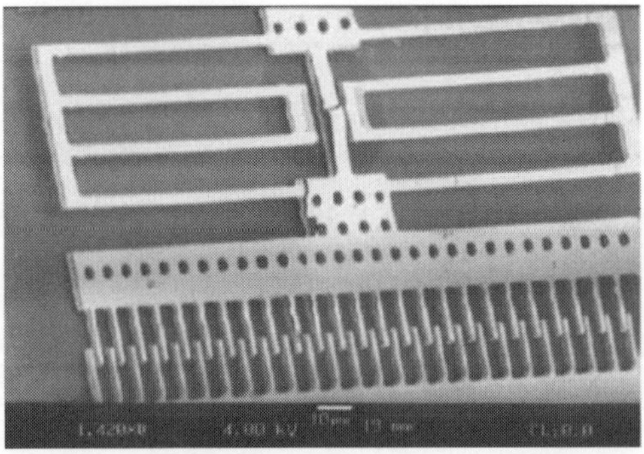

Figure 9.8 SEM photos of the delaminated silicide layers in microstructures with PtSi on the top (400 Å thick Pt)

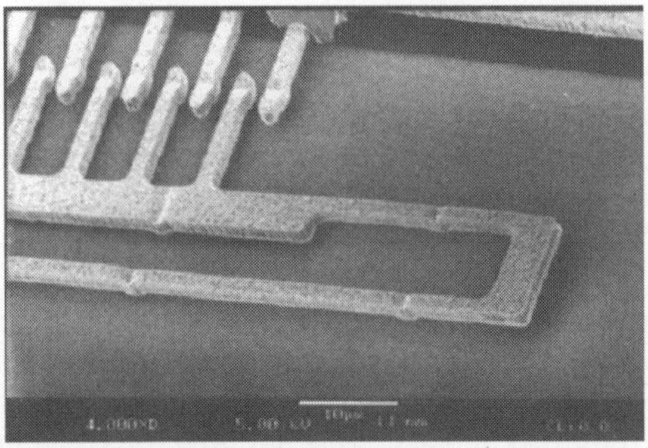

Figure 9.9 A SEM photo of microstructures with PtSi on the top (200 Å thick Pt)

The warpage came from the stress gradient caused by the asymmetric structure; the PtSi film was formed on the top surface and the sidewalls, but not on the bottom surface of the polysilicon. The method to make the structure symmetric is to add a PtSi film at the bottom or to remove the PtSi from the top surface. We chose the latter, because it is very difficult to form a self-aligned PtSi layer at the polysilicon bottom. Through a modified process, silicide was only formed on the sidewall, because the top surface was covered by oxide. No warpage was observed after the structure was released. For a structure with a large area, the decrement of resistance was not significant, because there was no silicide on most of the area. However, for narrow and long polysilicon lines which main series resistance came from, the silicide could greatly decrease the series resistance. For example, the series resistance of a 100 μm long, 2 μm thick and 2 μm wide polysilicon line (Poly1) was decreased to about 70 Ω from about 3 kΩ.

9.1.3.2 Electroless Metal-Plated Capsulation

To take the advantage of both electrical properties of metal and mechanical properties of silicon, a technique to selectively encapsulate polysilicon micromachined structures with copper was reported by J. -L Andrew Yeh et al.[45, 46, 60]. Electroless copper deposition with selective activation on the polysilicon surface was applied for metallization on all sides of polysilicon micromachined structures (as shown in Fig. 9.10). Using this technique, some fabrication difficulties of metal surface micromachining are overcome, and the stress induced by bimorph metal-on-silicon structures is minimized and further balanced due to the metal encapsulation on the silicon structures.

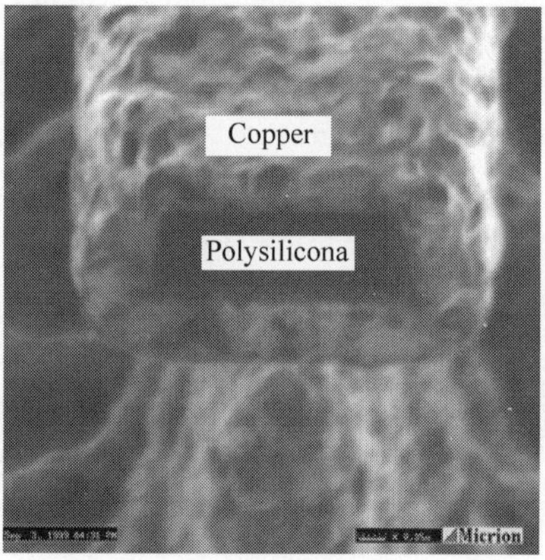

Figure 9.10 Focus-ion-beam micrograph of the cross section of a copper-encapsulated polysilicon beam. The plated copper is about 0.75 μm in thickness[30] (© 2000 IEEE)

The basic procedure of copper plating on polysilicon is described as follows: first, a sample is dipped into an activation bath which consists of diluted hydrofluoric

(HF) acid (100 – 250 ml/L) and palladium chloride ($PdCl_2$). In this wet activation step, native silicon oxide on the polysilicon surface is stripped off by HF, and a catalytic Pd activation film is formed on it; the palladium activation creates catalytic sites (nucleation centers) on the silicon surface, enabling subsequent electroless copper deposition. However, inert surfaces such as oxide, nitride or glass substrates are not activated during this step; therefore, they remain inactive to Cu deposition and provide isolation. The plating process is autocatalytic; in other words, the deposition continues once it starts. The sample is dipped in a base solution that contains cupric sulphate as the oxidation agent and formaldehyde as the reduction agent. The governing chemical reaction is given by[47]:

$$Cu^{2+} + 2HCHO + 4OH^- \longrightarrow Cu + 2HCOO^- + 2H_2O + H_2\uparrow$$

The recipe of the base solution is shown in Table 9.1, where Ethylenediamine-tetraacetic acid (EDTA) is a complexing agent. Potassium hydroxide is added to adjust the pH value of the plating bath to 12-13. 2,2'-Dipyridyl works as a brightening agent. It causes the randomization of the crystal growth, and subsequently reduces the average roughness. The plating temperature is set at 60℃.

Table 9.1 The recipe of the copper-plating solution

Chemical	Quantity
$CuSO_4 \cdot H_2O$ as copper resource	5 g/L
Formaldehyde for reduction	5 ml/L
Ethylenediaminetetraacetic acid (EDTA)	15 g/L
Potassium hydroxide for adjusting pH value	18 g/L
2,2'Dipyridyl as brightener	25 mg/L
RE-610 as surfactant	2.4 mg/L

Experiments showed that Cu could be selectively deposited on polysilicon but not on standard silicon nitride after 10 minutes of deposition[30]. However, some sporadic Cu precipitation was observed at the top of low-stress silicon nitride which is rich in silicon, but no continuous layer that would affect isolation was formed. Silicon oxide was not active to Cu deposition either. Hence, metallization of selected silicon/polysilicon structures and electric isolation by silicon nitride and/or silicon oxide could be realized by selective Cu plating. Figure 9.11 shows an SEM image of polysilicon structures on a single chip[30]. Cu was selectively plated onto the polysilicon structures without covering silicon oxide, while other areas covered by silicon oxide were not plated and kept isolated.

A suspended spiral inductor constructed by polysilicon and encapsulated with copper process was fabricated by utilizing this technology (see Fig. 9.12)[48]. The inductor had been measured of the inductance as 2 – 12 nH and quality factors over 30 at 5 GHz[45, 46]. In this design, the polysilicon provided structural rigidity, and the copper transmitting the electrical signals minimized the series resistance.

Figure 9.11 Selective deposition of Cu on structures in selected areas of a chip. The bright structures are where Cu was deposited on polysilicon[30] (© 2000 IEEE)

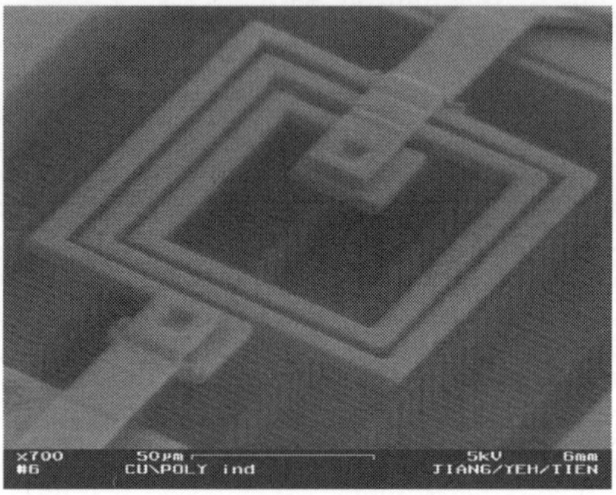

Figure 9.12 SEM image of a suspended rectangular spiral inductor[45, 46] (© 2000 IEEE)

This technique can also be applied to bulk micromachining technology.

9.1.4 Isolation

In some MEMS devices, such as microrelays and tunable capacitors, the movable structures have to be mechanically connected but electrically isolated. Here we take a laterally-actuated MEMS switch as an example to show how to isolate the surface-micromachined polysilicon structures[49–51]. Lateral switches can be fabricated with surface-micromachined polysilicon process[50, 51], bulk-micromachined silicon process[54–56], thick metal plating process[57], or other nonstandard processes[58].

One major benefit from the lateral switch is the ability to fabricate actuators, contacts, conductor paths, and to support all structures in one single lithographic step[59]. However, an extra isolation structure is necessary for mechanical coupling and electrical isolation between the actuator and the contacts. It usually requires extra process steps or special materials for this isolation structure. Reference[60] reported an isolating method of creating insulative regions in conductive materials for SOI (silicon-on-insulator) substrates. An inverse approach of creating conductive regions in dielectric materials was developed for the molded structures[61]. Both methods required combining process steps including etching trenches, refilling dielectric/conductive materials, and etching back to form the isolation structure. To simplify the process, maskless anisotropic etching was used to form a dielectric sidewall for isolation in the thermal actuator[62], but this method could not avoid forming dielectric sidewalls between the contact head and the signal lines in lateral switches (Fig. 9.13). Reference[63] reported a lateral switch in which a SiO_2 layer was used as the isolation structure. In this case, the switch with the SiO_2 layer was released with an unusual epoxy sacrificial layer and oxygen plasma etching. It is not applicable to other cases such as surfaced-micromachined switches because the epoxy layer significantly limits the thermal budget of the following processes. Photoresist was also employed as the isolating material in a thermal actuated lateral switch[52] (Fig. 9.14), but no detailed performance of the photoresist isolation structure was shown.

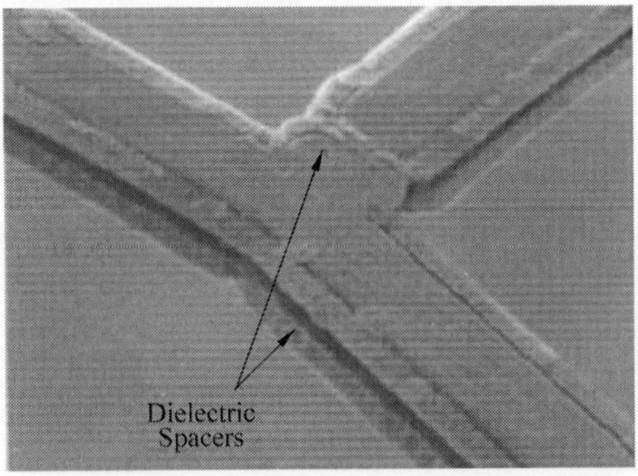

Figure 9.13 The isolation structure applied to lateral thermal actuation[62] (© 2001 IEEE)

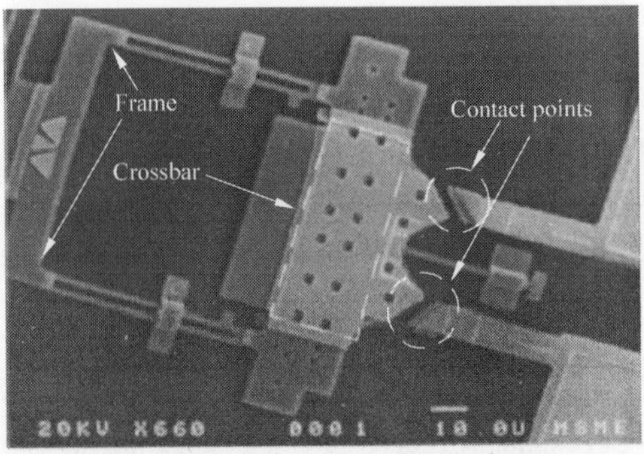

Figure 9.14 A lateral MEMS relay with gold contacts reported by UC Berkeley in the United States[52] (© 1999 IEEE)

Ye Wang et al. in UC Davis demonstrated a thermal actuated lateral switch that had advantages of low driving voltage, high RF performance, and simple fabrication process[50, 51, 53]. This switch adopted a piece of low-stress silicon nitride film as the isolation structure between the polysilicon actuator and the contact head (Shown in Fig. 9.15).

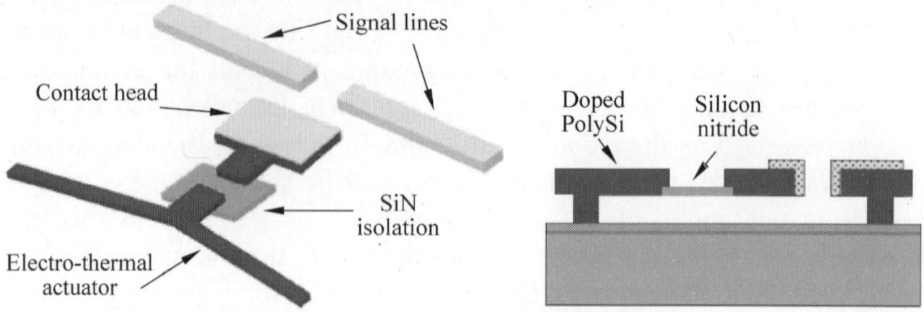

Figure 9.15 A thermal actuated lateral switch with nitride film as the isolation structure[51] (see color figure at the end of this book)

The lateral switch can be fabricated on both low-resistivity (10 Ω–cm) and high-resistivity silicon substrate (5,000 Ω–cm) to compare their RF performances. Figure 9.16 shows the cross-sectional schematic illustration of the fabrication sequence. First, the substrate is deposited with a 0.6 μm low-pressure chemical-vapor deposited (LPCVD) low-stress silicon nitride at a temperature of 850℃. The low-stress nitride forms an insulation layer to reduce substrate parasitics at high frequencies due to the lossy nature of the silicon substrate. Then, 2 μm of sacrificial low-temperature oxide (LTO) is deposited, and the anchors are patterned. Afterwards, another layer of LPCVD low-stress silicon nitride is deposited and

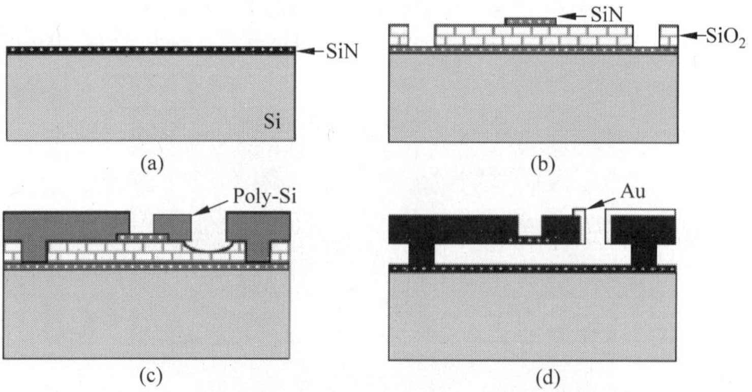

Figure 9.16 Cross-sectional illustration of the process flow: (a) deposition of the low-stress Si_3N_4 as isolation; (b) deposition and patterning of sacrificial SiO_2 and low-stress Si_3N_4 connection; (c) deposition and patterning of poly-Si and partial release, and (d) sputtering and lift-off of Au and HF release

patterned. It serves as the structural connection as well as the electrical and thermal isolation between the driving structure and the contact structure. In the next step, in situ doped n-type polysilicon film is deposited at 620℃. It is patterned through 0.4 μm oxide as a hard mask. After the formation of the polysilicon actuator, a partial released step is performed by dipping the wafer into 6∶1 BHF while exposing only a small region between the contact head and the RF signal lines. Approximately 1 μm of the sacrificial oxide in the closing gap area is removed to ensure the separation of sputtered gold on sidewalls of the contact head and on the signal lines, as well as the removal of unwanted gold in the area between them.

About 300 nm of Cr is deposited to serve as the adhesive and diffusing barrier layer for gold. Afterwards, 0.3 – 0.5 μm of gold is sputtered and lifted off, and gold is left only on the contact sidewalls and signal routing lines. Finally, the device is released in concentrated HF acid for 5 min, and the polysilicon and silicon nitride structures are released and suspended above the substrate. A supercritical drying after HF release is adopted to avoid the surface stiction of thin actuator beams.

The fabrication is completed with standard MEMS processes with only four masks including lift-off. No postprocessing is required. Contact metal is realized in one-step lithography and gold sputtering. The simplicity of this process ensures design flexibility and possible integration of this microrelay with other passive RF MEMS components. Utilizing this process, an electrothermally actuated lateral-contact microrelay for RF applications was fabricated on both silicon substrate and high-resistivity substrate. The microrelay utilizing the six-beam actuator required an actuation voltage of only 2.5 – 3.5 V, and had an off-state isolation –20 dB at 40 GHz and a low insertion loss of 0.1 dB up to 50 GHz.

However, the nitride isolation structure was a weak point (shown in Fig. 9.17), which might cause reliability and yield problems, because the nitride-polysilicon adhesion was not very strong. During operation of the switch, it was found that nitride-polysilicon connection was easily broken, particularly, when contact force was increased to achieve low contact resistance. Besides, the nitride-polysilicon

(a) (b)

Figure 9.17 (a) SEM image of the SiN structure connecting two polysilicon structures; (b) SEM images of structural connections[49] interface might be attacked by hydrofluoric acid (HF) etching during structure release.

In our following work, a modified thermal actuated lateral switch which utilized undoped polysilicon as the isolating material was proposed. The undoped-polysilicon isolation structure has advantages of simple process, robust mechanical strength and high reliability. Due to this robust structure, a stable pull-type actuation design and an optimized actuator can be employed to reduce the switching time and the power consumption. The performance and the lifetime of the switch were systematically investigated. Figure 9.18 shows the schematic overview of the proposed microswitch.

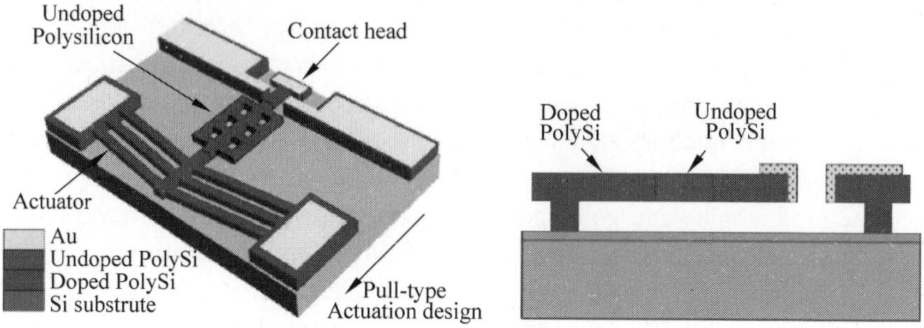

Figure 9.18 a modified thermal actuated lateral switch using undoped polysilicon as isolation structure[49] (see color figure at the end of this book)

An electrothermal V-shaped actuator, which is made of doped polysilicon, is employed to provide the in-plane motion of the switch. The contact head, signal lines of the doped polysilicon, and their sidewalls are coated with a gold film. The microswitch is fabricated with the polysilicon surface-micromachined process, and a silicon wafer with a 0.3 μm thick thermal oxide layer is used as the substrate. Figure 9.19 shows the cross-sectional schematic view of the process.

Firstly, a 0.2 μm-thick Si_3N_4 film is deposited on the substrate with LPCVD process. Then a sacrificial layer of 2 μm thick LPCVD SiO_2 film is deposited and patterned to form the anchor position, as shown in Fig. 9.19(b). The sacrificial SiO_2 layer remains undoped, different from the usual doped SiO_2 sacrificial layer such as borosilicate glass (BSG) or phosphosilicate glass (PSG), to prevent the dopant from diffusing from the sacrificial layer into the polysilicon structures.

Secondly, a 2 μm thick undoped LPCVD polysilicon film is deposited at 610℃, and a 2 μm thick photoresist film is coated, patterned and baked as the shelter layer for following implantation. As shown in Fig. 9.19(d), the polysilicon film is implanted with the P^+ at a dosage of 1×10^{16} cm^{-2} and the energy of 80 keV, while the patterned photoresist layer keeps the isolation area undoped. The undoped area forms the undoped-polysilicon isolation structure in the following sequences. After a 0.5 μm thick LPCVD oxide layer is deposited to avoid the self-diffusion

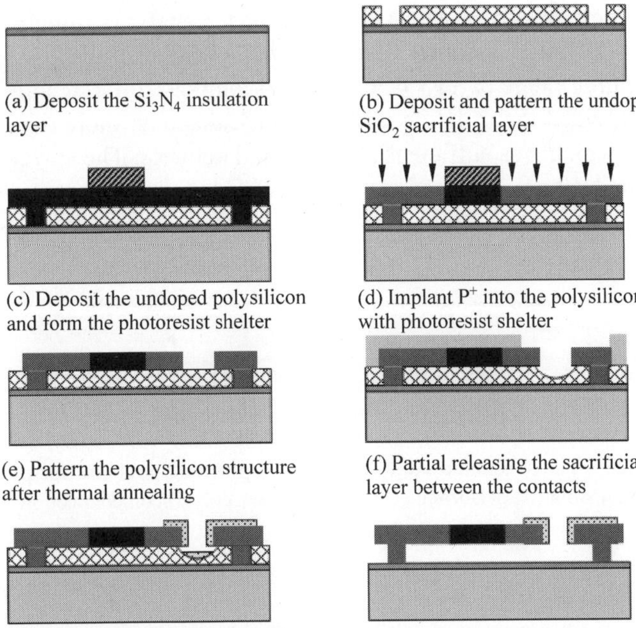

(a) Deposit the Si_3N_4 insulation layer

(b) Deposit and pattern the undoped SiO_2 sacrificial layer

(c) Deposit the undoped polysilicon and form the photoresist shelter

(d) Implant P^+ into the polysilicon with photoresist shelter

(e) Pattern the polysilicon structure after thermal annealing

(f) Partial releasing the sacrificial layer between the contacts

(g) Sputter and lift-off the gold film to form the sidewall contacts

(h) Release the whole microswitch

Figure 9.19 The cross-sectional illustration of the fabrication process sequence[49]

effect, thermal annealing (1,050℃, 1 hour) is carried out to drive and activate the dopant. Annealing also contributes to reduction of the residual stress in the polysilicon film. Then, the top oxide layer is removed by buffered hydrofluoric acid (BHF) etching, and the polysilicon film is patterned with inductively coupled plasma (ICP) etching process, as shown in Fig. 9.19(e). In this step, the undoped area forms the isolation structure while the doped area forms the actuator, the contact head and the signal lines.

Thirdly, similar to the process mentioned previously, the method of partial release combined with lift-off process is employed to form the sidewall metal contacts and the metal on signal lines (shown in Fig. 9.19(f)).

Finally, the device is fully released in the concentrated HF acid for 15 min as shown in Fig. 9.19(h). The sublimation drying after HF release is employed to reduce stiction of the thin actuator beams. The whole fabrication sequence is completed by standard MEMS processes with only four masks. The undoped-polysilicon connection is realized by one step of sheltered implantation without extra processes.

The electrical isolation performance of the undoped-polysilicon connection was investigated through on-chip testing structures as shown in Fig. 9.20. The testing structures were 8 μm wide, 2 μm-thick and 200 μm long doped polysilicon bridges with undoped-polysilicon connection in the center. The structures' $I \sim V$

curves were measured by a HP 4156B parameter analyzer. Figure 9.21 shows that undoped-polysilicon connection provided good electrical isolation in the switch's operating range of ±15 V. The 10 μm long, 20 μm long and 40 μm long connection provided the isolation with current leakage no more than 3 nA under 15 V voltage, which was sufficient for a thermal actuator. The current leakage of 20 μm long and 40 μm long connection remained no more than 5 nA when the voltage rose to 40 V.

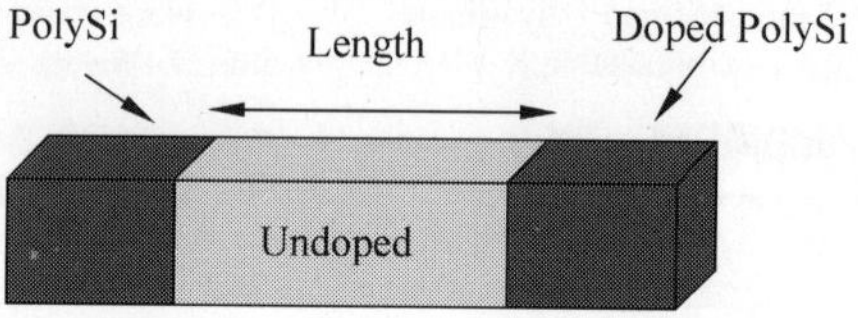

Figure 9.20 The schematic view of the on-chip testing structure for measuring the electrical isolating performance of the undoped-polysilicon connection[49]

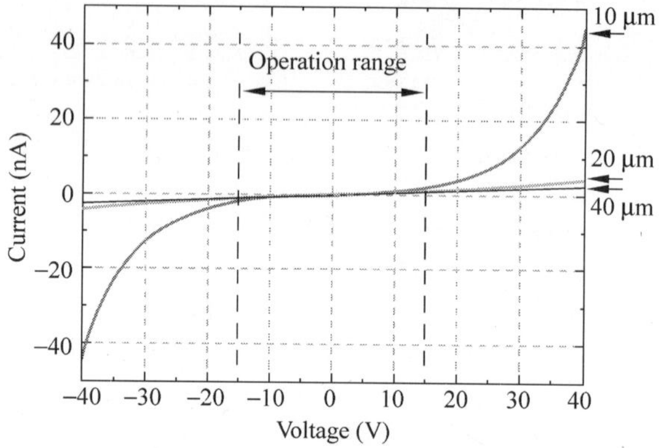

Figure 9.21 The $I \sim V$ curves of the undoped-polysilicon connections with three different lengths of connection:10, 20, and 40 μm[49]

It is well known that residual stress plays important roles in MEMS structures. If the dopant causes any stress mismatch between doped and undoped polysilicon, then out-of-plane deformation of the released structure may occur. Therefore, released doped polysilicon cantilevers, with and without undoped-polysilicon connection, have been employed to investigate the possible stress mismatch. Compared with the cantilevers without undoped-polysilicon connection, as shown in Fig. 9.15, cantilevers with undoped-polysilicon connection show no observable out-of-plane deformation. It seems that the stress mismatch could be ignored, which is also verified in the fabricated microswitch.

The fabricated microrelay was operated over 1 billion cycles without significant degradation of the contact resistance, and the electrical isolating performance of the undoped-polysilicon connection showed no observable degradation.

9.1.5 Monolithic Integrated Surface Micromachining Technology

Monolithic integration of MEMS and IC has been a hot issue in this field. The integration can improve the performance and save the processing and packaging costs. Since circuits and mechanical structures are quite different in process and performance requirements, research on the integration technology is full of challenges, particularly when regarding issues of the compatibility of materials and technological issues such as electrical connection, isolation and mechanical connection, etc. For example, as for the surface micromachining, the issue of thermal compatibility is such a problem. High-temperature techniques, such as deposition and annealing of polysilicon have negative impacts on metal layers, resistors, and active devices.

According to the sequence of process, the integrated fabrication technologies fall into three categories: pre-CMOS[64], post- CMOS[65] and intermediate-CMOS (or called Hybrid-CMOS). In the pre-CMOS approach, MEMS structures are fabricated before the regular CMOS process sequence. Pre-CMOS (or 'MEMS-first') micromachining fabrication technologies avoid thermal budget constraints during the MEMS fabrication, which may degrade the performance of CMOS circuitry. However, CMOS foundries usually do not accept the preprocessed wafers due to the risk of contamination, and some CMOS process steps have to be modified. In the intermediate-CMOS approach, the CMOS process sequence has to be interrupted for fabrication steps of MEMS structures, and some CMOS standard steps may be modified. Therefore, the process cannot be done in a commercial IC foundry, but, instead, manufacturers have to possess their own facility or contractor for specially-designed processes. The successful examples of this approach are Analog Devices' iMEMS and SOIMEMS processes. In the post-CMOS (or 'circuitry-first') approach, MEMS structures are fabricated after CMOS processes are completed. The circuits can be fabricated in any IC foundry using conventional IC technology first without any MEMS or other process steps, so low cost and high efficiency can be achieved. Therefore, the post-CMOS approach is most promising for commercial MEMS products.

Figure 9.22 is the cross-sectional schematic diagram of the integration of microstructure and circuit technology, which was made with the Post-CMOS process and developed by UC Berkeley[66]. The CMOS integrated part is firstly made, and then the micro-mechanical structures. It avoids the uneven surface caused by making the mechanical parts first, which consequently reduces the difficulty in lithography of electrical parts. The circuit part is realized with double-layer polysilicon, single-layer metal and *P*-well technology. As the metal in circuits has to survive from the high-temperature technique, it makes the whole process difficult. Tungsten is adopted as a part of the circuit connection material to replace aluminum, because tungsten is refractory metal and has a similar coefficient of thermal expansion to silicon but a lower resistivity. Therefore, in the following micro-machining process, high-temperature process can still be used. Doped polysilicon is used for local interconnection between circuits and structures. A major problem is that refractory metal used as the interconnection line is not the standard CMOS process, which means the standard foundry process cannot be applied directly. Moreover, its resistivity is higher than copper or aluminum, so the circuit performance is degraded. In recent years, UC Berkeley has developed a new Post-CMOS technology, in which polysilicon is replaced by polycrystalline silicon-germanium (Poly-Si_xGe_{1-x}) as the structural material[67]. The growing temperature of Poly-Si_xGe_{1-x} is less than 450℃, thus aluminum can be used as the interconnection material to achieve post-CMOS MEMS integration. IMEC at Belgium has also made great efforts on developing this technology.

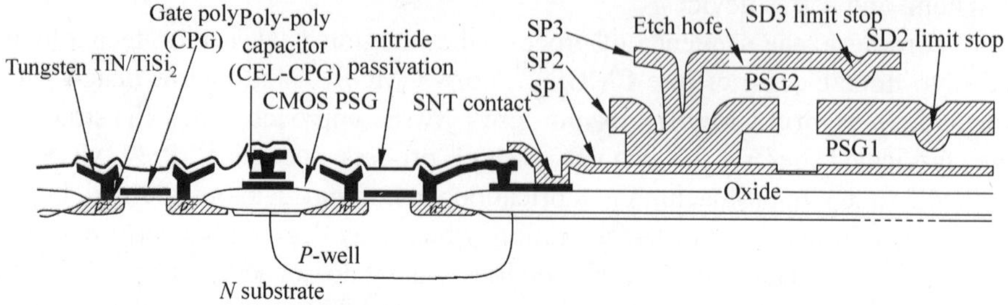

Figure 9.22 The section schematic diagram of the Post-CMOS integration of microstructure and circuit technology by UC Berkeley[66] (© 1994 Springer)

Figure 9.23 shows the BiMEMS integration technology developed by ADI, which merges the integrated circuits and micromechanical process to achieve integration. The circuit part is realized through BiCMOS technology, and the mechanical structure is made from polysilicon. The connection between the mechanical structure and the circuit is achieved through N^+ layer. This approach costs lower than producing the circuit and the structure separately, but it is not transplantable to other foundries.

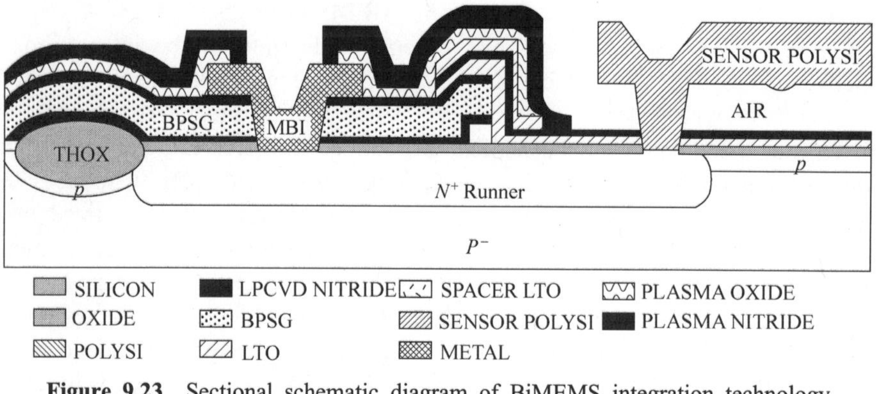

Figure 9.23 Sectional schematic diagram of BiMEMS integration technology made by ADI (© ADI)

Sandia National Laboratories in the United State have designed an integration technology in which the mechanical structure is made before the circuitry[68]. The cross-sectional schematic diagram of this integrated chip is shown in Fig. 9.24. Firstly, the silicon substrate is recessed with wet etching process, and silicon nitride as the insulating layer is deposited. Secondly, silicon dioxide and polysilicon are orderly deposited and patterned to form the sacrificial layer and mechanical structures, respectively; then, LPCVD silicon dioxide is refilled into the trench and planarized by CMP. Then, annealing is applied in order to release the stress of polysilicon, and silicon nitride is deposited as a passivation layer. After the completion of the mechanical structure, standard CMOS process is applied to the fabrication of the circuit part. Finally, passivation of the CMOS circuit, removal of the passivation layer on the mechanical structures, and release of the structures are applied successively. Since thermal annealing is applied before circuit processing and CMP planarization is adopted, the restriction of circuit fabrication on temperature and flatness is overcome.

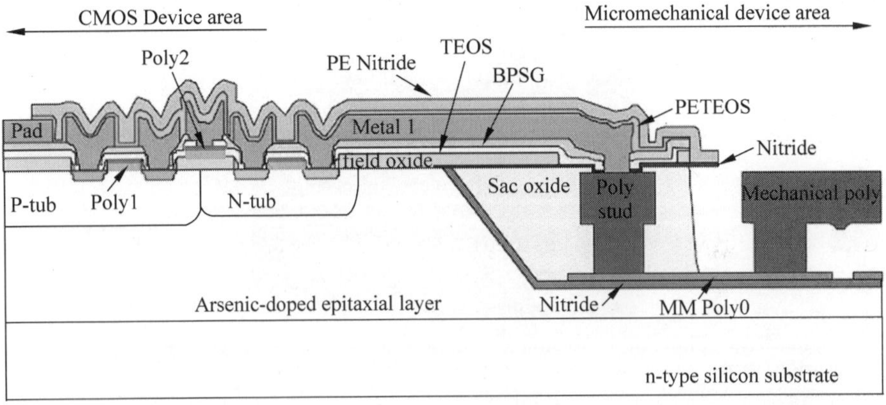

Figure 9.24 Sectional schematic diagram of Pre-CMOS integration technology developed by Sandia (© Sandia National Lab see color figure at the end of this book)

The so-called CMOS MEMS technology is a fully integrated post-CMOS process, developed by Carnegie-Mellon University in the United States[69, 70]. The basic process sequence is shown in Fig. 9.25. The mechanical structure is accomplished by the interconnecting metal and the dielectric between metal layers. Therefore, after the completion of the CMOS circuit processing, only a few steps of anisotropic or isotropic dry etching are needed to complete the device processing. This process has the feature that all the process steps are on the same side of the wafer, so it can easily be transplanted to other foundries based on different sizes or substrates. It makes the selection on processing service providers more flexible. The main drawbacks of this process are limitation on the thickness of the mechanical structure, and large residual-stress gradient in the multilayer. As shown in Fig. 9.26, the microstructure fabricated with this process is seriously warped[71].

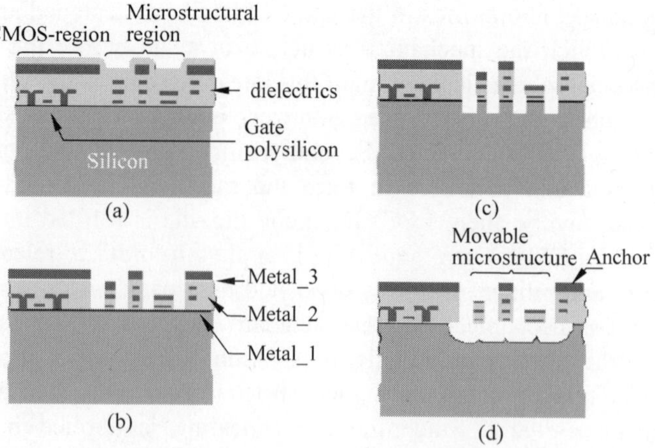

Figure 9.25 Basic process sequence chart of CMOS MEMS technology[69] (© 1996 Elsevier see color figure at the end of this book)

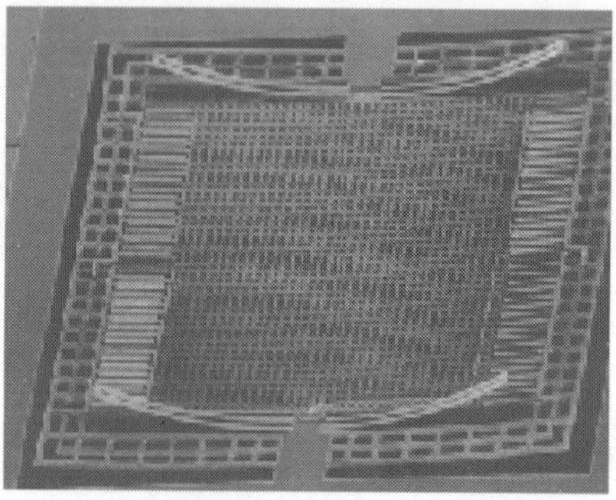

Figure 9.26 Photo of micro-structure fabricated with CMOS MEMS technology[71] (© 2001 IEEE)

9.1.6 3D Surface Maching

Owing to the characteristics of surface micromachining technology, normally only two-dimensional structures can be fabricated with the process. While, through a number of special structural designs and assembly methods, quasi three-dimensional surface processing can be achieved.

One of the most basic structures is the hinge shown in Fig. 9.27[72, 73]. This structure can be achieved through two-layer of polysilicon micromachining. The hinge made of the first polysilicon layer is surrounded by a frame constructed with substrate and the second polysilicon layer, and there is no connection between them. The movable structure can freely rotate upwards around the axis of hinge. In order to determine the position of the structure to form the final structure, some mechanical fixtures are also needed. Figure 9.28 shows the latches which can lock the actual structure against different directions through specific design. Plastic materials[74] are also used for fixation, as illustrated in Fig. 9.29. The materials can be some strong plastic metals (such as copper) or other special polymers. At a certain angle, plastic materials will stay at the targeted position due to plastic deformation.

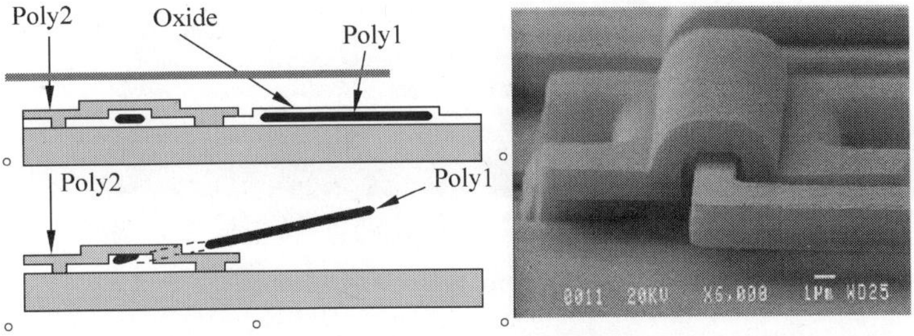

Figure 9.27 The schematic and SEM micrograph of off-plate structure by applying hinges and double-layer polysilicon[72, 73] (© 2001 IEEE)

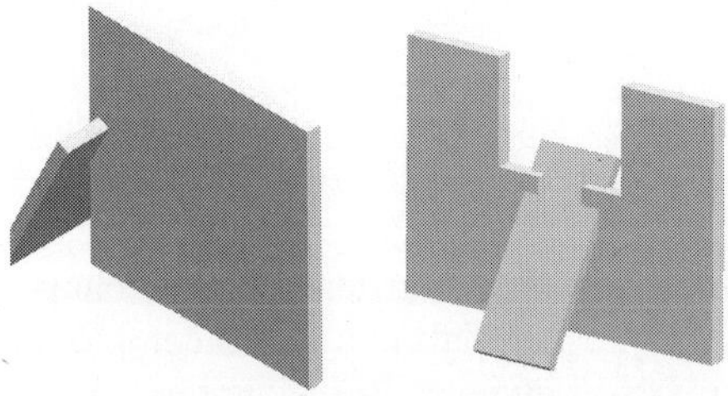

Figure 9.28 Applying latches to fix the off-plate structure (see color figure at the end of this book)

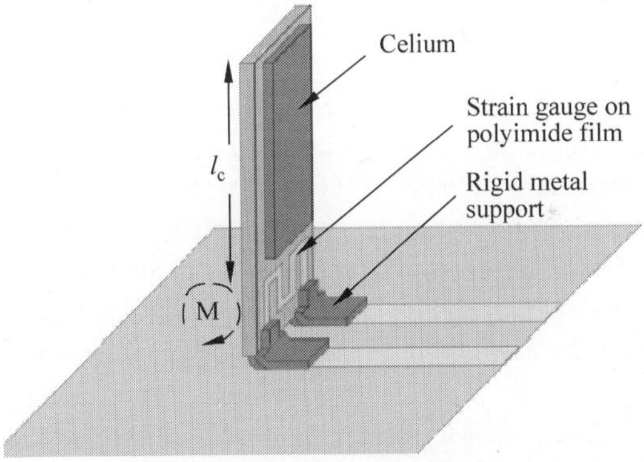

Figure 9.29 Applying plastic-metal to fix the off-plate structure[74] (© 1994 IEEE)

It is also an important issue how to assemble the micro structures. In early experiments, the microstructures were assembled manually with probes, but the efficiency of this method is too low to meet requirements of production. Therefore, other assembling methods are developed continually, such as water flow, electrostatic, magnetic and electromagnetic force, etc[75, 76]. Figure 9.30 shows pictures of the assembled quasi three-dimensional structures.

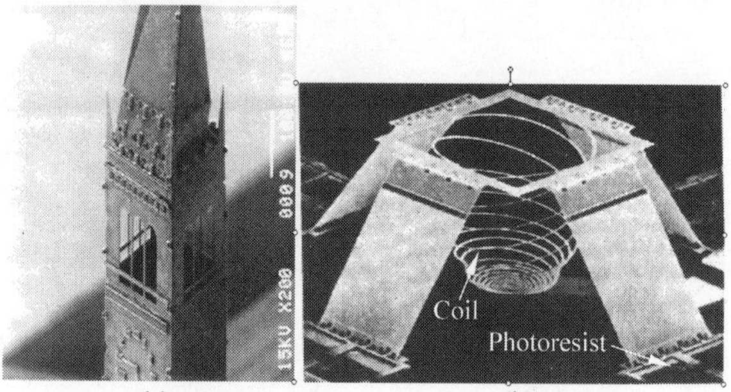

(a) (b)

Figure 9.30 The picture of a quasi three-dimensional structure applying surface technology and assembly techniques. (a) 3D model of the UC Berkeley Campanile clock tower. The tower stands 1.8 mm high. The steeple is an example of non-orthogonal plates. (b) Scanning electron micrograph of the suspended inductor supported by the MESA structure[75, 76] (© 2000 IEEE)

9.1.7 Other Surface Micromachining Technology

In addition to polysilicon surface sacrificial layer technology, other structural materials and sacrificial layer materials can also be employed for making devices so as to meet different requirements. For example, in RF MEMS, generally, sputtering or electroplating is used for making structural layers, while photoresist or other polymer materials are used as the sacrificial layer. This results in low resistance, which meets the low-loss requirement. At the same time, this technology also has the merit of low temperature[77, 78].

Owing to its low receptivity and fabrication feasibility, aluminum is one of the most common materials in CMOS foundries, but its use in surface micromachining is significantly less than that of polysilicon. The reason is that the mechanical properties of aluminum are inferior to those of polysilicon, and the residual stress in the aluminum film is not easy to control. However, a few notable MEMS devices constructed with aluminum have been fabricated successfully[79].

Until now, the most successful MEMS devices utilizing aluminum as the mechanical structure are DMD (micro-mirror display) invented in 1987 at Texas Instruments[80−85]. The DMD is a fast, reflective digital light switch, which (Fig. 9.31, Fig. 9.32) has a MEMS structure fabricated with surface micromachining processes with a polymer sacrificial layer. A yoke structure rotates about two compliant torsion hinges, and the mirror is connected to the yoke. The yoke is electrostatically driven by electrodes. The mirror and the yoke rotate until the yoke comes to rest against mechanical stops that are at the same potential as the yoke.

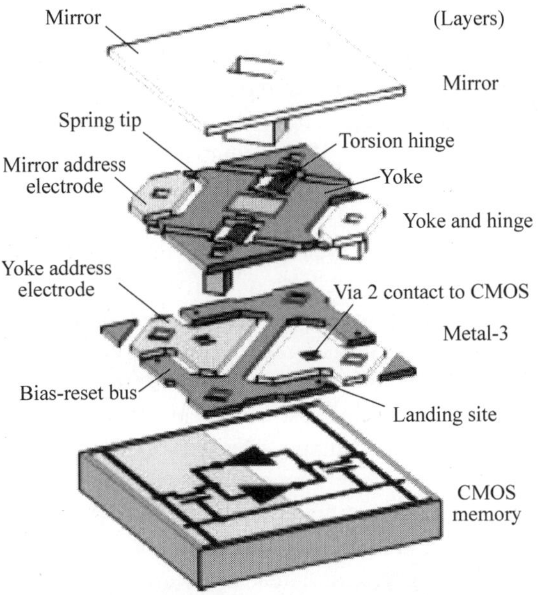

Figure 9.31 DMD pixel exploded view[86] (© 1998 IEEE)

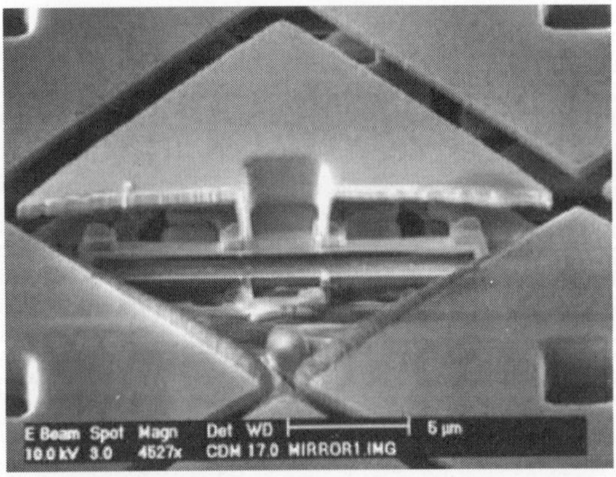

Figure 9.32 Ion mill sectioning of DMD pixel to reveal cross section[82] ((© 1996 IEEE) see color figure at the end of this book)

Both aluminum layer and polymer layer are deposited and etched at a low temperature, and therefore, the DMD can be monolithically integrated with CMOS SRAM cells. By writing to the memory cells, the mirrors can be individually controlled. The high reflectivity of aluminum is an important property for this application. Furthermore, combining DMD with image processing, memory, a light source and optics, a DLP system is capable of projecting large, bright, seamless, high-contrast color images. The DLP (Digital Light Processing) products include TV sets, VGA monitors, projectors and other projection displays.

The fabrication process flow of DMD structure is shown in Fig. 9.33. The structure process begins with a completed SRAM address circuit employing double level metal CMOS technology. A thick oxide is deposited over Metal-2 of the CMOS and then planarized through chemical mechanical polish (CMP) in order to obtain a flat surface. Then a layer of aluminum (marked as Metal-3) is deposited and patterned. An organic sacrificial layer (marked as Spacer-1) is then spin-coated, lithographically patterned, and hardened to form metal supporting posts after the yoke metal covers their sidewalls. Next, a 600 Åthick metal layer is sputtered as the hinge material. This metal is covered with PECVD SiO_2 layer, which is patterned in the shape of the hinges and used as an etching mask for the hinges later. A thicker layer of aluminum is sputtered on the yoke layer, followed by a second layer of PECVD SiO_2 which is deposited and patterned over the yoke metal, serving as a mask. Utilizing the single mask, the yoke and metallized layers of the hinge as well as the hinge geometries are defined by RIE. Through this technique, the hinge metal is continuous everywhere under the metallized layer of the yoke. Afterwards, a second organic sacrificial layer (Spacer-2) is spin-coated, lithographically patterned, and hardened to form the supporting posts that secure the mirrors to the underlying yokes. Then, an aluminum layer is sputtered and patterned over Spacer-2 to form the mirrors. Finally, the sacrificial layers are removed, and the mirrors and the yokes are released.

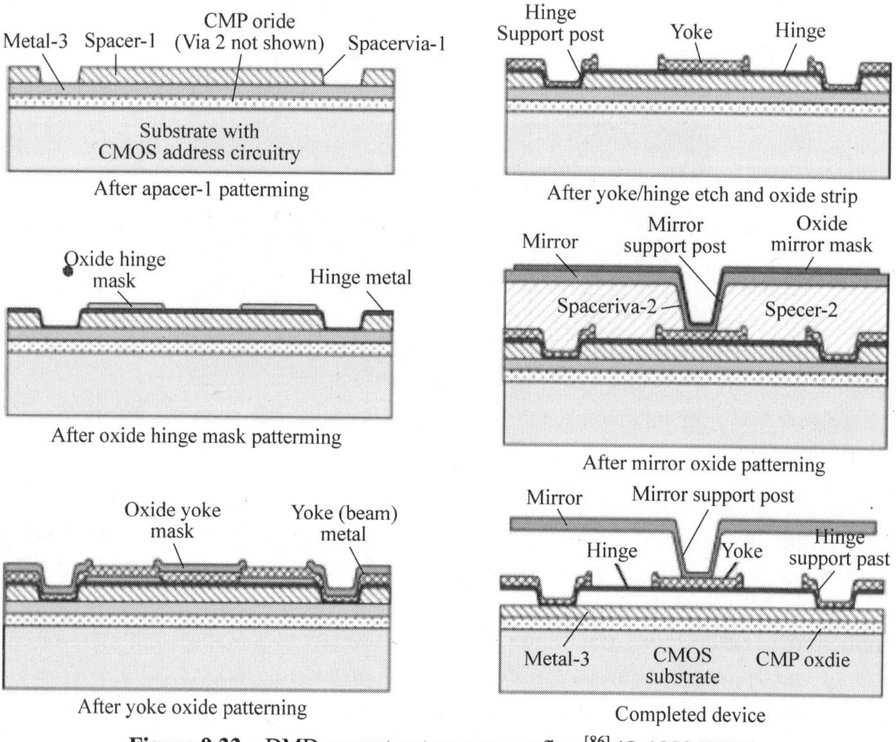

Figure 9.33 DMD superstructure process flow[86] (© 1998 IEEE)

Another successful example is a RF MEMS shunt switch reported by Yao et al. at Raytheon.[78, 87, 88]. Surface micromachining techniques were utilized to fabricate the switch. High-resistivity (>5,000 Ω-cm) silicon wafers were used as substrates. Figure 9.34 shows the process flow. Firstly, 1 μm of thermal oxide is grown on the substrate. Then, a layer of tungsten (<0.5 μm) is sputtered and patterned to define the bottom electrodes. Next, less than 2,000 Å of PECVD silicon nitride is deposited and patterned as the dielectric layer. A 4 μm thick aluminum layer is evaporated and wet etched to define the transmission lines and the posts for the membranes. A photoresist sacrificial spacer layer is spin-coated and patterned as the sacrificial layer. An aluminum alloy layer is sputtered and wet etched to define the membrane. Finally, the photoresist sacrificial layer is etched by oxygen plasma to release the membrane. Figure 9.35 shows a micrograph of a fabricated shunt switch. Major issues in this process are how to control the residual stress in the structural aluminum layer and the surface roughness of the bottom electrodes, which are critical for the switch performance.

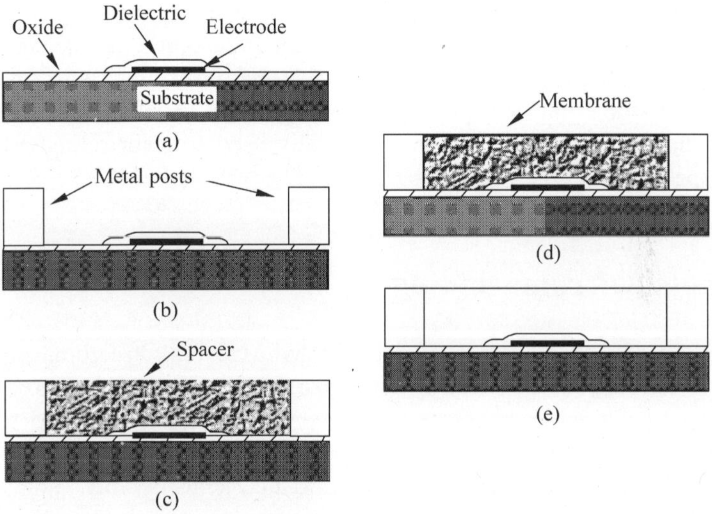

Figure 9.34 Schematic illustration of process flow: (a) oxide deposition, electrode, dielectric deposition and patterning; (b) metal posts deposition and patterning; (c) spacer coating and patterning; (d) membrane deposition and patterning; and (e) removal of the spacer by dry etching[78] (© 1999 IEEE)

Young and Boser of UC Berkeley used aluminum to fabricate variable capacitors for RF applications[34, 89, 91]. Sputtered 1.0 μm-thick aluminum was employed as the structural layer, while 1.5 μm of baked photoresist served as a sacrificial layer, which was released by oxygen plasma.

For infrared detectors and ultrasonic sensors, normally Si_3N_4 can be applied as structural layer material, and polysilicon or polymers are used as sacrificial layer material. Si_3N_4 is insulating material with higher Young's modulus and more light

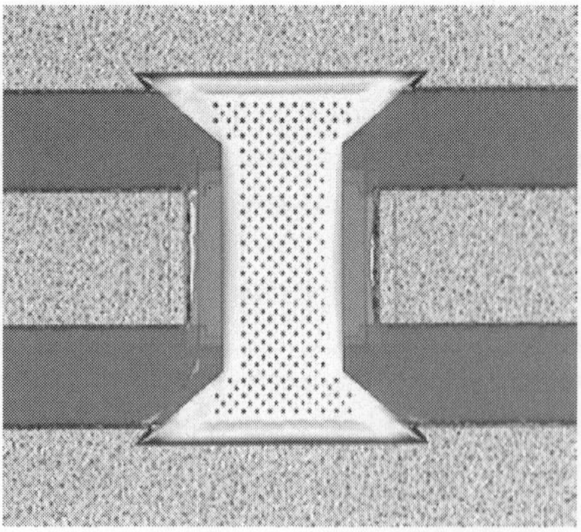

Figure 9.35 Micrograph of a shunt RF switch fabricated by Raytheon Systems Company[78]

absorption than silicon, which meets the special requirements of those devices.

Infrared (IR) detectors in wide applications can be divided into cooled detectors (photonic detectors) and uncooled ones (thermal detectors). The MEMS technology has been used for fabricating cantilever-based uncooled IR detector whose mechanism is based on the bending of a bimaterial beam upon absorption of IR energy. The surface micromachining technology with LPCVD SiN_x as structure material and Al as reflector material is widely used for fabricating the IR FPA (focal plane array)[92–96].

9.2 Bulk Micromachining

As a technology specially developed for MEMS, bulk micromachining can selectively etch the silicon substrate to realize functional structures. By using this technique, the whole-thickness of the silicon wafer can be utilized to form a relatively thick and complex 3D structure. This will be helpful to fabricate more devices and improve the devices' performance considerably. For example, resolution and sensitivity of capacitor-based micro inertial devices are increased through the introduction of the large proof-mass and the detecting capacitor. Some actuators prepared by the bulk micromachining technology can provide large driving forces and displacements. Moreover, single crystal silicon has excellent mechanical properties which are favorable to improving the device performance. Bulk micromachining has the major drawback that its compatibility with IC is not as good as the surface micromachining approach, which makes monolithic integration difficult to be achieved and the production cost comparatively high.

Bulk micromachining can be used for preparing complex 3D MEMS devices, such as membranes (of pressure sensors, RF devices and microphones, etc.), chambers (of pumps, reservoirs and microchannels), needles, tweezers, mirrors, switches, and so on. Different from the surface micromachining, the bulk micromachining has some special processes, such as anisotropic wet etching, deep reactive ion etching (DRIE), silicon/glass anodic bonding and silicon-silicon direct bonding, etc. In addition to paying attention to each single process, it is more important to study how to combine different individual processes to develop a whole-set bulk micromachining process. In the following sections, we will only give a brief introduction of several individual processes, but discuss more on different sets of processes.

9.2.1 Introduction of Key Processes

9.2.1.1 Silicon Wet Etch

Silicon wet etch process has been developed and applied in IC productions since 1960s. Based on etching performances, the process can be divided into isotropic etchi and anisotropic etch[14, 97]. (See Fig. 9.36)

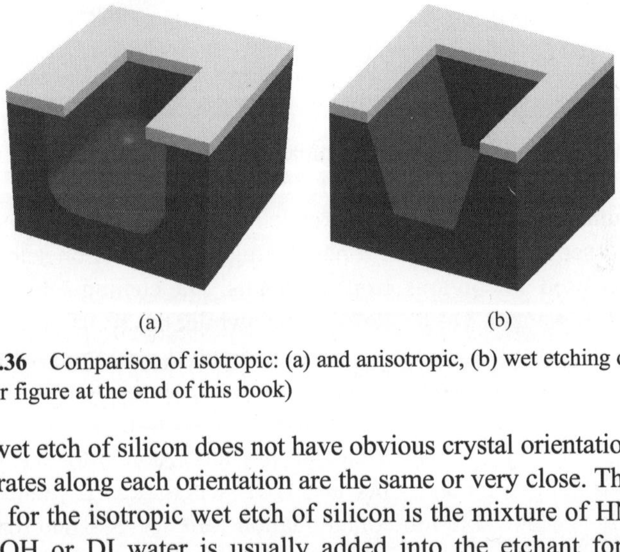

Figure 9.36 Comparison of isotropic: (a) and anisotropic, (b) wet etching of silicon (see color figure at the end of this book)

Isotropic wet etch of silicon does not have obvious crystal orientation selectivity. The etching rates along each orientation are the same or very close. The commonly used etchant for the isotropic wet etch of silicon is the mixture of HNO_3 and HF, and CH_3COOH or DI water is usually added into the etchant for dilution. If CH_3COOH is used, the etchant is also named as HNA[14, 97]. Different etchant composition leads to different silicon etching rates and surface roughness.

On the contrary, anisotropic etch refers to a special etching process in which the etch rate varies with the substrate crystal orientation, and the final etched profile is strongly dependent on the wafer's crystal plane. This will happen in the microfabrication of not only silicon, but nearly all crystals such as quartz. Anisotropic wet etch of silicon is a key process of the bulk micromachining technology and possesses an excellent feature of wafer-orientation-dependent etch. The silicon crystal has a diamond structure. For some etchants, there is a very slowly-etched plane, i.e. self-stopped etching plane, (111), while the etch rate of the (100) plane is considerably fast[98].

Figure 9.37 indicates the wafer-orientation-dependent anisotropic wet etch of (100) silicon wafer. If the mask patterns along the <110> direction, then the bottom surface is the fastest etch plane during etching (100), while the side wall will stop at the (111) plane. The angle between the side wall and the wafer surface is 54.74°. Finally, an inverted trapezoidal pit will be formed by this anisotropic etching.

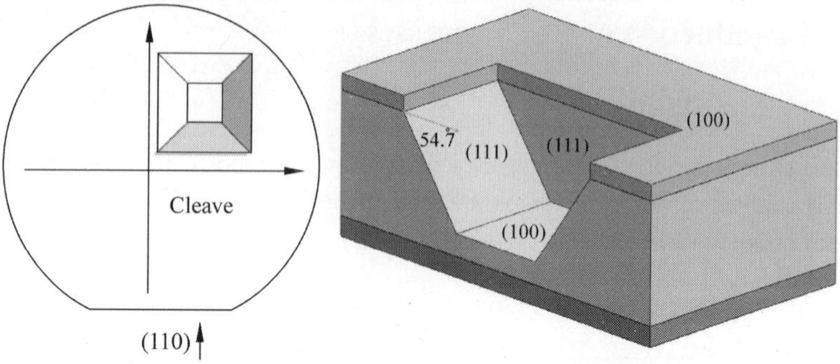

Figure 9.37 Illustration of the anisotropic etching performance of (100) silicon (see color figure at the end of this book)

The commonly used silicon anisotropic etchants are KOH, TMAH (Tetra Methyl Ammonium Hydroxide), and other alkaline etchants. Considering the low cost, simple instrument requirement, and excellent etching controllability, KOH is the most widely used silicon etchant. It has the highest orientation selectivity among all commonly used silicon anisotropic etchants. The etching selectivity of (111), (110) and (100) plane is 1:400:200[99]. Meanwhile, the KOH etch rates of Si_3N_4 and SiO_2 are very low, 20 Å/min for SiO_2, and only 1.4 Å/min for LPCVD Si_3N_4. Therefore, Si_3N_4 can be used as excellent mask material for KOH etching, and 1000 Å thick Si_3N_4 can successfully protect a 400 μm thick silicon wafer during through-wafer etching. The KOH etchant has the problem that its compatibility with CMOS is not good, mainly because KOH will attack Al simultaneously and potassium ion is a movable ion contamination for CMOS. Therefore, KOH etch process is restricted in the CMOS-integrated fabrication.

TMAH is another very commonly used anisotropic etchant of silicon The biggest advantage of TMAH is its compatibility with IC process. TMAH is free of any basic metal ion and has been widely used as a main component of positive photoresist developer for a period of time after diluted to a low concentration. By adding dissolved silicon into TMAH or using other methods to tune the final pH value of the etchant, it is possible to realize silicon anisotropic wet etch without significantly attacking the exposed Al[100]. This makes the TMAH applications much more flexible. Additionally, the alkalinity of TMAH is much lower than that of KOH, and thereby compared with the KOH-based one, TMAH-based etchant is much safer. The problem of TMAH as a silicon anisotropic etchant is that its orientation selectivity is not as good as that of KOH. The ratio of etch rates on the (111) and (100) planes varies from 1∶10 to 1∶35. What's more, the selectivity of heavy B+-doped silicon is not good, either, and it cannot be used for achieving self-stopped etching. Compared with KOH, TMAH etches silicon oxide much slower, and therefore, we can use SiO_2 as a deep TMAH etching mask.

9.2.1.2 DRIE: A Deep Silicon Etch Technique

Although wet etch of silicon is very simple and does not need any complex facilities, a high-aspect-ratio structure with vertical sidewalls is hard to be prepared merely by the wet etching technique. Moreover, conventional dry etch process cannot satisfy some of MEMS requirements, such as high etch rate, high selectivity of mask materials and high aspect ratio. Deep silicon etch technique was developed in the context of these requirements.

Deep reactive ion etch (DRIE) is one of the most important technologies in MEMS fabrication. The most popular silicon DRIE technique is Bosch process, a patented process developed by Robert Bosch GmbH (Bosch Gmbh, 1994). Bosch Process applies etch and passivation alternatively to obtain high-aspect-ratio structures (HARS). Advanced Silicon Etcher (ASE), Surface Technology System (STS), utilizing the Inductively Coupled Plasma (ICP) technique is a typical tool of Bosch process[101], in which SF_6 and C_4F_8 are employed as etch and passivation reactants respectively. Typical DRIE process features include high etch rate (several microns/min), high aspect ratio capability (up to 30∶1), high selectivity to mask (75∶1 to photoresist), and anisotropic sidewall profile ($A > 0.99$). In June 2005, STS launched the latest generation source for ASE processing, named Pegasus, which provides a 30% increase in etch rate compared to the ASE and

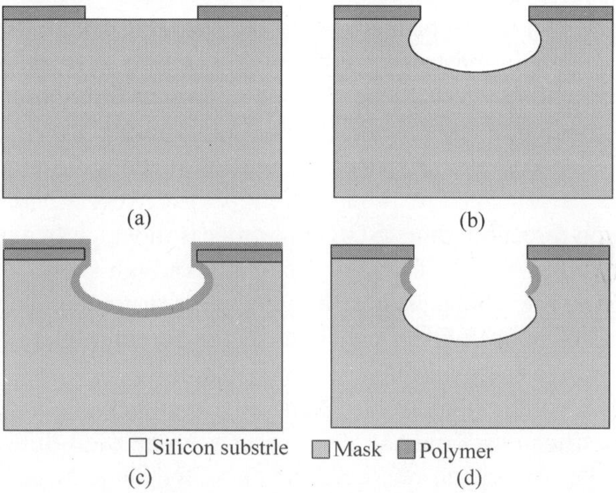

Figure 9.38 Principle of DRIE using Bosch process: (a) Pattern silicon substrate, (b) etching step, (c) passivation step, and (d) etching step

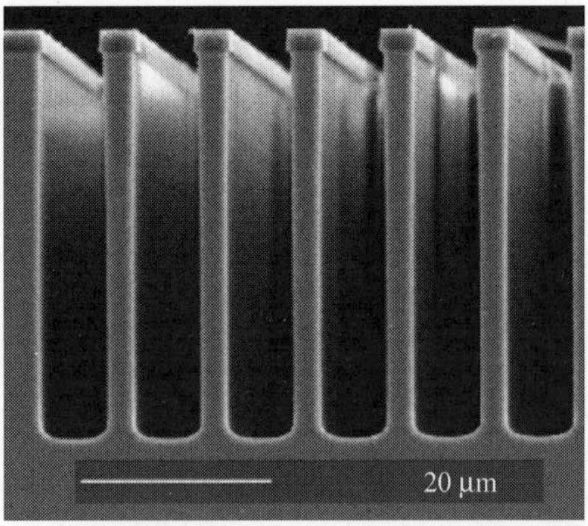

Figure 9.39 Comb-structure fabricated with deep silicon etching technique

significantly improves selectivity and the cross-wafer uniformity on substrates up to 200 mm. Utilizing the 'Pegasus' source, STS has demonstrated that etch rates > 50 μm/min (1% exposed area), with improved cross-wafer uniformity, smoother sidewalls, reducing structural tilting at the wafer edge as well. Owing to its outstanding advantages, the Bosch DRIE process has been widely utilized to fabricate a variety of MEMS devices including inertial, optical, biological, and RF devices[102–104]. Combined with other technologies, DRIE can also be utilized in various situations, e.g. an isolation technology with the combination of DRIE and polysilicon refill[105, 106] and a general technology with the combination of DRIE and silicon fusion bonding[107].

9.2.1.3 Wafer Bonding

In bulk silicon micromachining, wafer bonding is a key technique. Usually, wafer bonding refers to the process in which two wafers (of either the same or different materials) are mechanically coupled through different wafer-to-wafer interactions[14, 97, 108]. In most cases, there should be new chemical bonds between the two wafers/materials to achieve a stable coupling. Bonding can be used for packaging, providing support, adding additional electrodes, forming sealed chambers realizing complex 3D structure and introducing different materials as substrates, etc.

Silicon-silicon direct bonding (SDB) is a process in which two polished silicon wafers are combined face to face and bonded after high temperature annealing, and the process is also called as thermal bonding or fusion bonding[109–110]. After annealing, Si-O-Si bonds will be generated at the bonding interface, which have very strong cohesive energy, even larger than that of the bulk materials. Although silicon-silicon direct bonding seems like a simple process, considering the large stiffness of the silicon material and the difficulty of the Si-O-Si bond generation, a successful SDB has critical requirements on wafer flatness, surface roughness, and particles or other contaminations. If these requirements cannot be satisfied, cavities will be generated at the interface easily, which even leads to bonding failure. Consequently, besides strict requirements of the silicon wafer, operation and environments of bonding should be strictly controlled to ensure a successful bonding. Some special cleaning procedures and surface modifications will be helpful to improve the bonding quality. Related information can be found in literature[111]. The principle and the process of direct bonding of silicon wafers with oxide layer are the same as the bare silicon-to-silicon direct bonding.

Silicon-glass anodic bonding, also called as electrostatic bonding, is another commonly used bonding process. During the bonding process, the silicon wafer and the sodium-rich glass wafer are piled up and added with electrostatic bias through probes. The glass wafer is connected to the cathode, while the silicon wafer to the anode. The typical working voltage ranges from 200 – 1,500 V. To activate the sodium ions inside the glass and make them movable, the silicon and the glass wafers should be heated up to 180℃ – 500℃[112]. After the bias is applied, the sodium ions will move towards the cathode, and this drift will generate a several-micron-thick depletion layer at the interface. Because nearly all voltages are applied across this depletion layer, a very high electric field is generated at the silicon/glass interface, which pulls the two surfaces together and facilities bonding. As the bonding process is carried out at a relatively high temperature, chemical reaction will occur at the contacted silicon-glass interface and generate strong chemical bonds. Therefore, the bonding strength is even stronger than the mechanical strength of silicon or glass itself. However, when the bonded wafer is cooled down to the room temperature, thermal stress will be generated due to the thermal expansion coefficient difference between the bonded silicon and glass. The bonded wafer can be warped or even broken due to this serious mismatch. To minimize the thermal stress, we should use glass with thermal expansion coefficients close to that of silicon, such as Pyrex7740, and the bonding temperature should be as low as possible.

Adhesive bonding is also a commonly used bonding process. Here, an adhesive layer is added between two wafers to realize bonding[113]. The simplest adhesive bonding is the process in which different organic glues, such as epoxy, BCB and polyimide are used. Although using adhesive material to realize bonding is very simple, this process suffers a lot of drawbacks: low bonding strength, high stress, easy generation of bubbles, poor thermal stability at the interface, and so on. Other adhesive bonding methods include eutectic bonding[114], solder (deposit solder layer) bonding[115], low melting point glass (frit) bonding[116] and thermocompression (soft metal layer) bonding[117], etc.

9.2.2 Sets of Bulk Micromaching Process

None of the aforementioned single process can be used alone for preparing a real micro/nano device. Only combining some of them reasonably, and also with the integration with other IC fabrication techniques to develop a complete set of fabrication process, can a complex device be realized. For IC applications, usually, there are only several sets of processes required, and it is easy to build up a standard fabrication process to achieve foundry production. By separating IC designers and producers into different independent parts, foundry production mode is a highly efficient collaboration method and is a key factor to promote the rapid development of integrated circuits. However, for MEMS/NEM devices, because of their various functions, structures, and shapes, it is really difficult to find out a universal fabrication process.

Compared with the surface micromachining approach, the bulk silicon micromachining is more complicated and has more processes to utilize. By combining different processes, it is possible to realize several sets of processes and fulfill the requirements from different devices. MEMS research has improved the development of whole-set processes in breadth and depth. Relations between device research and whole-set processes can be divided into two categories. One is to develop process just according to the specific device requirements. Here, the process could be a totally new process or modifications based on the existing one. Although this method makes the device design very flexible, there are some drawbacks as stated below. A new process usually requires a comparatively long period to get a stable and reliable result, which will thereby prolong the device development period. Meanwhile, this non-standard process is difficult to be provided by a foundry and requires developers to solve the fabrication problems by themselves with considerably high cost for research and development. All of these problems make MEM devices difficult to get into real applications, especially when the market is not big enough. Another method is to select established and reliable standard processes for the device design. Although this method restricts the design procedure to some extent, without developing new process, the designer can focus on the device design to get a good result. By this way, the devices can be mass produced in foundry and developers need no (or very little) investment on the facilities. This approach is very important for those small-batch produced MEMS products.

9.2.3 Combining Wafer Bonding with DRIE

For bulk micromachining, the silicon-on-glass (SOG) process, which combining anodic bonding and DRIE techniques, is receiving great attentions[118–122]. The fabrication procedure is relatively simple, because only two or three masks and process steps are employed. In addition, all the technologies used in the process are now mature. In contrast, the surface micromachining process and the bulk micromachining process based on anisotropic wet etching generally need more than five masks and process steps. The process will not be at risk of stiction, since no wet process is used during structure release. This method can fabricate large proof mass and capacitors and it can precisely control the geometry of the microstructures. The mechanical structures are made of single-crystal silicon, which has excellent mechanical performances such as low residual stress, good fatigue resistance and high yield strength. Besides, since the SOG wafer employs the dielectric glass as the operating substrate, the parasitic capacitance noise can be significantly reduced. This characteristic is especially attractive for capacitive MEMS sensors. Therefore, the process is a good candidate to be chosen to fabricate MEMS devices with high performance. The SOG process has been applied to the fabrication of various MEMS devices including inertial sensors[56, 102, 122–127], RF switches[128], microactuators[129], BioMEMS devices[120–129], and so on, which shows that this kind of process has gained importance in recent years.

9.2.3.1 Basic SOG Process

The detailed SOG processes are different in literature with one another. Firstly, we show a two-mask process we developed. The silicon wafers used in the experiment were 4 in. 525 μm thick and heavily boron-doped. The resistivity of the wafers was 0.01 – 0.02 Ω-cm, which resulted in ohmic contact characteristics between the boron-doped silicon and aluminum[119, 130].

Figure 9.40 shows the schematic technological process. The technology is started from reactive ion etch (RIE) or wet etch to form a 4 μm deep recess on the silicon wafer. The *x*-axis and *y*-axis should be aligned to (110) orientation, because the Young's modulus of crystalline silicon is dependent on the crystal orientation. Any misalignment can bring about a variation of mechanical performance. Then the silicon wafer is anodic bonded with a 4 in. 525 μm thick Pyrex 7,740 glass. The typical bonding voltage, temperature and time are 1,000 V, 400℃ and 60 min., respectively. The silicon wafer is then ground and polished or etched by KOH to a 60 – 100 μm thickness, which could be varied according to need. The new obtained silicon wafer surface is then sputtered with thin aluminum followed by RIE etching. These photoresist patterns are formed after double-side aligning through the glass wafer. The aluminum patterns are sintered at 440℃ for 40 min. in nitrogen ambient to get good contact characteristics between the

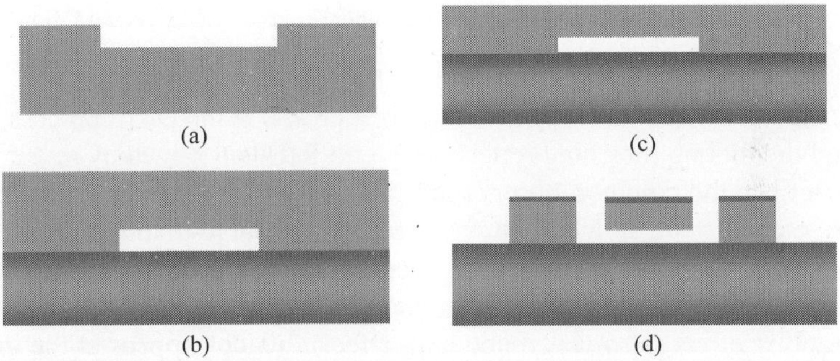

Figure 9.40 Schematic illustration of basic SOG process flow, (a) shallow trench etching, (b) silicon/glass anodic bonding, (c) silicon wafer thinning, (d) deep trench etching to release structure (see color figure at the end of this book)

silicon and the aluminum. Then, the wafers are diced from the silicon surface. The dicing trench was about 400 μm deep. The left 200 μm thick glass makes the further etching process possible and makes it easy to separate chips after the full process. After carefully cleaning, DRIE (ASE, STS Inc.) is used to form the mechanical structures. The ICP high aspect ratio etch makes the thickness of the mechanical layer fabricated with this technology as large as 20 – 200 μm, which could result in a small thermal–mechanical noise. The aluminum film acts as the mask material for DRIE and also as the electrodes. The large-area aluminum film also makes the serial resistance minimal. This technology only needs two masks. The accelerometer fabricated with this technology showed a ~mg resolution and a 3 dB bandwidth of 1.45 kHz for open-loop application[121].

An alternative SOG process is illustrated in Fig. 9.41. Contrast to the aforementioned process, a shallow recess is etched on the glass substrate to form an air gap (Fig. 9.41(a)). Then, a standard silicon wafer is in anodically bonded with the glass substrate (Fig. 9.41(b)). After the silicon wafer is thinned to 120 μm by using standard chemical mechanical polishing (CMP) (Fig. 9.41(c)), the metal contacts (Cr/Au) are evaporated and patterned. Finally, the wafer is DRIE etched to define the mechanical structures. An accelerometer fabricated with this process is shown in (Fig. 9.42)[102].

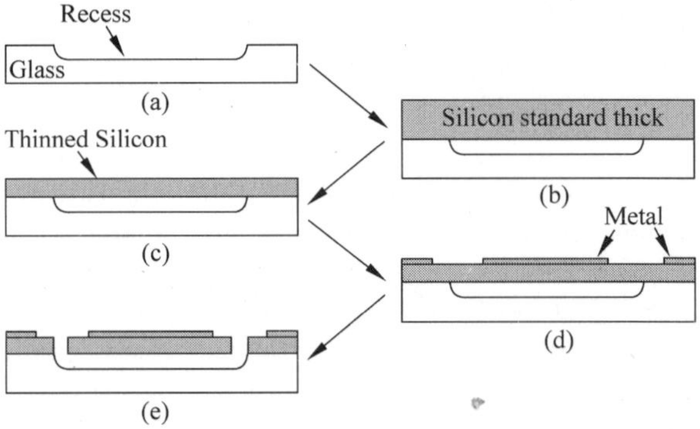

Figure 9.41 Schematic illustration of another kind of SOG process flow[102] (© 1999 IEEE)

It is well-known that there are two important effects in the DRIE process, the lag effect and the footing (notching) effect. The term RIE-lag, named by researchers at IBM, describes the common observation that narrow trenches or small-diameter holes are etched more slowly than wide trenches or large-diameter holes[131, 132], as shown in Fig. 9.43(a). In the SOG process, the lag effect will cause that wide trenches are etched through earlier than the narrower ones.

The footing effect (also called notching effect), which happens at the interface between silicon and glass in the SOG process or between silicon and SiO_2[134] in the SOI MEMS process, is another critical effect in the DRIE process[135, 136]. When the etch front reaches the isolation layer (glass or SiO_2, sometimes with an air gap

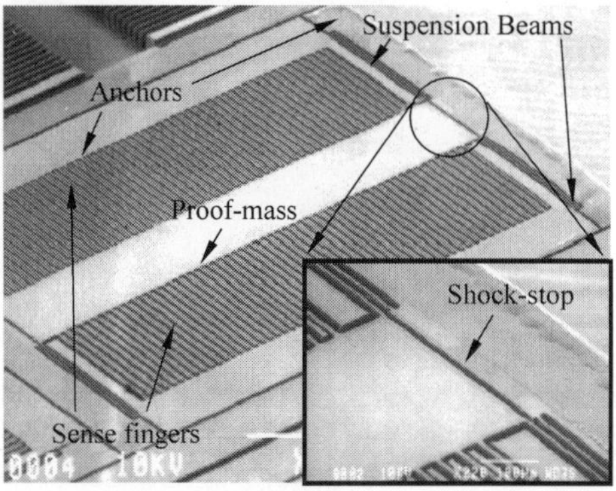

Figure 9.42 Top view of fabricated SOG accelerometer and shock stop[102] ((© 1999 IEEE) see color figure at the end of this book)

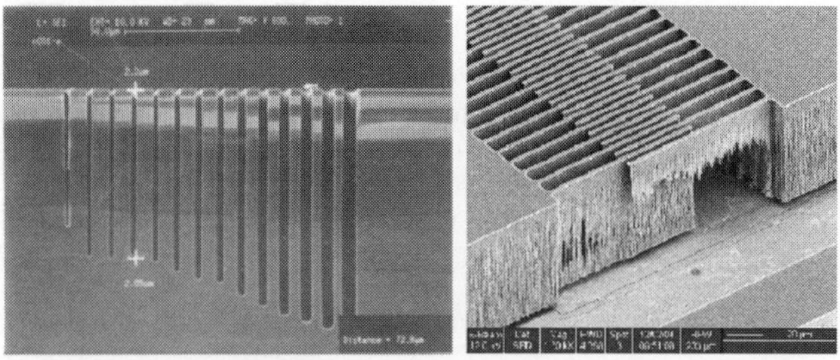

(a) (b)

Figure 9.43 Two important effects in the DRIE process. (a) Lag effect in DRIE Process[133], (b) Footing effect in DRIE process ((© 2004 IOP) see color figure at the end of this book)

in between), the undercut etching will happen, and the damage will occur on the bottom and the sidewall of the structure. The mechanism of the footing effect has been studied extensively, and most conclusions focused on the electron charging effect[136, 137].

In SOG process, wide trenches are etched through first due to the lag effect, and etching has to be continued though the narrow ones. Consequently, the footing effect is normally unavoidable and may damage the structures significantly as shown in Fig. 9.43(b). A simple and straightforward method is optimization of the layout in order that the size difference of trenches is minimized. However, it is not always available due to the device diversity. Therefore, how to eliminate or minimize the footing effect has become a major topic in SOG process research.

An effective method is to place a shielding metal layer between the silicon and the glass substrate (shown in Fig. 9.44)[138]. In doing so, both silicon and glass are set at the same electrical potential, which prevents the dielectric substrate from being charged up and alleviates the footing effect.

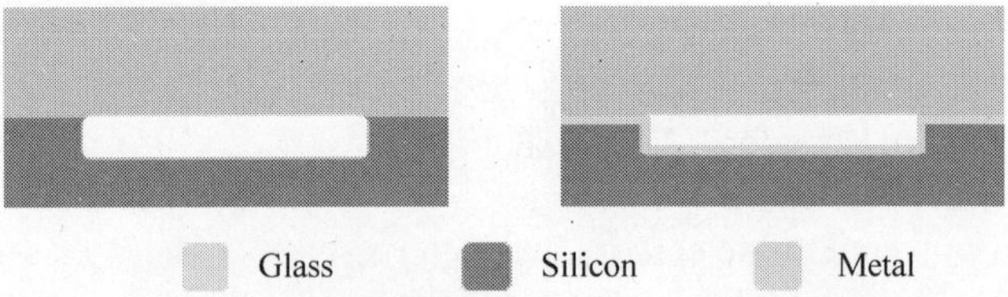

Figure 9.44 Illustration of a shielding metal layer between silicon and glass substrate, which can reduce the footing effect (see color figure at the end of this book)

As for the process shown in Fig. 9.40, adding a shielding layer on the glass substrate or the bottom of the silicon layer is also effective to protect the structure from damage[139].

In the new DRIE machine, e. g. Pegasus, a low-frequency power source is employed to prevent the footing effect efficiently. In this case, the anti-footing process is less important[140].

We developed a microswitch with lateral contact by utilizing the modified SOG process[55]. The only difference from the process shown in Fig.9.40 is that a layer of gold was sputtered on the structure to obtain low contact resistance (Fig. 9.45). To prevent structures from being shorted by the gold layer on the glass, all anchors had at least a 10 μm undercut. A fabricated device is shown in Fig. 9.46. The measured contact was below 1 Ω and the stand-off voltage was more than 300 V.

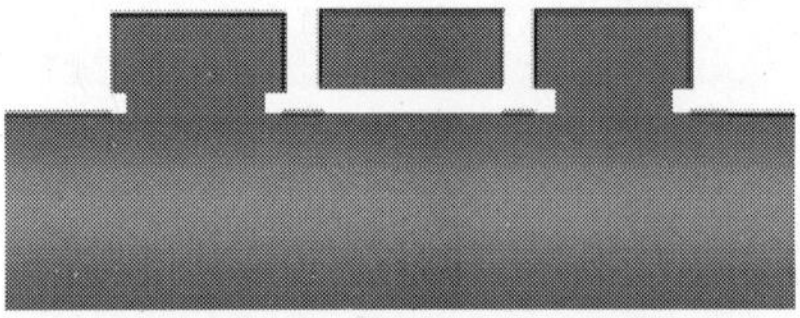

Figure 9.45 A layer of gold was sputtered on the structure to obtain a low contact resistance

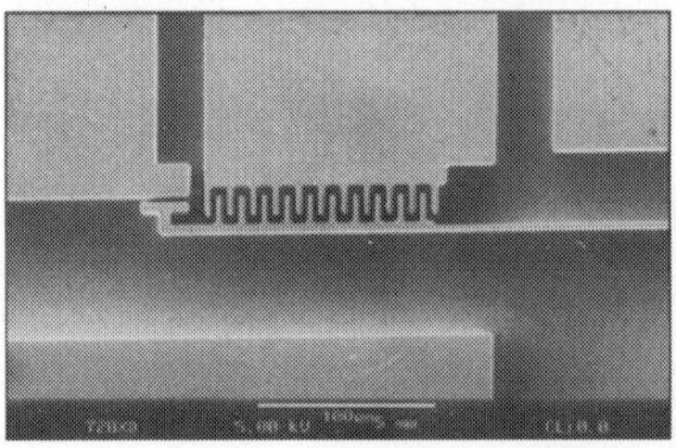

Figure 9.46 A fabricated device employed the modified SOG process[55]

9.2.3.2 SOG Process with Interconnection on Glass Substrate

For more complicated MEMS devices, such as gyroscopes, an electrode layer could be placed on the glass substrate to provide interconnection between different silicon parts. Moreover, placing electrodes on the substrate offers more flexibility for wire bonding, and, even more important, allows mechanical structures to be packaged on wafer level. A typical SOG process with interconnection on the glass substrate is shown in Fig. 9.47. The process starts with (100), medium doped or heavily doped 4 in. Si wafers. After shallow recess (about 4 μm) is etched by either RIE or chemical etching, a heavy surface doping is done with diffusion or ion implantation to form Ohmic contact with interconnects fabricated on glass wafers later. A Ti/Pt/Au or Cr/Au layer with thickness of about 200 nm on the Pyrex glass wafer is sputtered, and patterned by using lift-off to form interconnects, followed

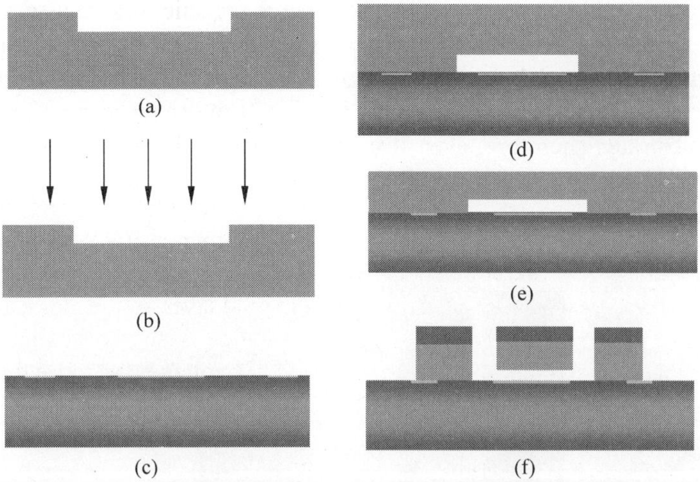

Figure 9.47 A typical SOG process with interconnection on the glass substrate, (a) shallow trench etching, (b) surface doping, (c) life-off to form electrodes, (d) silicon/glass anodic bonding, (e) silicon wafer thinning, (f) deep trench etching to release structure (see color figure at the end of this book)

by anodic bonding of Si and glass wafers at 400℃, for 60 min. Silicon wafers are thinned to 60 – 100 μm through either mechanical grinning/polishing or chemical etching with KOH. Finally, structures are formed through deep etching with DRIE.

9.2.3.3 SOG Process with Isolation Structure

A microstructure in a MEMS device generally acts as both a mechanical unit and an electric unit. Therefore, the isolation and interconnection of microstructures are important for some MEMS devices. In the surface micromachining technology, we have discussed how to realize isolation and interconnection. In bulk micromachining, however, isolation is also not an easy task. Some efforts to insulate a moveable microstructure from a fixed structure (substrate) have been reported[141–143]. However, each isolation technology was developed for a special process, such as SOI micromachining[143] or the SCREAM process[143], but none of them are suitable for SOG process. In some applications, such as microrelays[33, 145, 146], voltage tunable capacitors[34, 144], and phase shifters[147], some moveable structures should be electrically isolated from actuators to prevent electrical coupling. In this case, we should electrically isolate two moveable microstructures, which have mechanical (flexible or rigid) connection.

Based on the process shown in Fig. 9.47, a process was developed to realize isolation between movable microstructures[148]. The schematic isolation structure is shown in Fig. 9.48(a). A moveable microstructure (marked as Mass 1) is linked to a bonded anchor by a flexible beam, while the microstructure is linked to the other microstructure (marked as Mass 2) by an isolation structure. The isolation structure may be flexible or rigid, depending upon its application. Because a Pyrex glass wafer is used in process, no high-temperature sequence can be used after wafer bonding. Therefore, the isolation process, in which some high-temperature sequences will be carried out, must be completed before wafer bonding. In fact, the moveable structures must be suspended, and there is a gap between these structures and the bonded substrate. Therefore, even if using silicon-to-silicon wafer bonding, it is also very difficult to form an isolation structure after wafer bonding.

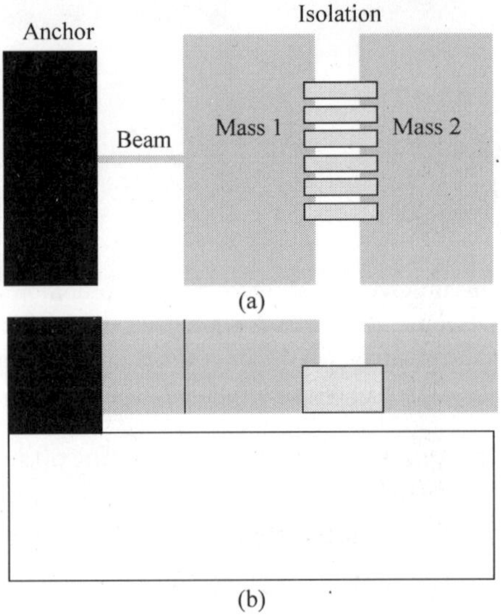

Figure 9.48 A schematic drawing of an isolation structure. A movable microstructure (marked as Mass 1) is linked to a bonded anchor by a flexible beam, while the microstructure is linked to another microstructure (marked as Mass 2) by an isolation structure: (a) is the top view and (b) is cross section view[148] (see color figure at the end of this book)

Figure 9.49 shows the process sequence to achieve mechanical microstructures with isolation structures. The wafer is the same as that mentioned previously. After shallow recess (Fig. 9.49(a)) is etched, narrow and deep trenches are formed by DRIE (Fig. 9.49(b)). The depth of trenches can be less than, but should be not more than, that of the mechanical structure. The depth and the width of the trenches are also dependent on etching and refilling capability. A 0.3 μm thick thermal oxide is formed on the surface (Fig. 9.49(c)), which acts as an isolation layer between the polysilicon and the substrate. After oxide growth, a conformal LPCVD undoped polysilicon is deposited to refill the trenches (Fig. 9.49(d)). The thickness of the polysilicon is dependent on the width of trenches, and has at least half of the trenches' width. A RIE etch back step is employed to remove the polysilicon on the surface, but not in the trenches (Fig. 9.49(e)). The oxide layer on the surface is removed by buffered HF rinsing (Fig. 9.49(f)). The wafer with refilled trenches is anodically bonded with a Pyrex glass wafer with metal electrodes, followed by silicon wafer thinning (Fig. 9.49(g)). Finally, the mechanical structures with isolation are formed by DRIE. During this step, the single-crystal silicon among the polysilicon bars at the center is etched out to form the isolation structure. The polysilicon bars are protected from etching by a thermal oxide layer. Both ends of the silicon bar are embedded in single-crystal silicon to form the mechanical connection. The undoped polysilicon bars covered by thermal oxide serve as the isolation structure. Fig. 9.48(b) shows the cross section of the isolation structure.

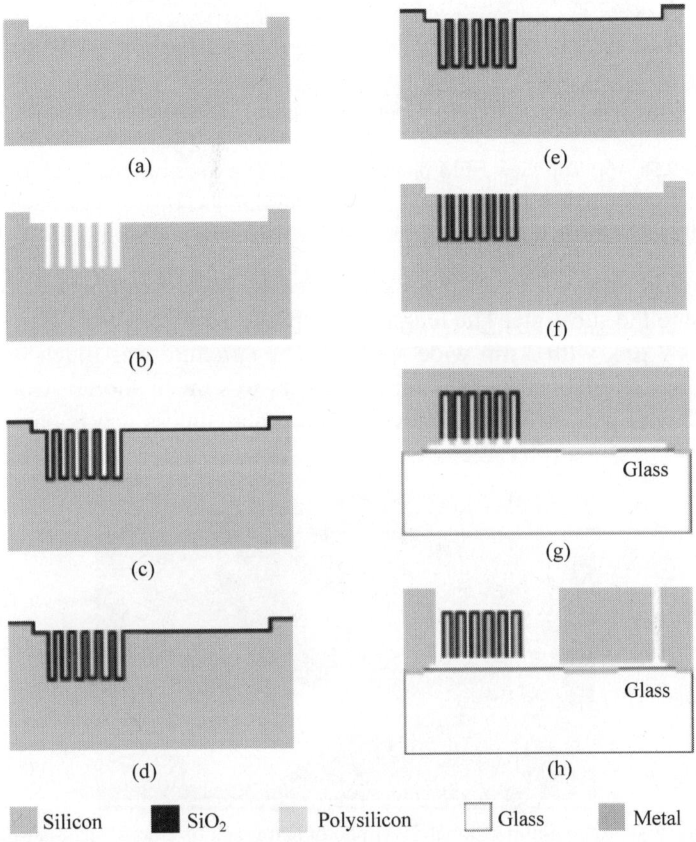

Figure 9.49 The process sequence to achieve the mechanical microstructures with isolation structures[148] (see color figure at the end of this book)

A top-view SEM micrograph of a test structure is shown in Fig. 9.50(a). The larger block of silicon on the right was bonded to a glass substrate, while the other block was suspended above it through a series of polysilicon bars. The length of the bars was 500 μm, and widths of the bars were 3, 4, and 5 μm from bottom to top, respectively. The spacing was 3 μm for the 3 μm wide bars, and 4 μm for the 4 and 5 μm-wide bars. Figure 9.50(b) shows a close-up SEM photomicrograph of the suspended proof mass. No visible bending was found along such a long distance. In the probe stage, we used a probe to apply a lateral force to the proof mass; it could be moved laterally over a large distance through the bending of the polysilicon bars. After the probe was moved out, the proof mass returned to its original position without any visible excursion or damage. The test indicates the structure has the potential to be used for a flexible connection.

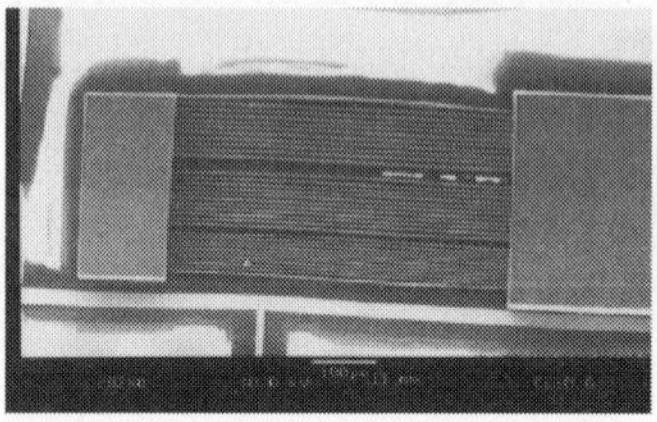

(a)

(b)

Figure 9.50 (a) Top-view SEM photomicrograph of a test structure. The larger block of silicon on the right is bonded onto a glass substrate, while the other block is suspended on it through a series of polysilicon bars. (b) Close-up three-dimensional view[148]

Figure 9.51 shows a proof mass suspended by polysilicon bars to two blocks bonded onto the substrate. The length of the polysilicon bars were 50 μm, and the width was 3 μm, with 3 μm wide spacing. The structure was much more robust than the former one, because the length of bars was much shorter. Consequently, the proof mass was difficult to move with a probe, unless it was damaged. This

Figure 9.51 Three-dimensional SEM photomicrograph of a proof mass suspended on two blocks bonded to the substrate[148]

kind of bar was suitable for rigid connection. Using an HP4156b, we measured the resistance between two bonded blocks, which could be considered as the resistance of the polysilicon silicon bars and the covered oxide, because the bulk silicon was heavily doped. The average resistance was more than 10^8 Ω at the applied voltage ranging from 0 V to 100 V. No breakdown was observed even at a voltage of 200 V. The result indicates the structure had good isolation performance.

9.2.4 SOI MEMS

In recent years, the SOI-MEMS technology becomes very popular and has been utilized to fabricate various MEMS devices, such as tunable capacitors, accelerometers, in-plane gyroscopes, optical mirrors and RF switches[149, 151]. The SOI-MEMS process has advantages of both surface micromachining technology and SOG bulk micromachining technology. Similar to surface micromachining, the SOI-MEMS technology utilizing buried oxide (BOX) as the sacrificial layer is compatible with CMOS process without special equipment or process requirements. Besides, the SOI-MEMS technology is suitable for realizing the integration of MEMS structures and ICs, because no high temperature is required in the process. Similar to SOG bulk micromachining, in SOI process, the thick single-crystal silicon, which has excellent mechanical properties, such as high yield strength, low residual stress and good fatigue resistance, is used to construct the mechanical structures. The technology for fabricating SOI wafers is mature currently. The SOI wafers with a well-controlled thickness of the active layer ranging from few microns to more than hundred microns are commercially available. Therefore, MEMS manufacturers can control the thickness of MEMS structures precisely without need to have a bonding machine and the wafer-thinning capability. A convincing example is that ADI has utilized SOI-MEMS process to replace the surface micromachining process and manufacture their famous integrated accelerometers since 2004. MEMS and electronics are integrated on the SOI layer and isolated from the circuitry by isolation trenches (see the Integrated Bulk micromachining section).

The basic SOI-MEMS process only needs one mask as shown in Fig. 9.52(a). As an example, the process starts with the 4 in. SOI wafer with a 2 μm buried oxide layer, a 20 – 100 μm thick top silicon layer, and a 500 μm thick handle wafer. A DRIE process is used to etch the top silicon layer till to the buried oxide layer, and then the HF solution is utilized to etch the buried oxide and release the mechanical structure after drying. The release time is determined by the maximum etching distance. The process is quite simple but several issues should be addressed. First, the release holes have to be designed on the structure in order to reduce release time and avoid intolerable undercut under the fixed area. For inertial sensor application, the release holes reduce the mass of the structure, which will degrade performance; while for optical MEMS application, the fill factor will be reduced dramatically. Second, stiction becomes more severe than that in surface micromachining because both surfaces risking stiction are very smooth, and dimples are not easy to form. Third, the parasitic capacitance between the structure and handle wafer is relatively large. The problem can be solved by employing high resistivity substrate, but it will increase the cost. Last but not least, similar to SOG process, the footing effect is a big issue when etch reaches the buried oxide, and it is impossible to replace the shielding layer under the structure. Even though, this kind of process is still widely used because of the simplicity.

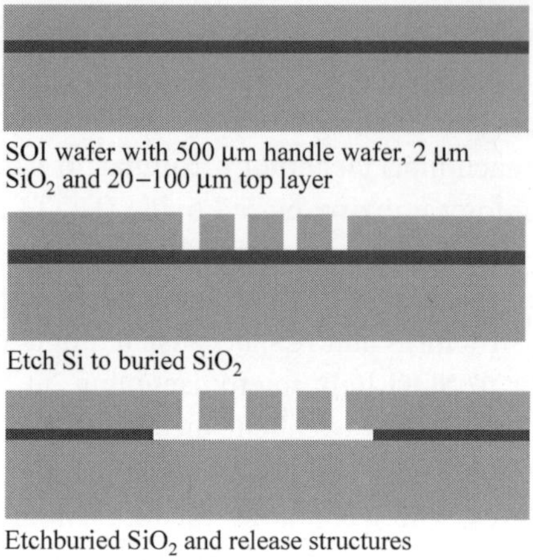

Figure 9.52 Basic SOI-MEMS process flow (see color figure at the end of this book)

A shadow mask could be used to provide metallization on the top and/or sidewall of structures (shown in Fig. 9.53). Utilizing this technique, A. Liu et al. reported low-loss lateral micromachined switches as shown in Fig. 9.54[150, 151].

An alternative process is shown in Fig. 9.5. The handle wafer is firstly etched through with either DRIE or KOH wet etch. Then the buried oxide layer is removed by RIE or HF etch. Finally, DRIE is used to etch through the top silicon layer and release the structure. This process can solve, at least partially, the problems in the process shown in Fig. 9.52. First, no release holes are required to release the structure. Second, no stiction occurs since dry release method is employed. Third,

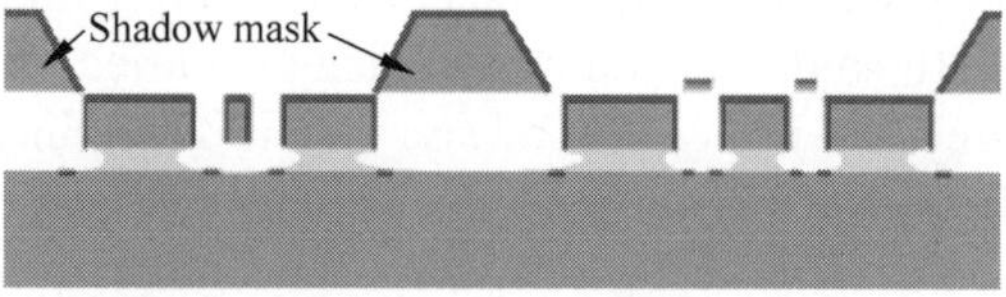

Figure 9.53 A shadow mask is used to provide metallization on the top and/or sidewall of structures (© 2004 IEEE)

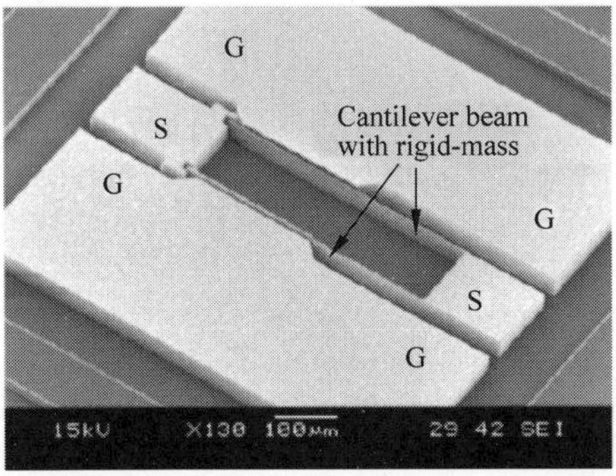

Figure 9.54 SEM micrographs of the lateral double-beam switch[151] (G: ground, S: signal) (© 2004 IEEE)

parasitic capacitance is significantly reduced because the part of handle wafer below the structure is removed. Last, the footing effect is alleviated, and a metal shielding or protecting layer is allowed to deposit at the bottom of the structure. However, this process has its own disadvantages. If KOH wet etch is utilized to etch the back side, then the front side has to be protected by a silicon nitride mask, and the sloped sidewall due to the crystal-orientation dependent anisotropic etching may decrease the device density. On the contrary, use of DRIE does not suffer from these problems, but the process cost is much higher.

MEMSCAP offers a Multi-User MEMS Processes (or MUMPs®) service for SOI-MEMS fabrication [152], called SOIMUMPs, which is similar to the process shown in Fig. 9.55. A difference is that the structure DRIE is preformed before a backside window is opened. Metallization with 50 nm Cr and 600 nm Au is realized through a shadow mask (shown in Fig. 9.55). As a standard process, the top silicon thickness is (10 ± 1) μm or (25 ± 1) μm, the oxide thickness is (1 ± 0.05) μm, and the handle wafer thickness is (400 ± 5) μm.

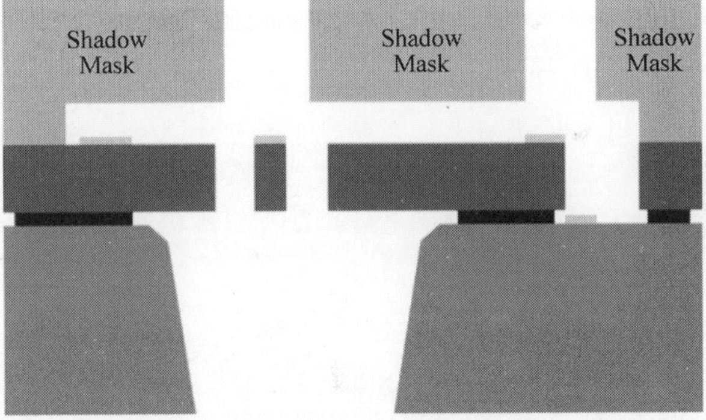

Figure 9.55 The shadow mask is aligned and temporarily bonded to the SOI wafer. The Metal layer, consisting of 50 nm Cr and 600 nm Au, is deposited through the shadow mask (© MEMSCap) (see color figure at the end of this book)

An interesting SOI-MEMS process was reported by B. V. Amini et al[4−6]. In this process, an extra seismic mass formed by the handle layer and a reduced air gap with a LPCVD polysilicon layer are utilized to improve the performance of inertial sensors. The schematic diagram of a SOI accelerometer fabricated with this process is shown in Fig. 9.56. The simplified process flow is shown in Fig. 9.57. The process starts with a low-resistivity (0.01 Ω-cm) 120 μm thick SOI substrate. After thermal oxidation, the device layer is patterned and etched with DRIE first, followed by backside oxide layer patterning. Then LPCVD polysilicon is deposited to reduce the air gap between the comb-fingers. Then, the front-side polysilicon is anisotropically etched back to make the floor clean. Next, the handle layer is

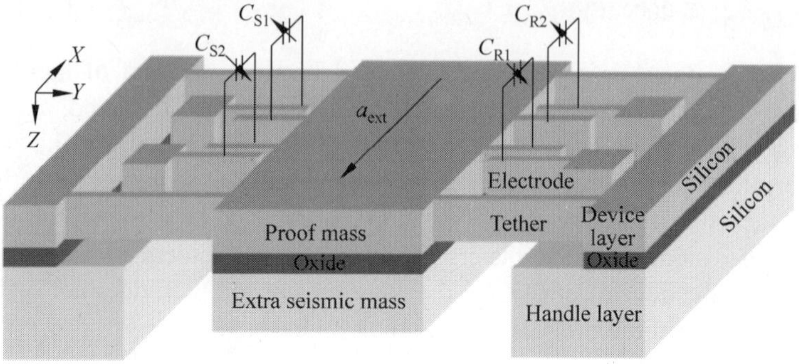

Figure 9.56 Schematic diagram of an SOI accelerometer with added seismic mass (© 2005 IOP)

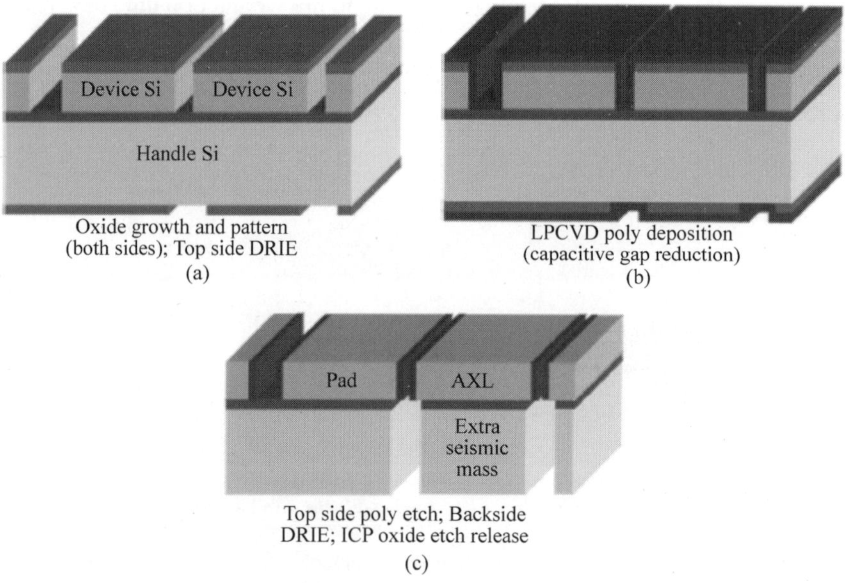

Figure 9.57 Fabrication process flow of a micro-g SOI accelerometer with reduced capacitive gaps and added mass (© 2005 IOP)

etched through to the buried oxide by DRIE. Different from the above-mentioned process, a part of the handle layer is left under the proof mass acting as an extra mass to improve the resolution of the accelerometer. Finally, the oxide layer is removed by RIE to release the device. By utilizing these process improvements and a well designed circuitry, a measured resolution of 4 μg $\sqrt{\text{Hz}}$ and an output dynamic range of 95 dB at 20 Hz were achieved.

9.2.5 SCREAM

SCREAM (Single Crystal Reactive Etching And Metallization) is a bulk micromachining process which was invented by McDonald et al. at Cornel University in 1993, and is still in wide use. The SCREAM only employs a single mask and a normal silicon wafer[156].

The process flow is shown in Fig. 9.58. First, a thermal oxide is grown and patterned as a mask followed by a DRIE process to create high-aspect-ratio trenches. The depth depends on the device specification and DRIE capability. Then, a 0.3 μm thick PECVD oxide layer as passive material is deposited to cover all surfaces of trenches. The conformality of the deposited oxide layer is very important. If the performed structure can endure a high temperature, then thermal oxidation or LPCVD can be used for higher conformality. Then, the oxide layer at the bottom is removed by RIE; while the layer of the oxide layer attached to the sidewall still remains due to the anisotropy of RIE, and the top surface is still protected by the thermal oxide. Next, DRIE is used to etch the trenches further down 3 – 5 μm. The microstructure is then released by isotropic ICP etch, so the suspended microstructures are completed. Finally, an aluminum layer is deposited for electrical interconnection.

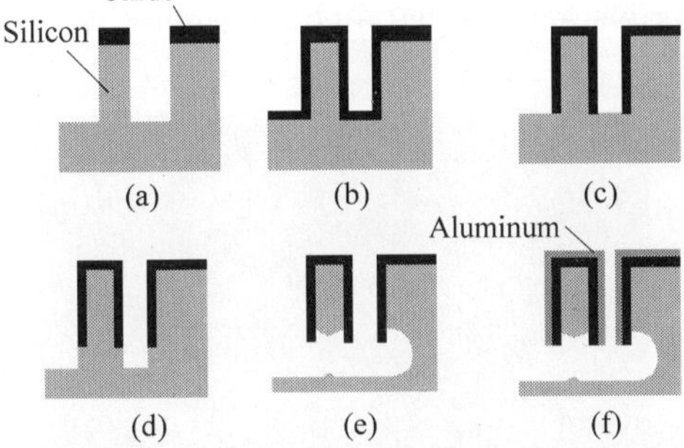

Figure 9.58 SCREAM basic processing sequence

There are some drawbacks in SCREAM process. The microstructures fabricated with SCREAM are constructed by a multi-layer composed of metal, silicon and oxide, which implies a large residual stress and stress gradient, as well as the bimorph effect caused by the thermal coefficient mismatch. During the release step, isotropic etch not only etches the exposed silicon laterally and downwards, but also etches the silicon structure upwards. Therefore, the thickness of structures is not easy to control precisely. Besides, the RIE-lag effect will result in ununiformity of the structure depth.

In the SCREAM process, SiO_2 is commonly used for passivation. There are two approaches for SiO_2 deposition, PECVD and LPCVD. LPCVD SiO_2 has excellent conformality, and therefore is a good candidate as a passivation layer. However, LPCVD process requires relatively high temperature and, consequently, it cannot be employed in some cases if the temperature budget is limited (e.g. in a post-CMOS process). On the contrary, the PECVD approach brings relatively low stress and requires a relatively low temperature (200℃ – 250℃). With the extension of applications of the suspended microstructures fabricated with SCREAM process, especially in microfluidic and bio-MEMS fields, some alternative materials are introduced for sidewall passivation[157]. For example, D. Vrtacnik et al reported a plasma polymerized fluorocarbon (FC) thin film to realize trench sidewall passivation[144]. The film has properties of high chemical inertness, high electrical resistivity, low surface free energy, low dielectric constant, selective etchant and biocompatibility. However, the mechanical performance of the FC film has not been well characterized yet.

The parylene-C (it is called as parylene herein) film was utilized as a sidewall passivation layer in SCREAM process[158]. Parylene is widely used in MEMS recently owing to its promising properties[159 – 162] such as excellent conformality, chemical inertness and mechanical performance. Besides, parylene has low residual stress and low Young's modulus, which may ease the deformation of mechanical structures, and reduce influences on the mechanical performance of the structures introduced by the extra coating layer. Furthermore, an outstanding merit of the parylene film is its unique vapor deposition polymerization (VDP) coating process at the room temperature.

Figure 9.59 shows a SEM of a cantilever fabricated with the SCREAM process using parylene as passivation material. In these figures, the parylene films protect

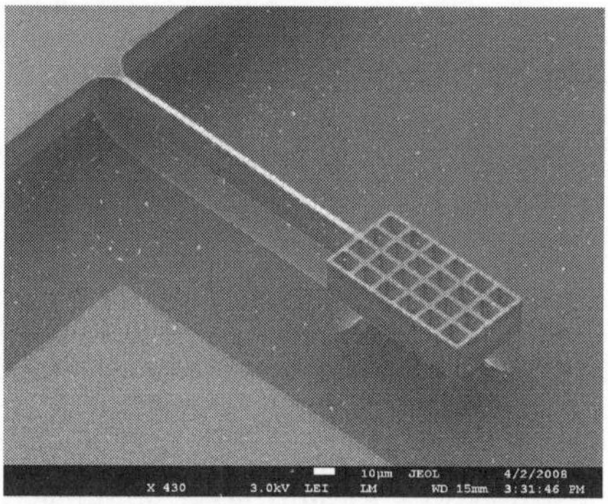

Figure 9.59 SEM photo of the released microstructures with parylene as passive material

the sidewall from ICP etching very well. The micro-cantilever can be bent freely by a probe tip, which shows it is completely released.

9.2.6 Integration of Bulk Micromachined MEMS with IC

Similar to surface micromachining process, integrating bulk micromachined MEMS devices with circuitry on the same substrate promises to improve the performance of MEMS devices and potentially lower the cost of device manufacture and packaging. Therefore, many efforts have been made to develop monolithic integration technology of bulk micromachining. However, it is more difficult to integrate bulk micromachined MEMS devices with ICs since bulk micromachining technology is less compatible with the microelectronics fabrication technology than surface micromachining technology is.

9.2.6.1 Integrated SOI MEMS Technology

Since SOI MEMS technology is similar to surface micromachining technology, it is more readily for integration than other bulk micromachining technologies[163, 164].

A successful example is the integrated SOI MEMS process developed by ADI. The process integrates MEMS and electronics using a 10-μm-thick SOI layer for both electronics and MEMS structures. It is an intermediate-CMOS integration method, in which the CMOS process sequence has to be interrupted for MEMS structure fabrication steps, and some CMOS standard steps may be modified. The process flow is shown in Fig. 9.60. The process starts with a SOI wafer with 10-μm active layer. At first, isolation trenches around the MEMS region are formed by DRIE, polysilicon refilling and CMP planarization. Then the wafer is sent to a standard CMOS foundry to finish all CMOS fabrication, so that the cost can be reduced. The challenge is that the preprocessed wafers should meet all strict requirements of the CMOS foundry; otherwise no foundry would accept them.

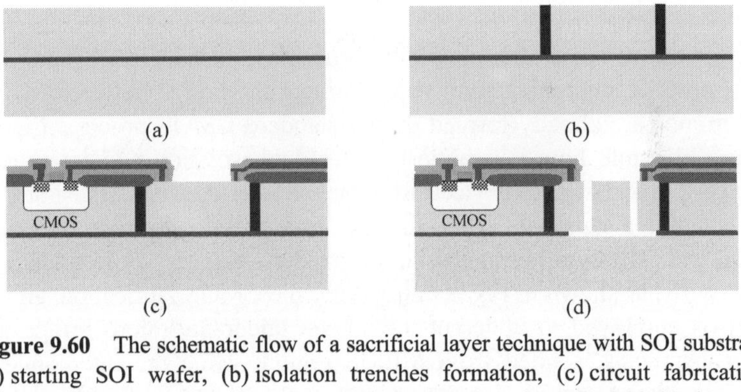

Figure 9.60 The schematic flow of a sacrificial layer technique with SOI substrate, (a) starting SOI wafer, (b) isolation trenches formation, (c) circuit fabrication, (d) MEMS structure etch and release (see color figure at the end of this book)

After circuit fabrication, the passivation layer over the MEMS region is removed and the MEMS structural pattern is etched through the SOI device layer. Finally, HF is used to etch the sacrificial oxide layer and the structures are released. ADI's SOIMEMS process uses a special release process in which temporary photoresist pedestals prevent the structures from stiction during drying.

Figure 9.61 shows the evolution of ADI's four generations of accelerometers. Obviously, as the technology changes from surface micromachining to new SOI MEMS process, the chip size is reduced but the performance is improved[163, 164].

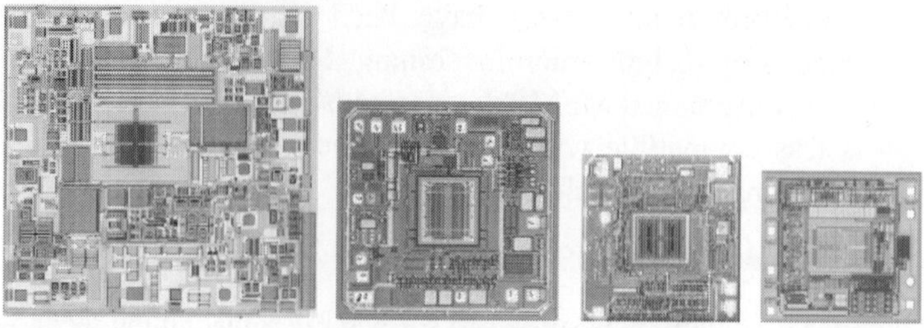

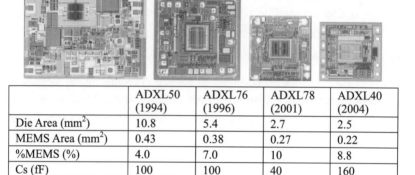

	ADXL50 (1994)	ADXL76 (1996)	ADXL78 (2001)	ADXL40 (2004)
Die Area (mm^2)	10.8	5.4	2.7	2.5
MEMS Area (mm^2)	0.43	0.38	0.27	0.22
%MEMS (%)	4.0	7.0	10	8.8
Cs (fF)	100	100	40	160
fo (kHz)	25.0	24.5	24.5	12.5
Noise (mgee/rt.Hz)	6.0	1.0	1.0	1.0
Offset (gee)	3.0	1.0	0.5	0.5

Figure 9.61 Performance comparison of ADI's four generations of accelerometers with the technology changing from surface micromachining to new SOIMEMS process (© 2005 IOP)

Recently, a post-CMOS integration technology of SOI MEMS devices using micro bridge interconnections was reported by H. Takao et al[165]. Compared to the refilled isolation trench, the micro bridge is formed at a low temperature, and therefore, it can be made after all CMOS processes finished.

In this process, interconnection wires through the bridge between MEMS and CMOS circuits are already formed during standard CMOS process. Figure 9.62 shows the principle how to realize the electrical isolation and interconnection between CMOS and MEMS devices using the micro bridge. First, integrated circuits are fabricated in a standard CMOS foundry, and Al wires for the interconnection of CMOS and MEMS are formed with the standard metal layers in CMOS module simultaneously, as shown in Fig. 9.62(a). After the CMOS fabrication, an isotropic etch step is employed to undercut the silicon under the micro bridge, and the CMOS substrate is isolated from MEMS region; while the interconnection is provided by the Al wires, as shown in Fig. 9.62(b). Afterwards, the MEMS structures are etched with DRIE from the front-side and released from the back side. The hard masks for bridge etching and structure etching are previously formed during CMOS fabrication, and an ordinary lithography is required for MEMS structure fabrication.

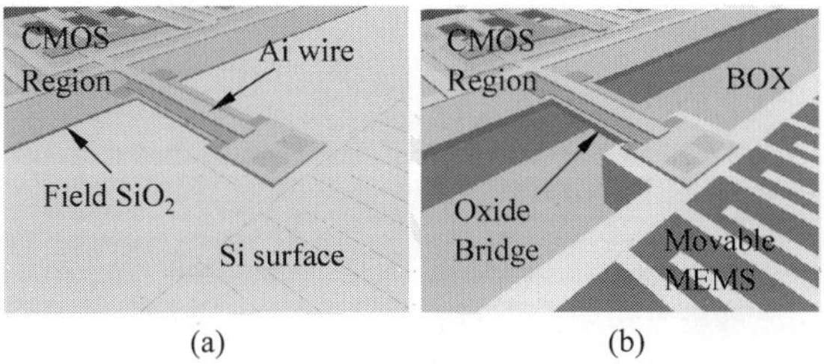

Figure 9.62 Conceptual Diagram of Post-CMOS MEMS Integration Steps Using Micro Bridge Interconnection. (a) Interconnection between MEMS and CMOS is Formed in Standard CMOS Process. (b) Micro Bridge Formation for Isolation of MEMS from CMOS Substrate (© 2008 IEEE)

9.2.6.2 CMOS MEMS Process with High-Aspect-Ratio Structure

In the surface micromachining section, the CMOS MEMS process developed at Carnegie Mellon University has been discussed. However, all of the microstructures in that process are made of thin films and are normally multi-layered. The multi-layered thin-film structures made of CMOS materials, including polysilicon, aluminum, LPCVD oxide and PECVD oxide, usually have large residual stress gradients which cause curling. Therefore the maximum layout size of microstructures is limited. Besides, mismatches of the thermal coefficient and mechanical properties between different materials degrade the temperature response and reliability. Moreover, release holes and unwanted curvature of microstructures degrade their performance in optical applications[166].

H. Xie et al. at Carnegie Mellon University improved the CMOS MEMS process by employing bulk micromachining and back-side Si DRIE[167]. After this modification, the process still keeps the post-CMOS merits and the process flow is shown in Fig. 9.63. The whole CMOS fabrication is done in a standard CMOS foundry. After that, the silicon wafer is etched at the back side with DRIE, and a membrane, whose thickness depends on device specifications, is formed. Then, with the top metal interconnect layer as a etch mask, the multilayer on the MEMS region is etched with RIE down to the silicon surface. In contrast to the surface CMOS MEMS process, an anisotropic DRIE is employed to etch through the membrane to define and release the high-aspect ratio structures. The final optional silicon isotropic etch step can be performed to remove the silicon under small beams to achieve the electrical isolation of certain silicon areas. Compared with the surface CMOS MEMS technology, the high-aspect-ratio structures of single-crystal silicon improve the mechanical strength and reduce the influence of the residual stress and stress gradient, providing large proof mass and capacitance as well.

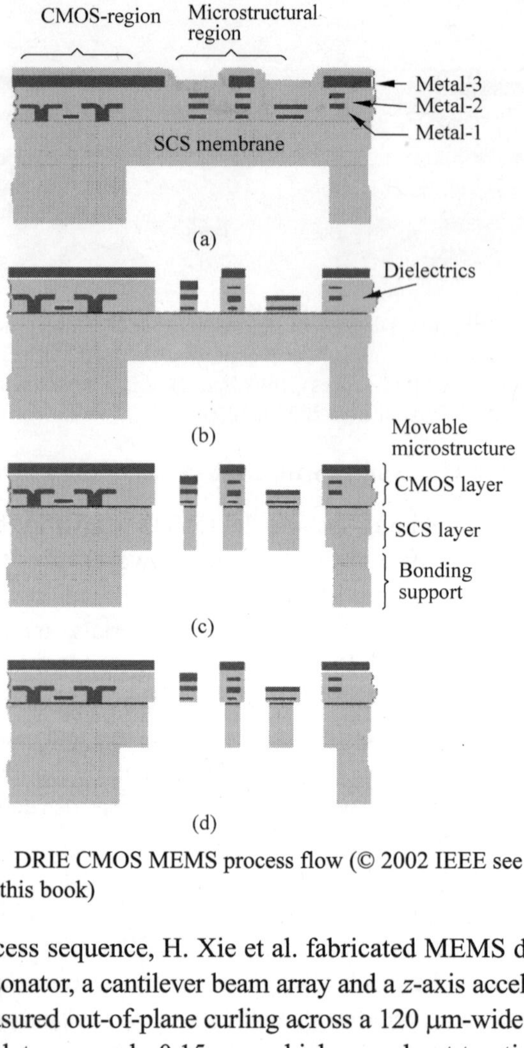

Figure 9.63 DRIE CMOS MEMS process flow (© 2002 IEEE see color figure at the end of this book)

Using this process sequence, H. Xie et al. fabricated MEMS devices including a comb-driven resonator, a cantilever beam array and a *z*-axis accelerometer (shown in Fig. 9.64). Measured out-of-plane curling across a 120 μm-wide and 25 μm-thick silicon-released plate was only 0.15 μm, which was about ten times smaller than the curling with identical design of surface CMOS MEMS microstructure.

9.2.6.3 Integrated SCREAM Process

K. A. Shaw and N. C. MacDonald reported the post-CMOS integration of SCREAM process with IC process[168]. After ICs were fabricated, only two masks were added to form mechanical structures and the patterned metal interconnects. The process flow is shown in Fig. 9.65. The whole CMOS fabrication was done in a CMOS foundry (Figure 9.65(a)). After that, an oxide layer (marked as Oxide-1) is deposited and patterned as the mask for following the SCREAM process (Fig. 9.65(b)). Then, the standard SREAM process is carried out before the metallizing step. The majority of Oxide-1 is back-etched to expose bonding pads. Finally, a metal layer is deposited and patterned to form the interconnection between MEMS and IC. This patterning process is a major difficulty of this technology, because the photoresist should cover the high-aspect-ratio movable MEMS structures and be patterned.

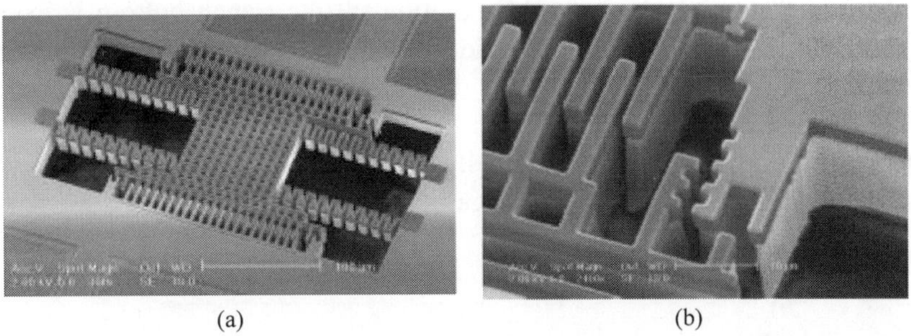

Figure 9.64 (a) SEM of a comb-driven resonator fabricated in the DRIE CMOS process. (b) Close-up of one corner of the comb-driven actuator (© 2002 IEEE)

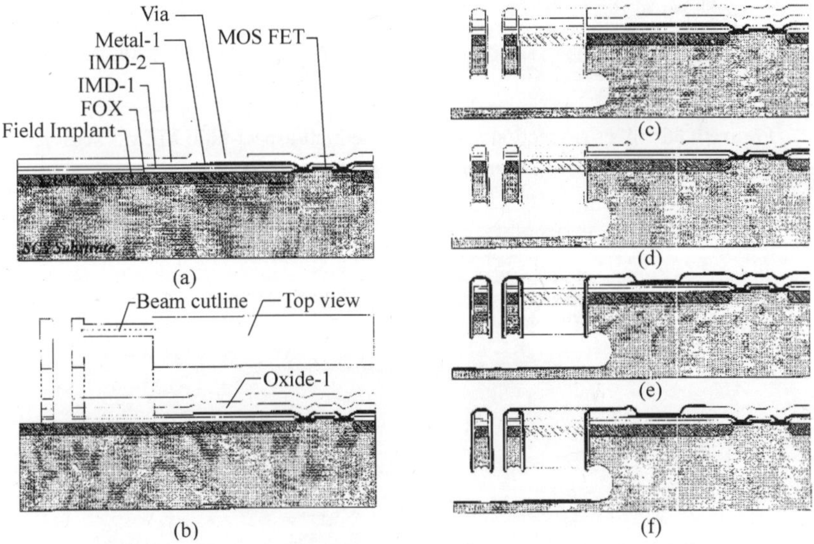

Figure 9.65 Integrated SCREAM process flow (© 1996 IEEE)

9.2.6.4 IBMURIT

G. Z. Yan et al. at Peking University developed a monolithic integration process, named IBMURIT (Integrated Bulk Micromachining Utilizing Refilled Isolation

Trench)[105, 106, 170]. A high-aspect-ratio MEMS structure with integrated CMOS circuits fabricated with this process is depicted in Fig. 9.66. Similar to integrated SOI MEMS technology, isolation trenches are used to isolate different mechanical elements from one another and from the circuit region. Figure 9.67 shows the process flow of the integrated technology. First, deep and high-aspect-ratio silicon trenches are etched with DRIE around the mechanical structure region. The trench depth depends on the height of the MEMS device structure. The silicon trenches are refilled by LPCVD SiO_2 and polysilicon. After electrical isolation trenches are fabricated, the trench and the structure region are etched from the wafer backside by using TMAH solution till the trench bottom is exposed (Fig. 9.67(a)). The etching time should be controlled to ensure that the trench bottom is exposed completely and the desired proof mass thickness is obtained. CMOS circuits are then fabricated in the circuit region through conventional CMOS processing (Fig. 9.67(b)). Finally, the structures are etched and released with DRIE by using a thick photoresist as a mask (Fig. 9.67(c)).

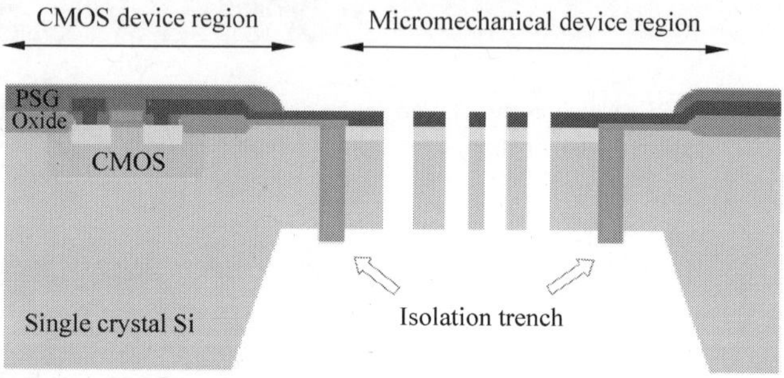

Figure 9.66 A cross-section scheme of the high-aspect-ratio MEMS sensor with CMOS circuits (see color figure at the end of this book)

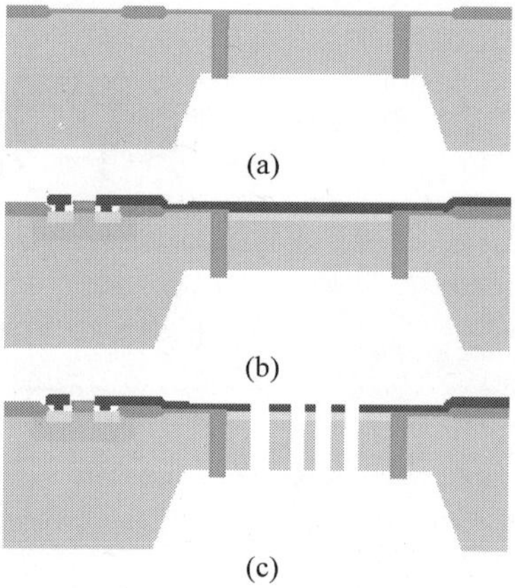

Figure 9.67 The process flow of IBMURIT (see color figure at the end of this book)

An alternative process is shown in Fig. 9.68. In this process, the CMOS front-end fabrication is done before the formation of the isolation trenches. Then the isolation trenches are etched, refilled and planarized, followed by etching of a back side window. After metallization, the structures are etched and released by DRIE. If a low-temperature trench-refilling material is used, then the process could be a post-CMOS process. A SEM photo of the fabricated MEMS structure integrated with IC devices is shown in Fig. 9.69.

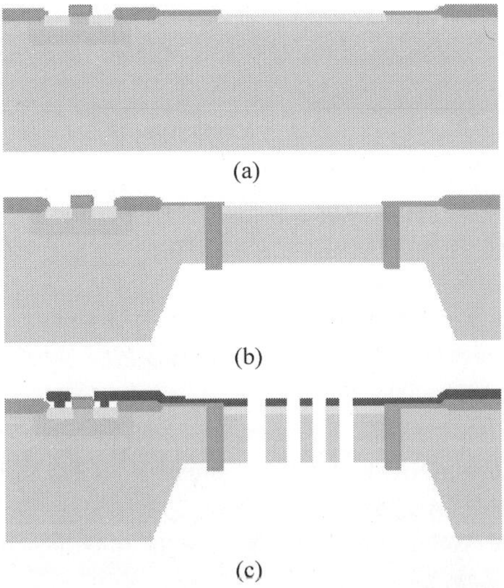

Figure 9.68 The alternative process flow of IBMURIT (see color figure at the end of this book)

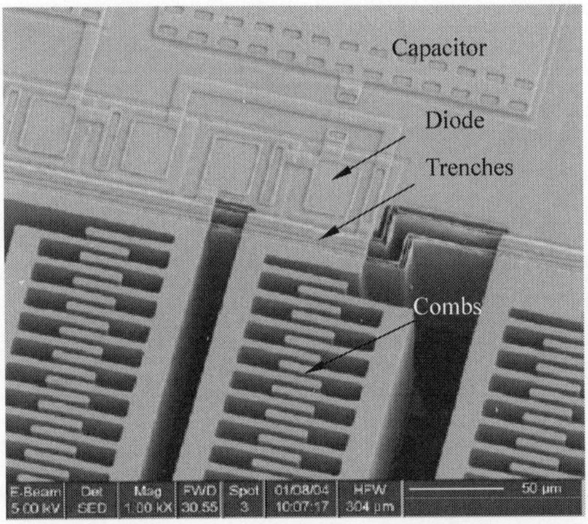

Figure 9.69 SEM front close-up view of the integrated bulk gyroscope using deep and high-aspect-ratio isolation trenches after backside TMAH etching and DRIE structure release

References

[1] Howe R. T., (1995), Recent advances in surface micromachining. *IEEJ Tech. Dig. 13th Sensor Symp.*, 1 – 8

[2] Petersen K. E., (1982), Silicon as a mechanical material. *In Proc. IEEE* **70**: 420 – 457

[3] Bustillo J. M., R. T. Howe, and R. S. Muller, (1998), Surface micromachining for microelectromechanical systems. *Proc. IEEE*, **86**: 1552 – 1574

[4] Core T. A., W. K. Tsang, and S. J. Sherman, (1993), Fabrication technology for an integrated surface-micromachined sensor. *Solid State Technol*, **36**: 39 – 47

[5] Hornbeck L. J., (1995), Projection displays and MEMS: timely convergence for a bright future. *Proceedings of SPIE*, Texas, USA, 1995, 2

[6] Howe R. T., and R. S. Muller, (1983), Polycrystalline Silicon Micromechanical Beams. *J. Electrochem. Soc.*, **130**: 1420 – 1423

[7] Howe R. T., (1985), Polycrystalline Silicon Microstructures, In *Micromachining and Micropackaging of Transducers*. Fung C. D., P. W. Cheung, W. H. Ko, Fleming DG, Eds. New York: Elsevier, 169 – 187

[8] Alley R. L., R. T. Howe, and K. Komvopoulos, (1988), The effect of release-etch processing on surface microstructure stiction. In *Proceedings of the IEEE Solid-State Sensor and Actuator Workshop, SC, USA*, 1988, 202 – 207

[9] Hoffman R. W., (1976), Mechanical Properties of Non-Metallic Thin Films, In Physics of Nonmetallic Thin Films, (NATO Advanced Study Institutes Series: Series B, Physics), Dupuy CHS and Cachard A., Eds., Plenum Press, 273 – 353

[10] Hoffman R. W., (1975), Stresses in Thin Films: The Relevance of Grain Boundaries and Impurities. *Thin Solid Films* **34**: 185 – 190

[11] Juan W. H., S. W. Pang, (1995), High aspect ratio Si etching for microsensor fabrication. *J. Vac. Sci. Technol. A* **13**: 834 – 838

[12] Juan W. H., S. W. Pang, (1996), Released Si microstructures fabricated by deep etching and shallow diffusion, *J. Microelectromech. Syst*, **5**: 19 – 23

[13] Seidel H., L. Csepregi, A. Heuberger, and H. Baumg et al, (1990), Anisotropic Etching of Crystalline Silicon in Alkaline Solutions, *J. Electrochem. Soc.* **137**: 3612

[14] Kovacs G. T. A., N. I. Maluf, K. E. Petersen, (1998), Bulk micromachining of silicon. In Proceedings of the IEEE, 1998, **86**(8): 1536 – 1551

[15] Tong Q. Y., and U. Gösele, (1999), Semiconductor Wafer Bonding: Science and Technology. New York: Wiley

[16] Nathanson H. C., and R. A. Wickstrom, (1965), A resonant gate surface transistor with high-q bandpass properties. *IEEE Transactions on Electron Devices*, **12**: 507

[17] Tai Y. C., L. S. Fan, and R. S. Muller, (1989), IC-processed micro-motors: Design, technology, and testing. In Proc. IEEE Micro Electro Mechanical Systems (MEMS) Salt Lake City, UT, 1 – 6

[18] Hao Y., Z. Li, and D. Zhang, (1999), Surface Sacrificial Layer Process, *Electronics Science and Technology Review* (*Chinese*), **12**: 16

[19] Koester D. A., R. Mahadevan, A. Shishkoff, and K. W. Markus, (1996), Smart-MUMPs Design Handbook Including MUMPs Introduction and Design Rules, rev 4. MEMS

Technology Application Center MCNC

[20] Koester D. A., R. Mahadevan, B. Hardy, and K. W. Markus, (2000), MUMPs Design Handbook, Revision 5.0. Cronos Integrated Microsystems, Research Triangle Park, NC

[21] Nasby R., J. Sneigowski, J. Smith, S. Montague, C. Barron, W. Eaton, and P. McWhorter, (1996), Application of chemical-mechanical polishing to planarization of surface-micromachined devices. In proceedings of Solid-State Sensors and Actuators Workshop, Hilton Head SC, 48 – 53

[22] Schriner H., B. Davies, J. Sniegowski, M. S. Rodgers, J. Allen, (1998), Sandia Agile MEMS Prototyping, Layout Tols, Education and Services Program. In proceedings of 2nd international conference on engineering design and automation, Maui, Hawaii, 1998

[23] Tang W., T. H. Nguyen, M. W. Judy, and R. T. Howe, (1990), Electrostatic-comb drive of lateral polysilicon resonators, *Sensors Actuators*, A **21**: 328 – 331

[24] Rodgers M., and J. Sniegowski, (1998), 5-level polysilicon surface micromachine technology: application to complex mechanical systems. In *Tech. Dig. Solid-State Sensor and Actuator Workshop*, Hilton Head, SC, 1998, 144 – 149

[25] Nguyen C. T., L. P. B. Katehi, and G. M. Rebeiz, (1998), Micromachined devices for wireless communications. *In Proc. IEEE* **86**: 1756 – 1768

[26] Yao J. J., (2000), RF MEMS from a device perspective, *J. Micromech. Microeng*, **10**: R9 – R38

[27] Dec A., and K. Suyama, (2000), A 1.9-GHz CMOS VCO with micromachined electromechanically tunable capacitors. *IEEE J. Solid-State Circuits* **35**: 1231 – 1237

[28] Ashby K. B., I. A. Koullias, W. C. Finley, J. J. Bastek, and S. Moinian, (1996), High Q inductors for wireless applications in a complementary silicon bipolar process. *IEEE J.Solid-State Circuits*, **31**: 4 – 9

[29] Burghartz J. N., D. C. Edelstein, K. A. Jenkins, and Y. H. Kwark, (1997), Spiral inductors and transmission lines in silicon technology using copper-damascene interconnects and low-loss substrates. *IEEE Trans. Microw. Theory Tech.* **45**: 1961 – 1968

[30] Yeh J. A., H. Jiang, H. P. Neves, and N. C. Tien, (2000), Copper-encapsulated silicon micromachined structures. *ASME/IEEE J. Microelectromech. Syst.* **9**: 281 – 287

[31] Read D. T., and J. W. Dally, (1994), Mechanical behavior of aluminum and copper thin films. AMD Mechan, *Materials for Electron. Packag.* **187**: 41 – 49

[32] Taylor W. P., and M. G. Allen, (1997), Integratedmagnetic microrelays: normally open, normally closed, and multi-pole devices. In Tech. Digest, 1997 Int. Conf. on Solid-State Sensors and Actuators, 1149 – 1152

[33] Zavracky P. M., S. Majumder, and N. E. McGruer, (1997), Micromechanical switches fabricated using nickel surface micromachining, *J. Microelectromech. Sys.*, **6**: 3 – 9

[34] Young D. J., and B. E. Boser, (1996), A micromachined variable capacitor for monolithic low noise VCO's. In Tech Dig. Solid State Sensor and Actuator Workshop, Hilton Head Island, SC, 1996, 86

[35] Pierret R. F., (1996), Semiconductor Device Fundamentals. Addison-Wesley

[36] Murarka S. P., (1983), Silicides for VLSI Applications. Academic

[37] Wolf S., (1990), Silicon Processing for VLSI Era Vol. 2. Lattice Press

[38] Lee H., (2000), Characterization of shallow silicide junctions for sub-quartermicron

ULSI technology—extraction of silicidation induced Schottky contact area. *IEEE Trans Electron Devices*, **47**: 762 – 767
[39] Lukyanchikova N. B., M. V. Petrichuk, N. Garbar, E. Simoen, A. Poyai, and C. Claeys, (2000), Impact of cobalt silicidation on the low-frequency noise behavior of shallow P–N junctions. *IEEE Electron Device Lett*, **21**: 408 – 410
[40] Osburn C. M., J. Y. Tsai, and J. Sun, (1996), Metal silicides: active elements of ULSI contacts. *J. Electron Mater*, **25**: 1725 – 1739
[41] Ohguro T., M. Saito, E. Morifuji, T. Yoshitomi, T. Morimoto, H. S. Momose, Y. Katsumata, and H. Iwai, (2000), Thermal stability of $CoSi_2$ film for CMOS salicide. *IEEE Trans. Electron Devices*, **47**: 2208 – 2213
[42] Fuji K., K. Kikuta, K. Inoue, K. Mikagi, S. Chikaki, T. Kikkawa, (1996), A thermally stable Ti–W salicide for deep-submicron logic with embedded DRAM. In IEDM Tech. Dig., San Francisco, CA, USA, 1996, 451 – 454
[43] Ohguro T., et al., (1994), Analysis of resistance behavior in Ti- and Ni-Salicided polysilicon films. *IEEE Trans. Electron Devices*, **32**: 2305 – 2317
[44] Li Z., G. Zhang, W. Wang, Y. Hao, T. Li, G. Wu, (2002), Study on the application of silicide in surface micromachining. *Journal of Micromechanics and Microengineering*, **12**: 162 – 167
[45] Jiang H., Y. Wang, J. A. Yeh, N. C. Tien, (2000), On-chip spiral inductors suspended over deep copper-lined cavities. *IEEE Trans. Microwave Theory Techniques*, **48**: 2415 – 2423
[46] Jiang H., J. A. Yeh, Y. Wang, N. C. Tien, (2000), Electromagnetically shielded high-Q CMOS-compatible copper inductors. In Tech. Dig. IEEE Int. Solid-State Circuits Conference (ISSCC), San Francisco, CA, USA, 2000, 330 – 331
[47] Kiang M. H., et al., (1992), Planarized copper interconnects by selective electroless plating. In MRS Symp. Dig., 260, 1992, 745 – 755
[48] Jiang H., (2001), A MEMS Fabrication Technology for On-chip Radio-frequency Passive Components. Thesis, Cornell University
[49] Shi W., N. C. Tien, Z. Li, (2007), A Highly Reliable Lateral MEMS Switch Utilizing Undoped Polysilicon as Isolation Material. *Journal Of Microelectromechanical Systems*, **16**: 1173 – 1184
[50] Wang Y., Z. Li, D. T. McCormick, N. C. Tien, (2002), Low-voltage lateral-contact microrelays for RF applications. In Proc. 15th IEEE Int. Conf. Micro-Electro-Mechanical Systems, Las Vegas, NV, USA, Jan. 2002, 645 – 648
[51] Wang Y., Z. Li, D. T. McCormick, N. C. Tien, (2004), A low-voltage lateral MEMS switch with high RF performance. *J. Microelectromech. Syst.* **13**: 902 – 911
[52] Kruglick E. J. J., K. S. J. Pister, (1999), Lateral MEMS microcontact considerations. *J. Microelectromech. Syst.* **8**: 264 – 271
[53] Wang Y., Z. Li, D. T. McCormick, N. C. Tien, (2002), Low-Voltage Lateral-Contact Microrelays For RF Applications. In proceedings of the Fifteenth IEEE International Conference on Micro Electro Mechanical Systems (MEMS'02), Las Vegas, NV, USA, Jan. 2002, 645 – 648
[54] Moseley R. W., E. M. Yeatman, A. S. Holmes, R. R. A. Syms, A. P. Finlay, and P. Boniface, (2006), Laterally actuated, low voltage, 3-port RF MEMS switch. In Proc. 19th

IEEE Int. Conf. Micro-Electro-Mechanical Systems, Istanbul, Jan. 2006, 878 – 881

[55] Li Z., D. Zhang, T. Li, W. Wang, G. Wu, (2000), Bulk micromachined relay with lateral contact. *J. Micromech. Microeng*, **10**: 329 – 333

[56] Li Z., Z. Yang, Z. Xiao, Y. Hao, T. Li, G. Wu, Y. Wang, (2000), A bulk micromachined vibratory lateral gyroscope fabricated with wafer bonding and deep trench etching. Sensors and Actuators A: Physical **83**: 24 – 29

[57] Wood R., R. Mahadevan, V. Dudley, A. Cowen, E. Hill, K. Markus, (1998), MEMS microrelays. Mechatronics **8**: 535 – 547

[58] Simon J., S. Saffer, F. Sherman, C. Kim, (1998), Lateral polysilicon microrelays with a mercury microdrop contact. IEEE Trans. Industr. Electron. **45**: 854 – 860

[59] Rebeiz G. M., (2003), RF MEMS: Theory, Design and Technology. Hoboken, NJ: Wiley

[60] Brosnihan T. J., J. M. Bustillo, A. P. Pisano, R. T. Howe, Embedded interconnect and electrical isolation for high-aspect ratio, SOI inertial instruments. In Proc. 9th IEEE Int. Conf. on Solid-State Sensors & Actuators (Transducers '99), Jun. 1999, 1002 – 1005

[61] Muller L., J. M. Heck, R. T. Howe, A P. Pisano, (2000), Electrical isolation process for molded, high-aspect-ratio polysilicon microstructures. In Proc. 13th IEEE Int. Conf. Micro-Electro-Mechanical Systems, Jan. 2000, 590 – 595

[62] Que L., J. Park, Y. B. Gianchandani, (2001), Bent-beam electrothermal actuators-Part Ⅰ: Single beam and cascaded devices. *J. Microelectromech. Syst.* **10**: 247 – 254

[63] Borwick R. L., P. A. Stupar, and J. DeNatale, (2003), A hybrid approach to low-voltage MEMS switches. In Proc. 12th IEEE Int. Conf. on Solid-State Sensors, Actuators and Microsystems (Transducers'03), Jun. 2003, 859 – 862

[64] Yun W., (1992), A Surface Micromacined Accelerometer with Integrated CMOS Detection Circuitry. Ph.D. Thesis, U.C.Berkeley

[65] Howe R. T., (1995), Polysilicon Integrated Microsystems: Technologies and Applications. In Tech. Digest. 8th Int. Conf. Solid-State Sensors and Actuators (Transducers '95)/Eurosensors IX, Stockholm, Sweden, 1995, 43 – 46

[66] Bustillo J. M., G. K. Fedder, C. T. Nguyen, and R. T. Howe, (1994), Process technology for modular integration of CMOS and polysilicon microstructures, *Microsystem Technologies*, **1**: 30 – 41

[67] Franke A. E., J. M. Heck, T. King, R. T. Howe, (2003), Polycrystalline silicon-germanium films for integrated Microsystems. *J. Microelectromechanical Systems*, **12**: 160 – 171

[68] Smith J. H., S. Montague, J. J. Sniegowski, and J. R. Murray, et al., (1995), Embedded micromechanical devices for the monolithic integration of MEMS with CMOS. In Proc. Int. Electron Devices Meeting, Washington, DC, 1995, 609 – 612

[69] Fedder G. K., S. Santhanam, M. L. Reed, S. C. Eagle, D. F. Guillou, M. S. Lu, and L. R. Carley, (1996), Laminated high-aspect-ratio micro-structures in a conventional CMOS process, *Sens. Actuators A*, **57**: 103 – 110

[70] Zhu X., D. W. Greve, R. Lawton, N. Presser, and G. K. Fedder, (1998), Factorial experiment on CMOS-MEMS RIE post processing. In Proc. 194th Electrochemical Society Meeting, Symposium on Microstructures and Microfabricated Systems Ⅳ, Boston, MA, 1998, 33 – 42

[71] Xie H., and G. K. Fedder, (2001), A CMOS-MEMS lateral-axis gyroscope. In Tech. Dig. 14th IEEE International Conference on Micro Electro Mechanical Systems (MEMS 2001) Interlaken, Switzerland, 2001, 162 – 165

[72] Burgett S. R., K. S. Pister, and R. S. Fearing, (1992), Three Dimensional Structures Made with Microfabricated Hinges. In proceedings of ASME Micromechanical Sensors, Actuators, and Systems, Anaheim, CA, 1992, 1 – 11

[73] Lin L. Y., S. S. Lee, M. C. Wu, and K. J. Pister, (1995), Micromachined integrated optics for free-space interconnections. In Proc. IEEE Microelectromech. Syst. Amsterdam, the Netherlands, 1995, 77 – 82

[74] Suzuki K., I. Shimoyama, and H. Miura, (1994), Insect-model based microrobot with elastic hinges, *J. Microelectromechanical Syst.*, **3**: 4 – 9

[75] Hui E. E., R. T. Howe, and M. S. Rodgers, (2000), Single-step assembly of complex 3-D microstructures. In Proc 13th Int. Conf. Microelectromechanical Systems Miyazaki, Japan, 2000, 602 – 607

[76] Fan L., R. T. Chen, A. Nespola, M. C. Wu, (1998), Universal MEMS platforms for passive RF components: suspended inductors and variable capacitors. In Proc. IEEE, 11th Ann. Int. Workshop on Micro Electro Mechanical Systems, 1998, 29 – 33

[77] Goldsmith C. L., Z. Yao, S. Eshelman, and D. Denniston, (1998), Performance of low-loss RF MEMS capcitive switches, *IEEE Microwave Guided Wave Lett.*, **8**: 269 – 271

[78] Yao Z. J., S. Chen, S. Eshelman, D. Denniston, and C. Goldsmith, (1999), Micromachined low-loss microwave switches, *J. Microelectromech. Syst.*, **8**: 129 – 134

[79] Honer K. A., (2001), Surface Micromachining Techniques for Integrated Microsystems. Thesis, Stranford University

[80] Hornbeck L. J., (1983), 128 × 128 deformable mirror device. *IEEE Transactions on Electron Devices*, **30**: 539 – 545

[81] Hornbeck L. J., (1996), Digital Light Processing and MEMS: An Overview. In Digest of the IEEE/LEOS 1996 Summer Topical Meetings, Keystone, CO, USA, 1996, 7 – 8

[82] Hornbeck L. J., (1996), Digital Light Processing: A New MEMS-Based Display Technology. In Technical Digest of the IEEJ 14th Sensor Symposium, Kawasaki, Japan, 1996, 297 – 304

[83] Hornbeck L. J., (1990), Deformable-mirror spatial light modulators. In Proceedings of the SPIE-The International Society for Optical Engineering, 1990, 86 – 102. at texas instruments

[84] Amm D. T., R. W. Corrigan, (1999), Optical performance of the grating light valve technology. In: Proceedings of the SPIE-The International Society for Optical Engineering, 1999, 71 – 78

[85] Sampsell J. B., (1994), An Overview of the Performance Envelope of Digital Micromirror Device (DMD) Based Projection Display Systems. In: Digest of Technical Papers, Society for Information Display International Symposium, San Jose, CA, 1994, 1 – 4

[86] Van Kessel P. F., L. J. Hornbeck, R. E. Meier, M. R. Douglass, (1998), A MEMSA MEMS-Based Projection Display. *In proceedings of the IEEE* **86** (8): 1687 – 1704

[87] Goldsmith C., T. Lin, B. Powers, W. Wu, B. Norvell, (1995), Micromechanical membrane switches for microwave applications. In Tech. Digest, IEEE Microwave Theory and Techniques Symp., 1995, 91 – 94

[88] Goldsmith C., J. Randall, S. Eshelman, T. Lin, D. Denniston, S. Chen, B. Norvell, (1996), Characteristics of micromachined switches at microwave frequencies. In Tech. Digest, IEEE Microwave Theory and Techniques Symp., 1996, 1141

[89] Young D. J., B. E. Boser, (1997), A micromachine-based RF low-noise voltage-controlled oscillator. In Proceedings of the IEEE 1997 Custom Integrated Circuits Conference, New York, USA, 1997, 431 – 434

[90] Young D. J., V. Malba, J. J. Ou, A. F. Bernhardt, B. E. Boser, (1997), Monolithic high-performance three-dimensional coil inductors for wireless communication applications. In International Electron Devices Meeting 1997. IEDM Technical Digest, New York, NY, USA, 1997, 67 – 70

[91] Young D. J., V. Malba, J. Ou, A. F. Bernhardt, B. E. Boser, (1998), A low-noise RF voltage-controlled oscillator using on-chip high-Q three-dimensional coil inductor and micromachined variable capacitor. In proceedings of Solid-State Sensor and Actuator Workshop, Cleveland, OH, USA, 1998, 128 – 131

[92] Zhao Y., M. Mao, R. Horowitz, A. Majumdar, J. Varesi, P. Norton, J. Kitching, (2002), Optomechanical uncooled infrared imaging system: design, microfabrication, and performance, *J. Microelectromech. Syst.*, **11**(2): 136 – 146

[93] Mao M., T. Perazzo, O. Kwon, A. Majumdar, (1999), Direct-view uncooled micro-optomechanical infrared camera. In Proceedings of 12th IEEE International Conference on MEMS, New York, NY, 1999, 100 – 105

[94] Choi J., J. Yamaguchi, S. Morales, R. Horowitz, Y. Zhao, A. Majumdar, (2004), Design and control of a thermal stabilizing system for a MEMS optomechanical uncooled infrared imaging camera, *Sensors and Actuators A: Physical*, **104**: 132 – 142

[95] Ishizuya T., J. Suzuki, K. Akagawa, T. Kazama, (2002), 160 × 120 pixels optically readable bimaterial infrared detector. In Proceedings of 15th IEEE International Conference on MEMS, New York, NY, USA, 2002, 578 – 581

[96] Grbovic D., N. V. Lavrik, P. G. Datskos, D. Forrai, E. Nelson, J. Devitt, B. McIntyre, (2006), Uncooled infrared imaging using bimaterial microcantilever arrays, *Applied Physics Letters*, **89**: 073118

[97] Kovacs G. T. A, (1998), Micromachined Transducers Sourcebook. McGraw-Hill

[98] Frühauf J., B. Hannemann, (1997), Anisotropic multi-step etch processes of silicon. *J. Micromech. Microeng.* **7**: 137 – 140

[99] Kendall D. L., (1990), A new theory for the anisotropic etching of silicon and some underdeveloped chemical micromachining concepts. *J. Vac. Sci. Technol.* **8**(4): 3598 – 3605

[100] Yan G., G. Chan, I. Hsing, R. Sharma, J. Sin, Y. Wang, (2001), An improved TMAH Si-etching solution without attacking exposed aluminum, *Sensors and Actuators A: Physica*, **89**(1 – 2): 135 – 141

[101] STS, (1997), "Anisotropic Dry Silicon Etching", presented at The symposium on microstructures and microfabricated systems at the Annual meeting of the electrochemical society, Montreal, Quebec, Canada, May 4 – 9, 1997

[102] Ishihara K., C. Yun, A. A. Ayón, M. A. Schmidt, (1999), A Inertial sensor Technology Using DRIE and Wafer Bonding with Interconnecting capability, *Journal of Microelectromechanical Systems*, **8**(4): 403 – 408

[103] Ishihara K., C. F. Yung, A. Ayon, M. A. Schmidt, (1999), An inertial sensor technology using DRIE and wafer bonding with enhanced interconnect capability. In 10th Int. Conf. on Solid-State Sensors and Actuators (Transducers'99), Sendai, Japan, 1999, 254

[104] Docker P. T., P. Kinnell, M. C. L. Ward, (2003), A dry single-step process for the manufacture of release MEMS structures. *J. Micromech. Microeng*, **13**: 790 – 794

[105] Zhu Y., G. Yan, J. Fan, J. Zhou, X. Liu, Z. Li, Y. Wang, (2005), Fabrication of keyhole-free ultra-deep high-aspect-ratio isolation trench and its application. *J. Micromech. Microeng*, **15**: 636 – 642

[106] Zhu Y., G. Yan, J. Fan, X. Liu, J. Zhou, Y. Wang, (2005), Post-CMOS process for high-aspect-ratio monolithically integrated single crystal silicon microstructures. In Proceedings of Transducers '05, 2005, 1130 – 1133

[107] Klaassen E. H., K. Petersen, J. M. Noworolski, J. Logan, N. I. Maluf, J. Brown, C. Storment, W. McCulley, G. T. A. Kovacs, (1996), Silicon fusion bonding and deep reactive ion etching: a new technology for microstructures. *Sensors and Actuators A: Physical*, **52(1 – 3)**: 132 – 139

[108] Schmidt M. A., (1998), Wafer-to-wafer bonding for microstructure formation. In Proceedings of the IEEE, **86**(8): 1575 – 1585

[109] Petersen K., P. Barth, J. Poydock, J. Brown, J. Mallon, J. Bryzek, (1988), Silicon fusion bonding for pressure sensors. In Proceedings of Solid-State Sensor and Actuators Workshop, IEEE, 1988, 144 – 147

[110] Harendt C., H. G. Graf, B. Hofflinger, E. Penteker, (1992), Silicon fusion bonding and its characterization. *J. Micromech. Microeng*, **2**: 113 – 116

[111] Haisma J., B. A. C. M. Spierings, U. K. P. Biermann, A. A. van Gorkum, (1994), Diversity and feasibility of direct bonding: a survey of a dedicated optical technology. Appl. Opt., **33**: 1154 – 1169

[112] Albauqh K. B., P. E. Cade, D. H. Rasmussen, (1988), Mechanisms of anodic bonding of silicon to pyrex glass. In Proceedings of Solid-State Sensor and Actuators Workshop, IEEE, 1988, 109 – 110

[113] Dragoi V., T. Glinsner, G. Mittendorfer, B. Wieder, P. Lindner, (2003), Adhesive wafer bonding for MEMS applications. In Proceeding of SPIE, 2003, **5116**(1): 160 – 167

[114] Cheng Y., L. Lin, K. Najafi, (2000), Localized silicon fusion and eutectic bonding for MEMS fabrication and packaging. *Journal of Microelectromechanical Systems*, **9(1)**: 3 – 8

[115] Sparks D., G. Queen, R. Weston, G. Woodward, M. Putty, L. Jordan, S. Zarabadi, K. Jayakar, (2001), Wafer-to-wafer bonding of nonplanarized MEMS surfaces using solder. *J. Micromech. Microeng*, **11**: 630 – 634

[116] Knechtel R., (2005), Glass frit bonding: an universal technology for wafer level encapsulation and packaging. *Microsystem Technologies*, **12**(1-2): 63 – 68

[117] Wolffenbuttel R. F., and K. D. Wise, (1994), "Low temperature silicon wafer-to-wafer bonding using gold at eutectic temperature," *Sensors and Actuators A*, **43**: 223 – 229

[118] Lin C., C. Hsu, H. Yang, W. Wang, W. Fang, (2008), Implementation of silicon-on-glass MEMS devices with embedded through-wafer silicon vias using the glass reflow process for wafer-level packaging and 3D chip integration. *J. Micromech. Microeng*, **18**: 1 – 6

[119] Chae J., H. Kulah, K. Najafi, (2005), A CMOS-compatible high aspect ratio silicon-on-glass in-plane micro-accelerometer. *J. Micromech. Microeng*, **15**: 336 – 345

[120] Chen B. T., J. M. Miao, F. E. H. Toy, (2007), Fabrication and characterization of DRIE-micromachined electrostatic, microactuators for hard disk drives. *Microsys. Technol*, **13**: 11 – 19

[121] Xiao Z., G. Wu, D. Zhang, Y. Hao, Z. Li, (1999), Lateral capacity sensed accelerometer fabricated with the anodic bonding and the high aspect ratio etching. In proceedings of 10th Int. Conf. on Solid-State Sensors and Actuators (Transducers'99), Sendai, Japan, 1999, 1518

[122] Li Z., Z. Xiao, Y. Hao, T. Li, G. Wu, Y. Wang, (1999), A bulk micromachined vibratory lateral gyroscope fabricated with wafer bonding and deep trench etching. In 10th Int. Conf. on Solid-State Sensors and Actuators (Transducers'99), Sendai, Japan, 1999, 1594

[123] Baek S. S., Y. S. Oh, B. J. Ha, A. D. An, B. H. An, H. Song, C. M. Song, (1999), A symmetrical Z-axis gyroscope with a high aspect ratio using simple and new process. In Proc. IEEE 12th Int. Workshop on Micro Electro-Mechanical Systems (MEMS'99), 1999, 612

[124] Mochida Y., M. Tamura, K. Ohwada, (1999), A micro micromachined vibrating rate gyro with independent beams for drive and detection modes. In Proc. MEMS'99, 1999, 618

[125] Kobayashi S., T. Hara, T. Oguchi, Y. Asaji, K. Yaji, K. Owada, (1999), Double-frame silicon gyroscope packaged under low pressure by wafer bonding. In proceedings of 10th Int. Conf. on Solid-State Sensors and Actuators (Transducers'99), Sendai, Japan, 1999, 910

[126] Alper S. E., T. Akin, (2005), A single-crystal silicon symmetrical and decoupled MEMS gyroscope on an insulating substrate. *J. Microelectromech. Syst*, **14**: 707 – 717

[127] Lee M., S. Kang, K. Jung, S. Choa, Y. C. Cho, (2005), A high yield rate MEMS gyroscope with a packaged SiOG process. *J. Micromech. Microeng*, **15**: 2003 – 2012

[128] Iliescu C., G. L. Xu, V. Samper, F. E. H. Tay, (2005), Fabrication of a dielectrophoretic chip with 3D silicon electrodes. *J. Micromech. Microeng*, **15**: 494 – 500

[129] Chen B., J. Miao, (2007), Influence of deep RIE tolerances on comb-drive actuator performance. *J. Phys. D: Appl. Phys*, **40**: 970 – 976

[130] Chae J., H. Kulah, K. Najafi, (2002), A Hybrid Silicon-On-Glass (SOG) Lateral Micro-Accelerometer with COMS Readout Circuitry. In proceedings of MEMS 2002, 623 – 626

[131] Richard A. Gottscho, and C.W. Jurgensen, (1992), "Microscopic uniformity in Plasma etching," *J. Vac. Sci. Technol. B*, **10**(5): 2133 – 2147

[132] Jansen H., M. de Boer, R. Wiegerink, N. Tas, E. Smulders, C. Neagu, M. Elwenspoek, (1997), RIE lag in high aspect ratio trench etching of silicon. *Microelectronic Engineering*, **35**: 45 – 50

[133] Chung C., (2004), Geometrical pattern effect on silicon deep etching by an inductively coupled plasma system. *J. Micromech. Microeng.*, **14**: 656 – 662

[134] Ayon A. A., K. Ishihara, R. A. Braff, H. H. Sawin, M. A. Schmidt, (1999), Microfabrication

and testing of suspended structure compatible with silicon-on-insulator technology. *J. Vac. Sci. Technol. B*, **17**(4): 1589 – 1593

[135] Fan J., Y. Zhu, Z. Yang, J. Zhou, X. Liu, G. Yan, (2004), An improved method employed in anodic bonded glass-silicon gyroscopes to avoid footing effect in DRIE. In Proc. of ICSICT'04, Oct. 2004, 1896 – 1899

[136] Kinoshita T., M. Hane, J. P. McVittie, (1996), Notching as an example of charging in uniform high density plasmas. J. Vac. Sci. Technol. B, Microelectron. *Process. Phenom.* B, **14**(1): 560 – 565

[137] Nozawa T., T. Kinoshita, T. Nishizawa, A. Narai, T. Inoue, A. Nakaue, (1995), The electron charging effects of plasma on notch profile defects. *Jpn. J. Appl. Phys.*, **34**(4B): 2107 – 2113

[138] Matsuura T., M. Chabloz, J. Jiao, Y. Yoshida, K. Tsutsumi, (2001), A method to evade silicon backside damage in deep reactive ion etching for anodically bonded glass-silicon structures. *Sensors and Actuators A*, **89**: 71 – 75

[139] Yoshida Y., M. Kumagai, K. Tsutsumi, (2003), Study of silicon backside damage in deep reactive ion etching for bonded silicon-glass structures. *Microsystem Technology*, **9**: 167 – 170

[140] McAuley S. A., H. Ashraf, L. Atabo, A. Cambers, S. Hall, J. Hopkings, G. Nicholls, (2001), Silicon micromachining using a high-density plasma source. *Journal of Physics D: Applied Physics*, **34**: 2769 – 2774

[141] Shridhar U., et al, (1999), Single crystal silicon microstructures using trench isolation. In Proc. 11th Int. Conf. Solid-State Sensors and Actuators (Transducers'99), Sendai, Japan, 1999, 258

[142] Hofmann W., N. C. MacDonald, (1997), Fabrication of multi-level electrically isolated high-aspect-ratio single crystal silicon microstructures. In Proc. IEEE 10th MicroElectro Mechanical Systems (MEMS'97), Negoya, Japan, 1997, 460

[143] Brosnihan T. J., J. M. Bustillo, A. P. Pisano, R. T. Howe, (1997), Embedded interconnect and electrical isolation for high-aspect-ratio SOI inertial instruments. In Proc. 9th Int. Conf. Solid-State Sensors and Actuators (Transducers'97), Chicago, IL, 1997, 637 – 640

[144] Young D. J., J. L. Tham, B. E. Boser, (1999), A micromachine-based low phase-noise GHz voltage-controlled oscillator for wireless communications. In proceeding of 10th Int. Conf. on Solid-State Sensors and Actuators (Transducers'99), Sendai, Japan, 1999, 1386

[145] Sun X. Q., K. R. Farmer, W. N. Carr, (1998), A bistable microrelay on two-segment multimorph cantilever actuators. In Proc. IEEE 11th Int. Workshop on Micro Electro-Mechanical Systems (MEMS'98), 1998, 154

[146] Zhou S., X. Q. Sun, W. N. Carr, (1997), A micro variable inductor chip using MEMS relays. In Proc. 9th Int. Conf. Solid-State Sensors and Actuators (Transducers'97), Chicago, IL, 1997, 1137

[147] Park J. H., H. K. Kim, Y. W. Kwon, Y. K. Kim, (1999), A tunable millimeter filter using coplanar wave guide and micromachined variable capacitor. In proceeding of 10th Int. Conf. on Solid-State Sensors and Actuators (Transducers'99), Sendai, Japan, 1999, 1272

[148] Zhang D., Z. Li, T. Li, G. Wu, (2001), A Novel Isolation Technology in Bulk Micromachining Using DRIE and Polysilicon Refill. *Journal of Micromechanics and Microengineering*, **11**: 13 – 19

[149] Liu A. Q., M. Tang, A. Agarwal, A. Alphones, (2005), Low-loss lateral micromachined switches for high frequency applications. *J. Micromech. Microeng*, **15**: 157 – 167

[150] Tang M., A. Liu, A. Agarwal, Q. X. Zhang, P. Win, (2004), A new approach of lateral RF MEMS. switch. *Analog Integr.Circuits Signal Process*, **40**: 165 – 173

[151] Tang M., P. Win, W. L. Goh, A. Agarwal, L. C. Law, A. Liu, (2004), A single-pole double-throw (SPDT) circuit using deep etching lateral metal-contact switches. In IEEE MTT-S Int. Microwave Symp. Digest., 2004, 581 – 584

[152] Miller K., A. Cowen, G. Hames, B. Hardy, (2004), SOIMUMPs Design Handbook. MEMScAP.f

[153] Amini B. V., R. Abdolvand, F. Ayazi, (2005), Sub-micro-gravity capacitive SOI microaccelerometers In Proceedings of Int. Conf. Solid State Sensors, Actuators and Microsystems (Transducers '05), 515 – 518

[154] Amini B. V., R. Abdolvand, F. Ayazi, (2006), A 4.5-mW Closed-Loop DS Micro-Gravity CMOS SOI Accelerometer. In Proceedings of ISSCC, San Francisco, CA, Feb. 2006

[155] Amini B. V., F. Ayazi, (2005), Micro-gravity capacitive silicon-on-insulator accelerometers. *J. Micromech. Microeng*, **15**(11): 2113 – 2120

[156] Kevin A. Shaw, Z. L. Zhang, and N. C. MacDonald, (1994), "SCREAM I: a single mask, single-crystal silicon, reactive ion etching process for microelectromechanical structures," *Sensors and Actuators A*, **40**: 63 – 70

[157] Vrtacnik D., D. Resnik, U. Aljancic, et al., (2007), Thin FC film for sidewall passivation in Scream process for MEMS. In Proceedings of Africon'07, Africa, Africon, 2007, 26 – 28

[158] Ji X., H. Yu, X. Huang, Y. Lei, Z. Li, Parylene Film for Sidewall Passivation in SCREAM Process, *Science in China Series E: Technological Sciences*, in press

[159] Wu J, T. Pike, C. P. Wong, (1999), Novel bi-layer conformal coating for reliability without hermeticity MEMS encapsulation. *IEEE Trans. Comp. Packag., Manufact. Technol. C* **22**: 195

[160] Sun C., C. H. Wang, M. H. Tsai, et al., (2008), A novel double-side Cmos-Mems post processing for monolithic sensor integration. In Proceedings of IEEE 21st International Conference on Micro Electro Mechanical Systems (IEEE MEMS'08), Tucson, 2008, 90 – 93

[161] Yang Y. J., W. C. Kuo, (2005), A novel fabrication method for suspended high-aspect-ratio microstructures. *J. Micromech. Microeng,* **15**: 2184 – 2193

[162] You L., G. R. Yang, C. I. Lang, et al., (1992), Vapor deposition of parylene films from precursors. In Proceedings of 3rd Biennial Meeting Chem. Perspectives Microelectron. Mater., Boston, 1992

[163] Judy M. W., (2004), Evolution of Integrated Inertial MEMS Technology. In proceedings of Solid-State Sensor, Actuator and Microsystems Workshop, Hilton Head Island, South Carolina, 2004, 27 – 30

[164] Chen T. D., T. W. Kelly, D. Collins, D. Bain, B. Berthold, T. J. Brosnihan, T. Denison, J. Kuang, M. OKane, J. W. Weigold, (2005), The Next Generation Integrated MEMS and CMOS Process on SOI Wafers for Overdamped Accelerometers. In proceedings of Transducers'05, 2005, 1122 – 1125

[165] Takao H., T. Ichikawa, T. Nakata, K. Sawada, M. Ishida, (2008), Post-CMOS Integration Technology Of Thick-Film SOI MEMS Devices Using Micro Bridge Interconnections. In proceedings of MEMS 2008, 359 – 362

[166] Ghosh S., M. Bayoumi, (2005), On integrated CMOS-MEMS system-on-chip. In Proceedings of The 3rd International IEEE-NEWCAS Conference, 31 – 34

[167] Xie H., L. Erdmann, X. Zhu, K. J. Gabriel, G. K. Fedder, (2002), Post-CMOS processing for high-aspect-ratio integrated silicon microstructures. *J. Microelectromechan. Syst.*, **11**: 93 – 101

[168] Shaw K. A., N. C. MacDonald, (1996), Integrating SCREAM micromachined devices with integrated circuits. In Proceedings of IEEE MEMS '96, 1996, 44 – 48

[169] Yan G., et al., (2004), Integrated bulk micromachined gyroscope using deep trench isolation technology. In Proceedings of. IEEE MEMS04, 2004, 605 – 608

10 Optical MEMS and Nanophotonics

Ming C. Wu[1], Jui-che Tsai[2], and Wibool Piyawattanametha[3], and Pamela R. Patterson[4]

[1] University of California, Berkeley, EECS Department, 261M Cory Hall, Berkeley, CA 94720-1770, USA
E-mail: wu@eecs.berkeley.edu

[2] Graduate Institute of Photonics and Optoelectronics and Department of Electrical Engineering, Taiwan University
E-mail: jctsai@cc.ee.ntu.edu.tw

[3] National Electronics and Computer Technology Center, Thailand

[4] HRL Laboratories LLC, 3011 Malibu Canyon Road Malibu, CA 90265-4797, USA

Abstract Micro-electro-mechanical systems (MEMS) technology ignites major breakthroughs in several research areas. Optics/photonics is one of these research fields impacted by MEMS techniques. Generally, micro-optical elements with sizes ranging from a few microns to a few millimeters belong to the category of optical MEMS. They are inherently suited for cost effective wafer scale manufacturing as the processes are derived from the semiconductor industry. The advantages of applying microelectronics technology to silicon micromechanical devices were presented by Petersen in his classic paper, 'Silicon as a Mechanical Material'[1].

The ability to steer or direct light is one of the key requirements in optical MEMS. In the past two decades since Petersen published his silicon scanner[2], the field of optical MEMS has experienced explosive growth[3,4]. In the 80's and early 90's, displays were the main driving force for the development of micromirror arrays. Portable digital displays are common places and head mount displays are now commercially available. In the past decade, telecommunications has become the market driver for Optical MEMS. The demand for routing internet traffic through fiber optic networks pushes the development of both digital and scanning micromirror systems for large port-count all-optical switches. In the biomedical arena, microoptical scanners promise low-cost endoscopic 3D imaging systems for in vivo diagnostics.

Thanks to the ongoing improvement of fabrication technologies, nano-electro-mechanical systems (NEMS) have become feasible and have steadily attracted attention in the fields of optics and photonics. Nano-photonics is particularly promising in guided-wave devices as the structural dimensions (a few hundred nanometers) are close to the optical wavelengths of interest.

This chapter summarizes the state of the art of Optical MEMS and nano-photonics technologies and applications. It is organized into the following sections: Section 10.1 describes the generic actuation mechanisms commonly used for MEMS and NEMS devices. Section 10.2 discusses the applications, dividing into three categories including 'Display, Imaging, and Microscopy,' 'Optical Communication,' and 'NanoPhotonics.'

Keywords Optical MEMS, nanophotonics, integrating MEMS with nanophotonic, MEMS, applications

10.1 Actuation Mechanisms

10.1.1 Electrostatic Actuation

Electrostatic MEMS devices with torsional rotation can be described as follows: when voltage is applied between the movable and the fixed electrodes, the moving part rotates about the torsion axis until the restoring torque and the electrostatic torque are equal. The torques can be expressed as:

$$T_e(\theta) = \frac{V^2}{2}\frac{\partial C}{\partial \theta} \tag{10.1}$$

$$T_r(\theta) = k\theta \tag{10.2}$$

where, V is the applied voltage across the fixed and movable electrodes, C is the capacitance of the actuator, θ is the rotation angle, and k is the spring constant. The capacitance is determined by the area of the electrode overlap and the gap between the electrodes. For simple parallel plate geometry, the capacitance can be expressed by

$$C = \frac{\varepsilon_0 A}{g} \tag{10.3}$$

where, ε_0 is the permittivity of free space, A is the area of electrode overlap, and g is the gap between fixed and moving electrodes.

There are two major types of electrostatic actuators. The first is based on parallel-plate capacitance, and the other is based on comb-drive capacitance. For the parallel-plate type devices (Fig. 10.1), the area of the electrode overlap is essentially the area of the fixed electrode. The gap for the parallel-plate actuator is a function of the rotation angle, and there is a tradeoff as the initial gap spacing needs to be large enough to accommodate the scan angle, but small enough for reasonable actuation voltage. The stable scan range is further limited by a pull-in phenomenon to 34% – 40% of the maximum mechanical scan angle[5, 6].

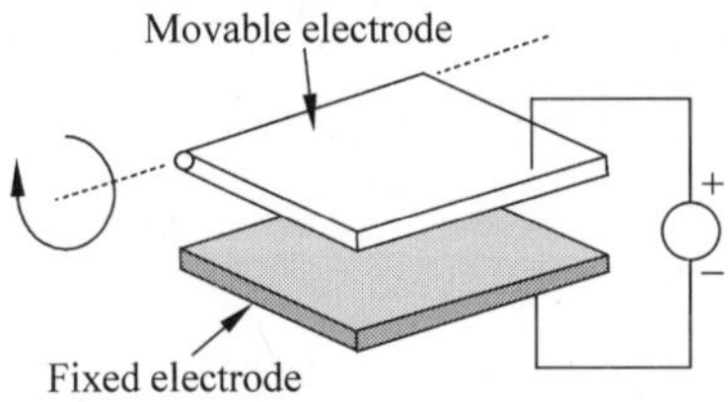

Figure 10.1 Schematic of a parallel-plate actuator

Figure 10.2 shows the schematic of a vertical comb-drive actuator. The vertical comb-drive offers several advantages: the structure and the actuator are decoupled, and the gap between the interdigitated fingers of the comb-drive is typically quite small, in the order of a couple of microns[7, 8]. Large rotation angle and low actuation voltage can be achieved simultaneously. In the comb-drive, the gap is constant and the area of the electrode overlap is a function of the rotation angle. The maximum rotation angle is typically the point where the overlap area of electrodes reaches the maximum.

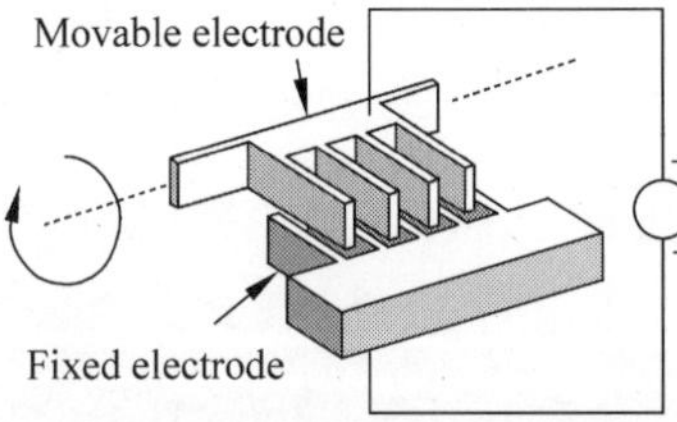

Figure 10.2 Schematic of a vertical combdrive actuator

10.1.2 Magnetic Actuation

Magnetic actuation is practical when the structural dimensions are on the millimeter scale since the magnetic torque (generated by the magnetic device interacting with an external magnetic field) scales with volume for permanent magnetic materials and with total coil area for electromagnets. For an analysis of magnetic torque, see Judy and Muller[9]. The overall system size must accommodate the magnets (permanent or electric coils) used to generate the external magnetic field. Therefore, the motivations for this type of scanner are usually cost reduction through batch fabrication and lower power consumption rather than miniaturization. In addition, magnetic actuation also has the advantage of operating in liquid environment.

Magnetic field can be induced by electrical current. This current-induced magnetic field can generate the force exerted on the moving magnetic material[9]. While the moving structure is not made of magnetic material, electromagnetic coils can be integrated on the movable part, making it quasi-magnetic by current injection[10]. Figure 10.3 shows an example of the electromagnetic scanner that is being used in table-top confocal microscopes.

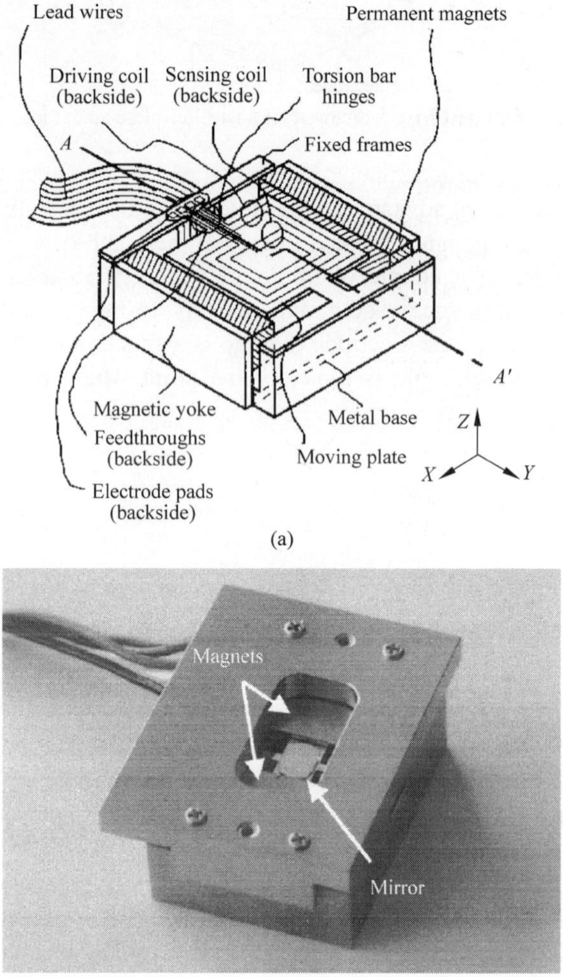

(b)

Figure 10.3 (a) Schematic and (b) Photograph of packaged electromagnetic 1D scanner in[10] (© 2003 IEEE Picture courtesy of Hiroshi Miyajima reprinted from [10] with permission)

10.1.3 Thermal Actuation

Thermal actuation utilizes the mismatch between thermal expansion coefficients of materials, which yields structural stress after temperature change. The structure deforms due to this built-in stress. The major advantage of thermal actuation is its ability to generate large deflection. Electrical current injection is one of the common mechanisms used for heating up the structure. However, temperature control and power consumption are issues for this type of actuators. Electro-thermal micromirror has been reported[11, 12].

10.1.4 Other Actuation Mechanisms

Piezoelectric material deforms when electric field is applied across the structure. This property can be used as the driving mechanism in MEMS and NEMS. 2D scanning mirror actuated by PZT has been demonstrated[13].

Magnetostrictive materials transduce or convert magnetic energy to mechanical energy and vice versa. As a magnetostrictive material is magnetized, it strains; i.e., it exhibits a change in length per unit length. Conversely, if an external force produces a strain in a magnetostrictive material, the material's magnetic state will change. This bidirectional coupling between the magnetic and mechanical states of a magnetostrictive material provides a transduction capability that is used for both actuation and sensing devices. It has the advantage of remote actuation by magnetic fields. 2D optical scanners using magnetostrictive actuators have been reported[14].

10.2 Applications

10.2.1 Display, Imaging, and Microscopy

10.2.1.1 Texas Instruments' Digital Micromirror Device (DMD)

The Digital Micromirror Device (DMD) was started in 1977 by Texas Instruments. The research initially focused on deformable mirror device. Eventually DMD became the preferred device. TI uses Digital Light Processing™ (DLP) to denote optical projection dislays enabled by the DMD technologies[15].

The DMD is a reflective spatial light modulator (SLM) which consists of millions of digitally actuated micromirrors. Each micromirror is controlled by underlying complementary metal-oxide-semiconductor (CMOS) electronics, as shown in Fig. 10.4. A DMD panel's micromirrors are mounted on tiny hinges that enable them to tilt either toward the light source (ON) or away from it (OFF) depending on the state of the static random access memory (SRAM) cell below each micromirror. The SRAM voltage is applied to the address electrodes, creating an electrostatic attraction to rotate the mirror to one side or the other. The details of operating principle, design, fabrication, and testing of DMD have been discussed in Ref. [16] and will not be repeated here.

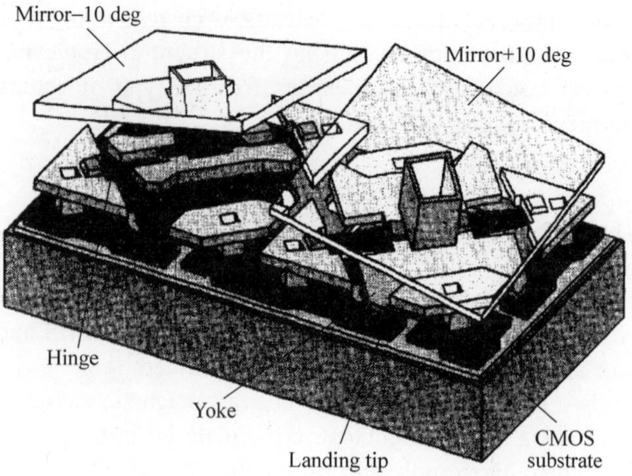

Figure 10.4 Schematic drawing of two DMD mirror with underlying structures (Picture courtesy of TI. Reprinted from [15] with permission) (© 1997 SPIE)

In projection systems, brightness and contrast are the two primary attributes that impact the quality of the projected image. The DMD has a light modulator efficiency in the range of 65%, and enables the contrast ratio ranging from 1000∶1 to 2000∶1. Because of the fast switching speed of the mirror, it enables the DLP to have a wide range of applications in video and data projectors, HDTVs, and digital cinema. Though DMD was developed primarily for projection display applications, there are some interesting non-display applications. An emerging new DMD application is volumetric display, in which DMDs are used to render three-dimensional images that appear to float in space without the use of encumbering stereo glasses or headsets. It is realized by using 3 DMD's to create 3D images viewed without glasses or headsets [17,18]. DMD also has applications in maskless lithography and telecom. Traditionally, the patterns in lithographic applications, such as print settings, printed circuit board (PCB) and semiconductor manufacturing, have been provided via film or photomasks. However, it is desirable to write on the UV-sensitive photoresist directly from digital files. DMD can be used as the spatial light modulator to generate the designed patterns [19]. Analog micromirror arrays with either tilting or piston motions are needed for maskless lithography in sub-100 nm semiconductor manufacturing. Smaller mirror size is also desired.

DMD also has interesting applications in microscopy and spectroscopy. In microscopy application, DMD is used as a spatial modulator of the incident or collected light rays. It replaces the aperture in conventional optical system. The DMD can shape or scan either the illumination or collection aperture of an optical microscope thus to provide a dynamic optical system that can switch between bright field, dark field and confocal microscopy [20−23]. In spectroscopy application, the DMD is used as an adaptive slit selectively routing the wavelength of interest to a detector. It can also chop the light reaching the detector to improve detection sensitivity [24].

10.2.1.2 GLV Display

The schematic of the Grating Light Valve™ (GLV™) shown in Fig. 10.5 is a diffractive spatial light modulator[25]. The GLV device switches and modulates light intensities via diffraction rather than by reflection. Distinct advantages of GLV include high speed modulation, fine gray-scale attenuation, and scalability to small pixel dimensions.

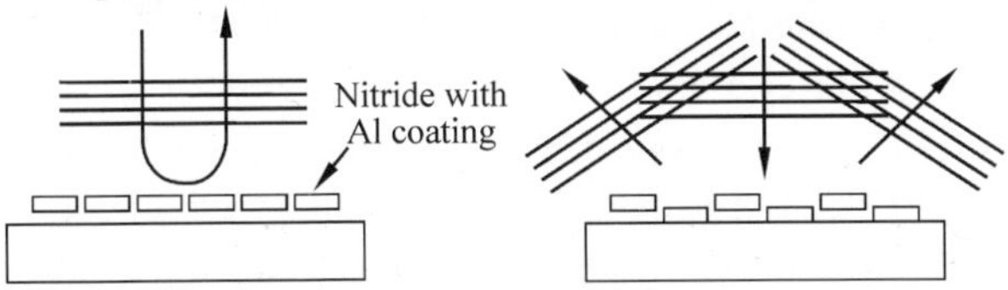

Figure 10.5 Cross-section of the GLV device showing the specular and diffraction states (after [25]) (Source: 'Chapter 7-Free–Space Optical MEMS,'/MEMS: A Practical guide to design, analysis, and applications/, William Andrew, Inc., and Springer-Verlag GmbH & Co.KG, 2006: reprinted with permission: @2006 Elsevier.)

The GLV device is built on a silicon wafer and is comprised of many parallel micro-ribbons that are suspended over an air gap above the substrate. Alternative rows of ribbons can be pulled down approximately 1/4 wavelength to crcatc diffraction effects on incident light by applying an electrical bias between the ribbons and the substrate. When all the ribbons are in the same plane, the GLV device acts like a mirror and incident light is specularly reflected from their surfaces. When alternate ribbons are deflected, the angular direction in which incident light is steered from the GLV device is dictated by the spatial frequency of the diffraction grating formed by the ribbons. As this spatial frequency is determined by the photolithographic mask used to form the GLV device in the fabrication process, the departure angles can be very accurately controlled, which is useful for optical switching applications. The linear deflection of the GLV is quite small, with no physical contact between moving elements, thus avoiding wear and tear as well as stiction problems. There are also no physical boundaries between the pixel elements in the GLV array. When using as a spatial light modulator in imaging applications, this seamless characteristic provides a virtual 100% fill-factor in the image.

The ribbons are made of suspended silicon nitride films with aluminum coating to increase its reflectivity. The silicon nitride film is under tensile stress to make them optically flat. The tension also reduces the risk of stiction and increases their frequency response. The GLV materials are compatible with standard CMOS foundry processes. GLV can be made into 1D or 2D arrays for projection display applications. Today, the GLV technology is used in high resolution display, digital imaging systems and WDM telecommunications [25].

10.2.1.3 Microvision Retinal Display

Retinal scanning display (RSD) uses a different approach than other microdisplays. Rather than a matrix array of individual modulators or sources for each pixel as seen in liquid crystal display (LCD), organic light-emitting diodes (OLED), and DMD microdisplays, a RSD optimizes a low power light source to create a single pixel and scans this pixel with a single mirror to paint the displayed image directly onto the viewers' retina. With this technique, it offers high spatial and color resolution and very high luminance. There are several papers that provide an overview of the RSD and its applications [26, 27]. This technology is developed by Microvision. The RSD systems typically employ two uniaxial scanners or one biaxial scanner. The combinations of two actuation mechanisms, electrostatic (for faster response) and electromagnetic (for larger force) actuations, were selected for a MEMS scanner[28]. Figure 10.6 shows a schematic drawing of the MEMS scanner.

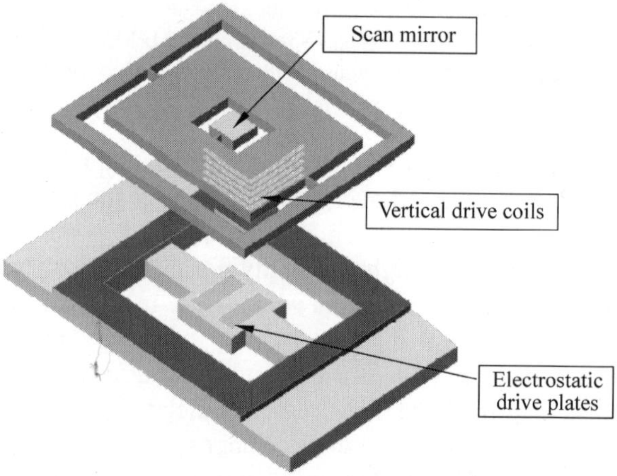

Figure 10.6 Schematic drawing of the electrostatic/electromagnetic scanner (© 2002 SPIE Picture courtesy of H. Urey. Reprinted from[28] with permission)

The horizontal scanner (the inner mirror axis) is operated at resonance by using electrostatic actuation. The drive plates are located on the substrate below the MEMS mirror. The inner mirror axis has a resonant frequency of 19.5 kHz with the maximum mechanical scan excursion of 13.4 degrees. The vertical scanner (the outer mirror axis) is magnetically driven by means of permanent magnets within the package and cols with a 60 Hz linear ramp waveform. The magnets need to be positioned carefully and provided sufficient magnetic field to move the mirror to the desired angular deflection. The maximum mechanical scan excursion of 9.6 degrees is achieved on the outer mirror axis. The devices are bulk micromachined utilizing both wet and dry anisotropic etching, and electroplating is used to form electromagnetic coils on the outer frame. These scanners must be stiff to remain flat and withstand the forces developed in resonant scanning mode. The dynamic mirror flatness of 0.05 microns rms is measured. The scanners also incorporate piezoresistive strain sensors on the torsion flexures for closed loop control. The scanners are designed to meet SVGA video standards that require 800×600 resolution. The design, fabrication, and control details of this bi-axial scanner can be found in ref. [28] and [29].

10.2.1.4 OCT (Optical Coherence Tomography) and Confocal Microscopy

Confocal microscopy offers several advantages over conventional optical microscopy, including controllable depth of field, the elimination of image degrading out-of-focus information, and the ability to collect serial optical sections from thick specimens. The concept was introduced by Marvin Minsky in the 1950's when he was a postdoctoral fellow at Harvard University. In 1957, he patented his 'double-focusing stage-scanning microscope'[30], which is the basis for the confocal microscope.

In a conventional widefield microscope, the entire specimen is bathed in light from a mercury or xenon source, and the image can be viewed directly by eye or projected onto an image capture device or photographic film. In contrast, the method of image formation in a confocal microscope is fundamentally different. Figure 10.7 shows the schematic drawing of the confocal imaging system. Illumination is achieved by scanning one or more focused beams of light, usually from a laser or arc-discharge source, across the specimen. This point of illumination is brought to focus in the specimen by the objective lens, and laterally scanned using some form of scanning device under computer control. The sequences of points of light from the specimen are detected by a photomultiplier tube (PMT) through a pinhole (or in some cases, a slit), and the output from the PMT is built into an image and displayed by the computer.

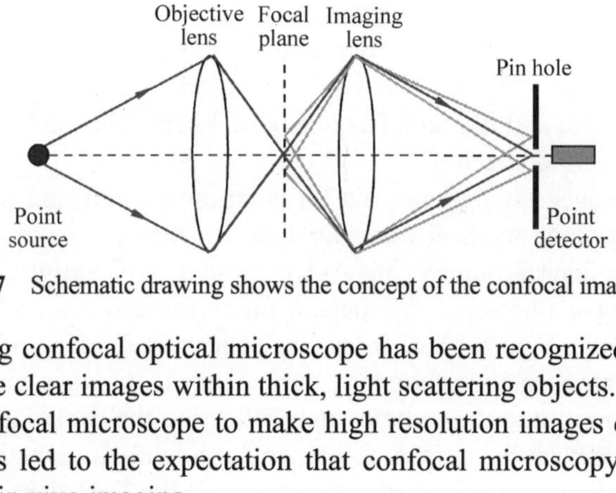

Figure 10.7 Schematic drawing shows the concept of the confocal imaging system

The scanning confocal optical microscope has been recognized for its unique ability to create clear images within thick, light scattering objects. This capability allows the confocal microscope to make high resolution images of living, intact tissues and has led to the expectation that confocal microscopy has become a useful tool for in vivo imaging.

The first compact rectangle shape endoscope (2.5 mm(w) × 6.5 mm(l) × 1.2 mm(t)) based on MEMS scanning mirrors was developed by D. L. Dickensheets et al. [31]. The architecture of the micromachined confocal optical scanning microscope, illustrated in Fig. 10.8, consists of a single-mode optical fiber for illumination and detection, two cascaded one-dimensional bulk micromachined electrostatic scanners with orthogonal axes of rotation to accomplish *x*-*y* scanning, and a binary transmission grating as the objective lens. The maximum mechanical scanned angle is ±2 degrees. The resonant frequencies of both axes are over 1 kHz.

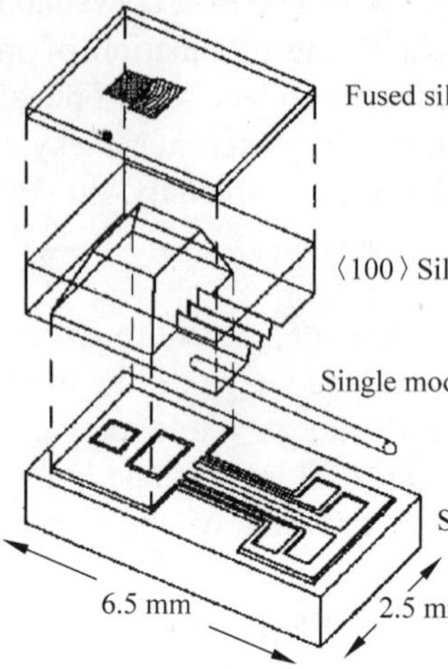

Figure 10.8 Schematic drawing of the endoscope head showing various components of the assembly (© 1998 IEEE Picture courtesy of D. L. Dickensheets. Reprint from[31] with permission)

Later, Olympus Optical Company, Ltd. developed the first commercialized cylindrical shape confocal endoscope with an outside diameter of 3.3 mm and a length of 8 mm [32]. Figure 10.9 shows a cross sectional drawing of the endoscope head. The scanner is a gimbal based two-dimensional bulk micromachined electrostatic scanner [33] with the size of 1.3 mm × 1.3 mm. The mirror has a diameter of 500 μm and resonant frequency of 3 kHz. The maximum mechanical scanned angle is ±3 degrees.

Optical coherence tomography (OCT) is an optical imaging technique that is analogous to B-mode medical ultrasound except that it uses low coherent light (low coherence interferometry) instead of sound. Generally, OCT imaging is performed using a fiber-optic Michelson interferometer with a low-coherence-length light source. Figure 10.10 shows the schematic drawing of the Michelson-type interferometer. One interferometer arm contains a modular probe that focuses and scans the light onto the sample, also collecting the backscattered light. The second interferometer arm is a reference path with a translating mirror or scanning delay line. Optical interference between the light from the sample and reference paths occurs only when the distance traveled by the light in both paths matches to within the coherence length of the light [34]. The interference fringes are detected and demodulated to produce a measurement of the magnitude and echo delay time of light backscattered from structures inside the tissue. The obtained data constitute a 2D map of the backscattering or back reflection from internal architectural morphology and cellular structures in the tissue. Image formation is obtained by performing repeated axial measurement at different transverse positions as the optical beam is scanned across the tissue.

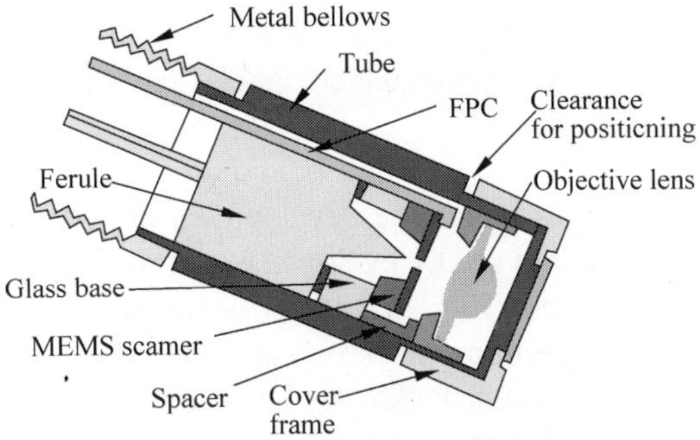

Figure 10.9 A cross sectional drawing of the endoscope head (© 2003 IEEE Picture courtesy of Olympus Optical Company, Ltd. Print from [32] with permission) (see color figure at the end of this book)

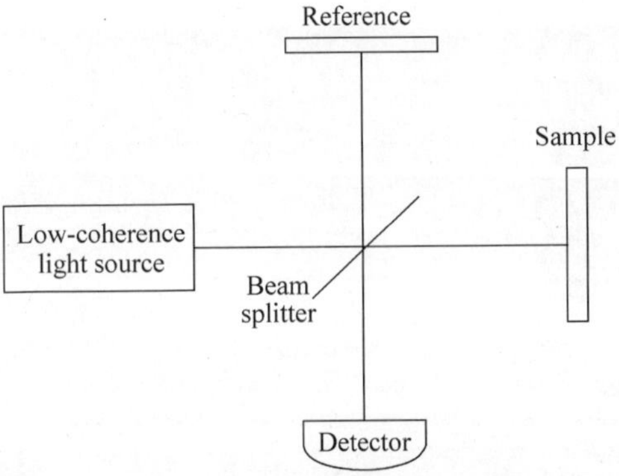

Figure 10.10 Schematic drawing of a michelson-type interferometer

Since its initial use for imaging the transparent and low-scattering tissue of eyes [35], OCT has become attractive for noninvasive medical imaging. Real time in vivo endoscope based OCT imaging systems [36] of the gastrointestinal and respiratory tracts of a rabbit was demonstrated with an axial resolution of 10 μm and sensitivity of more than 100 dB. The catheter-endoscope consisted of an encased, rotating hollow cable carrying a single-mode optical fiber.

Previously, the scanning element inside the OCT probe head used in clinical trials used a spinning reflective element to scan the light beam across the tissue in circumferential scan geometry [36, 37]. This scanning arrangement allowed the imaging probe to view only targets that were directly adjacent to the probe. The scan control of the probe was located outside the probe (proximal actuation). This type of actuation had some drawbacks such as a non-uniform and slow speed scanning. In addition, by applying a rotating torque on the optical fiber, it could cause unwanted polarization effects that could degrade image quality.

By using MEMS scanning mirrors, the scan control is located inside the probe head (distal actuation) which can reduce the complexity of scan control and potentially have a lower cost. Because of the scanner's miniature size, the overall diameter of the endoscope can be very small (< 5 mm). High speed and large transverse scan can also be achieved which enables real time in vivo imaging and large field of view, respectively.

Therefore, a need for compact, robust, and low cost scanning devices for endoscopic applications has fueled the development of MEMS scanning mirrors for OCT applications. Y. Pan et al. developed a one-axis electro-thermal CMOS MEMS scanner for endoscopic OCT [38]. The mirror size is 1 mm by 1 mm. The SEM is shown in Fig. 10.11. The bimorph beams are composed of a 0.7 μm thick Al layer coated on top of a 1.2 μm thick SiO_2 layer embedded with a 0.2 μm thick poly-Si layer. The mirror is coated with a 0.7 μm thick Al layer, and the underlying 40 μm thick single-crystal Si makes the mirror flat. The maximum optical scanned angle is 37 degrees (only in one direction).

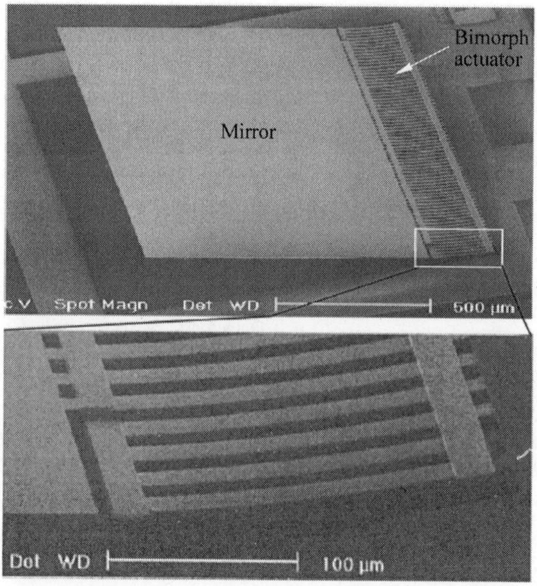

Figure 10.11 SEM of electro-thermal CMOS MEMS scanner with an inset shows a close-up view of the bending springs (© 2003 OSA Picture courtesy of T. Xie Reprint from[38] with permission)

Later, J. M. Zara et. al. fabricated one dimensional bulk micromachined MEMS scanner [39]. The scanner (1.5 mm long) is a gold-plated silicon mirror bonded on a 30 μm thick flat polyimide surface (2 mm long and 2.5 mm wide) that pivots on 3 μm thick polyimide torsion hinges. Figure 10.12 shows an optical image of the endoscope head. The actuator used to tilt the mirror, the integrated force array (IFA), is a network of hundreds of thousands of micrometer-scale deformable capacitors. The capacitive cells contract because of the presence of electrostatic forces produced by a differential voltage applied across the capacitor electrodes.

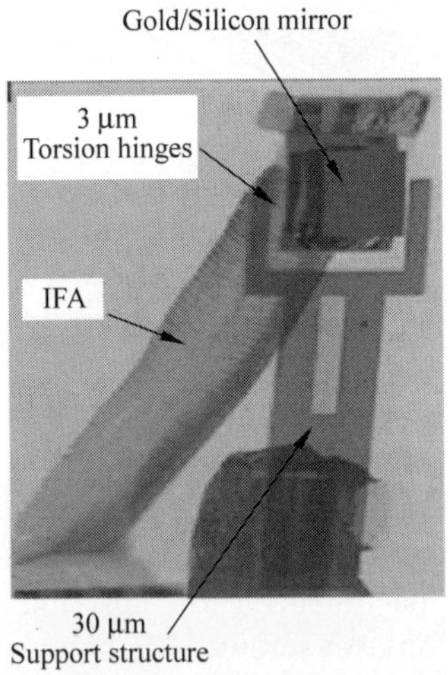

Figure 10.12 An optical image of the endoscope head (© 2003 OSA Picture courtesy of J. M. Zara. Reprint from [39] with permission)

Researchers at MIT and UCLA [40] have developed the first two-dimensional endoscopic MEMS scanner for high resolution optical coherence tomography. The two dimensional scanner with angular vertical comb actuators (AVC) is fabricated by using surface and bulk micromachining techniques [41]. The angular vertical comb (AVC) bank actuators provide high-angle scanning at low applied voltage [42]. The combination of both fabrication techniques enable high actuation force, large flat micromirrors, flexible electrical interconnect, and tightly-controlled spring constants [42, 43]. The schematic drawing of the 2D scanner is illustrated in Fig. 10.13. A single-crystalline silicon (SCS) micromirror is suspended inside a gimbal frame by a pair of polysilicon torsion springs. The gimbal frame is supported by two pairs of polysilicon torsion springs. The four electrically isolated torsion beams also provide three independent voltages ($V_1 - V_3$) to inner gimbals and mirrors. The torsion spring is 345 μm long, 10 μm or 12 μm wide, and 3.5 μm thick. The scanner has 8 comb banks with 10 movable fingers each. The finger is 4.6 μm wide, 242 μm long, and 35 μm thick. The gap spacing between comb fingers is

4.4 μm. The mirror is 1,000 μm in diameter and 35 μm thick. The AVC banks are fabricated on SCS. The movable and fixed comb banks are completely self-aligned [42].

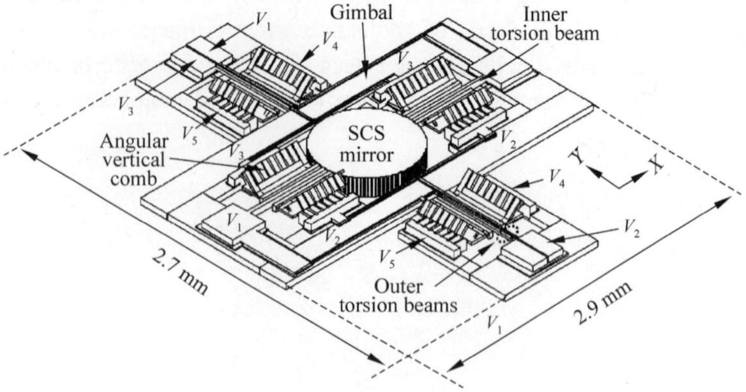

Figure 10.13 Schematic of 2D AVC gimbal scanner (© 2005 IEEE Reprinted from[42] with permission)

The endoscope head is 5 mm in diameter and 2.5 cm long, which is compatible with requirements for minimally invasive endoscopic procedures. Figure 10.14 shows a schematic of the fiber coupled MEMS scanning endoscope. The compact aluminum housing can be machined for low cost and allows precise adjustment of optical alignment using tiny set screws. The optics consists of a graded-index fiber collimator followed by an anti-reflection coated achromatic focusing lens producing a beam diameter (2w) of ~ 12 μm [40].

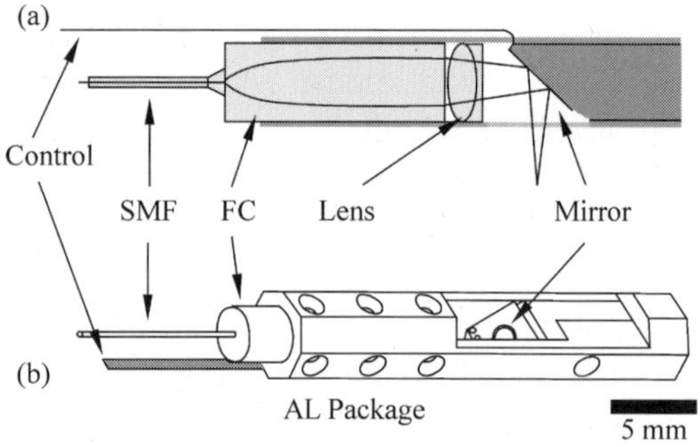

Figure 10.14 Schematic drawing of the endoscope head (© 2007 OSA Reprinted from[40] with permission)

The 2D MEMS scanner is mounted at 45 degrees and directs the beam orthogonal to the endoscope axis in a side-scanning configuration similar to those typically used for endoscopic OCT procedures. Post-objective scanning eliminates off-axis optical aberration encountered with pre-objective scanning. Figure 10.15 shows a scanning electron micrograph of the 2D AVC scanner located inside the endoscope package. The large 1 mm diameter mirror allows high-numerical-aperture focusing.

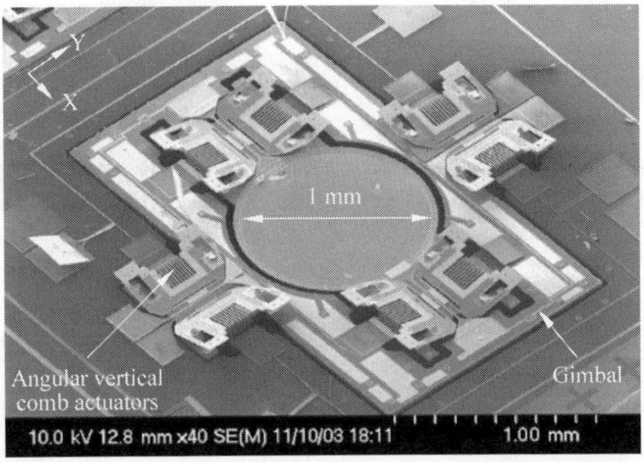

Figure 10.15 SEM of 2D AVC gimbal scanner (© 2005 IEEE Reprinted from[42] with permission)

10.2.1.5 Adaptive Optics

Optical MEMS devices offer a promising alternative to piezoelectric and other deformable mirror types used in adaptive optics applications. Adaptive optics refers to optical systems which adapt to compensate for undesirable optical effects introduced by the medium between the object and its image. It provides a means of compensating for these effects, leading to appreciably sharper images approaching the theoretical diffraction limit. These efforts include wave front correction, aberration cancellation, etc. With sharper images comes an additional gain in contrast—for astronomy, where light levels are often very low, this means fainter objects can be detected and studied[44, 45]. Other interesting applications using adaptive optics are confocal microscopy[46], adaptive laser wavefront correction [47], cryogenic adaptive optics[48], and human vision[49]. Several groups have developed MEMS deformable mirrors.

A two-level silicon surface micromachining approach was employed by researchers at Boston University to produce MEMS deformable mirrors using an original architecture described in Fig. 10.16 [50, 51]. The kilo-pixel spatial light modulator is made up of 1024 individually addressable surface-normal electrostatic actuators with center posts that support individual optical mirror segments. Each electrostatic actuator consists of a silicon membrane anchored to the substrate on two sides above a silicon electrode. These devices were manufactured at a commercial MEMS foundry [52]. A post centered on each actuator supports a 338 μm × 338 μm × 3 μm optically coated mirror segment. The spatial light modulator has an aperture of 10 mm, an actuator stroke of 2 μm, and a position repeatability of 3 nm. The resonant frequency of the mirror is around 60 kHz.

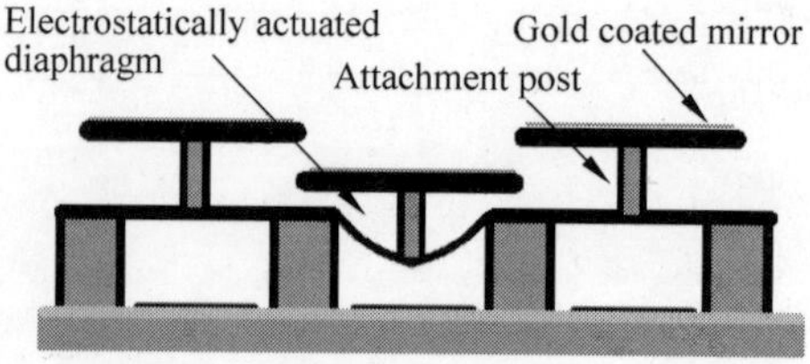

Figure 10.16 Schematic cross section of a gold coated spatial light modulator with a central deflected actuator (© 2004 TRF Picture courtesy of Thomas G. Bifano. Reprinted from [50] with permission)

Researchers at Jet Propulsion Laboratory (JPL) developed a single crystal silicon continuous membrane deformable mirror with underlying piezoelectric unimorph actuators as shown in Fig. 10.17 [53]. A PZT unimorph actuator of 2.5 mm in diameter with optimized PZT/Si thickness and design showed a deflection of 5 μm at 50 V. Deformable mirrors consisting of 10 μm thick single-crystal silicon membranes supported by 4×4 actuator arrays were fabricated and optically characterized. An assembled deformable mirror showed a stroke of 2.5 μm at 50 V with a resonant frequency of 42 kHz.

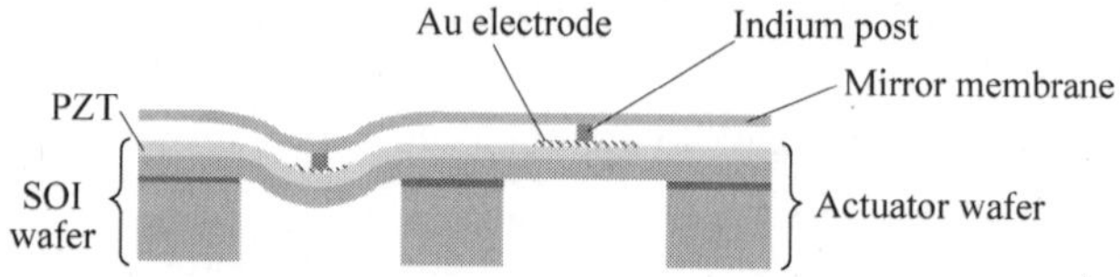

Figure 10.17 Cross-sectional drawing of the deformable mirror (© 2006 IEEE Reprinted from[53] with permission)

10.2.1.6 Other Examples

Researchers at UCLA fabricated two cascaded, two-dimensional scanners for optical surveying instruments[54]. Currently, cascaded acousto-optic deflectors are used in optical surveying instruments. MEMS scanners are very attractive candidates for replacing those scanners. They offer many advantages, including lower power consumption, smaller size, and potentially lower cost. Optical surveying instruments require mirrors with reasonably large scan range ($\sim \pm 6°$ mechanical), high resonant frequencies (5 – 10 kHz for fast axis), large radius of curvature, and low supply voltage (< 50 V).

Typically, the target, a highly reflective surface consisting of corner cubes, is located several meters to several kilometers away from the instruments. The required scanning angular range is relatively small, in the order of a few degrees. The angular divergence of the measurement laser beam is typically a few milliradians or narrower. Hence, the target search system needs to resolve several tens of spots in the entire scan range. Raster scanning has been used because the laser beam needs to search the entire area within the field of view to find the target. A combination of fast and slow scanning scanners has been employed. Both are fabricated by using bulk micromachining techniques with 25 μm thick SOI wafer. The fast scanner has a circular shape and achieves a resonant frequency of 7.5 kHz with the maximum mechanical rotation in DC mode of ±3.2 degrees. The slow scanner has an elongated circular shape and achieves a resonant frequency of 1.2 kHz with the maximum mechanical rotation in DC mode of ±0.74 degree. Figure 10.18 shows the SEM of the fast mirror.

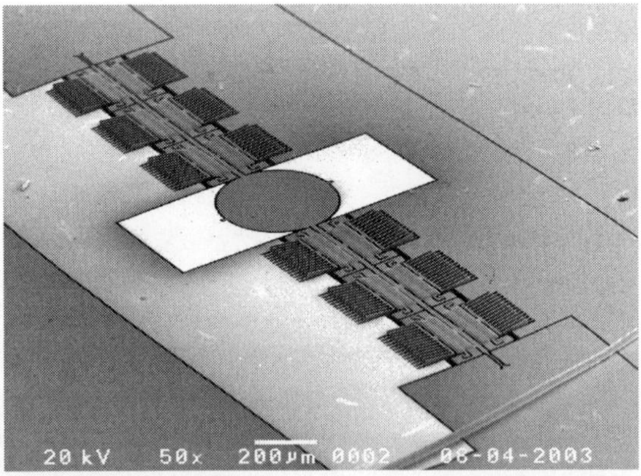

Figure 10.18 SEM of the fast mirror (© 2004 IEEE Reprinted from [54] with permission)

10.2.2 Optical Communication

10.2.2.1 2D MEMS Switch

The two-dimensional (2D) MEMS optical switch is basically an optical crossbar switch with N^2 micromirrors that can selectively reflect the optical beams to orthogonal output ports or pass them to the following mirrors. They are often referred to as '2D switches' because the optical beams are switched in a 2D plane. This is in contrast to the 3D switch (discussed in the following section) in which the optical beams are steered in 3D space. A generic configuration of the 2D switch is shown in Fig. 10.19. The core of the switch is an $N \times N$ array of micromirrors for a switch with N input and N output fibers. The optical beams are collimated to reduce diffraction loss. The micromirrors intersect the optical beams at 45°, and can be switched in and out of the optical beam path. The micromirrors are 'digital' that is, they are either in the optical beam path (ON) or completely out of the beam path. When the mirror in the i-th row and j-th column (M_{ij}) is ON, the *i*-th input beam is switched to the *j*-th output fiber. Generally, only one micromirror in a column or a row is ON. Thus during operation of an N_xN switch, only N micromirrors are in the ON position while the rest of the micromirrors are in the OFF position. MEMS 2D switches were first reported by Toshiyoshi and Fujita [55]. Several different ways of switching micromirrors have been reported, including rotating, sliding, chopping, and flipping motions. The switches are usually actuated by electrostatic, electromagnetic, or piezoelectric mechanisms.

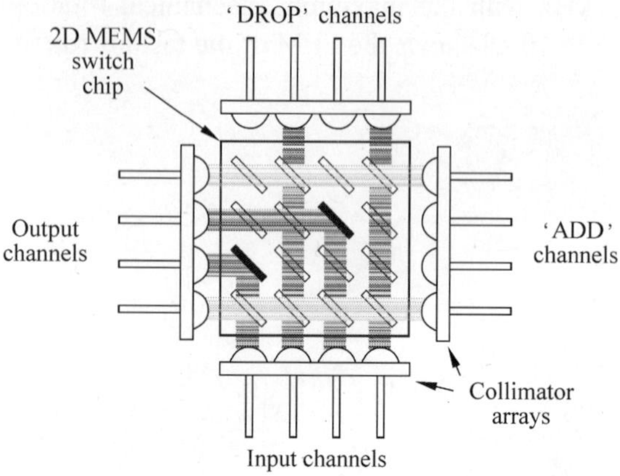

Figure 10.19 Schematic of 2D MEMS optical switches (see color figure at the end of this book) (Source: 'Chapter 7-Free –Space Optical MEMS,'/MEMS: A Practical guide to design, analysis, and applications/, William Andrew, Inc., and Springer-Verlag GmbH & Co. KG, 2006: reprinted with permission: @2006 Elsevier.)

2D switches using various types of flip-up (or pop-up) mirrors have been reported [55 – 58]. They are realized by either the bulk- [55] or the surface-micromachining [56] technology, or a combination of both [57]. The mirror lies in the plane of the substrate during OFF state and pops up in the ON state. Since the mirror angle is changing continuously during switching, a common challenge for this type of switch is the reproducibility of mirror angle. This is a critical issue as the mirror angles and their uniformity play a critical role in the performance and the scalability of 2D switches. The reproducibility of mirror angles over switching cycles determines the repeatability of insertion loss.

The first 2D matrix optical switch reported by Toshiyoshi and Fujita employed pop-up-type switching elements, as shown in Fig. 10.20 [55]. It consists of two bonded wafers. The mirrors are suspended by a pair of torsion beams in the plane of the top wafer. The biasing electrodes are fabricated on the bottom wafer. When a voltage is applied between the mirror and the bottom electrode, the mirror rotates downward by 90° by electrostatic actuation. The mirror angle in the ON (down) state is controlled by a stopper on the bottom wafer. Since the mirror angle is defined by the relative positions of two wafers, precise alignment is necessary to achieve accurate and uniform mirror angles. A single-chip electrostatic pop-up mirror has recently been reported [59]. The actuation and mechanical stopper are realized between a back-flap and a vertical trench etched in the silicon substrate. The angular accuracy and uniformity of their mirrors depend on the etched sidewall profile and the lithographic alignment accuracy.

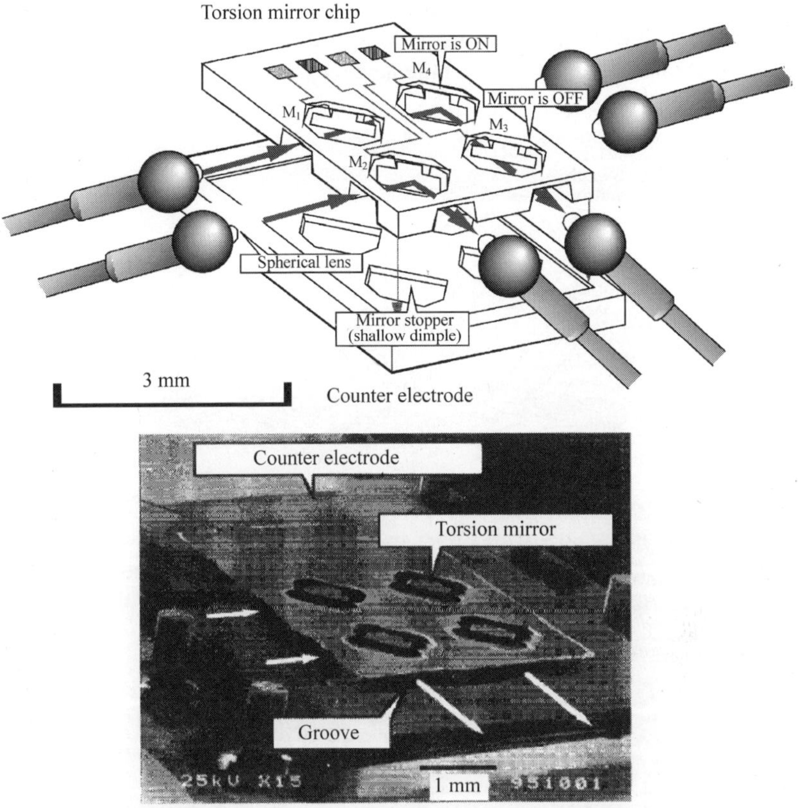

Figure 10.20 Schematic and SEM of bulk-micromachined 2D switch with free-rotating torsion mirrors (© 1996 IEEE Pictures courtesy of Hiroshi Toshiyoshi. Reprinted from [55] with permission) (see color figure at the end of this book)

AT&T Labs has reported surface-micromachined 2D switches with free-rotating hinged mirrors [56, 60, 61]. The schematic drawing and the SEM of the switch are shown in Fig. 10.21. It is fabricated using the MUMPs process. The mirror is pivoted on the substrate by microhinges. A pair of pushrods are used to convert in-plane translations into out-of-plane rotations of the mirrors. The switch is powered by scratch drive actuators [62]. Though scratch drive actuators do not move at high speed, fast switching time is achieved (700 μsec) because only a short traveling distance (22 μm) is needed for the mirror to reach 90°. The free-rotating microhinges have an inherent 0.75-μm clearance between the hinge pins and the staples, which could result in large variations in mirror angles. Using improved design and mechanical stoppers that are insensitive to lithographic misalignment during fabrication, mirror angular repeatability of better than 0.1° has been experimentally demonstrated [63]. The mirror flatness was improved by using a multi-layer structure with phosphosilicate glass (PSG) sandwiched between two polysilicon layers. The largest switch size demonstrated is 8×8 due to the foundry-imposed chip-size limits of 1 cm×1 cm. One of the potential issues is the constant tear and wear of the free-rotating hinges and actuators. This might affect the reliability of the switch and the accuracy and uniformity of mirror angles over many switching cycles.

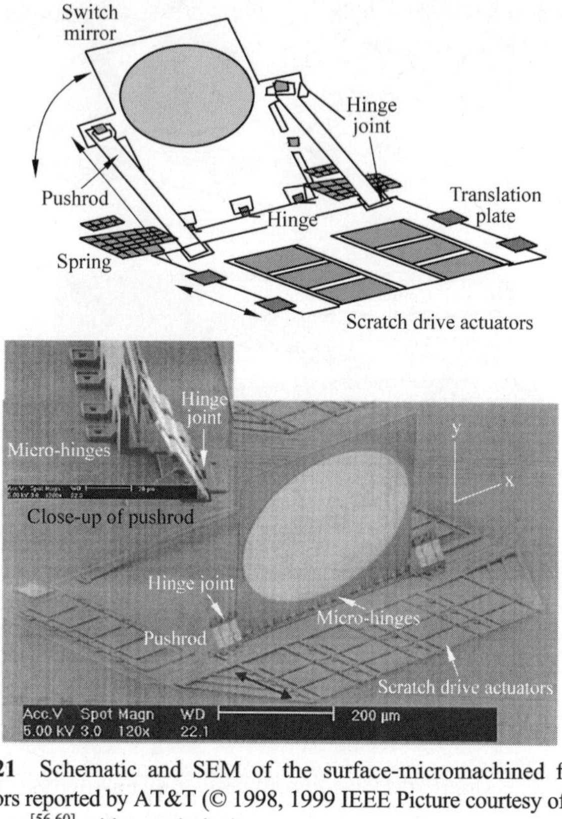

Figure 10.21 Schematic and SEM of the surface-micromachined free-rotating hinged mirrors reported by AT&T (© 1998, 1999 IEEE Picture courtesy of Lih Y. Lin. Reprinted from[56,60] with permission)

On the other hand, the 'chopper type' 2D switch employs a vertical mirror whose height can be changed by MEMS actuators [64, 65]. The mirror angle is fixed during switching, and excellent repeatability of insertion loss has been reported. Figure 10.22 shows the schematic diagram of OMM's 2D switch [64]. The mirror is assembled vertically at the tip of a long actuator plate. The plate is tilted upward and fixed by microlatches to raise the mirror height. Large traveling distance is achieved by extending the actuator arm. Several hundred microns displacement can be achieved with this configuration. The switch is actuated electrostatically by applying a voltage between the actuator plate and a bottom electrode on the substrate. The mirror moves in the vertical direction and the mirror angle is maintained at 90° during the entire switching cycle. The actuator is basically a gap-closing actuator. A mechanical stopper defines the lower position of the mirror. OMM employs a curved landing bar with a single point contact to minimize stiction and increase reliability (see Fig. 10.22). More than 100 million cycles have been demonstrated with repeatable mirror angle and performance. The landing bar also provides a cushion that helps reduce mirror ringing and improves switching time. They have demonstrated a switching time of 12 ms using a square-wave driving voltage without pre-shaping the waveform. OMM's switch is fabricated with polysilicon surface-micromachining technology. The mirrors and the actuators are batch-assembled into the 3D structures. Figure 10.23(a) shows the SEM of a 16×16 switch. The distribution of mirror angles is shown in Fig. 10.23(b). The uniformity is better than ±0.1 degrees for 256 mirrors. The switch is hermetically packaged with optical collimator arrays. Extensive testing has been performed for the packaged switches. The maximum insertion loss is less than 3.1 dB and the crosstalk is less than –50 dB. Loss variation over the wavelength range of 1,280 – 1,650 nm range is less than 1 dB. Return loss is greater than 50 dB, and maximum temperature variation is <1 dB over a temperature range of 0℃ – 60℃. Polarization dependent loss (PDL) is <0.4 dB and polarization mode dispersion (PMD) is <0.08 ps. Vibration tests showed <0.2 dB change under operation, and 3 axis shock tests confirm no change of operational characteristics under 200 G.

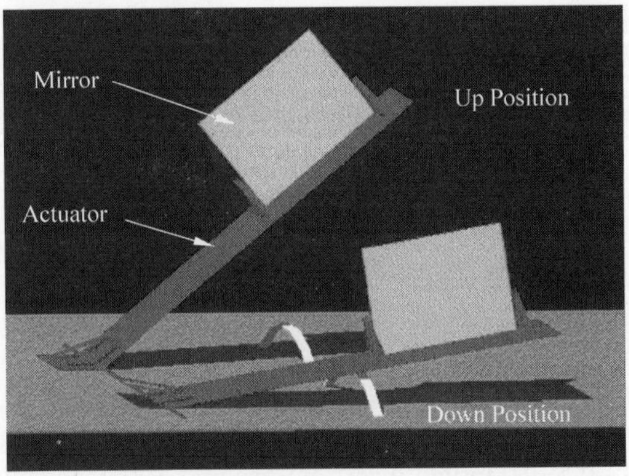

Figure 10.22 Schematic of a switching element in OMM's 2D switch (© 2002 OSA Picture courtesy of Li Fan. Reprinted from [64] with permission)

The structure of a 2×2 2D MEMS switch can eventually be simplified so that it requires only one single micromirror between two pairs of orthogonal fibers. A simple, elegant solution for 2×2 switches is using SOI-based Optical MEMS [66, 67].

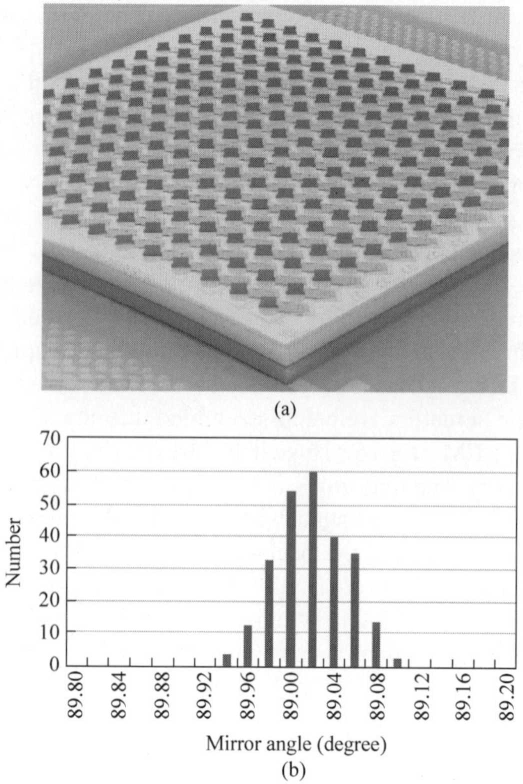

Figure 10.23 (a) SEM of OMM's 16x16 switch. (b) Measured distribution of mirror angles for the 16×16 switch (© 2002 OSA Picture courtesy of Li Fan. Reprinted from[64] with permission)

The schematic and SEM picture (only fiber grooves shown) of the 2×2 switch are shown in Fig. 10.24. Electrostatic comb drive actuators and vertical micromirrors are fabricated on 75 μm SOI wafers. The mirrors can be coated with metal by angle evaporation to increase their reflectivity. The most critical part of the process is the etching of thin (< 2 μm) vertical mirrors with smooth sidewalls. Thin vertical mirror is required for such a 2×2 switch because the offset of the reflected optical beams from the opposite sides of the mirror caused by the finite thickness of the mirror will introduce additional optical loss. The Institute of Microtechnology (IMT) at Neuchatel has perfected the mirror etching technology by DRIE [68]. A surface roughness of 36 nm has been achieved. The switch has excellent optical performance: 0.3 – 0.5 dB optical insertion loss and 500 μsec switching time, and very low polarization dependence [67].

10.2.2.2 3D MEMS Switch

Telecommunication switches with large port count have been the main driver for the two-axis scanner in the past few years. With increasing number of wavelengths

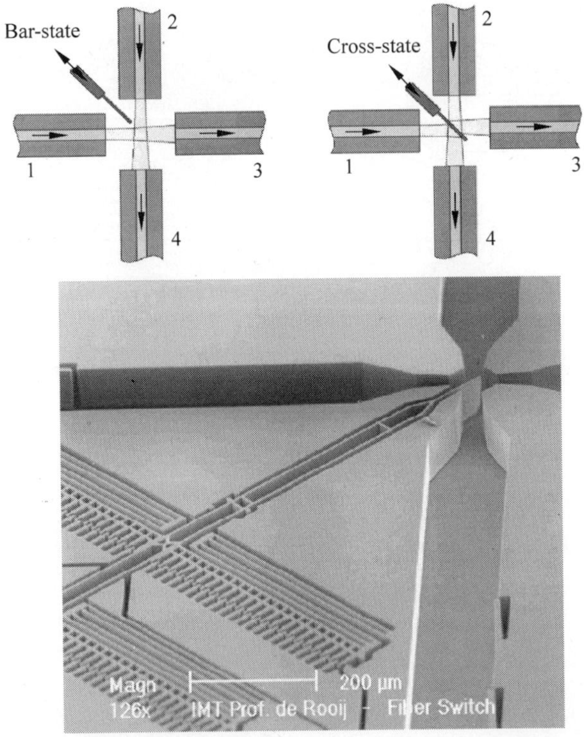

Figure 10.24 Schematic and SEM of 2×2 switch fabricated by SOI MEMS (© 1999 IEEE Picture courtesy of Nico de Rooij. Reprinted from [66] with permission)

and bandwidth in dense wavelength-division-multiplexed (DWDM) networks, there is a need for optical crossconnect (OXC) with large port count [69–71]. The dual axis analog scanning capability is the key for these applications since each mirror associated with the input fiber array can point to any mirror associated with the output fiber array. Implementation of $N \times N$ OXC using two arrays of N analog scanners is illustrated in Fig. 10.25. Even though the implementations may vary, we can always conceptually refer to this illustration. This switch is often called a 3D MEMS switch because the optical beams propagate in three-dimensional space. 3D switch is a better choice for larger port-count $N \times N$ OXC compared to 2D switch as the number of mirrors for a 2D switch is N^2. Since the optical path length is independent of the switch configuration, uniform optical insertion loss (2 – 3 dB) can be achieved. The port count of the 3D MEMS switch is limited by the size and flatness of the micromirrors, as well as their scan angle and fill factor. For a complete discussion of scaling laws for MEMS free space optical switches, see Syms[71]. For large port count (approaching 1,000×1,000), single crystal micromirror scanners are necessary to achieve large mirror size with required flatness.

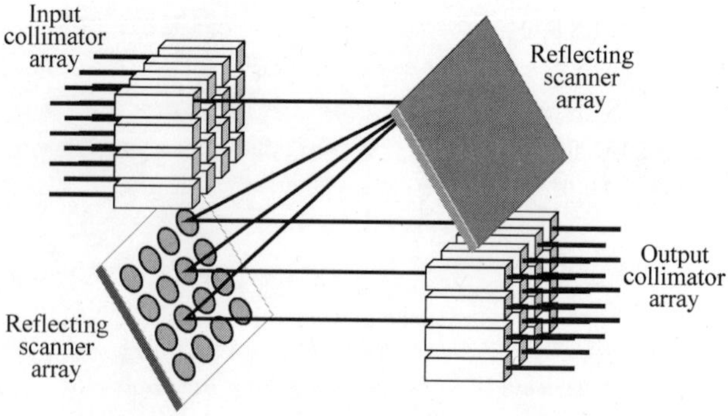

Figure 10.25 Configuration for 3D optical switch ($N \times N$) with $2N$ analog scanning mirrors (Source: 'Chapter 7-Free–Space Optical MEMS,'/MEMS: A Practical guide to design, analysis, and applications/, William Andrew, Inc., and Springer-Verlag GmbH & Co.KG, 2006: reprinted with permission: @2006 Elsevier.)

During the telecom boom, several companies invested heavily to develop 3D MEMS OXC's. These companies include (but not limited to) Lucent Technologies[69, 71–77], Corning[78–80], NTT Corp.[81, 82], Fujitsu Laboratories, Ltd.[83, 84], Tellium, Inc.[85–87], and Calient Networks[88]. They have demonstrated various designs of two-axis scanners, which are the key components of these 3D MEMS switches.

Lucent technologies employed a self-assembly technique which was driven by the residual stress in deposited thin films (Cr/Au on polysilicon) to raise two-axis polysilicon scanners (500 μm mirror diameter) to a fixed position 50 μm above the substrate [89, 90]. The scanning electron micrograph (SEM) is shown in Fig. 10.26. Two-axis scanning is achieved by electrostatic force between the mirror and the

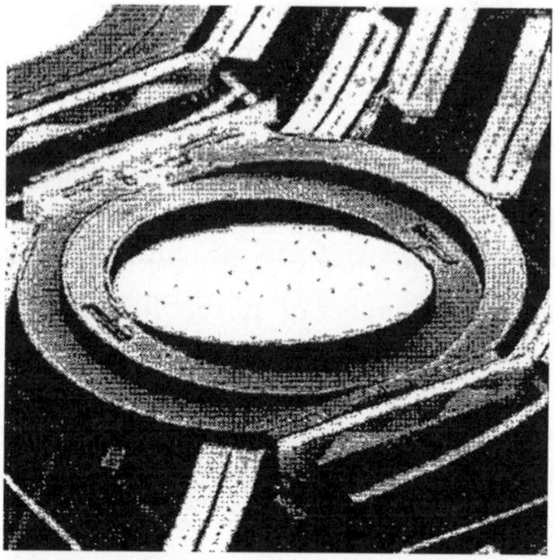

Figure 10.26 SEM photo of the surface-micromachined 2-axis scanners of Lucent Technologies (Reprinted from[92] with permission; © 2002 OSA)

quadrant electrodes on the substrate. SCS two-axis scanner with long-term stability and high shock resistance has also been developed by Lucent Technologies for 3D MEMS switches [91]. SCS is used to improve the mirror flatness. The long-term stability is achieved by the removal of exposed dielectric to avoid electrostatic charge-up effect (Fig. 10.27). The scanning angle is 7 degrees.

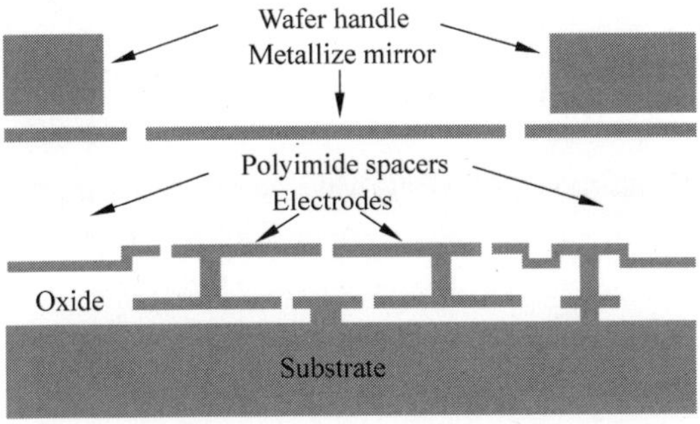

Figure 10.27 Cross section of the SCS two-axis mirror developed by Lucent Technolgies (© 2003 OSA Picture courtesy of A. Gasparya. Reprinted from [91] with permission)

NTT Corp. has reported a two-axis micromirror array driven by terraced electrodes. The mirrors and the electrodes are fabricated on separate chips and then bonded together. The use of terraced electrodes reduces the applied voltage by half, compared to regular parallel-plate-driven mirrors. The mirror is tilted by 5.4 degree at a maximum of 75 V. The resonant frequency of the fabricated mirror is approximately 1 kHz [81].

The two-axis scanner developed by Fujitsu Laboratories, Ltd. is based on vertical comb-drive actuators. SOI with 100 μm top and bottom (substrate) silicon layers has been used to fabricate the device [83]. The top silicon is for the moving comb fingers and mirror while the fixed fingers are made of the bottom silicon. V-shape torsion springs are adopted to improve the lateral stability which is a critical issue in comb-drive actuators. Rotation angle of ±5 degrees has been achieved with 60 V driving voltage.

Tellium, Inc. has demonstrated an electrostatic parallel-plate actuated two-axis scanner, featuring nonlinear, servo closed-loop control [85]. The nonlinear, servo closed-loop control enables the mirror to operate beyond the pull-in angle. Figure 10.28 shows the comparison of switching under open-loop and closed-loop operation. The closed-loop angular trajectory can exceed the pull-in (snap-down) angle and shows no overshoot. They have also developed a two-axis micromirror driven by both sidewall and bottom electrodes [87]. The addition of sidewall electrodes improves the linearity of the DC transfer characteristic. The mirror with sidewall electrodes also exhibits a larger scan angle than that driven by merely bottom electrodes (Fig. 10.29).

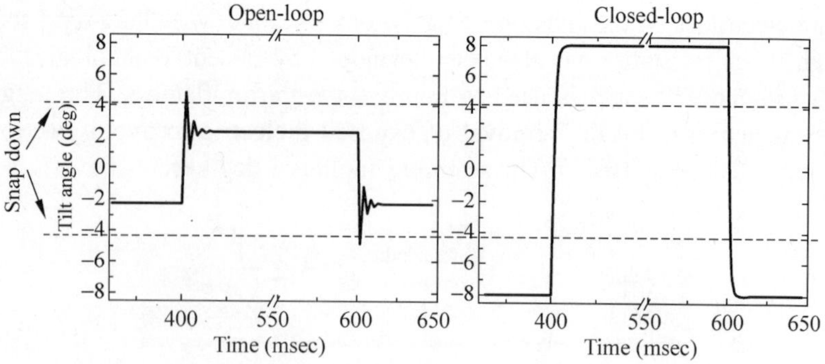

Figure 10.28 Comparison of switching under open-loop and closed-loop operation (© 2005 IEEE Picture courtesy of P.B.Chu Reprinted from[85] with permission)

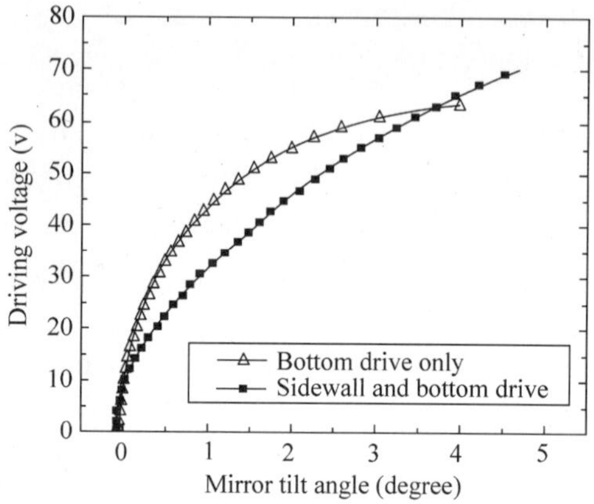

Figure 10.29 DC transfer characteristics of the two-axis scanner of Tellium, Inc., with and without sidewall driving (© 2004 IEEE Picture courtesy of C. Pu. Reprinted from[87] with permission)

10.2.2.3 Wavelength-Selective Switches (WSS)

(1) Wavelength add-drop multiplexer (WADM)

Wavelength-selective devices are important components in WDM networks and have attracted a great amount of efforts for implementation. One example is the dynamically reconfigurable wavelength add-drop multiplexer (WADM). It can be realized by placing a one-dimensional (1D) digital micromirror array in the focal plane of a grating spectrometer. The concept of the MEMS-based WADM is shown in Fig. 10.30. Light from an input optical fiber is collimated and then dispersed by a diffraction grating. The diffracted signal is focused by a lens onto the micromirror array. Each mirror corresponds to a WDM channel. The mirrors operate in bi-stable mode and the state of each micromirror decides whether its corresponding wavelength is set to THRU or ADD/DROP state.

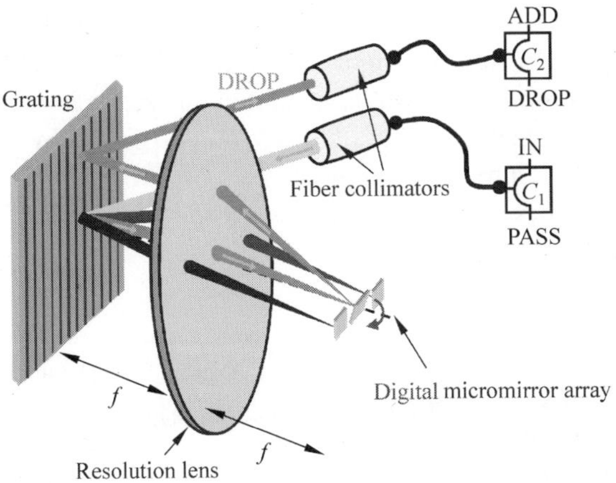

Figure 10.30 Concept of WADM (see color figure at the end of this book)

Joe Ford et al. have reported the first MEMS-based WADM [93]. The SEM of the digital micromirror is shown in Fig. 10.31. It is fabricated using the three-polysilicon layer surface-micromachining process through the MUMPs service offered by a foundry [52]. The mirror has an area of $30\times50\ \mu m^2$ and a pitch of 57 μm to match the 200 GHz WDM channel spacing. It has a pull-in angle of ±5° at 20 V bias. The mirror is driven by AC voltage to avoid electrostatic charging. The fiber-to-fiber optical insertion loss is from 5 – 8 dB, and the switching contrast ranges from 32 – 47 dB. Switching time is 20 μsec. A quarter-wave plate is employed in the actual apparatus. It rotates the polarization of the reflected beam by 90° to minimize the polarization dependent loss (0.2 dB).

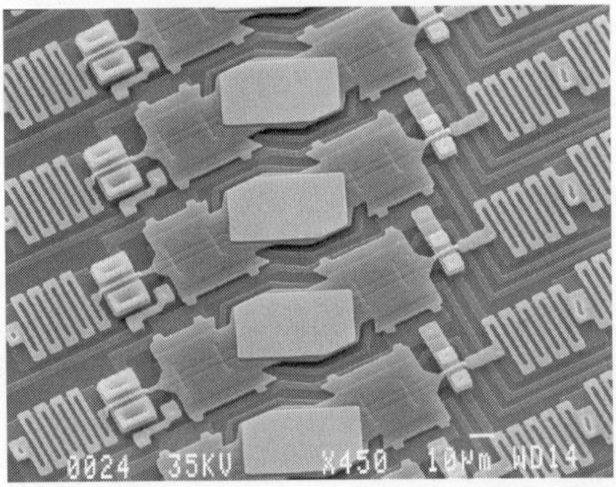

Figure 10.31 SEM of digital micromirror array used in WADM (© 1999 IEEE Picture courtesy of Joe Ford. Reprinted from [93] with permission)

(2) $1\times N$ wavelength-selective switches (WSS)

The WADM concept can be extended to switches with more than one output port, as illustrated in Fig. 10.32. This is generally called $1\times N$ wavelength-selective switch (WSS), multi-port WADM, or WDM routers [94–96]. To address more than two input/output ports, the micromirrors need to have more than two discrete angles. Analog micromirrors with large continuous scan range enable individual wavelengths to be directed to any of the N output fibers. In addition, high fill factor is desired to minimize the gaps between WDM channels. The mirror size is usually several times larger than the focused spot size of the Gaussian beam to attain a flat spectral shape for the passband ('flat-top' spectral response).

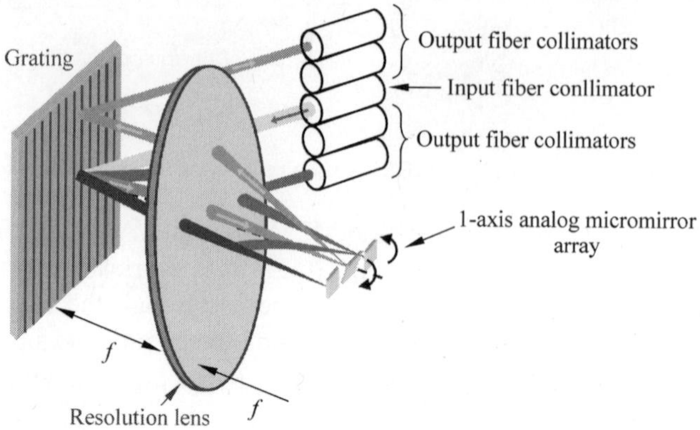

Figure 10.32 Concept of multi-port WADM or $1 \times N$ wavelength-selective switch (WSS) (© 2004 IEEE Reprinted from [96] with permission)

UCLA has developed a low-voltage analog micromirror array for $1 \times N$ wavelength-selective switches [97]. The schematic and the SEM of the micromirror are shown in Fig. 10.33. The actuator and the torsion spring are completely covered by the mirror; so high fill factor is achieved along the array direction. The vertical comb-drive actuator provides much larger torque than the parallel-plate actuator. Furthermore, the maximum scan angle will not be limited by the pull-in instability inherent in parallel plate actuators. The analog micromirror arrays are fabricated using the Sandia Ultra-planar, Multi-level MEMS Technology-5 (SUMMiT-V) [98] foundry process, which is a five-polysilicon layer surface-micromachining process with two chemical-mechanical planarization (CMP) steps. The first CMP process separates the lower and upper vertical combs so that narrow finger gap spacing (0.5 μm) can be achieved. Significantly higher force density (160 times larger than that of comparable parallel plate actuators) is attained since it is inversely proportional to the square of the gap spacing. This enables the design to achieve low operating voltage and large scan angle, while still maintaining a high resonant frequency. The second CMP process produces a smooth, flat micromirror surface without reflecting the mechanical structures underneath the mirror. The maximum mechanical scan angle of $\pm 6.1°$ is achieved at 8.8 V actuation voltage for 1 μm gap spacing. For 0.5 μm gap spacing, the actuation voltage is as low as 6 V.

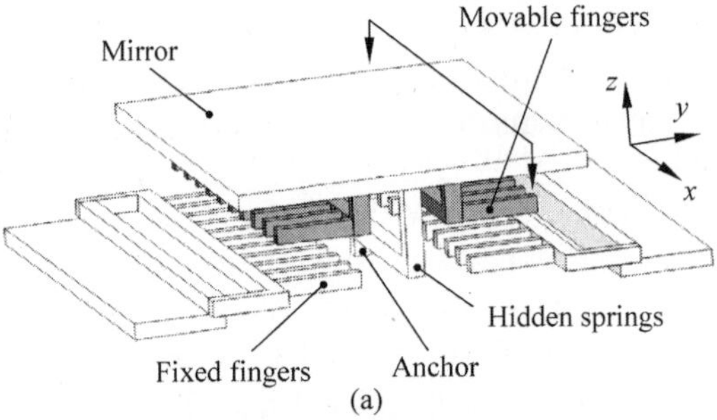

(b)

Figure 10.33 (a) Schematic (Reprinted from [97] with permission; © 2004 IEEE) and (b) SEM photo of the analog micromirror with hidden vertical comb drive actuators (photo taken by David Scharf ©; Reprinted from [96] with permission)

Lucent Technologies was the first to report the full system-level performance of the 1×4 wavelength-selective switch with 128 WDM channels at 50 GHz spacing [94]. The optical setup for the Lucent's switch is shown in Fig. 10.34. The fibers are first imaged onto a common spot by a magnification of 3*x*. A resolution lens and an 1,100 gr/mm grating provide the necessary spatial dispersion. Using a

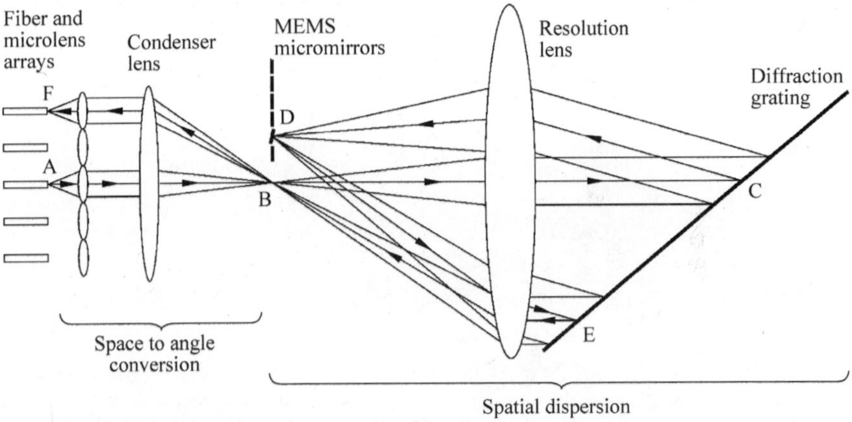

Figure 10.34 Schematic of the optical system for wavelength-selective 1×4 switch (© 2002 OSA Picture courtesy of Dan M. Marom. Reprinted from [94] with permission)

micromirror with $\pm 8°$ at 115 V made on an SOI wafer, a flat-top spectral response and an optical insertion loss of 3 – 5 dB are attained. Their modified system was reported later on [99] and new mirrors have been developed to match the requirement of the improved system [100, 101]. UCLA and JDS-U have also demonstrated the system performance of their 1×4 WSS's [95, 96]. Corning IntelliSense Corp. has reported an electromagnetically actuated micromirror array for this application [102].

(3) $1 \times N^2$ Wavelength-selective switches (WSS)

The maximum port count of the reported $1 \times N$ WSS is 4, which is limited by optical diffraction. A larger port count ($N > 10$) is desirable in telecommunication. The number of port count can be readily increased from $N - N^2$ by simply using a 2D collimator array. 2D beam steering mechanism has to be developed and can eventually be accomplished by a two-axis MEMS mirror array, which replaces the one-axis micromirror array at the focal plane (Fig. 10.35). UCLA has reported a two-axis analog micromirror array with high fill factor (96%), which is achieved by hiding the springs and actuators underneath the mirrors [103]. The device is electro-statically actuated by terraced electrodes. The terraced-electrode actuator utilizes parallel-plate-like driving mechanism. However, it reduces the actuation voltage without compromising the maximum rotation angle. Figure10.36 shows the schematic and SEM of the two-axis micromirror. Crossbar torsion springs for two-axis rotation and four terraced electrodes are deployed underneath the mirror. The devices are fabricated using the SUMMiT-V surface micromachining process provided by Sandia National Laboratory. As mentioned previously, it has five polysilicon layers, including one nonreleasable ground layer (mmpoly0) and four structural layers (mmpoly1 to mmpoly4). The terraced electrodes are made of the bottom four polysilicon layers (mmpoly0 to mmpoly3), whereas the top polysilicon layer (mmpoly4) is designated for the mirror. In the SEM picture, half of the mirror is intentionally removed to reveal the underlying structures. Large mechanical scan angles ($\pm 4.4°$ and $\pm 3.4°$) have been achieved. The resonant

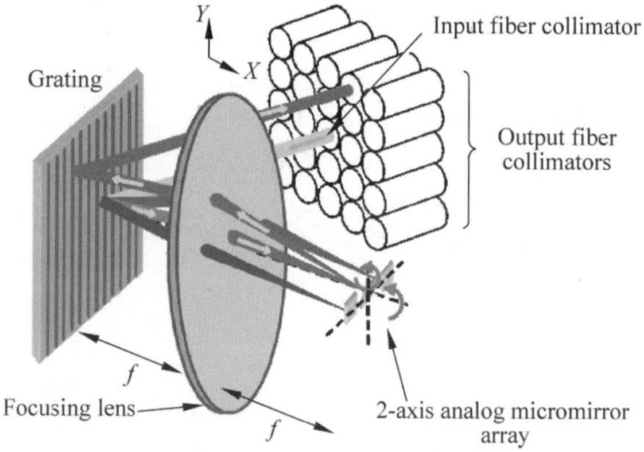

Figure 10.35 Concept of $1 \times N^2$ wavelength-selective switch (WSS) (© 2004 IEEE Reprinted from [103] with permission)

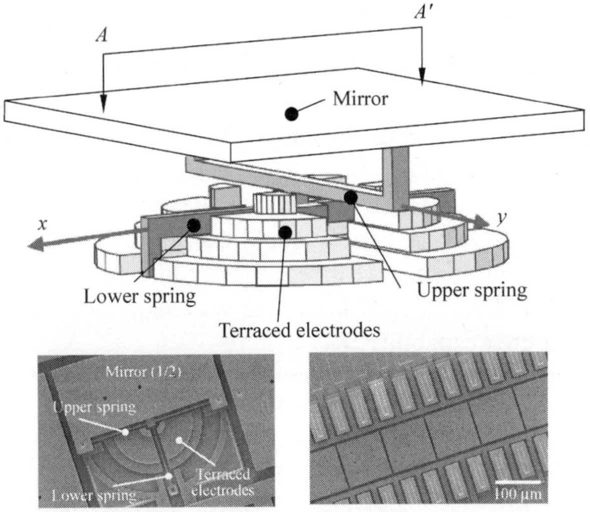

Figure 10.36 Schematic and SEM of the high fill-factor two-axis scanner (© 2004 IEEE Reprinted from [103] with permission)

frequency of the mirror is greater than 20.7 kHz. A 1×14 WSS (3×5 collimator array) was also constructed using the two-axis mirror array. The channel spacing is 50 GHz, and the fiber-to-fiber insertion is 8.2 dB.

Alternatively, the 2D beam steering mechanism for each WDM signal can be implemented by a pair of one-axis scanners with orthogonal scanning direction, instead of a monolithic two-axis scanner [104]. The cross-scanning one-axis analog micromirror arrays are arranged in a 4-f optical system (Fig. 10.37). UCLA has reported a 1×8 WSS (3×3 collimator array) using this architecture [104].

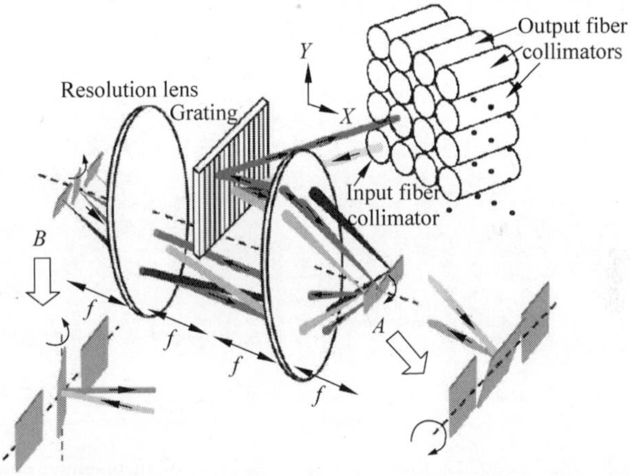

Figure 10.37 Concept of $1\times N^2$ wavelength-selective switch (WSS) using cross-scanning one-axis analog micromirror arrays arranged in a 4-f optical system. (© 2006 IEEE Reprinted from [104] with permission)

10.2.2.4 Dynamic Sspectral Eequalizers

Dynamic spectral equalizers (DSEs) are important components for advanced lightwave communication systems. Because channel power disparity in DWDM systems can result in detection errors due to the reduced optical signal-to-noise ratio and finite detector sensitivity, DSEs have been deployed to flatten the spectral profile across wavelength channels. There are two types of DSEs: ① continuous DSEs for flattening the gain of optical amplifiers [105]; and ② channelized DSEs that attenuate each optical channel independently to an extinction ratio greater than 30 dB [106]. The latter is used in optical systems with broadcast-and-select topologies and add-drop capability.

The basic optical setup for DSE is similar to that for WADM except that the digital micromirror array is replaced by a spatial modulator that creates variable reflectivity. A folded 4-*f* imaging system consisting of a lens and a grating in Littrow configuration images individual wavelengths onto micromirrors. A continuous mirror surface with individual electrodes for modulating the reflectivity offers a continuous operating wavelength spectrum with no passbands. This is useful for equalizing gain profiles of optical amplifiers. It was implemented by modifying the mechanical anti-reflection switch (MARS) [105]. The schematic cross-section and photograph of the MARS are shown in Fig. 10.38. It consists of

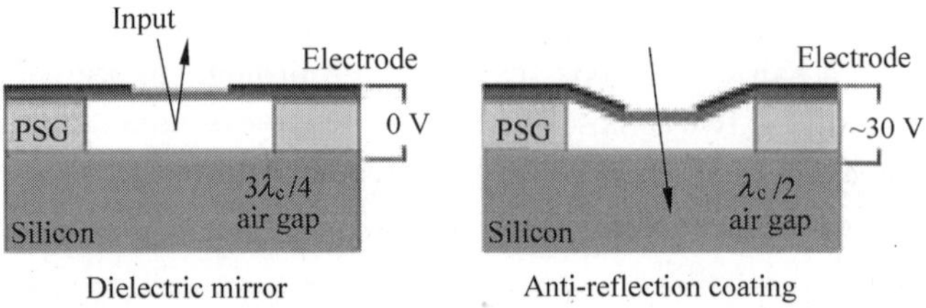

(a)

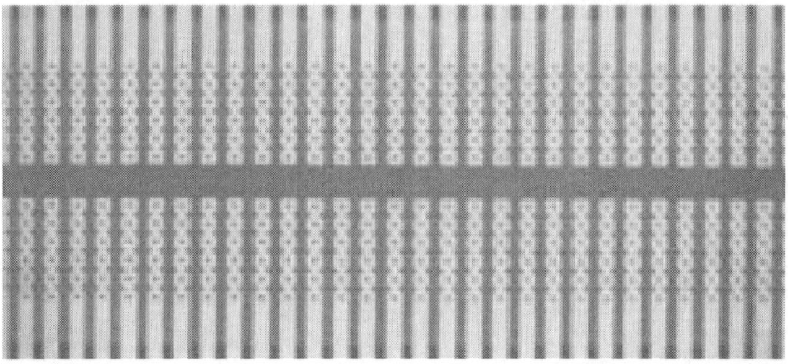

(b)

Figure 10.38 (a) Schematic illustrating the principle of mechanical anti-reflection switch (MARS). (b) Photograph of MARS variable reflectivity strip mirror (© 1998 IEEE Picture courtesy of Joe Ford. Reprinted from [105] with permission) a 1/4-λ-thick silicon nitride suspended above the silicon substrate by a 3/4-λ gap, where λ is the optical wavelength. At zero bias, MARS acts as a mirror with 70% reflectivity. When the nitride is pulled down to 1/2-λ above the substrate, the layer becomes an anti-reflection coating and reflectivity becomes nearly zero. By patterning an array of 32 electrodes spaced at a 28 μm pitch, a 32-channel equalizer is realized. The packaged component exhibits 9 dB excess loss, 20 dB dynamic range, and 10 μsec response time.

The micromirror array used in channelized DSE is very similar to those used in $1 \times N$ wavelength-selective switches. By fine-tuning the angle of the analog micromirror array, each wavelength channel can be attenuated independently. Unlike continuous DSE, large variation between adjacent channels is possible. The DSE reported by Lucent Technologies includes a 1×64 micromirror array with a pitch of 27 μm [106]. The insertion loss of the DSE is 5 dB with PDL <0.25 dB. With adjacent channels actuated, it exhibits a 3 dB pass band of >85 GHz. 40 dB attenuation is achieved. Corning IntelliSense also developed micromirror array for this application [107]. Their DSE is capable of handling 84 wavelength channels. 21 dB attenuation is observed at snap-down.

The mirror tilting direction plays an important role in the response of inter-channel regions. It has been shown that micromirrors tilting in the direction orthogonal to the array can minimize the undesirable inter-channel response [108].

10.2.2.5 Optical Attenuator

The variable optical attenuator (VOA) is a simple but important component in optical networks and subsystems. The main applications include power management of optical crossconnects or reconfigurable add-drop multiplexers, gain control of optical amplifiers, and power tuning of lasers and detectors. The advantages of MEMS-based VOAs compared with other technologies are better optical performance (large dynamic range, low optical insertion loss, low polarization, and wavelength dependent loss), lower power consumption, compact size, and low-cost batch manufacturing. These are particularly attractive in WDM networks in which a large number of VOAs in array form are required.

There are two main types of MEMS-based VOAs: the transmission type using moving shutters and the reflection type with moveable mirrors. Both can be fabricated by either bulk or surface micromachining processes. In many applications, the VOAs are actually integrated with other components such as a 2D switch or a wavelength add-drop multiplexer. The technology choice would be clear in those cases. For discrete VOA, consideration will be based on manufacturing cost, especially the packaging cost.

Bulk-micromachined VOAs using a one-step DRIE process have been reported [109]. A mirror or shutter is fabricated at the same time as the combdrive actuator on a 75 μm thick SOI wafer. U-grooves for input and output fiber are also fabricated at the same time. Both transmission and reflection VOAs have been reported [110]. The schematics and the SEM of the fabricated device are shown in Fig. 10.39. In the transmission type VOA, a shutter is moved back and forth by an electrostatic comb-drive actuator. This design is more compact and easier to package since the input and output fibers are co-linear. When the fiber ends are separated by 20 μm, the theoretical optical insertion loss is only 0.2 dB. No imaging lens or other components are needed. Index-matching liquid is used to reduce the optical insertion loss from 2.5 – 1.5 dB [109]. To reduce the back reflection, the shutters and the fiber end faces are tilted by 8°. A dynamic range of 50 dB, maximum voltage of 32 V, backreflection less than –37 dB, and a switching time of 5 msec have been achieved. The reflection type device uses a mirror that can either be tilted or translated to vary the coupling loss of reflected light. The reflective design shows better polarization dependent loss (PDL). The mean PDL for the reflective design is 0.085 dB while the shutter-based VOA has a mean PDL of 0.3 dB, both measured at 10 dB attenuation. On the other hand, the shutter-based VOA has less wavelength dependent loss.

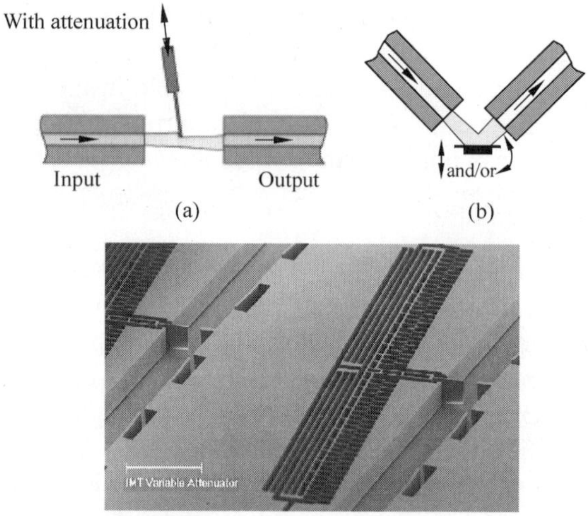

(c)

Figure 10.39 (a) Shutter type and (b) Reflection type VOAs. (c) SEM photo of shutter type VOA (© 1999 IEEE Reprinted from [109] with permission)

Researchers from University of Tokyo and Santec Corporation have reported a microelectromechanical VOA for high shock tolerance and low temperature dependence [111]. The VOA is based on the scheme of reflection type with a movable MEMS mirror. A collimating lens is inserted between the fibers and the mirror (Fig. 10.40(a)). The mirror is actuated by parallel-plate actuator and low voltage operation (5 V) is achieved. The device is made by DRIE of a 30 μm SOI with a 2 μm thick buried oxide. The schematic and SEM of the micromirror are shown in Fig. 10.40(b) and (c), respectively. The mirror is 600 μm in diameter. Despite the small rotation angle (approx. 1 degree at full contact) limited by the actuator width and buried oxide thickness, peripheral optics has been designed to attain attenuation up to –40 dB. The fluctuation of attenuation under mechanical impact of 25 G is 7 dB (at –10 dB attenuation level). No mechanical failure was observed up to 500 G.

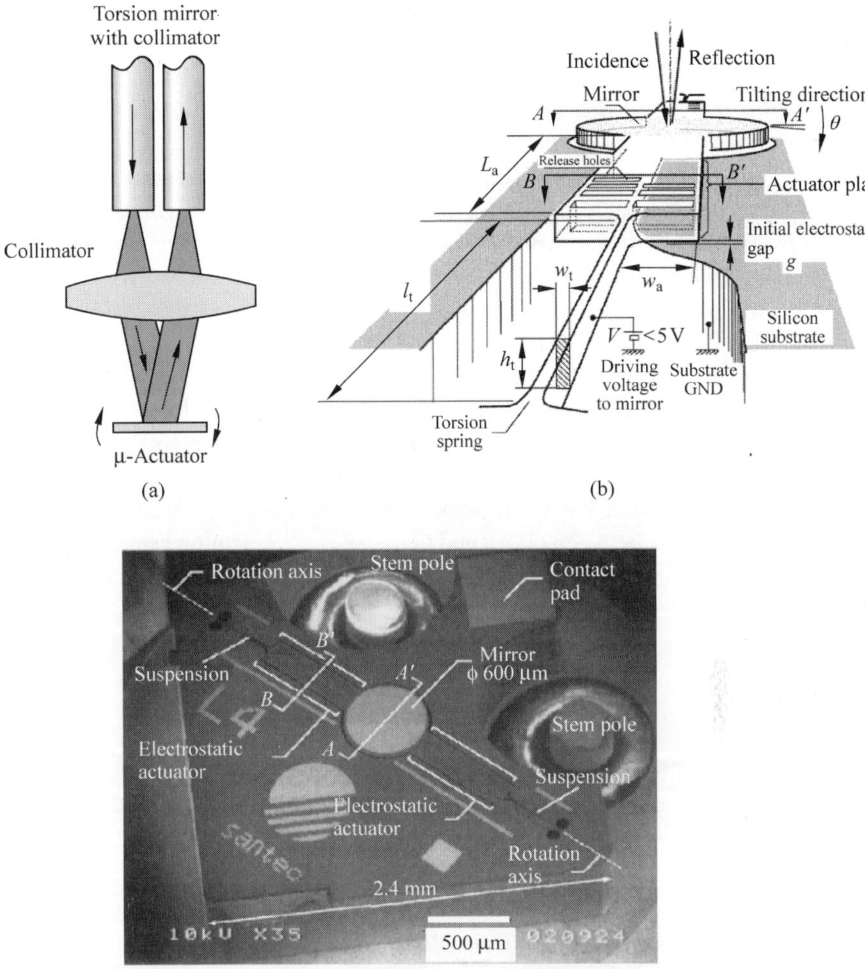

Figure 10.40 (a) Schematic of MEMS VOA in [111], (b) Schematic of the MEMS mirror, and (c) SEM of the MEMS mirror. (© 2004 IEEE Reprinted from [111] with permission)

10.2.2.6 Tunable WDM Devices

(1) Tunable filters

MEMS technologies have been widely used to implement tunable filters. MEMS-actuated tunable Fabry-Perot (FP) filters are of special interest because they offer advantages such as wide continuous tuning range (~100 nm at 1,550 nm wavelength), polarization insensitive operation, and monolithic integration of 2D arrays. Their applications include WDM networks, spectroscopy, and optical sensing systems. The filter consists of two partially transmitting mirrors separated by a variable air gap. Distributed Bragg reflector (DBR) is one of the most common structures for the mirrors. Usually the top DBR is attached to a cantilever or membrane that is actuated electrostatically or thermally. The large tuning range stems from the wide free spectral range ($\lambda_0^2/2d$, d: gap) of the short optical cavities. Figure 10.41 shows various designs of MEMS actuated FP tunable filters. Two original designs are based on electrostatically actuated cantilevers (Fig. 10.41(a)) [112] and a deformable membrane (Fig. 10.41(d)) [113, 114]. As in general gap-closing actuators, the displacement of the top DRB is restricted to 1/3 of the total gap spacing due to pull-in instability. This limits the maximum tuning range that can be achieved. Two approaches have been proposed to overcome this limit. The first is to employ an asymmetric see-saw structure suspended by torsion springs (Fig. 10.41(b)) [115]. The top DBR is attached to the long arm of the see-saw while the actuator is implemented on the short, wide arm. Using the lever effect, a small displacement on the short arm can move the top DBR over one free-spectral range without running into the pull-in limit. A tuning range of over 100 nm has been achieved. An alternative approach is to use thermal bimorph actuation (Fig. 10.41(c)). A thermally tunable filter has been demonstrated using the difference of thermal expansion coefficients between GaAs and GaAlAs [116, 117]. Tuning range of 23.2 nm has been demonstrated. To increase the finesse of the FP cavity, a concave top DBR has been proposed to form a stable cavity. As shown in (Fig. 10.41(e)), the

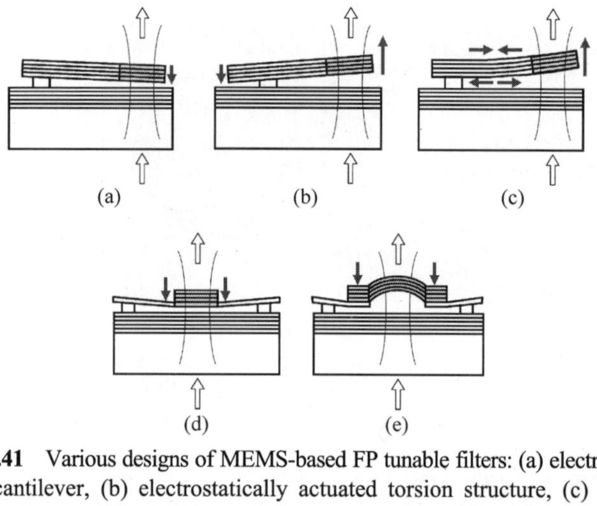

Figure 10.41 Various designs of MEMS-based FP tunable filters: (a) electrostatically actuated cantilever, (b) electrostatically actuated torsion structure, (c) thermally actuated cantilever, (d) electrostatically actuated membrane, and (e) electrostatically actuated membrane with spherical refector (Source: 'Chapter 7-Free–Space Optical MEMS,'/MEMS: A Practical guide to design, analysis, and applications/, William Andrew, Inc., and Springer-Verlag GmbH & Co.KG, 2006: reprinted with permission: @ 2006 Elsevier.)

stress gradient in the top DBR layers is controlled such that it forms a concave spherical shape when released [118, 119]. The line width of the passband was measured to be between 0.25 nm to 0.27 nm for wavelengths around 1.55 μm, which is narrower than filters with flat DBRs. Fiber-to-fiber coupling loss can also be reduced by mode matching (1.1 dB reported in [118]).

M. J. Little has particularly developed a compliant MEMS structure for a tunable Fabry-Perot filter [120]. The device is shown in Fig. 10.42. The mirrors are formed by dielectric high-reflection (HR) coating. The tunable Fabry-Perot filter is composed of three individual parts. This enables the design of the optical performance characteristics to be independent of the electrical actuation of the device. The bending element (spring) of the moving mirror is made of highly compliant material, elastomer. The Young's modulus is 200 – 300 kPa, which is 10^6 times lower than that of traditional MEMS materials (silicon, silicon nitride, etc.). The voltage required to tune over the 50 nm is 30 V.

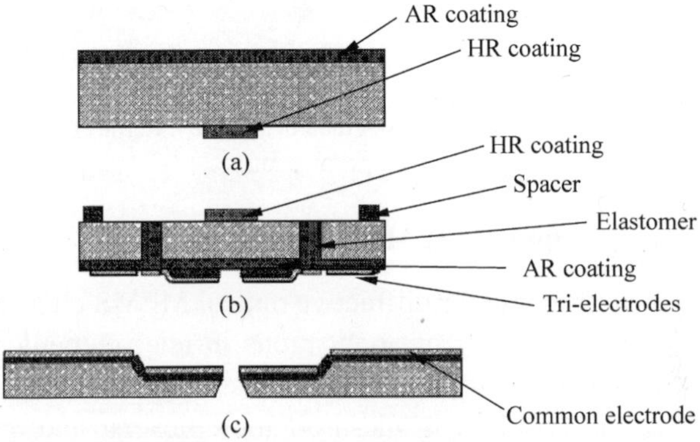

Figure 10.42 Sketch of the three individual parts that makes up the tunable filters (© 2002 OSA Reprinted from [120] with permission)

(2) Tunable lasers

Widely tunable semiconductor lasers have many uses in DWDM networks, including wavelength conversion, optical routing and multi-wavelength sparing. Micromechanical vertical cavity surface-emitting lasers (VCSEL) [121, 122] have been demonstrated as tunable lasers. The tunable VCSEL structures are very similar to those of tunable FP filters except active layers are embedded inside the FP cavity.

External cavity diode lasers (ECL) is another approach to achieve wide tenability [123, 124]. It offers significant advantages, including wide tune range, high output power, narrow line widths with good side mode suppression and accurate wavelength control. Iolon, Inc. has reported an external cavity diode lasers tuned with silicon MEMS mirror [123]. Schematic of the ECL is shown in Fig. 10.43.

The tuning of the laser wavelength is accomplished by applying a voltage to the comb elements of the MEMS actuator to produce an electrostatic force that rotates the mirror about their virtual pivot. ±2.5 degrees rotation angle with ±140 V has been used to tune up to 37 nm, almost half the 80 nm gain band width of the laser diode. An improved version of the MEMS mirror by the same team exhibits a rotation angle up to ±6 degrees at 130 V [125]

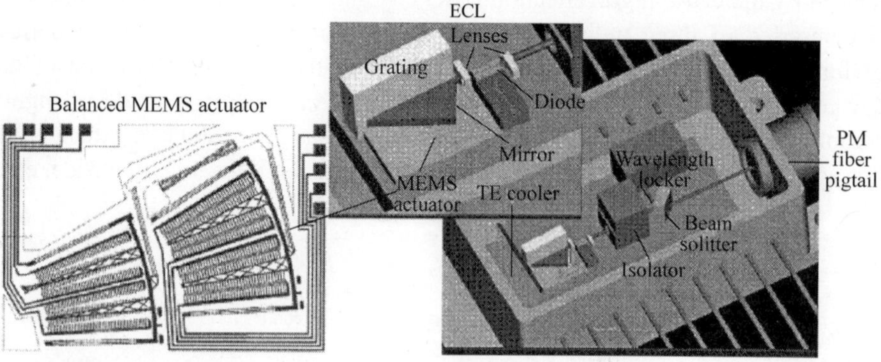

Figure 10.43 Schematic of MEMS-actuated tunable external cavity diode laser (© 2002 OSA Reprinted from [123] with permission)

10.2.2.7 Diffractive Optical MEMS

The GLV is a typical example for diffractive optical MEMS elements. In addition to display, it also has a variety of applications in telecommunication since the GLV eventually functions as an intensity modulator. Applications include dynamic spectral equalization, wavelength add-drop multiplexers, and variable optical attenuator [126, 127]. Recently, the MIT/Honeywell/Sandia National Laboratories team has developed a different MEMS-based programmable diffraction grating using polysilicon surface-micromachining technologies[128, 129]. The device, called a polychromator, consists of a parallel array of 20 μm wide mirror elements, each one of which can be individually pulled down with an analog signal. An aperiodic grating is realized with a fully programmable optical transfer function. When illuminated with white light, the spectral content at a fixed viewing angle can be controlled by adjustment of the various mirror element positions, as illustrated in Fig. 10.44. The polychromator enables a new form of correlation spectroscopy. It can synthesize the spectrum of a molecule and replace the reference cell containing that molecule in the correlation radiometers. It can also be used as a programmable spectral filter to enhance the selectivity of the detection process. The polychromator is actuated by a two-level structure that separates the top reflective optical layer from the lower actuation layer. The structure also permits a very long (1 cm) grating beam without bending. This enables large aperture programmable grating which is needed in correlation spectroscopy. The leverage bending mechanism enables the beam to move across the entire gap [130]. The device was designed for operation in the 3 – 5 μm spectral range for remote sensing.

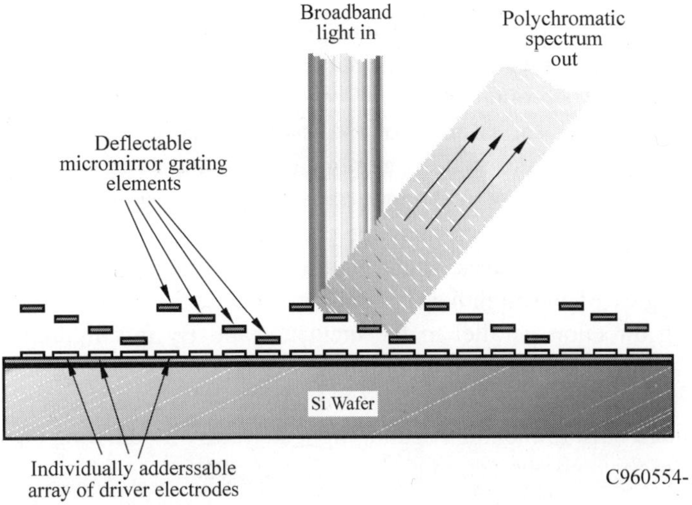

(a)

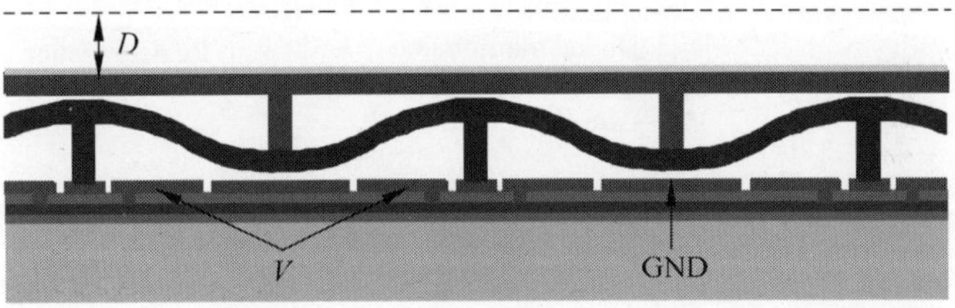

(b)

Figure 10.44 (a) Schematic cross section of the polychromator illustrating its operating principle. The spectral content of the diffracted beam can be varied in real time (~msec) for correlation spectroscopy. (b) Cross section of the polychromator (© 2001 IEEE Pictures courtesy of Steve D. Senturia and Mike Butler. Reprinted from[129] with permission)

Although the original motivation of the above mentioned programmable diffraction grating is to enable a new form of correlation spectroscopy, another application of this technology is the manipulation of individual wavelengths (or 'channels') in telecommunication networks. In telecommunication application, the polychromator is used to selectively and controllably attenuate each wavelength in a Dense Wave Division Multiplexed (DWDM). The product operates over the telecommunications C-band (wavelengths near 1.55 microns), controlling the power in 100 channels spaced 59 GHz apart over a 40 dB dynamic range [131].

Another example of application using diffractive optics is interference-based optical MEMS filter. It can be realized with diffractive micromirror arrays. O. Solgaard et al. have demonstrated a pulse shaping filter and a Gires-Tournois interferometer/filter using diffractive MEMS mirror arrays [132].

10.2.2.8 Free-Sspace Ooptical Ccommunication

The applications described in the previous Section 3.2.1 – Section 3.2.7) are mainly related to telecommunication. In this subsection, we focus on a different field, free-space optical communication. Free-space communication has attracted considerable attention for a variety of applications, such as wireless long-distance remote interrogation, inter-satellite communication, and communication between unmanned aerial vehicles (UAVs). One of the most promising optical components for these applications is the corner cube retroreflector (CCR). It consists of three orthogonal reflective surfaces. Light incident on an ideal CCR (within a proper range of angles of misalignment) is reflected back to the source with a back-propagating direction parallel to the incident path. By misaligning one of the three surfaces, the retro-reflection condition is destroyed and the incident light will be deflected to another direction. An on-off-keyed digital signal can therefore be transmitted back to the interrogating light source by modulating the CCR. The schematic of the communication is shown in Fig. 10.45.

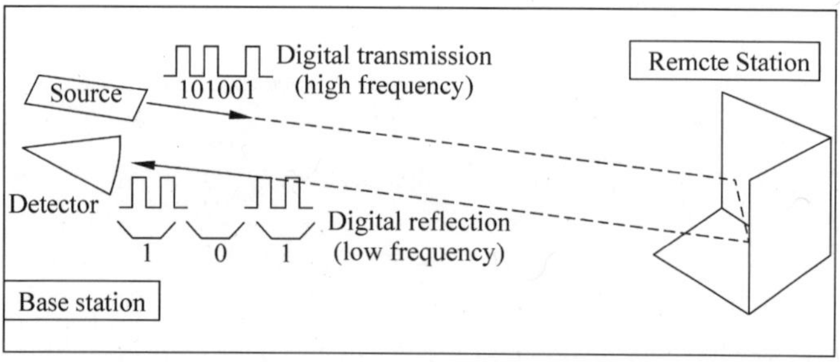

Figure 10.45 Schematic of free-space communication process. (© 1995 Elsevier B.V. Pictures courtesy of D. S. Gunawan. Reprinted from [133] with permission)

D. S. Gunawan et al. reported a MEMS-based polysilicon CCR using MUMP surface micromachining process [133]. The schematic diagram of the CCR is shown in Fig. 10.46. The bottom mirror can be tilted off the horizontal position by electrostatic actuation. Assembling of the two vertical mirrors is done by out-of-plane rotation using hinge structures. The measured optical efficiency of the CCR is 1.35% and the required actuation voltage is 8 V. The tilt angle corresponding to this voltage is measured to be 1.4 degrees, which is more than sufficient to spoil the orthogonality in the cube. An improved version of CCR using the same MUMP process was proposed by the same research group later on [134]. The efficiency is increased to 77% by coating the polysilicon mirror with gold.

Transmittance of digital signals was also demonstrated over a range of 2 meters in free space.

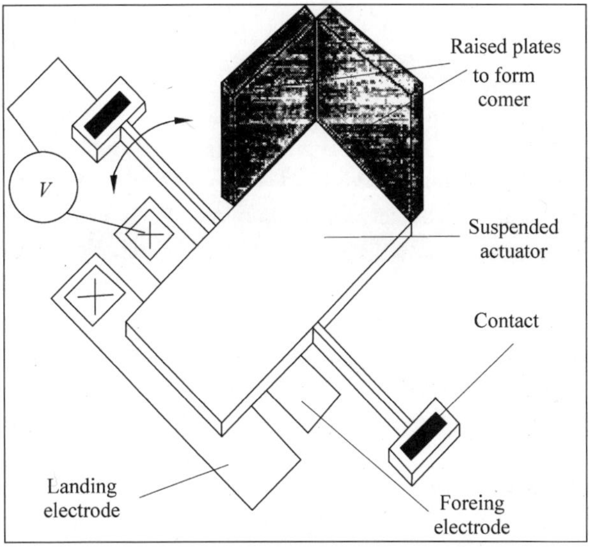

Figure 10.46 Schematic of the MEMS corner cube reflector in [133]. (© 1995 Elsevier B. V. Pictures courtesy of D. S. Gunawan. Reprinted from [133] with permission)

Polysilicon mirrors usually have relatively smaller radii of curvature than SCS mirrors. L. Zhou et al. have proposed quad MEMS CCRs fabricated with single crystal silicon [135, 136]. Each CCR comprises three mirrors fabricated from SOI wafers and is designed to facilitate manual assembly with accurate angular alignment. The SEM picture of the CCRs is shown in Fig. 10.47(a). The bottom mirror can be tilted by gap-closing actuation to spoil the retro-reflection condition. Fig. 10.47(b) shows the sequence of assembling the two vertical side mirrors and the bottom mirrors. The reflectivity of the CCRs can be modulated up to 7 KB/s by a drive voltage less than 5 V. 180 m free-space optical link has also been demonstrated using these CCRs.

CCRs combined with modulation approaches other than tilting mirrors have also been demonstrated. D. Pederson et al. integrated a grating light modulator (GLM) into a CCR [137] (Fig. 10.48). The GLM is used as the bottom mirror in the CCR and also serves as an intensity modulator. The major advantage of using GLM is its high resonant frequency (290 kHz). The switching time can be as fast as 10 μs with a pre-shaped actuation signal (35 μs for normal square-wave actuation). J.E. Ford has proposed a CCR integrated with a membrane modulator for free-space optical communication [138]. The membrane modulator was formed over a hexagonal array of cavities so that electrostatic force could deform the normally flat reflector into a shape like the surface of a golf ball. It then phase-modulates the back-propagating wavefront so that the signal is dispersed and cannot arrive at the remote detector. CCR arrays [139, 140] and other non-retroreflecting techniques [141–144] have also been reported.

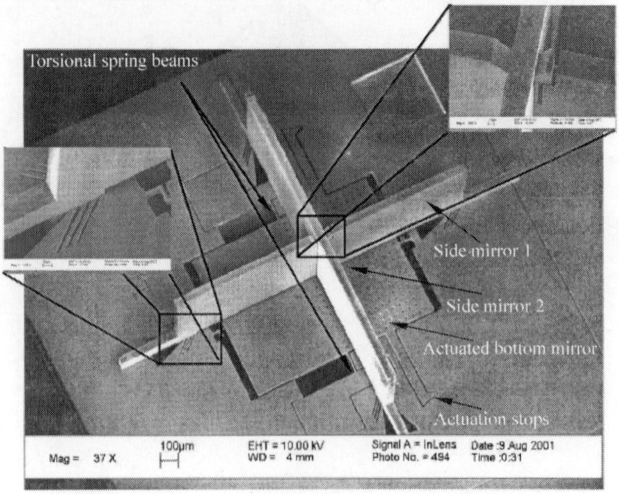

(a)

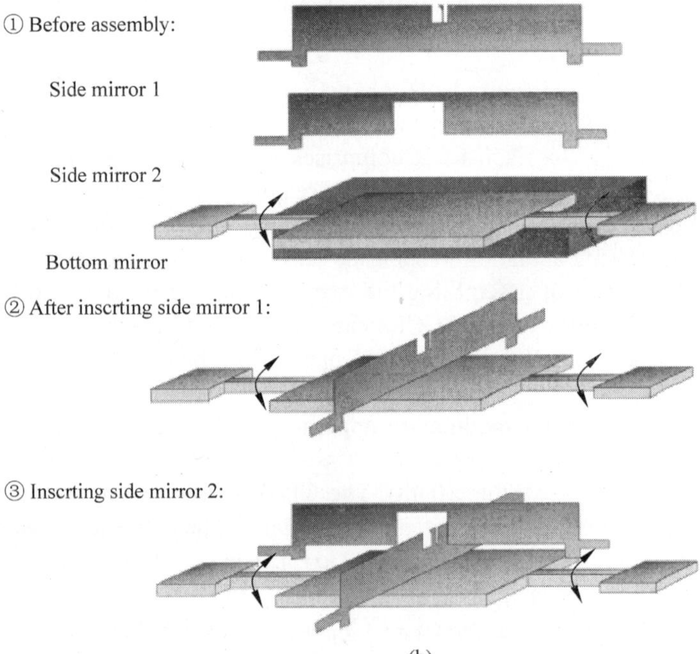

(b)

Figure 10.47 (a) SEM of the CCRs using bulk micromachining process, and (b) The sequence of assembling the CCRs. (© 2003 IEEE Pictures courtesy of L. Zhou. Reprinted from [136] with permission)

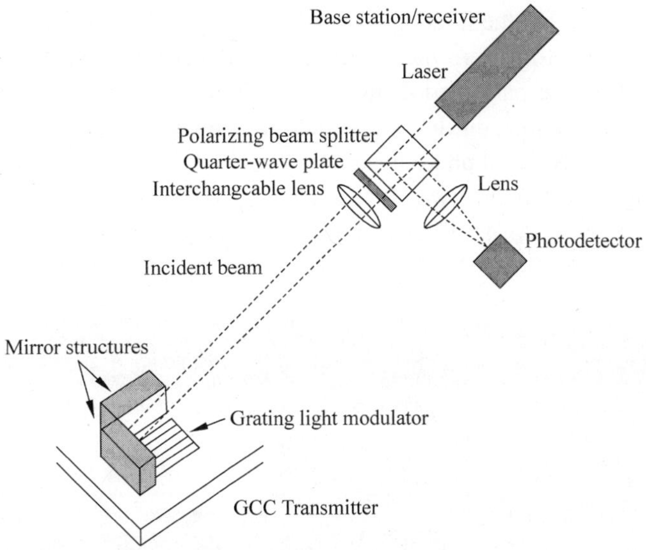

Figure 10.48 Free-space communication link using GLM CCR. (© 2000 Elsvier B. V. Pictures courtesy of D. Pederson. Reprinted from [137] with permission)

10.2.3 Nanophotonics

10.2.3.1 Photonics Crystal Switches

A photonic crystal (PC) is a periodical structure which consists of at least two different materials with distinct refractive indices [145, 146]. The PCs have the ability to confine light propagation within small volumes for specific frequency ranges, known as photonic crystal bandgaps (PBG). They can be classified as 1D, 2D, and even 3D structures, depending on how many dimensions the PC confines light. A comprehensive review of photonic crystals has been given in [146]. The discussion here is limited to tunable/reconfigurable photonic crystals with MEMS actuations.

The ability to tune or switch photonic crystals will enable us to build very compact, dynamic photonic integrated circuits. Researchers at UCLA have reported the first integrated 1D photonic crystal switch with MEMS actuators [147]. The input and output waveguides are linked by a 1D PBG active component. Two separate PC structures are designed: ① a reflection state that serves as a broadband notch filter center at 1.55 μm wavelength and extending from 1.0 μm to 2.1 μm, ② a transmission state with the same notch filter properties but allowing a narrow pass band at 1.55 μm. The device is fabricated on a SOI wafer. The thickness of the device layer is 1.5 μm and the silicon dioxide layer is 0.5 μm. Silicon is selected as the material for photonic crystal because of its high refractive index that enhances the quality factor (Q) of the filtering with only a few periods in the structure. E-beam lithography is used to pattern the photonic crystal and the waveguides, while the MEMS actuators are patterned using optical lithography. Comb-drive actuators are fabricated for displacing the PC structures. Figure 10.49(a) shows the SEM photo of the MEMS-based photonic crystal switch. A 70 V DC voltage is required for switching between the two different states. The transmittance spectrum is show in Fig. 10.49(b). An 11 dB extinction ration is observed at 1.56 μm.

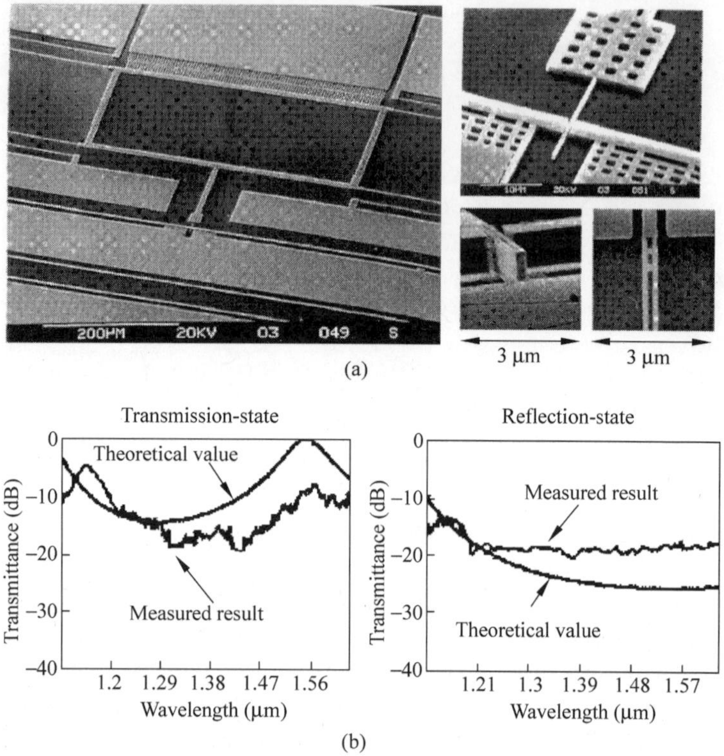

Figure 10.49 (a) SEM of the PBG switch, and (b) Spectrum in the transmission state and reflection state. (© 2002 OSA Pictures courtesy of M. C. M. Lee. Reprinted from [147] with permission)

Switching functionality can also be implemented by generating/canceling 'defects' in photonic crystals. A line defect in a 2D photonic crystal forms a waveguide. An ON-OFF switch is formed by introducing an array of holes with movable plugs. When the plugs are removed form the holes, the periodical structure is restored and the photonic bandgap blocks the light [148, 149]. Figure 10.50 shows this switching concept [148]. M. G. Salt et al. have proposed the use of an AFM tip to introduce perturbation in a photonic crystal cavity. A slight perturbation can lead to a significant change in the resonant wavelength [150].

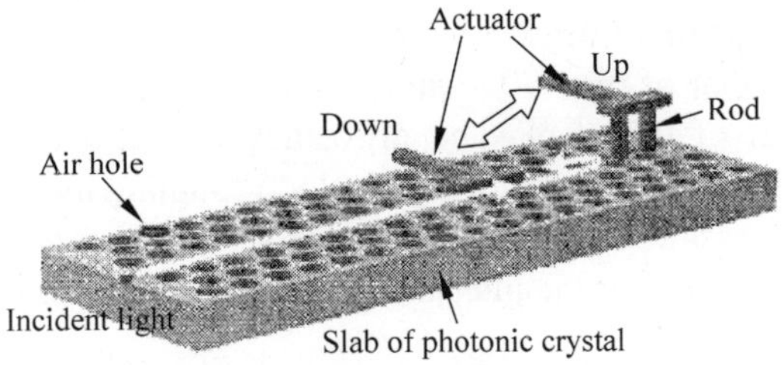

Figure 10.50 Photonic crystal switch using movable plugs (© 2003 IEEE Pictures courtesy of Y. Kanamori. Reprinted from [148] with permission)

10.2.3.2 Superprism

One of the extraordinary properties of PC is the 'superprism' phenomena. In the vicinity of the photonic bandgap, the propagation direction of light becomes extremely sensitive to its wavelength and incident angle. Although superprism is not a MEMS device, it is discussed here because of its potential to shrink the size of the WDM Demux/Mux components in MEMS-actuated photonic integrated circuits (PIC).

The prism function of PC was first discovered by Lin et al. in millimeter-wave frequencies [151]. Kosaka et al. demonstrated the superprism phenomena in 3D PCs at 1 μm wavelength [152, 153]. It showed 500 times stronger dispersion than that of a conventional prism. However, the 3D PC realized by multilayer deposition on patterned substrate is essentially a bulk optical element and is difficult to integrate with other photonic elements [154]. On the other hand, 2D PCs also exhibit superprism phenomena. They have simpler fabrication process and are compatible with planar lightwave integrated circuits. Using GaAs-based 2D PCs, L. Wu et al. have reported a dispersion of 0.5°/nm for wavelengths from 1,290 nm to 1,310 nm [155, 156]. Jin Yao et al. have demonstrated the first superprism in the 1,550 nm range using silicon-on-insulator (SOI) 2D PCs [157]. An angular dispersion of 0.34°/nm (10° shift for wavelength from 1,528 nm to 1,557 nm) has been experimentally achieved. The photonic crystal slab is fabricated on a SOI substrate with a 270 nm thick silicon layer and a 1 μm thick buried oxide. The SEM of the superprism test structure is shown in Fig. 10.51(a). The PC superprism has a semicircular shape with a radius of 24 μm. PCs with hexagonal lattice and air holes are employed. The lattice constant, a, is 670 nm and the hole radius, r, is 153 nm, as shown in Fig. 10.51(b). The superprism is integrated with waveguides. The output waveguides are arranged in a radial configuration with receiving angles from −80° to +80° (with increment of 10°). This ensures the output light to be perpendicular to interface of the PC area. The superprism chip is cleaved along the flat edge of the superprism, which is parallel to the Γ-K direction, as shown in Fig. 10.51(a). A wedge-shaped cylindrical lensed fiber is used to couple directly to the superprism. Incident angle can be varied by rotating the input fiber. The spectral response from various output waveguides are shown in Fig. 10.51(c), with an incident angle of 12 degrees. The peak wavelength for the –60° waveguide is 1,528 nm while that of the –70° waveguide is 1,557 nm. This corresponds to dispersion strength of 0.34°/nm. The efficiency is found to be approximately 0.31% at 1,528 nm. The sources of losses include coupling into the leaky modes in this high-index-contrast 2D slab, scattering from sample imperfections and sidewall roughness, and reflections at the interface between the PC and the slab areas.

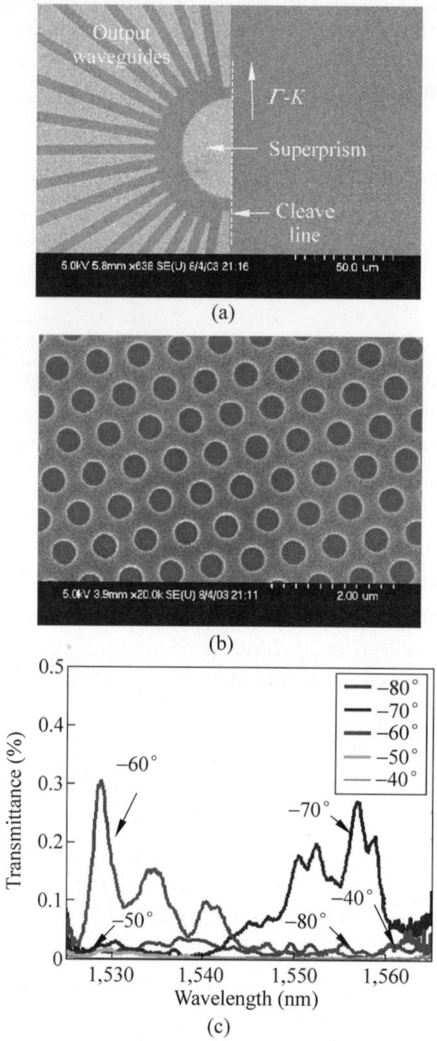

Figure 10.51 (a) SEM of the semicircular PC superprism and surrounding output waveguides, (b) Top view (SEM) of the hexagonal PC lattice, and (c) Transmittance spectra of output light from different waveguides at 12° incident angle. (© 2004 OSA Pictures courtesy of Jin Yao. Reprinted from [157] with permission) (see color figure at the end of this book)

10.2.3.3 Waveguide-Based Switches

Waveguide-based switches are attractive because the entire circuit can be monolithically integrated on wafer scale and they can be batch fabricated. Tedious optical alignment and manual assembly in free-space optical systems can be eliminated. In the past, waveguide-based switches have suffered from high crosstalk. With the advances of design and precision of fabrication, there is a renewed interest in MEMS-based guided-wave devices.

M. W. Pruessner et al. have developed optical switches composed of evanescently-coupled optical waveguides [158]. The structure of the device is shown in Fig. 10.52, which is essentially an InP-based waveguide coupler. Coupling is controlled by changing the gap and the coupling length between the two waveguides via electrostatic pull-in. This enables both optical switching (between the BAR and CROSS waveguides) and variable optical coupling at voltages below 10 V. The channel isolation can be as high as –47 dB. A coupling efficiency of up to 66% to the CROSS port is obtained with a switching loss of <0.45 dB. They also demonstrate voltage-controlled variable optical coupling over a 17.4 dB dynamic range. The active area is 500 μm×5 μm. InP is chosen as the waveguide material due to its potential for integration with active optoelectronic devices with optical gain at 1,550 nm. Other reported waveguide-based switches can be found in [159, 160].

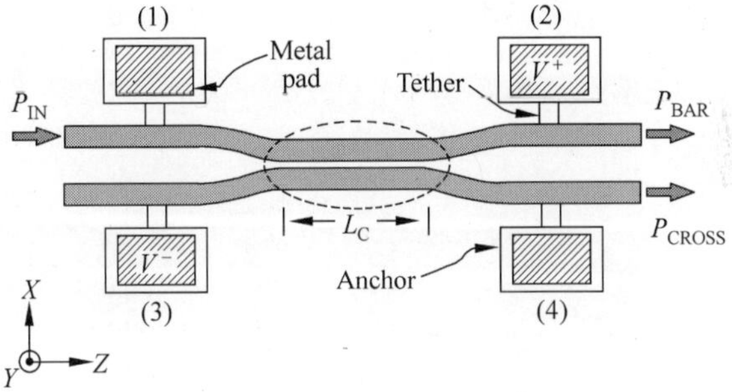

Figure 10.52 The structure of the InP-based waveguide coupler. (© 2005 IEEE Pictures courtesy of M. W. Pruessner. Reprinted from [158] with permission)

Waveguide-based switches capable of handling multiple wavelengths independently are key enabling components in WDM networks. Researchers at Xerox Corp. have reported a SOI-array waveguide grating (AWG)-based optical add-drop multiplexer [161]. Due to the high index of silicon ($n=3.4$), the minimum bending radius of a silicon waveguide (3 mm) is much smaller than that of a comparable silica waveguide (10 mm). Therefore, the size of their device (1.5 cm×2 cm) is smaller than conventional silica-based planar lightwave circuits (PLC's) (~15 cm× 15 cm). The layout of the OADM is shown in Fig. 10.53(a). The first AWG splits different wavelengths into individual waveguides. Each wavelength channel can be switched to ADD/DROP or THRU states, determined by the positions of the waveguide (Fig. 10.53(b)). Thermal driving and latching actuators with switching time less than 12 msec are designed and fabricated for moving the waveguides. No power is required to maintain the state. The second AWG combines all wavelengths into the output port. The optical spectrum (8 wavelength channels) of the OADM output is shown in Fig. 10.53(c). The fiber-to-fiber insertion loss is 19 dB. The extinction ratio is 40 dB, and the adjacent crosstalk is < –30 dB. The device is fabricated by a custom process on SOI wafers.

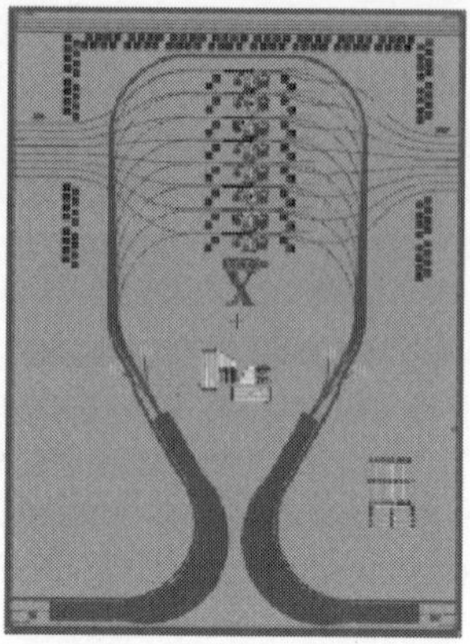

(a)

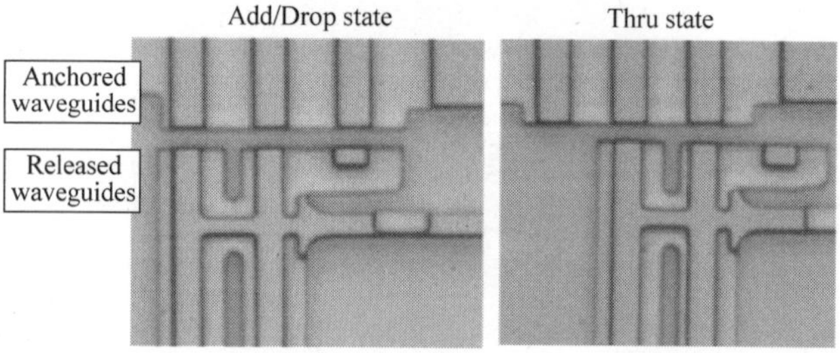

(b)

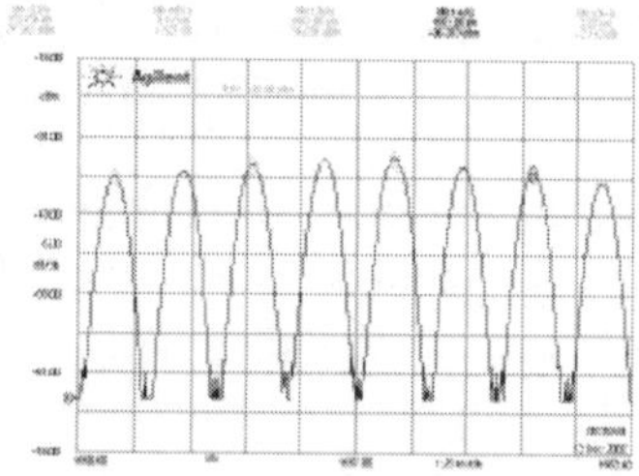

In → Out output sectrum

(c)

Figure 10.53 (a) Layout of the OADM in [161], (b) Waveguides in both ADD/DROP and THRU states, and (c) Output optical spectrum. (© 2004 TRF Pictures courtesy of Peter Gulvin. Reprinted from [161] with permission)

10.2.3.4 Microdisk and Microring Optical Add-Drop Switches

The wavelength add-drop switches using either AWGs or free-space gratings occupy significant areas (or volume). A very compact optical channel dropping filter was proposed by Marcatili in 1969 [162]. Using a microring resonator coupled to an input and an output waveguide, the resonant wavelength can be completely dropped from the input waveguide and directed to the output waveguide. Cascading such resonators can produce high-order filters with flat passband and sharp roll off [163]. To achieve good optical performance, the optical losses in the resonator must be minimized, including bending loss, scattering loss, and material absorption loss. Though the concepts have been proposed long time ago, making of high quality microring resonators in high-index contract waveguides has been possible only quite recently. Using high-index contrast materials, the ring size can be reduced significantly without suffering from bending loss. Recently, an 11-th order filter has been realized by B. E. Little et al. [164].

The input/output coupling between the optical waveguides and the microresonator is a very important parameter for the microresonator circuit. In microfabricated microring or microdisk resonators, the coupling coefficient is fixed by the microfabrication process. The ability to vary the microresonator coupling opens up many new opportunities. A reconfigurable optical add-drop multiplexer (ROADM) can be realized by switching the resonator between non-coupling to strong coupling. Ming-Chang Lee et al. (UCLA) have demonstrated the first MEMS-actuated tunable microdisk resonator [165]. The schematic and the SEM of the device are shown in Fig. 10.54. The waveguide-disk coupling is tuned by changing the gap spacing between them. In high-Q resonators, gap change of simply a fraction of micron can lead to many orders of magnitude change in the output transmission. The ability to tune the gap spacing not only relieves tight fabrication tolerance but also enables many new tunable WDM components such as wavelength-selective switches and dynamic add-drop filters. The device is fabricated on SOI wafer, with initial waveguide-disk gap spacing of 0.9 μm. There is no coupling between the waveguide and disk. The suspended waveguides can be pulled towards the microdisk by four electrostatic gap-closing actuators. Therefore, the coupling can be controlled by voltage. The radius of the disk is 10 μm and the waveguide width is 0.7 μm. Full displacement of the waveguide from 0 μm to 0.9 μm is achieved without experiencing pull-in. The voltage at maximum displacement (i.e., at contact) is 120 V. When both waveguides touch the microdisk, clear resonance peaks are observed at the DROP port. The highest peak is 8 dB above the noise floor and the loaded Q at contact is estimated to be 6,200.

With a similar structure, the same research group has also demonstrated a compact dynamic dispersion compensator [166]. The waveguide width, microdisk radius, and initial gap are 0.3 μm, 5 μm, and 2 μm, respectively. The device area is very small (100×50 μm^2). The measured group delay as a function of wavelength

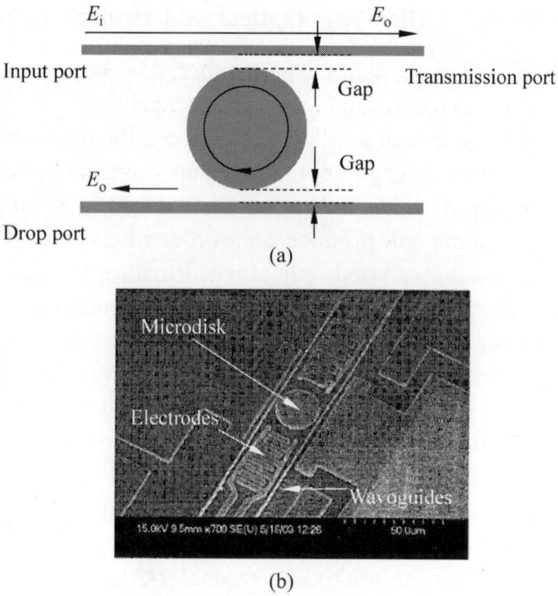

Figure 10.54 (a) Schematic and (b) SEM of the MEMS-based tunable microdisk resonator. (© 2003 IEEE Pictures courtesy of M. C. M. Lee. Reprinted from [165] with permission)

at three different voltages is plotted in Fig. 10.55. The group velocity dispersion is tunable from 0 – 400 ps/nm on the positive slope. The passband is 10 GHz. A wider passband can be obtained by cascading multiple disks.

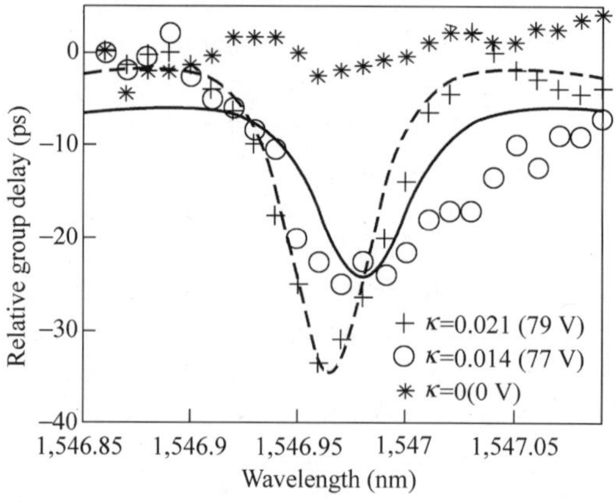

Figure 10.55 Group velocity v. wavelength at three different voltages. (© 2004 OSA Pictures courtesy of M. C. M. Lee. Reprinted from [166] with permission)

Changing the loss in the microdisk or microring can also lead to switching functions. Researchers in MIT/Pirelli Labs have reported a wavelength-selective optical switch based on variable-Q microring resonator [167]. The loss in the microring resonator can be increased by attaching it to a lossy material, such as an aluminum plate. When the plate is up, the resonant wavelength couples to the drop port. When the plate is down into the resonator's evanescent field, the resonant wavelength passes by the ring resonator unaffected (see Fig. 10.56(a)). The waveguide and the ring are made of silicon nitride and patterned by E-beam lithography. Polysilicon is used as the sacrificial layer for releasing the aluminum plate. The optical micrograph of the device is shown in Fig. 10.56(b). The aluminum plate is brought to the ring surface by electro-mechanical pull-in effect and the required voltage is 24 V.

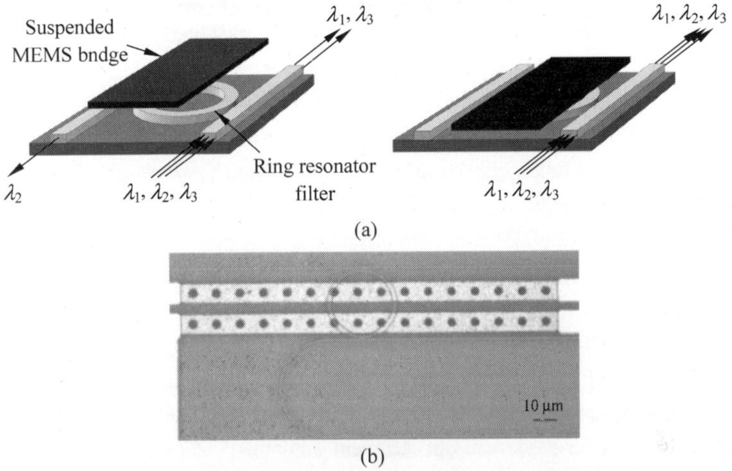

Figure 10.56 (a) Concept of switching by tuning the loss of the microring, and (b) optical micrograph of the fabricated device. (© 2005 IEEE Pictures courtesy of Gregory *N*. Nielson. Reprinted from [167] with permission)

10.3 Conclusion

In this chapter, we have described the physical design and fabrication of various Optical MEMS devices for display, imaging, and telecom applications. Both free-space and guided-wave optical systems were discussed. The emerging trend of integrating MEMS with nanophotonic integrated circuits such as photonic crystals or microresonators was also addressed.

References

[1] Petersen, K. E., (1982), Silicon as a Mechanical Material. *Proc. IEEE*, **70**(5): 420 – 457

[2] Petersen, K. E., "Silicon torsional scanning mirror," (1980), *IBM J. R&D*, **24**: 631 – 637

[3] M. C. Wu, (1997), "Micromachining for Optical and Optoelectronic Systems," *Proc. IEEE*, **85**: 1833 – 1856

[4] Muller R. S., and K. Y. Lau, "Surface-micromachined microoptical elements and Systems," Proc. IEEE, **86**: 1705 – 1720

[5] Degani, O., E. Socher, A. Lipson, T. Leitner, D. J. Setter, S. Kaldor, and Y. Nemirovsky, (1998), "Pull-In Study of an Electrostatic Torsion Microactuator," *IEEE J. Microelectromech. Syst.*, **7**(4): 373 – 379

[6] Hah D., H. Toshiyoshi, and M.C. Wu, (2002), "Design of Electrostatic Actuators for MOEMS," Proc. SPIE, Design, Test, Integration and Packaging of MEMS/MOEMS 2002, May 2002, Cannes, France

[7] Conant R. A., J. T. Nee, K. Lau, R. S. Mueller, (2000), "A Flat High-Frequency Scanning Micromirror", 2000 Solid-State Sensor and Actuator Workshop, Hilton Head, SC, 6 – 9

[8] Patterson P. R., D. Hah, H. Chang, H. Toshiyoshi, M. C. Wu, (2001), "An Angular Vertical Comb Drive for Scanning Micromirrors", IEEE/LEOS International Conference on Optical MEMS, Sept. 25-28, 2001, Okinawa, Japan, 25

[9] Judy J. W. and R. S. Muller, (1997), "Magnetically Actuated, Addressable Microstructures," *IEEE J. Microelectromech. Syst.*, **6**(3): 249 – 256

[10] Miyajima H., et al., (2003), "A MEMS electromagnetic optical scanner for a commercial confocal laser scanning microscope," *Journal of Microelectromechanical Systems*, **12**(3): 243 – 251

[11] Jain A., et al., (2003), "A two-axis electrothermal SCS micromirror for biomedical imaging", 2003 IEEE/LEOS International Conference on Optical MEMS 3, 14 – 15

[12] Jain A., H.W. Qu, S. Todd, G. K. Fedder, and H. K. Xie, (2004), "Electrothermal SCS micromirror with large-vertical-displacement actuation," *2004 Solid-State Sensor and Actuator Workshop Tech. Digest*, June 2-6, Hilton Head, SC, 228 – 231

[13] Nam H. J., Y. S. Kim, S. M. Cho, Y. Yee, and J. U. Bu, (2002), "Low Voltage PZT Actuated Tilting Micromirror with Hinge Structure," 2002 IEEE/LEOS International Conference on Optical MEMS, Lugano, Switzerland, 89 – 90

[14] Bourouina T., E. Lebrasseur, G. Reyne, A. Debray, H. Fujita, A. Ludwig, E. Quandt, H. Muro, T. Oki, and A. Asaoka, (2002), "Integration of Two Degree-of-Freedom Magnetostrictive Actuatio and Piezoresistive Detection: Application to a Two-Dimensional Optical Scanner," *IEEE J. Microelectromech. Syst.*, **11**(4): 355 – 361

[15] Hornbeck L. J., (1997), "Digital Light Processing™ for High Brightness, High Resolution Applications," *Proc. SPIE*, vol. 3013 (Electronic Imaging EI'97, Feb. 10 – 12, 1997, San Jose, CA)

[16] See for example, S. Senturia, Microsystem Design, Chapter 20, Kluwer Academic Publishers, 2001

[17] The Perspectra® product from Actuality Systems

[18] Z20/20™ product from VIZTA3D

[19] UV-Setter™ print-setting product from BasysPrint GmbH

[20] Liang M., R. L. Stehr, A.W. Krause, (1997), "Confocal pattern period in multiple aperture confocal imaging systems with coherent illumination," *Opt. Lett.*, **22**: 751 – 753

[21] MacAulay C., A. Dlugan, (1998), "Use of digital micro mirror devices in quantitative microscopy," *Proc. SPIE*, **3260**: 201
[22] Dlugan A.L.P., C. E. MacAulay, and P. M. Lane, (2000), "Improvements to quantitative microscopy through the use of digital micromirror devices," *Proc. SPIE*, **3221**: 6 – 11
[23] Hanley Q. S., P. J. Verveer, M. J. Gemkow, D. Arndt-Jovin, T. M. Jovin, (1999), "An optical sectioning programmable array microscope implemented with a digital micromirror device," *Journal of Microscopy*, **196**(3): 317 – 331
[24] Wagner II E. P., B. W. Smith, S. Madden, J. D. Winefordner, M. Mignardi, (1995), "Construction and Evaluation of a Visible Spectrometer Using Digital Micromirror Spatial Light Modulation." *Applied Spectroscopy*, **49**: 1715
[25] Bloom D. M., (1997), "The Grating Light Valve: revolutionizing display technology," Proc. International Society for Optical Engineering (SPIE), vol. 3013, Projection Displays Ⅲ, 1997, 165 – 71
[26] Urey H., (2003), "Retinal Scanning Displays, in Encyclopedia of Optical Engineering," to be published by Marcel-Dekker
[27] Freeman M., (2003), "Miniature high-fidelity displays using a biaxial MEMS scanning mirror," MOEMS Display and Imaging Systems, Proc. SPIE, Vol. 4985, San Jose, CA, Jan. 2003
[28] Urey H., (2002), "Torsional MEMS scanner design for high-resolution display systems," Proc. International Society for Optical Engineering (SPIE), vol. 4773, Optical Scanning Ⅱ: 27 – 37
[29] Yan S, F. A. Luanava, I. V. Dewitt, V. Cassanta, H. Urey, (2003), "Magnetic actuation for MEMS scanners for retinal scanning displays," Photonics West, SPIE vol. 4985, 106 – 114
[30] Minsky M., Microscopy Apparatus. US Patent # 3013467. 1957
[31] Dickensheets D. L. and G. S. Kino, (1998), "Silicon-micromachined scanning confocal optical microscope," *Journal of Microelectromechanical Systems*, **7**(1): 38 – 47
[32] Murakami K., A. Murata, T. Suga, H. Kitagawa, Y. Kamiya, M. Kubo, K. Matsumoto, H. Miyajima, and M. Katashiro, (2003), "A Miniature Confocal Optical Microscope with MEMS Gimbal Scanner," The 12th International Conference on Solid State Sensors, Actuators and Microsystems, Boston, June 8 – 12, 587 – 590
[33] Murakami K. et.al., (2002), "A MEMS gimbal scanner for a miniature confocal microscope", Optical-MEMS, TuA2 9 – 10
[34] Swanson E. A., D. Huang, M. R. Hee, J. G. Fujimoto, C. P. Lin, and C. A. Puliafito, (1992), "High-speed optical coherence domain reflectometry," *Optics Letters*, **17**(2): 151 – 153
[35] Huang D., E. A. Swanson, C. P. Lin, J. S. Schuman, W. G. Chang, M. R. Hee, T. Flotte, K. Gregory, C. A. Puliafito, and J. G. Fujimoto, (1991) "Optical Coherence Tomography," *Science*, **254**: 1178 – 1181
[36] Tearney G. J., M. E. Brezinski, B. E. Bouma, S. A. Boppart, C. Pitvis, J. F. Southern, and J. G. Fujimoto, (1997), "In vivo endoscopic optical biopsy with optical coherence tomography," *Science*, **276**(5321): 2037 – 2039

[37] Rollins A. M., R. Ung-arunyawee, A. Chak, R. C. K. Wong, K. Kobayashi, M. V. Sivak, Jr., and J. A. Izatt, (1999), Opt. Lett., **24**: 1358

[38] Tuqiang X., H. K. Xie, G. K. Fedder, and Y. T. Pan, (2003), "Endoscopic optical coherence tomography with a modified microelectromechanical systems mirror for detection of bladder cancers," *Applied Optics*, **42**(31): 6422 – 6426

[39] Zara J. M., S. Yazdanfar, K. D. Rao, J. A. Izatt, and S. W. Smith, (2003), "Electrostatic micromachine scanning mirror for optical coherence tomography," *Optics Letters*, **28**(8): 628 – 630

[40] Aguirre A. D., P. R. Herz, Y. Chen, J. G. Fujimoto, W. Piyawattanametha, L. Fan, M. C. Wu, (2007), "Two-axis MEMS scanning catheter for ultrahigh resolution three-dimensional and en face imaging," *Optics Express*, **15**(5): 2445 – 2453

[41] Piyawattanametha W., P. Patterson, D. Hah, H. Toshiyoshi, and M. Wu, "A 2D Scanner by Surface and Bulk Micromachined Angular Vertical Comb Actuators," International Conference on Optical MEMS, August 18 – 21, Hawaii, USA, 93 – 94

[42] Piyawattanametha W., P. R. Patterson, D. Hah, H. Toshiyoshi, and M. C. Wu, (2005), "Surface- and Bulk-Micromachined Two-Dimensional Scanner Driven by Angular Vertical Comb Actuators," *Journal of Microelectromechanical Systems*, **14**(6): 1329 – 1338

[43] Kudrle T. D., C. C. Wang, M. G. Bancu, J. C. Hsiao, A. Pareek, M. Waelti, G. A. Kirkos, T. Shone, C. D. Fung, and C. H. Mastrangelo, (2003), "Electrostatic Micromirror Arrays Fabricated with Bulk and Surface Micromachining Techniques," MEMS 2003, Kyoto, Japan, Jan. 2003, 267 – 270

[44] Tyson R. K., and B. W. Frazier, (1999), "Microelectromechanical system programmable aberration generator for adaptive optics," *Applied Optics*, **38**(1): 168 – 178

[45] Paterson C., I. Munro, and J. C. Dainty, (2000), "A low cost adaptive optics system using a membrane mirror," *Optics Express*, **6**(9): 175 – 185

[46] Albert O., et al., (2000), "Smart microscope: an adaptive optics system using a membrane mirror," *Optics Express*, **6**(9): 175 – 185

[47] Vdovin G., and V. Kiyko, (2001), "Intracavity control of a 200-W continuous-wave Nd:YAG laser by a micromachined deformable mirror," *Optics Express*, **26**(11): 798 – 800

[48] Dyson H. M., R. M. Sharples, N. A. Dipper, G. V. Vdovin, (2001), "Cryogenic wavefront correction using membrane deformable mirrors," *Optics Express*, **8**(1): 17 – 26

[49] Zhu L., et al., (1999), "Wave-front generation of Zernike polynomial modes with a micromachined membrane deformable mirror, " *Applied Optics*, **38**(28): 6019 – 6026

[50] Perreault J. A., and T. G. Bifano, (2004), "High-resolution Wavefront Control Using Micromirror Arrays," The proceedings of Solid-State Sensor, Actuator and Microsystems Workshop, Hilton Head Island, South Carolina, June 6 – 10, 83 – 86

[51] Krishnamoorthy R., T. G. Bifano, N. Vandelli, and M. Horenstein, (1997), "Development of MEMS deformable mirrors for phase modulation of light," *Optical Engineering:* 542 – 548

[52] Currently MEMSCAP, Inc. Durham, NC

[53] Hishinuma Y., and E. H. Yang, (2006), "Piezoelectric Unimorph Microactuator Arrays for Single-Crystal Silicon Continuous-Membrane Deformable Mirror," *Journal of Microelectromechanical Systems*, **15**(2): 370 – 379

[54] Fujino M., P. R. Patterson, H. Nguyen, W. Piyawattanametha, and M. C. Wu, (2004), "Monolithically Cascaded Micromirror Pair Driven by Angular Vertical Combs for Two-Axis Scanning," *IEEE Journal of Selected Topics in Quantum Electronics*, **10**(3): 492 – 497

[55] Toshiyoshi H., and H. Fujita, (1996), "Electrostataic Micro Torsion Mirrors for an Optical Switch Matrix," *IEEE J. Microelectromechanical Systems*, **5**: 231

[56] Lin L. Y., E. L. Goldstein, and R. W. Tkach, (1998), "Free-space micromachined optical switches with submillisecond switching time for large-scale optical crossconnects," *IEEE Photonics Technology Letters*, **10**: 525 – 527

[57] Hehin B., K. Y. Lau, and R. S. Muller, (1998), "Magnetically actuated micromirrors for fiber-optic switching," Solid-State Sensors and Actuator Workshop, Hilton Head Island, South Carolina

[58] Wood R. L., R. Mahadevan, and E. Hill, (2002), "MEMS 2-D matrix switch," 2002 Optical Fiber Communication (OFC) Conference, Paper TuO2, Anaheim California, 2002

[59] Yoon Y., K. Bae, and H. Choi, (2002), "An optical switch with newly designed electrostatic actuators for optical cross connects," 2002 IEEE/LEOS International Conference on Optical MEMS, Lugano, Switzerland, 2002

[60] Lin L. Y., E. L. Goldstein, and R. W. Tkach, (1999), "Angular-precision enhancement in free-space micromachined optical switches," *IEEE Photonics Technology Letters*, **11**: 1253 – 1255

[61] Lin L. Y., E. L. Goldstein, and R. W. Tkach, (1999), "Free-space micromachined optical switches for optical networking," IEEE Journal of Selected Topics in Quantum Electronics, **5**: 4 9

[62] Akiyama T., and H. Fujita, (1995), "A quantitative analysis of scratch drive actuator using buckling motion," Proc. 8th IEEE International MEMS Workshop, 1995, 310 – 315

[63] Lin L. Y., E. L. Goldstein, R. W. Tkach, (2000), "On the expandability of free-space micromachined optical cross connects," *J. Lightwave Technology*, **18**: 482 – 489

[64] Fan L., S. Gloeckner, P. D. Dobblelaere, S. Patra, D. Reiley, C. King, T. Yeh, J. Gritters, S. Gutierrez, Y. Loke, M. Harburn, R. Chen, E. Kruglick, M. Wu and A. Husain, (2002), "Digital MEMS switch for planar photonic crossconnects," 2002 Optical Fiber Communication (OFC) Conference, Paper TuO4, Anaheim, California, 2002

[65] Chen R. T., H. Nguyen, M. C. Wu, (1999), "A high-speed low-voltage stress-induced micromachined 2×2 optical switch," *IEEE Photonics Technol. Lett.*, **11**: 1396 – 1398

[66] Marxer C., N. F. de Rooij, (1999), "Micro-opto-mechanical 2×2 switch for single-mode fibers based on plasma-etched silicon mirror and electrostatic actuation," *J. Lightwave Technology*, **17**(1): 2 – 6

[67] Noell W., P.-A. Clerc, L. Dellmann, B. Guldimann, H.-P. Herzig, O. Manzardo, C.R. Marxer, K. J. Weible, R. Dandliker, N. de Rooij, (2002), "Applications of SOI-based optical MEMS," *IEEE J. Selected Topics in Quantum Electronics*, **8**(1): 148 – 154

[68] Marxer C., C. Thio, M. A Gretillat, N.F. de Rooij, R. Battig, O. Anthamatten, B. Valk, P. Vogel, (1997), "Vertical mirrors fabricated by deep reactive ion etching for fiber-optic switching applications," *J. Microelectromechanical Systems*, **6**(3): 277 – 285

[69] D. T. Neilson, et al., (2000), "Fully Provisioned 112×112 Micro-Mechanical Optical Crossconnect With 35.8Tb/s Demonstrated Capacity," Optical Fiber Communication Conference, OFC 2000, March 7-10, Baltimore, MD, **4**: 202 – 204

[70] Lin, L. Y., E. L. Goldstein, (2002), "Opportunities and Challenges for MEMS in Lightwave Communications," *IEEE J. Sel. Topics Quantum Elec.*, **8**(1): 163 – 172

[71] Syms R. R. A., (2002), "Scaling Laws for MEMS Mirror-Rotation Optical Cross Connect Switches," *IEEE J. Lightwave Tech.*, **20**(7): 1084

[72] Kim J., et al., (2005), "1100×1100 port MEMS-based optical crossconnect with 4-db maximum loss," *IEEE Photonics Technol. Lett.*, **15**: 1537 – 1539

[73] Neilson D. T., and R. Ryf, "Scalable micro mechanical optical crossconnects," 2000 IEEE/LEOS Annual Meeting, Paper ME2

[74] Aksyuk V. A., et al., (2003), "238×238 micromechanical optical cross connect," *IEEE Photonics Technol. Lett.*, **15**: 587 – 589

[75] Aksyuk V. A., et al., (2003), "Beam-steering micromirrors for large optical cross-connects," *IEEE J. Lightwave Tech.*, **21**(3): 634

[76] Kozhevnikov M., et al., (2004), "Micromechanical optical crossconnect with 4-F relay imaging optics," *IEEE Photonics Technol. Lett.*, **16**: 275 – 277

[77] Ryf R., et al., "1296-port MEMS transparent optical crossconnect with 2.07Petabit/s switch capacity," in Proceedings of 2001 OFC postdeadline paper, PD28

[78] Yazdi N., H. Sane, T. D. Kudrle, and C. H. Mastrangelo, (2003), "Robust sliding-mode control of electrostatic torsional micromirrors beyond the pull-in limit," 12th International Conference on Solid-State Sensors, Actuators and Microsystems, Transducers 2003, 8 – 12 June 2003, **2**: 1450 – 1453

[79] Kudrle T. D., G. M. Shedd, C. C. Wang, J. C. Hsiao, M. G. Bancu, G. A. Kirkos, N. Yazdi, M. Waelti, H. Sane, and C. H. Mastrangelo, (2003), "Pull-in suppression and torque magnification in parallel plate electrostatic actuators with side electrodes," 12th International Conference on Solid-State Sensors, Actuators and Microsystems, Transducers 2003, 8 – 12 June 2003, **1**: 360 – 363

[80] Kudrle T. D., C. C. Wang, M. G. Bancu, J. C. Hsiao, A. Pareek, M. Waelti, G. A. Kirkos, T. Shone, C. D. Fung, and C. H. Mastrangelo, (2003), "Electrostatic micromirror arrays fabricated with bulk and surface micromachining techniques," IEEE The Sixteenth Annual International Conference on Micro Electro Mechanical Systems, MEMS 2003, 19 – 23 Jan. 2003, 267 – 270

[81] Sawada R., J. Yamaguchi, E. Higurashi, A. Shimizu, T. Yamamoto, N. Takeuchi, Y. Uenishi, (2002), "Single Si crystal 1024ch MEMS mirror based on terraced electrodes and a high-aspect ratio torsion spring for 3-D cross-connect switch," 2002 IEEE/LEOS International Conference on Optical MEMs, 2002, 11 – 12

[82] Sawada R., J. Yamaguchi, E. Higurashi, A. Shimizu, T. Yamamoto, N. Takeuchi, Y. Uenishi, (2003), "Improved single crystalline mirror actuated electrostatically by terraced electrodes with high aspect-ratio torsion spring," 2003 IEEE/LEOS International Conference on Optical MEMs, 153 – 154

[83] Mizuno Y., et al., (2002), “A 2-axis comb-driven micromirror array for 3D MEMS switches,” 2002 IEEE/LEOS International Conference on Optical MEMs, 2002, 17 – 18
[84] Kouma N., et al., “A multi-step DRIE process for a 128×128 micromirror array,” 2003 IEEE/LEOS International Conference on Optical MEMs, 2003, 53 – 54
[85] Chu P. B., et al., “Design and Nonlinear Servo Control of MEMS Mirrors and Their Performance in a Large Port-Count Optical Switch,” *Journal of Microelectromechanical Systems*, **14**(2): 261 – 273
[86] Dadap J. I., et al., “Modular MEMS-based optical cross-connect with large port-count,” *IEEE Photonics Technol. Lett.*, **15**: 1773 – 1775
[87] Pu C., et al., (2004), “Electrostatic Actuation of Three-Dimensional MEMS Mirrors Using Sidewall Electrodes,” *IEEE Journal of Selected Topics in Quantum Electronics*, **10**(3): 472 – 477
[88] Zheng X., et al., (2003), “Three-dimensional MEMS photonic cross-connect switch design and performance,” *IEEE J. Sel. Topics Quantum Elec.*, **9**(2): 571
[89] Aksyuk V. A., F. Pardo, C. A. Bolle, S. Arney, C. R. Giles, D. J. Bishop, (2000), “Lucent Microstar micromirror array technology for large optical crossconnects,” Proceedings of the SPIE, MOEMS and Miniaturized Systems, Sept. 2000, Santa Clara, CA, 320 – 324
[90] Aksyuk V. A., M. E. Simon, F. Pardo, S. Arney, D. Lopez, and A. Villanueva, (2002), “Optical MEMS Design for Telecommunications Applications,” 2002 Solid-State Sensor and Actuator Workshop Tech. Digest, June 2 – 6, Hilton Head, SC, 1 – 6
[91] Gasparyan A., et al., (2003), “Drift-free, 1000 GB mechanical shock tolerant single-crystal silicon two-axis MEMS tilting mirrors in a 1000×1000-port optical crossconnect,” Proceedings of 2003 OFC postdeadline paper, PD36
[92] Aksyuk V. A., et al., (2002), “238×238 surface micromachined optical crossconnect with 2dB maximum loss,” OFC (Optical Fiber Communication) 2002, Postdeadline paper, FB9-1 – FB 9 – 3
[93] Ford J. E., V. A. Aksyuk, D. J. Bishop, and J. A. Walker, “Wavelength add-drop switching using tilting micromirrors,” *J. Lightwave Technology*, **17**(5): 904 – 911
[94] Marom D. M., et al., (2002), “Wavelength-selective 1×4 switch for 128 WDM channels at 50 GHz spacing,” Proceedings of 2002 OFC postdeadline paper, FB7
[95] Ducellier T., et al., “The MWS 1×4: a high performance wavelength switching building block,” Proceedings of ECOC 2002, session 2.3.1
[96] Tsai J. C., S. Huang, D. Hah, H. Toshiyoshi, and M. C. Wu, (2004), “Open-loop operation of MEMS-based 1×N wavelength-selective switch with long-term stability and repeatability,” *IEEE Photonics Technology Letters*, **16**(4): 1041 – 1043
[97] Hah D., S. T. Y. Huang, J. C. Tsai, H. Toshiyoshi, and M. C. Wu, (2004), “Low-voltage, large-scan angle MEMS analog micromirror arrays with hidden vertical comb-drive actuators,” *IEEE/ASME Journal of Microelectromechanical Systems*, **13**(2): 279 – 289
[98] http://mems.sandia.gov/tech-info/summit-v.html
[99] Marom D. M., et al., (2003), “Wavelength selective 4×1 switch with high spectral efficiency, 10 dB dynamic equalization range and internal blocking capability,” ECOC 2003, Paper Mo3.5.3

[100] Lopez D., et al., (2002), "Monolithic MEMS optical switch with amplified out-of-plane angular motion," Proc. 2002 IEEE/LEOS International Conf. Optical MEMS
[101] Greywall D. S., et al., (2003), "Monolithic fringe-field-activated crystalline silicon tilting-mirror devices," *J. Microelectromechanical Systems*, **12**(5): 702 – 707
[102] Taylor W. P., et al., (2004), "A high fill factor linear mirror array for a wavelength selective switch," *Journal of Micromechanics and Microengineering*, **14**(2004): 147 – 152
[103] Tsai J. C., S. Huang, and M. C. Wu, (2004), "High fill-factor two-axis analog micromirror array for 1 ×N2 wavelength-selective switches," Proc. of MEMS 2004, 101 – 104
[104] Tsai J. C., S. Huang, D. Hah, and M. C. Wu, (2006),"$1\times N^2$ wavelength-selective switch with two cross-scanning one-axis analog micromirror arrays in a *4-f* optical system," *IEEE/OSA Journal of Lightwave Technology*, **24**(2): 897 – 903
[105] Ford J. E., and J. A. Walker, (1998), "Dynamic spectral power equalization using micro-opto-mechanics," *IEEE Photonics Technology Letters*, **10**(10): 1440 – 1442
[106] Neilson D. T., et al., (2002), "High-dynamic range channelized MEMS equalizing filters," 2002 Optical Fiber Communication (OFC) Conference, Paper ThCC3, Anaheim, CA, 2002
[107] Bernstein J. J., et al., "MEMS tilt-mirror spatial light modulator for a dynamic spectral equalizer," *J. Microelectromechanical Systems*, **13**(2): 272 – 278
[108] Marom D. M., and S. H. Oh, (2002), "Filter-shape dependence on attenuation mechanism in channelized dynamic spectral equalizers," 2002 IEEE/LEOS Annual Meeting, Paper WG3, Glasgow, Scotland, 2002
[109] Marxer C., P. Griss, and N. F. de Rooij, (1999), "A variable optical attenuator based on silicon micromechanics," *IEEE Photonics Technologies Letters*, **11**(2): 233 – 235
[110] Marxer C., B. de Jong, and N. F. de Rooij, (2002), "Comparison of MEMS variable optical attenuator designs," 2002 IEEE/LEOS International Conference on Optical MEMS, Paper FA1, Lugano, Switzerland, 2002
[111] Isamoto K., et al., "A 5-V operated MEMS variable optical attenuator by SOI bulk micromachining," *IEEE Journal of Selected Topics in Quantum Electronics,* **10**(3): 570 – 578
[112] Vail E. C., M. S. Wu, G. S. Li, L. Eng, C. J. Chang-Hasnain, (1995), "GaAs micromachined widely tunable Fabry-Perot filters," *Electronics Letters*, **31**(3): 228 – 229
[113] Larson M. C., J. S. Jr. Harris, (1995), "Broadly-tunable resonant-cavity light-emitting diode," *IEEE Photonics Technology Letters*, **7**(11): 1267 – 1269
[114] Tayebati P., P. D. Wang, D. Vakhshoori, and R. N. Sacks, "Widely tunable Fabry-Perot filter using Ga(Al)As/AlOx deformable mirrors," Optical Fiber Communication (OFC) 1998, Paper TuB2
[115] Mateus C. F. R., C. H. Chang, L. Chrostowski, S. Yang, D.C. Sun, R. Pathak, H. C. J. Chang, (2002), "Widely tunable torsional optical filter," *IEEE Photonics Technology Letters*, **14**(6): 819 – 21
[116] Amano T., F. Koyama, M. Arai, (2002),"GaAlAs/GaAs micromachined thermally tunable vertical cavity filter with low tuning voltage," *Electronics Letters,* **38**(14): 738 – 740

[117] Peerlings J., A. Dehe, A. Vogt, M. Tilsch, C. Hebeler, F. Langenhan, P. Meissner, H.L. Hartnagel, (1997), "Long resonator micromachined tunable GaAs-AlAs Fabry-Perot filter," *IEEE Photonics Technology Letters*, **9**(9): 1235 – 1237

[118] Tayebati P., P. Wang, M. Azimi, L. Maflah, D. Vakhshoori, (1998), "Microelectromechanical tunable filter with stable half symmetric cavity," *Electronics Letters*, **34**(20): 1967 – 1968

[119] Halbritter H., M. Aziz, F. Riemenschneider, P. Meissner, (2002), "Electrothermally tunable two-chip optical filter with very low-cost and simple concept," *Electronics Letters*, **38**(20): 1201 – 1202

[120] Little M. J., (2002), "Compliant MEMS and their use in optical components," Optical Fiber Communication (OFC) 2002, Paper TuO6

[121] Wu M. S., E. C. Vail, G. S. Li, W. Yuen, and C. J. Chang-Hasnain, (1995), "Tunable micromachined vertical cavity surface emitting laser," *Electronics Lett.*, **31**: 1671 – 1672

[122] Harris, Jr. J. S. (2000), "Tunable long-wavelength vertical-cavity lasers: the engine of next generation optical networks?" *IEEE J. Selected Topics in Quantum Electronics*, **6**(6): 1145 – 1160

[123] Anthon D., J. D. Berger, J. Drake, S. Dutta, A. Fennema, J. D. Grade, S. Hrinya, F. Ilkov, H. Jerman, D. King, H. Lee, A. Tselikov, and K. Yasumura, (2002), "External cavity diode lasers tuned with silicon MEMS," Optical Fiber Communication (OFC) 2002, Paper TuO7

[124] Hal J. and J. D. Grade, (2002), "A mechanically-balanced, drie rotary actuator for a high-power tunable laser," 2002 Solid-State Sensor and Actuator Workshop Tech. Digest, June 2 – 6, 2002, Hilton Head, SC

[125] Grade J. D., K. Y. Yasumura, and H. Jerman, (2004), "Electrostatic actuators with mechanical brakes," *2004 Solid-State Sensor and Actuator Workshop Tech. Digest*, 4 – 7, Hilton Head, SC

[126] Solgaard O., (2002), "Dynamic diffractive optical elements based on MESM technology," Proc. 2002 Optics-Photonics Design and Fabrication (ODF) conference, Paper WP01, Tokyo, Japan, 2002

[127] Oh S. H., and D. M. Marom, (2004), "Attenuation mechanism effect on filter shape in channelized dynamic spectral equalizers," *Applied Optics*, **43**: 127 – 131

[128] Senturia S. D., (2002), "Diffractive MEMS: the polychromator and related devices," Digest 2002 IEEE/LEOS International Conference on Optical MEMS, 5 – 6

[129] Butler M. A., E. R. Deutsch, S. D. Senturia, M. B. Sinclair, W. C. Sweatt, D. W. Youngner, Hocker, (2001), "A MEMS-based programmable diffraction grating for optical holography in the spectral domain," Technical Digest 2001 International Electron Devices Meeting (IEDM), 41.1.1 – 41.1.4

[130] Hung E. S., and S. D. Senturia, (1992), "Extending the travel range of analog-tuned electrostatic actuators," *J. Microelectromechanical Systems*, **8**: 497

[131] Senturia S. D., (2003), "Programmable Difrraction Grating and Their Uses in Displays, Spectroscopy, and Communications," Proc. International Society for Optical Engineering (SPIE), vol. 5348, MOEMS and Imaging Systems Ⅱ, 2003, 1 – 6

[132] Solgaard O., R. Belikov, K. Yu, "Interference-based optical MEMS filters," Optical Fiber Communication (OFC) 2004, Paper TuD3

[133] Gunawan D. S., L. Y. Lin, and K. S. J. Pister, (1995), "Micromachined corner cube reflectors as a communication link," *Sensors and Actuators A*, 46 – 47: 580 – 583

[134] Chu P. B., N. R. Lo, E. C. Berg, and K. S. J. Pister, (1997), "Optical communication using micro corner cube reflectors," Proc. of MEMS 1997, 350 – 355

[135] Zhou L., K. S. J. Pister, and J. M. Kahn, (2002), "Assembled corner-cube retroreflector quadruplet," Proc. of MEMS 2002, 556 – 559

[136] Zhou L., J. M. Kahn, and K. S. J. Pister, (2003), "Corner-cube retroreflectors based on structure-assisted assembly for free-space optical communication," *J. Microelectromechanical Systems*, **12**(3): 233 – 242

[137] Pedersen D., and O. Solgaard, (2003), "Free space communication link using a grating light modulator," *Sensors and Actuators A*, **83**(2000): 6 – 10

[138] Ford J.E., (2004), "Optical MEMS: legacy of the telecom boom," Proc. 2004 Solid State Sensor, Actuator and Microsystems Workshop, (Hilton Head 2004), Hilton Head, South Carolina, June 2004

[139] Chu T. S., L. S. Huang, C. Y. Chang, C. S. Chang, W. F. Ye, M. H. Wen, and C. C. Yang, (2002), "A new addressable corner micromirror array for free-space optical applications," 2002 IEEE/LEOS International Conference on Optical MEMS, Paper WA5, Lugano, Switzerland, 2002

[140] Chang C. S., T. S. Chu, L. S. Huang, C. Y. Chang, S. Y. Zeng, M. H. Wen, and Y. K. Yen, (2002), "A novel addressable switching micro corner cube array for free-space optical applications," Proc. of MEMS 2002, 279 – 282

[141] Kruger M. V. P., M. H. Guddal, R. Belikov, A. Bhatnagar, O. Solgaard, C. Spanos, and K. Poolla, (2000), "Low power wireless readout of autonomous sensor wafer using MEMS grating light modulator," 2000 IEEE/LEOS International Conference on Optical MEMS, Paper WA3

[142] Peter Y. A., E. Carr, and O. Solgaard, (2002), "Segmented deformable micro-mirror for free-space optical communication," 2002 IEEE/LEOS International Conference on Optical MEMS, Paper FA5

[143] Zhou L., M. Last, V. Milanovic, J. M. Kahn, and K. S. J. Pister, (2003), "Two-axis scanning mirror for free-space optical communication between UAVs," 2003 IEEE/LEOS International Conference on Optical MEMS, Paper WP14

[144] Ford J. E., (2004), "Optical MEMS: legacy of the telecom boom," 2004 Solid-State Sensors and Actuator Workshop, Hilton Head Island, South Carolina, 2004, 1 – 3

[145] Yablonovitch E., (2001), "Photonic Crystals: Semiconductors of Light," *Scientific American (International Edition)*, **285**(6): 47 – 55

[146] Joannopoulos J. D., R. D. Meade, J. N. Winn, (1995), Photonic Crystals: Molding the Flow of Light, Princeton University Press, 1995

[147] Lee M. C. M., D. Hah, E. Lau, and M. Wu, (2002), "Nano-electro-mechanical photonic crystal switch," Optical Fiber Communication (OFC) 2002, Paper TuO5

[148] Kanamori Y., K. Inoue, K. Horie, and K. Hane, (2003), "Photonic crystal switch by inserting nano-crystal defects using MEMS actuator," 2003 IEEE/LEOS International Conference on Optical MEMS, Paper WA3

[149] Zhou W. M., M. T. Lara, G. Dang, L. Harrison, D. Mackie, M. Ervin, and P. G. Newman, (2004), "Design and fabrication of a reconfigurable photonic bandgap waveguide device with MEMS features," Proc. of CLEO 2004, Paper CWG3

[150] Salt M. G., I. Maerki, S. Gautsch, F. Schaedlin, U. Staufer, and H. P. Herzig, (2003), "Photonic crystal waveguide characterisation for MEMS applications," 2003 IEEE/LEOS International Conference on Optical MEMS, Paper WA4

[151] Lin S. Y., V. M. Hietala, L. Wang, and E. D. Jones, (1996), "Highly dispersive photonic band-gap prism," *Opt. Lett. 21*, 1996: 1771 – 1773

[152] Kosaka H., T. Kawashima, A. Tomita, M. Notomi, T. Tamamura, T. Sato, and S. Kawakami, (1998), "Superprism phenomena in photonic crystals," *Phys. Rev. B, Condens. Matter,* **58**: 10096 – 10099

[153] Kosaka H., T. Kawashima, A. Tomita, M. Notomi, T. Tamamura, T. Sato, and S. Kawakami, (1999), "Superprism phenomena in photonic crystals: Toward microscale lightwave circuits," *J. Lightwave Technol.*, **17**: 2032 – 2038

[154] S. Kawakami, (1997), "Fabrication of submicrometer 3-D periodic structures composed of Si/SiO2," *Electron. Lett.*, **33**: 1260 – 1261

[155] Wu L., M. Mazilu, T. Karle, and T. Krauss, (2002), "Superprism phenomena in planar photonic crystals," *J. Quantum Electron.*, **38**(2002): 915 – 918

[156] Wu L., M. Mazilu, T. Karle, and T. Krauss, (2003), "Beam Steering in Planar-Photonic Crystals: From Superprism to Supercollimator," *J. Lightwave Technol.* **21**: 561 – 566

[157] Yao J., M. C. M. Lee, and Wu M. C., (2004), "1550-nm superprism demultiplexers in 2-D silicon-on-insulator slabs," Optical Fiber Communication (OFC) 2004, Paper ThR1

[158] Pruessner M. W., K. Amarnath, M. Datta, D. P. Kelly, S. Kanakaraju, P. T. Ho, and R. Ghodssi, (2005), "InP-Based Optical Waveguide MEMS Switches with Evanescent Coupling Mechanism," *Journal of Microelectromechanical Systems*, **14**(5): 1070 – 1081

[159] Ollier E., (2002), "Optical MEMS devices based on moving waveguides," *IEEE J. Sel. Top. Quan. Elec.*, **8**: 155 – 162

[160] Bakke T., C. P. Tigges, J. J. Lean, C. T. Sullivan, and O. B. Spahn, (2002), "Planar microoptomechanical waveguide switches," *IEEE J. Sel. Top. In Quan. Elec.*, **8**(1): 64 – 72

[161] Gulvin P., et al., (2004), "Silicon-on-insulator-based optical add-drop multiplexers," 2004 Solid-State Sensors and Actuator Workshop, Hilton Head Island, South Carolina, 2004, 356 – 359

[162] Marcatili E. A. J., (1969), "Bends in optical dielectric guides," *Bell System Technical Journal*, **48**(7): 2103 – 2132

[163] Little B. E., S. T. Chu, H. A. Haus, J. Foresi, J. P.Laine, (1997), "Microring resonator channel dropping filters," *Journal of Lightwave Technology*, **15**(6): 998 – 1005

[164] Little B. E., S. T. Chu, P.P. Absil, J.V. Hryniewicz, F.G. Johnson, F. Seiferth, D. Gill, V. Van, O. King, M. Trakalo, (2004), "Very High-Order Microring Resonator Filters for

WDM Applications," *Photonics Technology Letters*, IEEE, **16**: 2263 – 2265

[165] Lee M. C. M., and M. C. Wu, (2003), "A MEMS-actuated tunable microdisk resonator," 2003 IEEE/LEOS International Conference on Optical MEMS, Paper MC3

[166] M. C. M. Lee, S. Mathai, and M. C. Wu, (2004), "Dynamic dispersion Compensator using MEMS-actuated microdisk resonators," CLEO 2004, Paper CThMM4

[167] Nielson G. N., D. Seneviratne, F. Lopez-Royo, P. T. Rakich, Y. Avrahami, M. R. Watts, H. A. Haus, H. L. Tuller, and G. Barbastathis, (2005), "Integrated Wavelength-Selective Optical MEMS Switching Using Ring Resonator Filters," *IEEE Photonics Technology Letters*, **17**(6): 1190 – 1192

11 Introduction to MEMS Packaging

Mu Chiao[1], Yu-Ting Cheng[2], and Liwei Lin[3]

[1] Department of Mechanical Engineering, University of British Columbia, Canada

[2] Electronics Department, Hsinchu Chiao Tung University

[3] Department of Mechanical Engineering, University of California, Berkeley, USA
E-mail: lwlin@me.berkeley.edu

Abstract Scientific and engineering advancements during the past decades in micro and nano devices have brought previously unthinkable applications to reality, such as in space systems, environmental instruments, and daily life appliances. However, a low cost and reliable packaging solution for MEMS/NEMS products remains a very difficult task. This chapter presents the fundamentals of MEMS/NEMS packaging technology, including packaging processes, hermetic and vacuum encapsulations, thermal issues, packaging reliability, and future packaging trends.

Keywords MEMS packaging, vacuum packaging, electronic packagin, hermetic testing, soldering, flip-chip bonding, accelerated testing

11.1 Introduction

MEMS devices are miniaturized components that may have mechanical, chemical, or biomedical features and integrated IC circuitry for sensor or actuator applications[1]. For example, pressure[2], temperature, flow[3] accelerometers[4], gyroscopes[5], and chemical sensors[5] can be fabricated by MEMS technologies for sensing applications. Fluidic valves[6], pumps[7], and inkjet printer heads are examples of actuation devices for medical, environmental, office, and industrial applications.

Silicon is typically used as the primary substrate material for MEMS because it can: ① provide unique electrical, thermal, and mechanical properties, ② be easily micromachined in a form of batch-processing, and ③ be incorporated with microelectronic circuitry. As a result, smaller size, lighter weight, lesser power consumption, and cheaper fabrication costs are the advantages of MEMS devices as compared with the existing macro-scale systems with similar functionalities. With the advancements of MEMS fabrication technology in the past decades, the MEMS market at the component-level exceeded 5 billion dollars, and is driving the end-product markets of more than 100 billion[8].

Nevertheless, the road to commercialization of MEMS does not look as promising as expected. Many industrial companies gained from the advantages of MEMS technology, specifically of high production volumes and high added value created by product integrations. However, cost-efficiency becomes the major factor driving MEMS toward commercialization. Several MEMS devices with high production volumes have been developed for the automotive industry and the information technology sectors. Most other custom-designed MEMS products are still waiting to be utilized in different applications since their costs in small-to-medium-scale production are still higher than the general market-acceptable levels. Consequently, high packaging and testing costs have slowed the commercialization of MEMS. Furthermore, based on the past experience of the IC industry, the cost of packaging processes is about 30%, and sometimes can be more than 70%, of the total manufacturing cost. MEMS packaging process is expected to be even more costly because of the challenging and stringent packaging requirements with regard to the fragile MEMS components in a typical MEMS product[9].

11.2 MEMS Packaging Fundamentals

The functions of conventional IC packaging are to protect, power, and cool the microelectronic chips or components, and to provide electrical and mechanical connections between the microelectronic parts and the outside world. With the increase in needs of high performance and multifunctional consumer electronic products, IC packaging processes have incorporated more complex designs and advanced fabrication technologies, such as Cu interconnects[10], flip chip bonding [11], ball grid arrays[12], wafer level chip scale packaging[13], 3-D packaging[14], and so on, in order to satisfy the necessities of high I/O density, large die area, and high clock frequency. In addition to the needs of electrical interconnects, MEMS components may need to interface with external environment (e.g., fluidic interconnectors[15]) and some other components may need to be hermetically sealed in vacuum (e.g., accelerometers[4]). Therefore, MEMS packaging processes may have to provide several functionalities such as better mechanical protection, thermal management, hermetic sealing, and complex electricity and signal distributions.

It has been suggested that MEMS packaging should be incorporated in the device fabrication stage as part of the micromachining process. Although this approach solves the packaging need for specific devices, it does not solve the packaging need for general microsystems. Especially, many MEMS devices are now fabricated by various foundry services[16, 17], and there is a tremendous need for a universal packaging solution after the foundry process. Figure 11.1 shows a typical MEMS device being encapsulated by a packaging cap. The most fragile part is the suspended mechanical sensor, which is a freestanding 'mass-spring' microstructure. It is desirable to protect this mechanical part during the packaging and handling process. Moreover, vacuum encapsulation may be required for these microstructures in applications such as resonant accelerometers[4], or gyroscopes[5, 18]. A 'packaging cap' with properly designed micro cavity is to be fabricated to encapsulate and protect the fragile MEMS structure as the first-level MEMS post-packaging process. The wafer can be diced afterwards, and well-established packaging technology in IC industry can follow and finish the final packaging step. However, unlike the packaging requirements for ICs, one common MEMS packaging requirement is hermetic seal and sometimes vacuum encapsulations. Hermetic seal is important to assure that no moisture or contaminant can enter the package and affect the functionality of microstructures. This tremendously increases the difficulty of common IC packaging processes. Although most single function MEMS chips can employ typical IC packaging techniques such as die-attached processes, wiring interconnects, molded plastic, ceramic, and metal for packaging[19], the increasing complexity of MEMS devices necessitates more advanced packaging techniques, especially wafer-level packaging, for the integration of multi-chips for multifunctional applications.

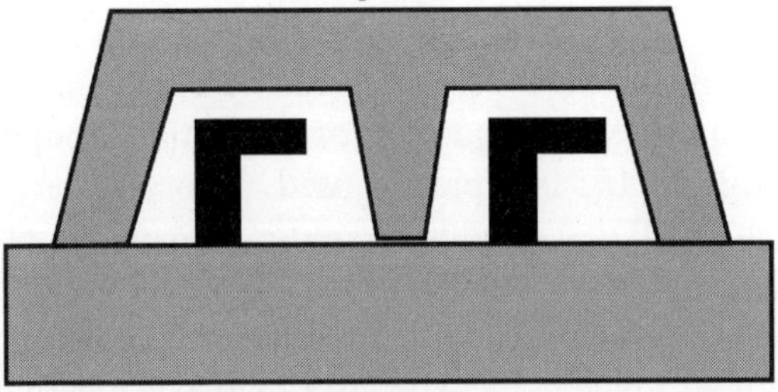

Figure 11.1 A typical MEMS packaging illustration where a MEMS structure is encapsulated and protect

Several primary micro fabrication processes for packaging applications have been briefed before discussing about the state-of-the-art MEMS packaging processes'. These processes may include Flip Chip (FC) technique, Ball Grid Arrays (BGA), and through wafer etching, and plating. Other silicon-based processes, such as thin film deposition, wet and dry chemical etching, lithography, lift-off, and wiring bonding processes can be found in many textbooks[20].

Flip chip technique (FC):

This technique is commonly used in the assembly process between a chip with microelectronics and a package substrate[11]. The microelectronic chip is 'flipped joined' with the packaging substrate, and metal solder bumps are used as both bonding agents and electrical paths, between bond pads on the microelectronic chip and metal pads on the package substrate. Because the vertical bonding space can be very small as controlled by the heights of the solder bumps, and because the lateral distributions of bond pads can be on the whole chip instead of being only on the edge, this technique can provide high density Input/Output (I/O) connections. In the FC technique, solder bumps are generally fabricated by means of electroplating. Before the bumping process, multiple metal layers, such as TiW-Cu, Cr-Cu, Cr-Ni, TaN/Ta/Ni, have to be deposited as seed layers for electroplating and as diffusion barriers to prevent the diffusion of solder into its underneath electrical interconnect.

Ball grid arrays (BGA):

This technology is very similar to the FC technique. An area array of solder balls on a single chip module or muti-chip module are used in the packaging process as electrical, thermal, and mechanical connects to join the module with the next level package, usually a printed circuit board.[12]. The major difference between a typical BGA and FC chips is the size of solder bump. In BGA chips, the bumps are in the order of 750 μm in diameter, which is 10 times larger than those commonly used in FC chips.

Through wafer etching:

This is a chemical etching process to make through wafer channels on a silicon substrate for the fabrication of vertical through wafer interconnects. The chemical etching process can be either wet or dry. Anisotropic or isotropic etching solutions can be used in the wet etching process. The dry etch process is based on plasma and ion-assisted chemical reactions, which can be either isotropic or anisotropic. In order to create high density and high aspect ratio through wafer vias, deep reactive ion etching (DRIE) is typically used. Two popular DRIE approaches, Bosch, and Cyro, are well described in literature[21].

Electroplating:

Electroplating is another common microfabrication process. It can be conducted for the deposition of an adherent metallic layer onto a conductive or nonconductive substrate. The process on a conductive substrate is called electrolytic plating, which utilizes a seed layer as the anode to transfer metal ions onto the cathode surface when a DC current is passed through the plating solution. The plating process without applying electrical current is called electroless plating, which can happen in both conductive and nonconductive surfaces. Electroless plating process requires a layer of noble metal such as Pd, Pt, or Ru on the substrate as a catalysis to trigger the self-decomposition reaction in the plating solution. The electroplating processes are very important for electrical interconnect, and solder bump fabrications are very important for packaging applications because of low process temperature and cost. These processes are generally developed for providing electrical and thermal paths for various IC/MEMS packaging approaches.

11.3 Contemporary MEMS Packaging Approaches

Several MEMS packaging issues and approaches before 1985 were discussed in the book, Micromachining and Micropackaging of Transducers[22], and researchers have been working on MEMS packaging approaches continuously. For example[23], discussed the packaging and partitioning issues for microsystems. Smith and Collins[24] used epoxy to bond glass and silicon for chemical sensors. Several MCM methods have been proposed. Butler et al.[25] proposed adapting multi-chip module foundries using a chip-on-flex (COF) process. Schuenemann et al.[26] introduced a 3D stackable packaging concept for the Top-Bottom Ball Grid Array (TB-BGA) that includes electric, fluidic, optic, and communication interfaces. Lee et al.[27] and Ok et al.[8] presented a direct-chip-attach MEMS packaging using through wafer electrical interconnects. Laskar and Blythe[28] developed a multichip modules (MCM) type packaging process by using epoxy. Reichl[29] discussed about different materials for bonding and interconnection. Grisel[30] designed a special process for packaging micro-chemical sensors. Special processes have also been developed for MEMS packaging, such as packaging for microelectrodes[31], packaging for biomedical systems[32], and packaging for space systems[33]. These specially designed, device-oriented packaging methods are aimed for individual systems. There is no reliable method yet that would qualify as a versatile post-packaging process for MEMS with the rigorous process requirements of low temperature, hermetic sealing, and long-term stability.

Previously, an integrated process had been developed by using surface-micromachined microshells[34]. This process applied the concepts of sacrificial layers and LPCVD sealing to achieve wafer-level post-packaging. Many similar processes have been demonstrated. For example, Guckle[35] and Sniegowski et al.[36] developed a reactive sealing method to seal vibratory micromachined beams. Ikeda et al.[37] adopted epitaxial silicon to seal microstructures. Mastrangelo et al.[38] used silicon nitride to seal mechanical beams as light sources. Smith et al.[39] accomplished a new fabrication technology by embedding microstructures and CMOS circuitry. All these methods have integrated the MEMS process together with the post-packaging process such that no extra bonding process is required. However, these schemes are highly process dependent, and not suitable for pre-fabricated circuitry.

Recently, several new efforts for MEMS post-packaging processes have been reported. Butler et al.[25] demonstrated an advanced MCM packaging scheme. It adopts the high density interconnect (HDI) process consisting of embedding bare die into pre-milled substrates. Because MEMS structures have to be released after the packaging process, it is undesirable for general microsystems. Van der Groen et al.[40] reported a transfer technique for CMOS circuits based on epoxy bonding. This process overcomes the surface roughness problem, but epoxy is not a good material for hermetic sealing. In 1996, Cohn et al.[41] demonstrated a wafer-to-wafer vacuum packaging process by using Silicon-Gold eutectic bonding with a 2 μm-thick polysilicon microcap. However, experimental results showed substantial leakage after a period of 50 days. Cheng et al.[42] developed a vacuum packaging technology using localized aluminum/silicon-to glass bonding. In 2002, Chiao and Lin[43] demonstrated vacuum packaging of microresonators by rapid thermal processing. These recent and on-going research efforts indicate a strong need for a versatile MEMS post-packaging processes.

11.4 Bonding Processes for MEMS Packaging Applications

Previously, silicon-bonding technologies such as epoxy bonding, eutectic bonding, anodic bonding, fusion bonding, and solder bonding had been used in many MEMS fabrication and packaging applications. For example, devices like pressure sensors, micropumps, bio-medical sensors, or chemical sensors require mechanical interconnectors to be bonded on the substrate[5, 15, 44]. Glass has been commonly used as the bonding material by anodic bonding at a temperature of about 300℃ – 450℃[45–48] have demonstrated different types of silicon fusion bonding and $Si\text{-}SiO_2$ bonding processes at very high temperatures of over 1000℃. Ko et al.[22], Tiensuu et al.[49], Lee et al.[50] and Cohn et al.[41] have used eutectic bonding for different applications. All these bonding techniques have different mechanisms that determine the individual bonding characteristics and process parameters. This section discusses the details of these processes.

11.4.1 Fusion Bonding for MEMS Packaging

Silicon fusion bonding is an important fabrication technique of SOI (Silicon On Insulator). The bonding process is based on Si-O, Si-N, or Si-Si strong covalent bonds. However, very high bonding temperatures (higher than 1000℃) and flat bonding surfaces (less than 6 nm) are the two basic requirements for strong, uniform, and hermetic bonding. Although hydrophilic surface treatment can lower the bonding temperature, an annealing step higher than 800℃ is still needed to remove possible bubble formation at the bonding interface. Bower et al.[51] proposed that low temperature Si_3N_4 fusion bonding could be achieved at temperatures under 300℃. Takagi et al.[52] proposed that silicon fusion bonding could be done at room temperature by using Ar+ beam treatment on the wafer surface, and also said that the bond strength is comparable to the conventional fusion bonding. In summary, fusion bonding has been a popular fabrication technique in MEMS fabrication and packaging.

11.4.2 Anodic Bonding for MEMS Packaging Applications

The invention of anodic bonding dates back to 1969 when Wallis and Pomerantz[53] found that glass and metal could be bonded together at about 200℃ – 400℃ below the melting point of glass with the aid of a high electrical field. This technology has been widely used for protecting on-board electronics in biosensors[54–56] and sealing cavities in pressure sensors[50, 57]. The silicon-to-glass anodic bonding process uses a high electrical field (more than 1000 Volts) to generate high electrostatic force to pull two bonding surfaces together for bonding. It is known that under high electric fields, the sodium ions in the glass migrate away from the silicon-glass interface, thus creating a local, high electrical field, and a bond is formed by electrochemical effects as demonstrated by Wallis and Pomerantz[53]. Figure 11.2 shows the setup for anodic bonding where two wafers are brought together and heated to an elevated temperature to supply the bonding energy. Care must be taken if free standing, conductive micromechanical structures exist on any bonding wafer, since the high voltage tends to pull the micromechanical structure, thus damaging it. A thin-film metal pattern on the glass cap can be formed to provide the shielding for solving this problem, as shown in Fig. 11.2.

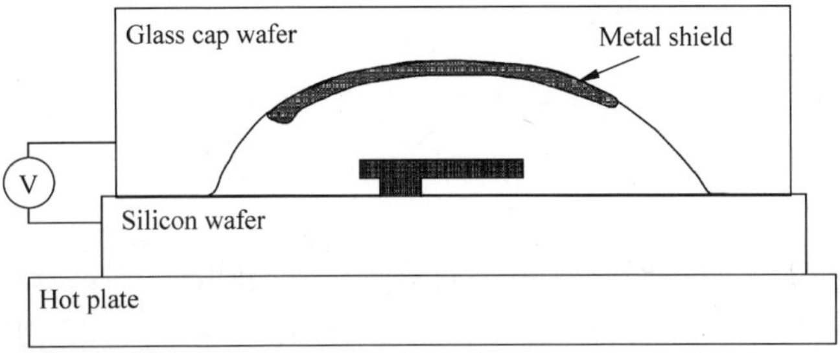

Figure 11.2 Schematic diagram of the setup for the silicon-to-glass anodic bonding process.th

Chavan and Wise[57] have reported absolute pressure sensors fabricated by using the anodic bonding technique. In this process, a silicon cap with a thin, heavily doped boron layer and a recess cavity, was bonded in vacuum environment to a glass substrate with pre-fabricated interconnection lines. An etch stop process was used to dissolve the silicon wafer in EDP (ethylenediamine pyrocatechol)[58] such that only heavily boron doped silicon regions such as the sensor membrane structures were left and sealed to the glass substrate. The problem of oxygen out-gassing due to the high electrical field in the anodic bonding process presents a challenge for the vacuum sealing process[59]. A thin Ti/Pt layer pre-deposited on the glass surface had shown to provide a good diffusion barrier, and the resulting pressure in the cavity could reach 200 mTorr[57].

In another example, micro gyroscopes were fabricated using the anodic bonding technique[60]. These gyroscopes were based on resonant MEMS structures, and Fig. 11.3 shows the fabrication process. First, a micromechanical structure was formed on the single crystalline silicon substrate using RIE (Reactive Ion Etching) and bonded to the bottom glass substrate with a pre-fabricated recess cavity. A second glass substrate with a machined (sand blasted) venting via was bonded to the other side of the silicon substrate. A degassed solder ball (64% Sn, /36% Pb) was applied on the venting holes. The package was then put into a vacuum chamber to allow air inside the cavity to evacuate through the venting via. Sealing was done by heating the package in vacuum to 200℃ to reflow the solder ball. The reported pressure level inside the cavity was 10 Pa, and remained stable for more than 70 days.

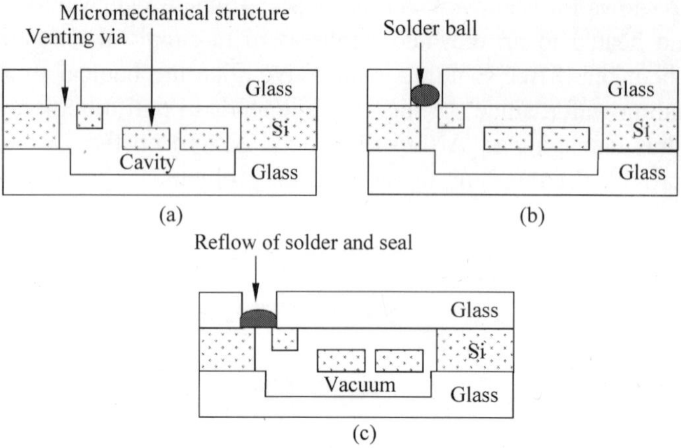

Figure 11.3 Fabrication process of a vacuum encapsulated MEMS gyroscope by the anodic wafer bonding process and reflow of solder material. (After T. Hara et al.) Drawn not to scale

Many reports have also discussed the possibility of lowering the bonding temperature by different mechanisms[61, 62]. Anodic bonding forms Si-O or Si-Si covalent bond are the strongest chemical bonds available for silicon-based systems. The bonding process can be accomplished on a hot plate with temperatures between 180℃ and 500℃ in atmosphere or vacuum environment. When a static electrical field is built within the Pyrex glass (7,740 from Dow Corning) and silicon, the electrostatic force can pull two surfaces close for a strong bond. A flat bonding surface with less than 50 nm roughness is required for creating high electric fields. In addition, the electrical field required for bonding is larger than 3×10^6 V/cm[22]. Such a high electrical field is generated by a power supply of 200 V to 1,000 V, which may damage the integrated circuits.

Hanneborg et al.[63] have successfully bonded silicon with other thin solid films, such as silicon dioxide, nitride, and polysilicon, together with an intermediate glass layer using anodic bonding techniques. In practice, electrostatic bonding has become widely accepted in MEMS fabrications and packaging applications. Unfortunately, the possible contamination due to excessive alkali metal in the glass; possible damage to microelectronics due to the high electrical field; and the requirement of flat surfaces for bonding limit the application of anodic bonding to MEMS post-packaging applications[64].

11.4.3 Epoxy Bonding (Adhesive Bonding)

Epoxy comprises four major components: epoxy resin, filler like silver slake, solvent or reactive epoxy diluent, and additives like hardener and catalyst[65, 66]. The bonding mechanism of epoxy is very complicated, which depends on the type of epoxy. In general, the main source of bonding strength is the Van Der Wall force. Low residual stress and process temperatures are the major advantages of epoxy bonding because epoxy is a soft polymer material and its curing temperature for bonding is only around 150℃. However, the properties of epoxy can be easily changed with environmental humidity and temperature; so the bonding strength decays over time. In addition, epoxy bonding has low moisture resistance and is a dirty process due to its additives. These disadvantages have made epoxy unfavorable for the special MEMS packaging needs of hermetic or vacuum sealing.

11.4.4 Eutectic Bonding

Many binary systems have an eutectic point corresponding to the alloy composition with the lowest melting temperature. If the environmental temperature is kept higher than the eutectic point, two contacted surfaces containing two elements with the eutectic composition can form a liquid phase alloy. The solidification of the eutectic alloy forms 'eutectic bonding' at a temperature lower than the melting temperature of either element in the alloy. Eutectic bonding can be a strong metal bonding. For example, in the case of Au/Si alloy systems, eutectic temperature is only 363℃ when the composition is at the atomic ratio of 81.4% Au to 18.6% Si, and bonding strength is higher than 5.5 GPa[67]. Because other alloy systems may have lower eutectic temperatures than Au/Si system, they present great potential for MEMS packaging applications. For example, in addition to Au/Si, Al/Ge/Si, Au/SnSi, and Au/Ge/Si systems have been applied for MEMS packaging.

11.4.5 Solder Bonding

Solder bonding has been widely applied in microelectronic packaging[68]. Both low bonding temperature and high bonding strength are good characteristics for packaging. Furthermore, there are a variety of choices of solder material for specific applications. Singh et al.[69] have successfully applied solder bump bonding in the integration of electronic components and mechanical devices for MEMS fabrication[70]. In this case, indium metal was used for bonding two separated silicon surfaces together by applying 350 MPa pressure, and the bonding strength was as strong as 10 MPa. Glass frits can also be treated as solder material, and have been extensively used for vacuum encapsulation in MEMS industry. Glass frits are ceramic materials that can provide strong bonding strength with silicon, with good hermeticity. Its bonding temperature is lower than 400℃, and is suitable for electronic components. However, more than 200 μm wide of bonding area is required to achieve good bonding results, and this may become a drawback because area is the measure of manufacturing cost in the IC industry. Nevertheless, glass frit is the most popular bonding process used in current MEMS products.

11.4.6 Localized Heating and Bonding

Low bonding temperature and short process time are desirable process parameters in MEMS packaging fabrication to provide less thermal budget and high throughput. However, most chemical bonding reactions require a minimum and sufficient thermal energy to overcome the reaction energy barrier, also called activation energy, to start the reaction and to form a strong bond. As a result, high bonding temperature generally results in shorter processing time to reach the same bonding quality at a lower bonding temperature[71]. The common limitations for the above bonding techniques are their individual bonding characteristics and temperature requirements. In general, MEMS packaging requires a good bonding for hermetic sealing, while the processing temperature must be kept low at the wafer-level to have less thermal effects on the existing devices. For example, a MEMS device may have pre-fabricated circuitry, biomaterial, or other temperature sensitive materials like organic polymer, magnetic metal alloy, or piezo-ceramic. Since the packaging step comes after the MEMS device fabrication processes, bonding temperature should be kept low to avoid effects of high temperature on the system. Possible temperature effects include residual stress due to the mismatch of thermal expansion coefficients of bonding materials and substrates, electrical contact failure due to atom inter-diffusion at the interface, and contamination due to the outgas or evaporation of materials. In addition to the control of bonding temperature, the magnitude of applied force to create intimate contact for bonding, and atmospheric environment control are other factors that should be considered. Based on the heat transfer simulation study[72], it is possible to confine high temperature area in a small region by localized heating without heating the whole substrate. Therefore, assembly steps can always be processed after the device fabrication processes without having detrimental effects. As such, localized heating and bonding technique is introduced and implemented for the fabrication of MEMS packaging for post-processing approaches[72, 73].

Table 11.1 summarizes these MEMS packaging technologies and their limitations, including the localized heating and bonding approaches. The localized heating approach introduces several new opportunities. First, better and faster temperature control can be achieved. Second, higher temperature can be applied to improve the bonding quality. Third, new bonding mechanisms that require high temperature such as brazing[74] may now be explored in MEMS applications. As such, it has potential applications for a wide-range of MEMS devices.

Table 11.1 Summary of Bonding Mechanisms

Bonding Methods	Temperature	Roughness	Hermeticity	Post-Packaging	Reliability
Fusion bonding	very high	highly sensitive	yes	yes by LH	good
Anodic bonding	medium	highly sensitive	yes	difficult	good
Epoxy bonding	low	low	no	yes	???
Integrated process	high	medium	yes	no	good
Low Temp. bonding	low	highly sensitive	???	no	???
Eutectic bonding	medium	low	yes	yes by LH	???
Brazing	very high	low	yes	yes by LH	good

???: no conclusive data LH: Localized Heating.

11.5 Hermetic/Vacuum Packaging and Applications

Hermetic packaging is desirable in most cases because it provides a moisture free environment to avoid charge separation in capacitive devices, corrosion in metallization, or electrolytic conduction, in order to prolong the lifetime of the electronic circuitry. Vacuum encapsulation is necessary in several device applications, but can be costly. Many surface micro-machined resonant devices may need vacuum to improve their performances such as comb-shape μ-resonators and ring-type μ-gyroscopes that have very large surface-to-volume ratios and vibrate in a very tight space[18, 37]. Two major approaches of MEMS hermetic and vacuum packaging have been demonstrated: ① the integrated encapsulation approach and ② the post-process packaging approach. Both these have been discussed in this section. Moreover, vacuum encapsulation by means of localized heating and bonding is discussed separately as another example for issues related to hermetic and vacuum packaging.

11.5.1 Integrated Micromachining Processes

Several MEMS hermetic and vacuum packaging processes have been demonstrated before, based on the integrated micromachining processes. Figure 11.4 illustrates typical steps that use surface-micromachined micromechanical components for the integrated encapsulation process. As depicted in Fig. 11.4, these steps include: (a) the completion of surface-micromachined devices with sacrificial spacer layer remaining on the wafer; (b) more sacrificial layer deposition and patterning,

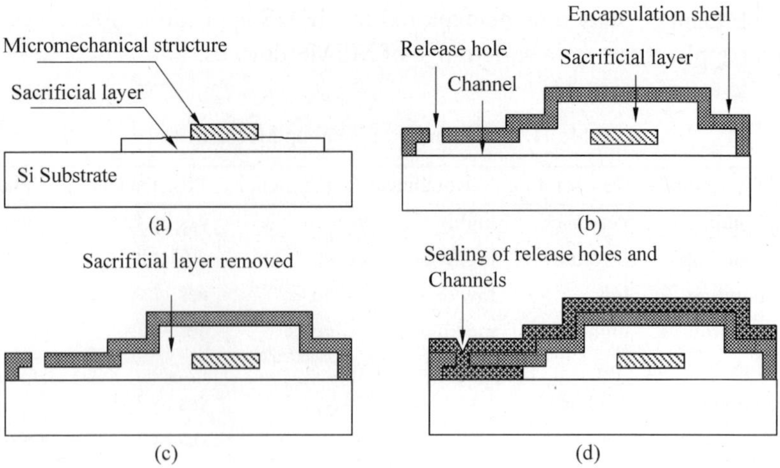

Figure 11.4 Schematic diagram of the concept of the integrated encapsulation process

followed by packaging cap layer deposition and patterning for the formation of the encapsulation shell with release etching channels and holes; (c) removal of sacrificial spacer layer to release mechanical microstructures; and (d) sealing of etching channels and holes by another deposition process. An integrated vacuum sealing process by LPCVD is presented here as the illustration example. This integrated process can encapsulate comb shape microresonators[75] in vacuum at the wafer-level. Micro resonators were first fabricated using a 4-mask process[76]. A thick LPCVD PSG (phosphorous silicate glass) sacrificial layer was then deposited to cover the resonators. Etch holes/channels were defined around the resonators. An LPCVD low stress silicon nitride layer was used as the packaging cap and release holes were defined on the nitride layer. A subsequent releasing procedure of comb-drive resonators was carried out by using concentrated HF (49% Hydrofluoric acid) to remove the PSG layer through the etch holes/channels, and the super critical CO_2 drying procedure[77] was used to prevent the surface tension force that would pull down the microstructures. Afterwards, the etch holes/channels were sealed by another LPCVD silicon nitride deposition at a pressure of 300 mTorr. The residual gas in the nitride shell would continue to react such that the resulting pressure inside the micro package was expected to be lower than the deposition pressure. Moreover, the microstructure inside the shell was expected to add a new layer of thin film due to the continual reaction of the residual gas. Figure 11.5 shows the fabrication result of a sealed micro resonator after the package was cleaved in half and the polysilicon microresonator was overhanging on the edge. The total packaging area (microshell) was about $400 \times 400\ \mu m^2$. The total height of the nitride shell was 12 μm as seen standing above the substrate. Spectrum measurement of the comb resonator inside the packaging revealed that a vacuum level of about 200 mTorr had been accomplished[78].

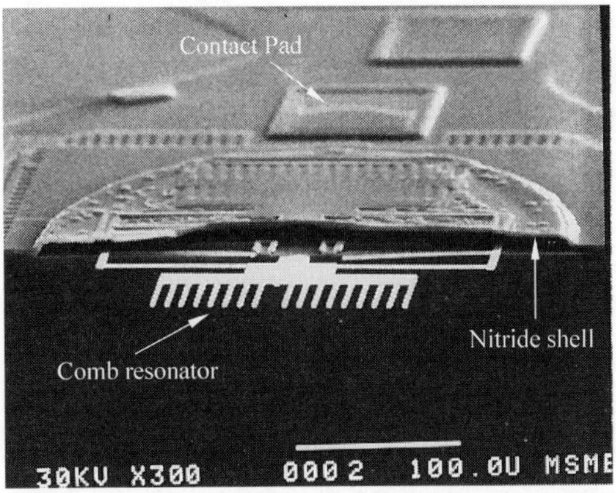

Figure 11.5 SEM microphoto of a comb-resonator with a sealing nitride cap. The sealing was conducted in a LPCVD tube

A Bi-CMOS compatible, integrated vacuum encapsulation process has been demonstrated by[31] as shown in Fig. 11.6. The integrated circuits were constructed using the Bi-CMOS process first, and micromechanical components and electrodes were formed afterwards. A sacrificial material and a protecting shell were deposited to encapsulate microstructures, and release holes were patterned and etched on the encapsulating shell. A dry release process was then carried out to release micro mechanical structures inside the shell. Finally, a PECVD (plasma enhanced chemical vapor deposition) process was used to seal the release holes. The demonstrated encapsulation pressure level was about 100 mTorr.

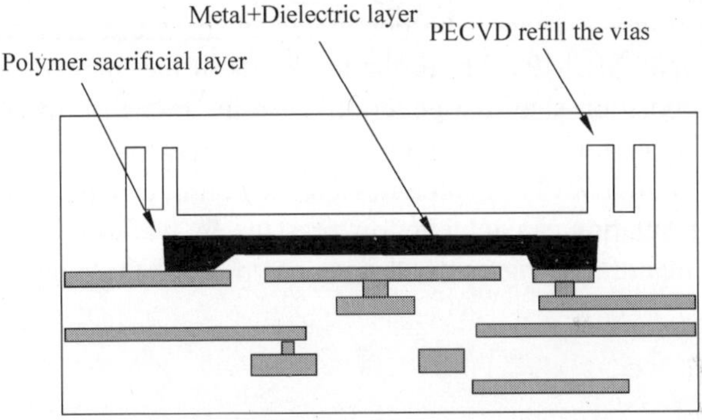

Figure 11.6 A Bi-CMOS compatible MEMS vacuum packaging process. (After Lund et al). Drawn not to scale

An integrated sealing process by evaporation of aluminum has also been reported[79], as shown in Fig. 11.7. A silicon substrate was deposited with an n-type, 4 μm thick epitaxial silicon layer. A controlled plasma etching and oxidation process formed a sharp tip, and a layer of BPSG (Boro-phosphosilicate glass) was used to fill the trench as the sacrificial layer. The nitride-sealing cap was deposited and patterned, and a 290 nm thick PSG sacrificial release via was deposited and patterned followed by the deposition and patterning of the polysilicon anode. After the release etching process, aluminum evaporation was done in a 2×10^{-6} Torr vacuum chamber, and an 800 nm thick aluminum layer was deposited to seal the release via. The resulting pressure was estimated as 1 MPa by measuring the vacuum diode characteristics.

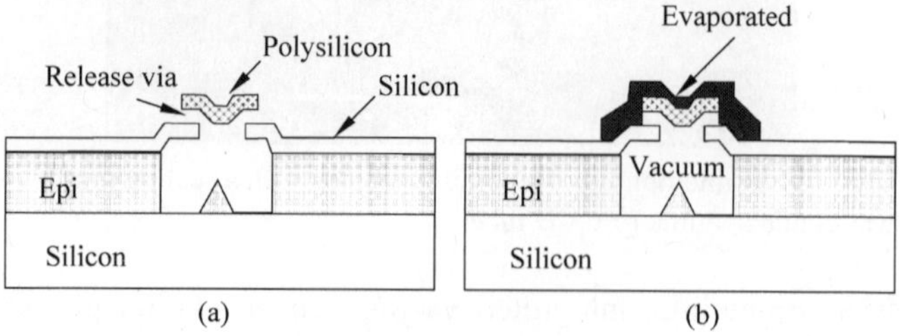

Figure 11.7 An integrated encapsulation process for a micro vacuum diode. (After M. Bartek et al.) Drawn not to scale

Although the above vacuum sealing process successfully achieved MEMS hermetic or vacuum packaging, it had several drawbacks. First, several high temperature steps were used after the standard surface-micromachining process. As such, no circuitry (such as those shown in Fig. 11.1) or temperature-sensitive materials will survive due to the global heating effect. Second, this post-packaging process is very specific and process dependent. MEMS companies or researchers have to adopt this post-packaging process with their own device manufacturing process. It can't be conducted in the multi-user MEMS process such as the MCNC MUMPs. Third, the thickness of the microshell is limited by the thin film deposition step that generally is in the range of a few micrometers. There is a big concern if the thin microshell can survive the high-pressure plastic molding process afterwards in some device packaging designs. Finally, although integrated encapsulation can achieve low pressure by wafer-level fabrication, and provide lower manufacturing costs, it does not provide the controllability of the cavity pressure.

11.5.2 Post-Packaging Process

The second approach is defined as post-packaging process. The packaging process starts when the device fabrication processes are completed, due to which this approach has high flexibility for various microsystems. For example, Fig. 11.8 shows a common industrial post-hermetic packaging that is called Dual-in-line packaging (DIP)[80, 81]. A die is placed inside a ceramic holder covered by a sealing lid. Solder or ceramic joining is generally used for assembling lid and holder under a pressure-controlled environment. High cost is the major drawback of this method because of expensive ceramic holder and low fabrication throughput.

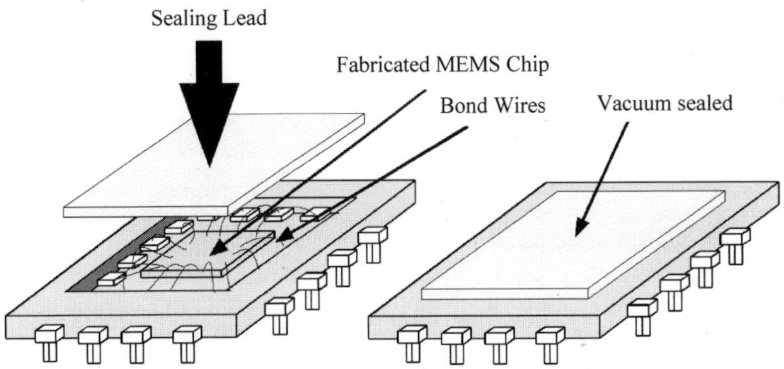

Figure 11.8 The schematic diagram of industrial post-packaging (DIPS) using a ceramic holder to be covered by a sealing lid

Another example of post-packaging method is based on wafer bonding techniques combined with microshell encapsulation. Devices are sealed by stacking another micromachined silicon or glass substrate as illustrated in Fig. 11.1. Integrated microsystems and protection shells are fabricated on different wafers, either silicon or glass, at the same time. After the two substrates are assembled together using silicon fusion, anodic, or low temperature solder bonding to achieve final encapsulation, these micro shells shall provide mechanical support, thermal path, and/or electrical contact for the MEMS devices. Low packaging cost can be expected due to wafer-level processing.

Moreover, by combining the integrated sealing process and wafer bonding technique, a wafer-level sealing process[41, 70] by transferring pre-fabricated caps to seal MEMS structures is shown in Fig. 11.9. A thin film cap made of 4 μm thick polysilicon was fabricated on the cap wafer with breakable tethers made of gold/polysilicon layer attached to the sides. Gold bumps were patterned around the edges of the cover cap, and MEMS devices were fabricated on the silicon substrate and surrounded by sealing rings with electrical interconnection line that went underneath the sealing rings. The sealing process was conducted by thermal compression bonding, and the gold bumps on the polysilicon cover were sealed to the sealing rings on the silicon substrate. The bonding condition varies with the material used on the sealing ring. For example, cold welding can be used to bond the gold bump to the gold sealing ring and hot press can be used to bond the gold bump to the aluminum surface at about 200℃. After the sealing process, the breakable tether was forcefully broken. Cohn et al.[41] demonstrated this packaging process could be accomplished in vacuum environment. However, experimental results showed substantial leakage after a period of 50 days.

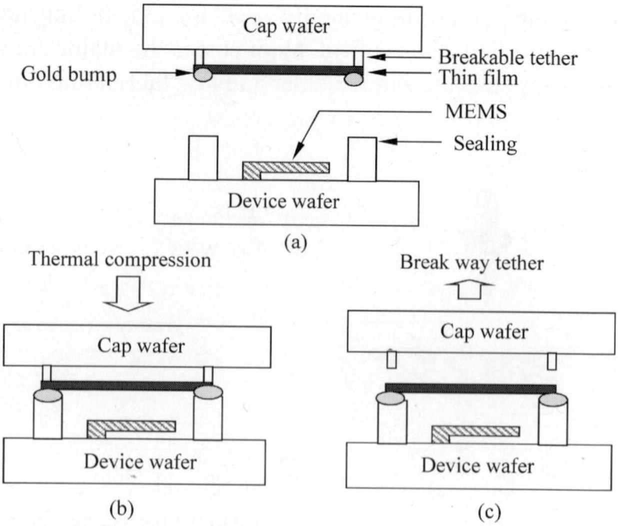

Figure 11. 9 Wafer-level packaging process (a) Fabrication of cap and device (b) Thermal compression bonding of cap and device wafers (c) Break away tether. (After M. Cohn.) Drawn not to scale

The related packaging issues are discussed by using a specific example of post-packaging by rapid thermal processing (RTP) that provides the advantages of wafer-level processing and low thermal budget. Figure 11.10 shows the schematic illustration of the RTP MEMS vacuum packaging process. Comb-shape microresonators have been chosen as the vacuum packaging examples in this chapter, and a standard surface-micromachining process is used to fabricate these microresonators[17]. One major addition to a regular microstructure is that an

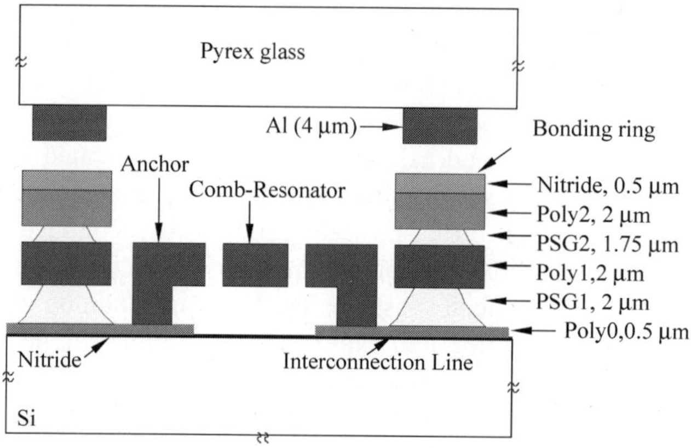

Figure 11.10 The schematic diagram of the RTP (Rapid Thermal Processing) aluminum-to-nitride bonding set up. (Chiao and Lin, 2002)

integrated sealing ring made of silicon nitride is incorporated in the manufacturing process as the topmost layer for the purpose of aluminum-to-nitride bonding[43]. A glass cap wafer is deposited and patterned with 4 μm thick aluminum sealing-rings, with width ranging from 100 μm to 250 μm and bonding area ranging from $450\times450\ \mu m^2$ to $1{,}000\times1{,}000\ \mu m^2$. Before the vacuum packaging process, both the device and cap wafers are baked in vacuum at 300℃ for over 4 hours to dry out water and gas species adhered at the surface. Afterwards, the device and cap wafers are flip chip assembled immediately, loaded into a quartz chamber, and put into a RTP chamber. The base vacuum estimated at 10 mTorr inside the quartz chamber is achieved by using a mechanical pump. The aluminum-to-nitride bond is formed after heating for 10 seconds at 750℃. Figure 11.11 shows the measured spectrum of a vacuum-packaged, double-folded beam comb-drive resonator by using a micro-stroboscope (SensArray Corporation). The central resonant frequency is about 18,625 Hz and the quality factor is extracted as 1800 ± 200 corresponding to a pressure level about 200 mTorr inside the package[82].

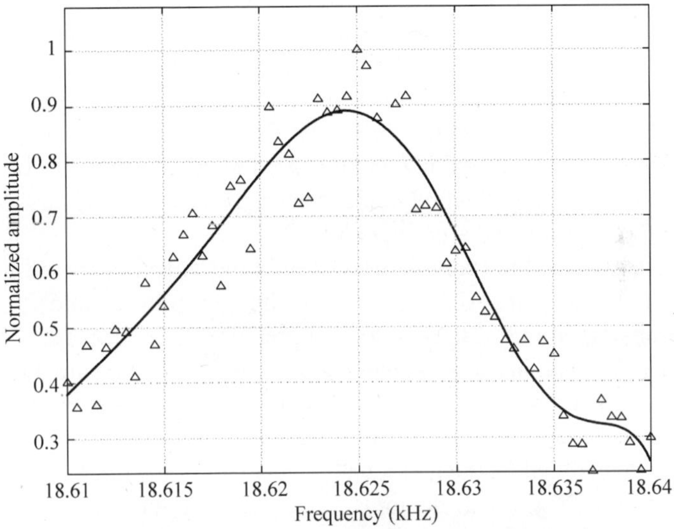

Figure 11.11 Spectrum measurement results of a vacuum encapsulated comb-shape resonator by using the RTP aluminum-to-nitride bonding method. (Chiao and Lin, 2002)

This type of post-packaging process at wafer-level has become the favorite approach to accomplish hermetic encapsulation because it can provide lower cost and process flexibility. However, the packaging process relies on 'good' bonding techniques. A strong and reliable bonding process between two substrates should be provided, and this bonding procedure should be compatible with other microsystem fabrication processes.

11.5.3 Localized Heating and Bonding

The approach of MEMS post-packaging by localized heating and bonding is proposed to address the problems of global heating effects. Previously, resistive microheaters were used as examples to provide localized heating[42], and several other means of localized heating were demonstrated recently, including laser welding[83], inductive heating[84], and ultrasonic bonding[85]. The principle of localized heating is to achieve high temperature for bonding while maintaining low temperature globally at the wafer-level. Resistive heating on top of the device substrate is applied by using microheaters to form a strong bond with silicon or glass caps. According to the results of a 2D heat conduction finite element analysis, the steady-state heating region of a 5 μm wide polysilicon microheater capped with a Pyrex glass substrate can be confined locally as long as the bottom of the silicon substrate is constrained to the ambient temperature. The physics of localized heating behind this design can be understood by solving the governing heat conduction equations of the device structure without a cap[86]. As long as the width of microheater and the thickness of silicon substrate are much smaller than the die size, and a good heat sink is placed underneath the silicon substrate, the heating can be confined locally. The temperature of silicon substrate can be kept low and close to room temperature. Several localized, resistive heating and bonding techniques have been successfully developed for packaging applications including localized silicon-to-glass fusion bonding, gold-to-silicon eutectic bonding, and localized solder bonding. Several solder materials have been successfully tested, including PSG, indium, and aluminum alloy[87].

The vacuum packaging example presented in this chapter is based on localized aluminum/silicon-to-glass solder bonding technique. Built-in folded-beam comb drive μ-resonators are used to monitor the pressure of the package. The detailed fabrication and packaging process can be found in[86]. To evaluate the integrity of the resonators packaged using localized aluminum/silicon-to-glass solder bonding, the glass cap is forcefully broken and removed from the substrate. It is observed that no damage is found on the μ-resonator and a part of the microheater is stripped away as shown in Fig. 11.12, demonstrating that a strong and uniform bond can be achieved without detrimental effects on the encapsulated device.

The post-process packaging using localized heating and bonding technique includes four basic components: ① an electrical and thermal insulation layer such as silicon dioxide or silicon nitride for localized heating, ② resistive microheaters fabricated to provide the heating source for localized bonding, ③ materials, including metal and polysilicon that can provide good bonding and hermeticity with silicon or glass substrates that can be considered as bonding materials, and ④ a good heat sink under the device substrate for localized heating provided during the bonding experiments.

MEMS devices will be fabricated on the device chip and hermetically sealed in the cavity formed by the device chip, resistive microheaters, and protection cap.

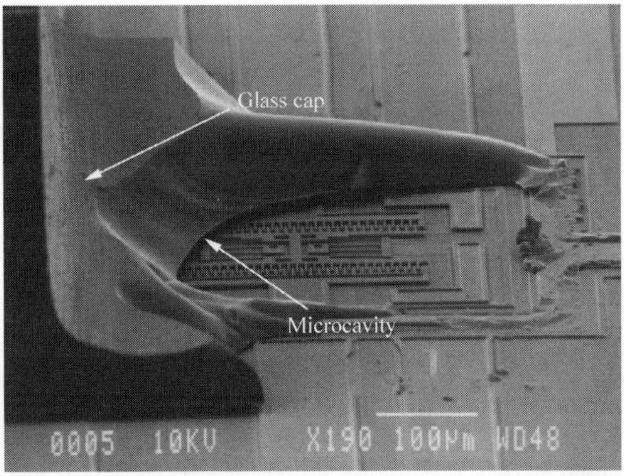

Figure 11.12 The SEM microphoto of encapsulated microresonators after the glass cap is forcefully broken

The process can be either die level or wafer level. The resistive microheaters are parallel to each other and connected together in order to ensure that identical current density is applied for individual packages at the same time. These heaters can be either fabricated on the chip or protection cap and can be built in a larger wafer for current inputs. The interconnections for these packaging cavities can be built in the dicing area such that no extra space is required for the packaging process.

Localized heating and bonding can also be achieved by ultrasonic bonding[85]. Figure 11.13 shows the experimental setup of ultrasonic bonding experiment for MEMS packaging. Au/In and Al/Al bonding systems have been tested, where In

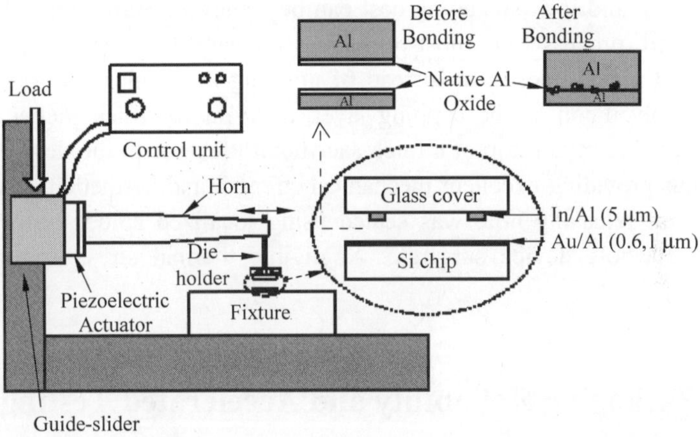

Figure 11.13 Schemetic diagram of localized bonding and packaging by ultrasonic bonding

or Al of 5 μm in thickness is patterned into a ring shape on the glass cap and Au (0.6 μm) or Al (1 μm) are deposited on the silicon side. The chips are filp chip assembled and ultrasonic energy is provided to vibrate the top chip as shown in Fig. 11.13. The ultrasonic energy can break the surface oxide and allow materials to have an intimidate contact, and form bonds. Figure 11.14 shows the packaging results and successful sealed rings can block water from leaking in.

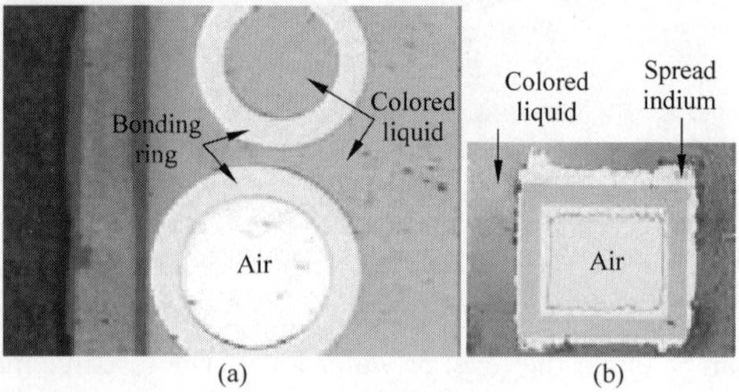

Figure 11.14 The optical microphoto of encapsulated microcavities by ultrasonic bonding: (a) Al-to-Al bonding system and (b) In-to-Au bonding system

11.5.4 Hybrid Approach

Although the fabrication of hermetic encapsulation can be generally divided into two kinds of processes as described previously, and each process has its own advantages and challenges, recent advancement in the encapsulation technique has contended the hybrid approach in which high mechanical reliability, process controllability, and low packaging cost can be achieved. Stark et al.[88] proposed an integrated process for 'post-packaging' release and vacuum sealing of electroplated nickel packages. Instead of utilizing 2 – 3 micros LPCVD silicon nitride or polysilicon as the capping layer, a 40 micros thick nickel shell was electroplated directly on top of a thick sacrificial PR prior to the device structure release, thus providing excellent mechanical strength and hermeticity. In addition, the structural releasing hole was sealed using localized solder reflow without heating the whole device substrate. Negligible thermal stress effects can be expected.

11.6 Packaging Reliability and Accelerated Testing

The thermal stress induced by the CTE mismatch is one of the main factors to affect the packaging reliability. As a matter of fact, stress can form not only during the packaging process, but also during the in-use operation of the device. In particular, the package may go through various temperature cycles in practical usage. Such temperature variations could cause the expansion of packaging materials. As a result of thermal mismatch, significant stress could be generated and could impact the device performance or cause failure. In addition to thermal mismatch, corrosion, creep, fracture, fatigue crack initiation and propagation, and delamination of thin films are all possible factors to cause package failure[89]. These failure mechanisms could be prevented or deferred under proper packaging designs. For instance, cyclic loading can generate and accumulate stresses that are initially small and eventually cause failure. Several common design practices in IC packaging have been adopted to prolong the lifetime of devices. For example, the strain in solder interconnects of BGA or flip chip packaging can be effectively reduced by introducing a polymer underfill material between the chip and the substrate to uniformly distribute thermal stress induced by CTE mismatch[90]. The strain can be further reduced if excellent thermal paths are built around interconnects to diminish the thermal stress originated from the temperature gradient between ambient and operation temperatures. Delamination phenomenon is another source to cause reliability problems, and it happens in the interface of adjacent material layers. In MEMS, components made of dissimilar materials are commonly bonded together to provide specific functions. Delamination can result in electrical or mechanical failures of devices such as mechanically cracking through the electrical via wall to make an electrical open circuit. The stress and thermal loading problems are complicated in MEMS device development, and require extensive investigations.

Reliability testing is required during the commercialization process. The reliability study is needed to provide guidelines on the improvement of packaging design and process. Hence, ‘reliability metrology,’ or ‘how to analyze the failure data,’ is very important in the packaging industry. Mathematical tools involving probability and statistical distributions are used to evaluate reliability testing data to characterize the patterns of failure and to identify the sources of failure. For example, a failure density function is defined as the time derivative of the cumulative failure function:

$$f(t) = \frac{\mathrm{d}F(t)}{\mathrm{d}t} \tag{11.1}$$

$$F(t) = \int_0^t f(s)\mathrm{d}s \tag{11.2}$$

The cumulative failure function, $F(t)$ is the fraction of a group of original devices that have failed at time t. The Weibull distribution function is one of the analytic mathematical models commonly used in the packaging reliability evaluation to represent the failure density function[19].

$$f(t)=\frac{\beta}{\lambda}\left(\frac{t}{\lambda}\right)^{\beta-1}\exp\left[-\left(\frac{t}{\lambda}\right)^{\beta}\right] \tag{11.3}$$

Where β and λ are the Weibull parameters. The parameter β is called a shape factor, which measures how the failure frequency is distributed around the average lifetime. The parameter λ is called the lifetime parameter, which indicates the time at which 63.2% of the devices fail to operate. By integrating both sides of the equation (x), $F(t)$ becomes:

$$F(t)=1-\exp\left[-\left(\frac{t}{\lambda}\right)^{\beta}\right] \tag{11.4}$$

Using the Weibull distribution function with the two parameters extrapolated by experimental data, one can estimate the number of failures at any time during the test. Moreover, knowing the meaning and values of the parameters, one can compare two sets of test data. For example, the λ with greater number means this set of samples has longer lifetime. Because all the mathematical models are statistically approximations based on real experimental data, more testing samples can provide better estimation.

The reliability of MEMS packages is best characterized by means of long-term tests with statistical data analyses. However, it is very difficult and time-consuming to obtain these experimental data from accelerated tests that put samples in extreme environments, and accelerated failures are commonly used to predict the lifetime of the devices. Unfortunately, there are not many research publications that deal with these two issues. In this section, two MEMS packaging examples that aim to address these two tests are discussed.

Figure 11.15 shows long-term measurements of Q factors of vacuum packaged μ-resonators using localized aluminum/silicon-to-glass bonding[72]. The vacuum encapsulation process is described in detail in[72]. It is found that the vacuum package provides stable vacuum environments for the μ-resonator by means of localized heating and bonding. A quality factor of 9600 has been achieved with no degradation for at least one year. Since the performance of high Q μ-resonator is very sensitive to environmental pressure variations, any leakage can be easily detected. The fact that this high Q value can hold for one year indicates the packaging process is well performed and both aluminum and Pyrex glass are suitable materials for vacuum packaging applications. According to a previous study of hermeticity in different materials, metal has lower permeability to moisture than other materials such as glass, epoxy, and silicon. With a width of 1 μm, metal can effectively block moisture for more than 10 years[19]. In this vacuum package system, the bonding width of the metal bonding ring is 30 μm, such that it can sufficiently block the diffusion process of moisture. On the other hand, the diffusion effects of air molecules into these tiny cavities have not been studied extensively, and the design guidelines for vacuum encapsulations are not clearly defined. Further investigations will be needed in this area, and the example presented here serves as a good starting point.

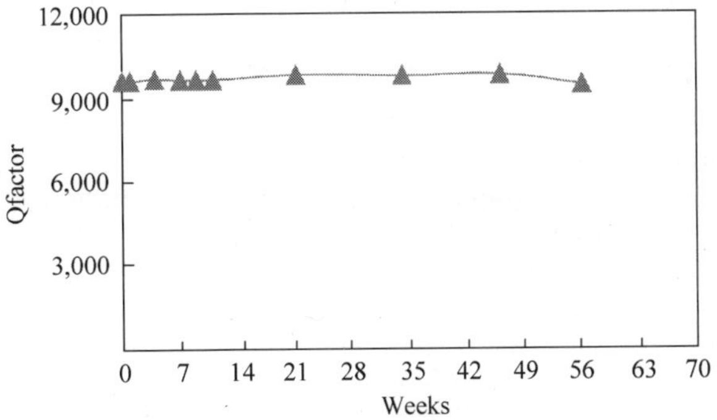

Figure 11.15 Long-term measurement of encapsulated μ-resonators. No degradation of Q factors is found after 56 weeks

On the other hand, accelerated testing puts a large amount of samples in harsh environment, such as elevated temperatures, elevated pressures, and 100% humidity, to accelerate the corrosion process. The statistical failure data are gathered and analyzed to predict the lifetime of packages under normal usage environment. As a result, the long-term reliability of the package can be predicted without going through the true long-term tests. Unfortunately, accelerated tests have not been addressed in MEMS research papers. Although the MEMS industry must have done some extensive reliability tests, they do not publish their results probably due to liability concerns. Among the very limited publications, this section uses a specific MEMS packaging system that has gone through accelerated tests as the illustration example[43].

The MEMS package is accomplished by means of RTP (Rapid Thermal Processing) bonding as described previously in this chapter. The goal of the accelerated test is to examine the failure rate at the bonding interface. The accelerated tests start by putting the packaged samples into the autoclave chamber filled with high temperature and pressurized steam at 130℃, 2.7 atm, and 100% relative humidity for accelerated testing. The pressurized steam can penetrate small crevasses if there is any defect at the bonding interface. Elevated temperature and humid environment speed up the corrosion process. A package is considered as failure if water is condensed or diffused into the package. Statistical failure data are gathered every 24 hours under optical examination for a period of 864 hours when new failure is seldom observed. Because of the robustness of the samples, it is difficult to conduct the tests all the way when all the packages may fail. The cumulative failure function is recorded and it is found that most failures occur at the first 96 hours, and such high early failure reflects the yielding issue of the bonding process. Weibull and Lognormal models are compared to predict the lifetime of the packages, and it is found that Lognormal model fits better to describe the statistical data. Figure 11.16 shows the inverse standard normal distribution function versus ln (time), and the maximum likelihood estimator (MLE) is used to predict the mean, standard deviation, and the MTTF (mean time to failure). Table 11.2 shows the MLE calculation results of MTTF. The wide interval of confidence level comes from the fact that only a small number of samples failed at the end of the test. It is also observed that packages with larger bonding width and smaller bonding areas have larger MTTF values. The lower bound of the MTTF provides the worst-case scenario. For example, only 4 out of 31 samples failed when tests stopped in the case of ring width of 200 μm and sealing area of 450 × 450 μm^2. The MTTF predicts, in the worst-case scenario, that there is 90% chance that a package will fail in 0.57 years in the autoclave environment.

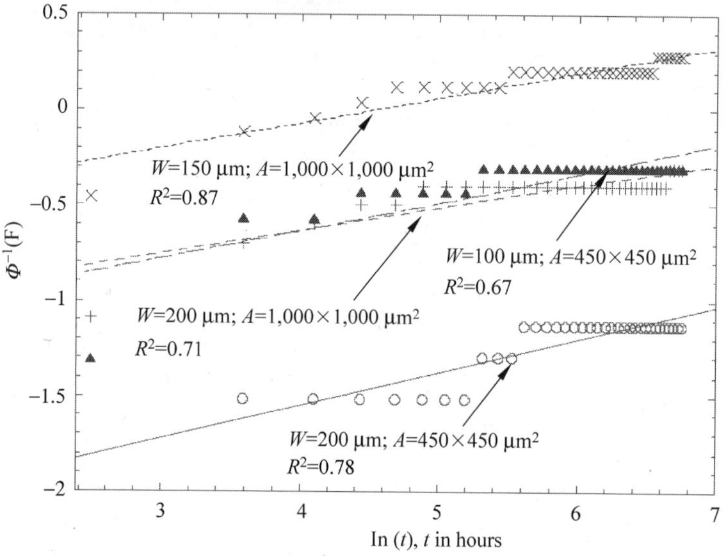

Figure 11.16 Life data fitted by Lognormal distribution. R^2 is the coefficient of determination

Table 11.2 The maximum likelihood estimation for mean time to failure (MTTF)

Bonding Area, A (μm^2) width W (μm)	MTTF		Worst cases in jungle condition (years)
	UB (years)	LB (years)	
200	450×450	1.8E7	1,700
100	450×450	5.3	300
200	1,000×1,000	6.5E3	270
150	1,000×1,000	0.50	50

It is widely accepted that the acceleration factor (AF) for autoclave tests follows the Arrhenious equation[19], and can be modeled as:

$$AF = \frac{(RH^{-n}e^{\Delta E_a/kT})_{\text{normal}}}{(RH^{-n}e^{\Delta E_a/kT})_{\text{accelerated}}} \tag{11.5}$$

Where RH is relative humidity (85%, $RH=85$), k is the Boltzmann constant and T is the absolute temperature. The recommended value for n, an empirical constant, is 3.0[90]; and ΔE_a, the activation energy, is 0.9 eV for plastic dip package and 0.997 eV for anodically bonded glass-to-silicon package[56]. If $\Delta E_a=0.9$ is used to estimate the AF for the accelerated testing condition as compared with the jungle condition (35℃, 1 atm and 95% RH), AF is about 3,000, and the worst case lifetime values in jungle condition are also listed in Table 11.2. The high values of estimated MTTF in jungle condition could be a result of over-estimation of AF because plastic dip package may have smaller AFs than those of glass packages. Nevertheless, these data and analyses provide important guidelines in the area of accelerated tests for MEMS packages.

Conventionally, MEMS devices are first fabricated and diced on a silicon wafer. After that, the freestanding micromechanical structures are released by removing the underneath 'sacrificial layer'[76]. However, dicing is a wet process that could result in a stiction problem to the freestanding microstructure. Furthermore, the cooling water jet and particle contamination during dicing could also cause device failure. Therefore, it is desirable to develop a low cost hermetic package process that can protect the microstructures during the following wet dicing operation. Reliability is not the only critical factor for MEMS packaging. Low packaging cost and minimal side effects induced by the packaging process are the other important packaging issues.

11.7 Future Trends and Summary

In the past, the development of MEMS packaging mainly originated from IC packaging advancement because existing packaging techniques could significantly reduce the development cost of MEMS. However, it is expected that the situation will change very soon in such a way that MEMS packaging approaches will assist the IC packaging development. Recent progresses in IC packaging are aimed to provide high I/O density and more chip integration capability for the needs of high speed and high data communication rates. In order to satisfy those requirements, several packaging concepts and techniques are developed, such as, 3D packaging, wafer level packaging, BGA, and flip chip technique. Although all concepts and methods can provide a package with more I/O density, flexibility in chip integration, and lower manufacturing cost for IC fabrication, they are still insufficient to provide solutions for the future applications because of the increase in complexity and requirements of MEMS packaging. On the contrary, with the progress of MEMS fabrication technologies, several key processes such as DRIE (Deep Reactive Ion Etching), wafer bonding, and thick photo resist processes[91] have been utilized for IC packaging fabrication. Therefore, technologies developed in MEMS fabrication can also assist the development of new IC packaging approaches.

In order to address the future needs of process integration, adaptive multi-chip module (MCM)[26] or 3D packaging combined with vertical through substrate interconnects[8, 92] are promising approaches for the development of future MEMS packaging processes. These packaging methods can provide more flexibility in device fabrication and packaging based on low temperature flip chip solder bonding techniques. Devices can be fabricated before they are integrated together to form microsystems to dramatically reduce the packaging costs. Vertical through substrate interconnects can have higher I/O density, smaller resistance and parasitic capacitance, and mutual inductance. Although this approach provides many possible advantages, technical challenges exist. For instance, metal is commonly used as the fill material inside the vertical vias as electrical interconnects, and it may introduce large thermal mismatch with respect to silicon substrate and generate huge thermal stress to cause packaging reliability problems. Moreover, it will be an interesting engineering challenge to fill the materials into those high aspect ratio vias.

The future development of MEMS packaging could depend on the successful implementation of unique techniques such as:

Development of mechanical, thermal, and electrical models for packaging designs and fabrication processes;

Wafer-level, chip-scale packaging with low packaging cost and high yield;

Effective testing techniques at the wafer-level to reduce the testing costs;

Device integrations by vertical through-interconnects as an interposer to avoid thermal mismatch problems.

In addition to these approaches and challenges, there are many other possibilities that have not been listed but also require dedicated investigations. For example, several key nanotechnologies have been introduced in recent years, but the packaging solutions for NEMS devices have not been addressed. Because it is feasible to use MEMS as the platform for NEMS fabrication, all the packaging issues discussed in the chapter can be directly applied to NEMS devices. On the other hand, nanotechnology may introduce new opportunities for MEMS/NEMS packaging applications by providing materials with superior electrical, mechanical, and thermal properties[93–96]. For example, carbon nanotubes have very high thermal conductivity [95] and may be suitable to increase the thermal cooling effects for better IC/MEMS/NEMS packaging applications.

In summary, MEMS packaging issues have been introduced in the areas of fabrication, application, reliability, and future development. Packaging design and modeling, packaging material selection, packaging process integration, and packaging costs are main issues to be considered when developing new MEMS packaging processes.

References

[1] Peterson K.E., (1982), Silicon as a mechanical material, *Proceedings of IEEE*, **70**(1982): 420 – 457

[2] Lin L. W., H. C. Chu, and Y. W. Lu, (1999) "A simulation program for the sensitivity and linearity of piezoresistive pressure sensors," *IEEE/ASME Journal of Microelectromechanical Systems*, **8**(1999): 514 – 522

[3] Tai Y. C. and R. S. Muller, (1988), "Lightly-doped Polysilicon Bridge as a Flow Meter," *Sensors and Actuators*, **15**: 63 – 75

[4] Hicks D., S. C. Chang, M. W. Putty, and D. S. Eddy, (1994) "Piezoelectrically activated resonant bridge microaccelerometer," *Solid-State Sensors and Actuators Workshop*,1994: 225 – 228

[5] Berstein J., S. Cho, A. King, A. Kourepenis, P. Maciel, and M. Weinberg, (1993), "A micromachined comb-drive tuning fork rate gyroscope," *6th IEEE, Int. Conf. on MEMS, 1993*, 143 – 148

[6] Zdeblick M. J., and J. B. Angell, (1987), "A Microminiature Electric-to-Fluidic Valve," Proceedings of Trandsucers'87, the 4th International Conference on Solid-State Transducers and Actautors, Tokyo, Japan, June 2 – 6, 827 – 829

[7] Tsai J.H. and L. Lin, (2002), "A thermal bubble actuated micro nozzle-diffuser pump," *IEEE/ASME Journal of Microelectromechanical Systems*, accepted

[8] Ok S. J. and D. Baldwin, (2002), "High density, aspect ratio through-wafer electrical interconnect vias for low cost, generic modular MEMS packaging," 8th IEEE *Int. Sym. On Adv. Pack. Mat.*, **2002**: 8 – 11

[9] Reichl H. and V. Grosser, (2001), "Overview and development trends in the field of MEMS packaging," 14th IEEE, *Int. Conf. on MEMS*, 2001: 1 – 5

[10] Kapur P., P. M. McVittie, and K. Saraswat, (2000), "Technology and reliability constrained future copper interconnects=Part II: performance implication," *IEEE, Trans. Electron Dev.*, **49**(2000): 598 – 604

[11] Lau J., (1996), "Flip chip technologies," McGraw-Hill. 1996

[12] Prasad R., "Surface mount technology: principles and practice," 2nd, New York, Chapman & Hall, 1989

[13] Töpper M., J. Auersperg, V. Glaw, K. Kaskoun, E. Prack, B. Keser, P. Coskina, D. Jäger, D. Petter, O. Ehrmann, K. Samulewicz, C. Meinherz, S. Fehlberg, C. Karduck, and H. Reichl, "Fab integrated packaging (FIP) a new concept for high reliability wafer-level chip size packaging,", IEEE, *ECTC*, 2000, 74 – 81

[14] Savastiouk S., O. Siniaguine, and E. Korczynski, (2000), "3D wafer level packaging," Int. Conf. High-Density Interconnect and Systems packaging, 26 – 31

[15] Tsai J. H. and L. Lin, (2001), "Micro-to-macro fluidic interconnectors with an integrated polymer sealant," *Journal of Micromechanics and Microengineering*, **11**: 577 – 581

[16] Core T. A., W. K. Tsang, and S. Sherman, (1993), "Fabrication technology for an Integrated Surface-Micromachined Sensor," *Solid State Technology*, October, **1993**: 39 – 47

[17] Koester K., R. Majedevan, A. Shishkoff, and K. Marcus, (1996), "Multi-user MEMS processes," (MUMPS) introduction and design rules, rev. 4, MCNC MEMS Technology Applications Center, Research Triangle Park, NC 27709, July 1996

[18] Lengtenberg R. and H. A. C. Tilmans, (1994), "Electrically driven vacuum-encapsulated polysilicon resonantor, Part I: Design and Fabrication," *Sensors and Actuators A*, **45**: 57 – 66

[19] Tummala R. R., E. J. Rymaszewski, and A. G. Klopfenstein, (1997), "Microelectronics packaging handbook, semiconductor packaging", Chapman & Hall, 1997

[20] Wolf S., 1995, "Silicon processing for the VLSI era, Vol Ⅰ: process technology," Lattice Press

[21] Bhardway J. K. and H. Ashraf, (1995), "Advanced silicon etching using high density plasmas," *SPIE Micromachining & Fabrication Technology*, **2639**: 224 – 233

[22] Ko W. H., J. T. Suminto, and G. J. Yeh, (1985), "Bonding techniques for microsensors," Micromachining and Micropackaging for Transducers, Elsevier Science Publishers

[23] Senturia S.D. and R. L. Smith, (1988), "Microsensor packaging and system partitioning," *Sensors and Actuators*, **15**: 221 – 234

[24] Smith R. L. and S. D. Collins, (1988), "Micromachined packaging for chemical microsensors," *IEEE Trans. on Electron Devices*, **ED 35**: 787 – 792

[25] Butler J. T., V. M. Bright, P. B. Chu, and R. J. Saia, (1998), "Adapting multichip module foundries for MEMS packaging," IEEE, *Int. Conf. on Multi. Mod. and High Den. Pack.,*" **1998**: 106 – 111

[26] Schuenemann M., A. J. Kourosh, V. Grosser, R. Leutenbauer, G. Bauer, W. Schaefer, and H. Reichl, (2000), "MEM modular packaging and interfaces," IEEE, *ECTC*, 2000: 681 – 688

[27] Lee D. W., Ono Takahito, Abe Takashi, and M. Esashi, "Fabrication of microprobe array with sub-100 nm nano-heater for nanometric thermal imaging and data storage," IEEE, Proceedings of IEEE Micro Electro Mechanical Systems Conference, Interlaken, Switzerland, Jan. 2001, 204 – 207

[28] Laskar A. S. and B. Blythe, (1993), "Epoxy multichip modules, a solution to the problem of packaging and interconnection of sensors and signal-processing chips," *Sensors and Actuators A*, **36**: 1 – 27

[29] Reichl R., 1991, "Packaging and interconnection of sensors," *Sensors and Actuators* A, **25 – 27**: 63 – 71

[30] Grisel A., C. Francis, E. Verney, and G. Mondin, (1989), "Packaging technologies for integrated electrochemical sensors," *Sensors and Actuators*, **17**: 285 – 295

[31] Lund J. L. and K. D. Wise, (2002), "Chip-level encapsulation of implantable CMOS microelectrode arrays," 1994 Solid-State Sensor and Actuator Workshop, Hilton Head, 29 – 32

[32] Akin T., B. Siaie, and K. Najafi, (1996), "Modular micromachined high-density connector for implantable biomedical systems," *Micro Electro Mechanical Systems Workshop, 1996*, 497 – 502

[33] Muller L., M. H. Hecht, L.M. Miller, et al., (1996), "Packaging Qualification for MEMS-Based Space Systems," *Micro Electro Mechanical Systems Workshop*. 1996: 503 – 508

[34] Lin L., (1993), "Selective encapsulations of MEMS: micro channels, needles, resonators, and electromechanical filters," Ph.D. Thesis, UC Berkeley, 1993

[35] Guckel H., (1991), "Surface micromachined pressure transducers," *Sensors and Actuators*, **A28**: 133 – 146

[36] Sniegowski J.J., H. Guckle, and R. T. Christenson, (1990), "Performance characteristics of second generation polysilicon resonating beam force transducers," IEEE Solid-State Sensor and Actuator Workshop, Hilton Head Island, 1990, 9 – 12

[37] Ikeda K., H. Kuwayama, T. Kobayashi, T. Watanabe, T. Nishikawa, T. Oshida, and K. Harada, (1990), "Three dimensional micromachining of silicon pressure sensor integrating resonant strain gauge on diaphragm," *Sensors and Actuators*, **A21 – 23**: 1001 – 1010

[38] Mastrangelo C. H. and R. S. Muller, (1989), "Vacuum-sealed silicon micromachined incandescent light source," IEEE, *IEDM*, 503 – 506

[39] Smith J., S. Montague, J. Sniegowski, R. Manginell, P. McWhorter, and R. Huber, (1996), "Characterization of the Embedded Micromechanical Device Approach to the Monolithic Integration of MEMS with CMOS," *SPIE*, 2879, Oct. 1996

[40] Van der Groen S., M. Rosmeulen, P. Jansen, K. Baert, and L. Deferm, (1997), "CMOS Compatible Wafer Scale Adhesive Bonding for Circuit Transfer," International Conference on Solid-State Sensors and Actuators, Transducers'97, 629 – 632

[41] Cohn M. B., Y. Liang, R. Howe, and A. P. Pisano, (1996), "Wafer to wafer transfer of microstructures for vacuum package," Solid State Sensor and Actuator Workshop, Hilton Head, 32 – 35

[42] Cheng Y. T., Y. T. Hsu, L. Lin, C. T. Nguyen, and Najafi K., "Vacuum packaging using localized aluminum/silicon-to-glass bonding using localized aluminum/silicon-to-glass bonding," 14th IEEE, *Int. Conf. on MEMS*, 2001, 18 – 21

[43] Chiao M..and L. W. Lin, (2002), "Vacuum packaging of microresonators by rapid thermal processing," Proceedings of SPIE on Smart Electronics, MEMS, and Nanotechnology, 4700, San Diego, 2002, 17 – 21

[44] Esashi M., S. Shoji, and A. Nakano, (1989), "Normally closed microvalve and micropump fabricated on a silicon wafer," *Sensors and Actuators*, **20**: 163 – 169

[45] Poplawski M. E., R. W. Hower, and R. B. Brown, (1994), "A simple packaging process for chemical sensors," *Solid-State Sensor and Actuator Workshop*, **1994**: 25 – 28

[46] Trautweiler S. F., O. Paul, J. Stahl, and H. Baltes, (1996), "Anodically bonded silicon membranes for sealed and flush mounted microsensors," *Micro Electro Mechanical Systems Workshop, 1996*, 61 – 66

[47] Klaassen E. H., K. Petersen, J. M. Noworolski, J. Logan, N. I. Malfu, J. Brown, C. Storment, W. McCulley, and G. T. A. Kovac, (1996), "Silicon fusion bonding and deep reactive ion etching: A new technology for microstructures," *Sensors and Actuators*, **A52**: 132 – 139

[48] Hsu C. H. and M. A. Schmidt, (1994), "Micromachined structures fabricated using a wafer-bonded sealed cavity process," Solid State Sensor and Actuator Workshop, Hilton

Head, 151 – 155

[49] Tiensuu A. L., J. A. Schweitz, and S. Johansson, (1995), "In situ investigation of precise high strength micro assembly using Au-Si eutectic bonding," Int. Conf. on Solid-State Sensors and Actuators, and Eurosensors IX, 1995, 236 – 239

[50] Lee Y. and K. Wise, (1982), "A batch-fabricated silicon capacitive pressure transducer with low temperature sensitivity," *IEEE Trans. on Electron Devices*,. **ED-29**: 42 – 48

[51] Bower R. W., M. S. Ismail, and B. E. Roberds, (1993), "Low temperature Si_3N_4 direct bonding," *Appl. Phys. Lett.*, **62**: 3485 – 3487

[52] Takagi H., R. Maeda, T. R. Chung, and T. Suga, (1997), "Low temperature direct bonding of silicon and silicon dioxide by the surface activation method," Int. Conf. on Solid-State Sensors and Actuators, Transducer 97, 1, 657 – 660

[53] Wallis G. and D. Pomerantz, (1969), "Filed assisted glass-metal sealing," *J. of Applied Physics*, **40**: 3946 – 3949

[54] Bowman L. and J. Meindl, (1986), "The packaging of implantable integrated sensors," *IEEE Trans. on Biomedical Engineering*, BME-33: 248 – 255

[55] Esashi M., (1994), "Encapsulated micro mechanical sensors," *Microsystems Technologies*, 1, 2 – 9

[56] Ziaie B., Arx J. Von, M. Dokmeci, and K. Najafi, (1996), "A hermetic glass-silicon micropackages with high-density on-Chip feedthroughs for sensors and actuators," *J. of Microelectromechanical Systems*, **5**: 166 – 179

[57] Chavan A. V. and K. D. Wise, (2001), "Batch-Processed Vacuum-Sealed Capacitive Pressure Sensors," *ASME/IEEE Journal of Microelectromechanical Systems*, **10**(4): 580 – 588

[58] Kim S. C. and K D. Wise, (1983), "Temperature Sensitivity in Silicon Piezoresistive Pressure Transducers," *IEEE Transactions on Electron Devices*, **ED-30**(7): 802 – 810

[59] Henmi H., S. Shoji, Y. Shoji, K. Yoshimi, and M. Esashi, (1994), "Vacuum Packaging for Microsensors by Glass-Silicon Anodic Bonding," *Sensors and Actuators A-Physical*, **A43**(1-3): 243 – 248

[60] Hara T., S. Kobayashi, and K. Ohwada, (1999), "A New Fabrication Mmethod for Low-Pressure Package with Glass-Silicon-Glass Structure and Its Stability," The 10th International Conference on Solid-State Sensors and Actuators, Transducers'99 Digest of technical papers, v2, 1999. 1316 – 1319

[61] Shoji S., H. Kicuchi, H. Torigoe, (1997), "Anodic bonding below 180 degree C for packaging and assembling of MEMS using lithium aluminosilicate-beta-quartz glass-ceramic," Proceedings of the 1997 10th Annual International Workshop on Micro Electro Mechanical Systems, Nagoay, Japan, 482 – 487

[62] Esashi M., N. Akira, S. Shoji, and H. Hebiguchi, (1990), "Low-temperature silicon-to-silicon anodic bonding with intermediate low melting point glass," *Sensors and Actuators*, **A23**: 931 – 934

[63] Hanneborg A., M. Nese, H. Jakobsen, and R. Holm, (1992), "Silicon-to-thin film anodic bonding," *J. Micromech. and Microengin.*, **2**: 117 – 121

[64] Audet S. A. and K. M. Edenfeld, (1997), "Integrated sensor wafer-level packaging," International Conference on Solid-State Sensors and Actuators, Transducers'97, 287 – 289

[65] Benson R. C., N. deHaas, P. Goodwin, and T. E. Phillips, (1992), "Epoxy adhesives in microelectronic hybrid applications," *Johns Hopkins APL Tech. Dig.*, **13**: 400 – 406
[66] Shimbo M. and J. Yoshikawa, (1996), "New silicon bonding method," *J. Electrochem. Soc.*, **143**: 2371 – 2377
[67] Zavracky P. M. and B. Vu, (1995), "Patterned eutectic bonding with Al/Ge thin film for MEMS," *SPIE*, **2639**: 46 – 52
[68] Humpston G. and D. M. Jacobson, (1993), "Principles of soldering and brazing," ASM International, 241 – 244
[69] Singh A., D. Horsely, M. B. Cohn, and R. Howe, (1997), "Batch transfer of microstructures using flip-chip solder bump bonding," International Conference on Solid State Sensors and Actuators, Transducer 97, 1, 265 – 268
[70] Maharbiz M. M., M. B. Cohn, R. T. Howe, R. Horowitz, and A. P. Pisano, (1999), "Batch micropackaging by compression-bonded wafer-wafer transfer," 12th International Conference on MEMS, 1999, 482 – 489
[71] Cheng Y. T., L. Lin, and K. Najafi, (2000), "Localized silicon fusion and eutectic bonding for MEMS fabrication and packaging," IEEE/ASME *Journal of Microelectromechanical Systems*, **9**: 3 – 8
[72] Cheng Y. T., L. Lin, K. Najafi, (2001), "Fabrication and hermeticity testing of a glass-silicon packaging formed using localized aluminum/silicon-to-glass bonding," IEEE/ASME *Journal of Microelectromechanical Systems*, **10**: 392 – 399
[73] Su Y. C. and L. Lin, (2000), "Localized plastic bonding for micro assembly, packaging and liquid encapsulation," Proceedings of IEEE Micro Electro Mechanical Systems Conference, 50 – 53, Jan., Interlaken, Switzerland, 2001
[74] Schwartz M., (1995), "Brazing," Chapman & Hall, London
[75] Lin L. W., R. T. Howe, and A. P. Pisano, (1998), "Microelectromechanical Filters for Signal Processing," *IEEE/ASME Journal of Microelectromechanical Systems*, **7**: 286 – 294
[76] Tang W. C., C. T. C. Nguyen, and R. T. Howe, (1989), "Laterally driven polysilicon resonant microstructures," *Sensors and Actuators*, **A20**: 25 – 32
[77] Mulhern G. T., D. S. Soane, and R. T. Howe, (1993), "Supercritical carbon dioxide drying of microstructures," *7th Int. Conference on Solid State Sensors and Actuators*, Yokohama, Japan, June 1993, 296 – 299
[78] Judy M., (1994), "Micromechanisms Using Sidewall Beams," Ph.D dissertation, EECS Department, University of California at Berkeley, 162
[79] Bartek M., J. A. Foerster, and R. F. Wolffenbuttel, (1997), "Vacuum Sealing of Mcirocavities Using Metal Evaporation," *Sensors and Actuators A*, **v61**: 364 – 368
[80] Leung A. M., J. Jones, E. Czyzewska, J. Chen, and B. Woods, (1998), "Micromachined accelerometer based on convection heat transfer," 11th International Conference on MEMS, 627 – 630
[81] Spark D. R., L. Jordan, and J. H. Frazee, (1996), "Flexible vacuum-packaging method for resonating micromachines," *Sensors and Actuators*, **A55**: 179 – 183
[82] Mu C. and L.W. Lin, (2006), "Device-Level Hermetic Packaging of Microresonators by RTP Aluminum-to-Nitride Bonding," *IEEE/ASME Journal of Microelectromechanical Systems*, **15**(3): 515 – 522

[83] Luo C. and L. Lin, (2002), "The Application of Nanosecond-Pulsed Laser Welding Technology in MEMS Packaging with a Shadow Mask," *Sensors and Actuators*, **A 97 – 98**: 398 – 404

[84] Cao A., M. Chiao, and L.W. Lin, (2002), "Selective and localized wafer bonding using induction heating," *Technical Digest of Solid-State Sensors and Actuators Workshop*, Hilton Head Island,.2002, 153 – 156

[85] Kim J. B., M. Chiao, and L. Lin, (2002), "Ultrasonic Bonding of In/Au and Al/Al for Hermetic Sealing of MEMS Packaging," Proceedings of IEEE Micro Electro Mechanical Systems Conference, Las Vegas, Jan. 2002, 415 – 418

[86] Cheng Y. T., W. T. Hsu, K. Najafi, C. T. Nguyen, and L. Lin, (2002), "Vacuum packaging technology using localized aluminum/silicon-to-glass bonding," *J. of Microelectromechanical Systems*, accepted, 2002

[87] Cheng Y. T., L. Lin, and K. Najafi, (1999), "Localized bonding with PSG or indium solder as intermediate layer," 12th International Conference on MEMS, 1999, 285 – 289

[88] B. H. Stark and K. Najafi, (2004), "A Low Temperature Thin Film Electroplated Metal Vacuum Package," *IEEE/ASME J. Micro Electro Mechanical Systems (JMEMS)*, **13**(2): 147 – 157

[89] Tummala R. R., (2001), "Fundamentals of Microsystems packaging," McGraw-Hill

[90] Brown W. D. (1999), "Advanced Electronic Packaging," IEEE Press

[91] Niklaus F., P. Znoksson, E. Käluesten, and G. Stemme, (2000), "Void free full wafer adhesion bonding," IEEE, Proceedings of IEEE Micro Electro Mechanical Systems Conference, 241 – 252

[92] Cheng C. H., A. S. Ergun, and B. T. Khuri-Yakub, (2002), "Electrical through-wafer interconnects with sub-picofarad parasitic capacitance," *IEEE*, *ECTC*, 18 – 21

[93] Routkevitch D., A. A. Tager, J. Haruyama, D. Almawlawi, M. Moskovits, and J. M. Xu, (1996), "Nonlithographic nano-array arrays: fabrication, physics, and device applications," IEEE, *Trans. Elec. Dev.*, **43**: 1646 – 1658

[94] Guo J., M. Lundstrom, and S. Datta, (2002), "Performance projections for ballistic carbon nanotube fieldeffect transistors," *Appl. Phys. Lett.*, **80**: 3192 – 3194

[95] Choi S. U. S., Z. G. Zhang, W. Yu, F. E. Lockwood, E. A. Grulke, (2001), "Anomalous thermal conductivity enhancement in nanotube suspensions," *Appl. Phys. Lett.*, **79**: 2252 – 2254

[96] Velikov K., A. Moroz, and A. Blaaderen, (2002), "Photonic crystals of core-shell colloidal particles," *Appl. Phys. Lett.*, **80**: 49 – 51

Nanotechnology

12 Advancement of Laser-Assisted and Roller-Based Nanoimprinting Technology

Yung-Chun Lee[1] and Fei-Bin Hsiao[2]

[1] Department of Mechanical Engineering, Tainan Cheng Kung University
E-mail: yunglee@mail.ncku.edu.tw

[2] Institute of Aeronautics and Astronautics, Tainan Cheng Kung University,
E-mail: fbhsiao@mail.ncku.edu.tw

Abstract Nanoimprinting technology was first developed in 1995 and is now recognized as one of the most promising approaches for large-area and low-cost fabrication of nanostructures. In this chapter, three types of laser-assisted and roller-based nanoimprinting and contact-printing methods developed in recent years will be addressed. First of all, a laser-assisted roller imprinting (LARI) method which can directly transfer the pattern from a quartz mold to a silicon substrate is introduced. The advantage of LARI is that the pattern transformation is direct, fast, and without any chemical etching processes. Secondly, a light-assisted metal film patterning (LAMP) method which transfers a patterned metal film directly from a silicon mold to a substrate is discussed. The pattern transformation relies on both mechanical contact pressure and optical heating at the interface. Metal patterns with 100 nm feature size can be easily transferred in laboratory using simple equipments and setups. Finally, a contact-transfer and mask-embedded lithography (CMEL) is proposed which cleverly arranges pure mechanical forces and surface energy difference to achieve the patterning of nano-structures on various kinds of substrates. Future developments and potential applications of these roller-based nanoimprinting and nano-patterning methods will be addressed.

Keywords Nanoimprinting, laser-assisted, roller-based, contact-printing, nanofabrication, nanostructure

12.1 Introduction

Nanopatterning and nanofabrication are fundamental and critical issues in the development of nanotechnology and nanoscience. The most commonly used method in nanopatterning and nanofabrication is photolithography which has being continuously improved in the past few decades so that now 90 nm and even 65 nm line-width is achieved in the semiconductor industry. However, the high capital investments and operating costs of conventional photolithography methods raise a barrier that denies access to many academic researchers. Furthermore, these photolithography systems are used only for silicon substrates and for large wafer sizes, and therefore may not be suitable for laboratory use for a variety of different purposes and/or requirements. In addition to conventional photolithography, other alternatives for nanopatterning and nanofabrication are:

(1) electron beam (E-beam) lithography, and

(2) focused ion beam (FIB) that are capable of line-widths down to 100 nm or less.

However, both E-beam and FIB systems are also very expensive and are extremely slow processes so that the final products are either limited to small area sizes or become very expensive.

To overcome the above-mentioned limitations and difficulties several non-conventional lithography methods have been developed in the past two decades. Among them, the most promising techniques for next-generation nanopatterning and nanofabrication are:

(1) imprinting printing lithography, and

(2) contact printing lithography.

These have the potential to overcome the disadvantages of conventional photolithography, which are:

(1) optical diffraction limit,

(2) complicated chemical etching processes, and

(3) huge costs in capital investments and operating costs.

Small feature sizes at sub-micrometer and nanometer scales can easily be achieved based on these imprinting/printing lithography techniques using relatively simple approaches and much lower costs. Well-known techniques in imprinting/printing lithography include nanoimprinting lithography (NIL)[1–8], step and flash imprint lithography (SFIL)[9–15], and micro-contact printing (μCP)[16–21]. Details of these methods as well as many other methods are given in several review papers[22–24].

For NIL, as shown in Fig. 12.1, a silicon mold is typically used and is pressed against a resist layer deposited on top of a substrate. At an elevated temperature beyond the glass transition temperature (T_g) of the resist layer, the mold can be embossed into the resist layer, which helps to transfer the patterns. Subsequent chemical etching processes on the residual resist layer will then complete the pattern transfer.

The SFIL is similar to NIL except that the mold is made of transparent materials (quartz, for example) and the resist layer is replaced by a UV-curable solution of low viscosity. The solution is trapped in the gaps between the mold and the substrate, when they are brought into contact, is solidified upon UV irradiation incident from the mold side, forming a replica of the mold's features on top of the substrate. Both NIL and SFIL have been very successfully developed and commercial systems are readily available.

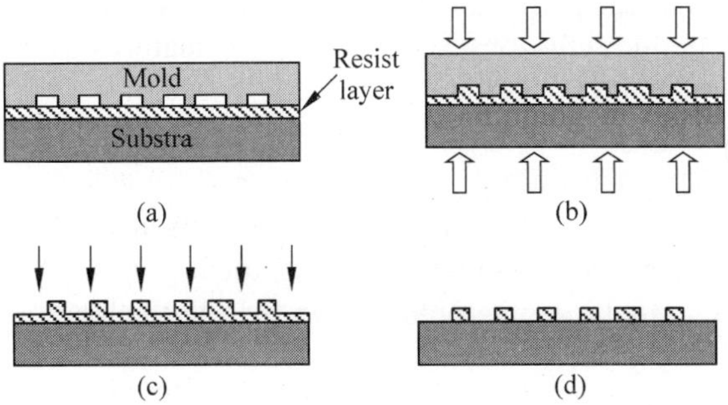

Figure 12.1 A standard nanoimprinting lithography (NIL) process, (a) a mold, resist-layer and substrate configuration, (b) heating up above T_g and mold embossing into the resist layer, (c) O_2 plasma etching, to remove the residual resist layer, and (d) completing the pattern transformation

Different from NIL and SFIL, the μCP utilizes a soft material poly (dimethylsiloxane) (PDMS) as a stamp, that is, a soft mold. Figure 12.2 shows a typical procedure of a μCP process. The mold surface is first coated with self-assembled monolayers (SAMs), which act like the ink to the PDMS stamp. After that the substrate is deposited with a gold film which has good adherence to SAMs. Therefore the patterned SAMs can be easily printed onto the gold film. The patterned SAM serves as the etching mask to ctch the gold film. The etched and patterned gold pattern serves as another etching mask for subsequent etching process on the substrate.

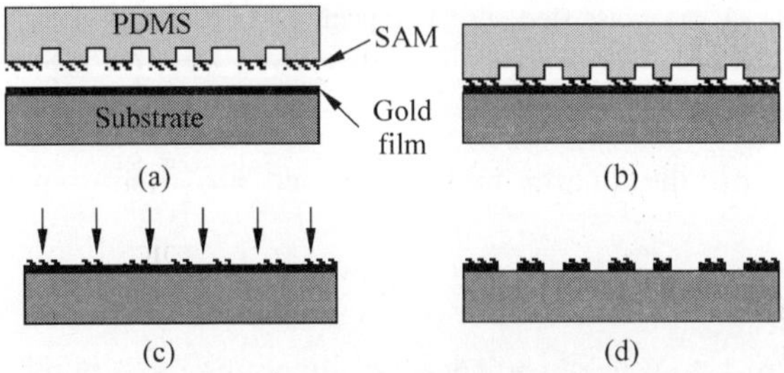

Figure 12.2 A standard micro-contact printing (μCP) process: (a) PDMS mold coated with self-assembly monolayers (SAMs) and a substrate coated with a gold film, (b) contact printing and transferring of patterned SAM to gold film, (c) Etching on gold film using patterned SAMs as the mask, and (d) completing the pattern transformation to substrate

As mentioned above, all the three imprinting and printing lithography methods requires several chemical etching processes and therefore the procedures are quite involved and time-consuming. A very different nanopatterning technique known as laser assisted direct imprinting (LADI) was proposed in 2002[25], which came to be a fast and direct way to fabricate micro- and nanoscaled structures. Figure 12.3 schematically illustrates the LADI process. Steps are:

(1) A quartz mold with some micro- or nanofeatures is pressed against a silicon substrate under a given loading pressure.

(2) Then a short UV laser pulse is irradiated through the quartz mold to the surface of the silicon substrate.

(3) The near-surface silicon is rapidly heated up, due to laser energy absorption, on which molten silicon layer is formed.

(4) Upon silicon melting, the mold, driven by a pre-loaded pressure, embosses into the molten silicon layer.

(5) After dissipation of heat, the molten silicon is re-solidified and the quartz is withdrawn.

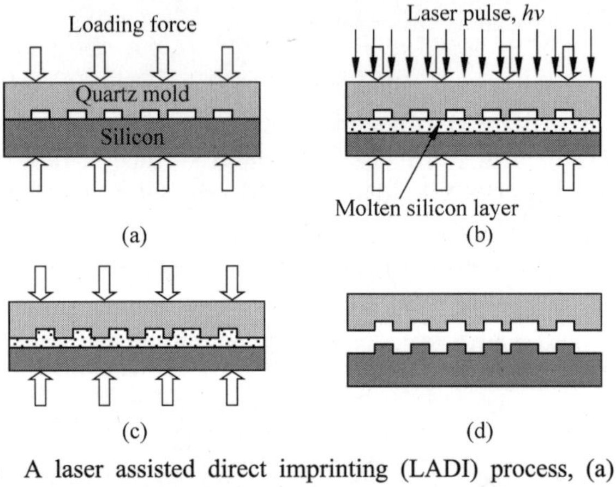

Figure 12.3 A laser assisted direct imprinting (LADI) process, (a) mold pre-loading, (b) pulsed laser heating and molten layer, (c) mold embossing, and (d) re-solidification and pattern transfer

The features on the quartz mold's surface are then transferred to silicon substrate.

The advantages of LADI are fast, direct, and no subsequent chemical etching processes are needed.

The concept of LADI has been successfully applied to a number of applications in microfabrication and nanofabrication[25–28]. However, the underlying mechanism of LADI is not well characterized as yet. As a consequence of this missing mechanism, the role and influence of each working parameter for a successful LADI process, such as laser fluence, applied loading pressure, imprinting feature size of the mold, and so forth, are not understood. As a starting point, the underlying mechanism of LADI will be first investigated theoretically and then verified by experiments. Inspired by the studies of the LADI's fundamental mechanism, a new type of roller-based LADI is proposed and tested experimentally. This roller-based LADI significantly improves the original planar type of LADI, so that the large-area and continuous formation of nanostructures based on the concept of LADI be fulfilled.

In the mean time, the LADI process demands quartz molds and high energy pulsed UV lasers, and both are not so easy to acquire. In response to this consideration, two new types of nanopatterning lithography methods have been developed, named as:

(1) Laser Assisted Direct Metal Film Patterning (LAMP) and

(2) Contact Transfer and Mask Embedded Lithography (CMEL).

Both methods can use silicon molds, which are much easier for fabrication, in comparison with their quartz counterparts, and utilizes either only infrared (IR) light sources or no energy sources. Therefore, these two methods can easily be implemented in most laboratories with minimum requirements on equipments as well as maintaining the capability on fabricating various kinds of micro/nano-structures on a variety of substrate materials.

Extract of this chapter is arranged as follows:

(1) A brief introduction on currently existing imprinting/printing lithography methods is given in Section 12.1 as well as the motivations for developing new types of laser-assisted and roller-based lithography methods;

(2) Section 12.2, focus on the fundamental mechanism of LADI process including both theoretical modeling and experimental verifications;

(3) Section 12.3, presents the roller-based LADI for direct, continuous, and large area fabrication of micro and nanostructures;

(4) Section 12.4, discusses a new type of contact printing method called LAMP for directly transferring a patterned metal film from a silicon mold to a substrate, based on using the contact pressure and optical heating from an IR source;

(5) Section 12.5, proposes a new method, CMEL, of contact printing that is based on pure mechanical forces only without using any other energy source.

This chapter is closed with some conclusions and discussions on all the laser-assisted and/or roller-based imprinting/printing lithography methods.

12.2 Fundamental Mechanism of Laser-Assisted Direct Imprinting (LADI)

In this section, a theoretical model that can quantitatively interpret the imprinting mechanism of the LADI process is first proposed and then followed by experimental verification. The model consists of three elements: ① the melting time-history of silicon when subject to irradiation of a high-energy laser pulse, ② the elastodynamic behaviors of the quartz mold due to relaxation of pre-stored strain energy, and ③ the squeezing out of the molten silicon during imprinting.

All these three physical problems are crucial in accurately explaining and modeling the LADI process and hence will be investigated properly in further topics.

12.2.1 Elastodynamic Modeling of Imprinting Process

First of all, the melting of silicon under irradiation of a high-energy laser pulse is numerically simulated. This laser annealing or melting problem on silicon substrate has been extensively studied in the past few decades and thereby theoretical and experimental results can be found in the literatures[29–31]. We will adopt a numerical approach based on finite difference method as proposed in Ref.[32] which takes into account the material absorption of laser energy, phase transformation, and heat transfer behaviors in a one-dimensional material system containing a silicon solid and a molten silicon layer of varying layer thickness. All the materials constants are temperature-dependent where a finite difference algorithm is developed for the calculation. Considering a KrF-248 nm excimer laser with a pulse duration of 25 ns (full-width-half-maximum, FWHM) and a Gaussian distribution profile, the thickness of melting silicon layer, $h_m(t)$, as a function of time is calculated and shown in Fig. 12.4 for a number of different laser fluences[33]. The calculated results are in good agreement with data in earlier literature. As shown in Fig. 12.4, the silicon surface starts melting when the laser fluence reaches 0.6 J/cm^2. With increasing laser fluence both the maximum melting depth and the overall time duration of melting silicon layer are increasing. For laser fluence higher than 1.6 J/cm^2, possible damages to silicon substrate may happen and therefore not suitable for LADI processes.

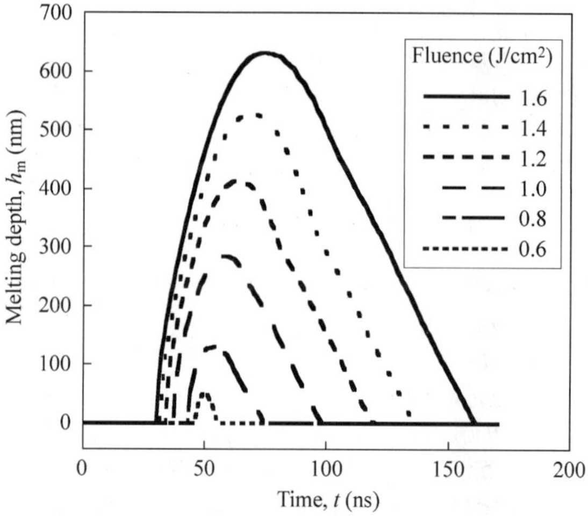

Figure 12.4 Calculated time-history of melting silicon layer when subjected to a KrF-248 nm laser pulse with 25 ns time duration[33] (from Ref.[33])

When the silicon surface starts melting, the pressure originally acting against the mold, suddenly drops to a very low level and the surface of mold starts advancing into the molten silicon. The mold advancement will be stopped finally by the re-solidified silicon and thus complete the LADI process. From Fig. 12.4, it shows the existence of melting silicon layer is typically less than 130 ns for laser fluence under 1.6 J/cm^2. Within such a short period of time, the movements of quartz mold, instead of being characterized in Ref.[25] as rigid body motion driven by external loading forces, should be more correctly described as the sudden relaxation of strain energy on one side of a pre-stressed elastic solid. For example, considering a linear spring with one end fixed in space and the other end compressed by a force F, and if the force is suddenly removed, the free end will move extensionally with a particle velocity v_{p},

$$v_{\mathrm{p}} = \frac{F}{\rho_{\mathrm{s}} \cdot k_{\mathrm{s}}}, \tag{12.1}$$

where ρ_{s} and k_{s} are the linear density and spring constant of the spring, respectively.

In the mean while, an extensional stress wave will propagate to the fixed end at a wave velocity v_{f},

$$v_{\mathrm{f}} = \sqrt{\frac{k_{\mathrm{s}}}{\rho_{\mathrm{s}}}}. \tag{12.2}$$

After reaching the fixed end, a reflected stress wave travels back to the free end and affects its subsequent movements. However, since the round trip time of the elastic wave propagation is twice the spring length divided by the wave velocity (v_{f}), the free end continues moving at the constant speed (v_{p}) until the arrival of reflected waves. This is the same situation in LADI. Given the quartz mold thickness as 0.5 mm and the longitudinal wave speed in quartz around 6,000 m/s, the round trip time for elastic wave is about 160 ns, which is long after the whole silicon melting (or the imprinting process) is completed. Therefore, during the imprinting time period, the movement of mold's surface is governed by elastodynamics or wave propagation theory for deformed elastic solids.

Figure 12.5 shows the extensional movement of the pre-compressed quartz mold, when the silicon surface starts melting. Since the pre-loaded pressure drops all of a sudden, the quartz mold surface is now impinging into the molten silicon with a velocity, v_{w}, which can be determined from basic elastodynamics[34] as,

$$v_{\mathrm{w}}(t) = \frac{P_0 - \sigma(t)}{\rho \cdot v}, \tag{12.3}$$

where P_0 is the pre-loaded pressure between quartz mold and silicon substrate, $\sigma(t)$ the pressure (or normal stress) exerted against the wall of quartz mold by the molten silicon fluid when the quartz surface is moving forward into the molten silicon, ρ and v the mass density and longitudinal wave speed of quartz, respectively. The product of the last two quantities, ρ and v, is also known as the longitudinal acoustic impedance.

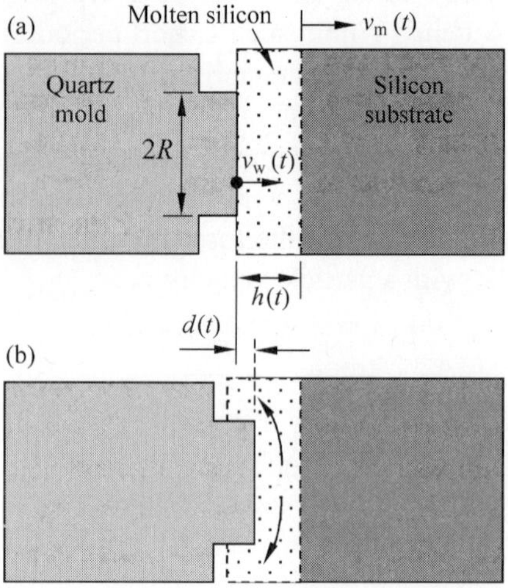

Figure 12.5 Imprinting processes of the pre-loaded quartz mold after silicon melting[33]

As shown in Fig. 12.5(b), the advancing quartz mold surface is driving molten silicon out and therefore suffers a reactive pressure $\sigma(t)$ from the fluid as indicated in Eq. (12.3). Apparently, there is a complicated relationship between the mold surface moving velocity, $v_w(t)$, the reacting stress, $\sigma(t)$, the melting layer thickness, $h(t)$, and the viscosity of molten silicon, μ. To simply this relationship and to derive an analytical expression, we will assume that the mold, as shown in Fig. 12.5(a), has disk-like embossing features with a diameter of *2R* and are regularly distributed on the mold surface. The distance between the adjacent features is far enough so that the molten silicon flows do not interact with each other. Finally, we will assume the feature size *2R* is much greater than the thickness of meting silicon layer. Under these assumptions, the Stefan equation[35] which describes the behavior of a thin film being squeezed out by two solid plates of finite sizes, is very close to model the impinging of quartz mold into the liquid silicon layer. However, to be more precisely in describing the LADI cases, we will adopt a modified Stefan equation[36] which characterizes a liquid film being squeezed out by a solid disk on one side and an infinite solid plate on the other side,

$$\sigma(t) = 3 \cdot \mu \cdot \left(\frac{R^2}{2 \cdot h(t)^3} + 1.238 \cdot \frac{R}{h(t)^2} \right) \cdot v_w(t) . \tag{12.4}$$

Equation (12.4) quantitatively characterizes the complicate relationship between moving velocity of mold surface, $v_w(t)$, the normal stress developed against the mold, $\sigma(t)$, the remaining melting layer thickness, $h(t)$, and the viscosity of molten silicon, μ. If the second term in the parenthesis is drop, Eq. (12.4) becomes a standard Stefan equation.

Substituting Eq. (12.4) into Eq. (12.3) gives,

$$\left[1+3\cdot\mu\cdot\left(\frac{R^2}{2\cdot h(t)^3}+1.238\cdot\frac{R}{h(t)^2}\right)\cdot\frac{1}{\rho c}\right]\cdot v_w=\frac{P_0}{\rho c}. \tag{12.5}$$

Equation (12.5) shows how the impinging velocity of quartz mold surface is related to the pre-loaded pressure (P_0), the layer thickness (h) and viscosity (μ) of molten silicon, as well as the imprinting feature size (R).

Finally, the thickness of molten silicon layer can be written as,

$$h(t)=h_m(t)-\int_0^t v_w(t)\cdot \mathrm{d}t, \tag{12.6}$$

where, the $h_m(t)$ is the time-varying layer thickness of molten silicon layer as being shown already in Fig. 12.4, and the integral $\int_0^t v_w(t)\cdot \mathrm{d}t$ can be defined as the imprinting depth of quartz mold, d(t). Equations (12.5) and (12.6) are coupled equations for unknown $h(t)$ and $v_w(t)$ with given $h_m(t)$ and other constant parameters, and therefore can be easily solved numerically using finite difference method.

12.2.2 Numerical Simulation Results

Figure 12.6, as an example, shows the calculated time-history of imprinting depth for a feature size of 10 μm (R) and a laser fluence of 1.6 J/cm^2[33]. The dash-line in Fig. 12.4 is the time-history of melting silicon layer and the solid lines are the imprinting depth as a function of time under different applied loadings. The viscosity of molten silicon is 0.3×10^{-3} N-s/m^2 and is applied in the calculation. For lower applied loadings such as 50 MPa, the initial moving velocity of mold surface is small and therefore can not catch up with the moving liquid/solid interface in silicon driven by laser heating. For increasing loadings such as 100 MPa or 200 MPa, the mold imprinting movement more closely follows the interface movement and therefore obtains a deeper imprinting depth. However, when further increasing the applied loading to 300 MPa, the thin film squeezing effect described by Eq. (12.4) starts to generate higher reactive pressure against the quartz mold and therefore limits its imprinting velocity. As shown in Fig. 12.6, when the solid lines intercept the dash-line, the LADI process is competed because the re-solidified silicon will stop the advancement of the quartz mold, hence the ultimate imprinting depth of LADI is determined.

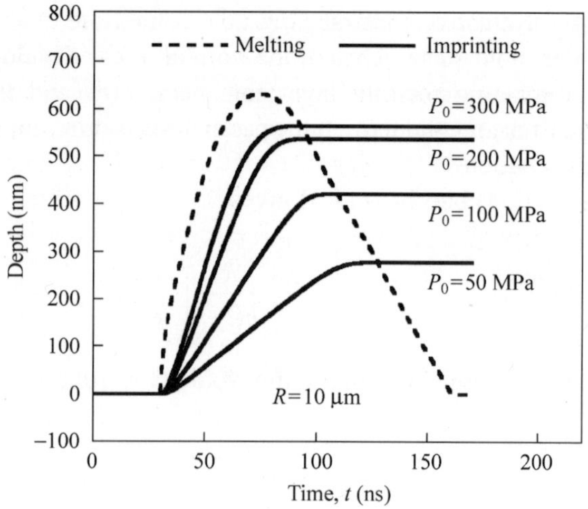

Figure 12.6 Imprinting depth as a function of time under different loading pressure for 1.6 J/cm^2 laser fluence and 10 μm feature size[33]

Figure 12.7 shows the ultimate imprinting depth as a function of applied loading pressure for different laser fluences and mold's feature sizes[33]. The general trend is that the imprinting depth is increasing for higher laser fluence and applied loading pressure. The influence of general trend are: ① Higher laser fluence provides a deeper molten silicon layer ② Higher loading pressure allows the quartz mold surface to obtain sufficient initial particle velocity to imprinting into the liquid silicon layer.

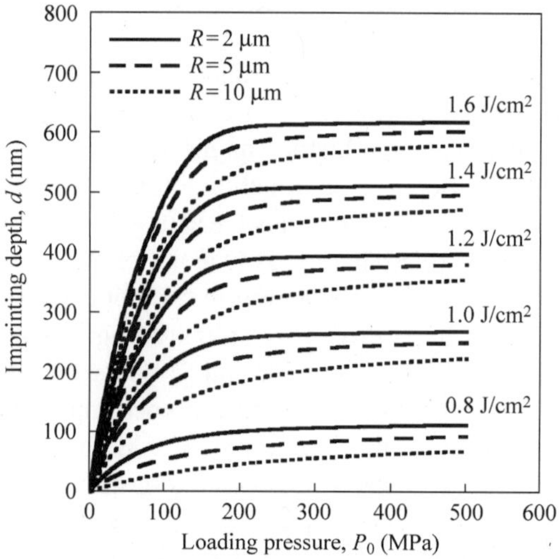

Figure 12.7 Ultimate imprinting depth of LADI for different laser fluence, applied loading, and feature size[33]

However, when the applied loading pressure is reaching some critical point, the imprinting depth is gradually saturated and approaching a constant value close to the silicon's maximum melting depth, which is dominated by the laser fluence only. The turning point or the critical loading pressure is somewhere around 100 MPa – 200 MPa. As for different imprinting feature sizes of mold (R=2 μm, 5 μm, and 10 μm shown in Fig. 12.7), smaller feature sizes will have deeper imprinting depth since it suffer-less reactive normal stress from the liquid silicon during the process of thin film squeezing.

12.2.3 Experimental Verification of LADI's Mechanism

To verify the modeling of this newly developed mechanism and its simulation results, experimental testing of LADI has been carried out in a systematic way. A quartz mold with features of three different sizes has been fabricated by photo-lithography. These surface features are basically linear gratings with line width of 5 μm, 10 μm, and 20 μm. These three features are arranged in a serial way right next to each other as shown in Fig. 12.8, and are continuously and repeatedly distributed on the whole mold surface. Since the three features of different sizes are close to each other, one can assure that the laser fluence and contact pressure for adjacent features are nearly the same during LADI processes. Therefore, if there is any difference in their imprinting depths, it must come from the feature size effect as been explained above based on liquid film squeezing theory.

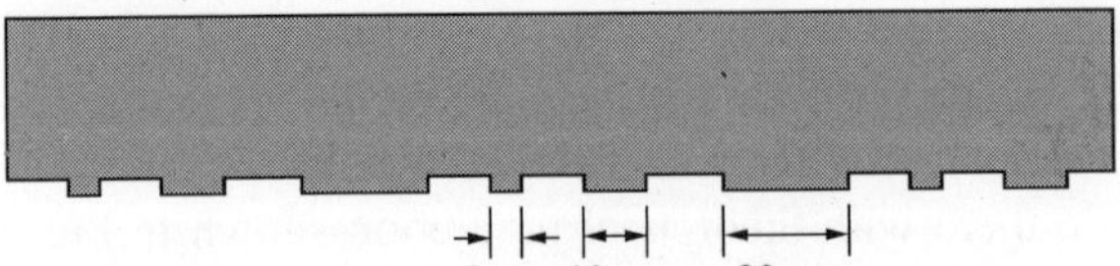

Figure 12.8 Three different feature sizes on the mold for LADI

A loading frame as shown schematically in Fig. 12.9 is designed and constructed. The loading frame is attached to an excimer laser micro-machining system (PS-2000, Excitech, Oxford, UK) which utilizes a KrF-248 nm excimer laser (COMPEX 101, Lamda Physics, Germany) with a pulse duration of 25 ns and maximum pulse energy of 300 mJ/pulse. The excimer laser micromachining system consists of laser beam homogenizer and optical projection system so that the laser beam, when reaching the silicon substrate surface as shown in Fig. 12.9, does have uniformly distributed laser fluence. This laser fluence is adjustable in the laser system by controlling the laser power directly and is measured by a laser power-meter. As shown in Fig. 12.9, a loading force is applied through a linear actuator in the loading frame and is measured by a load cell. The applied contact pressure is then derived from the loading force and the contact surface area between the mold and the silicon substrate. With the experimental setup as described above, the LADI process can now be carried out on silicon substrates under different loading contact pressure and laser fluence as well.

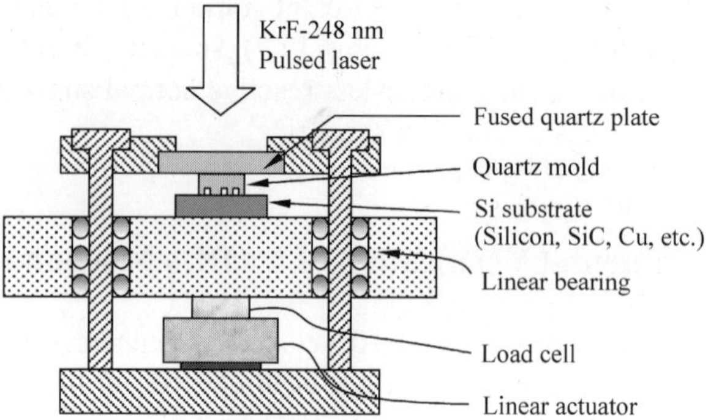

Figure 12.9 Loading frame for experimentally testing of LADI process

Figure 12.10 show the surface profiles of silicon sample after LADI with a laser fluence of 0.6 J/cm^2, 0.9 J/cm^2, and 1.3 J/cm^2, respectively. The surface profiles are measured by a confocal microscope with nm resolution in vertical depth measurement. As can be seen from Fig. 12.8, the imprinting depth of LADI is indeed proportional to laser fluence and contact pressure, as can be intuitively understood. However, it is also clear in Fig. 12.10, that the imprinting depth is inversely proportional to the feature's size. That is, the 5 μm features is always getting the deepest imprinting depth and the 20 μm is always the shallowest one, although the laser fluence and the contact pressure are the same. This is totally in agreement with the theoretical modeling and simulated results.

Figure 12.11 displays the experimental results in a quantitative way, so that, one can compare them with theoretical prediction shown in Fig. 12.2. The basic trend is the same with some discrepancy in magnitude, which may result from the model itself and/or the material properties used in the modeling. Furthermore, the theoretical model along with the experimental results point out one important fact, that is, LADI is basically an elastodynamic process for the mold to release its pre-loaded strain energy. The significance of this point is that LADI can be performed in a localized way, which leads to possible applications in large area LADI processes, which will be discussed in next section.

Extract of this paragraph:

(1) We successfully constructed a theoretical model which can comprehensively capture the underlying mechanism of LADI. The key point in this model is that the quartz mold in LADI needs to be modeled as a pre-compressed elastic solid with suddenly released stress at the mold/substrate interface;

(2) Through the elastodynamic modeling, we understood the roles of all important parameters in a LADI process and their influence on the ultimate imprinting depth both individually and collectively;

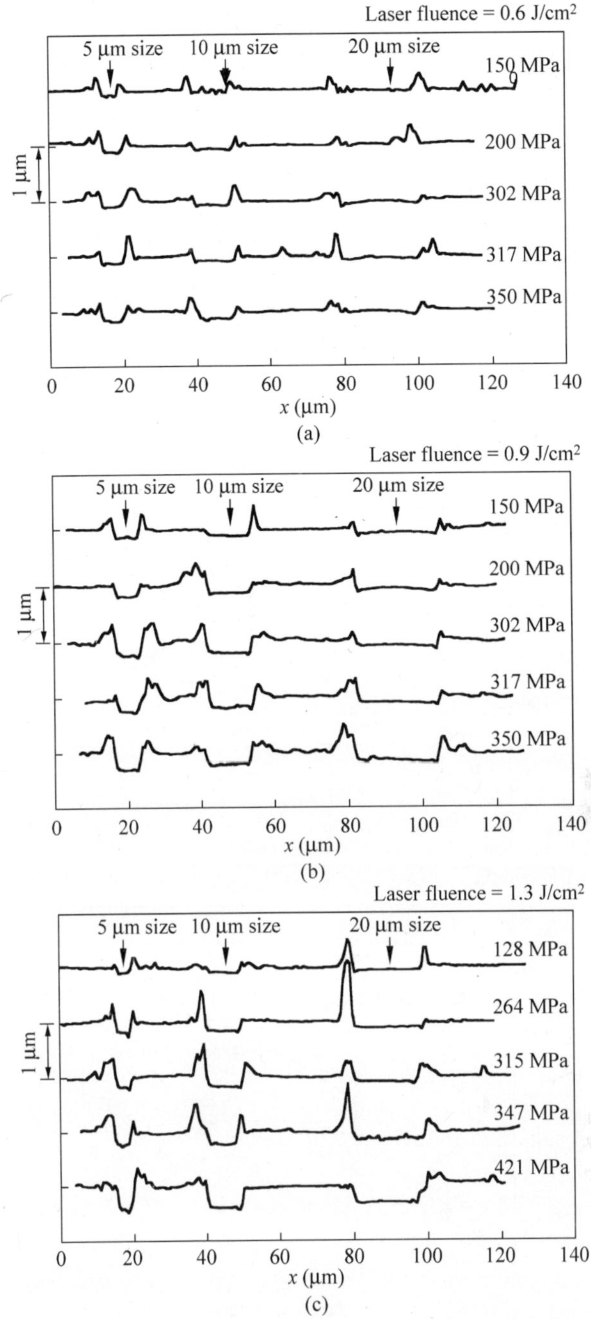

Figure 12.10 Cross-section of surface profiles of imprinted features on Si samples after LADI process

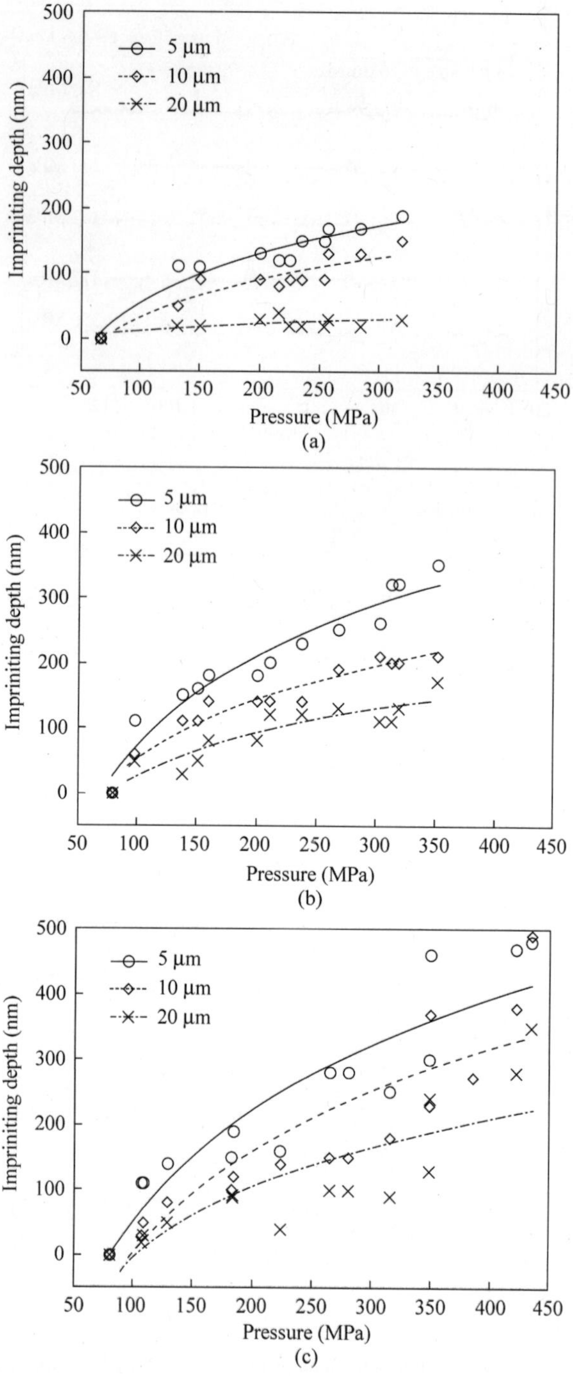

Figure 12.11 Imprinting depth as functions of contact pressure and feature sizes at different laser fluence of, (a) 0.6 J/cm^2, (b) 0.9 J/cm^2, and (c) 1.3 J/cm^2

(3) Quantitative information is given which can be very useful in designing and operating an imprinting system of LADI, as well as for applying LADI to other materials;

(4) In this work only micro-scaled and disk-shaped imprinting features are addressed because we would like to apply the analytical Stefan equation. However, the model can also be adapted for nanoscaled imprinting features or different profiles of imprinting features, for example, trench-type, as long as one can find a proper correlation between $\sigma(t)$, $v_w(t)$, and $h(t)$, similar to what is given in Eq. (12.5). Closed form solutions may not be possible sometimes but numerical simulations such as finite element analysis should be able to provide adequate data to keep the model running.

An experimental setup has been successfully applied to quantitatively determine the complicated relationship between the imprinting depth and important parameters of LADI such as laser fluence, contact pressure, and feature size of mold. Experimental data have been compared with the theoretical results calculated from a previously proposed theoretical model. Qualitative agreements between experimental results and theoretical predictions are observed. Particularly important are the critical contact pressures for saturated imprinting depth when the laser fluence is fixed, as well as, the effect of mold feature size on the imprinting depth. Both are well predicted and explained in the theoretical modeling and are first experimentally verified in this work. On the other hand, some quantitative discrepancies between the theoretical and experimental curves are observed, which may come from either the modeling parameters used or the theoretical model itself. Modifications on the theoretical modeling are indeed, needed to accurately account for the experimental data.

12.3 Roller-Based Laser-Assisted Direct Imprinting

The most important advantage of LADI is that it can be fast and directly form nanopatterns or nanostructures on a substrate, without using any resist layer or etching process. However, a serious drawback of LADI is that the imprinted area size of LADI is typically limited to only few mm^{2}, because the laser fluence required to melt the substrate is rather high, typically around 1 J/cm^2[25]. For a given laser pulse energy, the imprinting area size of LADI is therefore quite limited, not to mention, there is a significant reduction in laser pulse energy in transforming a laser beam of Gaussian distribution profile into a uniformly distributed one. Repeating and stepping the LADI process consecutively on the substrate surface is possible but will be very time-consuming and limited to repeating the same mold's pattern only. The mechanical alignment and positioning accuracy between individual imprinted patterns are very difficult to achieve nanoscaled precision. Furthermore, it is not trivial to maintain a constant, uniform mechanical contact between mold and substrate in such a planar type of LADI process.

The drawbacks and limitations in LADI as mentioned above can be solved by following steps:

(1) Introducing a quartz roller into the LADI setup. Figure 12.10 shows schematically the basic idea of this roller-based LADI process and its configuration of experimental setup[37];

(2) As shown in Fig. 12.10, a silicon substrate is carried by a servo-controlled motorized linear stage;

(3) A quartz mold with certain pre-designed and pre-fabricated features is placed on the top of the silicon substrate;

(4) A cylindrical quartz roller is mounted on a fixture with bearings so it can rotate freely, and the fixture is connected to a frame through a universal bearing;

(5) When an external loading force is applied at the end of the fixture, the quartz roller can press the quartz mold and silicon substrate against the carrier stage of the linear translation stage;

(6) Based on contact mechanics of elastic solids, one can image a contact pressure is developed in between the quartz mold and the silicon substrate with a distribution profile centered right beneath the contact line of the roller and the mold. In the mean time, the roller also acts like a cylindrical lens for focusing an incident laser beam into a line;

(7) Placing and positioning a cylindrical converging lens in the path of the laser beam as shown in Fig. 12.12 can help adjust the laser focusing position to be at the mold/substrate interface. If the laser focusing line is aligned with the high contact pressure line developed by the roller, once a laser pulse is triggered, LADI can be achieved locally in the area around the focusing line at the mold/substrate interface.

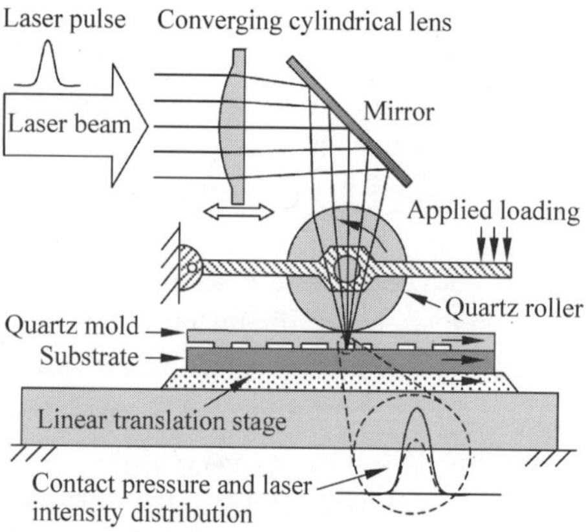

Figure 12.12 Basic idea and setup for roller-based LADI process[37] (see color figure at the end of this book)

By moving the mold/substrate and triggering the laser pulses simultaneously and continuously, it is possible to completely transform the whole pattern of the mold into the substrate through this roller-based LADI process. The ideas of using rollers for micro/nanofabrication can be found in Ref. [38] for conventional hot-embossing nanoimprinting lithography (NIL) and in Ref. [39] for micro-contact printing (μCP), but in their cases the rollers are for mechanical loadings only, and the underlying mechanisms are totally different.

12.3.1 Experimental Setup for Roller-Based LADI

The laser source used in this work for the roller-based LADI is a 248 nm KrF excimer laser (COMPEX Pro-201, Lamda Physik, Gottingen, Germany) with a pulse-duration of 25 ns (FWHM), maximum repetition rate of 10 Hz, and maximum laser pulse energy of 800 mJ/pulse. The output laser beam, as being measured directly by its burning mark on a photosensitive paper, have a rectangular beam profile with approximately a long axis of 24 mm and a short axis of 8 mm. The laser intensity distribution is Gaussian along its short axis. As shown schematically in Fig. 12.13, the KrF-248 nm laser beam is focused into a line along its long axis by a converging cylindrical lens and a quartz roller. The plano-convex cylindrical lens has a radius of curvature of 152.57 mm and a focus length of 300 mm, and the diameter of the quartz roller is 36 mm. Both are made of fused silica with high transmission coefficient at 248 nm wavelength. As depicted in Fig. 12.12, the roller is mounted on a plate-like fixture using bearings, and the fixture is connected to a frame through a universal joint so that, when a loading force is applied at the end of the plate, the roller can be in perfect line-contact with the quartz mold. The mold/substrate is placed on top of a carrier of a motorized linear translation stage (08PMT-150, UNICE E-O Services Inc., Chung Li,) which is servo-controlled by a personal computer (PC). The excimer laser is also connected to the PC through RS-232 interface and can be triggered by the PC.

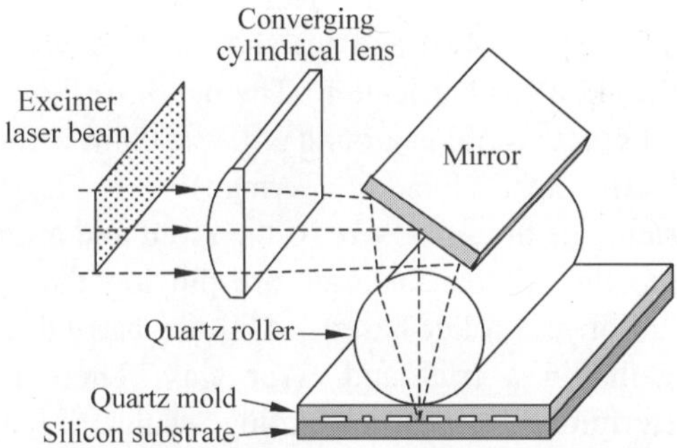

Figure 12.13 Optical arrangement of roller-based LADI process[37]

Therefore, the movement of mold/substrate and the triggering of laser pulses can be synchronized.

Two critical elements for a successful LADI are the laser fluence and the contact pressure, and both need to exceed certain levels. The laser fluence is limited by the maximum laser pulse energy. However, because of line-focusing, the laser intensity near the focusing line can be very high and can be adjusted by positioning the converging cylindrical lens to achieve an optimal laser fluence level and distribution profile for LADI. The idea is to have the laser intensity above the LADI's threshold but below the laser damage level of silicon, and in the meanwhile to spread out the laser distribution laterally to achieve wider imprinting area for each single laser shot. As for the contact pressure, its magnitude is directly determined by the applied loading force and its distribution profile is affected by the elastic material properties and geometries of the roller, quartz mold, and silicon substrate. Again there is an optimal contact pressure and its distribution which can best imprint into the silicon substrate wherever the irradiated laser fluence is high enough to melt the silicon surface. Finally, the laser and the optical components should be carefully aligned so that the laser fluence distribution profile is coincident with contact pressure distribution profile, as shown in the insert of Fig. 12.13, and the best imprinting result can be achieved.

12.3.2 Experimental Results of Roller-Based LADI

The quartz mold used in this work is made of a fused silica plate with thickness, width, and length of 1 mm, 5 mm, and 30 mm, respectively. The patterns on the surface of silicon mold are fabricated through a contact printing and transformation method using a silicon mold fabricated by photolithography, and followed by ICP etching on the quartz material. Figure 12.14(a) shows the SEM image of a basic pattern appeared on the quartz mold after ICP etching. It contains trench-type linear gratings with a line width of 500 nm, a center-to-center pitch of 1000 nm, a length of 30 μm, and a square area size of $30 \times 30\ \mu m^2$. The same patterns are repeatedly deployed into a 2D array all over the whole $5\ mm^2 \times 30\ mm^2$ surface area of the mold. Figures 12.14(b) and (c) show the SEM images of the detail structures of quartz mold after fabrication. The depth of the trench or the height of surface features of quartz mold is around 340 – 350 nm measured by a confocal microscope (NanoFocus μSurf®, Panduit, German).

The silicon substrate has the same size of the mold and a thickness of 500 μm. The quartz mold and the silicon substrate are put together under the roller. A series of experiments on the roller-based LADI are carried in searching for the best imprinting results in a trial and error way. There are basically three parameters to be determined for best imprinting results, the laser's pulse energy, the applied loading force, and the incremental step distance between two adjacent laser pulses. The first two parameters are directly related to the laser fluence and

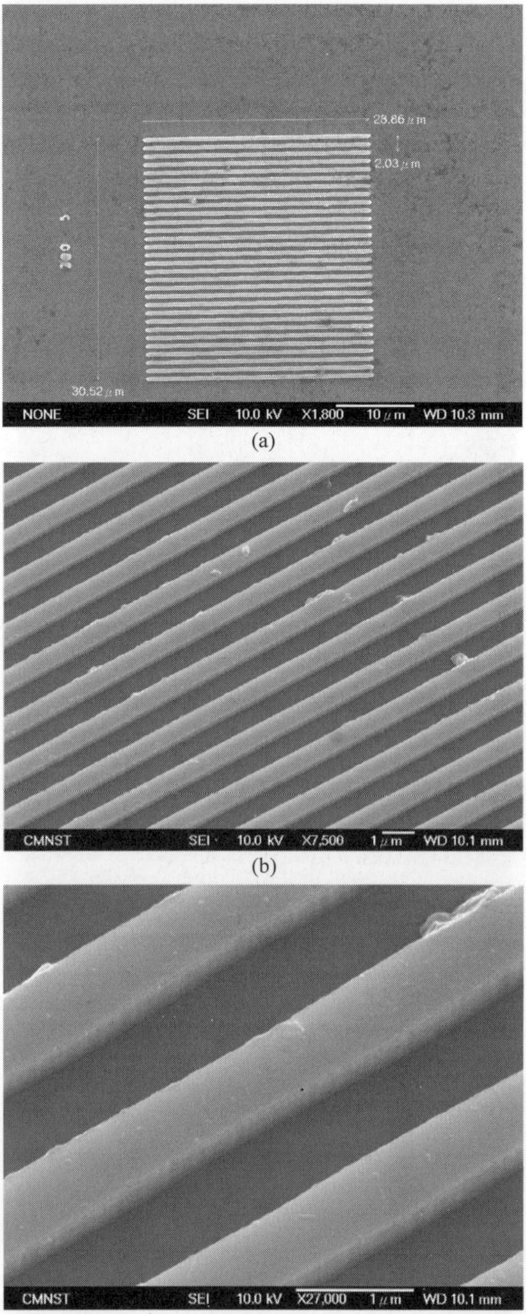

(c)

Figure 12.14 SEM images of a quartz mold with linear gratings of a line width of 500 nm and a center-to-center pitch of 1 μm[37]

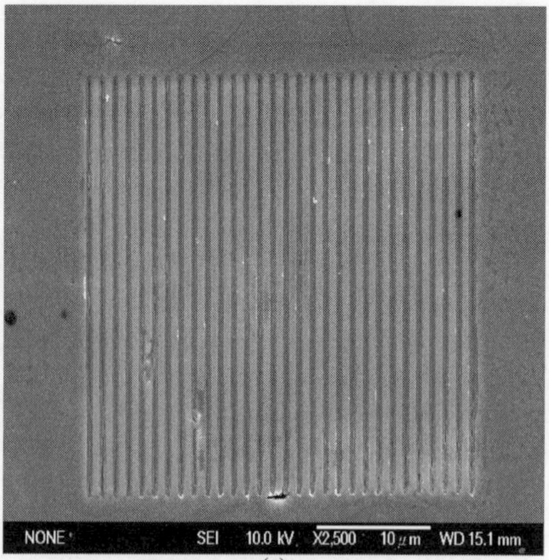

(a)

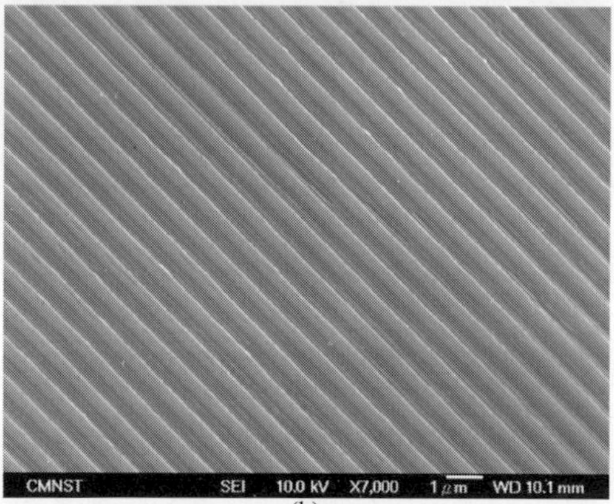

(b)

(c)

Figure 12.15 SEM Images of the silicon substrate after laser-assisted roller imprinting[37] the contact pressure, respectively, while the third one is related to the effective imprinting width of each single laser pulse and how to stitch two adjacent imprinted nanostructures together seamlessly. After several trials, the following combination of parameters gives a complete transformation of the mold's patterns to the substrate. The output laser energy is 680 mJ/pulse, the applied loading force is 8 kgf, and the stepping distance is 125 μm per laser pulse. The laser pulses are triggered at 8 Hz repetition rate and the linear stage is moving at a constant speed of 1 mm/sec. Figure 12.15 is the SEM image of different length- scales of the final imprinted surface structures on the silicon substrate. The patterns of the mold are directly and completely transferred to the substrate through this simple, fast, and direct type of roller-based LADI process. The imprinting depth is investigated by an SPM (SPA-400, SII Nanotechnology Inc., Japan) and the imprinting depth is around 320 – 330 nm and is very close to the trench depth of the mold.

12.3.3 Analysis and Conclusion

The distributions of both laser fluence and contact pressure for the optimal roller-based LADI experiment as mentioned above will be discussed. For the laser fluence, commercial optical modeling software ZEMAX (Focus Software Inc., San Diego, CA) is applied to simulate the fluence distribution at the focusing plane. The KrF-248 laser beam has a rectangular shape with Gaussian distribution profiles along the short axes. As shown in Fig. 12.13, the optical are all cylindrical and therefore the analysis can be done in a simple 2D domain. Imputing the optical parameters, geometries, and distance of the converging cylindrical lens, the quartz roller, and the quartz mold, one can calculate the laser fluence profile as shown in Fig. 12.16. The maximum or peak laser fluence at the center position is 1.6 J/cm^2, which is determined by directly measuring the pulse energy of laser after passing through the roller and assuming a Gaussian type distribution profile as shown in Fig. 12.17.

For the contact pressure, the finite-element method (FEM) is applied to simulate the magnitude and distribution of contact pressure between the quartz mold and the silicon substrate. For the applied loading force of 8 kgf, Fig. 12.17(a) shows the simulated deformation of the 5 mm wide and 30 mm long quartz mold which is on top of a silicon substrate and subjected to a concentrated loading from the quartz roller. The quartz mold is clearly bent towards the roller with a curvature and is in contact with the silicon substrate only in a much localized manner. The magnitude and distribution of contact pressure between mold and substrate are displayed in Fig. 12.17(b). The contact pressure has a maximum value of 128 MPa at the center and falls off quickly to both sides and covering a region about 400 μm wide where the mold and substrate are still in good contact.

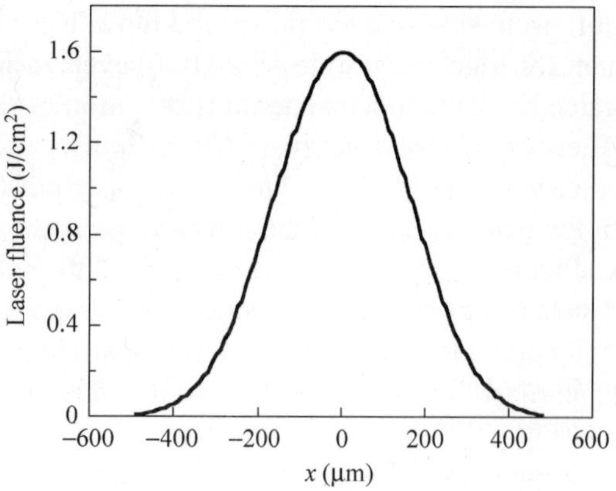

Figure 12.16 The laser fluence at focal position of the roller-based LADI setup[37]

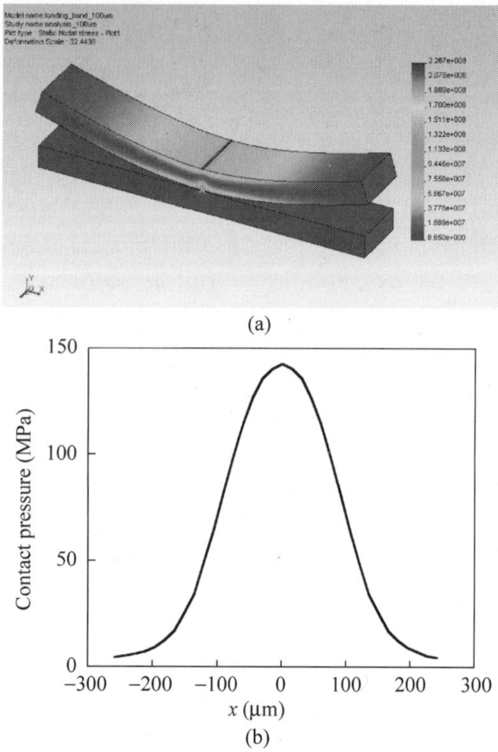

Figure 12.17 The (a) deformation of quartz mold and (b) the contact pressure distribution between mold and substrate in roller-based LADI for an 8 kgf loading force[37] (see color figure at the end of this book)

Comparing Fig. 12.16 and Fig. 12.17(b), one can see that they are very similar in their shapes and both with a bell-shape distribution. From the above analysis of laser fluence and contact pressure, it is clear that the roller-based LADI is carried out step by step in a localized and consecutive way. Both the optical energy and the mechanical energy are concentrated in a narrow, long, and small area so that LADI process can be achieved easily due to high laser fluence and high contact pressure. In the mean time, the formed nanostructure from each individual laser shot can be connected or partially overlapped with adjacent ones so that the full pattern can be seamlessly and continuously transformed, from the quartz mold to the silicon substrate. The ultimate imprinting speed of the roller-based LADI is determined by the length of laser focus line, the incremental step distance between laser shots, and the laser repletion rate. In the experiment of this work, the laser focusing line in 25 mm long but only 5 mm length is used because the quartz mold is 5 mm wide. With a 125 μm incremental step distance and 8 Hz laser repletion rate, or equivalently a 1 mm/s lateral translation speed, the nanostructures is directly fabricated in a rate of 3 cm^2/min, which conventional LADI method can not match, not to mentioned the imprinting of a large-area, continuous, and complex patterns. The imprinting speed can be significantly increased by using a wider quartz mold and a laser source of higher pulse energy and higher repletion rate. For example, assuming the same laser pulse energy but a 15 mm wide mold and an 80 Hz laser repetition rate, the imprinting rate could be increased by a factor of 30 cm^2/min and up to 90 cm^2/min for direct forming of nanostructures.

In short, a new type of nanofabrication method called roller-based LADI is proposed which inherits all the advantages of LADI, ① namely, ② direct, ③ fast, nanoscaled feature size, and ④ without using any photoresist layer and chemical etching. In the mean time, it eliminates the drawbacks and limitations of LADI and allows nanofabrication of large-area, continuous, and complex patterns from a whole quartz mold in a fast, smooth, and easily implemented way. The key concept in this roller-based LADI is to perform the LADI process in a localized way along a focusing line of the laser, and then continues the LADI process by moving the sample and triggering the laser continuously. In a sense, the proposed approach re-arranges the use of laser energy in LADI so that the potentials of the laser source as well as LADI itself are fully explored. The introduction of a quartz roller in the LADI process simultaneously achieves the goals of laser focusing and mechanical loading, and allows continuous processing of LADI.

12.4 Laser-Assisted Direct Metal Film Patterning (LAMP)

12.4.1 Direct Metal Film Patterning Using IR Laser Heating

As mentioned in Section 12.1 in reviewing the currently existing imprinting/printing methods such as NIL, SFIL, and μCP, the processes are still too complicated and indirect. For example, to pattern a metal film on a substrate may require several steps of processes and involve the deposition, patterning, and etching of several different materials. In this section, a novel contact printing method, which can directly transfer a patterned thin metal film from a mold to a substrate is proposed[40]. The basic idea of this direct contact printing and patterning of metal films is schematically depicted in Fig. 12.18. First of all, a silicon mold is fabricated using, for example, standard photolithography or E-beam lithography to have some micro- or nanofeatures on its surface. A thin anti-adhesion layer is first deposited on the mold surface, and a metal film is subsequently deposited on top of the anti-adhesion layer. The anti-adhesion layer serves the purpose for the metal film to be only weakly attached to the release layer and therefore can be easily taken off. After deposition of both films, the mold is pressed against a silicon substrate and a contact pressure is exerted between the mold and the substrate, as shown in Fig. 12.18(b). Finally, an infrared pulsed laser is applied from one side of the silicon substrate. Because of the optical properties of silicon,

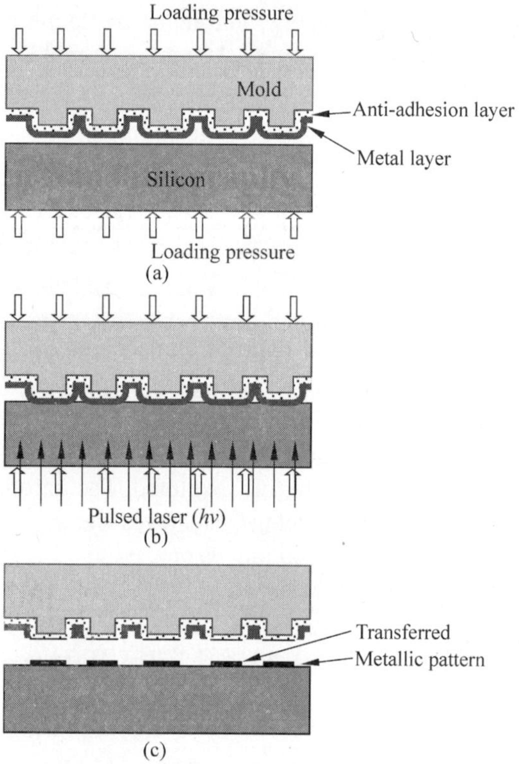

Figure 12.18 The processes of laser-assisted contact printing for direct metal pattern transfer (LAMP)[40]

the infrared light can partially pass through the silicon substrate and then reach the thin metal film. Depending on how much and how fast the laser energy is absorbed, the metal film is heated up and even start melting, especially at the film/substrate interface where laser energy is heavily absorbed. Under the combined action of both the loading contact pressure and the laser heating, it is possible to form a new interface between the metal film and the substrate, which is much stronger than the weakly bonded interface between the metal film and the anti-adhesion layer. Therefore, when the mold is withdrawn and separating from the substrate, the patterned metallic film defined by the features of the mold can be transferred to the substrate Fig. 12.18(c).

12.4.2 Experimental Details and Results

To demonstrate and verify this direct metal contact printing method, a series of experiments have been carried out. Figure 12.19 shows schematically the experimental setup built for this laser-assisted contact printing method. The Steps are:

(1) A 1064 nm pulsed Nd:YAG laser (LS-2137U, LOTIS TII, Minsk, Republic of Belarus) is used for the laser heating;

(2) A loading frame is constructed which can compress the mold and the substrate while allow the laser to pass through from the substrate side;

(3) A load cell is installed in the loading frame to measure the contact force and hence to derive the contact pressure;

(4) The laser spot size is smaller than the area size of the mold; the loading frame is fixed on a servo-controlled *x*-*y* stage so that the laser beam can sequentially scan across all the contact area of mold and substrate.

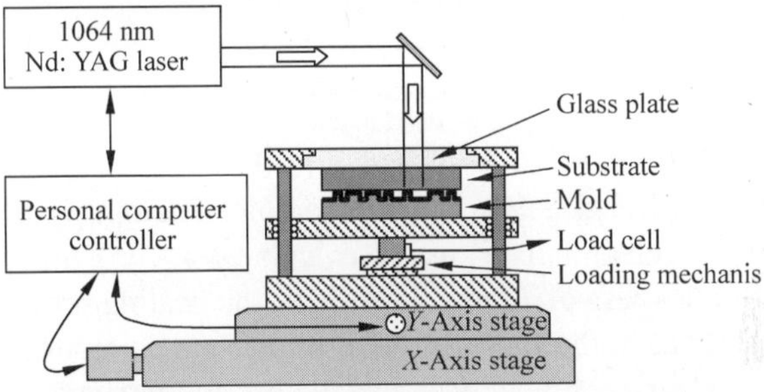

Figure 12.19 Experimental setup and configuration for laser-assisted direct contact printing of metallic films[40]

In other words, the laser-assisted printing is carried out in a localized but continuous manner. By carefully arranging the scanning path and laser pulse firing sequence, one can evenly distribute the laser energy over the whole contact area of the mold and the substrate, and hence achieve contact imprinting and pattern transfer in large area. A personal computer serves as the controller of the system and synchronizes the triggering of laser pulses and the movement of x-y stage.

Several silicon molds are fabricated using standard photolithography method. Both arrayed dot patterns and linear grating patterns with dot diameter or line-width around 450 – 500 nm are prepared. A releasing layer of 1H, 1H, 2H, 2H-Perfluorooctyltrichlorosilane[41] is first deposited on the silicon mold surface using vapor deposition method. Estimated layer thickness is around 10 nm. This releasing layer is known to have good adhesion with silicon substrate and has been widely used for anti-sticking layer. On top of the release laser, a 70 nm thick chromium film is deposited using an E-beam thermal evaporator (VT1-10CE, ULVAC, Kanagawa, Japan). The area size of the silicon molds is $10\ mm^2 \times 10\ mm^2$ with repeated patterns covering all over the mold's surface. Table 12.1 lists several combinations of laser fluence and contact pressure for testing the proposed contact printing method. The laser fluence is estimated by dividing the laser pulse energy by the laser spot size (3 mm in diameter). The contact pressure is derived by dividing the loading force with the help of contact surface area of the mold. The pulsed Nd:YAG laser used in this work has typical pulse duration of 6 – 7 ns, maximum pulse energy of 700 mJ, and a maximum pulse repetition rate of 10 Hz. The laser beam is continuously roaster scanning across the sample and the adjacent laser pulses are firing at a distance interval of 500 μm.

Table 12.1 Parameters for experimental testing of laser-assisted contact printing method [40]

Laser pulse energy (mJ)	Laser fluence (J/cm^2)	Loading contact pressure (MPa)
300	4.5	78.5
300	4.5	204
300	4.5	288
460	6.5	201

The laser heating process of bulk and thin-film materials by a pulsed laser have been well investigated before[42], for example. The optical absorption depth for chromium at wavelength 1064 nm is calculated as 10.8 nm, which is much less than the film thickness of 70 nm. Therefore, the heating process will result in a temperature gradient in the thin film with higher temperature on the surface in contact with the substrate. For thinner metal film, the temperature rising due to laser heating becomes more uniformly distributed in the film thickness direction. Since the absorption depths of most metal films are pretty much in the same range, one can expect the heating processes are similar when using metal films other than chromium.

The experimental testing results are shown in Fig. 12.20, Fig. 12.21, and Fig. 12.22. The patterned metal (Cr) films are successfully transferred to the silicon substrate for the given laser fluence and contact pressure listed in Table 12.1. Figure 12.20 shows the SEM images of the transferred pattern of Cr film by a mold with arrayed dot features. The diameter of dot is 450 nm and the center-to-center spacing is 1.5 μm. These arrayed dots are deployed all over the $10\ mm^2 \times 10\ mm^2$ area of the mold and are all successfully transferred to the substrate using the IR laser assisted direct contact printing method. Figure 12.21 show another arrayed dot patterns of Cr film transferred from different molds. The diameter of dot is still 450 nm but the spacing is 2.5 μm and 1 μm for Fig. 12.21, respectively. Figure 12.22 show the transferred patterns of Cr films by contact printing of a mold of linear grating features. The line width and length of the linear grating are 500 nm and 30 μm, respectively, and the period of grating is 1.5 μm. The complete linear grating patterns of Cr films are successfully transferred to the substrate.

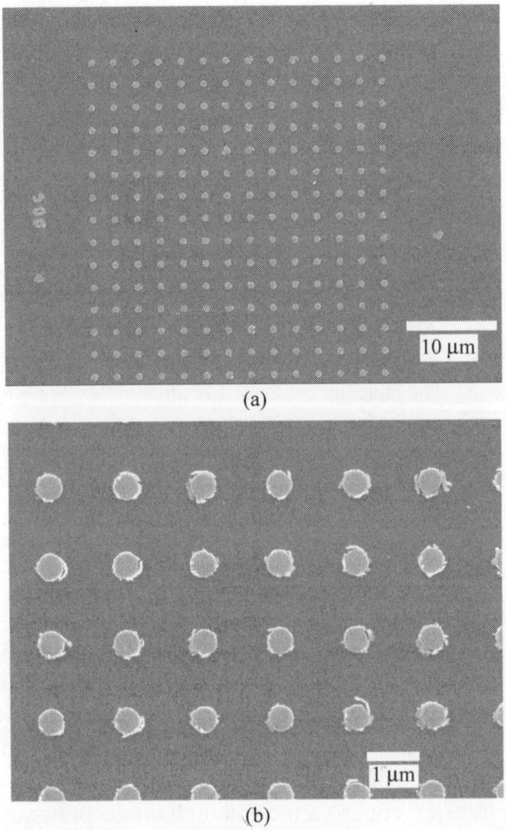

Figure 12.20 SEM images of two different magnification factors for the transferred pattern of Cr film from a mold with arrayed dot patterns. The diameter of dot is 450 nm and center-to-center spacing between dots is 1.5 μm[40]

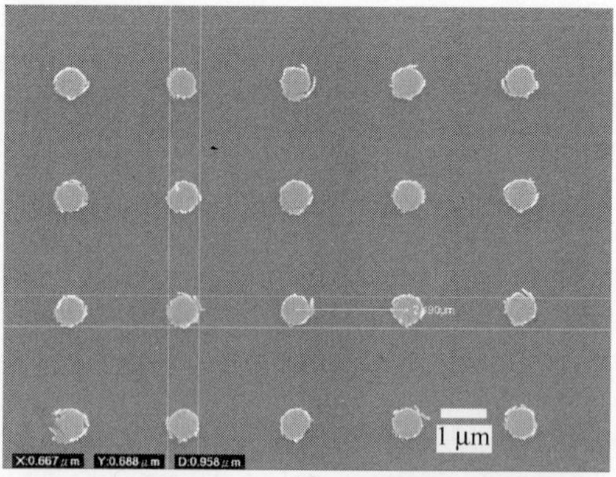

(a)

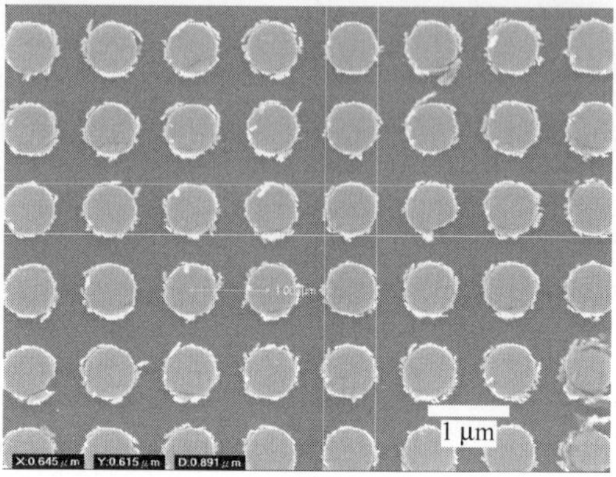

(b)

Figure 12.21 SEM images of the transferred patterns of Cr film from molds with arrayed dot patterns. The diameter of dot is 450 nm and the center-to-center spacing between dots is (a) 2.5 μm and (b) 1 μm[40]

For the successful and complete transfer of metal patterns, sufficient amounts of both contact pressure and laser fluence are required. Table12.1 lists a number of combinations of contact pressure and laser fluence which result in successful and complete pattern transfer in our experiments. If either the contact pressure or the laser fluence is reduced in a significant way, the pattern transfer will become incomplete. One can define a pattern transfer ratio as the ratio of successfully transferred area size to the overall area size of the mold. Obviously, this pattern transfer ratio is a function of contact pressure and laser fluence, as well as other minor parameters such as, pattern's feature size and metal film thickness. The exact relationship could be quite complicated and not clear now. However, to make sure a complete pattern transfer, conservative and high contact pressure and laser fluence should be used.

After the laser-assisted direct contact printing, the molds have been examined under a SEM (JSM-7000, JEOL, Tokyo, Japan) with an attached EDS (INCA Energy, OXFORD, Oxford, UK). Figure 12.23 shows the SEM image and the

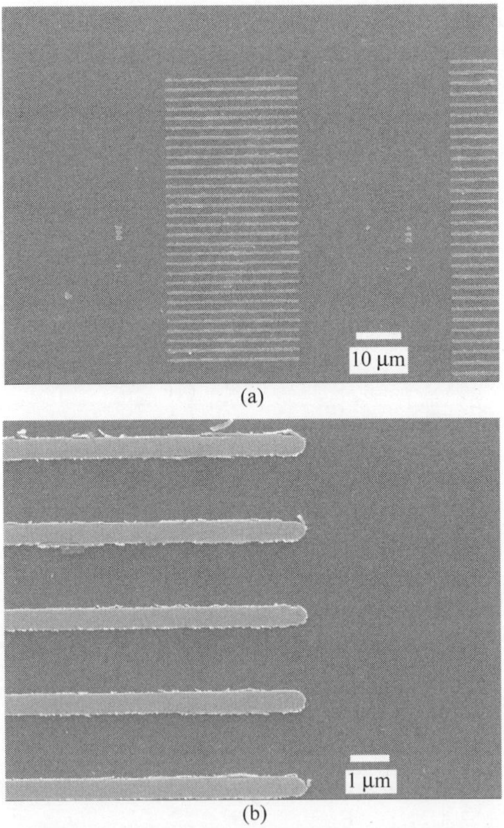

Figure 12.22 SEM images of two different magnification factors for the transferred pattern of Cr film from a mold with linear grating patterns. The line width and length of the linear grating are 500 nm and 30 μm, respectively, and the grating period is 1.5 μm[40]

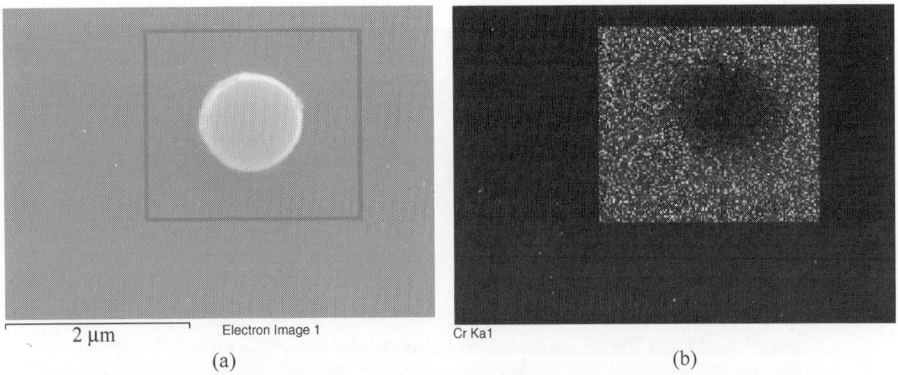

Figure 12.23 The mold after the direct metal contact imprinting: (a) the SEM image and (b) the EDS mapping images of Cr element[40]

EDS mapping image of Cr element, respectively, for an array-dot mold after contact printing. It also shows that the Cr film on the dot surface which is in contact with the substrate has been extracted away from the mold after contact printing.

To understand if the transferred Cr patterns can serve as an etching mask, the patterned substrate has been put into a RIE etching system. Important parameters of the RIE etching process are 100 W power, 4.2 min etching time, 20 sccm SF_6, 20 sccm CF_4, 20 sccm Ar, and 20 sccm O_2. After the RIE etching, the Cr film is removed and the etched silicon substrate is examined. Figure 12.24 is the SEM image and the AFM profile of the etched patterns on the surface of silicon

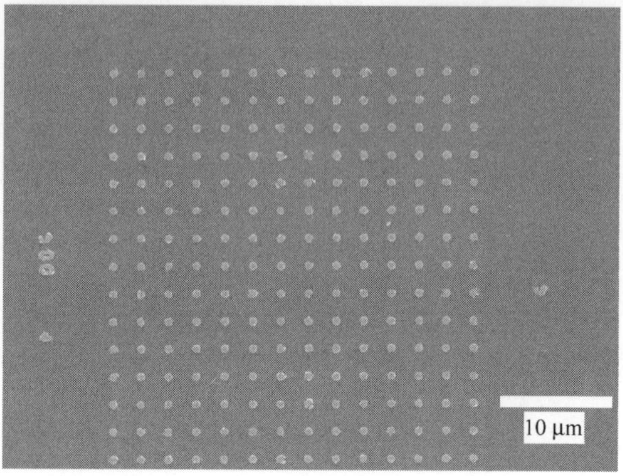

(a)

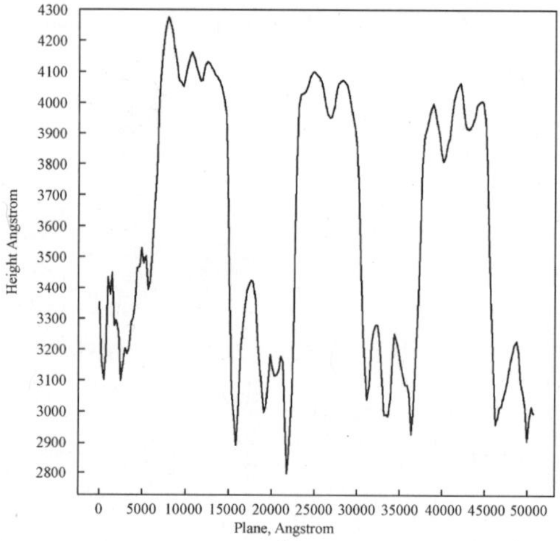

(b)

Figure 12.24 (a) The SEM image of the patterned substrate after RIE etching. (b) AFM cross-section view shows the etched depth or the dot height is around 80 nm[40] substrate. The etched depth on silicon by RIE is about 60 nm. It proves that the transferred Cr patterns are good enough for acting as the etching mask.

12.4.3 Discussions

To conclude, a laser-assisted contact printing method for directly patterning a metal film from a mold to a substrate has been proposed and experimentally demonstrated. The key elements in this method are the introducing of a releasing layer which serves as an anti-sticking layer and the IR pulsed laser to heat up the metal film from the substrate side. The mechanical contact pressure and pulsed laser heating help create a strong interface bonding between the metal film and the substrate, which overcomes the weakly bonded interface between the metal film and the releasing layer. Therefore, the patterned metal film defined by the mold's surface features can be directly and successfully transferred to the substrate.

Besides all the important advantages possessed by contact printing or imprinting lithography, there are several unique advantages of this laser-assisted direct contact printing method. First of all, it is a simple and direct way to transfer a metallic pattern without any etching processes. The transferred film can either serves as an etching mask of substrate or becomes part of the final structures of the device. Secondly, the method is applicable to a broad range of metal films and substrate materials, as long as the contact pressure and laser heating can induce a new and stronger interface between the metal film and substrate. One can envisage a variety of improvements or approaches based on the basic idea proposed in this work, such as using other light sources for transparent substrates and large area contact printing, and special surface treatments on the metal film and/or the substrate to enhance the interfacial bonding. Limited to our photolithography capability in fabricating the silicon molds, the feature size of transferred metallic pattern demonstrated in this work is only around 500 nm. It is conceivable that the smallest feature size of the proposed contact printing method can be far below 500 nm. However, for very small feature size such as less than 100 nm, the fidelity of pattern transfer could become an issue. It may require the use of thinner metal films in the order of 10 nm as well as a better thin film evaporation approach to minimize the film deposition on the side-wall of mold.

The proposed method is suitable for large-area patterning as long as the lasers or the light sources have enough power to reach certain level of laser fluence or optical intensity at the contact surface. It is also possible to adapt this planar-type printing method to curved surfaces with properly designed configurations and system setups. The underlying mechanism of this method is strongly related to interfacial and surface energy; hence a variety of materials for both films and substrates can be tested with this method.

12.5 Contact Transfer and Mask Embedded Lithography (CMEL)

12.5.1 Basic Idea and Experimental Setup

Inspired by the micro-contact printing (map) method as discussed in Section I and the laser-assisted direct metal film pattern transformation method discussed previously in Section IV, a new type of contact imprinting lithography is developed and is named Contact-Transferred and Mask-Embedded Lithography (CMEL)[43]. The CMEL process is much easier to implement for micro/nano- patterning and fabrication in comparison with the other currently existing methods. Figure 12.25 schematically depicts the basic idea and procedures of CMELand steps are as follows:

(1) First of all, a silicon mold with some micro/nano- scaled features is first coated with a thin releasing layer and then followed by a thin metal layer. The releasing layer is an anti-adhesion layer in between the mold surface and the metal layer so that the metal layer is only weakly attached to the mold's surface.

(2) This is complete the same as what has been applied in the LAMP process discussed in previous section. However, for the substrate, a polymer layer such as the photoresists commonly used in photolithography is spin-coated on top of the substrate. Without any hot baking, the polymer thin film will remain as a thin viscous liquid film with certain viscosity and mobility.

(3) After the mold and the substrate are prepared, the mold is placed on top of the substrate and a loading force is applied to imprint the convex features of the mold into the polymer layer on the substrate surface. When separating the mold from the substrate, a patterned metal film defined by the mold's convex feature surface can be transferred and embedded into the polymer film if the adhesion force between them overcomes the weak adhesion between the metal layer and the releasing layer.

(4) Once the patterned metal film is embedded in the polymer layer, it can serve as an etching mask for subsequent O_2 plasma etching to remove those polymers that are not protected by the transferred metal pattern. Finally, as shown in Fig. 12.25(d), the patterned substrate surface is exposed and is ready for subsequent processing such as chemical etching, electroplating, lift-off processing, and so forth.

There are several unique advantages of CMEL process when compared with other well-developed contact imprinting lithography methods mentioned in Section I in which three are listed below:

(1) The CMEL process is at room temperature without heating so that the process is much faster and there is no thermally induced dimensional change as commonly occurred in NIL;

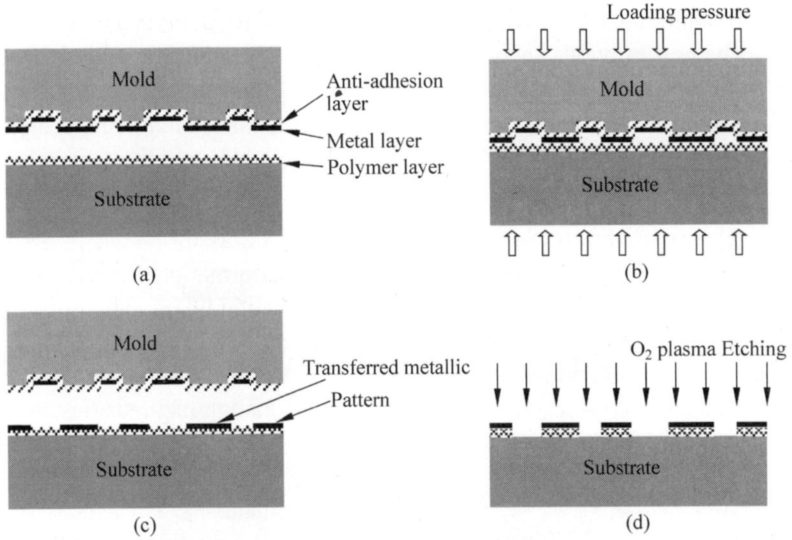

Figure 12.25 The basic idea and procedures of contact-transferred and mask-embedded lithography (CMEL)

(2) Unlike SFIL method which requires a transparent mold, the CMEL can utilize a silicon mold which is much easier and less expensive in preparation using standard photolithography or E-beam lithography;

(3) The CMEL utilizes a hard mold instead of a soft mold, as been used in micro-contact printing method, and the soft PDMS mold is known to have some mold sagging and adjacent feature sticking problems for certain feature dimensions.

Finally, since the basic mechanisms are all mechanical, the CMEL is applicable to a broad range of choices and combinations of materials in terms of the mold, the metal film, the polymer layer, and the substrate, and therefore is very flexible and versatile in micro/nano patterning and fabrication.

12.5.2 Experimental Details and Results

To demonstrate and verify this CMEL method, a series of experiments have been carried out which are as follows:

(1) First of all, several silicon molds are fabricated using standard photo-lithography methods;

(2) Both arrayed dot patterns and linear grating patterns with dot diameter or line-width around 500 nm are prepared;

(3) An anti-adhesion layer of 1H, 1H, 2H, 2H- Perfluorooctyltrichlorosilane is first deposited on the silicon mold surface using vapor deposition method, as mentioned before in previous section;

(4) On top of the release laser, a 60 nm thick chromium film is deposited using an E-beam thermal evaporator.

The preparation of molds in CMEL process is exactly the same as in LAMP process given in previous section. The area size of the silicon molds is 5 mm^2 × 5 mm^2 with repeated patterns covering all over the mold's surface. Figure 12.26 shows, as an example, the mold with linear grating features after being coated with a releasing layer and 60 nm Cr film. The length, line-width, and the center-to-center pitch of the linear gratings are 30 μm, 500 nm, and 1 μm, respectively.

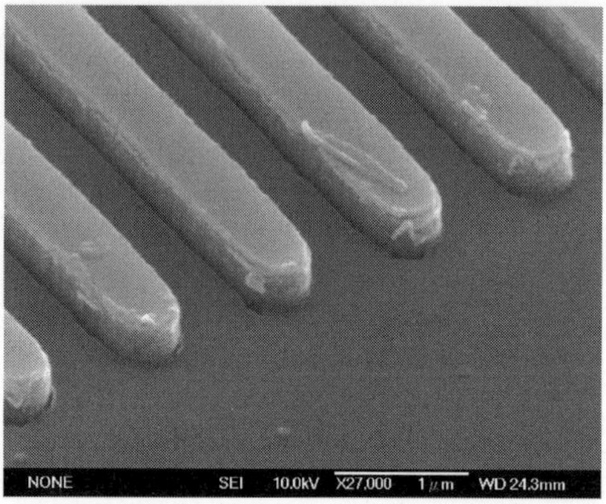

Figure 12.26 SEM images of silicon mold of linear grating features and coated with a thin releasing layer and a 60 nm thick Cr film. The width, center-to-center pitch, and the length of the linear gratings are 500 nm, 1 μm, and 30 μm, respectively[43]

Method for a silicon substrate:

(1) PMMA layer (PMMA 950K A6, MicroChem Corp., Newton, MA) is chosen as the polymer layer and is spin-coated on the substrate surface with a thickness around 390 nm.

(2) The films-coated mold is pressed on top of the PMMA/substrate with a loading pressure around 3 MPa for a few minute before separating the mold from the substrate.

(3) After the imprinting process, the PMMA-coated silicon substrates are examined by SEM. Figures 12.27(a) and (b) are the SEM images of the PMMA/Si substrates after imprinting by mold with linear grating and dot-arrayed features, respectively. As shown in Fig. 12.26.

(4) The patterned Cr films are now transferred to the PMMA layer. In Fig. 12.26, the irregular boundaries of the transferred patterns and some debris of polymer indicate the PMMA has been push aside by the mold's convex features during imprinting process and the metal films are actually embedded into the PMMA layer.

(5) The imprinted PMMA/Si samples are then dry-etched by O_2 plasma (RIE, OMNI-RIE, Duratex, Hsinchu) for 210 seconds to remove the PMMA material not covered by the metal film.

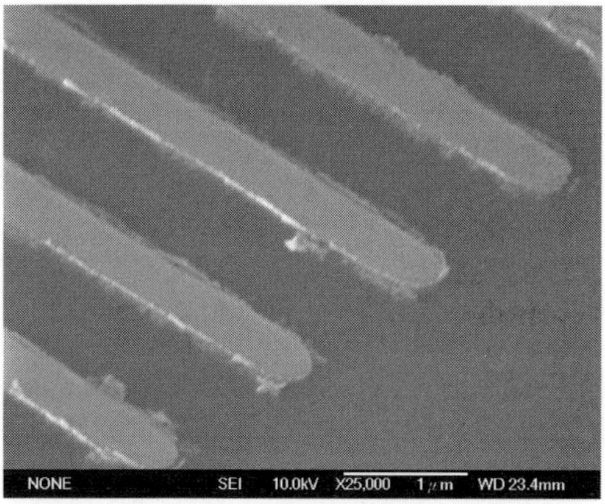

(a)

(b)

Figure 12.27 After contact imprinting, the patterned metal films are embedded into the polymer layer on top of the substrate surface, (a) linear grating features of 500 nm in width, 1.5 μm in center-to-center pitch, and 30 μm in length, (b). dot-array features with 400 nm in diameter and 1.5 μm in center-to-center pitch[43]

(6) The power of RIE is set to 150 Watts, the pressure of reaction chamber is 30 mTorr, and the flow rate of the reacting gas O_2 is controlled at 6 sccm.

(7) The unprotected PMMA is all etched off by O_2 plasma and the silicon surface is exposed. After then, it is etched using ICP (SLR-700, PlasmaTherm Inc., St. Petersburg, FL) with the Bosch process for one loop.

(8) Again, the patterned Cr film is serving as the etching mask during the ICP etching. Figures 12.28(a) and (b) are the SEM micrographs of the samples after silicon etching with linear-grating and dot-arrayed patterns, respectively.

(9) The PMMA materials which are not protected by the metal film patterns are etched out by O_2 plasma, and the patterned silicon structures are obtained after subsequent ICP etching as shown in Figs. 12.28(a) and (b).

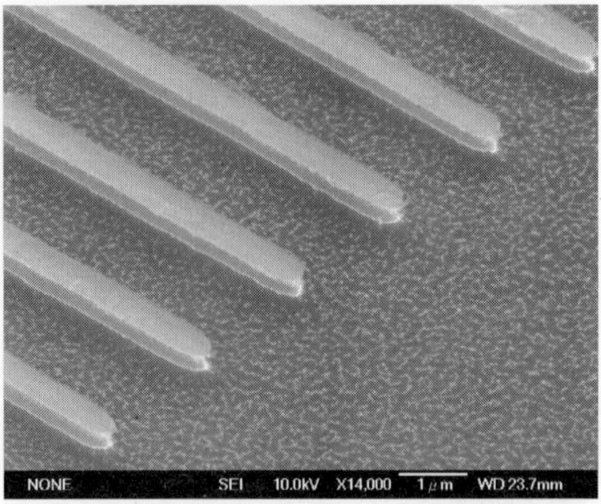

(a)

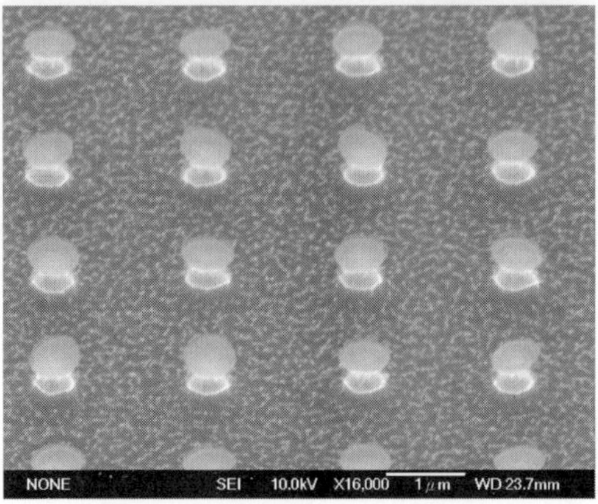

(b)

Figure 12.28 After O_2 plasma etching of polymer layer, the SEM images of the remained structures, from top to bottom, Cr film, polymer layer, and silicon, for (a) linear grating and (b) dot-arrayed patterns

(10) The remained PMMA polymer as well as the patterned metal films can be washed out by photo resist remover (Remover PG, MicroChem Corp., Newton, MA), and finally the silicon samples with the transferred patterns from the molds are fabricated as observed by SEM in Fig. 12.29.

Since metal films are good etching masks for O_2 plasma as well as for ICP process, one can obtain deeper etching depth and higher aspect ratio by enhancing the ICP etching process. Figure 12.30 shows, as an example, the fabricated structures by using the CMEL process and substantial ICP etching on the silicon substrate patterned with linear gratings. The fabricated linear grating structures in silicon have a line-width around 500 nm and a center-to-center pitch of 1.5 μm. The etching depth is around 1.5 μm which gives an aspect ratio of 3.

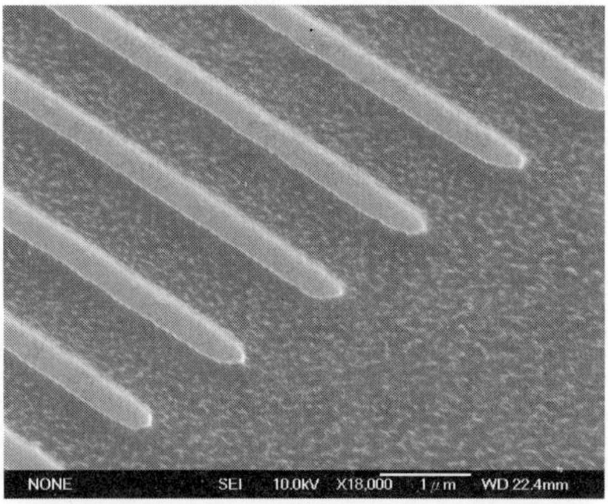

(a)

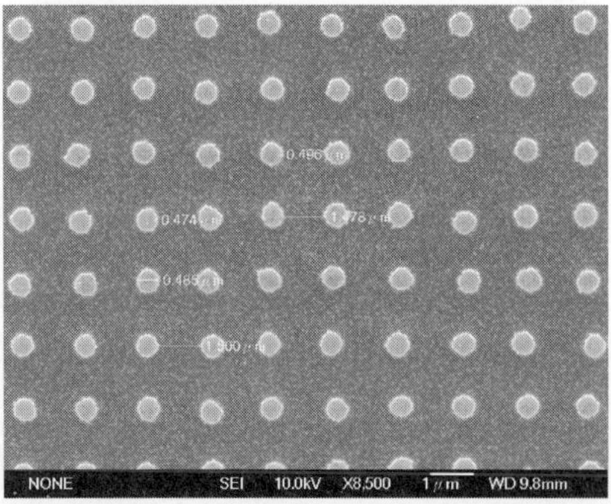

(b)

Figure 12.29 After removing the residual PMMA and metal films, the features of the mold is now replicated on the silicon substrate with (a) linear gratings and (b) dot-arrayed patterns[43]

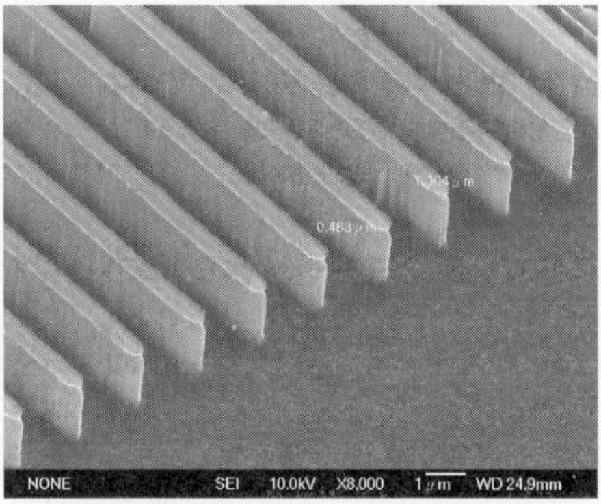

Figure 12.30 The linear grating structures of high aspect ratio fabricated by CMEL and ICP etching. The line-width, center-to-center pitch, and etching depth are 500 nm, 1.5 μm, and 1.5 μm, respectively[43]

Besides using molds with convex features, the CMEL can use molds with concave features too. To demonstrate this, a silicon mold with an array of small concave holes is applied to CMEL imprinting process on a PMMA/Si substrate. Figure 12.31(a) shows the transferred and embedded 60 nm Cr film patterns on top of the PMMA/Si substrate, and Fig. 12.31(b) shows the fabricated structures after O_2 plasma and ICP etching on the metal-film patterned silicon substrate. As seen from Fig. 12.31(b), a complete 2D array of deep holes with a diameter of 500 nm, an array pitch of 700 nm, and an etching depth of 1.5 μm is successfully fabricated on silicon substrate using this simple, fast, and powerful CMEL method. The center-to-center distance between adjacent holes is 700 nm and the narrowest part of the bridges between holes is only 200 nm, which is the smallest feature size we have demonstrated so far with this CMEL method.

(a)

(b)

Figure 12.31 CMEL processes using a mold with concave features of an array of holes, (a) patterned Cr film of 60 nm thick and embedded in a PMMA/Si sample, (b) after O_2 plasma and ICP etchings, the fabricated silicon structure with an array of concave holes of 500 nm in diameter, 700 nm in pitch, and 1.5 μm in etching depth[43]

12.5.3 Discussions and Conclusions

To conclude, a new method for micro/nano-lithography is proposed and demonstrated. This method utilizes an anti-adhesion layer to release a patterned metal film from a mold to a polymer-coated substrate. The key point is that the metal film is only weakly adhered to the mold and therefore can be transferred and embedded into the unbaked polymer layer through the contact imprinting process. The transferred metal film pattern then severs as a very good etching mask for O_2 plasma to etch out the polymer material that is not covered or defined by the transferred metal pattern. The proposed contact imprinting lithography is purely based on mechanical forces without using laser light, thermal heating, or any other kind of energy sources. Therefore, it is simple, fast, low-cost, at room-temperature, and easy to implement. The major equipments needed in this CMEL process, as demonstrated in this work, are all ordinary ones and readily available in many laboratories working on MEMS, semiconductors, and micro/nano-technologies. Fabrication of molds with nano scaled features is perhaps the most difficult part in this process, as is true for any other imprinting or contact printing methods currently exist. However, since silicon molds are relatively easy to fabricate or to acquire, this problem is less severe for CMEL. Another advantage of CMEL is that the contact pressure is much reduced since the polymer film is unbaked and is still like a viscous fluid film. Therefore, the life expectance of the mold is significant increased and the mold can be reused many times with proper processing. Finally, since the CMEL process and its underlying mechanisms are all purely mechanical, it is very flexible and versatile in terms of the choices of materials for the mold, the metal film, the polymer layer, as well as the substrate. This is very important for researches based on non-silicon materials.

Similar to many other nanoimprinting and contact printing methods, the smallest line-width of CMEL is not limited to optical diffraction limit since no light source is used. Although only 200 – 500 nm feature sizes are demonstrated in this work due to our limited fabrication capability of the molds, there is no obvious reason why this CMEL method can not achieve line-width down to 100 nm or less. Naturally, for smaller feature sizes, the thicknesses of the metal film and the polymer layer will have to reduce accordingly. Efforts are underway to achieve smaller line-width as well as to explore other potentials, possibilities, and applications of CMEL.

12.6 Conclusions and Future Perspectives

In this chapter, a number of innovative imprinting and printing methods for fabrication of micro-/nano- structures have been proposed and demonstrated. The ideas start from investigating and improving the Laser-Assisted Direct Imprinting

(LADI) process which utilizes a high-energy UV pulsed laser as the driving power for direct and fast transformation of the surface features of a quartz mold to a silicon substrate. However, in the process of searching for imprinting methods which are more effective and easily implemented in a typical laboratory with minimum requirements on equipments, the final approaches have been quite different from LADI.

This chapter begins with investigating the fundamental mechanism of LADI process with a goal to clarify the role played by each imprinting parameters including the laser fluence, contact pressure, and imprinted feature size in the LADI process as well as their correlation with the final imprinting depth of LADI. The most important discovery is that the LADI imprinting process has to take into account is the elastodynamic or wave-propagation characteristics of a pre-stressed elastic solid, that is, the mold, during the course of releasing of its pre-stored strain energy. By integrating this elastodynamic behavior with the laser-heating and melting characteristics as well as the film-squeezing phenomenon, a theoretical modeling is constructed. The numerical simulation based on this modeling is able to take all imprinting parameters into account, unveil the interaction between them, and yield a quantitative relationship which links the final imprinting depth to each and all individual imprinting parameters in LADI. It also reveals several interesting physic results such as saturation imprinting depth and feature size dependence of the final imprinting depth. To experimentally verify this theoretical model, a series of LADI tests have been designed and carried out. The experimental results, although not perfectly match with the theoretical modeling, but do show a similar trend predicted by the theoretical modeling and therefore support the basic idea of the theoretical modeling. Further modifications on the theoretical analysis are needed to cope with the complexity of the real LADI processes and bring theoretical results closer to experimental ones.

The most important implication revealed by this theoretical model is that, since LADI is a process of relaxation of pre-stored strain energy, it can be performed in a localized way or area by area. Based on this understanding, a new type roller-based LADI is proposed and experimentally demonstrated. The quartz roller, which plays the central role in the experimental setup of this new method, not only focuses the incident laser energy into a line at the mold/substrate interface but also create a line concentration of mechanical loading pressure coincided with the laser-focused line. Therefore, the LADI process can now be performed in a continuous and fast way for large-area fabrication of micro-/nano-structures. This shows that the roller-based LADI process explores almost all the advantages of LADI, avoids all major disadvantages of LADI, and also best utilizes the high repetition rate and the power of a pulsed UV laser source for LADI. The imprinting speed and the imprinting size of this roller-based LADI can be continuously increasing along with the increasing power of the laser sources without subjecting to small and discrete imprinting areas of the original LADI.

In searching for alternative laser energy sources other than expensive deep UV pulse laser, such as excimer lasers for imprinting/printing lithography, an IR-lased assisted, contact-printed, and direct metal film pattern transformation method is developed. The key element in this method are as:

(1) To deposit an anti-adhesion layer in between the mold surface and the metal film, which is to be transferred.

(2) The contact printing and IR laser heating from the silicon substrate side provide necessary contact pressure and temperature rising, respectively, and activate a new bonding interface between the metal film and the substrate.

(3) Finally, the patterned metal thin film of the mold can be transferred from the mold to the substrate in a direct way without any chemical etching process. The line-width of this direct metal film contact printing method can easily achieve sub-micrometer and few hundred nanometers, as being demonstrate in this chapter, and with further potentials to go below 100 nm or less.

There are two potential improvements on this contact-printing method which have significant impacts on future applications which are as mentioned below:

(1) Replace the IR laser with other types of IR radiation sources such as IR lamps with appropriate light focusing, which can significantly lower the cost and increasing the printing contact area size.

(2) Change the configuration from planar printing to roller-type configuration such as the one proposed for roller-based LADI. This turns the system into a continuous and roll-to-roll contact printing process for large area printing.

Finally, a contact-transfer and mask-embedded method for lithography, CMEL, is developed based on similar concepts but using the viscous and adhesive characteristics of a thin polymer layer as the driving force for pattern transformation from a mold surface to a substrate surface. It is a room-temperature process using pure mechanical forces only without other energy sources, and therefore is very to implement. It is demonstrated that complex structures of high aspect ratio and feature size around 300 nm or less can be easily fabricated using this CMEL approach along with RIE or ICP etching processes. Again, the CMEL can be further modified into a roller-based contact printing or imprinting process for large-area fabrication.

To conclude, laser-assisted or light-source-assisted and roll-based imprinting/printing methods as being discussed in this chapter have several distinguished advantages over conventional planar-type and thermally heated approaches which are highlighted as here:

(1) Lasers or light-sources can heat the samples much faster therefore significantly shorten the processing time. When an IR lasers or light sources are utilized, the molds for imprinting or printing can be still made of silicon crystals which are much easier to obtain due to the successful developments of semiconductor industries.

(2) Roller-based processing configurations are most suitable for high-speed, continuous, large-area, and therefore high throughput production of micro/nano-structures.

(3) And last but not the least, roller-based setup makes it much easier to achieve a uniformly distributed pressure along the contact surface between modes and substrates, which can be a troublesome problem in planar type imprinting/printing system especially for large area processing.

In the future developments of roller-based and laser or light source assisted imprinting/printing methods, several directions and areas of research are of particular importance. First of all, system integration to turn the proposed method into an integrated workstation or a tool for real world applications is very important and requires efforts in machine system design, automotive control, testing and integration. Optimal material design and new type of material for the proposed methods are also critical since all kinds of imprinting/printing methods require different combinations and matching in surface energies between materials used for molds, substrates, resist layers, and anti-adhesion layers, etc. Finally, multilayer alignment which has been always the most difficult challenge in imprinting/printing technologies still a big difficult issue open to innovative and creative ideas to solve.

Acknowledgements

The authors are grateful for supports from Taiwan Science Council of through projects NSC93-2120-M-006-009, NSC94-2120-M-006-009, and NSC95-2120-M-006-009. This work is also supported by Taiwan Industrial Technology Research Institute through jointed projects. The authors also thank to the Center for Micro/Nano Technology Research, Tainan Cheng Kung University for equipment access and technical support.

References

[1] Chou S. Y., P. R. Krauss, and P. J. Renstrom, (1995), Imprint of sub-25 nm vias and trenches in polymers, *Appl. Phys. Lett.*, **67**(21): 3114 – 3116

[2] Chou S. Y., P. R. Krauss, and P. J. Renstrom, (1996), "Nanoimprint lithography," *J. Vac. Sci. Technol., B* **14**(6): 4129 – 4133

[3] Chou S. Y., P. R. Krauss, and P. J. Renstrom, (1996), "Imprint lithography with 25-nanometer resolution," *Science*, **272**(5258): 85 – 87

[4] Chou S. Y., and P. R. Krauss, (1997), "Imprint Lithography with Sub-10 nm Feature Size and High Throughput," *Microelect. Eng.*, **35**(1 – 4): 237 – 240

[5] Guo L., P. R. Krauss, and S. Y. Chou, (1997), Nanoscale silicon field effect transistors fabricated using imprint Lithography, *Appl. Phys. Lett.*, **71**(13): 1881 – 1883

[6] Pepin A., P. Youinou, V. Studer, A. Lebib, Y. Chen, (2002), "Nanoimprint lithography for the fabrication of DNA electrophoresis chips," *Microelect. Eng.*, **61** – **62**: 927 – 932

[7] Zhang W., and S. Y. Chou, (2003), "Fabrication of 60-nm transistors on 4-in. wafer using nanoimprint at all lithography levels," *Appl. Phys. Lett.*, **83**(8): 1632 – 1634

[8] Li M., L. Chen, W. Zhang, and S. Y Chou, (2003), "Pattern transfer fidelity of nanoimprint lithography on six-inch wafers, *Nanotechnology*, **14**(1): 33 – 36

[9] Colburn M., S. Johnson, M. Stewart, S. Damle, T. Bailey, B. Choi, M. Wedlake, T. Michaelson, S. V. Sreenivasan, J. Ekerdt, and C. G. Willson, (1999), "Step and Flash Imprint Lithography: A New Approach to High-Resolution Patterning" *Proc. SPIE* **3676**: 379 – 389

[10] Bailey T., B. J. Choi, M. Colburn, M. Meissl, S. Shaya, J. G. Ekerdt, S. V. Sreenivasan, and C. G. Willson, (2000), "Step and flash imprint lithography: Template surface treatment and defect analysis," *J. Vac. Sci. Technol., B* **18**(6): 3572 – 3577

[11] Colburn M., T. Bailey, B.J. Choi, J.G. Ekerdt, S.V. Sreenivasan, C.G. Willson, (2001), "Development and advantages of step-and-flash lithography," *Solid State Technolgy*, **44**(7): 67 – 77

[12] Jung G. Y., S. Ganapathiappan, D. A. A. Ohlberg, D. L. Olynick, Y. Chen, W. M. Tong, and R. S. Williams, (2004), "Fabrication of a 34×34 Crossbar Structure at 50 nm Half-pitch by UV-based Nanoimprint Lithography," *Nano Letters,* **4**(7): 1225 – 1229

[13] Stewart M. D., S. C. Johnson, S. V. Sreenivasan, D. J. Resnick, C. G. Willson, (2005), "Nano-fabrication with step and flash imprint lithography," *J. Microlith., Microfab. and Microsys*, **4**(1): 1 – 6

[14] Dickey M. D., and C. G. Willson, (2006), "Kinetic Parameters for Step and Flash Imprint Lithography Photopolymerization," *AIChE Journal*, **52**(2): 777 – 784

[15] Khusnatdinov N., G. Doyle, M. Miller, N. Stacey, M. Watts, and D. L. LaBrake, (2006), "Fabrication of Nano and Micro Optical Elements by Step and Flash Imprint Lithography," *Proc. of SPIE*, **6110**: 61100K1 – 10

[16] Xia Y., M. Mrksich, E. Kim, and G. M. Whitesides, (1995), "Microcontact Printing of Octadecylsiloxane on the Surface of Silicon Dioxide and Its Application in Microfabrication," *J. Am. Chem. Soc.*, **117**(37): 9576 – 9577

[17] Xia Y., and G. M. Whitesides, (1995), "Reduction in the Size of Features of Patterned SAMs Generated by Microcontact Printing with Mechanical Compression of the Stamp," *Adv. Mater.*, **7**(8): 471 – 473

[18] Lahiri J., E. Ostuni, and G. M. Whitesides, (1999), "Patterning Ligands on Reactive SAMs by Microcontact Printing, *Langmuir*, **15**(6): 2055 – 2060

[19] Deng T., M. Prentiss, and G. M. Whitesides, (2002), "Fabrication of magnetic microfiltration systems using soft lithography," *Appl. Phys. Letts.*, **80**(3): 461 – 463

[20] Loo Y.-L., J. W. P. Hsu, R. L. Willett, K. W. Baldwin, K. W. West, and J. A. Rogers, (2002), "High-resolution transfer printing on GaAs surfaces using alkane dithiol monolayers," *J. Vac. Sci. Technol., B* **20**(6): 2853 – 2856

[21] Wolfe B. D., J. C. Love, B. D. Gates, G. M. Whitesides, R. S. Conroy, and M. Prentiss, (2004), "Fabrication of planar optical waveguides by electrical microcontact printing," *Appl. Phys. Lett.*, **84**(10): 1623 – 1625

[22] Xia Y., and G. M. Whitesides, (1998), "Soft Lithography," *Annu. Rev. Mater. Sci.*, **28**: 153 – 184

[23] Gates B. D., Q. Xu, M. Stewart, D. Ryan, C. G. Willson, and G. M. Whitesides, (2005), "New Approaches to Nano-fabrication: Molding, Printing, and Other Techniques," *Chem. Rev.*, **105**(4): 1171 – 1196

[24] Guo L. J., (2007), "Nanoimprint Lithography: Methods and Material Requirements," *Adv. Mater.*, **19**(4): 495 – 513

[25] Chou S. Y., C. Keimel, and J. Gu, (2002), "Ultrafast and direct imprint of nanostructures in silicon," *Nature*, **417**(6891): 835 – 837

[26] Cui B., W. Wu, C. Keimel, and S. Y. Chou, (2006), "Filling of nano-via holes by laser-assisted direct imprint," *Microelect. Eng.*, **83**(4 – 9): 1547 – 1550

[27] Li L. P., Y. F. Lu, D. W. Doerr, D. R. Alexander, J. Shi, and J. C. Li, (2004), "Fabrication of hemispherical cavity arrays on silicon substrates using laser-assisted nanoimprinting of self-assembled particles," *Nanotechnology*, **15**(3): 333 – 336

[28] Li L. P., Y. F. Lu, D. W. Doerr, and D. R. Alexander, (2004), "Parametric investigation of laser nanoimprinting of hemispherical cavity arrays," *J. Appl. Phys.*, **96**(9): 5144 – 5151

[29] Xu X., C. P. Grigoropoulos and R. E. Russo, (1994), "Measurement of solid–liquid interface temperature during pulsed excimer laser melting of polycrystalline silicon films," *Phys. Re. Lett.*, **65**(14): 1745 – 1747

[30] Sasik R., and R. Cerny, (1991), "Numerical solution of the non-isothermal moving boundary problem in heat conduction," *Comput. Phys. Communicat.*, **64**(2): 241 – 251

[31] Tokarev V. N., and A. F. H. Kaplan, (1999), "Analytical modeling of time dependent pulsed laser melting," *J. Appl. Phys.*, **86**(5): 2836 – 2846

[32] Hsiao F.-B., C.-P. Jen, D.-B. Wang, C.-H. Chuang, Y.-C. Lee, C.-P. Liu, H.-J. Hsu, (2006), "An analytical modeling of heat transfer for laser-assisted nano-imprinting processes," *Comput. Mech.*, **37**(2): 173 – 181

[33] Lee Y. C., M.-H. Chung, F.-Y. Chang, "An elastodynamic modeling of laser assisted direct imprinting (LADI) process," submitted to journal for publication

[34] Achenbach J. D., Wave Propagation in Elastic Solids (Elsevier North-Holland, New York, 1973), Chap. 1

[35] Bird R. B., R. C. Armstrong, and O. Hassager, (1987), *Dynamics of Polymeric Liquids*, 2nd ed. Wiely, New York, 20

[36] Kim M.-U., K. W. Kim, Y.-H. Cho, and B. M. Kwak, (2001), "Hydrodynamic force on a plate near the plane wall. Part II: Plate in squeezing motion," *Fluid Dynamics Research*, **29**(3): 171 – 198

[37] Lee Y.-C., C.-Y. Chiu, C.-H. Chen, F.-Y. Chang, "Roller-based laser assisted direct imprinting for large area and continuous nano-fabrication," *Microelectronic Engineering*, **87**(1): 34 – 40

[38] Tan H., A. Gilbertson, and S. Y. Chou, (1998), "Roller nanoimprint lithography" *J. Vac. Sci. Technol., B* **16**(6): 3926 – 3928

[39] Rogers J. A., Z. Bao, A. Makhija, and P. Braun, (1999), "Printing process suitable for reel-to-reel production of high-performance organic transistors and circuits," *Adv. Mater.*, **11**(5): 741 – 745

[40] Chen C.-H., and Y.-C. Lee, (2007), "Contact printing for direct metallic pattern transfer based on pulsed infrared laser heating," *J. Micromech. Microeng.*, **17**(7): 1252 – 1256
[41] Jung G. Y., Z. Li, W. Wu, Y. Chen, D. L. Olynick, S. Y. Wang, W. M. Tong, and R. S. Williams, (2005), "Improved pattern transfer in nanoimprint lithography at 30 nm half-pitch by substrate-surface functionalization," *Langmuir*, **21**(14): 1158 – 1161
[42] Poate J. M., and J. W. Mayer, *Laser Annealing of Semiconductors* (Academic Press, New York, 1982) Chapters 3 and 4
[43] Lee Y.-C., and C.-Y. Chiu, "A new micro/nano-lithography based on contact transfer of thin film and mask embedded etching," *J. Micromech. Microeng*; **18**(7): 075013 – 075019

13 The Application of STM and AFM in Nanoprocess and Fabrication

Yi Zhang[1], Jun Hu[1], and Xudong Xiao[2]

[1] Shanghai Institute of Aplied Physics, Chinese Academy of Sciences, Shanghai 201800, China
E-mail: yzhang@sinap.ac.cn

[2] The Chinese University of Hong Kong, Hong Kong, China

Abstract The scanning tunneling microscope (STM) and atomic force microscope (AFM) provide, not only 'eyes' but also 'hands' to investigate and modify nano-objects. Therefore, not only are high resolution images available to us, but they offer a means to construct objects in the microscopic world. In this chapter, we will introduce nanometer processing technologies based on STM and AFM.

During last decade fabrication and processing at the nanometer scale have achieved great advances, based on STM and AFM. Manipulation of individual atoms and molecules has been realized, and potential applications such as molecular devices have been demonstrated. Functionalized nanostructures have been fabricated with STM- and AFM-related techniques through various physical or chemical mechanisms. We expect that process and fabrication with STM and AFM will finally go from laboratory to factory as well as to thousands of families in the coming future.

Keywords Scanning tunneling microscope (STM), atomic force microscope (AFM), nanofabrication, nanomanipulation

13.1 Introduction

One of the ultimate goals of nanoscience and nanotechnology is to develop molecular machines that manipulate individual atoms or molecules and make products with unique functions. The well-known speech entitled 'There's Plenty of Room at the Bottom', delivered by the physicist R. Feynman in 1959, resulted in the bud of nanoscience and nanotechnology. Later, in one of Feynman's books, he suggested further that people might develop machines that work at the molecular level[1]. However, as there was no means or tools to manipulate a single molecule at that time, his idea was merely a purely academic discussion. In 1981, K.E. Drexler pointed out for the first time that artificial molecular machines might be constructed via advanced molecular engineering technology, by following the ways that nature adopted and presented in organisms for millions of years[2]. In 1992 he showed that complex structures could be built via precise control of atoms, the properties of which depend on the organization of atoms[3].

The invention of the scanning probe microscopes (SPM) family[4] provides strong support for the processing and fabrication at the nanometer level, and drives forward the development in nanoscience and nanotechnology. Originally, the SPM was used to investigate surface properties of samples by scanning the local surface with a tiny tip. Detailed information that can be obtained with very high spatial resolution by using the SPM is: ① topological, ② mechanical, ③ electrical, ④ magnetic and ⑤ optical. The most popular members of the SPM family are the scanning tunneling microscope (STM)[5] and atomic force microscope (AFM)[6]. STM is the first member of SPM family, invented by G. Binnig and H. Rohrer, who shared the Nobel Prize in Physics in 1986 for this invention. The STM measures the tunnel current between a conductive tip and a conductive sample, and can 'see' a single atom. The AFM, invented by G. Binnig et al. in 1986, measures the mechanical deflection of a cantilever, which has a nanometer sized tip that interacts with a local region of sample surfaces. The AFM is applicable for both conductive and non-conductive samples under various environmental conditions (in vacuum, ambient air, or liquid). In addition, AFM and STM are used as not only 'eyes' but also 'hands' so that they can probe and modify samples. Therefore, not only is high-resolution information available to us, but also a means to construct in the microscopic world.

The goal of this chapter is not to systematically review work in the field of SPM, but to introduce nanometer processing technologies based on STM and AFM, especially the developments in the last decade.

13.2 The Manipulation and Processing of Single Atoms and Molecules

Apart from high-resolution images obtained by STM, the tunneling current and the voltage exerted between the tip and the sample can be employed to achieve surface modifications at the atomic level, for example, to manipulate single atoms. Atomic manipulation by STM can be simply classed into ① vertical and ② lateral manipulation modes. Both modes are described below:

(1) In vertical mode, the STM tip is first located directly above the atom to be moved, and then lowered down to it to increase the attraction between them, which in turn leads to atom adsorption on the tip; then, the tip is lifted up, and kept in planar motion relative to the surface. Finally the atom is released from the STM tip and placed at the desired location (see Fig. 13.1(a));

(2) In the lateral mode, the STM tip can perform many operations on the atom,

including pushing, pulling and sliding, while at the same time the atom remains bound to the surface (see Fig. 13.1(b)).

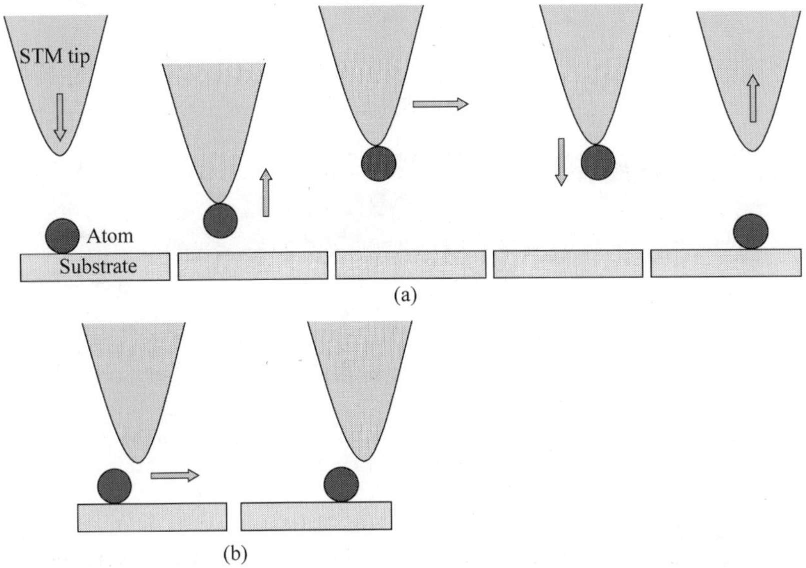

Figure 13.1 Schematic drawing of the nano-manipulation of atoms with STM. (a) Vertical manipulation mode. (b) Lateral manipulation mode (see color figure at the end of this book)

Manipulating single atoms on the conductor surface[7] was a milestone in nanoscience and nano-technology. In 1990, D. M. Eigler et al. used STM tips to move atoms and wrote down a company's name with 35 xenon atoms on a nickel surface (see Fig. 13.2), which meant that the long-standing desire of human beings to manipulate single atoms had been satisfied. In addition, vertical mechanical manipulation of single atoms using AFM has also been realized[8]. Recently, W. Ho et al. used STM to build 1D gold chains (see Fig. 13.3)[9] and studied the correlation between geometric and electronic properties, thus demonstrating that it is possible to carry out atomic-level fabrication.

Figure 13.2 A company name 'IBM' formed with 35 Xe atoms by using STM nano-manipulation[7]

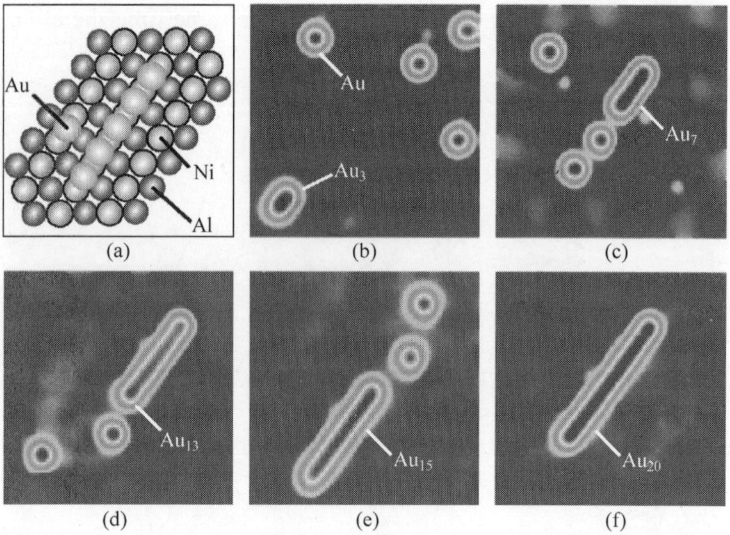

Figure 13.3 Moving and patterning individual Au atoms with STM. A atomic chain was formed with 20 Au atoms[9] (see color figure at the end of this book)

The manipulation of single molecules was realized a little later as molecules are more complex. Figure 13.4 shows images before and after the rearrangement of 6 Cu-TBPP molecules under the STM tip at room temperature[10]. Taking advantage of the repulsion between the STM tip and molecules, X. Xiao et al.

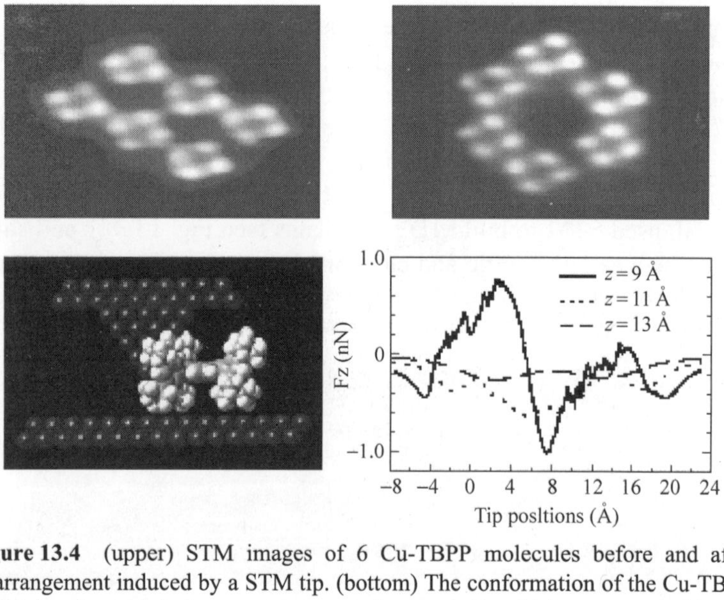

Figure 13.4 (upper) STM images of 6 Cu-TBPP molecules before and after re-arrangement induced by a STM tip. (bottom) The conformation of the Cu-TBPP molecules changed during re-arrangement (bottom left), which was revealed by the force curve (bottom right)[10] (see color figure at the end of this book)

managed to manipulate CO molecules and patterned the word 'HKUST' with 49 CO molecules on the copper surface in 2002 (see Fig. 13.5). The manipulation of biological macromolecules has also been accomplished. As shown in Fig. 13.6, complicated patterns, such as letters 'D', 'N', and 'A' were patterned with DNA molecules by employing AFM nanomanipulation including cutting, pushing and folding process[11].

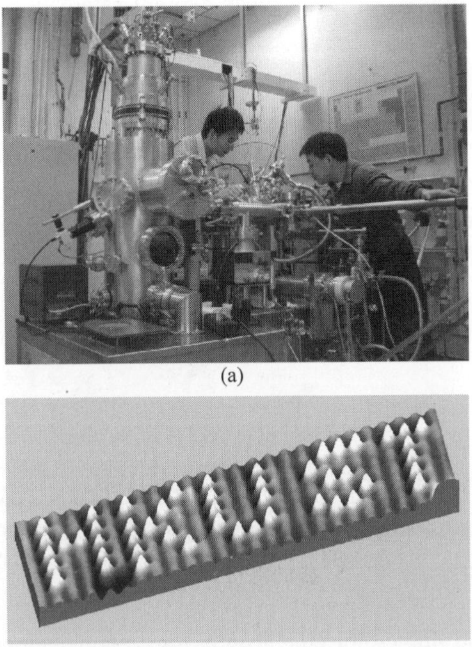

(a) (b)

Figure 13.5 Manipulation of CO molecules with STM. (a) Researchers working with a Low Temperature Omicron STM system; (b) the word 'HKUST' formed with 49 CO molecules on Cu surface. Images were provided by Prof. Xudong Xiao of the Hong Kong University of Science & Technology (see color figure at the end of this book)

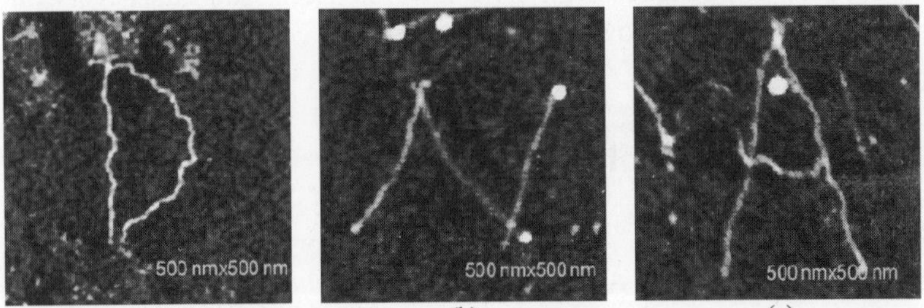

(a) (b) (c)

Figure 13.6 Human letters 'D', 'N', and 'A' formed with individual DNA molecules[11] (see color figure at the end of this book)

Nanomanipulation makes possible the single-atom or single-molecule reaction as shown in Fig. 13.7. A CO molecule was transferred and positioned over an Fe atom to form Fe (CO), and Fe $(CO)_2$ was formed when a second CO was added[12]. It should be noted that the reaction would not occur automatically when a CO molecule is close to a Fe atom. Tunneling electrons and possibly the electric field between the tip and the surface will be involved in overcoming the energetic barriers in the process to form new bonds. In addition, scanning tunneling current tip-induced chain polymerization has been demonstrated[13].

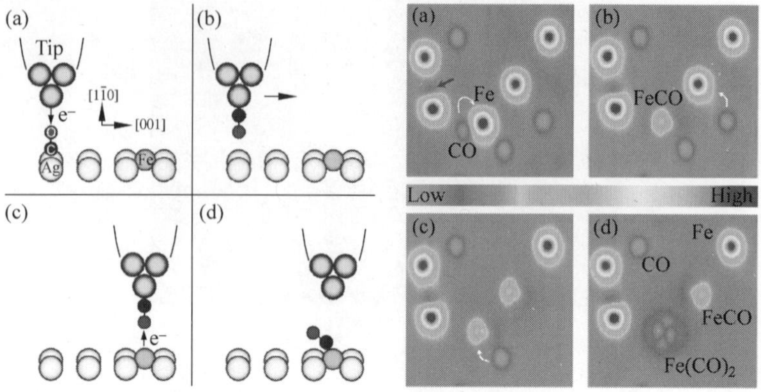

Figure 13.7 Single-molecule reaction induced with STM. (Left) Scheme. (Right) STM images indicating the reaction process. (a) Several Fe atoms and CO molecules on the substrate. (b) One CO molecule reacted with Fe atom to form a FeCO molecules. (c) Two FeCO molecules were formed. (d) One FeCO reacted with another CO and formed a $Fe(CO)_2$[12] (see color figure at the end of this book)

Manipulation at the single-molecule level has great applications, in manufacturing single-molecule devices. Scientists used a C_{60} molecule as a current amplifier[14]. This single-molecule device was produced by placing a C_{60} molecule between a STM tip and a surface of a conductor. When a bias was exerted to the STM tip to force it to approaching the surface, the resulting pressure caused a change in C_{60} conformation, which in turn decreased the resistance of the C_{60} molecule. The researchers found that the resistance was lowered nearly 100 times every time the C_{60} molecule was pressed down 0.1 nm by the tip.

13.3 Nanolithography on Surfaces

Development in STM and AFM provides tools for nanoscale processing and modifying. For instance, the AFM tip can exert a mechanical force to a local region of the surface so as to produce mechanical machine work in the nanometer scale. The process is programmable, making practical operation convenient. What is of great symbolic significance is that a famous Chinese poem of the Tang dynasty,

'Dawn of Spring' (see Fig. 13.8), was written with an AFM tip by Z. Liu's research group at Peking University[15].

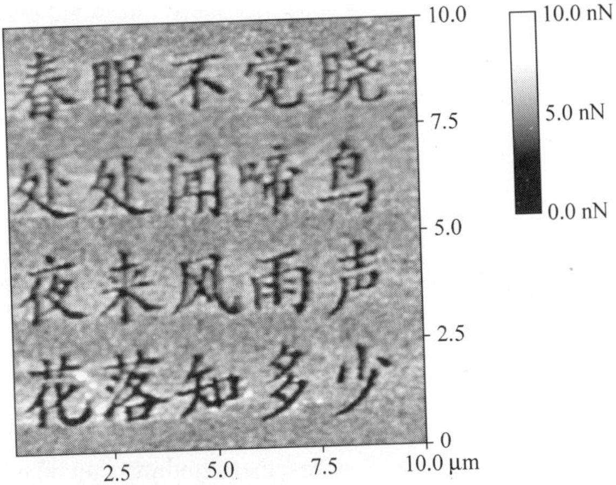

Figure 13.8 The famous Chinese poem of the Tang dynasty, 'Dawn of Spring', written with AFM nano-lithography[15]

Besides the mechanical force exerted by using an AFM tip, an 'electric' interaction can be introduced on the local surface by an STM tip. For instance, if a certain voltage is imposed locally on the self-assembled monolayer (SAM) formed with Au-S bonds on the Au surface, the SAM will be removed, resulting in nanoscale patterns (Fig. 13.9)[16]. As for AFM, the same operation can be achieved by scanning a conducting tip with a sufficient bias between the tip and

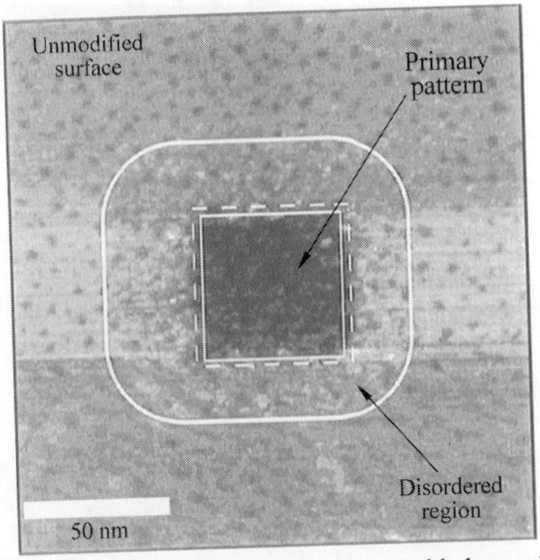

Figure 13.9 STM nano-lithography on the self-assembled monolayer. The center 50 nm × 50 nm square in the image was the exposed Au surface after nano-lithography[16]

the SAM surface[17]. In the experiments, the tip-sample bias needs to exceed a critical threshold value, while at the same time sufficient ambient humidity is demanded for some specific SAMs.

13.4 Nanoscale Surface Processing Based on Electrochemical Reactions

It has long been noted that the oxidation of hydrogen-passivated Si surfaces can be induced by a STM tip operating in air[18]. The study showed that a biased conducting AFM tip can locally induce surface oxidation of semiconductors (Si) or metals such as Ti. Researches have indicated that the water present on the surfaces play an important role in these processes. Therefore, it is believed that it is an electrochemical process.

Volume expansion of semiconductors or metals upon oxidation makes convenient, the characterization of the reactions. Besides, these findings can be used to construct nanostructures in the oxidation state. The size of nanostructure is determined by the bias voltage and the reaction time (Fig. 13.10(a))[19–22]. As aqueous solution of HF can be used to etch SiO_2 easily, a proper treatment of the nano-structures with HF solution resulted in nano-meter sized wells (Fig. 13.10(b))[19].

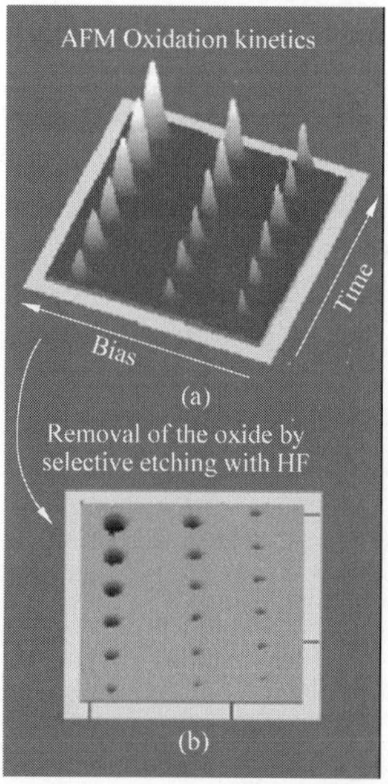

Figure 13.10 (a) AFM image of a locally oxidized Si substrate. (b) AFM image of the Si nano-structures after HF etching[19]

Since the AFM tip takes effect merely in a confined area, a direct idea is to take advantage of this kind of nanoscale electrochemical reactions to reduce metal ions, so that the metallic nanostructures can be constructed on surfaces. For example, when silver ions were chemisorbed on a thiol-terminated silane monolayer on silicon substrate, an appropriate bias applied to the AFM tip would result in release of Ag and formation of island-like Ag nanostructures on the substrate[23]. Another indirect way was that methyl-terminated silane monolayer on Si could be patterned via tip-induced electrochemical oxidation of the methyl group, in which the product –COOH group, would facilitate the adsorption of Ag^+ ions. Then the Ag^+ ions were reduced by reducing agent, and finally nanoscale silver islands were obtained (see Fig. 13.11)[24]. Similarly, the same strategy can be applied to construct nanostructures of Au, CdS and so on.

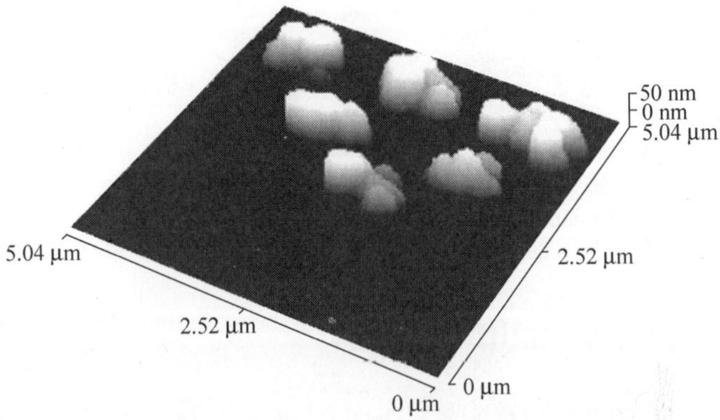

Figure 13.11 AFM image of Ag island formed after electrochemical reaction induced by conductive AFM[24]

13.5 Metal Nanostructures Fabricated with Field Evaporation

Field Evaporation is the phenomena where the atoms are ionized and evaporated in the presence of extremely high electric field of the order of a few V/nm. Such high electric field normally can be achieved by applying a high voltage between a sharp needle-like conductor and a plate-like conductor. Since the distance between the tip and the surface can be controlled accurately to 1 nm or less for STM or AFM, a few volts of supply will meet the ultra-high electric field required for field evaporation.

The field evaporation can be used to manipulate atoms or to construct nanostructures on the surface[25]. A simple idea is to use the STM tip as the emission source to construct nanostructures on the surface. Similarly, when an

AFM tip is coated with a metal film, such as a gold film, then the film can be used as the emission source to construct gold nanostructures on a conducting surface. As shown in Fig. 13.12, a nice array of gold nanodots was produced in this way[15].

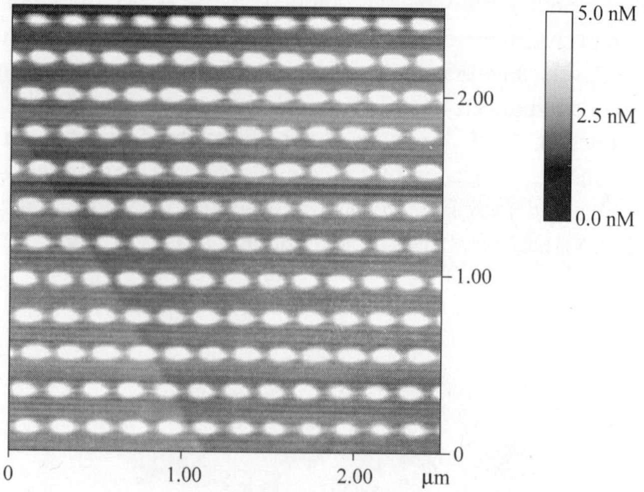

Figure 13.12 Au nano-array formed on a HOPG surface by field evaporation[15]

13.6 Dip-pen Nanolithography

Dip-pen Nanolithography (DPN)[26], based on atomic force microscope (AFM) is an approach for nanofabrication, which was developed by C. A. Mirkin et al. As shown in Fig. 13.13, molecules (inks) adsorbed on an AFM tip (as a nanopen) can be transferred to the substrate through the water meniscus, when the tip is

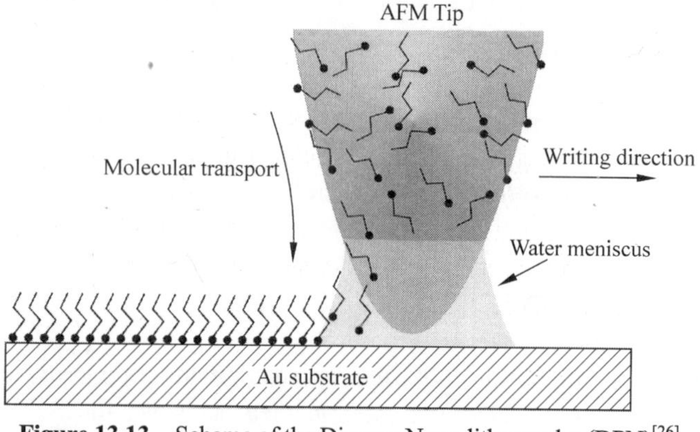

Figure 13.13 Scheme of the Dip-pen Nano-lithography (DPN)[26]

contacted with the surface of a substrate. The location and motion of the tip can be accurately controlled by the AFM system, thus the desired nanometer-sized pattern can be easily 'written' or 'drawn' with a variety of molecules as the inks. For example, biomolecules such as DNA and proteins have been patterned and their biological activities were demonstrated (Fig. 13.14)[27], which provided an efficient and convenient way for the manufacture of biochips. The concept of DPN can also be developed for site-specific capturing and deposition of nanoparticles in a one-particle-at-a-time fashion[28].

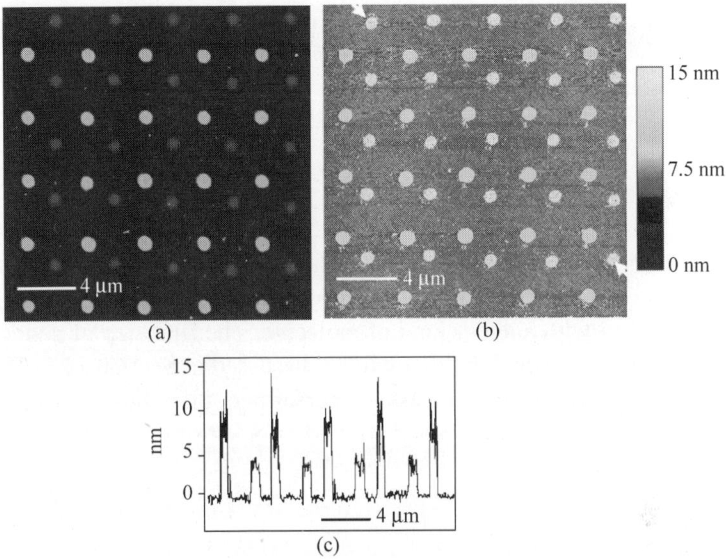

Figure 13.14 DPN-generated biomolecule patterns on substrate showing biological activities. (a) Fluorescent image indicating target DNA molecules binding to their complementary DNA spot. (b) AFM image indicating two kinds of DNA-functionalized Au nanoparticles bound to their complementary DNA spots. (c) Section analysis of the line along the arrows shown in 'B', indicating that two different nanoparticles, with 5 nm and 10 nm in dimensions, respectively, were bound to their complementary DNA spots[27] (see color figure at the end of this book)

DPN also provides a way for positioning reactions at the nanometer level. The ink molecules on the AFM tip could be served as source for synthesis of polymers (Fig. 13.15)[29], and the reaction could be well-controlled through regulating the tip-substrate contact time. Recently, we have also demonstrated that a positioning scission reaction of a single DNA molecule could be realized by delivering DNase I molecules onto the DNA strands[30].

By employing information technology, parallel-probe DPN can work with tens of thousands of probes[31, 32]. If every nanopen can be controlled separately and inked with different molecules, it could have prominent applications in the future.

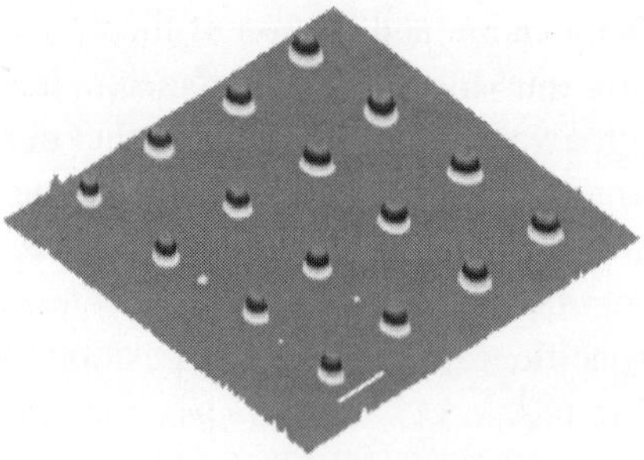

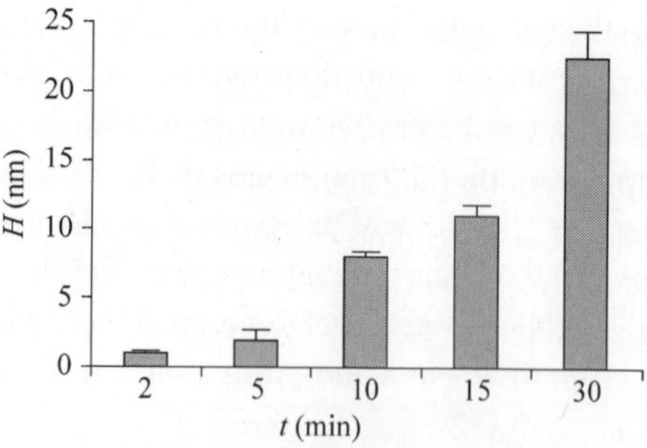

(a) (b)

Figure 13.15 AFM image of polymer synthesized in situ by using DPN technique. The polymer size was increased along with the increasing of the contact time of the inked AFM tip to the substrate[29]

13.7 Nanografting

In the nanografting method[33], closely-packed self-assembled mono-layers on the surface can be removed locally by AFM under a high load when the exposed surface was grafted with another kind of molecule. The first step of nanografting actually is AFM nanolithography that will be discussed in Section 13.3. The main difference is that the whole process is performed in a liquid environment. Figure 13.16(a) shows a smooth SAM formed on a substrate. When an AFM tip

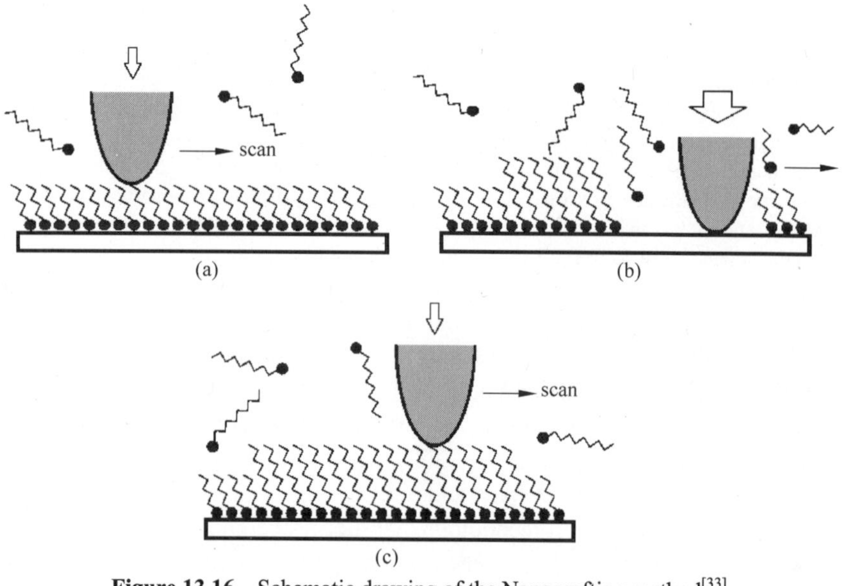

Figure 13.16 Schematic drawing of the Nanografting method[33]

applies a larger force to the surface while the tip keeps moving over it, local SAM would be mechanically removed, leaving a bare surface. Because the whole system is immersed in the liquid, other molecules in the liquid environment would take up places on the bare substrate (Fig. 13.16(b)) and form nanostructures, which can be revealed with AFM performed with a small force (Fig. 13.16(c)). To remove a pre-formed SAM, researches have also used STM and conductive AFM by applying a sufficient voltage between the STM (AFM) tip and the surface[17, 34, 35].

By this method, nanostructures with controlled chemical components, structures, and functions can be fabricated. For example, a hydrophilic nano-island with 70 nm × 300 nm size was formed on the Au surface coated with a hydrophobic monolayer (Fig. 13.17)[36]. In addition, nanostructures of proteins and oligonucleotides have also been constructed[37, 38].

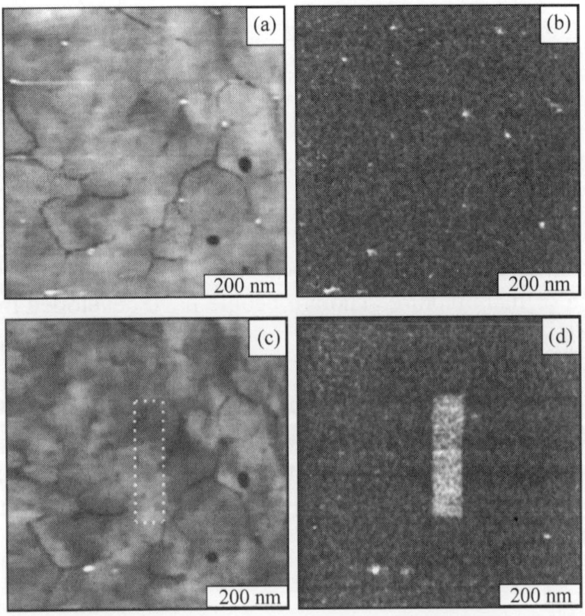

Figure 13.17 The formation of a 70 nm × 300 nm hydrophilic nanostructure by using Nano-grafting. (a, b) Topography and Friction mode AFM images before Nano-grafting. (c, d) Topography and Friction mode AFM images after Nano-grafting. The Friction mode AFM image clearly indicated the hydrophilic area[36]

13.8 Nanoprocess with Heatable AFM Tips

AFM-based techniques that employ a miniaturized thermal probe have exhibited great advantage in controlling polymer behaviors by locally heating the surfaces. AFM can be equipped with a nanoscale heatable tip, by which extreme conditions can be generated in terms of a very high temperature gradient on the surface (approx. 100℃/nm) for short time periods (μs – ms). In particular, the sample surface is only exposed very locally to the extreme condition and the induced new surface features are generated within an unchanged matrix. In this way it is possible to get insight into the structure, formation, the dynamics of polymers, and the control of surface properties on the nanometer scale.

Nanoscale control of the polymer surface is of great importance for both fundamental research and industrial applications. For example: ① work has been done on melting of polymer nanocrystals[39], ② high-density data writing and reading[40, 41], ③ local surface glass transition[42], and ④ nanodecomposition[43, 44].

13.9 Summary and Perspective

In summary, fabrication and processing at the nanometer scale based on STM and AFM have achieved great advances in the last decade. Manipulation of individual atoms and molecules has been realized, and potential applications such as molecular devices have been demonstrated. Functionalized nanostructures have been fabricated with STM- and AFM-related techniques through various physical or chemical mechanisms.

However, it should be noted that there are still some open problems in this field. For example, efficiency should be considered seriously in the process of any fabrication or manufacture. Though people have developed multiple probes or probe arrays to increase the efficiency, the SPM-based nanofabrication is still impractically time- consuming. On the other hand, the products of STM- and AFM-based nanomanipulation should reach to a certain amount for practical application. Ideally, if this kind of fabrication can result in molecular machines that can self-replicate, as DNA has done in nature, then it is expected that process and fabrication with STM and AFM will go from laboratory to factory, even to thousands of families in the future.

References

[1] Feynman R., (1961), Miniaturization, Reinhold

[2] Drexler K. E., (1981), Molecular engineering: an approach to the development of general capabilities for molecular manipulation. *Proc. Nat. Acad. Sci. USA*, **78**: 5275 – 5278

[3] Drexler K. E., (1992), Nano-systems: molecular machinery, manufacturing, and computation. Wiley Interscience

[4] Wickramasinghe H. K., (1989), *Scientific American*, **261**: 74 – 81

[5] Binnig G., H. Rohrer, Ch. Gerber, E. Weibel, (1982), Surface studies by scanning tunneling microscopy. *Physical Review Letters*, **49**: 57 – 61

[6] Binnig G., C. F. Quate, Ch. Gerber, (1986), Atomic force microscope. *Physical Review Letters*, **56**: 930 – 933
[7] Eigler D. M., E. K. Schweizer, (1990), Positioning single atoms with a scanning tunnelling microscope. *Nature*, **344**: 524 – 526
[8] Sugimoto Y., M. Abe, S. Hirayama, N. Oyabu, O. Custance, S. Morita, (2005), Atom inlays performed at room temperature using atomic force microscopy. *Nature Materials*, **4**: 156 – 159
[9] Nilius N., T. M. Wallis, W. Ho, (2002), Development of one-dimensional band structure in artificial gold chains. *Science*, **297**: 1853 – 1856
[10] Gimzewski J. K., C. Joachim, (1999), Nano-scale science of single molecules using local probes. *Science*, **283**: 1683 – 1688
[11] Hu J., Y. Zhang, H. B. Gao, M. Q. Li, U. Hartmann, (2002), Artificial DNA patterns by mechanical nano-manipulation. *Nano Letters*, **2**: 55 – 57
[12] Lee H. J., W. Ho, (1999), Single-bond formation and characterization with a scanning tunneling microscope. *Science*, **286**: 1719 – 1722
[13] Okawa Y., M. Aono, (2001), Materials science: nano-scale control of chain polymerization. *Nature*, **409**: 683 – 684
[14] Joachim C., J. K. Gimzewski, (1998), A nano-scale single-molecule amplifier and its consequences. *Proceedings of the IEEE*, **86**, 184 – 190
[15] Song J., Z. Liu, C. Li, H. Chen, H. He, (1998), SPM-based nano-fabrication using a synchronization technique. *Applied Physics A-Materials Science & Proceeding*, **66**: S715 – S717
[16] Schoer J. K., R. M. Crooks, (1997), Scanning probe lithography. 4. Characterization of scanning tunneling microscope-induced patterns in n-alkanethiol self-assembled monolayers. *Langmuir*, **13**: 2323 – 2332
[17] Zhao J., K. Uosaki, (2002), Formation of nano-patterns of a self-assembled monolayer (SAM) within a SAM of different molecules using a current sensing atomic force microscope. *Nano Letters*, **2**: 137 – 140
[18] Dagata J. A., J. Schneir, H. H. Harary, C. J. Evans, M. T. Postek, J. Bennett, (1990), Modification of hydrogen-passivated silicon by a scanning tunneling microscope operating in air. *Applied Physics Letters*, **56**: 2001 – 2003
[19] Avouris P. h., R. Martel, T. Hertel, R. L. Sandström, (1998), AFM-tip-induced and current-induced local oxidation of silicon and metals. *Applied Physics A -Materials Science & Procedding*, **66**, S659 – S667
[20] Gordon A. E., T. Fayfield, D. D. Litfin, T. K. Higman, (1995), Mechanisms of surface anodization produced by scanning probe microscopes. *Journal of Vacuum Science & Technology B*, **13**: 2805 – 2808
[21] Avouris P. h., T. Hertel, R. Martel, (1997), Atomic force microscope tip-induced local oxidation of silicon: kinetics, mechanism, and nano-fabrication. *Applied Physics Letters*, **71**: 285 – 287
[22] Dagata J. A., T. Inoue, J. Itoh, H. Yokoyama, (1998), Understanding scanned probe oxidation of silicon. *Applied Physics Letters*, **73**: 271 – 273

[23] Maoz R., E. Frydman, S. R. Cohen, J. Sagiv, (2000), Constructive nano-lithography: site-defined silver self-assembly on nano-electrochemically patterned monolayer templates. *Advanced Materials*, **12**: 424 – 429

[24] Maoz R., E. Frydman, S. R. Cohen, J. Sagiv, (2000), 'Constructive nano-lithography': inert monolayers as patternable templates for in-situ nano-fabrication of metal-semiconductor-organic surface structures-a generic approach. *Advanced Materials*, **12**: 725 – 730

[25] Hosaka S., S. Hosoki, T. Hasegawa, H. Koyanagi, T. Shintani, M. Miyamoto, (1995), Fabrication of nano-structures using scanning probe microscopes. *Journal of Vacuum Science & Technology B*, **13**: 2813 – 2818

[26] Piner R. D., J. Zhu, F. Xu, S. Hong, C. A. Mirkin, (1999), 'Dip-pen' nano-lithography. *Science*, **283**: 661 – 663

[27] Demers L. M., D. S. Ginger, S. J. Park, Z. Li, S. W. Chung, C. A. Mirkin, (2002), Direct patterning of modified oligonucleotides on metals and insulators by dip-pen nano-lithography. *Science*, **296**: 1836 – 1838

[28] Wang Y., Y. Zhang, B. Li, J. Lü, J. Hu, (2007), Capturing and depositing one nanoobject at a time: single particle dip-pen nano-lithography. *Applied Physics Letters*, **90**: 133102

[29] Liu X., S. Guo, C. A. Mirkin, (2003), Surface and site-specific ring-opening metathesis polymerization initiated by dip-pen nano-lithography. *Angewandte Chemie International Edition*, **42**: 4785 – 4789

[30] Li B., Y. Zhang, S. Yan, J. Lu, M. Ye, M. Li, J. Hu, (2007), Positioning scission of single DNA molecules with nonspecific endonuclease based on nano-manipulation. *Journal of the American Chemical Society*, **129**: 6668 – 6669

[31] Ginger D. S., H. Zhang, C. A. Mirkin, (2004), The evolution of dip-pen nano-lithography. *Angewandte Chemie International Edition*, **43**: 30 – 45

[32] Salaita K., Y. H. Wang, J. Fragala, R. A. Vega, C. Liu, C. A. Mirkin, (2006), Massively parallel dip-pen nano-lithography with 55000-pen two-dimensional arrays. *Angewandte Chemie International Edition*, **45**: 7220 – 7223

[33] Xu S., G. Liu, (1997), Nano-meter-scale fabrication by simultaneous nanoshaving and molecular self-assembly. *Langmuir*, **13**: 127 – 129

[34] Chen J., M. A. Reed, C. L. Asplund, A. M. Cassell, M. L. Myrick, A. M. Rawlett, J. M. Tour, P. G. Van Patten, (1999), Placement of conjugated oligomers in an alkanethiol matrix by scanned probe microscope lithography. *Applied Physics Letters*, **75**: 624 – 626

[35] Gorman C. B., R. L. Carroll, Y. He, F. Tian, R. Fuierer, (2000), Chemically well-defined lithography using self-assembled monolayers and scanning tunneling microscopy in nonpolar organothiol solutions. *Langmuir*, **16**: 6312 – 6316

[36] Xu S., S. Miller, P. E. Laibinis, G. Liu, (1999), Fabrication of nano-meter scale patterns within self-assembled monolayers by nano-grafting. *Langmuir*, **15**: 7244 – 7251

[37] Wadu-Mesthrige K., N. A. Amro, J. C. Garno, S. Xu, G. Liu, (2001), Fabrication of nano-meter-sized protein patterns using atomic force microscopy and selective immobilization. *Biophysical Journal*, **80**: 1891 – 1899

[38] Liu M., N. A. Amro, C. S. Chow, G. Liu, (2002), Production of nano-structures of DNA on surfaces. *Nano Letters*, **2**: 863 – 867

[39] Vasilev C., H. Heinzelmann, G. Reiter, (2004), Controlled melting of individual, nanometer-sized, polymer crystals confined in a block copolymer mesostructure. *Journal of Polymer Science: Part B: Polymer Physics*, **42**: 1312 – 1320

[40] Vettiger P., G. Cross, M. Despont, M. Drechsler, U. Duerig, B. Gotsmann, W. Haeberle, M. A. Lantz, H. E. Rothuizen, R. Stutz, G. K. Binnig, (2002), The 'millipede'—nanotechnology entering data storage. *IEEE Transactions on Nanotechnology*, **1**: 39 – 55

[41] Gotsmann B., U. Duerig, J. Frommer, C. J. Hawker, (2006), Exploiting chemical switching in a diels-alder polymer for nano-scale probe lithography and data storage. *Advanced Function Materials*, **16**: 1499 – 1505

[42] Fischer H., (2005), Probing the surface Tg of monodisperse PS by local thermal analysis. *Macromolecules*, **38**: 844 – 850

[43] King W. P., S. Saxena, B. A. Nelson, B. L. Weeks, R. Pitchimani, (2006), Nano-scale thermal analysis of an energetic material. *Nano Letters*, **6**: 2145 – 2149

[44] Szoszkiewicz R., T. Okada, S. C. Jones, T. D. Li, W. P. King, S. R. Marder, E. Riedo, (2007), High-speed, sub-15 nm feature size thermo-chemical nano-lithography. *Nano Letters*, **7**: 1064 – 1069

14 Nanoscale Fabrication

Ampere A. Tseng[1], Zuliang Du[2], Andrea Notargiacomo[3], and Shyankay Jou[4]

[1] Department of Mechanical and Aerospace Engineering, Arizona State University, Tempe, Arizona 85287-6106, USA
E-mail: ampere.tseng@asu.edu

[2] Key Lab for Special Functional Materials of Ministry of Education, Henan University, Kaifeng, Henan 475004, China

[3] Physics Department Universita Roma TRE, Rome, Italy

[4] Department of Materials Science and Engineering, Taiwan University of Science and Technology

Abstract Miniaturization is the central theme in modern fabrication technology. Following the introduction of nanofabrication and its significance the two major nanolithographic processes using electron and ion beams are first addressed. These processes are similar to the conventional photolithography by using energetic beams for pattern transfer to the target substrate. Subsequently, the lithographic techniques of nanoimprinting and scanning probe microscopy (SPM) are evaluated with the emphasis on their lithographic abilities and applications. Three major schemes in the family of SPM lithography, including ① scanning tunneling microscopy, ② atomic force microscopy, and ③ dip-pen nanolithography, are separately presented. The principles and associated procedures of these three schemes are discussed first and the differences among them are then elaborated. The bottom-up strategies for nanofabrication are also reviewed. Self assembling with and without externally controlled forces for patterning nanoscale structures has been examined. The associated principles and procedures of key assembling processes are given. Application examples for several self-assembly techniques are also included. Finally, the prospective areas for future research in nanofabrication are presented.

Keywords Atomic force microscopy, electron beam lithography, focused-ion beam lithography, nanofabrication, nanoimprinting, nanolithography

14.1 Introduction

Nanoscale fabrication or nanofabrication aims at building nanoscale material structures, components, devices, or systems with desired properties and performance characteristics in large-quantities with potentially low-costs. Generally, nanoscale feature refers to any characteristic size that is between 0.1 nm and 100 nm. Nanofabrication has been widely heralded as the most significant manufacturing frontier currently being explored. The major benefits in nanofabrication should be, but not limited to, minimizing the use of materials and energy, reducing waste and environmental impact, and enabling high-rate, cost-effective production suitable for industrial implementation. Towards this end, future research will focus on making heterogeneous nanostructures and multiscale nanosystems. Both approaches need to develop the ability to hierarchically integrate nanosystems with larger scale systems. This requires a high degree of process control in the sensing and actuation of matter at nano and sub-nano scales, as well as capabilities for scaling-up. Major innovations are anticipated in virtually every industry and public sector[1].

Nanoscale fabrication consists of two major approaches: ① top-down high-resolution and ② bottom-up directed assembling processes.

The top-down approach evolved from classical photolithography techniques. The approach takes a bulk material and modifies or breaks it down to smaller desired shapes which normally involves removing or etching (sometimes with forming or adding) materials out to make the final shapes. The approach becomes possible through the increasing precision of tools that have been developed largely with the progress of microelectronics and enables the fabrication of artificial functional objects with sizes down to the scale of nanometers. On the other hand, the bottom-up approach involves synthetic methods of chemistry and biochemistry, such as molecular recognition and self-assembly (SA), in the direct assembly of subnanoscale building blocks including atomic, molecular, and supramolecular elements[2]. With ever-increasing precision, the bottom-up assembly of complex molecules approach enables us to measure and manipulate with extreme precision molecular objects and their interactions with the potential to make various devices, including multiscale self-assembling elements, artificial biological materials, and scalable opto-electro-mechanical systems (OEMS).

Because of its commercial importance and technology maturity, the top-down approach is emphasized more than the bottom-up approach. More discussions are also dedicated towards the top-down techniques. In this chapter, three major top-down processes are presented: ① electron beam lithography (EBL), ② ion beam lithography (IBL), and ③ nanoimprinting lithography (NIL).

The first two processes are similar to the conventional photolithographic technology, i.e., using an energetic beam for transferring pattern to substrates, while the third one uses thermo-mechanical strategies for pattern transformation. All these three processes have been considered as the major candidates for the next-generation of lithographic (NGL) systems to be used in the semiconductor industry. For the bottom-up approach, several SA techniques are examined. These techniques are the emerging technologies based on simple bottom-up principles with an excellent ability to manufacture nanostructures and a potential for large-scale production. The specific techniques presented include synthetic methods of biochemistry in directly assembling sub-nanoscale building blocks, such as atomic, molecular, and supra-molecular elements, into required nanoscale patterns. Three scanning probe microscopy (SPM)-based lithographic techniques are also introduced. These three techniques are mainly evolving from the high-resolution image-probing instruments of SPM, including scanning tunneling microscopy (STM), atomic force microscopy (AFM) and dip-pen nanolithography (DPN). The principles and processes for each technique are presented while their differences are also discussed. In fact, these SPM-based techniques apply both top-down and bottom-up principles for fabricating nanostructures. For example, in DPN, SA techniques are frequently incorporated in the creation of the chemical and biological patterns, while the etching and deposition schemes based on the top-down approach are concurrently used for making nanostructures. Thus, in this chapter, these SPM-based techniques are not to be categorized into either a top-down or bottom-up approach. Finally, concluding remarks are provided to summarize the major technologies studied and to recommend the scopes for technology improvement and future research.

14.2 Electron Beam Lithography (EBL)

Lithography is the process of transferring patterns from one medium to another. For many years, particle beams of various types have been used in lithography. The electron source has the benefit of extremely high diffraction-limited resolution and has been used for transferring patterns having nanometer feature sizes. In EBL, two major schemes, projection printing and direct writing, are used. In projection printing, a relatively large-sized electron-beam pattern is projected in parallel through the mask onto a resist-coated substrate by using a high-precision lens system. In direct writing, on the other hand, a small spot of the electron beam is written directly onto a resist-coated substrate, eliminating the expensive and time-consuming production of masks. For many years, direct writing EBL has become the popular selection in prototyping nanoscale structures and devices[3]. In the semiconductor industry, e-beam direct writing has been routinely used to generate master masks and reticles from computer-aided design (CAD) files and these masks or reticles are usually used in photolithography to replicate the patterns onto silicon wafers. In this section, the techniques of projection printing and direct writing are presented.

14.2.1 Projection Printing EBL

Projection printing EBL systems have not been commercialized. Two major efforts have led in the development of the commercial projection EBL systems: ① SCALPEL and ② PREVAIL. Bell Laboratories started the SCALPEL (SCattering with Angular Limitation in Projection Electron-beam Lithography) project in 1989, while IBM had laid the foundation for its PREVAIL (Projection Reduction Exposure with Variable Axis Immersion Lenses) technology with the development of the variable-axis lens for electron-beam lithography systems during the 1980s[3]. Both systems project a small field image of a 4x mask onto a wafer to generate nanoscale subpatterns.

The short penetration length of electrons, however, precludes the use of a solid substrate, like quartz, for the mask. The strength of SCALPEL, which differentiates it from previous attempts at projection EBL, lies in its specially designed mask, also known as the scattering mask. The SCALPEL mask consists of a low-atomic number membrane, on which a layer of the pattern made of a high-atomic number material is coated. When the electrons pass through the high-atomic number material, they scatter more strongly and at higher angles than those that pass through the low-atomic number membrane. As illustrated in Fig. 14.1, an aperture located at the back focal plane of the projection lens blocks the strongly scattered electrons, while those passing through the membrane suffer little change to their trajectories and travel through the aperture. As a result, the unblocked electrons that pass through the aperture form a high contrast image are printed on the wafer or substrate surface. Since the incident electron energy is not only absorbed by the mask but also blocked by the aperture, thermal distortion of the mask can be minimized.

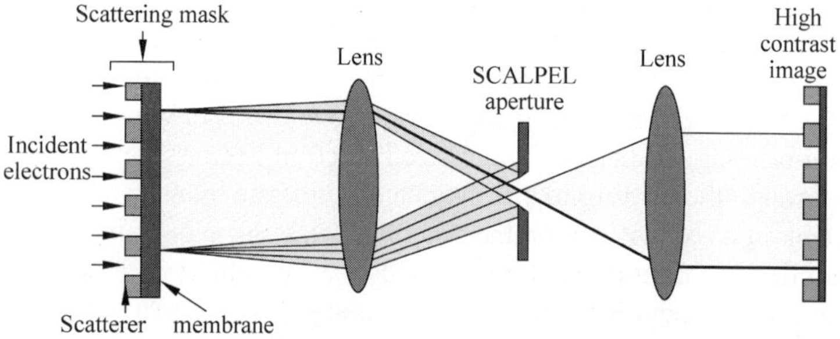

Figure 14.1 Schematic of projection electron-beam lithography system: SCALPEL (see color figure at the end of this book)

In the PREVAIL approach, the small fields in both reticle and wafer are stitched through a combination of high-speed electron-beam scanning and moderate-speed mechanical scanning. The cornerstone of the PREVAIL approach is a system of variable-axis lenses that permits shifting of the electron optical axis along with a predetermined curvature. The variable-axis lens also simultaneously deflects the electron beam to precisely follow the curvilinear variable axis so that the beam effectively remains on the axis, eliminating all off-axis aberrations. A proof-of-concept PREVAIL system has achieved an enhanced field size or printing area of 10 mm×10 mm[4]. This result makes the PREVAIL approach promising, but further improvement is needed because larger scan ranges are required for the illumination and projection of the 4x reticle, and also because the enhanced pattern field (10 mm) is still, orders of magnitude smaller compared to the size of the current 300-mm semiconductor wafer.

The challenge for projection EBL systems is to downscale the feature size while maintaining a high throughput. To increase the throughput and the quality of the product, it is expected that the advantages of techniques used in SCALPEL and PREVAIL will eventually be integrated into one system. Once integrated, the projection EBL can become the next generation of mainstream lithography in the semiconductor industry. Other recent developments on the 65 nm technology using projection EBL have been reported by Koba et al.[5], while the device performance evaluation has been conducted by Romeo et al.[6] showing the imaging results of features down to 50 nm imaged on a projection EBL tool.

14.2.2 Direct Writing and Lift-Off Process

The most popular process used in direct writing EBL is the lift-off process; it is an additive process that adds material to the substrate. The lift-off process consists of several steps: ① e-beam resists coating, exposure, and development; ② material evaporation; and ③ resist removal. The normal lift-off process is schematically explained in Fig. 14.2. As shown in Fig. 14.2(a), the resist coating is exposed by e-beam direct writing using a vector or raster scan, while Fig. 14.2(b) shows that the exposed resist (the nanostructure pattern) is developed and removed in a solvent. A metal layer (the nanostructure material) can be deposited by an e-gun or an evaporation process onto the substrate, as depicted in Fig. 14.2(c). The final step of the lift-off process is accomplished by soaking the substrate in a solvent bath to wash away the remaining resist and unwanted material. The final deposited nanostructure on a substrate is shown in Fig. 14.2(d).

Other etching processes are less frequently used in EBL. Wet etching requires good resist adhesion, whereas dry etching needs good resist selectivity over the etched material or substrate. To illustrate a non-standard lift-off technique and its application, the EBL process using a bilayer resist for a bowtie structure on an insulating substrate is presented. The bowtie is a major component of a nanoscale optical probe. The optical probe is based on a concept called the Wave Interrogated Near-Field Array (WINFA), which combines the sensitivity of near-field detection with the speed of optical scanning. It is expected that bowties having a 40 nm gap should act as resonant elements to provide spatial resolution well below the diffraction limit with the transmission efficiency approaching unity. It is expected that nanoscale defects or particles, 50 nm in size or smaller, can be detected by the probe while its inspection speed can be as fast as an ordinary optical probe, i.e., two to three orders of magnitude faster than that of the AFM or near-field optical microscopy. Based on the current design, a 300 mm wafer can be inspected within few minutes[7].

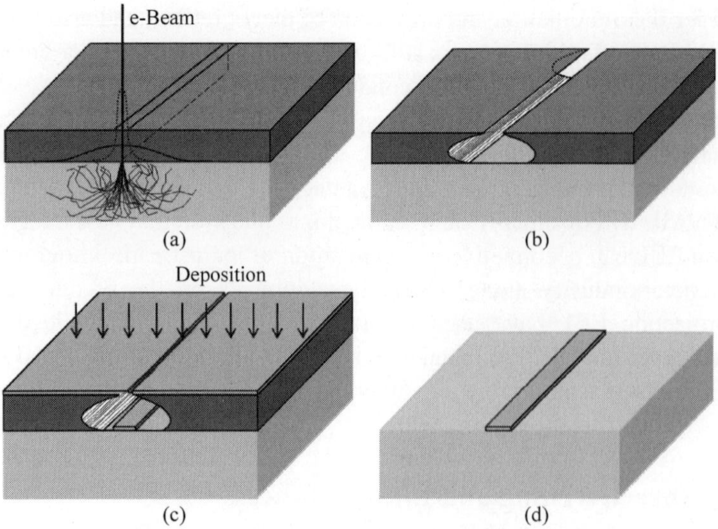

Figure 14.2 Schematic of EBL lift-off process: (a) *e*-beam injection, (b) exposed resist developed and removed, (c) deposition of desired materials by e-gun or vacuum evaporation, (d) lift-off of unwanted materials (see color figure at the end of this book)

As a design requirement, the substrate of the bowties should be transparent to the incident wave source, and thus, a glass—based substrate is used. However, when patterning an insulating glass substrate, the substrate charging causes considerable distortion. To cope with the distortion problem, also known as the discharge accumulation[3], a bi-layer resist is used in EBL. The bilayer resist consists of a conducting layer sandwiched by a polymer resist layer and the substrate, which is used to eliminate the charge accumulation problem. The bowtie array has been fabricated on a 0.5 mm thick Pyrex glass substrate and the gap of the fabricated bowtie is about 40 nm with a height of 60 nm, a 25 nm Au layer on the top of a 35 nm thick Cr layer[7].

The corresponding fabrication procedures begin with the preparation of a bi-layer system: a 30 nm thick Cr film is first coated on the Pyrex glass substrate by a thermal evaporation process, and then a PMMA (polymethylmethacrylate) resist film is spin coated to cover the Cr layer (Fig. 14.3(a)). As the pattern is defined on this top layer, a thinner film is preferred, as it produces a better pattern sharpness. A diluted PMMA resist (2% in anisole), spun at 3000 rpm, is used. After soft-baking at 135℃, a thin (~200 nm) PMMA resist film is formed. The bilayer resist is then exposed to an area dose of approximately 250 $\mu C/cm^2$ (Fig. 14.3(b)). The exposed region is developed, removed, and cleaned to ensure a residue-free image (Fig. 14.3(c)). A 5 nm Cr layer is deposited first and then a 25 nm Au layer is deposited (Fig. 14.3(d)). The unwanted materials are lifted off (Fig. 14.3(e)). The Au layer then acts as a mask while the unprotected Cr is removed by the chrome wet etching process (Fig. 14.3(f)). Figure 14.3(g) shows a SEM image of a bowtie array fabricated by this method on a 0.5 mm thick

Pyrex glass substrate; the gap of the fabricated bowtie can be observed to be approximately 40 nm. The thickness of the bilayer bowtie estimated by AFM imaging is around 60 nm; it has a 25 nm Au layer on top of a 35 nm thick Cr layer. In addition to producing a thick structure, the bilayer resist scheme not only copes with the charge accumulation problem caused by a non-conducting substrate but also eliminates the 'lift-off flag' defects, in which thicker materials appear along the bowtie edges when the standard or the single-layer-resist lift-off process is employed.

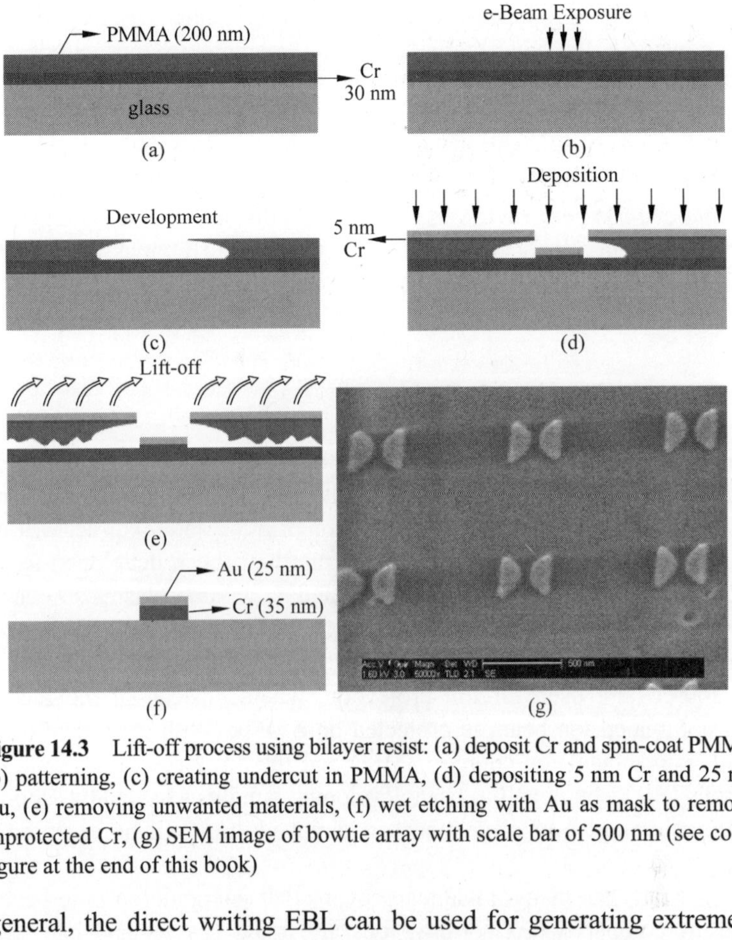

Figure 14.3 Lift-off process using bilayer resist: (a) deposit Cr and spin-coat PMMA, (b) patterning, (c) creating undercut in PMMA, (d) depositing 5 nm Cr and 25 nm Au, (e) removing unwanted materials, (f) wet etching with Au as mask to remove unprotected Cr, (g) SEM image of bowtie array with scale bar of 500 nm (see color figure at the end of this book)

In general, the direct writing EBL can be used for generating extremely fine patterns; in fact, when combined with evaporation processes, fabrication of future electronic devices with critical dimension as small as 10 nm has been demonstrated. Since direct writing EBL is capable of superior resolution and requires no expensive projection optics or time consuming mask production, it is the most desirable process for cutting-edge micro and nanofabrication. However, direct writing transfers the pattern by exposing one pixel or one image element at a time. This imposes a limitation on the exposure speed or the rate of the pattern to be transferred onto the wafer. This throughput hurdle has confined the direct writing system to a supporting role in the semiconductor industry. However, considerable effort has been dedicated to the variable shaped beam technology to increase its throughput by enhancing exposure speed and to widen its applications by integrating with other nanoscale processes. The shaped beam system uses parallel electron beams to write a primitive shape (mainly rectangles) in one shot. These primitive shapes are smaller than the field sizes achieved in the projection EBL systems mentioned earlier. In the shaped beam system, the upper aperture in the optics is typically used to form two sides of a rectangle, and the overlay of the lower aperture constructs the other two sides[3]. More complex shapes can be achieved by splitting the rectangle before the exposure. The shaped beam system gains the speed or throughput by compromising the resolution achieved by the single pixel of the Gaussian beam system. Recently, in the frame of the ALLIANCE program between Motorola, Philips Semiconductors and STMicroelectronics, the shaped beam technique has been reviewed for its integration capabilities and possibilities for high-throughput manufacturing of integrated circuit (IC) making the resolution down to 65 nm[8].

14.3 Ion Beam Lithography (IBL)

In semiconductor industry, ion beam lithography (IBL) is popular for mask repairing, device modification, failure analysis, and integrated circuit debugging. Similar to EBL, two basic working modes: ① projection printing and ② direct writing have been developed. Two types of ion sources that have been developed to produce nanometer resolution patterns are: ① point and ② volume-plasma sources.

The point sources are used in focused ion beam systems for direct ion writing, in which a sharp dot image is focused directly on the substrate, while the volume plasma sources are used for ion projection, where, instead of the focused ion beam, a collimated ion beam is projected on a mask. With the recent use of the powerful liquid metal ion source (LMIS) and the advances in ion optics in the last decade, IBL technology has been developing rapidly as have it has applications. Both the technologies of projection and direct writing will be explored in this Section.

The ion beam has many advantages over other energetic particle beams. For example, as compared to electrons, ions are much heavier and can strike the target with a much greater energy density at relatively short wavelengths to directly transfer patterns on hard materials (such as semiconductors, metals, or ceramics) without producing high-energy back-scattered electrons or ions. Thus the feature sizes of the patterns are directly dictated by the beam size and the interaction of the beam with the material fabricated. On the other hand, EBL or photolithography can only be effectively written on or exposed to soft materials (such as resists) and the corresponding feature sizes will be determined by the proximity of the back-scattered electrons or wave diffraction limits. The lateral exposure in IBL is also very low thus just exposing the right areas. Thus a fine beam of heavy ions can produce a structure that has a feature size at nanoscale ranges as reported by Tseng[9,10].

14.3.1 IBL Projection Printing

In IBL projection printing or IBLP processing, a collimated beam of ions passes through a mask and the reduced image of the mask is projected onto the substrate underneath. Because of its advantages in both high beam energies and short wavelengths, IBLP is one of the NGL to replace the conventional photolithography for making structures with feature sizes below 100 nm. The European and American programs on IBLP led by Infineon Technologies and Sematech have built a prototype, called the Process Development Tool (PDT) to investigate the industrial suitability for next-generation chip mass production[11]. Currently, the PDT has been charged with the development of a system suitable for 50 nm resolution. 4x reduction ion optics have been integrated using a concept similar to EBL projection, to stitch a printing area of 12.5 mm×12.5 mm into a full image, the whole wafer area. The PDT uses a co-axial multi-cusp ion source with a 1-eV FWHM (Full-Width-Half-Maximum) energy spread, which was developed by US Lawrence Berkeley National Laboratory. Multi-electrode electrostatic-ion-optics is used as the diverging electrostatic lens while an on-line diagnostic system and a field composable lens are used to compensate for mechanical manufacturing inaccuracies.

Most IBLP systems use two types of masks for pattern transformation and the mask needs to be of ion transparent substrate with a pattern made up of an absorber surface. The two type of masks is the all-silicon mask technology that uses varying thickness of the silicon acting as the absorber and the transparent membrane. Using the same single silicon crystal minimizes the problem created due to the thermal distortion and proton scattering in conventional masks[9]. This type is relatively easy to manufacture using conventional IC processes. The second type of masks is the stencil or open mask technology, which is made of open masks that are etched patterns on the metal foils. This type of mask has excellent contrast, as the ions are not affected by passing through the open hole before striking on the resist. However, since there is no sub-layer to hold the etched metal pattern, every section in the etched pattern must be connected and no island or detached sections can be included in the pattern. As a result, this type of mask can only be used for very limited geometries.

Single crystal Si stencils appear to be popular because of their compatibility with the existing semiconductor processes and good control of mask stress. Typically, the fabrication process consists of three major steps:① membrane etching, ② membrane implanting and framing, and ③ stencil patterning[12,13]. Since the mask in IPL is demagnified, the features on the mask are larger than those on the wafer, which makes the mask easier to fabricate from the point of view of resolution. Of course, this advantage has to be traded against the difficulties of making a larger area membrane mask. So far, equipments have been built with demagnification from 10:1 to 3:1. A stencil mask of 150 mm in diameter is shown in Fig. 14.4(a). The stencil pattern for structuring magnetic media is shown in Fig. 14.4(b), where the rectangular stencil openings are approximately 320 nm wide and 2000 nm long[14]. The stencil mask shown in Fig. 14.4(b) has also been used exposure resolution test, in which the 4X PDT systems is used to expose a 50-nm thick with 45 keV He^+ at a 2.0 μC/cm^2 dose. The CARL resist, developed by Infineon Technologies of Germany for thin film imaging, requires an exposure time of a few seconds. As expected, through the

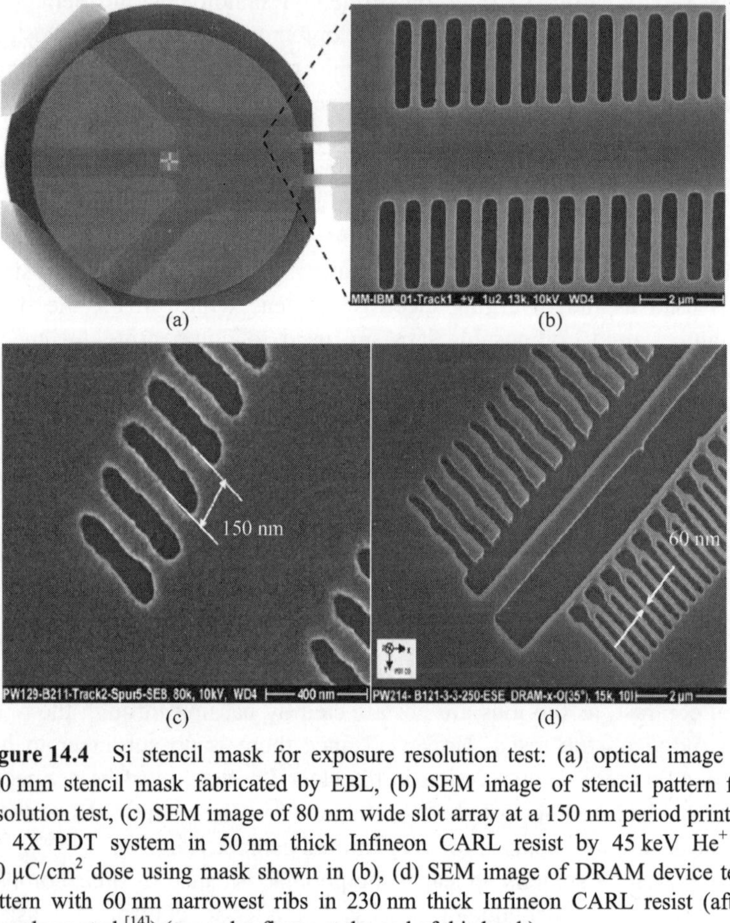

Figure 14.4 Si stencil mask for exposure resolution test: (a) optical image of 150 mm stencil mask fabricated by EBL, (b) SEM image of stencil pattern for resolution test, (c) SEM image of 80 nm wide slot array at a 150 nm period printed by 4X PDT system in 50 nm thick Infineon CARL resist by 45 keV He^+ at 2.0 μC/cm^2 dose using mask shown in (b), (d) SEM image of DRAM device test pattern with 60 nm narrowest ribs in 230 nm thick Infineon CARL resist (after Loeschner et al.[14]) (see color figure at the end of this book)

4X reduction ion-optics of PDT, the 320 nm wide slots in the mask have printed about 80 nm wide slot patterns in the resist as shown in Fig. 14.4(c). In addition to the above slot pattern, a pattern for a DRAM device test is also included in the same mask. The printed DRAM device image is shown in Fig. 14.4(d), and indicates that 60 nm wide ribs and spaces can be obtained. These results have demonstrated that mask-to-wafer transfer for isolated and arrayed lines/space can be performed within the required accuracy.

Other types of resists are appropriate for IPL. Similar to EBL, PMMA is also considered as one of the best positive resists for IBL. It has excellent resolution but minor sensitivity and etching resistivity. Other common resists used for IBLP include G-line, I-Line, and DUV (Deep-ultraviolet) resists with both positive and negative tones work well with IPL[15]. Especially, the deep-ultraviolet (DUV) chemical-amplified resists (CAR) is very popular for IPL resists. Other DUV resists appropriate for IPL include Hoechst's AZ series, Olin's HPR 506, OCG's HPR and ARCH[16]. In a recent study by Arshak et al.[17], by applying the Top Surface Imaging (TSI) principle and using Ga ion beam exposure associated with silylation and oxygen dry etching, a DNQ/novolak-based resist patterns can be obtained as small as 30 nm while maintaining a high aspect ratio of up to 15. In IBLP, at the present, the ion optics and stitching system still remain as the major challenges since the entire stitched image has to be projected with minimum distortion and stitched into the whole field at the same time.

14.3.2 FIBL Direct Writing/Milling

The ion beam direct write process, also known as focused ion beam lithography (FIBL), is a process of transferring patterns by direct impingement of the focused ion beam (FIB) on the target. A variety of ion-target interactions can occur, including swelling, etching, deposition, milling, implantation, backscattering, and nuclear reaction, when an energetic ion hits the target. In this subsection, the interactions related to material milling will be emphasized. The other interactions, including ion implantation and chemical deposition will also be presented separately in the next subsection. The FIB can also be used for enhancing the chemical etching process. However, since FIB etching has relatively high etching rates, too high to be used for removing materials in nanoscale amounts, it has seldom been used in nanofabrication[10]. Consequently the FIB assisted etching process is not discussed in this article.

In the process that a small and energetic FIB is used to directly remove the substrate materials is called ion milling. Ion milling possesses three distinguished phenomena: ① sputtering, ② redeposition, and ③ amorphization. Sputtering is a major mechanism for material removal in milling and its efficiency is normally represented by sputter yield, defined as the number of atoms (neutrals and ions) ejected from the target surface per incident ion. The sputtered atoms ejected from the solid near surface into the gas phase are not in their thermodynamic equilibrium state and tend to condense back into the solid phase upon collision with any solid surface nearby. The process, which a portion of the ejected atoms bump into the already sputtered surface and redeposit on it, is called redeposition[18]. However, if the energy or dose level of the incident ions is not high enough for sputtering, amorphization can occur in the bombarded area of a crystalline substrate and can induce the substrate to swell. Understanding these three distinguished phenomena should be the first step to control the milling process for making nanostructures from simplified two-dimensional (2D) structures (such as microchannels, microholes) to complicated three-dimensional (3D) structures[10].

Sputtering or sputtering yield is dependent not only on the substrate material, but also on many processing parameters, including the ion energy, the angle of incidence, and the milling conditions. The sputtering yield for different substrates at different processing conditions has been reviewed by Reyntjens and Puers[19] and Tseng[20] to characterize the basic sputtering phenomena. In amorphization, the incident ions in most cases are buried in the target material and may also displace the target atoms from their lattice sites, so that the displaced atoms are relocated to a nearby region. In the case of silicon, its density at the amorphous state is much lower than that of crystalline silicon. Also, since the volume of swelling is much larger than the volume of the buried or implanted ions, swelling can be largely caused by the density changes or the amorphization, rather than exclusively by the buried or implanted ions. The magnitude of the swelling due to amorphization can be as high as tens of nanometers. Thus amorphization can diminish the dimensional accuracy of nanostructures and an important consideration in nanofabrication. For example, in the case of a crystallized Si substrate bombarded by Ga ions, the dose level that causes amorphization is on the order of 10^{15} ion-cm^{-2}, while the effective sputtering dose should be at least two orders of magnitude higher than the amorphization dose[10].

The effects of redeposition can be characterized by a channel milling experiment. A set of nanochannels milled by a single-pass with 5 ms dwell time using a 90 keV As^{2+} FIB, with a beam current of 5 pA on a 125 nm thick gold film coated on a Si wafer is shown in Fig. 14.5. The pixel spacing (p_s) is set at 14.5 nm and the beam FWHM diameter (d_f) is set at 50 nm. Using raster scanning, several different sizes of 'ASU' patterns are milled with the dwell time varying from 5 – 50 ms. The insert in the left corner of Fig. 14.5 shows the corresponding cross-sectional contour and indicates that the channels milled by a single-pass possess a V-shaped profile with a maximum depth at the center and a maximum width at the mouth. Ridges are formed along the channel banks. The figure also shows that the four features are used to characterize the profile of the V-shaped channel: *A* is the ridge width, which is the distance between the ridge peaks, *B* is the mouth width, which is the channel width with respect to the original surface, *C* is the depth from the original surface, and *D* is the ridge height. As shown in the right insert, although all of the features increase with the dwell time, the increase rates are gradually reduced as the dwell time increases. This may indicate that a large amount of sputtered materials are redeposited into not only the ridge (outside the channel) but also inside the channel, and since the mouth width and the milling depth should increase proportionally with the dwell time without redeposition. Also, the measurements indicate that the mouth width is much larger than the FWHM diameter (d_f), by almost one order of magnitude. This may suggest that at a higher dwell time, the ion intensity outside the FWHM core region is sufficiently high to produce sizable sputtering.

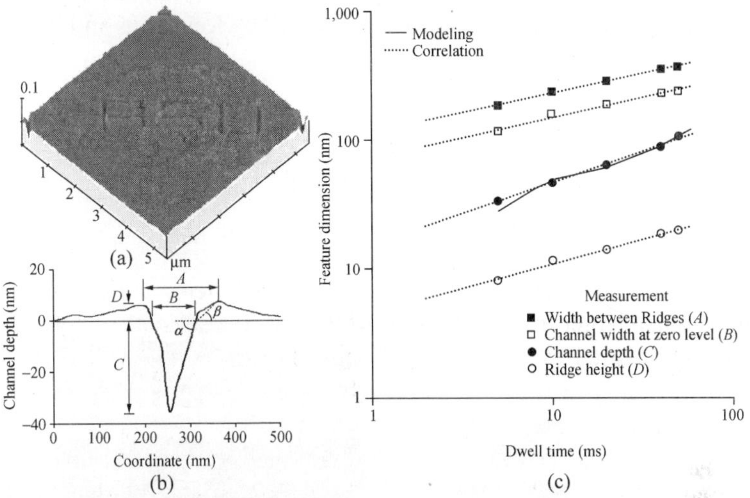

Figure 14.5 'ASU' nanochannel pattern on gold layer milled by 90 keV As^{2+} FIB: (a) AFM image at 5-ms dwell time, (b) channel cross-section and feature definition, (c) feature measurements for various dwell times

14.3.3 FIBL Direct Writing/Implantation

The FIBL system not only has capabilities of performing subtractive (milling) processes, but it can also perform additive (implantation and deposition) processes. In this subsection, this feature of FIBL will be explored by showing the specific procedure in creating different nanostructures. The first one is fabricated by using a combination of FIB implantation and wet etching. Figure 14.6 shows the process of fabricating a quad-cantilever. A shadow (20 – 30 nm) layer of Ga^+ ions is first implanted on top of a silicon substrate with the FIB ion energy varied typically from 10 – 50 keV (Fig. 14.6(a)). The layout of the FIB scanned area for implantation for making the quad-cantilever (Fig. 14.6(b)). A high concentration of p^+ doping in silicon is known to drastically reduce the etch rate of certain etchants such as potassium hydroxide (KOH) in the implanted region. Therefore, a selective etching is accomplished in this way. As the substrate is dipped in the KOH etchant, the silicon under the modified layer is etched away while the implanted region stays relatively unaffected (Fig. 14.6(c)). So in a sense, the doped region acts as an etch stop. Note that the critical implant dose is about 1×10^{15} ions cm^{-2} for the etch stop to be effective. This dose can be obtained in only a few seconds of time on small areas ($10\times10\ \mu m^2$) using moderate beam currents (typically 100 pA), and sputtering effects have to be taken into consideration for doses over 1×10^{16} ions cm^{-2}. This procedure results in a 3D quad-cantilever as shown in the SEM image (Fig. 14.6(d)). Using this combined implantation/wet etching method, other types of nanoscale freestanding structures, including a nanocup, and a U-shaped cantilever have also been reported by Reyntjens and Puers[19].

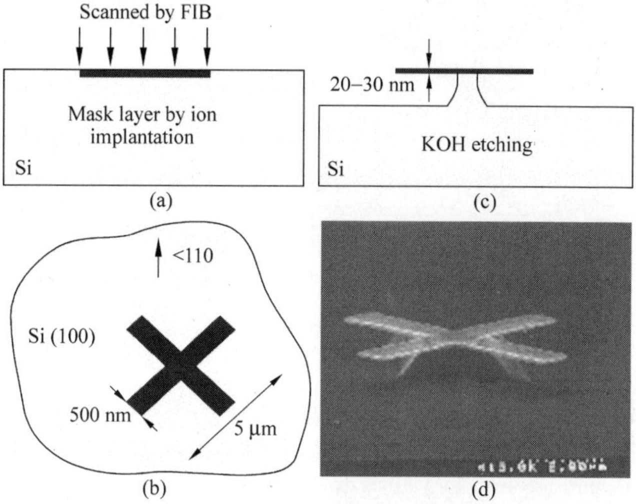

Figure 14.6 Fabrication of nanoscale quad-cantilevers: (a) implantation by FIB scanning (cross section), (b) top view of FIB scanned surface with quad-cantilever layout, (c) KOH etching for non-modified substrate (cross section), (d) SEM image of fabricated quad-cantilevers with 30 nm thick, 500 nm wide, and 2 μm long (courtesy of J. Brugger, IBM Zurich Research Lab, Switzerland)

14.3.4 FIBL Direct Writing/Deposition

The FIBL technique can also be used as a deposition tool for fabricating 3D nanostructures. FIBL deposition is also known as FIBCVD, in which a FIB is used to initiate and localize chemical vapor deposition (CVD) in a specific location by a direct writing technique. A typical FIBCVD system is equipped with a gas nozzle to inject a variety of gases on the target surface in a vacuum chamber as shown in Fig. 14.7(a). The injected precursor gas should be adsorbed by the target surface and then decomposed by the incident FIB. After that, the desired reaction product remains deposited on the target surface while the volatile reaction products that desorb from the surface should be eventually removed from the vacuum chamber. Many types of precursor gases have be used in FIBL to deposit a variety of metallic and ceramic structures; as reported by Melngailis[22], precursor gases of WF_6, $C_7H_7F_6O_2Au$, $(CH_3)_3NAlH_3$, $C_9H_{17}Pt$, and $TMOS+O_2$ can be used to produce W, Au, Al, Pt and SiO_2, respectively. Normally, the precursor gas is evaporated from a heated container and the gas nozzle is usually controlled at a height of 0.1 – 1 mm above the target surface with a angle of 30° – 60°.

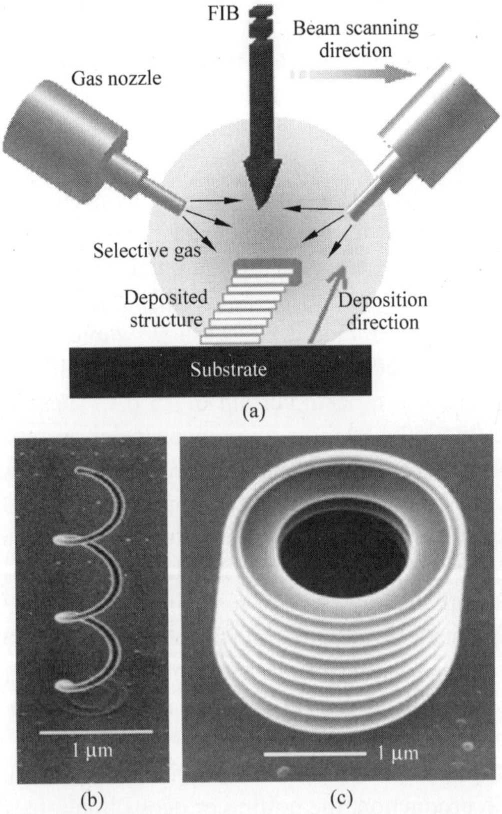

Figure 14.7 Nanostructures fabricated by FIBCVD: (a) schematic of FIBCVD, (b) SEM image of nanocoil with a 600 nm coil diameter, 700 nm coil pitch, and 80 nm wire diameter, (c) nanobellow with a 100 nm thickness, 800 nm pitch, 2750 nm external diameter, and 6,100 nm height (courtesy of Shinji Matsui of Himeji Institute of Technology, Japan) (see color figure at the end of this book)

The key for making 3D nanostructures by FIBCVD is the ability to deposit an overhung feature that extends beyond the previously deposited structure underneath. Figure 14.7(a) shows a schematic diagram of the procedure used by many investigators for fabricating 3D overhung structures. As shown, the deposition proceeds layer by layer. In each scan or layer, the new deposition extends a bit more over the previously deposited layer. Normally, the size of the extension or overhang in each layer should not be larger than the layer thickness. The moving speeds of FIB in the horizontal (x and y) directions are controlled by the beam deflectors, while the growth in the height (z) direction is determined by the deposition rate. This implies the height of the structure is proportional to the irradiation time when the deposition rate is constant. This layer-by-layer manufacturing process is similar to that commonly used by rapid prototyping or freeform fabrication. Many other techniques developed for rapid prototyping should also be adopted in FIBCVD as reported by He, Zhou, and Tseng[23].

Matsui et al.[24] fabricated several 3D nanostructures with 30 keV Ga^+ using the process discussed above (Fig. 14.7(a)). With an aromatic hydrocarbon precursor gas, FIB can be used to create diamond-like amorphous-carbon nanostructures. Figure 14.7(b) shows an SEM image of a microcoil structure made by the Ga^+ FIB. The beam diameter is 7 nm and the dwell time is 0.11 s with 40 s exposure time at 0.4 pA beam current. The basic vacuum chamber pressure is 2×10^{-5} Pa and becomes 5×10^{-5} Pa after introducing the gas. The FIB is scanned to write the desired pattern by computer control and the coil pitch can be changed by controlling the growth speed. The diameter of the microcoil is 600 nm with a 700 nm coil pitch and 80 nm wire diameter. Figure 14.7(c) shows a micro bellow with a 100 nm thickness, 800 nm pitch, 2,750 nm external diameter and 6,100 nm height. The total exposure time was 300 s at a beam current of 16 pA. These two nanostructures are considered an integral part in a micromechanical system. Using a similar technique, a number of other nanostructures have also been fabricated by Watanabe et al.[25]. The realization of these structures implies that FIBCVD is one of the promising techniques to fabricate 3D parts for a microsystem, although the mechanical performance has yet to be investigated.

Because of the relatively slow rate of deposition, and the sequential nature of the direct writing process, processing time becomes unacceptably long in case of making large structures. As a result, the size limitation is a major problem in the FIB deposition process. Although, in general, the ion milling and implantation processes are more efficient than the FIB induced deposition, the fabrication of sizable nanostructures is still a problem. To increase the throughput and the ability to be used in production, the milling or deposition rate of the existing FIB milling systems has to be improved. A variable-diameter beam system should be developed to provide multi-resolution milling to cope with different accuracy or tolerance requirements. It is ideal that the beam diameter can be continuously changed in situ. This type of system has been available for rapid prototyping processes[26]. With this system, a larger beam can be used for roughing 'cut' (or deposition) to increase the production rate in regions where lower resolution is needed. Once the high-performance FIBL system is used in production, it can be a vital candidate to become the mainstream tool for the future nanotechnology industry.

14.4 Nanoimprint Lithography (NIL)

Nanoimprint lithography (NIL) refers to a group of techniques developed for fabricating nanostructures using a patterned stamp by conformal contact between the relief pattern and the substrate for local pattern transformation. The origins of these imprint lithographic techniques can be traced to earlier generations of manufacturing methods, such as, the hot embossing process used to make copies of relief structures as found in compact disks. Imprint lithography as one of the candidates for NGL, is now under rapid development to meet the needs of a new generation of applications extended to the nanoscale arena.

14.4.1 Development of NIL

The typical NIL considered for NGL is essentially a molding process in which the topography of a mold (or template) defines the patterns created on a substrate. As shown in Fig. 14.8, the process consists of three major steps. Which follows as:

(1) In the first step, a mold (or stamp) with nanofeatures on its surface is pressed into a thin film, followed by subsequent cooling. Typically, the thin film is made of a printable polymer which is spun onto the substrate. The mold and substrate are placed on parallel stages and heated up to the imprinting temperature, which is normally above the glass temperature of the polymer to be printed. A certain amount of time is allowed for the thermal equilibrium to be reached. After the nanofeatures are cast on the thin film, the mold is removed (Fig. 14.8(b)).

(2) The second step is to create a thick contrast pattern in the polymeric film. Demounting and separation of the stamp and substrate takes place when both are just below the glass temperature. The temperature, pressure, and associated duration times are needed to be appropriately controlled to obtain the best pattern transfer.

(3) The third step is the pattern transfer where an anisotropic etching process, such as reactive ion etching (RIE), is used to remove the residual film in the compressed area, transferring the contrast pattern, through the entire film (Fig. 14.8(c)). The polymeric contrast pattern left on the substrate can be used as a mask for dry etching or deposition as well as a functional element for an electrical or optical device. As reported by Chou et al.[27], the NIL has the capability of patterning sub 10 nm features on a Si substrate transferred by an imprinted PMMA film.

The NIL can also be used to imprint the nanostructures directly in the polymeric film, i.e., without the last step (etching/transferring) shown in Fig. 14.8. Figure 14.9 shows SEM images of an array of nanochannels directly imprinted by a Si mold in a 300 nm thick polystyrene (PS) film that is coated on a Si substrate. The NIL is conducted at 170℃ with an imprint pressure of 4.5 MPa. As shown in Fig. 14.9(a), the channels have a width of 150 nm and a wall-thickness of 50 nm

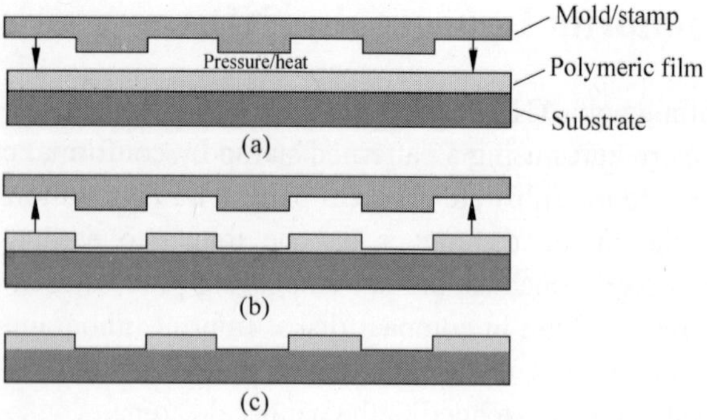

Figure 14.8 Schematic of nanoimprint lithography (NIL): (a) mold pressing, (b) mold casting and removing, (c) etching and pattern transferring

with an array period of 200 nm. The side view shown in Fig. 14.9(b) indicates that the channel has a V-shaped bottom with a depth of 150 nm from the surface to bottom tip. Normally, the V-shaped bottom with a wall having an aspect ratio of 3 should be difficult for fabrication by other nonconventional approaches, including SIL. In fact, with such a high aspect-ratio wall, the 'non-vertical' moving or unnecessary contact after separation, should be avoided during the final detachment step; otherwise, the channel walls can be tilted or damaged. Furthermore, the imprinted surface feature, such as roughness, can be deteriorated as compared with that of the mold, if the operating parameters, including the temperature, the uniformity of substrate material and thickness, and the clearness of mold and environment, are not controlled in the optimized conditions. Nevertheless, in general, the imprinted channels appear to be faithfully replicated by the imprinting features of the mold.

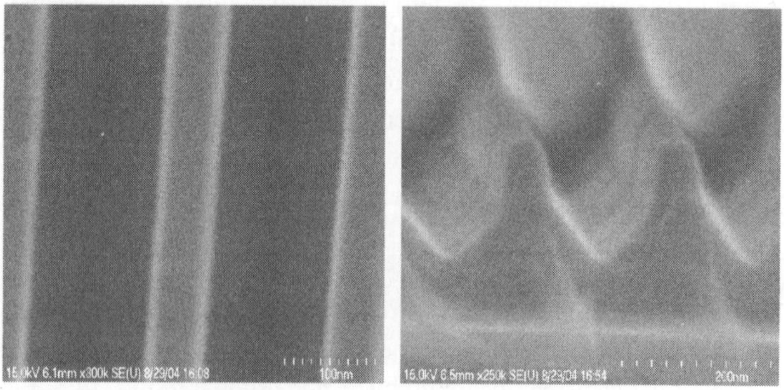

(a) (b)

Figure 14.9 SEM images of NIL imprinted array channels in PS film using Si stamp: (a) top view showing 150 nm channel-width with 50 nm wall-thickness and 200 nm array period, (b) side view showing 150 nm V-shaped bottom

14.4.2 Variations in NIL

Two major variants of NIL, step and flash imprint lithography (SFIL) and laser-assisted direct imprint (LADI), have been developed for making a variety of nanoscale structures. In SFIL, as shown in Fig. 14.10(a), two modifications are made from the normal NIL: the mold is made of transparent materials (to ultraviolet or UV light, such as quartz) and a photopolymerizable (UV curable, low-viscosity) organosilicon solution is coated on the top of the polymeric layer. The polymeric layer now acts as a transfer layer. As shown in Fig. 14.10(b), once the mold is pressed against the coated substrate, the organosilicon fluid fills the gap, including the cavities of the nanofeatures on the mold surface, under capillary reaction. The mold/substrate assembly is then irradiated with UV light, which cures the photopolymers to make it a solidified and silicon-rich replica of the nanofeatures of the mold (Fig. 14.10(c)). The mold is withdrawn leaving the low-aspect ratio features of the cured organosilicon polymer on the top of the transfer layer. The residual of the cured organosilicon polymer can be etched away (e.g. with a shot halogen plasma) and the nanofeatures are transferred into the transfer layer with anisotropic etching (such as RIE) for creating a high-aspect-ratio pattern. The high-aspect-ratio pattern can be used as a mask for the subsequent processes or as a functional element by itself.

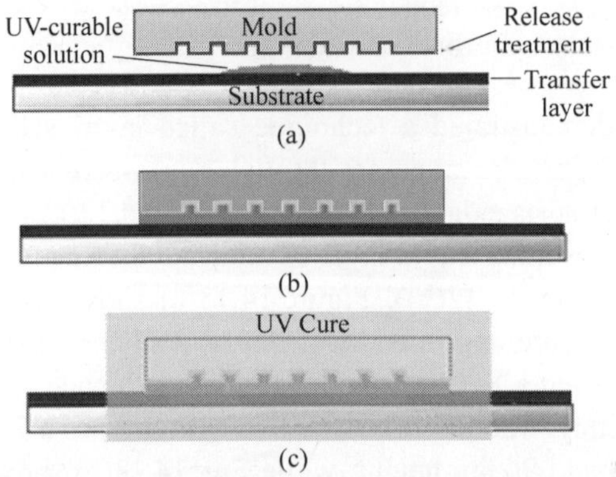

Figure 14.10 Major modified steps in step and flash imprint lithography (SFIL): (a) dispensing UV curable solution, (b) imprinting, (c) UV exposure (see color figure at the end of this book)

There are two advantages in SFIL. The first one is that the process can be conducted at room temperature under relatively low pressure, while the other is that the associated feature distortion due to the thermal shrinkage can be minimized. Choi[28] used SFIL to imprint sub-100 nm features on flat substrates and indicated that a uniform intimate contact between the mold and substrate surfaces is essential in transferring nanoscale features to the transfer layer. Figure 14.11 shows the SEM images of an SFIL imprinted pattern of 30 nm wide lines on an UV-cured polymer film reported by Resnick et al.[29]. The associated imprint and release pressures were less than 35 kPa and a crosslinking polymer: 1,3 bits(3-methacryloxypropyl)-tetramethyl disiloxane was employed as the UV cured agent. A separate imprint experiment yielded features as small as 20 nm. Also, as indicated by Bailey et al.[30], the mold contamination decreased with each successive imprint that may imply SFIL having a self-cleaning ability.

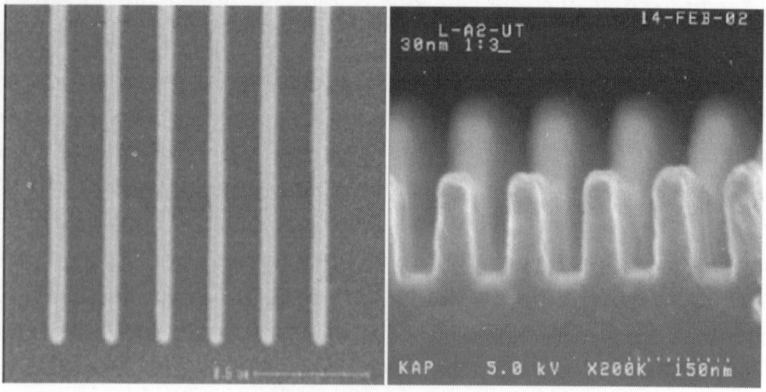

(a) (b)

Figure 14.11 SEM images of SFIL imprinted 30 nm wide line pattern on the cured polymer film: (a) top view, (b) cross-section view[29]

Chou et al.[31] demonstrated a technique called laser-assisted direct imprint (LADI), in which a laser beam passes through a transparent mold (e.g., a quartz mold) to melt a thin surface layer of substrate (Fig. 14.12(a)), and a mold is then impressed into the resulting liquid layer to replicate the nanofeatures of the same onto the substrate (Fig. 14.12(b)). Figure 14.13(a) shows an SEM image of a NPR-69 grating structure imprinted by LADI on a silicon substrate. NPR-69 is a thermoplastic resist and a XeCl excimer laser with a fluence of 0.56 J/cm pulse is used for resist melting. The imprinted NPR-69 grating has a 200 nm period with 100 nm line width and 90 nm height, while Fig. 14.13(b) shows an SEM image of the corresponding grating mold used by LADI[31]. The entire imprint from melting the polymer to completion of the imprint is in less than 500 ns. The mold has been treated with an anti-adhesion coating for better mold release after the imprint and has been used multiple times, without special cleaning between each imprint. A variety of other materials, such as Si and other polymers, have also been adopted for LADI. Also, the heating and expansion of the substrate and mold can be significantly reduced, leading to a better overlay alignment between the two.

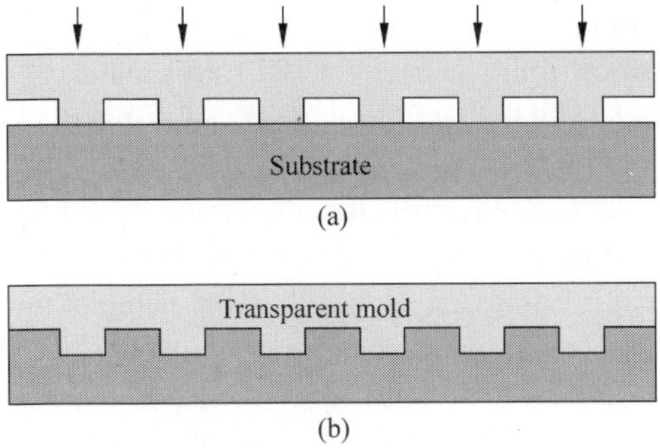

Figure 14.12 Major modified steps of laser-assisted direct imprint (LADI), (a) laser passes through transparent mold and melts substrate, (b) mold makes impression

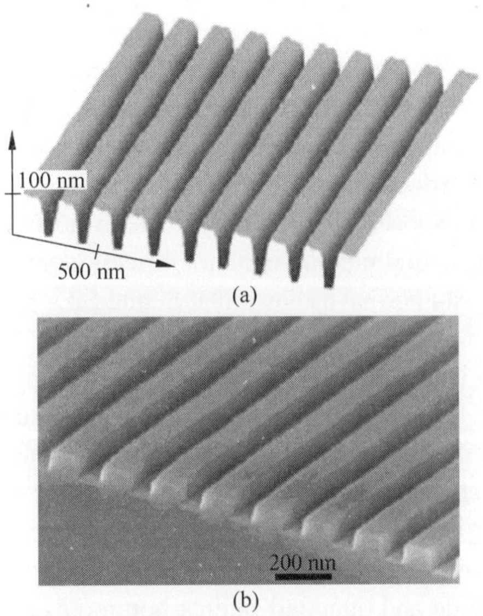

Figure 14.13 Nanograting structures: (a) AFM image of NPR-46 gratings imprinted by LADI, (b) SEM image of 200 nm period grating mold made from quartz. The gratings in mold are 90 nm high and precisely imprinted in NPR-46[32]

14.4.3 Critical Parameters and Challenges

Imprint lithography appears to be a simple and promising tool for pattern replication in the 10 – 100 nm range at affordable costs. Many issues remain to be solved, however, before the techniques can be commercialized for mass production. Some critical parameters are general enough and applicable to all the techniques discussed, while others apply only to specific techniques.

Level to level alignment is critical for imprinting multilevel structures and devices. A multilevel capability is one of major issues that have to be solved before commercialization. The first step is to develop an in-plane alignment approach, in which a rule of thumb is that alignment accuracy should be within 20% of the minimum feature size. Consequently, the alignment should be better than 10 nm for any feature size smaller than 50 nm, which is the target for NGL in 2007. In general, the alignment in NIL mainly depends on the stamp or mold size, the thermal and mechanical stability of the polymer, and the choice of stamp and substrate materials. These factors have to be carefully controlled to achieve required alignment during processing.

Furthermore, the rigid mold has to match its thermal expansion coefficient with that of the substrate. Most molds are made of Si or Si-based ceramics, including SiO_2, SiC, and Si_3N_4. Diamond and sapphire have also been used for imprint molds. Since NIL is a 1X method, the mold (or stamp in soft imprinting) should be able to fully mirror the nanoscale features with a precision at the accuracy level even higher. The fabrication of this ultra high resolution mold is a difficult task and advanced nanolithographic techniques, such as e-beam writing and other high resolution semiconductor processes, are used. As a result, Si or Si-based ceramics becomes the affordable choice for mold materials. Development of the capability for making nanoscale molds can be a significant hurdle to widespread adoption of imprint as a vital method in nanofabrication industry.

Nevertheless, many studies have shown that Si and SiO_2 have sufficient hardness and durability for nanoimprint needs. A matched thermal expansion coefficient with the imprint film is also critical, since hard imprinting is typically conducted at a temperature over 100℃. A thermal mismatch could result in pattern distortion or create undesirable thermal stresses during the heating and cooling cycles. As a result, a Si mold matched with a Si substrate is a good pair for NIL. However, the silicon or quartz (SiO_2) mold is somewhat brittle and has a relatively short lifespan. For increasing the mold life, focused ion beams (FIB) have been used to directly fabricate titanium nitride and diamond-like-carbon molds for NIL[18, 25, 33]. Lee et al.[34] used electroforming to produce metallic (Ni) molds. These molds, especially the metallic ones, are expected to endure imprinting cycles much longer, thereby offering a possibility of mass production.

Other issues that are important to throughput in mass production include the imprinting-area size, feature density, cycle time, and automation. The imprinting-area size determines how many elements can be printed in each cycle; it is mainly dictated by the limitation of stamp or mold sizes as well as the allowable misalignment. The feature density is limited by the flow of the displaced polymer, i.e., the separation distance between each feature to be appropriately printed. Currently, the total duration time for the whole imprinting process is still longer than the conventional photolithographic process. Finally, the imprinting techniques could be automated. However since many critical parameters are still not fully understood, the automation implementation should be evolutionary but not revolutionary.

14.5 Scanning Tunneling Microscopic Lithography (STML)

This Section addresses the lithographic applications of STM, the first type of instrument in the SPM family invented by Binnig and Rohrer in 1981[35]. STM uses a sharpened, conducting tip with a bias voltage applied between the tip and the target sample. When the tip is within 1 nm of the sample, electrons from the sample begin to tunnel through the gap to the tip. The resulting tunneling current varies with tip-to-sample spacing and is the signal for creating an STM image. It has become an effective tool to perform many lithographic activities, including atomic manipulation, material modification, material deposition, and material removal[2, 36].

14.5.1 Nanoscale Manipulation

In operating an STM, the tip is approaching the sample surface until the set-point current is reached (at a given bias voltage). An adsorbed atom, molecule or nanocluster, which is hereafter referred as an adparticle, is held on the surface by chemical bonds with the surface atoms. In an imaging mode, the distance between the tip apex atom(s) and adparticle is far enough such that any forces between them are negligible as compared to the forces binding the adparticle to the surface, and the adparticle is not disturbed by the passage of the tip over it. However, if the tip-adparticle distance is gradually decreased, the tip-sample interaction changes from the conventional tunneling regime to the electronic-contact regime and then to the mechanical-contact regime[37]. In the manipulation mode, the tip is in close proximity of the surface such that the adparticle bonds to the tip. It implies that by varying the distance between the STM tip and the sample, a force can be exerted on the nanoparticle adsorbed on the surface. A controlled manipulation experiment can thus be performed by lowering the tip towards the target adparticle to enhance the tip-adparticle interaction to overcome the forces between the adparticle and the surface. By adjusting the tip position and reducing bias voltage, and/or increasing the tunneling current, it is possible to adjust the magnitude and direction of the force, so that the tip can either push or drag an adparticle across a surface while the adparticle remains bound to the surface. This process is known as lateral manipulation (LM)[38]. The adparticle can also be picked up by the tip and relocated to another position with the assistance of the electric fields from the STM tip to increase or reduce the tip-adparticle interaction and this process is called vertical manipulation (VM).

The first pioneering work demonstrating the ability of positioning single atoms on a metallic surface by STM was conducted using lateral manipulation in 1990 by Eigler and Schweizer[39], in which a W-tip was used to arrange Xe atoms adsorbed in a company logo of 'IBM' on a single Ni(111) surface. Many geometrical configurations have been achieved by using lateral manipulation with different atoms and surfaces. For example, Fig. 14.14 shows an STM image of two Chinese characters for 'atom' made of iron atoms on a Cu(111) surface created by D. M. Eigler and C. P. Lutz of IBM. As indicated by Crommie, Lutz, and Eigler[40], the ripples around the characters shown in the figure are the standing-wave patterns in the local density of states of the Cu(111) surface. Using vertical manipulation, Eigler, Lutz, and Rudge[41] found that the direction of transferring Xe atoms between the tip and the substrate surface is the same as that of the tunneling electrons and the corresponding atom transfer rate is a power-law function of the tunneling current (I). For the specific experiment conditions considered, i.e., the voltage (V) ranging from 18 – 180 mV with a tunneling junction of V/I=906 kΩ±2%, and a varying transfer rate of 14.9±0.2. Lyo and Avouris[42] have shown that voltage pulses can be used for vertical manipulation by extracting atoms from a Si(111) surface to the tunneling tip and then depositing them elsewhere using an oppositely polarized pulse. They noted that the atom motion

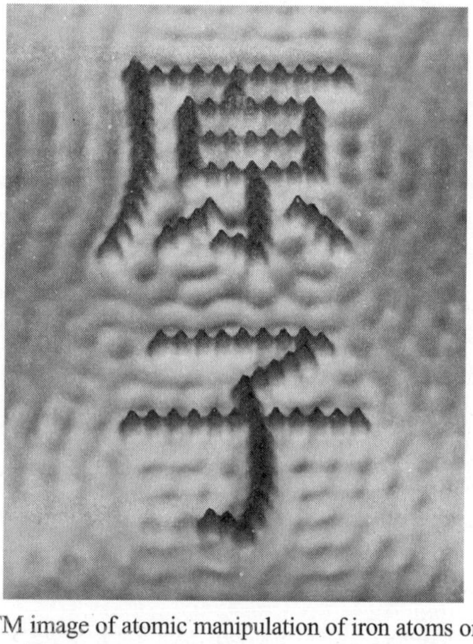

Figure 14.14 STM image of atomic manipulation of iron atoms on Cu(111) surface in writing Chinese characters for 'atom' by C. P. Lutz and D. M. Eigler, to which the literal translation is something like 'original child' (courtesy of IBM Almaden Research Center) (see color figure at the end of this book)

was in the same direction as the electron motion. Later, Shen et al.,[43] also observed that the transfer of atomic H to Si surfaces at relatively low voltages is strongly power-law dependent. Manipulation experiments are typically conducted using an STM at low temperatures under UHV (ultrahigh vacuum, less than 10^{-9} torr) conditions. After careful cleaning of the sample surface, the construction of quantum structures can be achieved by an atom-by-atom relocation on the surface.

Similar to atoms, single molecules, starting with small molecules such as CO, can be manipulated with an STM tip by managing the tip-adsorbate interaction force, by regulating the induced electric field, or by applying tunneling electrons from the tip. Stroscio and Eigler[44] were the first group to study the lateral manipulation of CO molecules adsorbed on Pt(111) surfaces using cryogenic STM. At this temperature, the molecules can be sufficiently frozen so that a large number of them can be precisely moved to the desired location. Also the manipulated structure can remain stable for a relatively long time. CO molecules have also been laterally manipulated on various surfaces, including Cu(111) and Ag(110)[45]. Gimzewski and Joachim[46] have demonstrated that the manipulation of single molecules at room temperature is also feasible; they have exploited the strong interaction with the surface shown by macromolecules such as porphyrins. Furthermore, on the issue of increasing the throughput and patterning speed, it is worth mentioning the 'automated atom assembly' approach of Stroscio et al.[47] in which a bottom-up fabrication of nanostructures was performed by providing the STM with computer controlled capabilities of lateral displacements of atoms. Most manipulations were performed under the constant-current mode, but the constant-height modes have also been used for manipulation of complicated molecules[48].

Recently, interest in STM manipulation of nanoclusters has grown significantly, because nanoclusters exhibit a wide range of physical and chemical properties and the ability to position nanoclusters can lead to many applications, including optics, electronics, mechanical materials, catalysis as well as biotechnology[49–51]. Significant efforts have been devoted to manipulating metallic nanoclusters on Si surfaces because of the popularity of Si substrates used in microelectronic devices. Meanwhile, the manipulation of metallic nanostructures on a clean reactive Si surface has been considered extremely challenging for reasons of surface wetting and strong interface bonding. Pretreatment of the clean Si surface is necessary for conducting manipulation. By using the buffer-layer-assisted growth technique, Chey, Huang, and Weaver[52, 53] demonstrated controlled manipulation of Ag, Cu, and mixed Ag-Cu nanoclusters on an Si(111)-(7×7) surface. The buffered [60 – 300 ML (monolayer)-thick layer of Xe] Si surface is used to deposit Ag and Cu atoms, and the Ag and Cu adatoms are sufficiently mobile on Xe to form nanoclusters. Unwanted Ag nanoclusters were removed by laterally pushing the nanoclusters with the STM tip using the following two approaches. In the first approach, which is also known as the fast-approach mode, a large area was scanned to derive the image and then a single line scan was performed over the desired feature with a fast scan speed (>10 μm/s), so that the feedback could not respond, to establish contact between the nanocluster and the tip to remove the Ag nanocluster. The second approach is typically involving a line scan at a slower scan speed (~ 0.1 μm/s) with the feedback disabled. Mn clusters can also be manipulated on C_{60} terminated Si surfaces, where the clusters can be removed and transferred to the tip but cannot be released from the tip[54]. In fact, the success of nanocluster manipulation is highly dependent on the competition of bonding strengths of nanoclusters with the substrate and the tip.

Hydrogen-terminated Si surfaces are another kind of Si for cluster manipulation. Butcher Jones, and Beton[55] demonstrated that by scanning at either large negative tunneling current or high positive bias voltage, it is possible to remove Ag nanoclusters from hydrogen terminated Si(100) surfaces. By lowering tunneling impedance below a threshold value, individual Ag nanoparticles could be controllably slid across the H-passivated Si(111) surface or picked up by the tip and subsequently re-deposited by applying an appropriate voltage pulse[56]. On the same H-terminated Si(111) surfaces, the manipulation can also be applied on Au nanoclusters prepared by means of field-induced transfer of Au tip material, but was restricted to the Au nanoclusters deposited by using relatively low-amplitude voltage pulses (< 8 V)[57]. Higher voltage pulses lead to the formation of an Au-Si alloy. Furthermore, it was observed that upon traversing the tip through a wet chemically prepared CdS nanocluster agglomeration, several individuals can be removed to form a desired structure[57]. Chemically passivated nanoclusters are also tried for such manipulation. For instance, it has been demonstrated that chemically passivated Au nanoclusters deposited on highly oriented pyrolytic graphite (HOPG) surfaces can be manipulated in a controlled way by using appropriate tunneling parameters[58]. In the cleared area after removal of these $C_{12}H_{25}S$ coated Au clusters, fragments resulted from the cluster dissociation process were observed. These fragments could be laterally displaced by further high current tunneling.

Recently, the STM manipulation technique has been used to pattern Co nanoclusters grown on an ordered Al_2O_3/NiAl(100) surface[59, 60]. The tip is placed over a specific cluster and the applied bias is reduced below a threshold value to attract the cluster and to subsequently remove it from the patterns. Through this approach, the patterns of the supported Co clusters can be systematically tailored. The removed clusters can also be relocated to other positions by reversing the polarity. Since uniform Co clusters formed from vapor deposition are only present on crystalline Al_2O_3 films and are highly aligned by protrusion structures of the crystalline Al_2O_3, the geometry of the crystalline Al_2O_3 film and the protrusion networks on it can be controlled through simple thermal treatments. Thereby the patterns of the Co clusters can be manipulated. This self-organized patterning in combination with the STM manipulation techniques enables one to fabricate desired cluster patterns and subsequently to investigate their physical properties. A sequence of STM images illustrating removal of the Co clusters by reducing the bias during scanning in a UHV condition can be found in Fig. 14.15. The STM image in Fig. 14.5(a) was obtained at 2.4 V bias and 0.8 nA tunneling current, where aligned Co nanoclusters are formed on crystalline Al_2O_3. As shown in the square of the zoom-in area in Fig. 14.15(b), the bias is lowered to different values during scanning (from left to right). As the tunneling current is kept the same, this process brought the tip close to the clusters, as illustrated schematically in the cartoon inset. It is evident that bias voltages below a threshold value of 0.8 V induce the motion of the Co nanoclusters. Figure 14.15(c) is the same surface region as shown in Fig. 14.15(a) scanned just after the manipulation process with the same imaging parameters. It can be observed from the figure image that where the bias is above the threshold value, the Co clusters are in fixed and well-defined locations. On the contrary, the regions where the bias is below the threshold value have no Co clusters. When a higher tunneling current is set, a higher threshold bias can be found. For instance, when 1.6 nA was used as the set point current, the threshold bias was found to be 1.6 V[60].

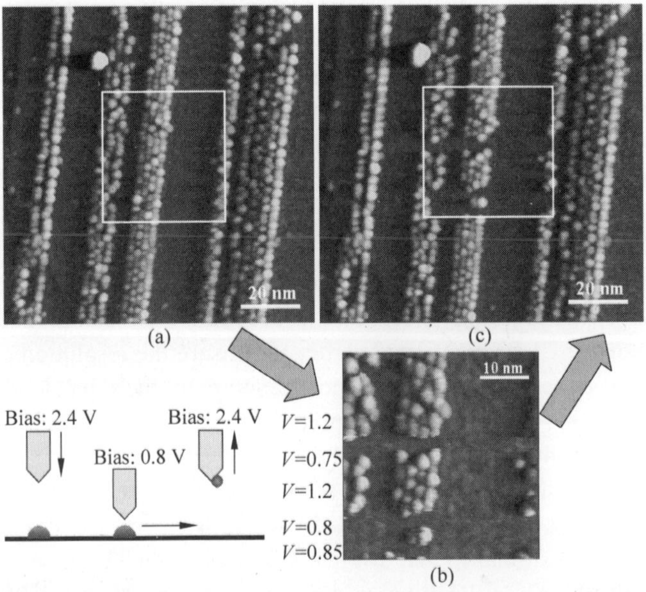

Figure 14.15 STM images showing removal of Co clusters by reducing bias during scanning: (a) Co clusters grown on ordered Al_2O_3/NiAl(100) surface (bias = 2.4 V and tunneling current = 0.8 nA), (b) zoom-in image of square area shown in Panel a, where bias was lowered to different values with I = 0.8 nA during scanning, (c) same surface region as in Panel (a) after removal of Co clusters scanned with same imaging parameters (2.4 V, 0.8 nA). The inset cartoon illustrates the procedure (after Tseng et al.[60]) (see color figure at the end of this book)

For realistic applications, attempts have been made to perform such manipulation at ambient pressure. Ohgi, Sheng, and Nejoh,[61] demonstrated that lower-density

Au nanoparticles supported on self-assembled monolayers (SAMs) of octanedithiol ($HS(CH_2)$:SH:C_8S_2) molecules formed on an Au(111) surface can be removed easily with lower bias and higher tunneling current than the imaging ones, although the manipulation is difficult at coverage above 1 ML. Rolandi et al.[62] have shown that alkanethiol-coated Au nanoparticles on HOPG substrate can also be removed by scanning at low bias voltages. Coulomb blockade was found to be the reason why the tip attracts nanoclusters at a low bias voltage. The results for the manipulation in ambient conditions are not abundant; however, they have implied the possibility for succeed.

14.5.2 Material Modification

Shortly after its invention by Binnig and Rohrer in 1981[35], STM had been discovered to be an effective tool for inducing modification to a material surface, in addition to its imaging capabilities. The first demonstration of STM modification to a material surface was achieved by producing lithographic patterns of nanoscale lines[63] and cones[64] on atomically flat surfaces in vacuum. The field of STM lithography has become notable after the study of Dagata et al.[65] who induced local oxidation on a hydrogen-passivated silicon substrate using an STM in air.

The ability for precise control of the tunneling current represents the basis for the STM imaging technique. The combination of precise spatial localization of the tunneling electron beam and low current intensity makes the STM set-up adaptable for exposure of very thin resist films. The low voltage applied, which is necessary to produce the electron beam, ensures limited back scattering and, in turn, minimizes the proximity effect that would normally dictate the resolution of the conventional EBL as mentioned earlier. To ensure the resolution or linewidth of the exposed pattern down to the nanoscale domain, the typical electron beam current and voltage, and scanning rate used for resist exposure in STM should be respectively controlled on the order of 1 nA, 10 V, and 1 m/s. Similar to EBL, the developed resist profile or structure are suitable for both lift-off and direct etching processes. By STM exposure of a PMMA resist, McCord and Pease[66] applied the lift-off process, similar to that of Fig. 14.2, to obtain a 22 nm wide and 12 nm thick gold-palladium (Au-Pd) line on a Si substrate, in which the PMMA resist film has to be thinner than those used in EBL because the lower energy electrons created in STM and the gap between the STM tip and conducting substrate is relatively small. Using a similar technique, McCord and Pease[66] also obtained a thin-film resistor device having a 2.5 kΩ resistance at room temperature. In addition to PMMA, several other polymer resists have also been adopted by STM for patterning structures with a line-width below 100 nm, such as SAL (Shipley Advanced Lithography) 601 negative resist[67] and SAM of molecules[68]. The latter, after exposure and ligation of catalyst, has also been used as templates for electroless plating thus producing a metallic etch mask for pattern transfer with a feature size at 15 nm[69].

14.5.3 Material Deposition

The STM has been used for local-field-induced deposition, in which the tip can be used as a miniature emission source. By applying a voltage, atoms or nanoparticles can be transferred from the STM tip to the target surface, which is within the tunneling range. Both positive and negative voltages, which should be higher than a certain threshold, have been used for the deposition. The threshold voltage, which is normally at a few volts, is influenced by the conditions of tip-target separation and polarity as indicated by Mamin et al.[70]. Houel et al.[71] also observed that the negative threshold voltage necessary to produce material deposition changes with the tip/target configuration but remains on the order of a few volts for depositing platinum and tungsten dots on Si and Au/mica substrates. Material deposition has also been observed with short pulses on the order of 10 ns, but little change in amount of materials deposited is observed with pulse duration larger than about 10 ms, which may imply the existence of a sort of saturation mechanism. Moreover, in deposition of Au particles on an Au substrate, Mamin et al.,[70] discovered that the gold dot or mound previously deposited can be removed by a subsequent pulse on the same location. Consequently, it can be argued that STM deposition can be used for a nanoscale write/erase device.

Recently, Fujita, Onishi, and Kumakura[72] used an Ag-coated W tip to deposit sequential Ag-dots on an n-type Si(111) substrate with the pitch equal to the dot size. As shown in the STM image of Fig. 14.16(a), a nanocharacter 'A' was formed by STM direct deposition using a negative 4.5 V bias for a 1 ms duration. The overlapped dots are about 20 nm in diameter and 2 nm in height. The size of the Ag-dots can be controlled by adjusting the pulse voltage and duration. Also, it is important to achieve 100% deposition probability so that overlapped dots or continuous lines can be created. Following similar procedures, Fig. 14.16(b) shows three Au nanolines using an Au-coated tip. Normally, by appropriately setting the deposition parameters, the feature size of the deposited wires or dots can be as small as tens of nanometers. In fact, a minimum linewidth of less than 5 nm has been obtained. Furthermore, Fujita, Onishi, and Kumakura[72] believed that the formation of the dots, shown in Fig. 14.16(a), can be attributed to the field-enhanced diffusion of silver atoms to the tip apex, but not by the process of tip evaporation enhanced by the high electric field at the tip/substrate gap, as explained by Mamin, Guethner, and Rugar[73]. However, in general, the mechanism of tip-target material transfer is not fully understood. For example, it is not clear why W from the tips cannot be effectively deposited onto Si or Au substrates, although

Ag, Au, and Pt tips have been successfully used for deposition onto Si and Au targets.

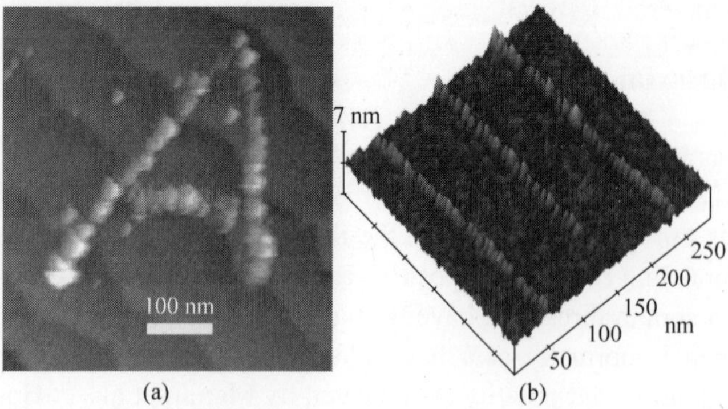

Figure 14.16 Nanostructures on Si substrates by direct STML deposition of sequential dots: (a) STM image of Ag-characters 'A' by Ag-coated tip (courtesy of Daisuke Fujita of National Institute for Materials Science, Japan), (b) AFM image of Au-lines by Au-coated tip (courtesy of H. Abed of Faculté des Sciences de Luminy, France) (see color figure at the end of this book)

Similar to IBL, STM can also be used to initiate a localized CVD for deposition of various metals, including Al, Cd, Ni, Pd and Si as reported by Pai et al.[74]. Again, since a precursor gas is needed for the CVD growth, the STM should also be equipped with a gas-nozzle in a vacuum chamber. The emission of free electrons from the STM tip interacts with the precursor molecules by decomposing the species and the desired decomposed species is deposited in the near proximity of the tip. A typical gas pressure on the order of 10^{-6} to 10^{-5} mbar is used. The voltages applied are on the order of tens of volts, while the typical current value during the process is on the order of tens of pA. Under these conditions, the duration of voltage pulse necessary for the material deposition is on the order of tens of seconds, depending on the gas used as precursor. Si and Ge based nanostructures with lateral size of about 10 nm were successfully deposited on Si(111) substrates starting from GeH_4[75], SiH_4, and SiH_2Cl_2[76] precursors.

Magnetic nanostructures with a lateral size of about 10 nm have also been created by Pai et al.[74] using decomposition of ferrocene as the metal-organic source gas. In an electrochemical variant of STM, Schindler, Hofmann and Kirschner[77] have used an aqueous electrolyte containing $CoSO_4$ on a gold substrate for the electrodeposition of 15 nm wide Co-nanoclusters. Furthermore, STM can be used to define a pattern for subsequent CVD by using electrons to remove hydrogen atoms (to depassivate) from a surface that had been hydrogen terminated (H-passivated). Using this depassivating technique for patterning, Mitsui, Hill and Ganz[78], and Adams, Mayer and Swartzentruber[79] have respectively deposited aluminum and iron nanostructures from highly reactive dimethylaluminum hydride and ferrocene gaseous precursors.

14.5.4 Material Removal and Etching

Nanoscale material removal can be achieved by e-beam induced thermal decomposition. Li, Yoshinobu and Iwasaki[80] have demonstrated that SiO_2 layers can be selectively removed by using a field-emitted electron beam extracted from the STM tip to trigger decomposition of SiO_2 at temperatures between 300℃ – 700℃ under UHV conditions. The oxide removal or decomposition is caused by the thermal desorption of SiO_2 onto a Si substrate, which is directly induced by e-beam radiation. Using STM, SiO_2 decomposition onsets around 100 eV, close to the value found previously for e-beam-induced dissociation by Auger electron spectroscopy and e-stimulation. Much higher energies, 30 – 50 keV, have also been applied to desorb oxides using focused e-beams provided by special non-STM equipment[81]. The schematic of this STM decomposition process is shown in Fig. 14.17(a), where the process is dependent on the electron dose and can be controlled by adjusting the emission current and exposure time. The opening feature size of 50 nm is typical but a minimum feature size of 10-nm is possible. Various open patterns and feature sizes can be obtained by controlling the tip scanning. As depicted in Fig. 14.17(b), a concentric-ring pattern can be obtained by setting the STM parameters of 80 eV in beam energy and 10 nA in emission current at 693℃ with less than 2.0×10^{-8} Pa vacuum[82]. The line width of the three rings shown in the figure varies from 25 – 56 nm where the applied line dose increases from 1.7×10^{-3} – 3.3×10^{-3} C/cm.

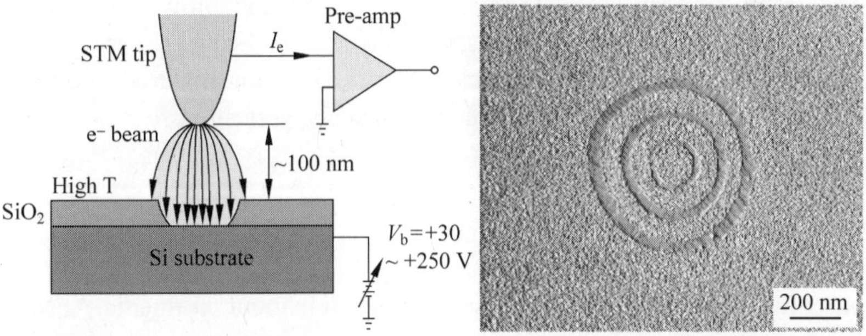

(a) (b)

Figure 14.17 Material removal by STM induced thermal decomposition: (a) schematic of decomposition of SiO_2 layer by an STM tip with negative bias, (b) concentric ring pattern with a minimum line width of 25 nm fabricated by STM tip scanning using computer controller (courtesy of Hiroshi Iwasaki of Osaka University, Japan) (see color figure at the end of this book)

The STM technique can be adopted for nanoscale etching, if the gas injected from the gas-nozzle can interact with the STM tip-electrons to induce a gas-assisted electrochemical etching. This kind of electrochemical etching process has been employed by Yau, Kaji and Itaya[83], and Kaneshiro and Okumura[84] to locally etch the Si (100) and GaAs(100) substrates, respectively, on areas down to a few nm^2.

14.6 Atomic Force Microscopic Lithography (AFML)

AFM is evolved from STM and uses a cantilevered tip to quantify the attractive or repulsive forces between the tip and sample. These forces vary with the spacing between the tip and sample, because the tip is located at the free end of a cantilever and the attractive or repulsive forces cause the cantilever to deflect. As a raster-scan drags the tip over the sample, an image of the surface topography can be generated by measuring the cantilever deflections and by knowing the tip position. In AFM, contact (repulse), non-contact (NC) or tapping modes can be operated depending on the application. In a contact operation, either the constant height or the constant force mode can be used. In a non-contact mode, the cantilever tip is made to vibrate at a frequency near to its resonant frequency near the sample surface with spacing on the order of a few nm without touches the surface at lowest deflection, while in a tapping mode (TM), the tip vibrates closer to the surface with intermittently touches the surface at lowest deflection[36].

Many techniques have been developed to use AFM to fabricate various structures on the nanometer scale. These AFM-based techniques are less restrictive than those of STM, because AFM can be conducted in a normal room environment and be used to image almost any kind of materials. Furthermore, AFM can be equipped with conductive tips to possess the typical capability of an STM, such as for low-energy exposure of resists, as indicated by Tseng, Notargiacomo, and Chen[85]. In this section, the applications of AFM for material modification, oxidation, deposition and removal are, respectively, presented.

14.6.1 Nanoscale Manipulation

Oyabu et al.[86] are believed to be the first group using a cryogenic AFM near a contact mode to study the vertical manipulation of Si atoms on Si(111)-(7×7) surfaces. The experiment was conducted at a temperature of 78 K under UHV (5×10^{-11} Torr). An n-doped Si cantilever with a spring constant of 48 N/m and a resonant frequency of 160 Hz was used. In manipulation, a soft nanoindentation was first performed by the tip to remove a selected Si atom from its equilibrium position at the surface without additional perturbation of the (7×7) unit cell. The short-range interaction force acting between the atom at the tip apex and closest adatom at the surface activated the removing process. Unloading the manipulated atom is achieved by depositing it on a previously created vacancy at the surface. These manipulation processes are purely mechanical, since only short-range chemical interaction forces are involved and neither bias voltage nor voltage pulse is applied between probe and surface. Kawai and Kawakatsu[87] applied an AFM under the frequency modulation mode to extend the lateral manipulation of Si adatoms on the Si(111)-(7×7) surface to room temperature under a UHV environment. Pushing and pulling steps were carried out with repulsive and attractive interaction forces between the cantilever tip and the adatom. A small amplitude of 0.4 nm was used to improve the detection sensitivity of the short-range interaction force gradient as well as to enhance the resolution of the manipulation. Nishi et al.[88] used the frequency modulation (FM) of AFM to investigate the atomic manipulation on an insulator surface, which normally is not suitable for STM manipulation. In a FM operation, the AFM feedback exploits the change in the amplitude of a cantilever's oscillation driven at a user-defined frequency due to the interaction of a tip mounted at the cantilever's end with a sample. They adopted the soft nanoindentation approach, similar to that used by Oyabu et al.[86], to manipulate atoms on a cleaved ionic crystalline KCl(100) surface in UHV at room temperature with limited success.

Similar to single atoms, individual molecules are difficult to be manipulated by sliding on or dragging from a surface to chosen sites. The most important reason is probably the presence of undesired interactions between the AFM tip and the surface, including van der Waals, electrostatic and adhesion forces. Also, the non-specificity of the attachments, residuals, and molecules often occurs between the tip and surface[89]. Although many efforts have been attempted to manipulate single molecules with AFM, all are with limited success. For example, Chyan et al.[90] have used the mechanical forces exerted by AFM to initiate the unfolding transition of individual protein molecules for the characterization of the unfolding and refolding process. However, actually sliding the molecule to the desired location in a stable and controllable manner is still unachievable.

Although AFM still has only limited success in manipulating both single atoms and molecules, it has been successfully used for manipulating a wide range of nanoparticles, especially for those having sizes larger than the order of 10 nm. Various techniques have been developed with the capabilities to be operated in different environments, including UHV, air, and liquid, using relatively simple sample preparation techniques[36]. Schaefer et al.[91] demonstrated that AFM in the contact mode under a dry nitrogen environment can be applied for moving Au particles with diameters ranging from 9 – 20 nm across a HOPG substrate to predefined locations. By employing the same approach these Au particles can be further manipulated on the WSe_2 substrate. The tapping mode of AFM can also be applied for the manipulation of nanoparticles. Junno et al.[92] used a tapping mode with a frequency of 170 kHz to manipulate and position individual 30 nm GaAs particles by connecting them to form letters 'nm' at room temperature in ambient air. The manipulation was achieved by physically pushing each individual particle with the AFM tip to the desired location.

More delicate manipulation was performed on aerosol Ag particles on SiO_2

substrate, in which several letters were written using 45 nm Ag particles[93]. It was found that Ag aerosol particles on an InP substrate were swept up by the AFM tip during scans[94]. Modeling based on this sort of aerosol particle manipulation implies again that the tip radius should be minimized in order to reduce the adhesion between tip and particle. Figure 14.18 shows the lateral manipulation of Au nanoparticles (approximately 24 nm in size) on a cleaved mica surface by FM-AFM in ambient environment at room temperature to create chain-like nanostructures. A positive coating of poly-L-lysine on the mica surface allows the negatively charged gold particles to be adsorbed onto the surface. Rectangular Si cantilevers (probe model TESP from Veeco Instruments) with a spring constant of approximately 50 N/m, and a setting frequency of approximately 300 kHz were utilized.

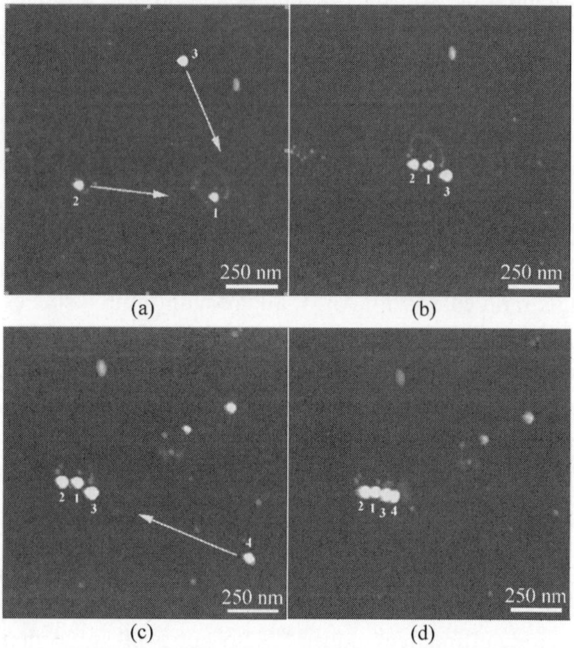

Figure 14.18 AFM images of lateral manipulation of 24 nm Au nanoparticles to create chain-like nanostructure by FM-AFM: (a) pushing nanoparticles labeled with 2 and 3 along direction shown by arrows, (b) nanoparticles 2 and 3 are pushed close to nanoparticle 1, (c) moving nanoparticle 4 towards nanoparticle 1, (d) final chain-like nanostructure

Currently, the AFM manipulation techniques are becoming mature enough to have a great potential of manufacturing various nanodevices. Junno et al.[95] had fabricated nanomechnical switches and atomic scale contacts with 50 nm Au nanoparticles in air at room temperature. The electrode patterns used were formed by EBL followed by evaporation of 3 nm Ti (for adhesion) and 25 nm Au with a gap of 20 – 50 nm onto a 300 nm thick SiO_2 layer on a Si substrate. Jennette et al.[96] had constructing devices that allow the measurement of the conductance of single molecules by using Au nanowires as the electrodes to the molecules. The nanowires were created by AFM manipulation of gold nanoparticles of diameter 2 – 15 nm. Decossas et al.[97] made a device of two metallic electrodes connected by AFM manipulation, with a 70 nm long Si nanocrystal (nc-Si) chain, in which the resonant tunneling effects resulting from the nc-Si multiple junctions were observed at room temperature. This implies that the manipulation of nc-Si is a promising way to fabricate single electron devices.

14.6.2 Material Modifications

Many attempts have been made to use AFM to induce modification of different materials at the nanometer scale. Majumdar et al.[98] demonstrated that an AFM equipped with a gold-coated tip can be used to provide a localized electron source for exposing ultrathin PMMA resists, in which a line pattern with a width of 35 nm and periodicity of 68 nm was realized. Davidsson et al.[99] have patterned a 10 nm thick SA resist by electron exposure using AFM. A conducting 50 nm line with a 6 nm thick film can be obtained by a subsequent Al vacuum evaporation using the patterned resist. Ishibashi et al.[100] used the field emission current as the feedback signal to control the amount of exposure for investigating the line-and-space patterns generated by AFM in a negative e-beam resist, RD2100N, on a p-type Si(100) substrate. The AFM tip is coated with Ti having a radius of 50 nm. A negative bias between 10 V and 100 V was used to obtain a constant current in the range of 10 – 100 pA. A range of line doses from 0.3 – 110 nC/cm with a scanning speed between 10 μm/s and 100 μm/s was used for resist patterning. The minimum line widths in the line-and-space resist pattern are 27 nm, 55 nm, and 110 nm for resist thicknesses of 15 nm, 40 nm, and 100 nm, respectively. The cross section of the pattern is an upside-down trapezoid at a low exposure dose, but becomes a right-side up trapezoid at a high exposure dose. By performing thermally induced surface modifications, AFM can increase its reproducibility. Mamin[101] used resistive heating of the AFM tip to temperatures up to 170℃ for 4 ms to produce an array of sub-100 nm pits on polycarbonate substrate.

14.6.3 Material Oxidation

AFM tip-induced local oxidation (LO) is an electrochemical process, in which an AFM conducting tip is biased negative with respect to the substrate to induce surface oxide features. By moving the tip close to the substrate surface, the negatively biased tip induces a high electric field which ionizes the water molecules from the ambient humidity between the tip (cathode) and the substrate (anode). The OH^- ions produced provide the oxidant for the electrochemical reaction. The electric field further enhances the vertical drift of these ion species away from the tip towards the surface where they react with underlying atoms to form a localized oxide beneath the tip, according to the formula: $Si + 4h^+ + 2OH^- \rightarrow SiO_2 + 2H^+$, where h^+ is a hole or vacancy in the substrate. The field strength decays across the growing oxide film and the oxide growth process self terminates at/below the critical electric field of the order of 10^9 V/m. Probes with conductive coatings ensure better performances while bare doped Si probes are also acceptable. The typical parameters used to produce oxide patterns are an applied voltage of several volts and a scanning rate on the order of 1 μm/s.

In dot formation, initially the oxide thickness increases almost linearly with both the applied voltage and the pulse duration until the diffusion efficiency of additional OH^- ions to the freshly formed oxide layer is reduced. In line formation, the oxide thickness increases as the scanning rate or tip moving speed decreases. The oxidation efficiency can be improved by increasing the environmental humidity, in which higher humidity leads to thicker oxide as well as an increased lateral size. The oxidation efficiency in Si also depends on doping type and concentration: n^+-doping produces thicker oxide with respect to p-type substrates. Before conducting LO, a dip of Si substrate in a HF diluted solution can ensure a clean Si surface effectively passivated by hydrogen. The typical effects of the applied voltage on the LO dots and lines patterned on Si substrate can be found in Fig. 14.19, in which a Si tip is scanned in contact-mode by increasing the voltage magnitude from –3 V to –9 V at 60% ambient humidity. While the oxide dots are created by applying a 500 ms DC pulse, the oxide lines are formed by constant DC voltages at a scanning rate of 1 m/s. The height and lateral size of the dots and lines are increasing almost linearly with the magnitude of applied voltages. For oxide dots, the FWHM diameter expands from 10 nm to 40 nm and the height grows from 0.6 nm to 2.2 nm on the Si substrate as the voltage decreases from –3 V to –9 V, where FWHM stands for full width at half maximum, while the corresponding height of the oxide lines increases from 0.4 nm to 1.1 nm.

The oxide patterns induced can act as robust masks for subsequent etching or deposition processes, which have been using for patterning a fairly wide range of devices, such as single electron transistors, nanomechanical structures, quantum electronic devices, and molecular templates[102, 103]. However, the oxide patterns induced for the existing efforts have been limited to relatively simple geometries: lines or dots as those shown in Fig. 14.19. Recently, an AFM oxidation technique has been developed to induce or create oxide masks with arbitrary shapes of area patterns, which can be generated by overlapping or superimposing a series of individual oxide lines. Different shapes of lines can also be formed by superimposing a series of individual oxide dots. Figure 14.20 shows AFM images of the overlapped oxide lines with appropriate pitch control. As shown in Fig. 14.20(a), oxide lines

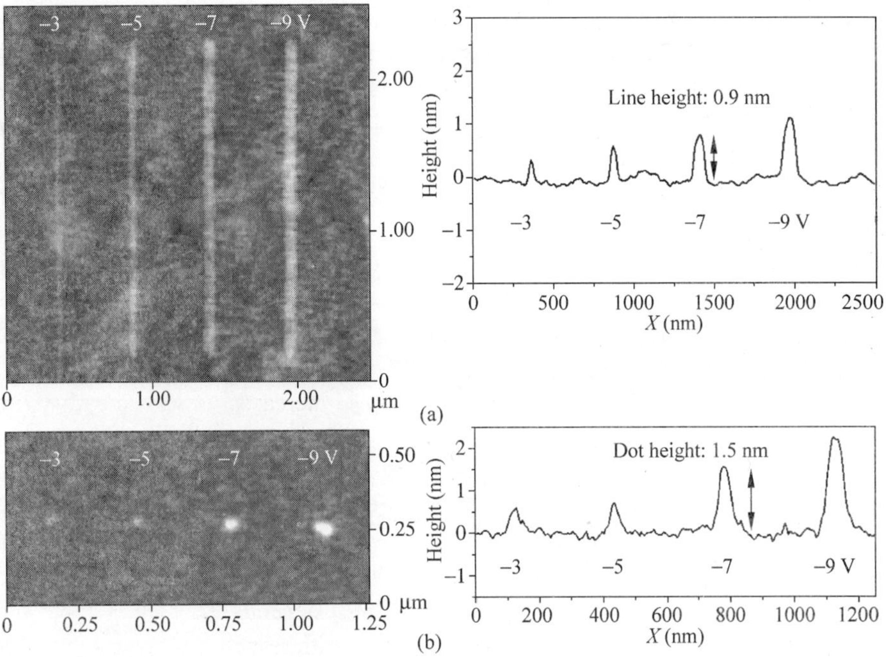

Figure 14.19 AFM tip-induced line and dot oxidation on Si substrate: (a) AFM image (left side) and section profile (right side) of oxide lines by applying DC voltage from −3 V to −9 V with scanning rate of 1 μm/s, (b) AFM image and section profile of oxide dots by applying DC voltage from −3 V to −9 V with 500 ms pulse

were induced using a DC of −8 V with a scanning speed of 1 μm/s and a pitch of 174 nm ($p/w = 1.5$). Here, w is the FWHM width of the oxide lines.

However, after careful examination of the line pattern created (Fig. 14.20(a)), it has been found that these lines are not perfectly parallel. For a 2 μm long line, the deviation can be more than several tens of nanometers. This type of deviation or drift is believed to be caused by the hysteresis-creep of the piezo-scanner used in AFM. A close-loop control with a careful designed feedback sensor can cope with this type of mechanical drift problems[104]. A thermal drift can also be significant, if the oxidation is conducted for a large amount area with a relatively long operating time. Nonetheless, as shown in Fig. 14.20(b), even with several tens of nm deviation, a relatively uniform oxide area of 2 μm by 2 μm can be formed by reducing the pitch to 58 nm or $p/w = 0.5$. The average line height in Fig. 14.20(a) is 1.5 nm, while the height of the area or fully overlapped lines in Fig. 14.20(b) is approximately 2.2 nm, a 45% increase in height. Software to provide the guidelines for AFM oxidation is developed by inputting the shape of the required oxide pattern and material and equipment parameters involved, while the output guidelines are the operating conditions, including scanning mode, scanning path, and scanning speed, overlapping pitch, pulse duration, applied voltage, ambient humidity, tip geometry, and tip material[105]. By controlling these operating parameters, the oxide masks can have not only the desired shape (or contour) but also the desired variation. These masks can be truly three-dimensional (3D) and can be used as grayscale masks for making intricate 3D nanostructures, similar to those used for photolithography or laser machining of microoptical devices[106, 107].

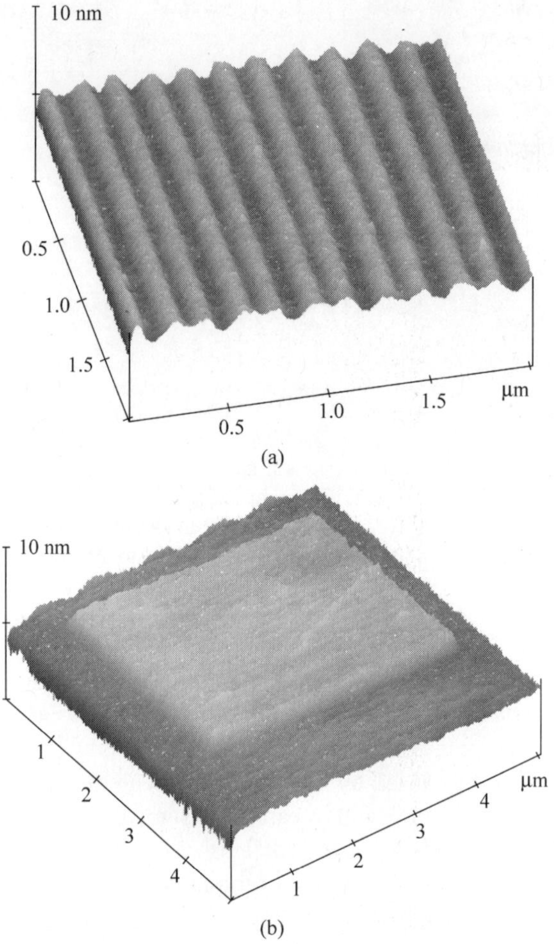

Figure 14.20 AFM images of AFM induced area oxidation on Si substrate by overlapping lines using –8 V DC and 1 μm/s scanning speed with pitch (*p*) equal to: (a) 174 nm ($p/w = 1.5$), (b) 58 nm ($p/w = 0.5$), where *w* is line width

14.6.4 Material Removal

AFM has been used for nanoscale material removal through both mechanical and chemical means. In the former, the materials are removed by direct tip scratching or plowing, while, in the latter, the materials are removed by the tip-induced electrochemical etching. By applying a certain amount of force on the tip or by controlling the cantilever deflection during scanning, the AFM tip has been successfully employed to 'scratch' several hard surfaces of metals, oxides and semiconductors, producing furrows with widths of tens of nm and depths of a few nm. Magno and Bennett[108] have used a Si_3N_4 cantilever tip in a contact mode to dig three 500 nm long grooves on a two-layer GaSb/InAs film. The stiffness of the cantilever is 0.37 N/m and the applied forces vary from 100 nN to 150 nN with a scanning rate of 0.02 μm/s. The grooves produced on the 5 nm GaSb/20 nm InAs substrate are down to 65 nm in width and several nm in depth. The resulting grooves of 50 – 100 nm width can form an arrangement of barriers in the electron layer of a conventional double-layer structure. A new type of heterostructure with a compensating p-type doped cap layer shows an electron enhancement if the cap layer is selectively removed. Machining a groove in these structures enables one to induce a one-dimensional electron system. Both types of structures are used to fabricate various ballistic quantum devices and Coulomb- blockade structures as indicated by Kunze[109].

Diamond tips have also been used to increase probe lifetime. Filho et al.[110] have equipped an AFM with a diamond tip operated in air under a contact mode to scratch an Al layer for patterning a Si-based mask. The diamond tip used has an apex radius of 25 nm and the scratch depth grows from 20 to 80 nm as the applied tip force increases from 15 μN to 30 μN. Tseng et al.[111] applied an AFM equipped with a diamond-coated tip to scratch Silicon and Nickel-iron thin films to study their nanoscale machining properties and a NiFe-based nanoconstriction was scratched to demonstrate the versatility of the scratching technique developed. Figure 14.21(a) shows an 'ASU' trench pattern on a p-type Si(100) surfaces scratched with a diamond coated tip in a contact mode at a speed of 10 μm/s and a normal force of 7 μN. The probe used was a Nanosensors DT-NCHR rectangular cross-section type with a diamond-coated tip having a spring constant of 42 N/m and a resonant frequency of 330 kHz. The V-shaped trench roughly resembles the tip profile and has a depth of 3 nm and a FWHM width of 30 nm approximately. Protuberances or ridges have been observed along the banks, the two sides near the groove mouth. Protuberances are partially the material plastically squeezed or deformed by the stresses generated by the tip during scratching and can also be formed by the pile-up of scratched debris or chips. It has been found that the depth and width of the scratched trenches increase logarithmically with the normal force[112].

The mechanical patterning of soft materials, including mica, polymers, and resist, by AFM tips has been more popular since it requires a lower tip force resulting in a longer tip lifetime. Trenches and pits with lateral sizes down to a few tens of nanometers can be obtained in mica substrate. Freshly cleaved mica is the most readily available surface with atomic-scale flatness and this makes it a promising substrate for nanoscale patterning and monitoring. It has been used

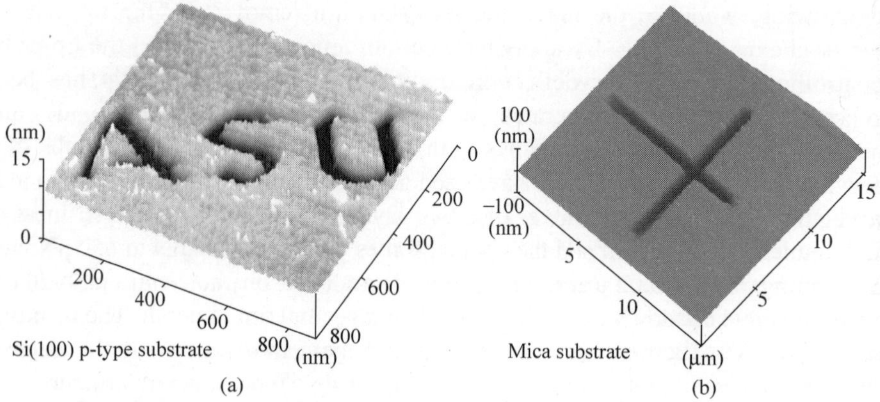

Figure 14.21 AFM images of grooves scratched by AFM at contact mode: (a) single scratch on Si(100) substrate with a normal force of 7 μN using diamond-coated tip, (b) five repeated scratches on mica substrate with a normal force of 5 μN using Si tip

as a substrate for patterning and observation of, DNA, RNA, protein and other bio and chemical materials[36, 113–115]. Both single and multiple scratches have been used to scratch trenches or grooves on mica surfaces with depths up to 1 μm. As shown in Fig. 14.21(b), a cross patterned trench on a mica substrate is created by five repeated scratches to have a depth of 25 nm and a mouth width of 300 nm, approximately. The groove is mechanically scratched by a TESP Si tip in a contact mode with a normal force of 5 μN. The TESP tip is pyramidal shaped with a tip height of 10 – 15 μm having a spring constant of 20 – 100 N/m and a resonant frequency of 240 – 280 kHz. For a freshly cleaved mica surface, the normal force to have a noticeable scratch should be larger than 100 nN, which is typical force threshold observed by other investigators [116, 117].

No debris was found outside the trenches, indicating that the material removing mechanism for multiple scratches is also dominated by atomic-scale abrasive wear due to sliding friction as those observed in single scratch[117]. During mica surface scratching, a top 0.2 nm thick layer, which is about the size of the molecular layer, is first removed. Then, the mica surface is removed layer by layer, sequentially, in which the layer thickness is about 1 nm[116]. With a proper design of the tip profile, nano- or micro-scale groove or channel with controlled profiles and patterns can be produced.

For polymer materials, most investigators have performed AFM scratch to study the deformation behavior and associated mechanical properties [118–121]. Figure 14.22 shows the mechanically scratched trenches on PMMA and PI (polyimide, Kapton VN) films, respectively. The PMMA film is prepared by depositing droplets of a 0.2 g solution of PMMA (Aldrich, M.W. 230,000) in 10 μL of acetone on a mica surface and letting the acetone slowly evaporate over a few days. The PMMA trench shown in Fig. 14.22(a) is scratched by a Si tip with a normal force of 17.5 μN in a contact mode. It possesses a V-shaped cross-section with ridges or bulges observed along the trench banks. The ridge is partially formed by the pile-up of debris, which is the material chips plowed from the trench and can be subsequently removed by dissolving them in solvents that do not alter the other parts of the film[119]. Also the ridge could be the material squeezed by the tip during scratch due to viscoplastic deformation, which is similar to those phenomena observed in nanoindentation of polymers. Except from the two end regions, the depth of the trench is gradually increases along the scratch direction, the arrow direction shown in the figure. The trench is 4 μm long and the depths are 150.0 nm, 190.6 nm, and 225.0 nm measured at the locations of approximately 1 μm, 2 μm, and 3 μm from the starting scratching position, respectively. The tip used is 110 μm long with a spring constant of 17.5 N/m and a resonant frequency of 210 kHz. The trench on the PI film is scratched by the same Si tip used for PMMA scratching but with a normal force of 8.5 μN. The depths of the PI trench are rather consistent and are 140.2 nm and 138.9 nm measured at the locations about 0.5 μm from the two ends. Similar to the PMMA trench, the PI trench also has sizable side ridges. Also it has been observed that at relatively high scratching forces, the plowed debris can cover the trench, which can not only greatly deteriorate the uniformity of the trench profile but also reduce the material removing rate. Trenches or grooves can be created by AFM tips in both tapping and contact modes. In the former, the trench is continuously carved by plowing forces. On the other hand, in the latter, the trench is formed by overlapping the indented holes. Kassavetis, Mitsakakis, and Logothetidis[121] have used an AFM tip in a tapping mode to pattern trenches on a PMMA film.

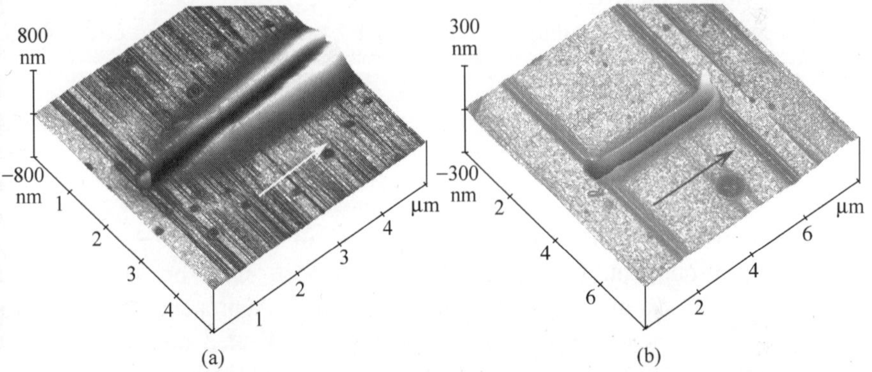

Figure 14.22 AFM images of trenches on polymer films by AFM using Si tip at contact mode: (a) one scratch on PMMA film with normal force of 17.5 μN, (b) one scratch on PI film with normal force of 8.5 μN

Normally a patterned polymer film made by mechanical scratching is used as a mask for the subsequent chemical etching process to obtain a final structure. This is a two-step process: mask patterning and subsequent etching. Koinuma and Uosaki[122] combined these two steps and developed an AFM tip induced electrochemical etching for material removing at an ambient temperature. Using an etchant of 10 mM H_2SO_4 solution, electrochemical dissolution of a single-crystalline Zn-doped p-GaAs(100) surface (act as an electrode) was accelerated by the scanning of a Si_3N_4 tip with a radius of 40 nm. At a potential of −0.05 V for 30 min and a tip force of 10 nN with a scan rate of 25 lines/s × 200 lines/image (100 × 100 nm^2 image taken in 8 s), a wedge groove with an 80 nm wide mouth and an 8 nm depth can be obtained. If the potential is increased to +0.05 V (0.1 V more positive potential), the groove depth is enhanced to ~ 18 nm. It has also been found that the depths of the modified or etched structures were dependent not on the scan rate but on the number of scans as well as on the electrode potential.

Recently, other energies, including the field-emission current originating from AFM tips, have been aided for material removing or cutting. Kim, Koo, and Kim[123] found that multi-walled carbon nanotubes of 30 nm in diameter on a Si substrate can be cut or broken by a conducting AFM tip with a negative bias. By scanning the AFM tip across the carbon tubes in a contact mode in air with 40% – 70% humidity, the tube can be cut, if the magnitude of the negative bias is higher than a threshold value. The threshold magnitude increases from –6 V to –8 V as the tip scanning speed increases from 0.1 μm/s – 1.0 μm/s. After cutting, it has been found that the inside of the cutting groove has been anodized by the negative bias voltage. In fact, an AFM tip with a negatively bias higher than a threshold can also cut or etch a graphite surface, which has a similar composition of carbon nanotubes. As the magnitude of the bias voltage increased, the depth of the etched graphite increased exponentially to reach 7.9 nm at a bias voltage of –10 V. Kim, Koo, and Kim[123] believed that the activation energy to break or to cut the atomic bonds in nanotubes (or graphite) is provided by the field-emission current from the negatively biased AFM tip.

14.6.5 Parallel Processing

One of the major challenges in the development of AFM nanofabrication is to increase its throughput. Extensive efforts have been made on using multiple probe arrays for parallel processing nanostructures. Approaches ranging from individual multifunction probes to independently activated array probes have been evaluated[124, 125]. For example, Minne et al.[126] have developed an expandable system to operate an array of 50 cantilevered probes in parallel at high speed for LO patterns. The oxide pattern over 1 cm^2 in size was then acting as a mask and transferred into Si substrate using KOH (potassium hydroxide) etching. IBM has extended this multiple-probe concept to data-storage applications. The extended system, called Millipede, uses large arrays (64 × 64) of AFM-type cantilevered tips to write, read, and erase data on very thin polymer films. The latest report on Millipede has indicated that the parallel indentation tracks can be achieved with spacing of 18 nm between tracks and 9 nm within a track, and depth of 1 nm leading to a storage density of more than 1 Tbit/in^2[127].

Extensive efforts have been made to enhance the Millipede-like system capability with emphasis on integrated MEMS systems, probe recording mechanisms, and media recording density. Rosenwaks et al.[128] reported on parallel AFM based writing in ferroelectric domains of $LiNbO_3$ and $RbTiOPO_4$, in which the writing speed of ferroelectric domain based devices is limited by both the physical processes in a single domain and the velocity of the scanning tip. Hagleitner, et al.[129] and Yang et al.[130] have developed tiny MEMS-based actuators and sensors to concurrently operate different probe arrays (up to 72×72) to achieve recording density at terabit per square inch and fast data manipulability or accessibility. These efforts on enhancing the parallel AFM-based recording technology should provide building blocks for the development of massively parallel TBN. Nevertheless, strong limitations, including the pattern uniformity and reliability of a large number of probes, represent the main weaknesses for this type of multi-probe lithography.

14.7 Dip-Pen Nanolithography (DPN)

As shown in Fig. 14.23(a), the AFM tip in DPN is coated with a thin film of ink molecules that can react with the substrate surface to create a chemical reaction, which can be controlled at the nanoscale level. A minute drop of ink is naturally condensed between the AFM probe and the substrate. The associated capillary transport from the probe towards the tip apex provides a resupply of new molecules for continuous writing, like a quill pen in writing. The molecules and substrates are chosen in order to have chemical affinity and favorable adhesion of

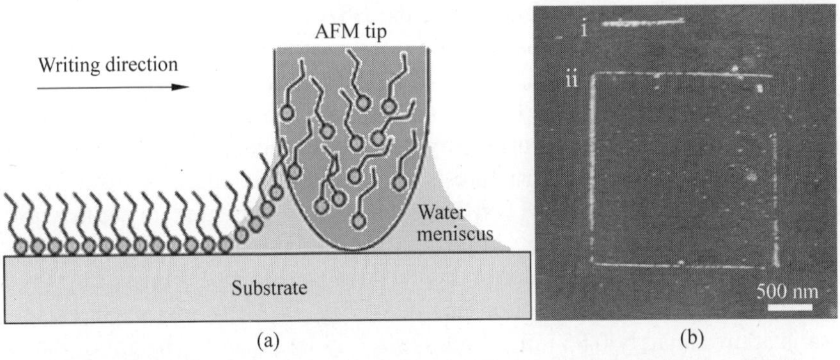

Figure 14.23 Nanostructures fabricated by dip-pen nanolithography (DPN): (a) schematic of DPN, (b) AFM image of Cu nanowires fabricated on mica surface, in which ascorbic acid was dropped onto freshly cleaved mica first, and then writing on mica surface with AFM tip adsorbed with $CuSO_4$ molecules (see color figure at the end of this book)

the deposited film. With the aid of the chemical induced forces associated with the tip, the manipulation of molecules becomes manageable. DPN has the special advantages in dealing with biological or chemical active materials. DPN has been used for generating molecule-based nanostructures on a wide variety of surfaces[131]. The technique has been used to create metal and semiconductor nanostructures[132–134] as well as biological[135, 136], CNT[137], and conducting polymer[138] arrays. Thus, in this section, the focus will be on the applications of DPN for the fabrication of biological or chemical active materials with subsequently self-assembly or chemical processes. The recent improvements in parallel processing are also included.

14.7.1 Biological-Based Nanostructures by DPN

A number of biological-ink materials, including DNA, RNA, virus, and protein, have been successfully used by DPN for patterning many nanostructures. For example, many biological arrays fabricated by DPN have become useful tools in proteomics and genomics, including probing gene expression, clinical-based diagnostic, studying protein profiling and screening of drag candidates[131, 139, 140]. Since the formation of immobilized biological structures by DPN is strongly dependent on the interaction between the ink and substrate, the biomolecules chosen should be biologically compatible with the substrate. It is always desirable that the patterned nanostructures can maintain their original bioactivities. As a result, it is essential that suitable modification of the adsorption and desorption of the biomolecular inks is made to ensure the biological integrity and functionality of the resulting patterns.

Lee et al.[139] also used DPN to directly print integrin $\alpha_v\beta_3$ and bovine serum albumin (BSA) nanoarrays on Au coated Si substrate. These nanoarrays provide a platform for investigating the molecular interaction between the integrin and vitronectin cell adhesion protein. Using the BSA nanoarrays as a control, it was further confirmed that the patterned integrin proteins retain their biological selectivity after surface immobilization. BSA biomolecules have also been patterned on the mica surface by DPN[36]. Figure 14.24(a) show a mesa-like BSA nanostructure directly written on the mica surface by AFM with a contact force of 5 nN. The square mesa-like BSA nanostructure is generated by scanning a 3 μm by 3 μm area at a scan rate of 1 Hz. Then the scan size is increased to 6 μm with an increased scan rate of 3 Hz while the image was recorded as shown in Fig. 14.24(a), in which the interior lighter area is the BSA film written by the AFM tip. As shown in the section profile of Fig. 14.24(b), the height of square mesa is approximately 0.95 nm, which is slightly less than the height of the BSA molecule backbone. This height difference is believed due to the applied contact force by the tip during scanning. The BSA molecules are believed to be flatly laid down to form a ML on the mica surface. Also, as shown in Fig. 14.24(a), the BSA molecules do not spread evenly in the periphery region. This may be due to the fact that the diffusion rate from the SBA solution to the mica surface is not fast enough to be spread wider and the molecules are self assembled into individual islands. It is expected that if the scanning or writing speed is slower, the mesa nanostructure can be more evenly formed. The BSA used has a molecular weight of 68,000 and is dissolved in water with a solution concentration of 2×10^{-4} M. It is one of the most widely studied proteins and is the most abundant protein in plasma and is a large globular protein with a good essential amino acid profile. BSA binds free fatty acids, other lipids and flavour compounds, which can alter the heat denaturation of the protein. It has been well characterized and the physical properties of this protein are well-known[141].

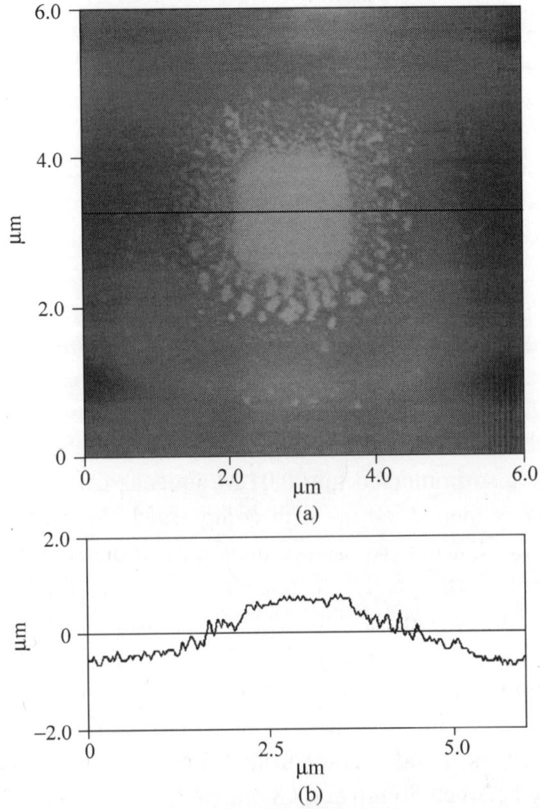

Figure 14.24 Mesa-like nanostructure of BSA on mica surface written by DPN with contact force of 5 nN: (a) AFM image, (b) cross-section profile along the black line shown in (a) (see color figure at the end of this book)

14.7.2 DPN of Chemical Materials

Both organic and inorganic nanostructures have been successfully patterned on different substrates by using DPN. The majority of DPN inks are organic materials, including thiols, silazanes, silanes, and alkynes. Typically, the thiol inks are written on the gold surface and their chemisorption is the driving force for the thiol ink transfer from the tip to the gold substrate[2]. These organic inks have been deposited on different substrates for making various nanostructures, which can be used as either the final functional structures or templates for subsequent processes. Alkylthiol inks such as ODT (1-octadecanethiol) and MHA (16-mercaptohexadecanoic acid) have been found to be very suitable for writing high resolution patterns on Au and mica surfaces. The closed-packed SAM can be formed by raster scanning an ODT-coated tip across the Au/mica surface ODT. The dot features can be formed by holding the tip at a fixed position for certain periods while ODT arrays and grids can be fabricated by either holding the tip stationary at one point or sweeping the tip for line scans. Hong, Zhu and Mirkin[142] demonstrated that dot and line patterns can be generated by multiple ink organic molecules with near perfect alignment and 5 nm spatial separation.

DPN has also been applied to inorganic materials, including metals, oxides, and magnetic compounds. In writing metallic nanostructures, the AFM tip can be coated with reducing or oxidizing regent ink molecules, which can react with the substrate surface, writing to form desired shapes. The substrate is then immersed into the oxidizing/reducing regent before writing the regent on it. Using this approach Tseng and Li[36] have fabricated several Cu nanostructures on a mica substrate. In their approach, freshly cleaved mica is first immersed in an aqueous ascorbic acid solution for a few minutes. After the rudimental water is removed by filter paper, the mica substrate is dried in a vacuum. Concurrently a Si_3N_4 cantilevered tip is also immersed into 0.01 M aqueous $CuSO_4$ for a few minutes and the cantilever is then dried up with compressed N_2 to remove the residual solvent from the tip. During patterning, the $CuSO_4$ molecules are written by the coated tip on the mica surface and Cu nanoparticles are formed after 40 – 50 minutes, in which the Cu^{2+} is deoxidized into Cu^0 by ascorbic acid. In DPN, the Si_3N_4 cantilevered tip is moved in the contact mode at a writing speed of 100 nm/s under 60% relative humidity at room temperature. The Cu nanostructures shown in Fig. 14.23(b) are imaged in the contact mode with a scan rate of 2 Hz. The height of the Cu nanowires is found to vary from 1.5 nm to 1.7 nm while their widths are approximately between 30 nm and 68 nm.

Moreover, DPN has been utilized to generate nanostructures by combining DPN with wet-etching and RIE techniques. In fabrication of Si structures, a three-step method has been developed. The DPN is first used to pattern MHA on an Au/Ti-layer-coated Si substrate. The MHA nanopatterns are used as etching resists for wet etching to generate Au structure patterns, which are then used as highly effective masks to fabricate Si nanostructures via RIE. Zhang et al.[143] reported that the smallest Au dots and narrowest Au lines obtained by this method are 35 nm (dot diameter) and 53 nm (line width), respectively.

14.7.3 Parallel Processing of DPN

Similar to AFM, DPN should also be capable of parallel processing with multiple probes to increase throughput. However, the tip in DPN is mainly used for ink material transfer for activating chemical or biological reactions on the substrate surfaces, unlike an AFM tip that is utilized for energy transfer between the tip and substrate. Thus the characteristics of DPN are different from AFM, so that the parallel processing strategies developed for AFM cannot be directly applied to DPN. For example, the DPN probe and its patterning procedure are quite different from that of AFM. Furthermore, the process of the molecule-based inking in DPN is less sensitive to tip-substrate contact force as compared to AFM. Consequently, in designing multiple probes, the soft and hard compatibility, array architecture, control strategy, and instrumentation requirements involved in DPN should be taken into consideration[144].

Recently, parallel DPN has been demonstrated by Salaita et al.[145] where they developed a 2D 55,000-pen array of AFM cantilevers to simultaneously pattern molecules across 1 cm^2 substrate areas at sub-100 nm resolution. The 55,000-pen array as shown in Fig. 14.25(a) involves a passive-pen array, where each pen is a duplication tool and a single-tip feedback system is needed. The passive-pen array is relatively easier to be implemented and operated than the active pens, in which each pen in the array can be independently actuated and used. Also the cost of passive-pen array is much less than the active pens, since fabrication constraints are minimal and the array design is conceptually simple. Using this 55,000-pen array a miniaturized replica of the face of the five-cent coin is generated by depositing 1-octadecanethiol on a gold-on-SiOx substrate followed with chemical etching. Figure 14.25(b) shows the miniaturized replica where the associated background is an optical micrograph of a representative region of the substrate on which approximately 55,000 duplicates are created[145].

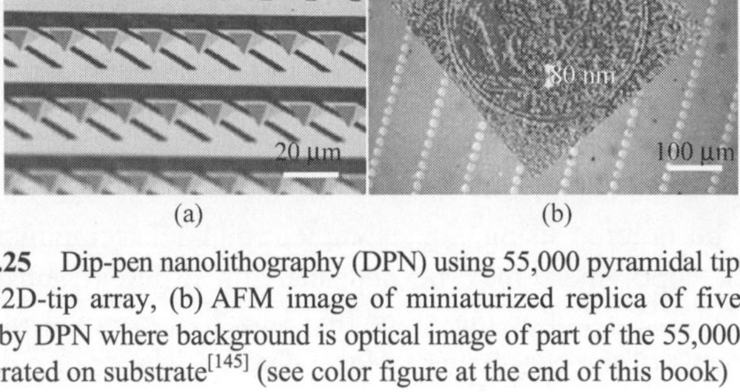

(a) (b)

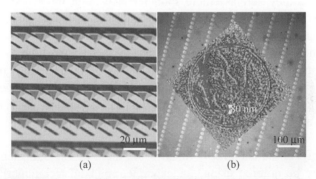

Figure 14.25 Dip-pen nanolithography (DPN) using 55,000 pyramidal tips: (a) SEM image of 2D-tip array, (b) AFM image of miniaturized replica of five-cent coin generated by DPN where background is optical image of part of the 55,000 duplicates were generated on substrate[145] (see color figure at the end of this book)

On the other hand, Bullen and Liu[146] have developed an active-pen array in which each pen is electrostatically actuated. Active-pen arrays offer the benefit of multiple shape and multiple ink flexibilities. Also, utilizing such arrays, one can prepare many nanostructures of differing feature size and shape in a single experiment. Although the active-pen array has been developed, much work needs to be done to increase the operation flexibility and probe density of the array.

14.8 Self-Assembly/Bottom-Up Approach

In this section, the bottom-up approaches for nanoscale fabrication and component integration are presented. Following an introduction of pattern formation by self-assembly, the self-organizing properties of biological molecules to template assembly of functional nanostructures are discussed. Then, the applications of externally-controlled force fields for discrete manipulation are addressed.

14.8.1 Pattern Formation and Transfer Mediated by Self- Assembly

It is envisaged that materials which spontaneously self-assemble at a substrate surface, with well defined nanostructures, may be exploited as nanoscale shadow masks or resists and should be attractive to NGL. Research efforts have been focused on self-assembly of a broad range of unconventional materials at technologically relevant substrates in order to facilitate pattern formation and transfer into the underlying supporting substrate. The self-assemblies of monolayers, protein layers, block copolymers, nanospheres, carbon nanotubes and nanowires have been developed for pattern formation and transfer.

SAMs of organic compounds on inorganic substrates are thermodynamically stable because they self assemble spontaneously with molecular ordering and tend to reject defects. A number of techniques have been successfully applied to large-area nanoscale (sub-100 nm) patterning of SAMs on a wide variety of substrates including microcontact printing, edge transfer lithography, dip-pen nanolithography and e-beam lithography[147, 148]. They have found applications in biotechnology, electrochemistry, molecular electronics and microelectronics.

Self-assembled block copolymers contain nanodomains with well defined periodicity arising from constrained nanophase separation of the polymer mixture[149]. The size, shape and chemical properties of these nanodomains (10 – 100 nm) can be chemically tuned while the location and orientation of the domains may be tailored using, for example, epitaxial techniques[149–151]. Thin films of block copolymers may be deposited on different substrates by spin casting techniques[152]. Following assembly, selective removal of the major or minor components of the copolymer to form discrete islands or porous structures on the underlying substrate is typically performed. These structures may then be used as a template or mask for further processing[153] and for fabrication of 20 nm silicon nanocrystals[154], for growth of GaAs-based quantum dots[152, 155], fabrication of 3D photonic band gap structures[156]. Figure 14.26 shows a fabrication process developed by Shin et al.[153] for assembling Cr dot arrays using a poly (styrene-b-methyl methacrylate) copolymer (upper pictures) and height images of tapping mode AFM of each step (lower pictures).

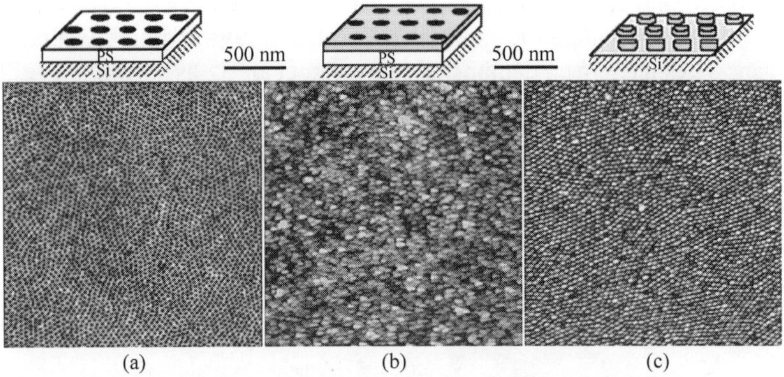

Figure 14.26 Fabrication process for Cr dot arrays: (a) nanoscopic holes in cross-linked polystyrene (PS) matrix following removal of minor component, (b) evaporated Cr onto the PS template, (c) removal of template to yield Cr nanodot array. The height range of AFM images is 10 nm[153] (see color figure at the end of this book)

Self-assembled carbon nanotubes and nanowires, have also been utilized as templates for fabrication of nanostructures. Single wall and multiwall carbon nanotubes have been used as shadow masks and direct contact masks, respectively, for metal evaporation and argon ion bombardment in the fabrication of electrodes with nanometer-size gaps and nanowires of various materials, respectively[157, 158]. However, completely removing the nanotubes following fabrication has proven to be difficult. A complimentary approach, to fabrication of metallic nanowires 15 – 20 nm in width with uniform cross section has been to employ vanadium-pentoxide (V_2O_5) fiber as an argon ion beam etch mask. Following fabrication, the fiber templates could be easily removed by dissolving in dilute acid[159, 160].

14.8.2 Templated Self-Assembly Using Biological Structures

Templated self-assembly based on the molecular recognition properties of biological molecules provides a good avenue for nanofabrication. The assembly information is programmed or encoded into the components, which then self-assemble according to that information.

Individual strands of DNA have been used to template the assembly of 1D gold nanoparticle arrays with close packed structures, where, Coulombic interactions between cationic ligand stabilized gold nanoparticles and anionic DNA were employed to drive the site selective localization and self-assembly of the nanoparticles at the DNA surface[161]. Parallel 1D and crossed 2D platinum nanowires arrays have also been fabricated by first using molecular-combed DNA to direct the assembly of positive metal ions at the DNA surface, followed by chemical reduction of the cations to yield 30 nm diameter nanowires[162]. Chemically modified DNA component tiles, comprising 4×4 DNA strands, have been successfully self-assembled into two lattice structures; nanoribbons and nanogrids, which were then employed to template the assembly of protein arrays and highly conductive, silver nanowires have been demonstrated by Yan et al.[163] as shown in Fig. 14.27. Schematics of the 4×4 DNA strand component tile and the self- assembled 2D nanogrids are shown in Figs. 14.27(a) and (b), respectively. The AFM images of self-assembled 2D lattices (nanogrids) displaying a square aspect ratio are shown in Figs. 14.27(c) and (d) with two different magnifications.

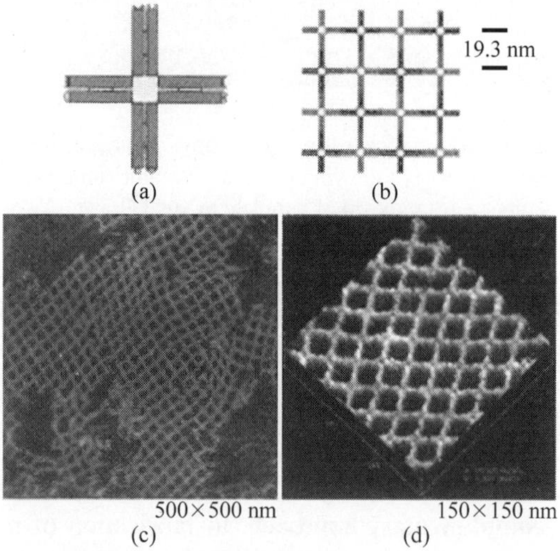

Figure 14.27 Self-assembly of 2D nano-grids with corrugated design: (a) schematic of 4×4 DNA strand component tile, (b) schematic of self-assembled 2D nano-grids, (c) AFM image of self-assembled 2D lattices (nano-grids) displaying a square aspect ratio, (d) surface plot of a magnified region from (c)[163] (see color figure at the end of this book)

14.8.3 Force Field Directed Self-Assembly

New technologies based on externally controlled force fields are under investigation for site-specific localization, positioning and integration of nanoscale inorganic materials. A number of self-assembly techniques based on externally controlled force fields, including those of a fluidic, magnetic or electric nature, are currently under investigation.

Fluidic flow as an approach for hierarchical self-assembly of 1D discrete semiconducting nanowires whereby each nanowire may be aligned using fluidic flow has been demonstrated by the Lieber group[164], while the external magnetic fields have also been applied to control the manipulation and self-assembly of isolated magnetic nanowires[165, 166]. The large magnetic shape anisotropy and high remnant magnetization parallel to the long axis of the nanowires enabled facile orientation and manipulation of the components to form self-assembled ordered structures, such as head-to-tail nanowire chains extending over hundreds of microns.

By imposing an external electric field, Thurn-Albrecht et al.[167] developed a method for the alignment of cylinder-forming of PS/PMMA (polystyrene-b-polymethylmethacrylate) copolymer patterns to create ultrahigh-density array of nanowires as shown in Fig. 14.28. If the copolymer is deposited between the two electrodes which is separated by a short distance of less than 1 μm, the electrostatic pressure added at the polymer/air interface causes an instability with well-defined wavelength inside the deposited polymer film. Gradually, the polymer columns spanned the gap between the two electrodes as shown in Fig. 14.28(a). After the minority component (PMMA) is removed, a hexagonal-array template between the electrodes is formed as shown in Fig. 14.28(b); dependent on the original composition, PS can also be the minor component with PMMA matrices. Also the dimensions and lateral density of the array could be determined by segmental interactions and the co-polymer molecular weight. The authors successfully grew over 1.93×10^{11} Co wires (14 nm in diameter) within just 1 cm^2 with the array period of 24 nm (Fig. 14.28(c)). Figure 14.28(d) shows the SEM image (on the left) of the corresponding array template using PS/PMMA (molecular weight = 42,000), while the SAXS (Small Angle X-ray Scattering) image of a single pore in a PS matrices. This technique might find many promising applications in broader areas, such as nanoreactors, templates for etching mask, and making nanoporous membranes.

Recently, Mesquida and Stemmer[168] reported self-assembly of 20 nm gold colloidal nanoparticles at electrostatically charged surfaces patterned by locally injecting electric charges into an insulating, thin fluorocarbon film using a conducting atomic force microscope tip to which voltage pulses were applied. The lateral charge pattern resolution was ~ 100 nm. The trapped charges generated electric fields above the fluorocarbon film attracting and trapping the oppositely charged gold nanoparticles at the film surface. Smith et al.[169] have reported self-assembly of gold nanowires using an electric-field assisted assembly technique to position individual nanowires, suspended in an isopropyl alcohol (IPA) dielectric medium, between electrode comb structures lithographically defined on a silicon chip.

In the future, the externally controlled force fields are expected to address the complex challenges associated with heterogeneous integration of pre-fabricated

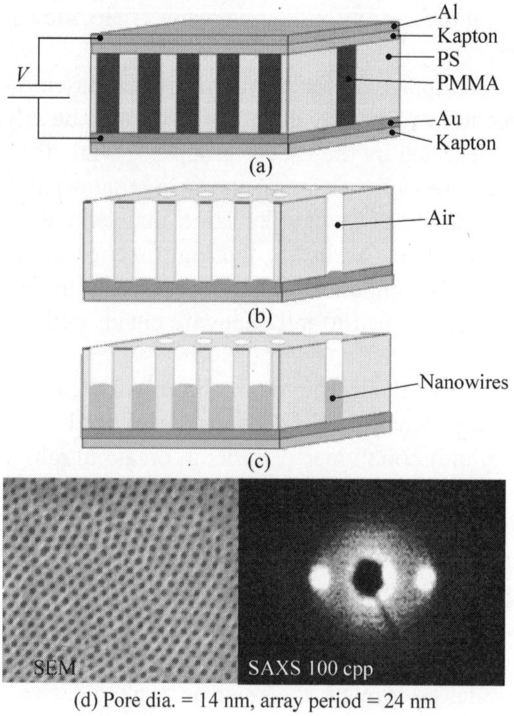

Figure 14.28 Nanopatterning by self assembly: (a) asymmetric diblock copolymer annealed above glass transition temperature of copolymer between two electrodes under applied electric field, forming hexagonal array of cylinders, (b) after removal of the minor component, a nanoporous film being formed, (c) by electrodeposition, nanowires being grown in porous template (after Thurn-Albrecht et al., 2000), (d) SEM and SAXS images of corresponding PS/PMMA template having array period of 24 nm and pore diameter of 14 nm (courtesy of T. P. Russell, UMass Amherst) (see color figure at the end of this book)

components at a nanoscale as functional building blocks for next-generation nanoelectronic and nanophotonics devices.

14.9 Concluding Remarks

Nanofabrication is an essential tool for the sustained evolution of electronic, photonic, biomedical, and microsystem technologies. Major technologies for both top-down and bottom-up approaches have been presented and discussed in this paper. Basically, the top-down approaches have evolved from the conventional semiconductor processes, which have been scrutinized by the industry for several decades, and proved to be reliable and productive, while the bottom-up approaches evolved from the fundamental chemical or biological syntheses. In commercialization, the top-down approaches are rather mature and will continue to encounter many the challenges as they approach their fundamental size limits, while the bottom-up approaches are in their infant stage and 'there's plenty of room at the bottom' as mentioned by Richard P. Feynman in 1959. The bottom-up approaches continue to build or assemble larger structures until they are no longer economically possible.

Three key top-down processes are addressed: electron beam lithography (EBL), ion-beam lithography (IBL), and nanoimprinting lithography (NIL). The associated principles, procedures, achievements and potential for each technique are presented. In EBL and IBL, two principle techniques: ① projection printing and ② direct writing, are examined, while, in NIL, the strengths and weaknesses of each imprinting technique are assessed and the current and potential capabilities have also been deliberated. The three different methods belonging to the SPML family: scanning tunneling microscopy (STM), atomic force microscopy (AFM), and dip-pen nanolithography (DPN) are evaluated individually. In self-assembly processing, applications of conventional and nonconventional biological materials for nanolithography are first introduced. Spontaneous self-assembling or self-organizing of biological molecules for templated assembly of functional nano-structures is then described. Manipulation or assembly with the aid of externally controlled forces for making nanocomponents is also presented.

In both EBL and IBL, a wide variety of equipment is available. While the equipment for projection printing is still largely under development, the direct-writing approach is a somewhat mature technology, mainly using a finely-focused Gaussian beam. The direct writing approach is flexible in making a variety of nanodevices with critical dimensions down to 10 nm. The direct-writing techniques will continue to play a major role in prototyping of nanostructures and be the de facto technique in high resolution mask-making for other lithographic processes. On the other hand, by considering the throughput, projection printing should have potential to be the most probable method among the next generation lithography (NGL) techniques for the semiconductor industry, although the prototype systems surveyed have indicated that further fine-tuning and improvement in their resolution and precision are needed. Particularly, the accuracy of the stitching scheme requires further refining, and resists with higher sensitivity and better processing characteristics need to be developed. It is also critical that projection writing should demonstrate the system level integrity to be included in next generation lithography for the semiconductor industry. The issues involved in enabling NIL for mass production, especially for NGL, are also discussed; potential remedies for some of these issues or hurdles have been suggested and elaborated.

The SPM-based techniques has been a vital alternative for nanofabrication, because of their low cost and potential to reach a resolution that may exceed those of other common lithographic processes, including EBL, IBL, and NIL presented. Taking also into account the possibility of imaging in real time on the processed area and the variety of possible approaches, SPM based techniques appear to be some of the most promising candidates for device fabrication at the nanoscale. However, due to its serial nature SPM-based nanofabrication has been extremely favored for applications in making prototypes. In the future, to increase the throughput of SPM-based techniques, a fully automated system with a robust parallel processing strategy to improve productivity (or throughput) as well as reliability (or reproducibility) is needed. Furthermore, better lithographic schemes that exploit the particular characteristics of STM, AFM, and DPN are also required to be developed and new applications in nanofabrication should be explored. Eventually, the SPM lithographic family will be one of the most popular methodologies used for nanoscale fabrication.

One of the common challenges for all the direct-writing techniques including, EBL, IBL, and SPM-based techniques, is to downscale the feature size while maintaining a high throughput. To increase the throughput and the ability to be used in production, the writing rate of the existing systems has to be improved. A variable-diameter beam system should be developed to provide multi-resolution writing to cope with different accuracy or tolerance requirements. It is ideal that the beam diameter can be continuously changed in situ. This type of system has been available for many macroscale fabrication processes[23]. With this system, a larger beam can be used for roughing 'cut' (writing) to increase the writing rate in regions where only lower resolution is needed. Once the two-beam system with improved automation is developed, it can be a vital candidate to become the mainstream tool for the future nanofabrication industry.

For self-assembly, the critical challenge in the fabrication of future nanoscale systems, which will employ molecular scale materials as functional building blocks, is the lack of suitable integration tools that enable site-specific localizations and integration of components on technologically relevant substrates. To provide a solution to this fabrication bottleneck, researchers have been investigating novel approaches for assembling and self-assembling nanocomponents. To date, much research has focused on the development of unconventional 'bottom-up' self-assembly routes, compatible with silicon processing techniques, as alternatives to replace or augment high resolution lithography-based methods. Self-assembly is a promising approach for formation of complex component architectures and offers a number of advantages for fabrication of future nanoscale devices, such as spatial control at the nanometer length-scale, parallel self-assembly mechanisms, and the tendency towards self-correction and defect minimization.

Finally, it is believed that in the foreseeable future, the techniques in both the top-down and bottom-up approaches presented in this paper will co-exist and be complementary to each other. This is simliar to the current situation: the batch and continuous systems are co-existing and complementary to each other. However, the major challenge will be how to integrate both approaches to build multiscale architectures or multi-resolution systems. Eventually in the post-nanofabrication or post-miniaturization era, both the top-down and bottom-up approaches will have to cross each others boundaries, i.e., if the top-down technique needs to be successful, it has to integrate with its counterpart in the bottom-up side, and vice versa. A wide variety of applications of nanofabrication have been presented. Many others from materials to energy and from cosmetics to health care all look promising. Nanofabrication will be a key technology in the 21st century and will have a revolutionary impact on every aspect of the manufacturing industry. Tremendous challenges and opportunities await for us to explore.

Acknowledgements

The first author gratefully acknowledges the support for this study by the US National Science Foundation under Grant Nos DMI-0002466, CMS-0115828 and DMI-0423457 and by Pacific Technology LLC of Phoenix USA. Special thanks are to Tsinghua University and Taiwan University for providing funding and help for the first author on sabbatical in Beijing and Taipei, respectively, in writing this manuscript. The support and encouragement from H. Abed of Faculté des Sciences de Luminy (France), Dr. Wilhelm H. Bruenger of Fraunhofer Institute in Berlin (Germany), Professor Jürgen Brugger of Swiss Federal Institute of Technology (Switzerland), Dr. Daisuke Fujita of National Institute for Materials Science (Japan), Professor Hiroshi Iwasaki of Osaka University (Japan), Professor M. F. Luo of Taoyuan Central University, Professor Shinji Matsui of Himeji Institute of Technology (Japan), Professor T. P. Russell of University of Massachusetts at Amherst (USA), Professor Jun-ichi Shirakashi of Tokyo University of Agriculture and Technology (Japan) and Professors Xiong-Ying Ye and Zhao-Ying Zhou of Tsinghua University (China) should be specifically acknowledged.

References

[1] Tseng A. A., (2008), "Nanofabrication: Fundamentals and Applications", World Scientific, Singapore

[2] Tseng A. A., A. Notargiacomo, (2005), "Nanoscale fabrication by nonconventional approaches". *J. Nanoscience & Nanotechnology*, **5**: 683 – 702

[3] Tseng A. A., K. Chen, C. D. Chen, K. J. Ma, (2003), "Electron beam lithography in nanoscale fabrication: recent development". *IEEE Trans. Electronics Packaging Manufacturing*, **26**: 141 – 149

[4] Dhaliwal R. S., W. A. Enichen, S. D. Golladay, R. A. Kendal, J. E. Lieberman, H. C. Pfeiffer, D. J. Pinckney, C. F. Robinson, J. D. Rockrohr, W. Stickle, E. V. Tressler, (2001), "PREVAIL: Electron projection technology approach for next-generation lithography". *IBM J. Res. & Dev.*, **45**: 615 – 638

[5] Koba F., T. Tsuchida, H. Sakaue, K. Koike, J. Yamamoto, N. Iriki, H. Yamashita, S. Kageyama, T. Nasuno, E. Soda, K. Takeda, H. Kobayashi, F. Shoji, H. Okamura, Y.

Matsubara, H. Arimoto, (2005), EPL performance in 65-nm node metallization technology and beyond. Emerging Lithographic Technologies IX. Progress in Biomedical Optics and Imaging, *Proceedings of SPIE*, **5751**: 501 – 508

[6] Romeo C., P. Cantu, D. Henry, H. Takekoshi, N. Hirayanagi, K. Suzuki, M. McCallum, H. Fujita, T. Takikawa, M. Hoga, (2005), Device based evaluation of electron projection lithography. Emerging Lithographic Technologies IX. Progress in Biomedical Optics and Imaging, *Proceedings of SPIE*, **5751**: 699 – 706

[7] Tseng A. A., C. D. Chen, C. S. Wu, R. E. Diaz, M. Watts, (2002), Electron-beam lithography of microbowtie structures for next generation optical probe. *J. Microlithography, Microfabrication, and Microsystems*, **1**: 123 – 135

[8] Pain L., M. Jurdit, Y. Laplanche, J. Todeschini, H. Leininger, S. Tourniol, R. Faure, X. Bossy, R. Palla, A. Beverina, M. Broekaart, F. Judong, K. Brosselin, L. Depoyan, Y. Le Friec, F. Leverd, V. De Jonghe, E. Josse, O. Hinsinger, P. Brun, D. Henry, M. Woo, P. Stolk, B. Tavel, F. Arnaud, (2004), 65 nm device manufacture using shaped E-beam lithography. *Jpn J. Applied Physics*, Part 1, **43**: 3755 – 3761

[9] Tseng A. A., (2005), Recent developments in nanofabrication using ion projection lithography. *Small*, **1**: 594 – 608

[10] Tseng A. A., (2005), Recent developments in nanofabrication using focused ion beams. *Small*, **1**: 924 – 939

[11] Kaesmaier R., A. Ehrmann, H. Löschner, (2001), Ion projection lithography: status of tool and mask development. *Microelectronic Eng.*, **57** – **58**: 145 – 153

[12] Pendharkar S. V., J. C. Wolfe, H. R. Rampersad, Y. L. Chau, D. L. Licon, M. D. Morgan, W. E. Horne, R. C. Tiberio, J. N. Randall, (1995), Reactive ion etching of silicon stencil masks in the presence of an axial magnetic field. *J. Vac. Sci. Technol. B*, **13**(6): 2588 – 2592

[13] Volland B., F. Shi, H. Heerlein, I. W. Rangelow, P. Hudek, I. Kostic, E. Cekan, H. Vonach, H. Loeschner, C. Horner, G. Stengl, H. Buschbeck, M. Zeininger, A. Bleeker, J. Benschop, (2000), Fabrication of open stencil masks with asymmetric void ratio for the ion projection lithography space charge experiment. *J. Vac. Sci. Technol. B*, **18**(6): 3202 – 3206

[14] Loeschner H., G. Stengl, H. Buschbeck, A. Chalupka, G. Lammer, E. Platzgummer, H. Vonach, P. W. H. de Jager, R. Kaesmaier, A. Ehrmann, S. Hirscher, A. Wolter, A. Dietzel, R. Berger, H. Grimm, B. D. Terris, W. H. Bruenger, G. Gross, O. Fortagne, D. Adam, M. Böhm, H. Eichhorn, R. Springer, J. Butschke, F. Letzkus, P. Ruchhoeft, J. C. Wolfe, (2003), *JM3*, **2**: 34 – 48

[15] Ngo V. V., B. Akker, K. N. Leung, I. Noh, K. L. Scott, S. Wilde, (2003), Demonstrations of electronic pattern switching and 10× pattern demagnification in a maskless microion-beam reduction lithography system. *J. Vac. Sci. Technol. B*, **21**: 2297 – 2303

[16] Melngailis J., A. A. Mondelli, I, L. Berry, R. Mohondro, (1998), A review of ion projection lithography. *J. Vac. Sci. Technol. B*, **16**: 927 – 957

[17] Arshak K., M. Mihov, A. Arshak, D. McDonagh, D. Sutton, (2004), Focused ion beam lithography-overview and new approaches. Proceedings of the International Conference on Microelectronics. *IEEE. Solid-State Circuits Society*, **24 II**: 459 – 462

[18] Tseng A. A., (2004), Recent developments in micromilling using focused ion beam technology. *J. Micromech. Microeng*, **14**: R15 – R34

[19] Reyntjens S., R. Puers, (2001), A review of focused ion beam applications in microsystem technology. *J. Micromech. Microeng*, **11**: 287 – 300

[20] Tseng A. A., (2007), Fabrication of nanoscale structures using ion beams. *Focused Ion Beam Systems: Basics and Applications*, Ed., N. Yao, Cambridge University, Cambridge, UK, 187 – 214

[21] Tseng A. A., B. Leeladharan, B. Li, I. A. Insua, C. D. Chen, (2003), Fabrication and modeling of microchannel milling using focused ion beam. *Int. J. Nanoscience*, **2**: 375 – 379

[22] Melngailis J., (2001), Applications of ion microbeams lithography and direct processing. Helbert J N, ed. Handbook of VLSI Lithography, 2nd ed. Park Ridge, NJ: Noyes, 791 – 855

[23] He Z., J. G. Zhou, A. A. Tseng, (2000), Feasibility study of chemical liquid deposition based solid freeform fabrication. *Materials and Design*, **21**: 83 – 92

[24] Matsui S., T. Kaito, J. Fujita, M. Komuro, K. Kanda, Y. Haruyama, (2000), Three-dimensional nanostructure fabrication by focused-ion-beam chemical vapor deposition. *J. Vac. Sci. Technol. B*, **18**: 3181 – 3184

[25] Watanabe K., T. Morita, R. Kometani, T. Hoshino, K. Kondo, K. Kanda, Y. Haruyama, T. Kaito, J. Fujita, M. Ishida, Y. Ochiai, T. Tajima, S. J. Matsui, (2004), Nanoimprint using three-dimensional microlens mold made by focused-ion-beam chemical vapor deposition, *Vac. Sc. Technol.*, B. **22**: 22 – 26

[26] Tseng A. A., M. Tanaka, (2001), Advanced deposition techniques for freeforming metal and ceramic parts, *Rapid Prototyping J.* **7**: 6 – 17

[27] Chou S. Y., P. R. Krauss, (1997), Imprint lithography with sub-10 nm feature size and high throughput. *Microelectronic Eng.*, **35**: 237 – 240

[28] Choi B. J., S. V. Sreenivasan, S. Johnson, M. Colburn, C. G. Wilson, (2001), Design of orientation stages for step and flash imprint lithography. *Precision Eng.*, **25**: 192 – 199

[29] Resnick D. J., T. C. Bailey, W. J. Dauksher, D. Mancini, K. J. Nordquist, E. Ainley, K. Gehoski, J. H. Baker, S. Johnson, M. Meissl, S. V. Sreenivasan, J. G. Ekerdt, C. G. Willson, (2002), High resolution templates for step and flash imprint lithography. Proceedings of SPIE, *Int. Society Optical Eng.*, **4688**: 205 – 213

[30] Bailey T., B. Smith, B. J. Choi, M. Colburn, M. Meissl, S. V. Sreenivasan, J. G. Ekerdt, C. G. J. Willson, (2001), *Vac. Sc. Technol.*, B. **19**: 2806 – 2810

[31] Chou S. Y., C. Keimel, J. Gu, (2002), Ultrafast and direct imprint of nanostructures in silicon. *Nature*, **417**: 835 – 837

[32] Xia Q., C. Keimel, H. Ge, Z. Yu, W. Wu, S. P. Chou, (2003), Ultrafast patterning of nanostructures in polymers using laser assisted nanoimprint lithography, *Appl. Phys. Lett.* **83**: 4417 – 4419

[33] Gao J. X., M. B. Chan-Park, D. Z. Xie, Y. H. Yan, W. X. Zhou, B. K. A. Ngoi, C. Y. Yue, (2004), UV embossing of sub-micrometer patterns on biocompatible polymeric films using a focused ion beam fabricated tin mold. *Chem. Mater.*, **16**: 956 – 958

[34] Lee N., Y. Kim, S. Kang, J. Hong, (2004), Fabrication of metallic nano-stamper and replication of nano-patterned substrate for patterned media. *Nanotech.*, **15**: 901 – 906

[35] Binnig G., H. Rohrer, C. Gerber, E. Weibel, (1982), Surface studies by scanning tunneling microscopy. *Phys. Rev. Lett.*, **49**: 57 – 61

[36] Tseng A. A., Z. Li, (2007), Manipulations of atoms and molecules by scanning probe microscopy. *J. Nanoscience & Nanotechnology.*, **7**(8): 2582 – 2595

[37] Wissendanger R., (1998), Scanning Probe Microscopy and Spectroscopy Methods and Applications, Cambridge Univ. Press, Cambridge, UK.

[38] Bartels L., G. Meyer, K. H. Rieder, (1997), Basic steps of lateral manipulation of single atoms and diatomic clusters with a scanning tunneling microscope tip. *Phys. Rev. Lett.*, **79**: 697 – 700

[39] Eigler D. M., E. K. Schweizer, (1990), Positioning single atoms with a scanning tunneling microscope. *Nature*, **344**: 524 – 526

[40] Crommie M. F., C. P. Lutz, D. M. Eigler, (1993), Confinement of electrons to quantum corrals on a metal surface. *Science*, **262**: 218 – 220

[41] Eigler D. M., C. P. Lutz, W. E. Rudge, (1991), An atomic switch realized with the scanning tunnelling microscope. *Nature*, **352**: 600 – 603

[42] Lyo I. W., P. Avouris, (1991), Field-induced nanometer- to atomic-scale manipulation of silicon surfaces with the STM. *Science*, **253**: 173 – 176

[43] Shen T. C., C. Wang, G. C. Abeln, J. R. Tucker, J. W. Lyding, P. Avouris, R. E. Walkup, (1995), Atomic-scale desorption through electronic and vibrational-excitation mechanisms. *Science*, **268**: 1590 – 1592

[44] Stroscio J. A., D. M. Eigler, (1991), Atomic and molecular manipulation with the scanning tunneling microscope. *Science*, **254**: 1319 – 1326

[45] Lorente N., H. Ueba, (2005), CO dynamics induced by tunneling electrons: differences on Cu(110) and Ag(110). *European Physical J. D.*, **35**: 341 – 348

[46] Gimzewski J. K., C. Joachim, (1999), Nanoscale science of single molecules using local probes. *Science*, **283**: 1683 – 1688

[47] Stroscio J. A., E. W. Hudson, S. R. Blankenship, R. J. Celotta, A. P. Fein, (2002), A facility for nanoscience research: an overview. Nanostructure Science, Metrology and Technology, *Proceedings of SPIE.*, **4608**: 112 – 115

[48] Moresco F., G. Meyer, K. H. Rieder, H. Tang, A. Gourdon, C. Joachim, (2001), Low temperature manipulation of big molecules in constant height mode. *App. Phys. Lett.*, **78**: 306 – 308

[49] Alivisatos A. P., (2004), The use of nanocrystals in biological detection. *Nature Biotechnology*, **22**: 47 – 52

[50] Schmid G., (2001), Nanoclusters-building blocks for future nanoelectronic devices. Adv. *Engg. Mater.*, **3**: 737 – 743

[51] Lee T. H., R. M. Dickson, (2004), Nanocomputing with nanoclusters. *Optics & Photonic News*, **15**: 22 – 27

[52] Chey S. J., L. Huang, J. H. Weaver, (1998), Manipulation and writing with Ag nanocrystals on Si(111)-7×7. *Appl. Phys. Lett.*, **72**: 2698 – 2700

[53] Chey S. J., L. Huang, J. H. Weaver, (1999), Interface bonding and manipulation of Ag and Cu nanocrystals on Si(111)-(7×7)-based surfaces. *Phys. Rev.*, B, **59**: 16033 – 16041

[54] Upward M. D., P. Moriarty, P. H. Beton, S. H. Baker, C. Binns, K. Edmonds, (1997), Measurement and Manipulation of Mn clusters on clean and fullerene terminated

Si(111)-7 × 7. *Appl. Phys. Lett.*, **70**: 2114 – 2116

[55] Butcher M. J., F. H. Jones, P. H. Beton, (2000), Growth and modfication of Ag islands on hydrogen terminated Si(100) surfaces. *J. Vac. Sci. Technol.*, B, **18**: 13 – 15

[56] Radojkovic P., M. Schwartzkopff, T. Garbrei, E. Hartmann, (1998), STM-assisted manipulation of Ag nanoparticles, *Appl. Phys.*, A, **66**: S701 – S705

[57] Hartmann E., M. Enachescu, P. Radojkovic, M. Schwartzkopff, F. Koch, (1996), Imaging and manipulation properties of nanoparticles in scanning tunneling microscopy. *Nanotechnol.*, **7**: 376 – 380

[58] Durston P. J., R. E. Palmer, J. P. Wilcoxon, (1998), Manipulation of passivated gold clusters on graphite with the scanning tunneling microscope. *Appl. Phys. Lett.*, **72**: 176 – 178

[59] Sartale S. D., K. L. Lin, C. I. Chiang, C. C. Kuo, M. F. Luo, (2006), Engineering patterns of Co nanoclusters on thin film Al_2O_3/NiAl(100) using STM manipulation techniques. *Appl. Phys. Lett.*, **89**: 063118: 1 – 3

[60] Tseng A. A., S. D. Sartale, M. F. Luo, C. C. Kuo, (2008), Atom, molecule, and nanocluster manipulations for nanostructure fabrication using scanning probe microscopy. Nanofabrication: Fundamentals and Applications, Chapter. 1, A. A. Tseng, Ed., World Scientific, Singapore

[61] Ohgi T., H. Y. Sheng, H. Nejoh, (1998), Au particle deposition onto self-assembled monolayers of thiol and dithiol molecules. *Appl. Surf. Sci.*, **130 – 132**: 919 – 924

[62] Rolandi M., K. Scott, E. G. Wilson, F. C. Meldrum, (2001), Manipulation and immobilization of alkane-coated gold nanocrystals using scanning tunneling microscopy. *J. Appl. Phys.*, **89**: 1588 – 1594

[63] Ringger M., H. R. Hidber, R. Schlogel, P. Oelhafen, H. J. Guntherodt, (1985), Nanometer lithography with the scanning tunneling microscope. *Appl. Phys. Lett.*, **46**: 832 – 834

[64] Staufer U., R. Wiesendanger, L. Eng, L. Rosenthaler, H. R. Hidber, H. J. Guntherodt, (1987), Nanometer scale structure fabrication with the scanning tunneling microscope. *Appl. Phys. Lett.*, **51**: 244 – 246

[65] Dagata J. A., J. H. Schneir, H. Harary, C. J. Evans, M. T. Postek, J. Bennett, (1990), Modification of hydrogen-passivated silicon by a scanning tunneling microscope operating in air. *Appl. Phys. Lett.*, **56**: 2001 – 2003

[66] McCord M. A., R. F. W. Pease, (1988), Lift-off metallization using poly(methyl methacrylate) exposed with a scanning tunneling microscope. *J. Vac. Sci. Technol.*, B, **6**: 293 – 296

[67] Dobisz E. A., C. R. K. Marrian, (1991), Sub-30 nm lithography in a negative electron beam resist with a vacuum scanning tunneling microscope. *Appl. Phys. Lett.*, **58**: 2526 – 2528

[68] Muller H. U., C. David, B. Volkel, M. Grunze, (1995), Nanostructuring of alkanethiols with ultrasharp field emitters. *J. Vac. Sci. Technol.* B, **13**: 2846 – 2849

[69] Perkins F. K, E. A. Dobisz, S. L. Brandow, J. M. Calvert, J. E. Kosakowsky, C. R. K. Marrian, (1996), Fabrication of 15 nm wide trenches in si by vacuum scanning tunneling microscope lithography of an organosilane self-assembled film and reactive ion etching. *Appl. Phys. Lett.*, **68**: 550 – 552

[70] Mamin H. J., S. Chiang, H. Birk, P. H. Guethner, D. Rugar, (1991), Gold deposition from a scanning tunneling microscope tip. *J. Vac. Sci. Technol. B*, **9**: 1398 – 1402

[71] Houel A., D. Tonneau, N. Bonnail, H. Dallaporta, V. I. Safarov, (2002), Direct patterning of nanostructures by field-induced deposition from a scanning tunneling microscope tip. *J. Vac. Sci. Technol B*, **20**: 2337 – 2345

[72] Fujita D., K. Onishi, T. Kumakura, (2003), *Jpn. J. Appl. Phys. Part 1*, **42**: 4773 – 4776

[73] Mamin H. J., P. H. Guethner, D. Rugar, (1990), *Phys. Rev. Lett.*, **65**: 2418 – 2421

[74] Pai W. W., J. Zhang, J. F. Wendelken, R. J. Warmak, (1997), Magnetic nanostructures fabricated by scanning tunneling microscope-assisted chemical vapor deposition. *J. Vac. Sci. Technol B*, **15**: 785 – 787

[75] Schoffel U. R., H. Rauscher, R. J. Behm, (2003), Scanning tunneling microscope mediated nanostructure fabrication from GeH_4 on Si(111)-(7×7). *Appl. Phys. Lett.*, **83**: 3794 – 3796

[76] Rauscher H., F. Behrendt, R. J. Behm, (1997), Studies of field related effects in the fabrication process on graphite using a scanning tunneling microscope. *J. Vac. Sci. Technol B*, **15**: 1373 – 1381

[77] Schindler W., D. Hofmann, J. Kirschner, (2000), Nanoscale electrodeposition: a new route to magnetic nanostructures. *J. Appl. Phys.*, **87**: 7007 – 7009

[78] Mitsui T., E. Hill, E. Ganz, (1999), Nanolithography by selective chemical vapor deposition with an atomic hydrogen resist. *J. Appl. Phys.*, **85**: 522 – 524

[79] Adams D. P., T. M. Mayer, B. S. Swartzentruber, (1996), Selective area growth of metal nanostructures. *Appl. Phys. Lett.*, **68**: 2210 – 2212

[80] Li N., T. Yoshinobu, H. Iwasaki, (1998), *Jpn. J. Appl. Phys*. Part 2, **37**: L995 – 998

[81] Fujita S., S. Maruno, H. Watanabe, M. Ichikawa, (1996), Nanostructure fabrication using the selective thermal desorption of SiO_2 induced by electron beams. *Appli. Phys. Lett.*, **69**: 638 – 640

[82] Iwasaki H., T. Yoshinobu, K. Sudoh, (2003), Nanolithography on SiO_2/Si with a scanning tunnelling microscope. *Nanotechnology*, **14**: R55 – R62

[83] Yau S., K. Kaji, K. Itaya, (1995), Electrochemical etching of Si(001) in NH_4F solutions: initial stage and {111} microfacet formation. *Appl. Phys. Lett.*, **66**: 766 – 768

[84] Kaneshiro C., T. Okumura, (1997), Nanoscale etching of GaAs surfaces in electrolytic solutions by hole injection from a scanning tunneling microscope tip. *J. Vac. Sci. Technol B*, **15**: 1595 – 1598

[85] Tseng A. A., A. Notargiacomo, T. P. Chen, (2005), Nanofabrication by scanning probe microscope lithography: a review, *J. Vac. Sci. Technol. B*, **23**: 877 – 894

[86] Oyabu N., O. Custance, I. Yi, Y. Sugawara, S. Morita, (2003), Mechanical vertical manipulation of selected single atoms by soft nanoindentation using near contact atomic force microscopy. *Physical Rev. Lett.*, **90**: 176102/1 – 4

[87] Kawai S., H. Kawakatsu, (2006), Atomically resolved amplitude modulation dynamic force microscopy with a high-frequency and high-quality factor cantilever. *App. Phys. Lett.*, **89**: 23113:1 – 3

[88] Nishi R., D. Miyagawa, Y. Seino, Y Insook, S. Morita, (2006), Non-contact atomic force microscopy study of atomic manipulation on an insulator surface by nanoindentation. *Nanotechnology*, **17**: S142 – S147

[89] Ritort F., (2006), Single-molecule experiments in biological physics: methods and applications. *J. Phys: Condensed Matter*, **18**: R531 – R583

[90] Chyan C. L., F. C. Lin, H. Peng, J. M. Yuan, C. H. Chang, S. H. Lin, G. Yang, (2004), Reversible mechanical unfolding of single ubiquitin molecules. *Biophysical J.*, **87**: 3995 – 4006

[91] Schaefer D. M., R. Reifenberger, A. Patil, R. P. Andres, (1995), Fabrication of two-dimensional arrays of nanometer-size clusters with the atomic force microscope. *Appl. Phys. Lett.*, **66**: 1012

[92] Junno T., K. Deppert, L. Montelius, L. Samuelson, (1995), Controlled manipulation of nanoparticles with an atomic force microscope. *App. Phys. Lett.*, **66**: 3627 – 3629

[93] Martin M., L. Roschier, P. Hakonen,Ü. Parts, M. Paalanen, B. Schleicher, E. I. Kauppinen, (1998), Manipulation of Ag nanoparticles utilizing noncontact atomic force microscopy. *App. Phys. Lett.*, **73**: 1505 – 1507

[94] Junno T., S. Anand, K. Deppert, L. Montelius, L. Samuelson, (1995), Contact mode atomic force microscopy imaging of nanometer-sized particles. *App. Phys. Lett.*, **66**: 3295 – 3297

[95] Junno T., S. B. Carlsson, H. Xu, L. Montelius, L. Samuelson, (1998), Fabrication of quantum devices by Ångstörm-level manipulation of nanoparticles with an atomic force microscope. *App. Phys. Lett.*, **72**: 548 – 550

[96] Jennette J., A. M. Ramson, R. A. J. Janssen, D. O'Mahony, C. F. J. Flipse, (2002), "Measurement and Manipulation of a conducting molecule." 7th Int. Conf. on Nanometer-Scale Science and Technology and 21st European Conf. on Surface Science, 2

[97] Decossas S., F. Mazen, T. Baron, G. Bremond, A. Souifi, (2003), Atomic force microscopy nanomanipulation of silicon nanocrystals for nanodevice fabrication. *Nanotechnology*, **14**: 1272 – 1278

[98] Majumdar A., P. I. Oden, J. P. Carrejo, L. A. Nagahara, J. J. Graham, J. Alexander, (1992), *Appl. Phys. Lett.*, **61**: 2293 – 2295

[99] Davidsson P., A. Lindell, T. Makela, M. Paalanen, J. Pekola, (1999), Nano-lithography by electron exposure using an atomic force microscope. *Microelectron. Eng.*, **45**: 1 – 8

[100] Ishibashi M., S. Heike, H. Kajiyama, Y. Wada, T. Hashizume, (1998), Characteristics of scanning-probe lithography with a current-controlled exposure system. *Appl. Phys. Lett.*, **72**: 1581 – 1583

[101] Mamin H. J., (1996), Thermal writing using a heated atomic force microscope tip. *Appl. Phys. Lett.*, **69**: 433 – 435

[102] Stievenard D., B. Legrand, (2006), Silicon surface nano-oxidation using scanning probe microscopy. *Progress in Surf. Sci.*, **81**: 112 – 140

[103] Takemura Y., J. Shirakashi, (2006), AFM lithography for fabrication of magnetic nanostructures and devices, *J. Magnetism & Magnetic Mater.*, **304**: 19 – 22

[104] Kuramochi H., K. Ando, T. Tokizaki, M. Yasutake, F. Perez-Murano, J. A. Dagata, H. Yokoyama, (2004), Large scale high precision nano-oxidation using an atomic force microscope. *Surf. Sci.*, **566 – 568**: 343 – 348

[105] Tseng A. A., S. Jou, A. Notargiacomo, T. P. Chen, (2008), Recent developments in tip-based nanofabrication and its roadmap, *J. Nanoscience & Nanotechnology*, **8** in press

[106] Chapman G. H., Y. Tu, C. Choo, J. Wang, D. K. Poon, M. Chang, (2006), Laser-induced oxidation of metallic thin films as a method for creating grayscale photomasks. Advances in Resist Technology and Processing XXIII, *Proceedings SPIE*, **6153** II: 61534G

[107] Tseng, A. A., (2007), Recent developments in micromachining of fused silica and quartz using excimer lasers. *Phys Status Solidi A*, **204**: 709 – 929

[108] Magno R., B. R. Bennett, (1997), Nanostructure patterns written in Ⅲ–Ⅴ semiconductors by an atomic force microscope. *Appl. Phys. Lett.*, **70**: 1855 – 1857

[109] Kunze U., (2002), Nanoscale devices fabricated by dynamic ploughing with an atomic force microscope. *Superlattices and Microstruct.*, **31**: 3 – 17

[110] Filho H. D. F., M. H. P. Mauricio, C. R. Ponciano, R. Prioli, (2004), Metal layer mask patterning by force microscopy lithography, *Mater. Sci. Eng. B*, **112**: 194 – 199

[111] Tseng, A. A., J. Shirakashi, S. Nishimura, K. Miyashita, and A. Notargiacomo(2009), Scratching properties of nickel-iron thin film and silicon using atomic force microscopy, *J. Applied Physics*, **106**: 044314

[112] Tseng, A. A., J. Shirakashi, S. Nishimura, K. Miyashita, Z. Li, (2010), Nanomachining of permalloy for fabricating nanoscale ferromagnetic structures using atomic force microscopy," *J. Nanoscience & Nanotechnology*, **10**: 456 – 466

[113] Henn A., O. Medalia, S. Shi, M. Steinberg, F. Franceschi, Sagi I. Visualization (2001), of unwinding activity of duplex RNA by DbpA, a DEAD box helicase, at single-molecule resolution by atomic force microscopy. *Proc. Nat. Acad. Sci.*, **98**: 5007 – 5012

[114] Czajkowsky D. M., Z. Shao, (2003), Inhibition of protein adsorption to muscovite mica by monovalent cations, *J. Microscopy*, **211**: 1 – 7

[115] Wang L., X. Feng, S. Hou, Q. Chan, M. Qin, (2006), Microcontact printing of multiproteins on the modified mica substrate and study of immunoassays. *Surface and Interface Analysis*, **38**: 44 – 50

[116] Kopta S., M. Salmeron, (2000), The atomic scale origin of wear on mica and its contribution to friction. *J. Chemical Physics*, **113**: 8249 – 8252

[117] Müler M., T. Fiedler, R. Gröger, T. Koch, S. Walheim, C. Obermair, T. Schimmel, (2004), Controlled structuring of mica surfaces with the tip of an atomic force microscope by mechanically induced local etching, *Surface and Interface analysis*, **36**: 189 – 192

[118] Heyde M., K. Rademann, B. Cappella, M. Geuss, H. Sturm, T. Spangenberg, H. Niehus, (2001), Dynamic plowing nanolithography on polymethylmethacrylate using an atomic force microscope, *Review of Scientific Instruments*, **72** (1): 136 – 141

[119] Cappella B., H. Sturm, (2002), Comparison between dynamic plowing lithography and nanoindentation methods, *J. Applied Physics*, **91**: 506 – 512

[120] Dvir H., J. Jopp, M. Gottlieb, (2006), Estimation of polymer-surface interfacial interaction strength by a contact AFM technique, *J. Colloid and Interface Science*, **304**: 58 – 66

[121] Kassavetis S., K. Mitsakakis, S. Logothetidis, (2007), Nanoscale patterning and deformation of soft matter by scanning probe microscopy. *Materials Science Eng. C*, **27**(5 – 8): 1456 – 1460

[122] Koinuma M., K. Uosaki, (1996), AFM tip induced selective electrochemical etching of and metal deposition on p-GaAs(100) surface. *Surf. Sci.*, **358**: 565 – 570

[123] Kim D. H., J. Y. Koo, J. J. Kim, (2003), Cutting of multiwalled carbon nanotubes by a negative voltage tip of an atomic force microscope: A possible mechanism. *Phys. Rev.*, **B68**: 113406 – 113409

[124] Takami K., M. Akai-Kasaya, A. Saito, M. Aono, Y. Kuwahara, (2005), Construction of

independently driven double-tip scanning tunneling microscope Jpn. *J. Appl. Phys*. Part 2, **44**: L120 – L122

[125] Wang X., C. Liu, (2005), Multifunctional probe array for nano patterning and imaging. *Nano Lett*., **5**: 1867 – 1872

[126] Minne S. C., G. Yaralioglu, S. R. Manalis, J. D. Adams, A. Atalar, C. F. Quate, (1998), Automated parallel high-speed atomic force microscopy. *Appl. Phys. Lett*., **72**: 2340 – 2342

[127] Pozidis H., W. Haberle, D. Wiesmann, U. Drechsler, M. Despont, T. R. Albrecht, E. Eleftheriou, (2004), Demonstration of thermomechanical recording at 641 Gbit/in(2). *IEEE Trans. Magnetics*, **40**: 2531 – 2536

[128] Rosenwaks Y., D. Dahan, M. Molotskii, G. Rosenman, (2005), Ferroelectric domain engineering using atomic force microscopy tip arrays in the domain breakdown regime. *Appl. Phys. Lett*., **86**: 012909

[129] Hagleitner C., T. Bonaccio, H. Rothuizen, J. Lienemann, D. Wiesmann, G. Cherubini, J. G. Korvink, E. Eleftheriou, (2007), Modeling, design, and verification for the analog front-end of a MEMS-based parallel scanning-probe storage device. *IEEE J. Solid-State Circuits*, **42**: 1779 – 1789

[130] Yang J. P., J. Q. Mou, N. B. Chong, Y. Lu, H. Zhu, Q. Jiang, W. G. Kim, J. Chen, G. X. Guo, E. H. Ong, (2007), Probe recording technology using novel MEMS devices. *Microsystem Technol*., **13**: 733 – 740

[131] Salaita K., Y. Wang, C. A. Mirkin, (2007), Applications of dip-pen nanolithography. *Nature Nanotech*., **2**: 145 – 155

[132] Xia Y., X. M. Zhao, E. Kim, G. M. Whitesides, (1995), A selective etching solution for use with patterned self-assembled monolayers of alkanethiolates on gold. *Chem. Mater*., **7**: 2332 – 2337

[133] Zhang H., S. -W. Chung, C. A. Mirkin, (2003), Fabrication of sub-50-nm solid-state nanostructures on the basis of dip-pen nanolithography. *Nano Lett*., **3**: 43 – 45

[134] Zhang H., C. A. Mirkin, (2004), DPN-generated nanostructures made of gold, silver, and palladium. *Chem. Mater*., **16**: 1480 – 1484

[135] Lee K. B., S. J. Park, C. A. Mirkin, J. C. Smith, M. Mrksich, (2002), Protein nanoarrays generated by dip-pen nanolithography. *Science*, **295**(5560): 1702 – 1705

[136] Liu M., N. A. Amro, C. S. Chow, G. Y. Liu, (2002), Production of nanostructures of DNA on surfaces. *Nano Lett*., **2**: 863 – 867

[137] Wang Y. H., D. Maspoch, S. L. Zou, G. C. Schatz, R. E. Smalley, C. A. Mirkin, (2006), Controlling the shape, orientation, and linkage of carbon nanotube features with nano affinity templates. *Proc. Natl. Acad. Sci. USA*, **103**: 2026 – 2031

[138] Lim J. -H., C. A. Mirkin, (2002), Electrostatically driven dip-pen nanolithography of conducting polymers. *Adv. Mater*., **14**: 1474 – 1477

[139] Lee M., D. -K. Kang, H. -K. Yang, K. -H. Park, S. Y. Choe, C. S. Kang, S. -I. Chang, M. H. Han, I. -C. Kang, (2006), Protein nanoarray on Prolinker (TM) surface constructed by atomic force microscopy dip-pen nanolithography for analysis of protein interaction. *Proteomics*, **6**: 1094 – 1103

[140] Vega R. A., C. K. F. Shen, D. Maspoch, J. G. Robach, R. A. Lamb, C. A. Mirkin, (2007), Monitoring single-cell infectivity from virus-particle nanoarrays fabricated by parallel dip-pen nanotithography. *Small*, **3**: 1482 – 1485

[141] Taha H., A. Lewis, C. Sukenik, (2007), Controlled deposition of gold nanowires on semiconducting and nonconducting surfaces. *Nano Lett.*, **7**: 1883 – 1887
[142] Hong S., J. Zhu, C. A. Mirkin, (1999), *Science*, **286**: 523
[143] Zhang H., N. A. Amro, S. Disawal, R. Elghanian, R. Shile, J. Fragala, (2007), *Small*, **3**: 81
[144] Mirkin C. A., (2007), The power of the pen: development of massively parallel dip pen nanolithography. *ACS Nano*, **1**: 79 – 83
[145] Salaita K., Y. Wang, J. Fragala, R. A. Vega, C. Liu, C. A. Mirkin, (2006), Massively parallel dip-pen nanolithography with 55,000-pen two-dimensional arrays. *Angewandte Chemie Inter. Ed.*, **45**: 7220 – 7223
[146] Bullen D., C. Liu, (2006), Electrostatically actuated dip pen nanolithography probe arrays. *Sens. Actuators A*, **125**: 504 – 511
[147] Cherniavskaya O., A. Adzic, C. Knutson, B. J. Gross, L. Zang, R. Liu, D. M. Adams, (2002), Edge transfer lithography of molecular and nanoparticle materials. *Langmuir*, **18**: 7029 – 7034
[148] Lee S. W., C. Mao, C. E. Flynn, A. M. Belcher, (2002), Ordering of quantum dots using genetically Engineered viruses. *Science*, **296**: 892 – 895
[149] Park C., J. Yoon, E. L. Thomas, (2003), Enabling nanotechnology with self assembled block copolymer patterns. *Polymer.* **44**: 6725 – 6760
[150] Deng T., S. Ha, J. Y. Cheng, C. A. Ross, E. L. Thomas, (2002), Micropatterning of block copolymer solutions. *Langmuir*, **18**: 6719 – 6722
[151] Cheng J. Y., C. A. Ross, E. L. Thomas, H. I. Smith, G. J. Vancso, (2002), Fabrication of nanostructures with long-range order using block copolymer lithography. *App. Phys. Lett.*, **81**: 3657 – 3659
[152] Li R. R., P. D. Dapkus, M. E. Thompson, W. G. Jeong, C. Harrison, P. M. Chaikin, R. A., Register, D. H. Adamson, (2000), Dense arrays of ordered GaAs nanostructures by selective area growth on substrates patterned by block copolymer lithography. *Appl. Physics Lett.*, **76**: 1689 – 1691
[153] Shin K., K. A. Leach, J. T. Goldbach, D. H. Kim, J. Y. Jho, M. Tuominen, C. J. Hawker, T. P. Russell, (2002), A simple route to metal nanodots and nanoporous metal films. *Nano Letters*, **2**: 933 – 936
[154] Guarini K. W., C. T. Black, Y. Zhang, I. V. Babich, E. M. Sikorski, L. M. Gignac, (2003), Low voltage, scalable nanocrystal flash memory fabricated by templated self assembly. *Technical Digest - International Electron Devices Meeting.* 541 – 544
[155] Haupt M., S. Miller, A. Ladenburger, R. Sauer, K. Thonke, J. P. Spatz, S. Riethmuller, M. Moller, F. Banhart, (2002), Semiconductor nanostructures defined with self-organizing polymers. *J. Appl. Phys.*, **91**: 6057 – 6059
[156] Fink Y., A. M. Urbas, M. G. Bawendi, J. D. Joannopoulos, E. L. Thomas, (1999), Block copolymers as photonic bandgap materials. *J. Lightwave Technology*, **17**:1963 – 1969
[157] Yun W. S., J. Kim, K. H. Park, J. S. Ha, Y. J. Ko, K. Park, S. K. Kim, Y. J. Doh, H. J. Lee, J. P. Salvetat, L. Forro, (2000), Fabrication of metal nanowire using carbon nanotube as a mask. *J. Vac. Sci. Technol.* A, **18**: 1329 – 1332
[158] Xu T., R. M. Metzger, (2002), Nanoditches fabricated using a carbon nanotube as a contact mask. *Nano Lett.*, **2**: 1061 – 1065

[159] Sordan R., M. Burghard, K. Kern, (2001), Removable template route to metallic nanowires and nanogaps. *Appl. Phys. Lett.*, **79**: 2073 – 2075

[160] Ancona M. G., S. E. Kooi, W. Kruppa, A. W. Snow, E. E. Foos, L. J. Whitman, D. Park, L. Shirey, (2003), Patterning of narrow Au nanocluster lines using V_2O_5 nanowire masks and ion-beam milling. *Nano Lett.*, **3**: 135 – 138

[161] Yonezawa T., S. Onoue, T. Kunitake, (1999), Formation of one-dimensional arrays of gold nanoparticles with DNA. *Kobunshi Ronbunshu*, **56**: 855 – 859 (in Japanese)

[162] Zhaoxiang D., M. Chengde, (2003), DNA-Templated fabrication of 1D parallel and 2D crossed metallic nanowire arrays. *Nano Lett.*, **3**: 1545 – 1548

[163] Yan H., S. H. Park, G. Finkelstein, J. H. Reif, T. H. LaBean, (2003), DNA-Templated self-assembly of protein arrays and highly conductive nanowires. *Science*, **301**: 1882 – 1884

[164] Huang Y., X. F. Duan, Y. Cui, L. J. Lauhon, K. H. Kim, C. M. Lieber, (2001), Logic gates and computation from assembled nanowire building blocks. *Science*, **294**: 1313 – 1317

[165] Chien C. L., L. Sun, M. Tanase, L. A. Bauer, A. Hultgren, D. M. Silevitch, G. J. Meyer, P. C. Searson, D. H. Reich, (2002), Electrodeposited magnetic nanowires: arrays, field-induced assembly and surface functionalization. *J. Magnetism Magnetic Materials,* **249**: 146 – 155

[166] Tanase M., L. A. Bauer, A. Hultgren, D. M. Silevitch, L. Sun, D. H. Reich, P. C. Searson, G. J. Meyer, (2001), Magnetic alignment of fluorescent nanowires. *Nano Lett.*, **1**: 155 – 158

[167] Thurn-Albrecht T., J. Schotter, G. A. Kästle, N. Emley, T. Shibauchi, L. Krusin-Elbaum, K. Guarini, C. T. Black, M. T. Tuominen, T. P. Russell, (2000), Ultrahigh-density nanowire arrays grown in self-assembled diblock copolymer templates. *Science*, **290**: 2126 – 2129

[168] Mesquida P., A. Stemmer, (2002), Maskless nanofabrication using the electrostatic attachment of gold particles to electrically patterned surfaces. *Microelectronic* Eng., **61 – 62**: 671 – 674

[169] Smith P. A., C. D. Nordquist, T. N. Jackson, S. A. Mayer, B. R. Martin, J. Mbindyo, T. E. Mallouk, (2000), Electric-field assisted assembly and alignment of metallic nanowires. *Appl. Phys. Lett.*, **77**: 1399 – 1401

15 Integrated Nanotechnology Based on MEMS

Xinxin Li

State Key Lab of Transducer Technology, Shanghai Institute of Microsystem and Information Technology, Chinese Academy of Sciences, China
E-mail: xxli@mail.sim.ac.cn

Abstract In this chapter, after a brief review of integrated silicon-based MEMS fabrication techniques, MEMS techniques for nano-metric fabrication is emphasized. Using high selectivity and anisotropy of specific top-down micromachining methods, nanometric feature size can be fabricated for NEMS applications. Fabrication techniques of typical MEMS-made NEMS structures, such as nanotips, nanoapertures, nano junction, nanolines and nano-beams, are detailed in the chapter. Then, by integrating the nanoscale feature structure with the micrometric main body, typical integrated NEMS devices and their applications are addressed. The chapter also relates key size-effects of the integrated nanomechanical structures that have shown significant difference in electromechanical properties compared to their microscale counterparts, likc thc big differcnce in silicon Young's modulus value. At last, the bright future of the integrated NEMS techniques and devices are outlooked.

Keywords Nanomachining techniques, micromachining techniques, nano-electromechanical systems, nanosize-effects

15.1 Introduction

15.1.1 Review of MEMS Fabrication Technologies

In the second half of the 20th century, microelectronic engineering and semi-conductor integrated circuits (IC) had developed rapidly. In addition to the IC manufacturing industry, microelectronic planar fabrication technologies have also been used for applications in other fields. As one of the technical methods for information acquisition, transducers are considered as sensing terminals to match microprocessor computation technology. Formed by micro fabrication, miniaturization and integration of sensors have been long-time investigated.

Since 1970's, driven by the demands of automation industry, automobile electronics and electronic medical systems, miniaturized solid-state sensors and integrated sensors had been developed to replace their conventional bulk counterparts. The intensive development was mainly due to their small volume, light weight and low energy consumption. More importantly, microsensors could make full use of the technical advantages of IC fabrication, especially in high-reliability and low-cost mass production. With the advantages of microsensors, they could be applied in brand new fields that had never been touched by conventional devices. Moreover, fabricated by a compatible process with ICs, it was much easier to monolithically integrate the sensors with interface and signal processing circuits to build integrated smart sensors.

In fact, many micro-sensors comprise of no mechanical parts, like ① Hall-effect sensors for magnetic field detection, ② Resistive thermometers and ③ Diodes for optical detection. However, indeed there are lots of sensors that use mechanical effects for sensing, such as ① Diaphragm-structured pressure sensors, and ② Spring-mass inertial sensors. To build the mechanical microsensors, both the electronic sensing elements and the micromechanical structures need to be integrated together. However, at early stage of MEMS development, micromachining fabrication techniques were not so mutual compared to the well-developed microelectronic integration techniques, thus, had to be emphasized for rapid promotion.

The first generation micro-machining techniques were focused on fabrication of piezoresistive pressure sensors. By borrowing anisotropic etching from semiconductor field, which had been used for digging air-insulating trenches between adjacent devices, anisotropic-etching based bulk micromachining technique has been long-time developed and applied for MEMS fabrication [1]. In the mean time, isotropic etching was also occasionally used for silicon micromachining [2], however, it's etching quality and process controllability were much worse than that of anisotropic etch that gradually became a main-stream micromachining technique. Besides the pressure sensors, anisotropic etching technique had found another successful application, information of ink-jet micronozzles for printers[3]. Following the demand of fabricating more complicated micro-structures, advanced anisotropic etching technique was further developed for three-dimensional (3D) multi-layer structures. A so-called masked-maskless combined etching technique was invented. With the technique, 3D micro-structures or arrayed structures can be formed by only one-time photolithography followed by continual etch [4, 5]. The SEM images in Figs. 15.1(a) and (b) shows the 'masked-maskless etching' formed silicon multi-layer tower-like structure and the beam-mass acceleration sensing array with sequentially varied beam thickness.

As pressure sensors need hermetic solid-state packaging at the pressure inlet, a kind of electrostatic bonding technique for silicon wafer and Pyrex glass piece was intensively developed [6]. Based on these techniques, capacitive pressure sensors, piezoresistive/capacitive microaccelerometers and microgyroscopes were developed one by one [7, 8]. In 1982, Dr. K. Peterson published a famous review

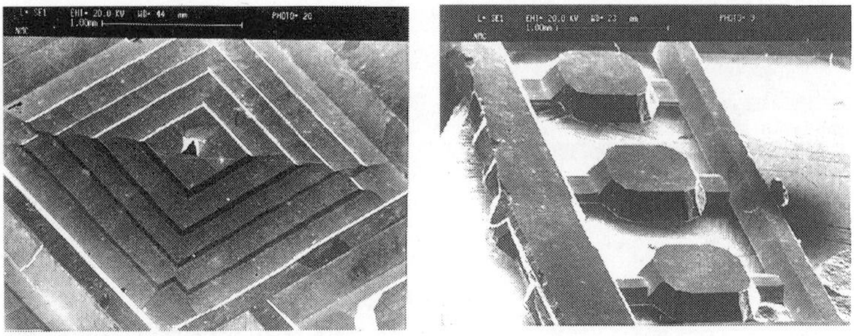

(a) (b)

Figure 15.1 SEM images of complicated 3D silicon micromechanical structures. (a) multi-layer tower-like structure; (b) thickness sequentially varied beam-mass acceleration switch array

paper entitled 'Silicon as a mechanical material'[9], which had been considered as the symbol of creation of MEMS technical field. The fabrication techniques reviewed above were also called conventional bulk micromachining and, even now, are used frequently. As an example, Fig. 15. 2 shows the SEM image and micrograph of a piezoresistive angular-rate gyroscope and its output properties. The sensor was fabricated by the above introduced bulk micromachining techniques.

To enhance the compatibility of integration between micromachining parts and microelectronics at a smaller size, surface micromachining techniques were then developed that uses thin-films for both structure layer and sacrificial layer. Surface micromachining techniques had been intensively investigated from the end of 1980's to the beginning of 1990's, with which not only microsensors but also microactuators, microfluidic systems, RF- and optical MEMS devices were fabricated [10–13]. A surface-micro-machined microchannel flow chip is illustrated in Fig. 15.3. A series of pressure sensors were integrated with the micro channel for monitoring the fluidic properties. In the structure a PSG thin film, which was used as sacrificial layer, low-stress silicon nitride was used as the structural layer and a doped poly silicon thin-film was used for piezoresistive sensing material. At the end of 1980's, NSF and DARPA of USA organized a meeting, in which a key-note report was given that was entitled 'An emerging technology—micro electro mechanical systems'. From that time on, the abbreviation of the word, MEMS came to be well known.

Surface micromachining bears a technical weakness in forming high aspect-ratio structures. As a complementary technique, LIGA technique was developed in Germany that used micro molding as the technical basis. However, LIGA process needed synchronous radiation X-ray as the lithographic light source that was very expensive. Later ultra violet light was used as the replacement to develop a quazi-LIGA technique [14, 15]. These non-silicon micromachining technologies were generally problematic in compatibility with silicon IC processes. Therefore people sought new solutions for silicon micromachining. As the result, a kind of ICP-DRIE (inductively coupled plasma-deep RIE) technique was developed to

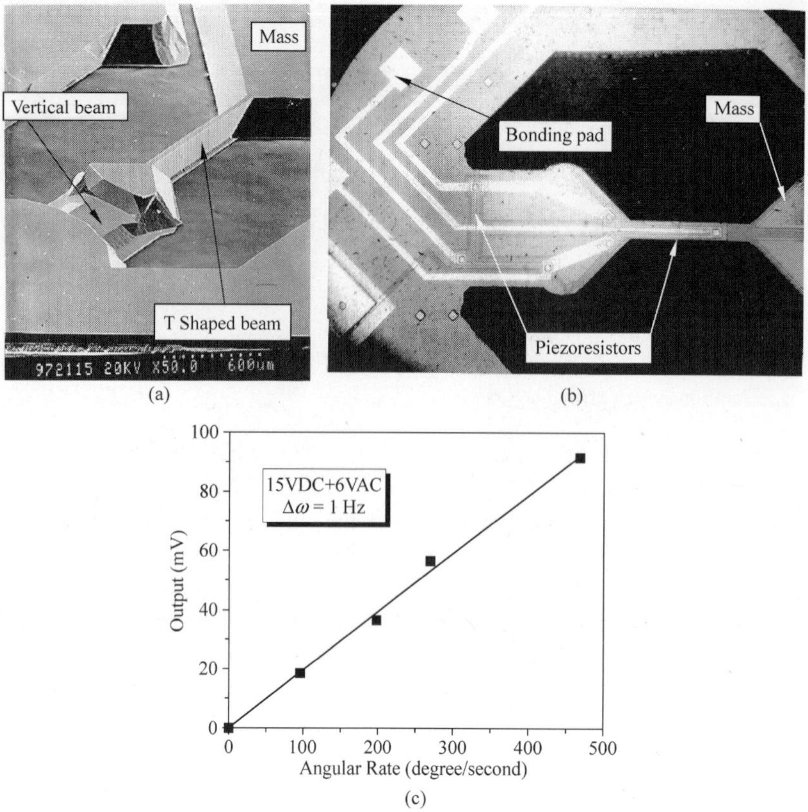

Figure 15.2 A composite-beam piezoresistive microgyro developed with bulk micromachining techniques. (a) Backside-view SEM of the microstructure, (b) front-side micrograph of the gyro, (c) measured gyro output signal in terms of angular rate

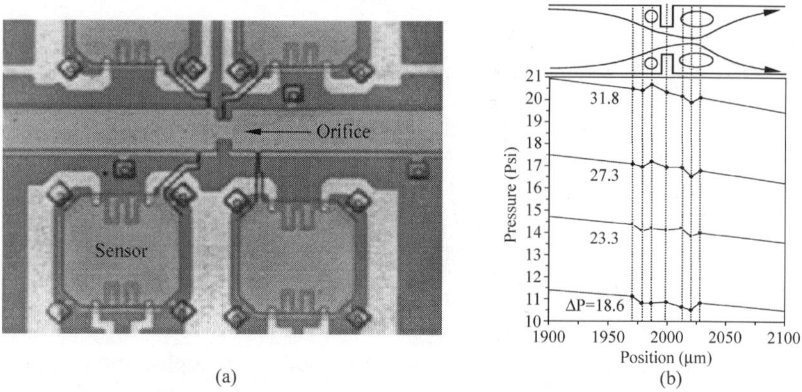

Figure 15.3 Integrated microchannel fluidic systems formed by surface micromachining techniques. (a) Micrograph showing the pressure sensor array with the pressure inlet connected to the microchannel, (b) measured microflow separation occurring behind the orifice

fabricate high aspect-ratio microstructure in silicon wafers [16, 17]. As an advanced bulk micromachining technique, ICP-DRIE could be used to form large seismic masses. Moreover, it can also imitate surface micromachining technique to fabricate comb-drive structures. Using this high aspect-ratio fabrication process, thicker silicon structure could be made free of the release static friction problem that was frequently encountered when using surface micromachining techniques [18]. Combined with silicon-silicon multi-wafer bonding technique [19, 20], the advanced silicon bulk micromachining has lead a general trend towards 3D microfabrication. Figures 15.4(a) and (b) show the SEM images of a microresonator by quazi-LIGA and a deeply etched trench structure by DRIE.

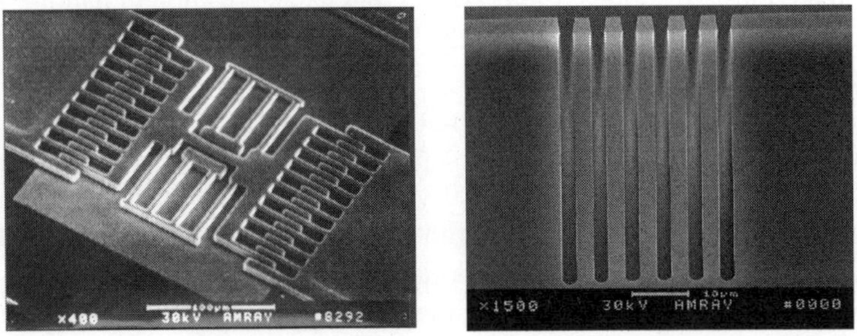

(a) (b)

Figure 15.4 (a) SEM of a micro resonator formed by Ni/Cu electroplating and quazi-LIGA, (b) high aspect-ratio silicon trenches made by ICP-DRIE

15.1.2 MEMS Techniques for Nanometric Fabrication

Along with the development of MEMS, the fabrication precision has been largely improved. Gradually MEMS has become to touch the fabrication of sub-micron structures. For example, MEMS is needed to be able to make sub-micron capacitor gap of capacitive sensors for improving sensing resolution [21]. In the market, the available capacitive inertial sensors have realized the mechanical resolution of the capacitive gap to a level as fine as nanometers or even sub-nanometers, i.e., the precision approaches the crystal length of silicon. For such a small size, the sensor noise floor us largely influenced by thermal fluctuation of the atoms at the capacitive plates. For further improving the resolution of MEMS inertial sensors, a kind of high-sensitivity sensor was developed that uses nanotip tunneling current to detect micromechanical displacement [22, 23]. When the tip physically approaches the counter electrode with a small gap of nanometers, the tunneling current will go through the air gap for detection of inertial force induced displacement. In fact such a method has used MEMS fabrication to form nano-structures. The nanotip is made by MEMS fabrication and the nanogap is also formed by MEMS technique.

In MEMS actuators, wear and friction are a problem when adjacent micromechanical parts contact to each other. Conventional friction is under the assumption that the contact area is much larger than the contacting distance. However, in MEMS structures like microgears and micromotors, the contacting area has been already small enough and the conventional theory is no longer suited. IBM ever conducted an experiment. They used an AFM probe tip to contact with a routing CD for many days to observe the wear phenomenon. The results show that there is no severe wear observed. They carried on another experiment to use a thermal-electrically heated nanotip for nanomechnical data-storage writing. The experiment shows that the heating transfer through the nanotip gets far deviates from conventional thermal-transfer theory. All these clearly indicate that some conventional theories are no longer to be suited for characterization of nanomechanical structures when the feature size of the structure or the operated object enters nanometric regime.

Most of MEMS-made structures comprise micrometric feature size and, in such size, many theories for macro things can still be used for MEMS modeling and design. In MEMS history of about 20 years, Newton mechanism based theory dominates the MEMS world, such as finite element method. People expected that many significant specimen size effects can be observed in MEMS but the answer is no. For a long period of time, many mechanical experts had worked on the size effect of MEMS materials, i.e., they tried to measure significant variation in microscale solid-state structures for important parameters like elastic modulus but they have not observed the drastic variation in microscale structure. In the fore mentioned microchannel flow experiment. What the authors observed is only slip flow instead of continuing flow when the channel cross-section is shrunk from macro down to microscale. The academic value of such kind of results is only telling us that the macrosize theory can still be used in microscale. That is all.

The things have been changed since the invention of AFM and STM [24, 25]. Using the MEMS-made probes, people know that nanomachine is relative not only with Newton mechanism but also with other mechanisms. The miracle work made by the scientists in IBM, i.e., moving and manipulating Ni atoms into the pattern of 'IBM', indeed has been related to atomic theory and quantum mechanism. With similar MEMS fabrication, near-field optical probe, nanomechanical data storage probe and gene detection probe can be formed. Such micro/nano combined devices really consist of nanometric feature size. In this way, MEMS can be down scaled into NEMS (Nanoelectromechanical systems).

15.1.3 Potential and Capability of MEMS for the Down-Scale Integration

Accompanying the development of IC industry, MEMS fabrication technology is also going ahead. Now the MOSFET size is entering deep sub-mircon or nanometers. Similarly, using the advanced exposure techniques like ultra-UV photolithgraphy, electro-beam direct writing or nanoimprinting, nano feature-size of MEMS structures can be realized. Moreover, some unique fabrication methods of MEMS, like silicon anisotropic etch and highly selective etch between different materials etc.; can be used for nanomechanical fabrication. Anisotropic etching is one of widely used MEMS techniques. The model of the etching technique shows that silicon anisotropic etch is processed by removing silicon molecules from one layer to another layer and, thus, can be used for nanometric precise fabrication. The nano tips for AFM probes have been formed with the anisotropic etching, by the aid of other technique. On the other hand, nanothick free-standing films can be formed by sacrificial layer release technique. With this kind of top-down nano fabrication techniques, wafer level mass production can be realized, which is advantageous in device uniformity, reliability and, of course, production cost. With all these advantages, the top-down nano-fabrication techniques are reasonably expected to be broadly applied.

15.2 Technical Trend from MEMS to NEMS

Bottom-up construction is considered an important methodology in nanoworld and, has been widely used for various nanomaterials. Equipped with the nanoscale properties, these nanomaterials feature unique functions like self-cleaning surface, etc. In fact, the bottom-up nanotechniques have been used in MEMS for many years. The researchers at U. C. Berkeley used bottom-up self-assembly to modify the structure surface, where the molecules feature low surface energy. In this way the surface shows hydro-phobic function to avoid stiction of MEMS structures during or after structure release.

By now, the developed bottom-up techniques have not been powerful enough to produce NEMS structures. The reason lies in that most of NEMS structures consists of different sizes from millimeters, micrometers to nanometers. In the multi-scale structures, NEMS only uses nano for the feature size. In fact the whole device size is, more often than not, in micro or even millimeter size. Take the tunneling inertial sensors as an example. Only the tip for tunneling current is in nanoscale. The cantilever body is in micrometer size and the whole device chip is packaged in millimeter scale. Therefore, top-down fabrication is still needed as the mainstream method to build such multi-scale NEMS structures. Based on the matured MEMS fabrication, some techniques can be developed to specifically form nanometric structures. Such kind of combined fabrication is suited for compatible integration of NEMS, which possesses both micro and nano. This combined fabrication trend can be considered the technical extension of MEMS for smaller structural size. Figure 15.5 shows the SEM images of an integrated thermal-electrically scanning probe and the close-up view of the nanotip. Apparently the whole cantilever-tip probe is in microscale. However the working part, i.e., the tip, is indeed in nanoscale. This NEMS device is fabricated using the MEMS-based NEMS techniques.

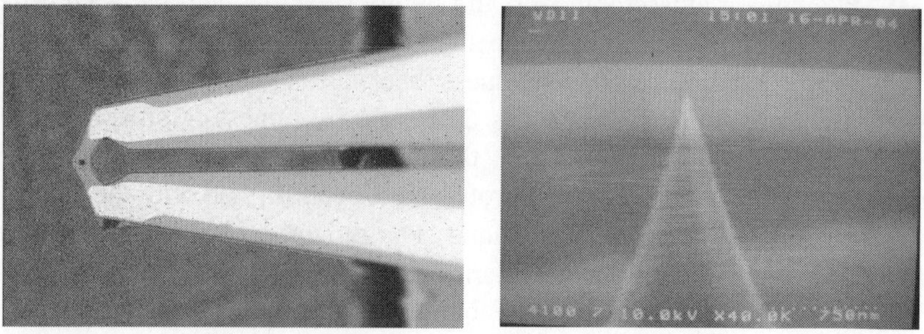

(a) (b)

Figure 15.5 (a) SEM of a thermal-electric scanning microscopic probe. (b) Close-up view of the nano tip (with the diameter as tens of nanometers) that is located at the apex of the microcantilever

Such technical solution is practically feasible, as the extension of achieved microelectronic technique to nano-electronic regime have proved it. Please recall the whole progress from microelectronic ICs to nanoelectronic ICs that was predicted by the well known Moore's law. For many times, people suspected the capability of microelectronic fabrication. Limited by the wave length of the exposure light, people suspected the photo-lithographic resolution when the line width entered deep submicron. However, the commercialization of 45 nm ICs has verified that the technical extension of top-down integration indeed can be used for nanothings. Theoretically, top-down fabrication has not a clear bottom limitation along the down scale road. More importantly, such top-down fabrication does follow the Moore's law. Every time when the proto type was fabricated by the top-down technique, the low-cost volume production would be not far.

Along the road from MEMS to NEMS, top-down and bottom-up cannot be separated. In contrast, they have been combining together very well. Some key parts with nanofeature size are indeed difficult to be fabricated by top-down method. Alternatively bottom-up may have advantage in integration of the nanometric key components of NEMS. For example, high aspect-ratio tip is needed for probing and imaging clustered nano-materials. Top-down made cone-shaped nanotip cannot meet the probing requirement. Carbon nanotube (CNT) is a typical bottom-up nanostructure that features a high aspect-ratio. In addition, CNT features light weight, high mechanical strength and small diameter. The difficult thing lies in the oriented and localized growth of CNT at the silicon tip end and, combined with top-down fabrication of silicon cantilever-tip, in order to form a top-down bottom-up compatible integration. Figure 15.6 demonstrates such an achievement by top-down and bottom-up compatible integration.

Another example on CNT NEMS is given as follows. It has been well known that CNT is a promising candidate for next generation nano MOSFET devices.

However, no matter how small the MOSFET itself is, a signal input/output is always needed. In other words, the leading out pads are always inevitable, those are in micrometric size and have to be formed by top-down. To adapt the mess CNT material to the highly arrayed layout of electrodes, the CNT segments should be well laid out into a parallel array by bottom-up method like L-B membrane technique. Then the CNT segments can be localized at the MOSFET sites to form an IC. Therefore, the process compatibility between top-down and bottom-up is indeed the key point for the combined NEMS technique.

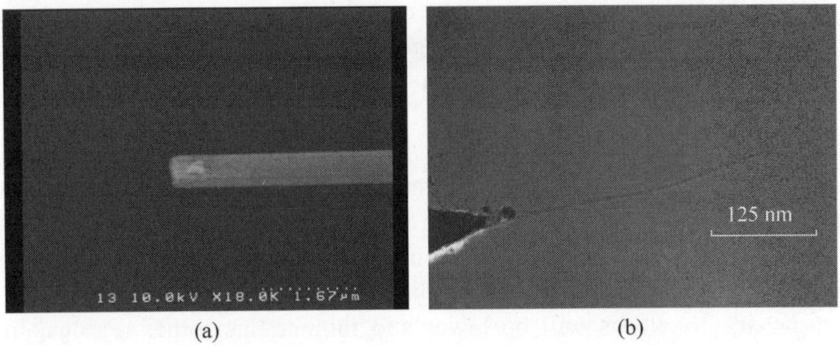

Figure 15.6 SEM images showing bottom-up selective growth of CNT on top-down formed microstructures. (a) CNT array locally grown at the end of a silicon microcantilever; (b) a single CNT is controllably grown at the apex of a silicon tip

15.3 Integrated Nanomachining Technologies

It is deserved to have a discussion before introducing the MEMS-based nanomachining fabrication. Why MEMS should be made as small as possible? The answer may be as follows: single wafer product yield can be increased when MEMS devices can be made smaller. Then, when the MEMS devices feature lighter weight and lower power consumption, the fabrication and application costs can be lowered. Now talk about NEMS. Why people would like to make the things even smaller? Is the reason the same as MEMS? The answer is no. From package view, a NEMS device can have a similar size with a MEMS one. In a NEMS device, only the feature size of important working parts is nanometric. The reason using the nanofeature size lies in that some size effects will appear at the size and new nanofunctions can be used for new applications.

SPM probes are a typical type of NEMS devices that are formed with MEMS-based techniques. A microscale cantilever is formed for atomic force detection. For surface imaging in atomic level, a scanning tip with the size matching the targeted atoms is equipped at the apex of the cantilever. Almost all the SPM probes available in the market are made by MEMS fabrication. It is a small piece for MEMS techniques to uniformly fabricate many microcantilevers in a silicon wafer. It is also easy for MEMS to form many micro silicon tips in the same way. However, pure MEMS fabrication is not capable of forming the tips with a uniform nanometric diameter. Based on MEMS fabrication, new nanomachining techniques is necessary to be developed to meet the nanofabrication requirements. Still, take the nanotip as example: The fabrication firstly utilizes anisotropic etching or plasma dry etching with lateral underetches function to form the contour of the tip, with the tip diameter ranged in 0.5 – 1 micron. Based on these MEMS fabrication process, a low-temperature oxidization nanomachining is then developed and used to further sharpening the tip end into a nanodiameter [26, 27]. The thermal oxidation will form a SiO_2 layer that covers the silicon tip. The following oxidation will be continued with the gaseous oxygen passing through the existing silicon-dioxide layer and reacting with the silicon at the Si-SiO_2 interface. There is a thermal mismatch stress in the existing silicon-dioxide film. At the tip end region, the geometric curving is more intensive and the stress is higher compared to that at the planar regions. Such kind of stress serves as a potential barrier for the oxygen passing process. The higher stress at the tip end region will exhibit a stronger resist against the oxygen molecules passing through the existing silicon-dioxide layer. In consequence, the oxidization rate at the tip end and the final silicon-dioxide thickness will be lower and thinner than other regions. In this way the tip is finally sharpened into nanometers. Since that high-temperature (higher than 1,000℃) formed in silicon-dioxide has a re-flow character that will release the stress at the tip region, low-temperature (below 950℃) oxidization has to be used in this fabrication. Herein we call the localized tip sharpening process as nanomachining technique. Figure 15.7 shows the probe tip evolution during the MEMS etching step and the nano-machining sharpening step.

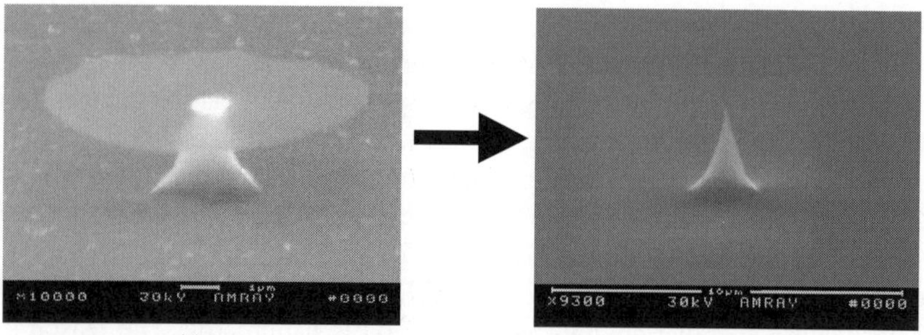

(a) (b)

Figure 15.7 SEM images showing the forming process of a nano probe-tip. (a) Anisotropic etching formed blunt silicon tip, with the tip end diameter ranged in 0.5 – 1 micron; (b) the nanotip is formed by further low-temperature oxidation sharpening process

Then another example of nanoaperture is given as: The localized limitation effect for nanomachining is also used for other nano structures. A nanoaperture located at the cantilever-end tip can be used for single-mode optical fiber feeding and surface near-field optical data storage or other nanomanipulation. The above mentioned localized limitation of oxidation is again used for a SiO_2 nanoaperture. Which is done as: Firstly anisotropic etching is performed at the cantilever apex to form a pyramid-shaped cavity. The sharp tip end is shaped by four ⟨111⟩ slow etching plane. Then the low-temperature oxidation is used to form a silicon-dioxide film, with the film thickness at the tip end being thinner than other regions. Herein, the curving induced stress effect still influences the oxidation at the tip region. After backside silicon etching to expose the silicon-dioxide tip, diluted wet HF etching is used to remove the silicon-dioxide. The etching is stopped when the tip is etching through while the silicon-dioxide at other regions is still remained. By careful control of the HF etching, nanometric aperture can be formed [28]. Figure 15.8 shows the nanomachining process flow and the SEM image of the nano aperture.

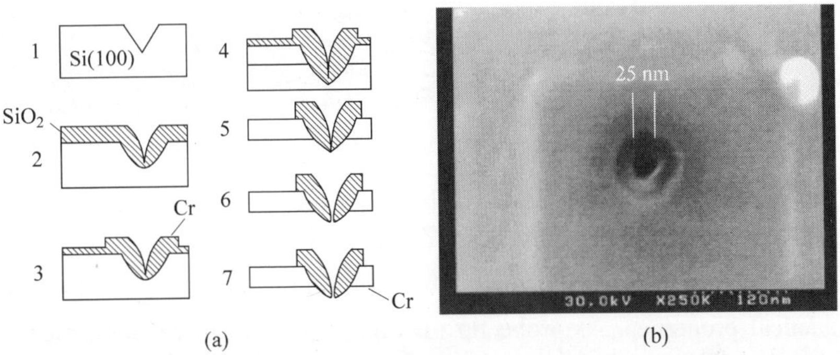

Figure 15.8 (a) Process flow including the steps of anisotropic etching, locally constrained low-temperature oxidation and HF removing of silicon dioxide; (b) SEM image of the formed 25 nm aperture

Using the same locally restricting nanomachining method, silicon dioxide nano probe tip can be also fabricated. The anisotropic etching formed silicon pyramid cavity is used as a mould. A thin film is deposited to form a pyramid-shaped tip shape. After patterning the thin film into a cantilever shape, backside silicon is removed and a cantilever-tip probe is fabricated [29]. If a metal film is deposited, an electrically conductive probe can be formed and, if a silicon nitride film is deposited, a dielectric probe can be formed.

The SPM probes can also be used for surface thermal imaging. Atomic level resolution of thermal distribution is expected to be realized. For this purpose a thermal nanotip is utilized where the heat capacitance and the thermal influence to the targeted surface temperature distribution should be very small. According to the requirement, a nano sized thermal couple is designed and formed at the nanoaperture by nanomachining fabrication. After the low-temperature oxidation is processed, Pt/Ti thin film is sputtered from the front side. Than after the HF backside etching forms the nano sized silicon dioxide hole, another Ni thin-film is sputtered from the backside to contact the front-side metal via the nanohole.

The nano sized thermal couple is therefore formed at the tip for thermal imaging [30]. Figure 15.9 shows the process flow and the cross-sectional SEM of the nano thermal-couple.

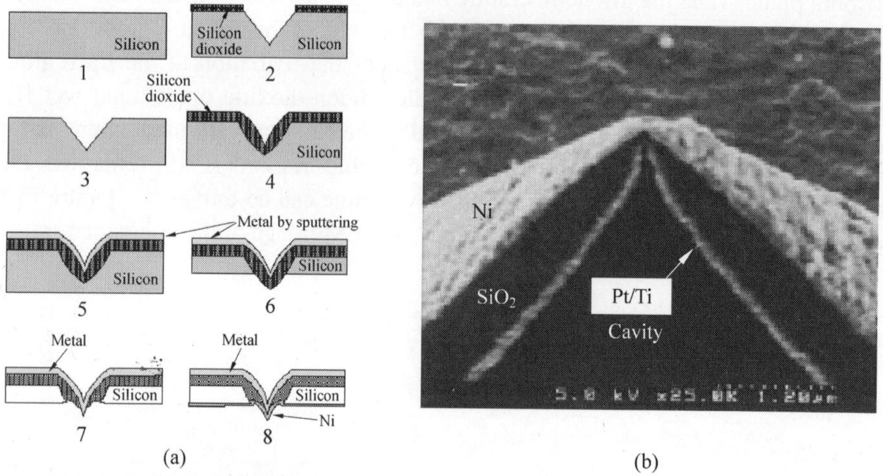

Figure 15.9 (a) Fabrication process, (b) SEM image of the double-metal thermal-couple formed at the nanohole

CNT is a high aspect-ratio nanostructure, with light weight and excellent mechanical properties. As probe tip material, CNT has many advantages. The problem lies in the local integration of the CNT tip at the microcantilever apex. Previous reports described many installation methods, in which the CNT was assembled at the cantilever apex by manual manipulation. Besides the complication and low yield, volume production of uniform probes was difficult. If the integration method was used, localized and oriented growth of CNT tips were the key technique. The catalyst material, like Ni nano particle, should be precisely placed at the tip location. To solve the problems, tip field emission effect is used to realize the localized Ni dot deposition. Even so, the nanonickel dot is still too large and can accommodate too many CNTs. To secure only one CNT grown at the tip, a critical CNT growing condition should be built. It is well known that the strongest electric field occurs at the sharp tip where the electric energy density is the highest. If an appropriate voltage is applied on the silicon tip, by precisely controlling the critical condition can be built. The energy at the very tip reaches the critical value where a CNT can be grown, while at other regions, the energy is lower than the critical value and no CNT will be grown [31]. For better controlling, the above mentioned nano aperture can also be used. After the oxidation sharpening, a nickel film is sputtered in the pyramid-shaped silicon cavity. By backside HF etching a nanosized nickel dot will be exposed at the etched nano-hole. Then by the critical electric field method, single CNT can also be grown at the tip end [32]. Equipped with the CNT tip, the probe surface scanning images shows a significantly finer resolution compared to the ones scanned by conventional probes. Moreover, the initial nickel nanodot, serving as the catalyst during CNT growth, leads the growth of the CNT and is finally located at the far end of the CNT. After magnetization of the nickel nanodot, a magnetic probe is formed and can be further used for surface magnetic field imaging. In conclusion, the CNT-tip probe is a typical achievement by combination of top-down and bottom-up fabrication that follows the technical trend of MEMS to NEMS. Figure 15.10 shows the growth mechanism as well as the fabrication and imaging results of the CNT-equipped probe tips.

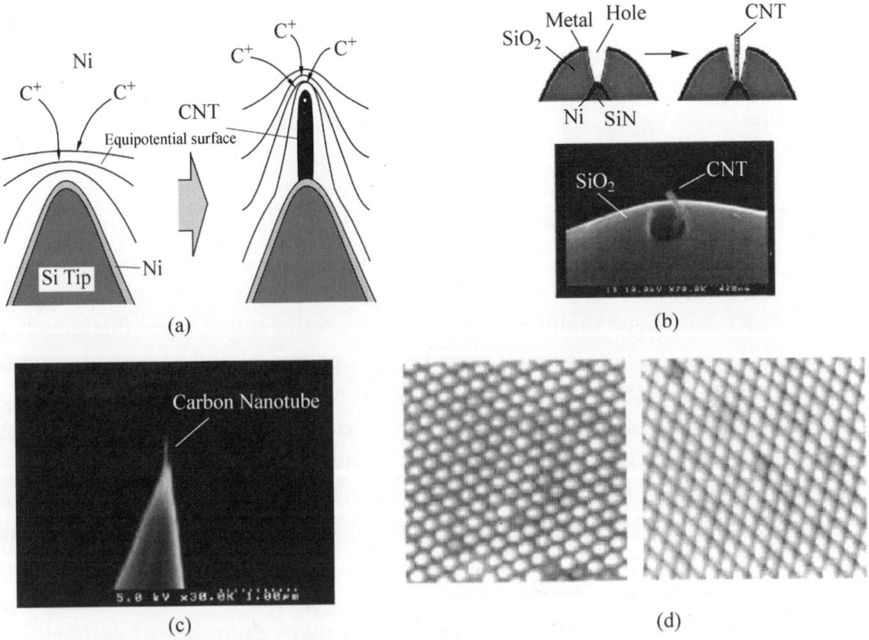

Figure 15.10 (a) Schematic of the electric field energy aided mechanism for selective growth of CNT at a silicon tip. (b) Mechanism and fabrication result of a single CNT growth in a nano aperture. (c) SEM image of a CNT grown at the far end of a silicon tip. (d) Surface scanning images by using the CNT tip probe and conventional silicon tip, respectively

Further thinning micro cantilevers can form nano-thick cantilevers which can be used to form ultra-sensitive surface-stress sensors or resonant mass sensors that are promising in trace bio/chemical detection. High resonance frequency is required for the resonant cantilever sensors and, thus, the cantilever mass is expected to be as small as possible. Besides, the thinner is the cantilever; the higher will be the mechanical sensitivity. To form the thin cantilevers, the routine method is thinning the active silicon layer of a SOI wafer into a desired thickness and then removing the substrate silicon by backside anisotropic wet etching. At last the cantilever shape can be formed by electro-beam direct writing and selective dry etching the nanodiaphragm [33]. With this technique the thickness of the cantilevers can only be thinned to 50 – 100 nm. When an even thinner cantilever needed, this technique will be lack of usability. The reason lies in that the etchant for backside wet etching causes hydraulic pressure that further causes a large deflection and plastic deformation of the nanothick silicon diaphragm. The silicon diaphragm suffers from plastic deformation and takes a shape of a wrinkled sheet. Such diaphragm will partly lose elastic properties and cannot meet the mechanical requirements. Besides, the front-side plasma dry etching will exert physical bombardment on the silicon surface and cause surface defects that will lower the quality factor of the resonant cantilever. Therefore, new etching methods free of plasma effect have to be developed.

Dry oxidation has a satisfactory control to the oxidization layer thickness and the thickness uniformity, by which the consumed silicon layer thickness can be precisely counted. The thinning method avoids plasma process induced surface defects. In addition, along with the increase in the oxidation layer thickness, the oxidization speed will slow down. In contrast, the oxidizing speed at the regions without the previous oxidation will be much higher. Using this oxidation speed difference in different regions, nanothick silicon cantilevers can be controllably formed. SOI wafers are firstly oxidized, by which the active layer thickness t is consumed into $t-t_1$. Then the oxidized layer is patterned and selectively etched off to form the cantilever shape. Thus the cantilever region still remains the SiO_2 layer, with the thickness as 2.27 t_1. Then a new oxidization is processed to consume up the entire silicon layer except for that at the cantilever region, where SiO_2 covers the silicon. At the cantilever region there is already a SiO_2 covering layer and the slower oxidation rate will finally cause a thin layer of silicon remained there. The remained silicon thickness is for the cantilever that can be precisely controlled by managing the two-time oxidation process. Then a window is opened and XeF_2 dry etching is used to laterally under-etch the substrate silicon beneath the cantilever. The etch is stopped when the designed cantilever length is reached. After the oxidation layer is removed by diluted HF, the cantilever is safely released in a CO_2 super critical point evaporation equipment [34]. Cantilevers as thin as 10 nm have been high-yield fabricated with the NEMS technique. Figures 15.11 and 15.12 show the fabrication flow and the formed cantilever image, respectively.

A simpler method is then developed for nano-mechanical beams. The beam is patterned and shaped by ion-beam etching. After oxidation, from the thin cantilever into the desired thickness, windows are opened at the double sides of the cantilever. With the photo-resist as mask, ion-beam etching is used to etch through the BOX layer and, the substrate silicon is exposed. Since the cantilever is along ⟨100⟩

orientation in the (100) wafer, anisotropic etching can be used to laterally under-etch the silicon beneath the cantilever. With this method, the beams of several tens of nanometer in thickness have been formed.

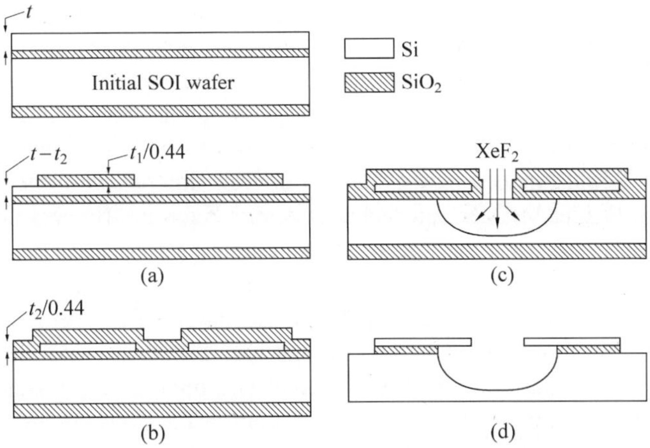

Figure 15.11 Fabrication flow for the silicon NEMS cantilever

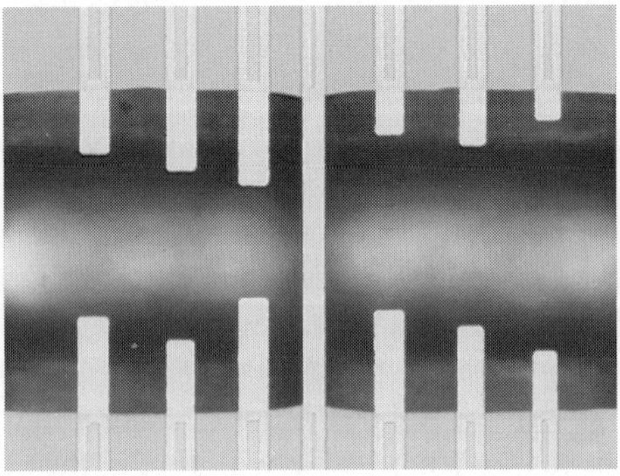

Figure 15.12 Micrograph of the formed 12 nm thick cantilever array (see color figure at the end of this book)

15.4 Nanoelectromechanical Size-Effect

As aforementioned, for a long run the theoretical basis of MEMS is still Newton mechanism and conventional electric knowledge. If MEMS history is reviewed, only two things are new that are: ① pull-in effect and, ② air-damping effect. For the macro structures, the two effects can be ignored but, in MEMS world, they have become significant and have to be taken into account. In MEMS, pull-in is an important effect. To analyze it we can solve two equations that are ① spring-mass force equilibrium equation and, ② electrostatic force balance equation. If air damping effect is taken into consideration, the solution will be perfect. Air damping control and positive application are indeed a brilliant achievement in MEMS field. In a macromachine, only when the moving speed of the structure is very high, e.g. a flying plane, the air damping effect needs to be analyzed. For slow moving ones, air damping is too weak to be considered. Sometimes people have to use the more viscous oil for damping control. When the structures are shrunk into microscale, air damping becomes to play an important role in MEMS dynamics. When people want to model the air damping, they should read the very old textbook to find the Reynolds equation that was published at the end of the 19th century. People indeed expect to find obvious micro size effects in MEMS. Especially in fluidic MEMS, microchannels with micrometric cross section were fabricated and the flow in the microchannel entered a so called slip flow regime, i.e., the flow rate at the channel wall cannot be assumed as zero. Using the micro-channels people hope to observe some unique flow properties that are significantly different from the conventional macroflow. A research fabricated a narrower orifice at the middle of the channel and integrated a series of pressure sensors along the channel and the orifice to monitor the flow-rate related pressure distribution. The experiment indeed showed that flow separation occurred just behind the orifice. However, such a floe character was already found for a macro-channel flow. In other words, the experiment only tells us that the macro flow theory can still be used for micro flow modeling. With a disappointment to the microscale phenomena, people hope to find real size effects in nanometric world.

Nonlinear resonance is the easiest observed size effect. When the resonating amplitude of a cantilever is much larger than the thickness, a harmonic resonance will occurs. The resonance frequency will largely shift and a hysteresis will take place when scanning the frequency forward and back. Such a nonlinear resonance effect is easily observed in nanothick cantilevers [35].

Nanometer is a size comparable with crystal lattice length, and NEMS structures possess relatively large surface to body ratio. If looking into it, the atom number at or near the surface, can be comparable with that in the body. Therefore many NEMS size effects are related to surface. At or near the surface of a NEMS structure, the binding condition in the lattice is quite different from that in the body, e.g. lattice relaxation effect, etc. Besides, the dangling bonds at the surface and the interaction among them will strongly influence the surface re-construction, surface oxidization and surface adsorption, etc. and, finally, induce significant surface effects.

Quality-factor (Q) value can be considered as a typical parameter for performance evaluation of mechanical resonators, as it reflects the energy dissipation of the resonant systems. For bulk structures, the Q value is mainly dominated by the material properties and is less influenced by the structural dimensions, for example, bulk single-crystal quartz is well known possessing of a high Q value. When the structure is shrunk into microscale, the environmental factors surrounding the resonator become to largely affect the Q factor. Besides, other factors like the imperfect of the supporting anchor structure also influence the Q. When the micro resonator is further shrunk into meso-scale, the energy dissipation from the inner material defects and that transferred through the anchor will dominate the Q. When the shrinkage touches nanoscale, surface atomic interaction induced fluctuation, deviation from conventional dynamics due to limited number of atoms involved in the resonance, imperfect in surface atoms and the absolute temperature determined thermal-mechanical noise, all will influence or even determine the Q. For a single-crystalline silicon cantilever, with the thickness continually decreasing from micron to nanometers, the Q value remains unchanged at first, then gradually decreases, and then linearly decreases and, finally, rapidly decreases. The different changing rates according to the difference sizes just demonstrate the acting sequence of the size-effects [36, 37]. Figure 15.13 shows the Q value of a nanothick silicon cantilever in vacuum. After special treatment, the Q value can be higher than 20,000. The results helps to elucidate that NEMS structures still bear excellent mechanical properties. The figure also shows the measured nonlinear resonance phenomena, i.e., the frequency shift due to too large resonant amplitude.

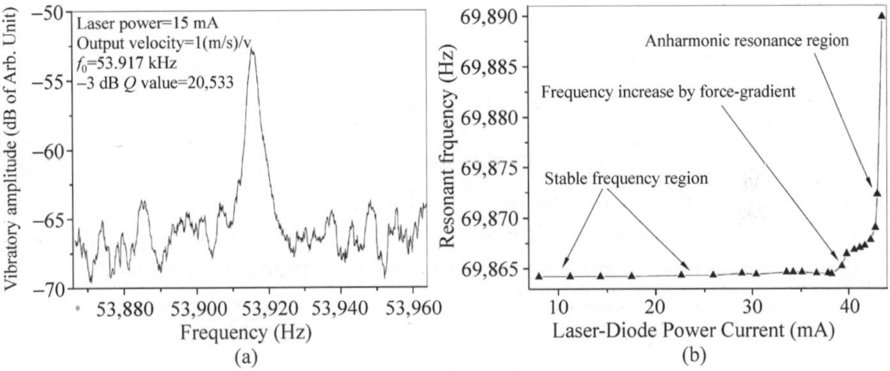

Figure 15.13 (a) 12 nm-thick cantilever is measured with a Q-factor of higher than 20,000 in vacuum. (b) Obvious nonlinear resonance phenomena (including resonance frequency shift) are measured when the amplitude is large enough

Quantum effects are easily observed in nanometric structures. As well known, the quantum effects can be at the aspects of electronics, semiconductor science, photo-electronics and magnetics, etc. Herein we would like to focus on NEMS effects, including the size effects and quantum effects, on mechanics and thermal dynamics.

The scientists at IBM California Research Center and Stanford University have studies the friction size effect when using the electric-heated NEMS probe-tip for ultra-high density data storage. Friction and wear have to be considered for the nanotip contact scanning on a high-speed rotating media thin-film. By common knowledge, such a high-speed contact scanning does cause severe wear on the tip. However, the experimental results show that the observed wear is far from expectation, i.e., a slight wear is observed after scanning for one week. In the definition of conventional friction, there is no contacting area as an effective factor, in other words, unlimited large area is assumed there. In the case of a nanotip, nonosize properties become to appear that the polymer thin-film will have both elastic and plastic deformation, under the heat and force-load applied by the nanotip. Therefore, the friction and wear under such nano situation should be redefined. Similarly, Dr. Binnig (a Nobel Prize gainer) and his colleagues found that, for nanotip thermal-mechanical data storage, the tip temperature required for thermal elastic writing is much higher than the glass transition point of the polymer film. That indicates the nano size effect on thermal transfer via the nanotip. Moreover, Dr. M. Roukes's group at Caltech, found thermal transfer quantum effect in a NEMS structure, with the results reported in Nature [38].

For 1D silicon nanowires, significant nanosize effects have been also observed. Japanese scientists fabricated the nanowires on SOI wafers by using electronic beam exposure and plasma dry etching. They further formed pressure sensors with the doped nanosilicon wires as piezoresistors [39]. They measured the piezoresistors and found that the piezoresistive sensitivity of the nanowires is significantly larger than the conventional microsized piezoresistors. Such a nanoeffect can therefore only be attributed to a lower dimensional semiconductor effect or, more precisely, attributed to quantum refinement effect.

As the broadest used material for microelectronics and MEMS, single-crystal silicon has been intensively studied about its physics parameters. At macroview point, Young's modulus of silicon acts on the relationship between elastic strain and stress and determines the MEMS deflection under a force and mechanical resonance frequency. In microview point, Young's modulus reveals the atomic bond strength in silicon crystal. Therefore, Young's modulus is considered one of important parameters of silicon. For a long period of time this parameter is treated as a fixed constant, i.e., $E = 170$ GPa. However, along with the size shrinkage, people just wonder whether its value will change or not. In 1999, American researchers used a giant computer in Navy Lab of USA to directly atomic-simulate a single-crystal silicon nanobeam structure. The atom number involved into the simulation is several million [40]. They obtained the results that, when the beam thickness is decreased into nanometers, the Young's modulus value significantly decreases, compared to that for bulk silicon. At that time, there was no experimental result to verify the size effect. However, people really expected the nanosize effect, as the atom number at or near the surface can be comparable with that in the body for a nanothick NEMS structure. In other words, surface effect will surpass the body effect to dominate the mechanical properties of a NEMS structure [41, 42]. It is easily imagined that, due to the different bond interaction style from the in-body tight-binding one, a 'skin' Young's modulus portion would contribute to the original body Young's modulus value.

Efforts have been made to fabricate ultra-thin NEMS structure for experimental testing the size effect. In 2000, Japanese researchers reported an AFM testing result for 255 nm thick silicon beams. Unfortunately, the specimen is not thin enough to observe the size effect [43]. Later, a nanomachining technique was developed (aforementioned in the last section) that can be used to fabricate 12 nm thick cantilevers. In vacuum, resonance method was used to experimentally test the significant size effect on silicon Young's modulus [44]. In details, the surface natural oxidation layer and adsorbate are removed by a pulsed heating treatment. The resonance of the nanocantilever is excited by pulsed laser light pressure. Another laser light is put near the cantilever with an optic fiber and the resonance signal is fed back to a Doppler vibration meter. The exciting signal is provided from the Doppler vibration meter. After the phase shifter, the signal is input into a chopper to generate the pulse of the driving laser to maintain the resonance of the nanocantilever. Figure 15.14 shows the measurement setup. The measured high Q-factor indicates that the resonance well satisfies the condition for mechanical energy conservation. Based on the energy conservation principle, validation of the following expression about the resonance frequency is confirmed [45]. The expression is

$$f_0 \approx 0.162(E/\rho)^{1/2} t/l^2$$

where E is Young's modulus, ρ is density, t and l are the cantilever thickness and length, respectively. Since that the measurement for t and l is very precise, the relationship between Young's modulus and resonant frequency can be calculated. For certain thickness, a cantilever array with various cantilever length is fabricated. By mathematic fitting and extraction from the relationship, the corresponding Young's modulus value can be obtained. Figure 15.14(b) shows the result of $E=68$ GP a for 38.5 nm thick silicon. By analogy, the Young's modulus values for various thicknesses can be obtained. Shown in Fig. 15.14(c), Young's modulus in terms of thickness is obtained based on measurement. It is clearly shown that the Young's modulus value drastically decreases with the thickness decrease. When the silicon is thinned to 12 nm, the Young's modulus is decreased from the bulk value of 170 GPa down to 53 GPa. To confirm the change in Young's modulus being induced by size effect but other influences, we should evaluate the change due to material heating by the exciting laser light. We heat the cantilever to different temperature and, simultaneously, measure the resonant frequency. The results shown in Fig. 15.14(d) indicate that, according to the temperature change from 20℃ to 753℃, the frequency changing is coefficient only –0.45 ppm/℃ and, the related Young's modulus variation within the whole temperature range is only 6%. In contrast, the measured Young's modulus for the 12 nm thick silicon has changed by several times. Therefore, the Young's modulus must be changed by surface size effect instead of temperature effect.

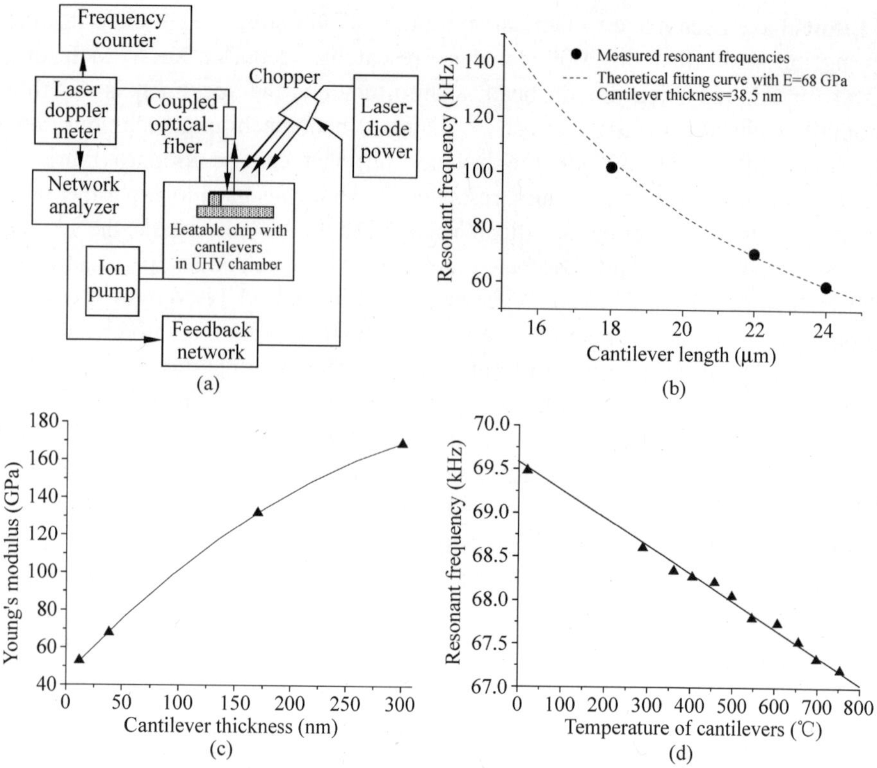

Figure 15.14 (a) Vacuum chamber and testing set-up for NEMS silicon cantilevers. (b) 68.5 GPa Young's modulus value for 38.4 nm thick cantilevers is extracted from the measured resonant frequencies of a group of cantilevers with identical thickness but different length. (c) Young's modulus in terms of silicon cantilever thickness is plotted for various silicon thickness. (d) Measured frequency of a nano-cantilever under different temperatures

Due to the very small structure of NEMS, the MEMS actuating methods, like electrostatic force or laser light pressure, really encounter difficulties in usage for NEMS. To enhance the actuating amplitude of a NEMS resonant cantilever, some effects can be used, for example, strong mechanical coupling of closely matched resonance modes can be used for this purpose. As shown in Fig. 15.15(a), two cantilevers can be mechanically linked together to form a two-degree-of-freedom system. One cantilever is very wide and another is very narrow, but, the two cantilevers have the same length, i.e.. the same resonance frequency. The wider one can be used as a light actuation. Due to the strong mode coupling, the resonance energy will be equally shared by the two cantilevers. The narrower cantilever has relatively a lower mechanical rigidity and, therefore, has a much amplified resonance amplitude for signal readout. Figure 15.15(b) shows the experimental results of the coupling induced amplitude enhancement [46]. Many such kind of effects can be developed to deal with the very small NEMS devices.

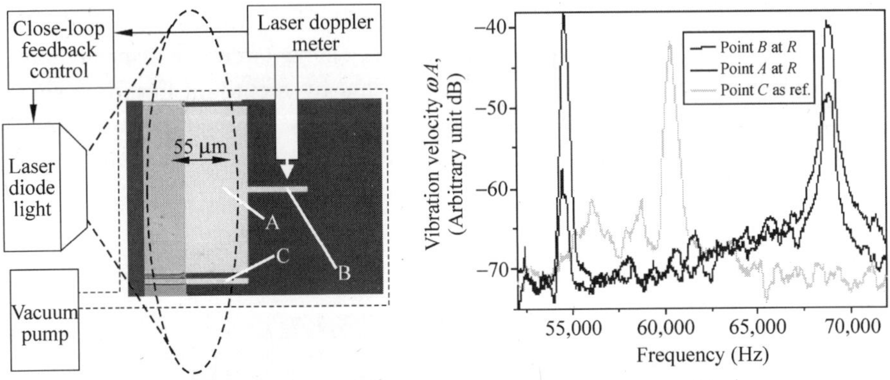

(a) (b)

Figure 15.15 (a) Micrograph of a two-degree-of-freedom NEMS resonant cantilever and the schematic of the testing setup; (b) Tested mechanical mode coupling induced sensitivity amplification (see color figure at the end of this book)

The performance just begins. In nanoscale, many NEMS effects are expected to be found. Made by integrated nanomachining technology, MEMS and NEMS can be combined to form micro/nano multi-scale systems. Many such kind of devices will be developed for detection of NEMS effects.

15.5 Typical MEMS-Made NEMS Devices

Talking about the devices made by MEMS-based NEMS techniques, people naturally recall the SPM probes. In 1980's, people learned to use AFM and STM for nanocharacterization and manipulation. The machines precisely detect the force on the microcantilever by laser light bending testing. Aided by electronic feedback circuits and piezoelectric actuators, atomic surface image was realized. In recent years, such kind of probing functions have been broadened to form a series of functional SPM probes. SPM family now consists of AFM, STP, BEEM, SICM, SThM, PSTM, SNOM, MFM and bio-dotting systems, etc. In addition to the nanoimaging functions, the SPM probes have been used for nanowriting, nanomask making and nanoline patterning, etc. and have become a kind of powerful tools for NEMS fabrication.

To make the SPM probe a high-efficient NEMS fabrication tool, people have made many efforts on solving the problem of slow scanning speed, of one probe. With the rapid development and wide applications of DSP microprocessor techniques, arrayed probes parallel work becomes a reality. A typical example is the NEMS data writing on thermal-plastic thin-film. IBM invented a 32×32 electric-heated probe array device that was named 'millipede' in which 1024 probes can parallel work, with each probe writing the nano-metric data pitches on a defined area unit. This high-speed parallel data storage technique is very promising in new generation fast ultra-high density data storage [47]. Besides the thermal writing function, piezoresistive sensing elements can be also integrated in the cantilever for electrically reading the data by recording the force signal when the probe touches and scans on the data pitches [48]. Figure 15.16 shows a 1×10 integrated probe arrays (that is made in our lab) and the nanobump data writing results.

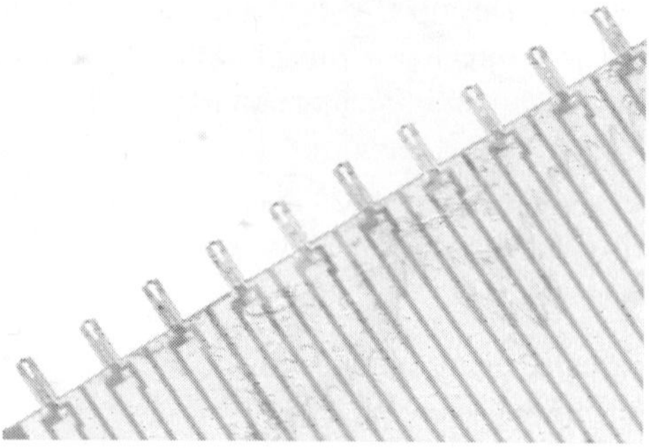

(a)

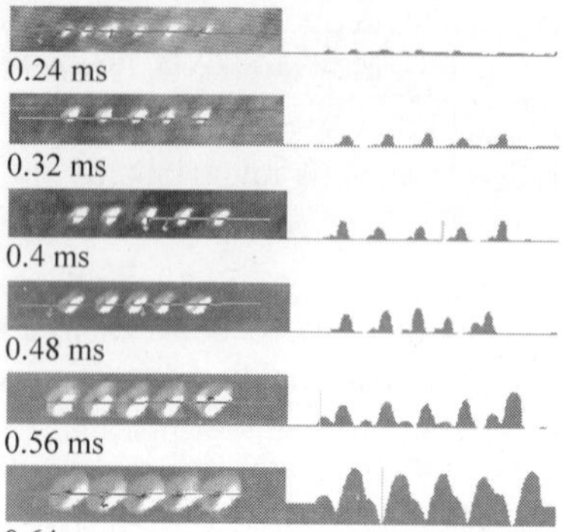

(b)

Figure 15.16 (a) Monolithically integrated 1×10 NEMS probe-array. The integrated probe consists of piezoresistive sensor in the cantilever and electric heater at the nanotip; (b) nanobump data dots writing results on a PMMA thin-film

NEMS techniques can be widely used for sensor applications. Refs. [22] and [23] have shown us the high-resolution tunneling inertial sensors. The nano story in this device lies in that, when the nanotip approaches the faced electric plate, the tunneling current across the air gap has a relationship with the air gap of

$$I \propto V_b \exp(-\alpha x \phi^{1/2})$$

where x is air gap, $\phi = 1.0251/(\text{Å}\text{eV})$ is the constant air potential barrier height, V_b is the biased voltage. Thanks to the ultra-sensitivity of tunneling current response to the air gap distance, theoretically the displacement resolution can be as high as 10^{-15} m. On the other hand, NEMS cantilever sensors have shown a great promise in ultra-sensitive bio/chemical sensor applications. Since 1990's various silicon nanomechanical cantilever biosensors have been developed and shown satisfactory resolution for detection of cells, viruses, DNAs and proteins. Although, still at a lab experiment stage, some prototypes of the products have been formed that need to be rapidly promoted into commercialization.

The cantilever-type NEMS sensors can be categorized into two kinds by operation modes, which are static cantilevers and dynamic cantilevers. The former detects bending of the cantilever. Specific reactions, like protein to protein combination, DNA stride hybridization and antigen-antibody reaction, will cause heat generation or surface stress that further cause cantilever bending. Dynamic mode means specific reaction induced mass adsorption will cause a shift in resonance frequency of the cantilever.

A kind of static stress cantilever DNA chip has been developed at IBM Zurich research center. They used the device to measure specific DNA hybridization induced cantilever bending, with an AFM-like laser light detecting method. The device works in a label-free mode, as well as, features repeatable and reliable operation. They published the achievement in Science, with the topic as 'Translating molecular recognition into nanomechanics' [49].

Such kinds of NEMS sensors use nanomachining response to characterize bio/chemical specific reaction. In other words, the sensors use a NEMS platform to detect various materials, by the aid of arrayed structures and smart algorithms. The NEMS sensors have been found possessing ultra-high sensitivity and, are called 'chemo-mechanical sensors'. These new generation sensors are expected for trace material detection [50]. Figure 15.17 shows the SEM image and the trace hydrogen detection results of a developed NEMS resonant cantilever sensor. CNTs are grown at the nanothick cantilever end and are then modified for specificity to hydrogen. Then the resonant cantilever is used to detect trace hydrogen in vacuum by recording the frequency shift. Experimental results show a high resolution of 5×10^{-18} g, i.e., the mass of tens of thousand hydrogen atoms [51]. It is predicted that the NEMS high-performance sensors will finally achieve single atom detection level [52].

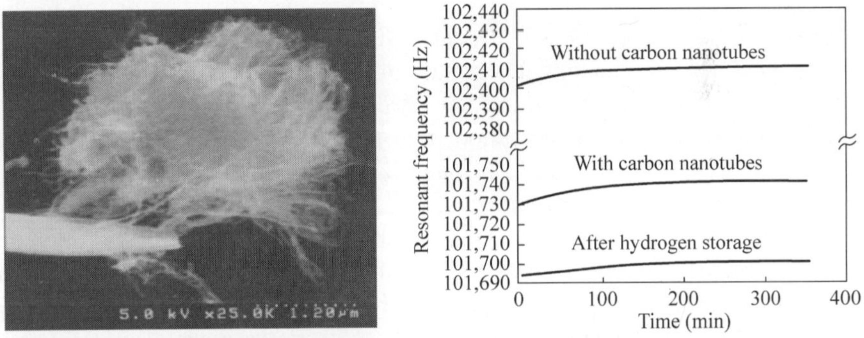

(a) (b)

Figure 15.17 (a) SEM image showing the NEMS resonant cantilever with a bound of CNTs grown at the apex for hydrogen detection. (b) Resonant detecting results for trace hydrogen gas

Due to the small dimensions of NEMS structures, its mechanical resonance frequency can be as high as the telecommunication frequency band of GHz. Making full use of the high *Q*-factor of mechanical structures, NEMS resonators can be made as resonator and band-pass filters for radio-frequency or microwave communication. Such devices have the potential of compatible integration with silicon ICs. With other advantages taken into consideration, such as low power consumption, the NEMS devices are expected to replace conventional independent components for integrated communication products [53].

NEMS cantilevers can also be used for ultra-resolution NEMS instrumentation. For example, people have tried to use cantilever to construct a micro-NMR analysis instrument. The instrument can be used for high-resolution magnetic characterization of materials by cutting and imaging the cross-section of the materials at a micron-resoluble level [54]. Further, NEMS cantilevers can be used to build micro-photo-thermal spectrum analysis systems [55]. The instrument shows a high analysis resolution to heat, with the resolution at the pJ level. The resolution is suited for analysis of a single cell or bacteria. Capable of ultra-high sensitivity and resolution of nanomechanical effects, NEMS structures and devices will contribute much to the new century applications.

15.6 Prospect of NEMS Technology

MEMS development history has generated many successful advances that can be directly applied to MEMS-based NEMS fabrication and devices. Along the MEMS path, though many techniques have been borrowed from nonsilicon precise fabrication techniques, the integration technology does serve as the mainstream fabrication methodology. The typical successful devices include air-bag accelerometers, industry- and medical- use pressure sensors, printer used nozzles, and display projectors with microoptic mirrors, etc. One important reason for the commercialization success lies in the integration mode that leads to high-reliable and low-cost mass production. The nature of the integration fabrication mode is that, the higher the producing volume, the lower the price of one device. To promote nanotechnology to commercialization, this integration-based NEMS technique should be promoted. On this basis, the nanosize effects should be applied in NEMS devices to further improve the performance.

Of course, there have been some unsuccessful examples during the development history of MEMS. We should bear them in mind when doing NEMS. Recall the electrostatic MEMS motors that were formed with surface micromachining fabrication. Such micromotors were not shrunk from the macroelectromagnetic ones simply by downward size scaling but by a new electrostatic driving method. Due to the weak force-loading capability of the electrostatic driving method, the micromotors are difficult to find applications. Unlike other microelectronic devices that have only electrical input and output signals, MEMS devices also need to contact the real word with nonelectrical signal output, e.g., force output for actuation. Integrated MEMS has to meet this kind of new requirements. On the other hand, MEMS can solve some problems in the microworld, but it cannot solve every problem. The people who want to use MEMS should learn to use the advantage of MEMS and avoid its inherent weakness. For NEMS, this kind of strategy is even more critical. More importantly, NEMS will exhibit even more size effects. How to coordinate the conventional properties with the new effects? This question deserves more consideration.

In the MEMS-based NEMS, a new model for micro- and nano- multi-size coupling is needed. Up to now, tight binding theory, coarsely grained molecule dynamics, and finite-element analysis have been independently used to deal with the nanoscale, micro/nanocombined scale and microscale problems. Recently some research aims to seamlessly couple the different theories for multi-scale modeling. In a nanosystem that consists only of a limited number of atoms, the models based on first principle or direct atomic simulation have been built. On the other hand, the finite-element analysis method is quite mature for microscale simulation. Future work will focus on micro-to-nano multi-scale modeling.

Currently the bottom-up method is frequently used in nanomaterials. However, when constructing nanodevices such as nano-sensors, a top-down dominant NEMS integration method will be a very useful tool. No matter how excellent the nano-materials, integration is the only method to encorporate them into a device structure. In fact, top-down and bottom-up combination method will dominate NEMS for a long time.

In conclusion, extended from MEMS fabrication and combined with bottom-up nanoscience and technology, top-down NEMS integration will become a very useful method for nanodevices, especially for NEMS commercialization.

The author would like to thank Prof. Masayoshi Esashi, Prof. Takahito Ono, Dr. Dong-Weon Lee, Dr. Phan Ngoc Minh, Dr. Jinling Yang and other investigators in Tohoku University for providing their micrographs. My colleagues in the State Key Lab of Transducer Technology of China also deserve deep appreciation for their help and advisory discussions. Xinxin Li also thanks to the support from the NSFC Project (60725414) and Korean WCU project (R32-2009-000-20087-0).

References

[1] Bean K. E., (1978), Anisotropic etching of silicon, *IEEE Trans.Electron Devices*, **ED-25**: 1185 – 1193

[2] Robbins H. R. and B. Schwartz, (1976), Chemical etching of silicon—Ⅳ. Etching technology, *J. Electrochem. Soc.*, **123**(12): 1903 – 1909

[3] Bassous E., (1978), Fabrication of novel three-dimensional micro-structures by the anisotropic etching of (100) and (110) silicon, *IEEE Trans. Electron Devices*, **ED-25**: 178 – 1185

[4] Li Xinxin, Minhang Bao and Shaoqun Shen, (1996), Maskless etching of three-dimensional silicon structures in KOH, *Sensors and Actuators A*, **57**(1996): 47 – 52

[5] Li Xinxin, Minhang Bao, (2001), Micro-machining of multi-thickness sensor array structures with dual-stage etching etching Technology, *Journal of Micromechanics and Microengineering*, **11**(2001): 239 – 244

[6] Schmidt M. A., (1998), Wafer-to-wafer bonding for microstructure formation, *Proceedings of the IEEE*, **86**(8): 1575 – 1585

[7] Li Xinxin, M. H. Bao, and S. Q. Shen, (1997), Study on linearization of silicon capacitive pressure sensors, *Sensors and Actuators A*, **63**(1): 1 – 6

[8] Li Xinxin, M. H. Bao, H. Yang, S. Q. Shen, D. R. Lu., (1999), A micro machined piezoresistive angular rate sensor with a composite beam structure, *Sensors and Actuators A*, **72**: 217 – 223

[9] Peterson K., (1982), Silicon as a mechanical material, *Proceedings of the IEEE*, **70**(5): 420 – 457

[10] Bustillo J. M., R. T. Howe, R. S. Muller, (1998), Surface micro-machining for microelectro-mechanical systems, *Proceedings of the IEEE*, **86**(8): 1552 – 1574

[11] Li Xinxin, W. Y. Lee, Man Wong, (2000), Yitshak Zohar, Gas flow in constriction micro-devices, *Sensors and Actuators A*, **83**: 277 – 283

[12] Muller R. S., K. Y. Lau, (1998), Surface-micromachined micro-optical elements and systems, *Proceedings of the IEEE*, **86**(8): 1705 – 1720

[13] Nguyen C. T. –C., L. P. B. Katehi, G. M. Rebeiz, (1998), Micromachined devices for wireless communications, *Proceedings of the IEEE*, **86**(8): 1756 – 1768

[14] Guckel H., (1998), High-aspect-ratio micro-machining via deep X-ray lithography, *Proceedings of the IEEE*, **86**(8): 1586 – 1593

[15] Lorenz H., et al., (1998), High aspect ratio, ultrathick, negative-tone near-UV photoresist and its applications for MEMS, *Sens. Actuators A*, **64**(1): 33 – 39

[16] Shaw K. A., Z. L. Zhang, and N. C. MacDonald, (1994), SCREAM I: A single mask, single-crystal silicon, reactive ion etching process for microelectromechanical structures, *Sens. Actuators A*, **40**: 63 – 70

[17] Madou M., (1997), Fundamentals of Microfabrication, CRC Press LLC

[18] Lee S., S. Park, D. Cho, (1999), The Surface/Bulk Micro-machining (SBM) Process: A New Method for Fabricating Released MEMS in Single Crystal Silicon, *J. Microelectromech. Syst.*, **8**(4): 409 – 416

[19] Mehra A., A. A. Ayon, I. A. Waitz, M. A. Schmidt, (1999), Microfabrication of high-temperature silicon devices using wafer bonding and deep reactive ion etching, *Journal of Microelectromechanical Syatems*, **8**(2): 152 – 160

[20] Mehra A., X. Zhang, X. Ayon, A. Waitz, M. Schmidt, C. Spadaccini, (2000), A 6-wafer combustion system for a silicon micro gas turbine engine, *Journal of Microelectromechanical Syatems*, **9**(4): 517 – 527

[21] Pourkamali S., A. Hashimura, R. Abdolvand, G. K. Ho, A. Erbil, F. Ayazi, (2000), High-Q single crystal silicon HARPSS capacitive beam resonators with self-aligned sub-100 nm transduction gaps, *Journal of Microelectromechanical Syatems*, **12**(4): 487 – 496

[22] Kenny T. W., W. J. Kaiser, et al, (1991), Micromachined silicon tunnel sensors for motion detection, *Appl. Phys. Lett.*, **58**(1): 100 – 102

[23] Chang D. T., F. P. Stratton, R. L. Kubena, D. J. V. Kirby, R. J. Joyce, T. R. Schimert, R. W. Gooch, (2000), New fabrication techniques for high dynamic range tunneling sensors, *Proceedings of SPIE*, **4176**: 68 – 73

[24] Binnig G., C. F. Quate, C. Gerber, (1986), Atomic force microscope, *Phys. Rev. Letters*, **56**(9): 930

[25] Binnig G., H. Rohrer, (1987), Scanning tunneling microscopy-from birth to adolescence, *Review of Modern Physics*, **59**(3), Part 1: 615

[26] Ravi T. S., R. B. Marcus, D. Liu, (1991), Oxidation sharpening of silicon tips, *J. Vac. Sci. Technol. B*, **9**(6): 2733 – 2737

[27] Y. Zunxian, Xinxin Li et al, (2003), Micro cantilever probe array with integration of electro-thermal nano tip and piezoresistive sensor, *Proceedings of IEEE Sensors'2003*, **2**: 830 – 833

[28] Minh Phan Ngoc, T. Ono, M. Esashi, (1999), Nonuniform silicon oxidation and application for the fabrication of aperture for near-field scanning optical microscopy, *APPLIED PHYSICS LETTERS*, **75**(26): 4076 – 4078

[29] Brugger J., R. A. Buser, N. F. de Rooij, (1992), Silicon cantilevers and tips for scanning force microscopy, *Sens. Actuators*, **34-3**: 193 – 200

[30] L. Dong-Weon, T. Ono, T. Abe, and M. Esashi, (2002), Microprobe Array With Electrical Interconnection for Thermal Imaging and Data Storage, *Journal of Microelectromechanical Syatems*, **11**(3): 215 – 221

[31] Takahito Ono, H. Miyashita and M. Esashi, (2002), Electric-field-enhanced growth of carbon nanotubes for scanning probe microscopy, *Nanotechnology*, **13**: 62 – 64

[32] Phan Ngoc Minh, Le T. T. Tuyen, et al, (2003), Selective growth of carbon nano-tubes on Si microfabricated tips and application for electron field emitters, *J. Vac. Sci. Technol.*, **B 21**(4): 1705 – 1709

[33] Yang Jinling, T. Ono, and M. Esashi, (2000), Mechanical Behavior of Ultrathin Microcantilever, *Sensors and Actuators*, **A82**: 102 – 107

[34] Takahito Ono, X. X. Li, and D. W. Lee, (2001), Hidetoshi,Miyashita,Nano-metric Sensing and Processing with Micromachined Functional Probe, *Technical Digest of Transducers'01*, **11**(1): 1062 – 1068

[35] Li Xinxin, T. Ono, Y. L. Wang, M. Esashi, (2002), STUDY ON ULTRA-THIN MEMS CANTILEVERS-HIGH YIELD FABRICATION AND SIZE-EFFECT ON YOUNG'S MODULUS OF SILICON, *Proceedings of IEEE International Conference on Micro Electro Mechanical Systems*, **15**: 427 – 430

[36] Yang J., T. Ono, M. Esashi, (2002), Energy Dissipation in Submicrometer Thick Single-Crystal Silicon Cantilevers, *Journal of Microelectromechanical Systems*, **11**(6): 775 – 783

[37] Yasumura K. Y., T. D. Stowe, E. M. Chow, T. Pfafman, T. W. Kenny, B. C. Stipe, and D. Rugar, (2000), "Quality factors in micro- and submicron-thick cantilevers," *J. Microelectromech. Syst.*, **9**: 117 – 125

[38] Schwab K., E. A. Henriksen, J. M. Worlock, M. L. Roukes, (2000), Measurement of the quantum of thermal conductance, *NATURE*, **404**(27): 974 – 977

[39] Toshiyuki Toriyamaa, D. Funai and S. Sugiyama, Piezoresistance measurement on single crystal silicon nanowires, *Journal of Applied Physics*, **93**(1): 561 – 565

[40] Broughton J. Q., C. A. Meli, P. Vashishta, K. Kalia, (1997), Direct atomistic simulation of quartz crystal oscillators: Bulk properties and nano-scale devices, *Phys. Rev.* **B 56**, 611

[41] Broughton J. Q., F. F. Abraham, N. Bernstein, E. Kaxiras, (1999), Concurrent coupling of length scales: Methodology and application, *Phys. Rev. B*, **60**: 2391

[42] Rudd R. E., J. Q. Broughton, (1999), Atomistic simulation of MEMS resonators through

the coupling of length scales, *Journal of Modeling and Simulation of Microsystems*, **1**: 29

[43] Namazu T., Y. Isono, T. Tanaka, (2002), *J. Microelectromechanical Sys*. **9**: 450

[44] Li Xinxin, T. Ono, Y. L. Wang, M. Esashi, (2003), Ultra thin single-crystalline-silicon cantilever resonators: Fabrication technology and significant specimen size effect on Young's modulus, *Applied Physics Letters, Volume* **83**(15): 3081 – 3083

[45] Bao Min-hang, (2000), Micro Mechanical Transducers—pressure sensors, accelerometers and gyroscopes, Ed. by Simon Middelhoek, ELSEVIER, 2000, Chapter 2

[46] Li Xinxin, T. Ono, R. Lin, M. Esashi, (2003), Resonance Enhancement of Micromachined Resonators with Strong Mechanical-coupling between Two Degrees of Freedom, *Microelectronic Engineering,* **65**: 1 – 12

[47] Vettiger P., T. Albrecht et al, (2003), Thousands microcantilevers for highly parallel and ultra-dense data storage, *IEEE International Electron Device Meeting—IEDM2003*, Washington DC, Dec. 2003: 763 – 766

[48] Yang Zunxian, X. X. Li, Y. L. Wang, H. F. Bao, M. Liu, (2004), Micro cantilever probe array integrated with Piezoresistive sensor, *Microelectronics Journal*, **35**: 479 – 483

[49] Fritz J., M.K. Baller, H.P. Lang, H. Rothuizen, P. Vettiger, E. Meyer, H.-J. Güntherodt, Ch. Gerber, J.K. Gimzewski, (2000), "Translating Biomolecular Recognition into Nanomechanics", *Science*, 288: 316 – 318

[50] Hagleitner C., A. Hierlemann, D. Lange, A. Kummer, N. Kerness, O. Brand, H. Baltes, (2001), Smart single-chip gas sensor microsystem, *Nature* **414**: 293 – 296

[51] Ono T., X. X. Li, and H. Miyashita, Masayoshi Esashi, (2003), Mass sensing of adsorbed molecules in sub-picogram sample with ultrathin silicon resonator, REVIEW OF SCIENTIFIC INSTRUMENTS, VOLUME 74, NUMBER 3, MARCH, 2003, 1240 – 1243

[52] Ekinci K., X. Huang, M. Roukes, (2004), Ultrasensitive nanoelectromechanical mass detection, APPLIED PHYSICS LETTERS, **84**(22): 4469 – 4471

[53] Xùe M., H. Huang, C. A. Zorman, M. Mehregany, M. L. Roukes, (2003), Nanodevice motion at microwave frequencies, Nature, **421**: 496

[54] Rugar D., O. Zuger, S. Hoen, C. S. Yannoni, H. M. Vieth, R. D. Kendrick, (1994), Force detection of nuclear magnetic resonance, *Science*, **264**: 1560 – 1563

[55] Barnes J. R., R. J. Stephenson, M. E. Welland, Ch. Gerber, J. K. Gimzewski, (1994), Photothermal spectroscopy with femtojoule sensitivity using a micromachined devices, *Nature*, **372**: 79 – 81

Application Issues

16 Applications of Microelectro-Mechanical Systems

Wen H. Ko

Pen-Tung Sah Research Center, Xiamen University, Xiamen, 361005, China
EECS Department, Case Western Reserve University, Cleveland, Ohio, USA
E-mail: whk@cwru.edu

Abstract The Chapter introduces the brief history and trends of MEMS, application of MEMS, an important opening application field—bio-medical applications, and applications of implantable MEMS—physical therapy, medical care and drug developments. The application of MEMS permeates broadly into all fields of Sciences and Engineering activities. MEMS applications will expand rapidly in all fields, in the near future.

Keywords MEMS, implantable MEMS, biomedicine, MEMS application

16.1 Brief History and Trends of Microelectro-Mechanical System

The micromachining technology has been derived from the semiconductor electronics and integrated circuit technologies. Early in the 5th decade of the 20th century, optical lithography was used in printed circuits fabrication, and semiconductor etching also was a process step in the fabrication of transistors and other electronic elements. The isotropic and anisotropic etching of germanium and silicon was discussed in many of papers in the Bell System Technical Journal around 1950. Many of microelectro-mechanical system (MEMS) fundamentals and theories were also formed by 1950. For example, Dr. C.C. Smith, in 1953, measured the piezoresistivity coefficients of germanium and silicon[1], and many members of Bell Laboratories studied the piezoresistive materials that opened the door for designing piezoresistive sensors and transducers. Similarly, the early studies of W. P. Mason and Bell Laboratories members on piezoelectric materials and devices[2] led to the piezoelectric sensors and actuators of today. All current MEMS elements and systems have been built upon the previous scientific research and technology advances.

In the 1960s, and 1970s, semiconductor microelectronics and integrated circuit technology advanced rapidly. These technological advances became the foundation of the sensor and actuator technology. Adding the bonding and packaging technologies, practical microsensors for strain, pressure, flow, gas, pH, biochemical, and other were realized. Early researchers in this field recognized that there was a need for a specialized journal in this new field, i.e., when the 'Sensors and Actuators' was boned in 1980.

By 1980, the precision technologies for mass production of microelectronics and integrated circuits were mature. The micromachining technology was adopted for mass-quantity fabrication of micromechanical elements, and chemical, physical, biological sensors and actuators, and when they were embedded with large scale I.C. and computing circuits, another industrial revolution was inaugurated. During the period 1986 to 1988, U.C. Berkeley and MIT fabricated micromotors and published papers on them, nearly at the same time. In November, 1987, the National Science Foundation of USA called a meeting at Hyannis, Massachusetts, to discuss possible research in microrobots, sensors, and actuators. By 1988 the term Microelectro-Mechanical System or MEMS was created which opened up a new field of engineering and industrial research and development. In the same year, the IEEE and ASME joint publication, the Journal of Microelectro-Mechanical Systems (J.MEMS) had its first issue. Many other journals, news-letters and publications related to MEMS, micromachining, sensors, and transducers were started throughout the world communities.

From 1980 – 1990, great progress was expected of MEMS, because it could use micromachining techniques to fabricate traditional mechanical, electrical, chemical, biological and medical devices with much smaller volume, higher performance, and lower unit cost. As one aspect, it could fabricate/compose all-new microsystems through new research and new development for new applications which were impossible without MEMS technology, such as devices/systems used in aerospace, military, and medical fields. As another aspect, it could be used to improve existing systems performance and manufacturing techniques of devices/systems, to have them integrated with microelectronics and computers, making them high performance, low cost, mass-manufactured functional devices or systems, such as microsensors and actuators, automated control systems, precision instruments, and other scientific research equipment.

In this period, every region of the world was investing large resources in MEMS research and development. US universities and research institutions set up MEMS curricula and research; aerospace and military organizations and large electronic industries also pushed aggressively on MEMS design and fabrication. Japan, in 1989, organized government, research institutes, universities and industries to establish the Micromachining Center, with the goal to develop technology and functional systems to survey, monitor, and repair various underground pipes and channels, as well as blood vessels and respiration channels in the body. The constituent units of the Center worked on the theory, design, fabrication, and operation needed for the final system, according to their specialty, while collaboratively aimed to build-up and advance the MEMS science, technology and applications. European countries also invested large resources to support universities, research institutes, and industries to engage in MEMS research and fabrication of functional highly-valued devices. The LIGA process for mass fabrication of delicate components and many optical MEMS devices are just a few successful examples.

By the decade of 1990, many MEMS industries were quickly established. The capital asset of each company increased, with time, from hundred thousands to ten millions of dollars. MEMS moved from laboratory curiosity to industrial products. Just like the other major industrial technologies, such as transistors, integrated circuits, and computers, MEMS progressed through the stages of discovery, laboratory trial, sample design, and pilot applications in 20 years, and is now ready for industrial product development, manufacturing, commercial applications and exploration of new uses. MEMS permeated through all industrial and research fields to improve product performance, working methods and tools to satisfy the high-tech needs in these areas.

In the 21st century, MEMS is expected to grow into a branch of the new industrial high-tech forces. MEMS integrated with the nanotechnology and materials will surely create another new era of research and applications.

Like all other new science and technology, the final goal of MEMS is the practical usage of the knowledge and products to satisfy people's needs, to improve social welfare, and to raise the living standard of humanity. MEMS involves methods, technology, and tools to fabricate microsize devices and systems. It is a way to satisfy some needs of industries and sciences. Its application can be in all fields of human activities and interests. Table 16.1, in the next section, gives some well-known examples of applications.

There are two categories of successful applications:

(1) For applications that are possible only with MEMS technology, such as microfabricated instruments for aerospace explosion, flight control devices embedded in the bullet head for military, and implant monitors, actuators and therapeutic systems for bio-medical fields. Only with the combination of MEMS and LSI-MOS circuits can the practical systems be realized, with the required small volume and weight.

(2) In successful applications where MEMS can provide better performance with lower unit cost. For example: connectors for optical cables, optical switches between fibers in optical communication systems, SiC coated nozzles for diesel engines, ink-jet heads in printers, CVD or DVD read- and write- heads in computers and consumer products, etc.

When developing MEMS applications, we should select the ones that can satisfy existing needs (markets). Actually, the needs usually are not just sensors and actuators but the functional working systems. Therefore, while designing an MEMS one should also consider the overall integration of packaging, interface circuits and computing or signal processing circuits. Good applications are those devices/systems that can meet existing needs and can fulfill desired functions

Table 16.1 Examples of existing applications of MEMS

Fields of Application	MEMS Products	Applications
Automotive	Accelerometer, gyroscopes pressure sensor flow sensor temperature	Air bag, vehicle dynamic control, roll-over sensing and control air intake, fuel injection, HVAC, brake, gearbox oil, tire air, oil humidity, vibration, cabin compact
Aeronautic/Aerospace Military	Accelerometer, gyroscope, barometer, sheer sensor, microactuator, pressure sensors, bio, chemical sensors, biochips, lap-on chip, RF MEMS	Inertial navigation, IFR imaging, air flow control on airplane wings, altitude control, engine control, detection of biochemical weapons, communication, smart munitions
Information Technology	Accelerometer, gyroscope, disk drive head (microcontrol system) inject printer head, microdisplay (mirrors) optical sensors	Joystick, disk and camera stabilization, data storage & retrieval printers, video projections, potable systems, computer mouse
Biomedical	Microsize microphone, speaker, stimulating electrodes, drug pumps, micronozzle, smart drug delivery system, pressure sensor	Hearing aids, cochlear implants, nerve, stimulator, insulin or other drug delivery, drug injection, smart pills, active patch, blood pressure, body fluid pressure
Process control automation	Pressure, acceleration, angle, temperature, and flow sensors, magnetic, gas, biosensors, micropumps, mechanical actuators	Quality control in food and manufacturing industries, automation of manufacturing, management and safety control
Tele communication	Microminors, tunable filters tunable capacitors, inductors optical source & detectors v-groove connector	Channel switching, optical attenuator signal routing, control optical communication, tunable lasers optical fiber alignment
Environmental	Acceleration, pressure, flow, biochemical sensor, biochips, ion sensor, particles sensors, uTAS analysis systems	Vibration/seismic detection pollution control, weather monitoring water and air quality monitoring
Science and instrumentation	Physical, chemical, biological sensors, actuators biochips, lab on chips, microspectrometer	New scientific research, such as dna study, protein, cell study, physical sciences studies surface physics, micro/nano material studies, engineering studies
Consumer/home	Pressure, acceleration, tough, sensors; flow, humidity, temperature sensor; flat panel display	Washing machine, iron, position sensing, HVAC, comfort control, automated house keeping robots, TV, DVD…

reliably. Frequently, one needed function can be met by several MEMS and circuit combinations; also frequently one MEMS device/system can satisfy several needs with minor changes in the design or system integration.

16.2 Application of MEMS

The application of MEMS permeates broadly into all fields of sciences and engineering activities. The few cases mentioned here are just small samples of the vast application fields. Table 16. 1 below lists some well-known samples in major science and technology fields. It is used to illustrate that MEMS applications spread over all scientific research, industrial, entertainment, information process, communication, military and space exploration fields. Furthermore, in each field, the samples are small representatives of the total applications. MEMS applications will expand rapidly in all fields in the near future.

Looking into the future, it is believed that applications of MEMS will expand in each field and there will be new application fields opening up as the technology moves forward. Table 16.2 lists possible growth area of MEMS applications in the next 10 years, according to some researchers. As it now appears, human society would develop new needs that require MEMS to provide technical methods, devices/system designs, and functional products to satisfy these new needs. The items listed in Table 16.2 are the views of a small group of MEMS workers. The inclusion of the list is aimed to stimulate reader's interest and questions leading to more serious search, examine, and explore future application fields.

Table 16.2 Examples of developing applications of MEMS

Application field	MEMS products	Applications/functions
Automation of agriculture	Sensors, actuators systems	Automated monitor and application of humidity, fertilizer, insecticide, farm animal monitor; improve farm product harvest, sorage, and packaging
Environment	Functional monitoring and data analysis systems MEMS network	Monitor, protect and regenerate fresh water resources, forest, ocean and atmosphere monitoring and study of large structures and nature's disastrous events
Biomedical	Medical instruments health monitoring system	Medical research, individualized health care, preventive medicine
	Functional health care instruments and processes	Diagnosis & therapy individualized health care
Home/consumer	Functional home appliances and systems	Safety, automated home environment control, automated appliances

16.3 An Important Opening Application Field-Bio-Medical Applications

The MEMS applications with the most social impact are those that can only be achieved with MEMS technology and that can meet the most important human needs. Besides aerospace exploration, biomedical research and clinical medicine are in this category. Biology and physiology research and clinical medical care often require: small, light-weight, fast-response, and easy to operate equipment and processes that can also be mass manufactured at low cost. These requirements can't be met with traditional technologies. In these aspects, MEMS has advantages as compared with traditional technologies. MEMS products, when incorporated with microelectronics, integrated circuits, and computing blocks, can become small-volume, low power consumption, on-line analysis, and quick-response equipments to satisfy the needs of biological research and clinical care. At the same time humanity has great interest and eagerness to understand the body's status as well as treatment of illness and pain in body or mind. Therefore, the applications in these areas, although much more difficult to develop, would have high impact and rapid advances.

Presently, there are products and applications in these fields but they accomplish a very small portion of the desired needs. In the past, the application of MEMS begins with automobile, military, industry, and communication. With limited trained personal and resources, the application in the biomedical field was tabled. Furthermore, MEMS is an engineering technology whose scientific base is different from biology and medicine. In order to develop MEMS applications in the biomedical field, the team has to have the collaboration of personnel from both classes of disciplines. Therefore the advances are more difficult. Owning to these factors, the application of MEMS in biomedical fields lagged behind. However, the situation is changing. The trained personnel has increased significantly, both in MEMS and in multidisciplinary fields, such as the now-popular biomedical engineering or MD/Ph. D programs. Many talented people are interested in biomedical applications of MEMS. The success of 'Bio-Chip' in genetic research and DNA therapy opened the door for MEMS to collaborate with biomedical researchers in research and applications. Therefore, the application of MEMS in biology / physiology research, clinical care, as well as drug screening should see accelerated advances.

There are three classes of biomedical applications of MEMS:

(1) Research in Biology, Medicine, and Pharmacology   Starting from recording the sequence of DNA to finding the relationship of each genetic segment (gene) of the body functions and illness, many new instruments, facilities, and research techniques would be needed. MEMS may contribute significantly in the research equipment and method or processes in these areas. Biochips have shown their great value in DNA and gene studies. In the work to recognize and record the

sequence of human DNA, biochips have sped up the work several thousand times as compared to traditional processes. MEMS will contribute in the system to uncover functions of each gene and their specific relation with the body function and diseases. MEMS will be needed to provide research instruments, equipment, and systems for research from DNA, to gene, to cells, to organs, to human body and to communities.

(2) Individualized Medicine The present medicines and procedures are developed based on an 'average person', derived from statistics. However, we know that no one is an 'average person'. Therefore, the current medicine and procedure can only expect to have 'average effects' on patients. There are some medical treatments that are non-effective or even with atypical reactions harmful to the unfortunate patients. We would like the future medical care to go beyond the 'average person' treatment to consider the individual's special situation and adjust the treatment according to the individual conditions. This is a monumental job. But it is believed that MEMS together with information technology and computers will make significant advances in this endeavor.

(3) Improved Medical Care to Patients In the diagnoses area, MEMS, with its fast, simple ways can acquire physiological parameters of a patient for quick, accurate diagnosis. MEMS also can be used to collect data on long-term physiological parameters in people, to establish the 'normal' of that person. By comparing normal data with the data when the person is ill, a better and more accurate diagnosis can be made. In the therapy area, various improved treatment techniques can be developed with MEMS, such as: remote control of microsurgery, painless injection, chronic automatic drug delivery, minimally invasive procedures, tissue engineering, speedy recovery with electrical stimulations, implant prostheses, and many others.

16.4 Applications of Implantable MEMS—Physical Therapy, Medical Care and Drug Developments

In biology and physiology research, medical care, and drug development areas, MEMS, with its small, fast and convenience characteristics, can provide many improved or new applications. One of the special areas is the 'Applications of Implantable MEMS', which means that the packaged, functional, MEMS system is implanted in or attached to a body for monitoring or therapy.

Early in the 1960s, implantable monitoring systems using electrode sensors and radio-frequency communication links were demonstrated in several universities called as 'biotelemetry systems' at that time. Nearly all the concepts and feasibility demonstrations in implantable remote sensing and control systems were explored in the 1960 – 1970 period[5–8]. For example: to implant multi-channel remote sensing, multiple channel remote stimulation, and closed-loop control systems were demonstrated; the experiment to use the voluntary EMG signals transmitted from an implanted telemetry sensing device; to control external machinery; experiments that use implanted sensing and stimulating systems to communicate with the central nervous system of the body to access the emotional status and to control a monkey's emotion and behavior was demonstrated, etc. All these experiments were made in the 1960 – 1970 period, with the 'miniaturization techniques' of the post second-world-war age. However, because the microelectronics and micromachining technologies were not yet developed, these implant systems which had large volume (in cm^3), consumed large power (in milliwatts) and did not have suitable packaging materials and techniques, the costs were very high and were not practical, except for the treatment of critical illness such as the heart pacemakers and aerospace experiments. There was a semi-hibernating period in this field from 1970 – 1990.

Now with MEMS incorporated with MOS Large scale IC and computer circuits, the total volume and power required has become thousands of to ten thousands of times smaller. The implantable MEMS systems have became practical and can now become an important application of MEMS in biomedical fields.

Implantable MEMS functional systems can be equipped with various sensors to monitor the body condition through RF links. The sensed signal may include EKG, EEG, EMG, blood pressure, flow, microcirculation, biochemical parameters and many others. The MEMS system can also incorporate electrodes or other mechanical, chemical, biological sensors and actuators for remote-controlled therapy, such as functional electrical stimulation (FES), automated drug release, pain suppression, epilepsy control, depression and psychological treatment, cancer therapy, etc.

One of the important undertakings of MEMS may be in the biological/physiological research and drug screening areas. When small animals are used for drug response experiments, small number of animals can be implanted with monitoring systems to record their responses toward several drugs in a time sequence to determine the relative merits of these drugs, instead of sacrificing the animals, as traditionally happened to get the response to a drug treatment. Because the same group of animals was used for different drugs, the variation in different experimental animals for different drugs was eliminated. The number of data samples can be reduced, thus reducing expense and time. Furthermore, when examining a drug response, not only are the final results obtained, but also the change of body response during the treatment period can be accessed thus saving much time and cost. Similarly, by implanting a monitoring system in the patient for long periods, continuous data on the patient condition and response to various treatments may be gathered to reach improved final outcomes. For example, for patients after cancer therapy or extensive heart surgery, the implant system can be used to release medicine on a controlled schedule, and to monitor the response to treatment and the state of recovery which allows adjustment in treatment when needed.

Besides common diagnosis and treatment, the MEMS system can have important application in orthotics and prosthesis[7]. Besides artificial limbs, by incorporating functional electrical stimulation[8] and neural control techniques, MEMS may be used in ① visual prosthesis; ② hearing aids, cochlear implant; ③ electrical stimulation for pain suppression; ④ diaphragm pacing; ⑤ heart pacing and de-fibrillation; ⑥ bladder control; ⑦ epileptic seizure suppression; ⑧ hand gripping aid, arm aid, mobility stimulation, muscle building, and many others.

Similarly, in the future, artificial organ or organ repair will benefit from implantable MEMS systems for monitoring, actuation and control.

Although 'Implantable MEMS Systems' may have many significant applications, they have to be attached on the surface or implanted in the body through some procedures. There are many additional problems to be resolved, beyond considerations for industrial applications that include: ① small total package volume; ② electrical power source, or body-powered converter devices; ③ micropower wireless communication techniques; ④ biocompatible packaging techniques that can protect the body and the implantable system; ⑤ sensors and actuators that can operate in the body for a long time without being damaged by antibodies or the environment; ⑥ sensors and actuators that can be fabricated with reasonable cost.

There are literatures on the implantable systems in animals[8, 9]. The implantable systems in the human body would have much more difficult problems to be resolved[10–12]. These are not simple problems; however, once they are resolved, the significance or impact also would be far larger than industrial applications. This field is a special application of MEMS in biomedical areas that deserves concentrated effort and attention.

References

[1] Smith C. S., (1954), Piezoresistive effect in germanium and silicon, *Phys. Rev.* **94**: 42 – 49

[2] Mason W. P., (1950), Piezoelectric Crystals and Their Application to Ultrasonics, Van Northland, New York, NY

[3] Fan L. S., Y. C. Tai, and R. S. Muller, (1988), IC Processed Electrostatic Micromotors, Proc. *IEEE Int. Elect. Dev Meeting*, San Francisco CA, 666 – 669

[4] Mehregany M., S. F. Bart, et al., (1989), A Study of three microfabricated Variable Capacitance Micromotors, *Proc. Transducer 89 and Euro sensor III.* Montreux, Switzerland, 173 – 179

[5] Ko W. H., (1966), Telemeter of Biological Signals: Biotelemetry.Handbook of Biochemistry and Biophysics. World Publishing Co., Cleveland, OH, USA, 636 – 643

[6] Ko W. H., and M. R. Neuman, (1967), Implant Biotelemetry and Microelectronics. *Science* **156**(773): 351 – 360

[7] Ko W. H., J. Mugica, A. Ripart, (1985), Implantable sensors for closed-loop prosthetic systems. Futura Pub. Co, Mount Kisco, New York, NY

[8] Hambrecht F. T., J. B. Reswick, (1977), Functional Electrical Stimulation: Applications in Neural Prostheses. Marcel Dekker, New York, NY

[9] Amlaner C. G., and D. M. MacDonald, (1980), *A Handbook on Biotelemetry and Radio Tracking.* Pergamon Press, Oxford and New York

[10] Ko W. H., (1996), The future of sensors and actuators systems. *Sensors and Actuators: A Physical*, **056** (1 – 2): 193 – 196

[11] Ko W. H., (2007), Trends and Frontiers of MEMS. *Sensors and Actuators: A Physical,* **136**: 62 – 67

[12] Updated references on "Implantable biomedical systems" from IEEE-EMNS, Google or other search engines

17 Microelectromechanical Sensor-Based System

Zhaoying Zhou, Rong Zhu, Xu Fu, and Ganghua Zhang

Department of Precision Instruments and Machanology, Tsinghua University, Beijing, 100084, China

E-mail: zhouzy@mail.tsinghua.edu.cn

Abstract The microelectromechanical sensor-based system refers to the microsensor group or the microsensor cluster and their composite application. The multi-sensor integration and fusion technology has been widely used in many fields. Because of its deficiency and limitation, an individual sensor can provide only partial information of the particular environment and thus lacks robustness, and composite application of multiple sensors of various types is needed to acquire integrated information about different environments or different types. The microsensor is an important part of a microelectromechanical system (MEMS). Development of a microsensor inevitably leads to the formation of a microelectromechanical sensor-based system, the properties, design, and application methods of which should be studied.

Keywords Microelectro-mechanical system, sensor-based system, data fusion, multi-sensor integration

17.1 Introduction

17.1.1 Microelectro-Mechanical Systems (MEMS)

With the development of a MEMS technology, we have gained much more profound understanding for MEMS and applications. Firstly, MEMS can be regarded as a technological platform for designing, manufacturing, and application, where many subjects and fields can be used to promote the development of the technology. Secondly, corresponding methodologies, such as design methodology, especially analyzing and synthesizing methods for these devices working in microspace, are formed with the development of the MEMS technology. Since the technology should eventually be transformed into production, new categories of MEMS products are emerging continuously and playing an important role in industry, agriculture, environment, military affairs and other fields.

MEMS grew up along with the development of a semiconductor-integrated circuit, a microfabrication technology, and an ultra-precision machining technology. Different from mere miniaturization, MEMS refers to miniature devices or systems that can be developed for batch manufacture, integrating with micromechanisms, microsensors, microactuators, signal processing and controlling circuits, interfaces, communication, power supplies, and etc.

MEMS can be divided into several independent functional units with the input of physical/chemical signals, which are converted into electrical signals through a sensor and interact with the external world through an actuator after signal processing (analogizing and/or digitizing). Each microsystem can communicate with other microsystems via digital or analog signals (electric, optical, magnetic, and other physical/chemical quantities).

As the MEMS technology develops, the diversity of MEMS units, and their combination are also growing. These units include: micromechanical structures, microsensors, microactuators, microenergy, signal processing and transmission units, etc. There are various different microsystems, such as optical MEMS, microfluid systems, bio-microsystems, communication microsystems, power microsystems, etc.

A microelectromechanical sensor-based system can be regarded as a functional unit or an independent system of MEMS involved in various fields, the general structure of which is shown in Fig. 17.1. If microsensors within are of the same type, multi-microsensors form an array, which could construct a distributed microsensor-based system. If microsensors within include different types, the combination system acquires and processes information through signal processing. Such a system is a composite microsensor-based system.

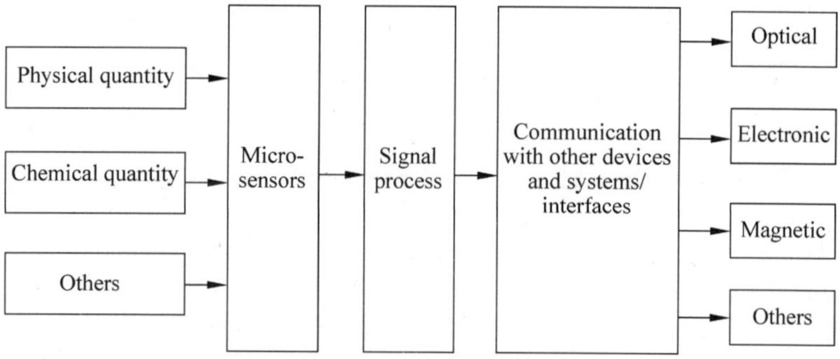

Figure 17.1 Microelectromechanical sensor-based system model

17.1.2 Microelectromechanical Sensor-Based System

The categories of commercial MEMS sensors are currently becoming more and more diversified, and their performances are continually improving. The microelectromechanical sensor-based system (in either multi-sensor combination or multi-sensor integration) will play an important role to realize an organic combination of miniaturization and smartness. The development of MEMS, system integration, and computer technologies contribute to the progress or growth of the microelectromechanical sensor-based system. To realize their performances and functions, multi-discipline knowledge is required, such as signal processing, data fusion, modeling, control algorithms, etc. Currently, the application demands of a microelectromechanical sensor-based system are mainly embodied in the following aspects.

17.1.2.1 Sensor-Based Application Systems

MEMS sensors take advantage of small size, light weight, low power consumption, anti-shock capability, and high reliability, etc. and have been able to replace some traditional sensors. For instance, MEMS accelerometers and gyroscopes with a weight of about 1 gram and a power consumption of 10 milliwatts have been widely applied to the field of automobile safety, navigation control, etc.

Utilizing specific sensors that measure concerned physical quantity can lead to a corresponding sensor application system. The multi-sensor integration application can accomplish specific tasks by synthesizing the information from multiple sensors. For example, a digital compass can be realized by 2 or 3 magnetometers, a level meter can be realized using 2 – 3 accelerometers, and an altimeter and an anemometer can be realized based on pressure sensors. Figure 17.2 is a functional block diagram of a combined pressure-based device for measuring altitude and airspeed. A micro absolute pressure sensor, a differential pressure sensor, and a pitot tube incorporating with a regulating circuit and signal processing device compose a composite altitude and airspeed measurement system.

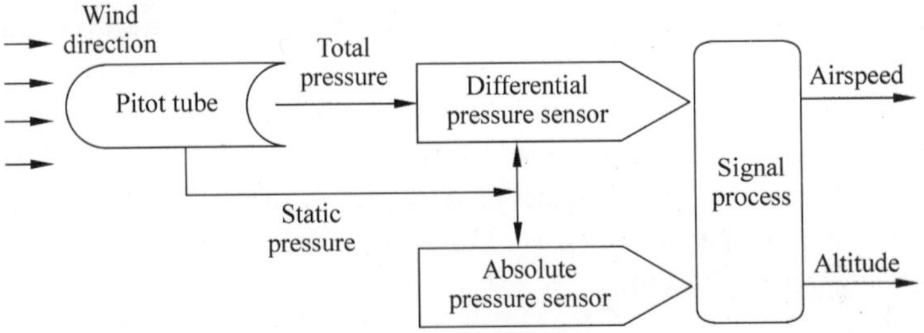

Figure 17.2 Block diagram of altimeter and airspeed meter

17.1.2.2 Multi-MEMS Sensor Information Fusion

Generally, the measurement accuracy may not be satisfied by merely using a sensor. Various physical parameters can be obtained by using multi-sensors, and signal fusion technology can fuse different sensing information into required forms (transition, mapping, or fusion) and thus improve the measurement accuracy and other performances.

A typical integrated microelectromechanical sensor-based system—a MEMS measurement and control system—is shown in Fig. 17.3. It combines more than ten MEMS sensors and microprocessors, such as microaccelerometers, gyroscopes, magnetometers, altimeters, and speed meters, etc., and also includes many interfaces for connecting micro-GPS, micro camera, micro-communication device, and micro recorder. The system has the functions of detection and control for the attitude, the position, and the movement of a moving object [1, 2]. The total weight of this microelectromechanical sensor-based system is less than 10 grams, and the power consumption is less than 1 W.

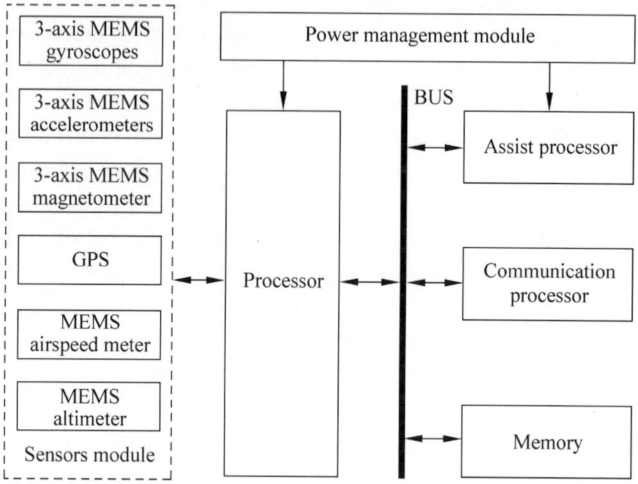

Figure 17.3 MEMS measurement and control system

The signal process of a multi-sensor integration system sometimes is complicated, and sometimes new problems occur in its application. Investigation of multi-sensor integration and fusion has become a new special research subject, including integration patterns, control structures, sensor-selective strategies, models, fusion methods, etc. Researchers can conduct their own study of the relevant literatures[3–9]. This chapter merely introduces a part of related contents concerning the application of the MEMS sensing system.

17.1.2.3 Integrated Design of Sensor-Based System

Higher requirements for miniaturization and integrated design of measurement and control systems have been proposed with the development of either large vehicles (such as automobiles, ships, aircrafts, etc.) or small vehicles (such as micro air vehicles, microrobots, etc.). Microautopilot is a typical micromeasurement and control system composed of multi-MEMS sensors. Considering that a traditional autopilot system in an unmanned air vehicle (UAV) might be replaced by a microautopilot, the airborne weight can be effectively reduced, the flight flexibility and carrying load capacity can be enhanced, the overall consumption can be decreased, the flight distance can also be extended, and the total cost can be reduced. To achieve this, an appropriate integrated design is necessary for a complex multi-sensor combination. Adopting systematical optimization technologies, such as integrated function and performance analysis, sensor and actuator selection, system design, signal processing and control algorithms, hardware and software realization, etc., the system can perform as desired.

In some applications, not only the sensor-based systems should be concerned, but also relevant controlled objects should be involved, optimized, and designed together. A typical example is the Micro Air Vehicle (s) or Micro Aerial Vehicle (s) (MAVs) with small size, light weight, and low cost [10]. MAVs are provided with many MEMS devices as shown in Fig. 17.4, indicating the various components. Under integration design and multi-disciplinary optimization technologies, the microelectromechanical sensor-based system can help the MAVs to achieve excellent flight performances [11].

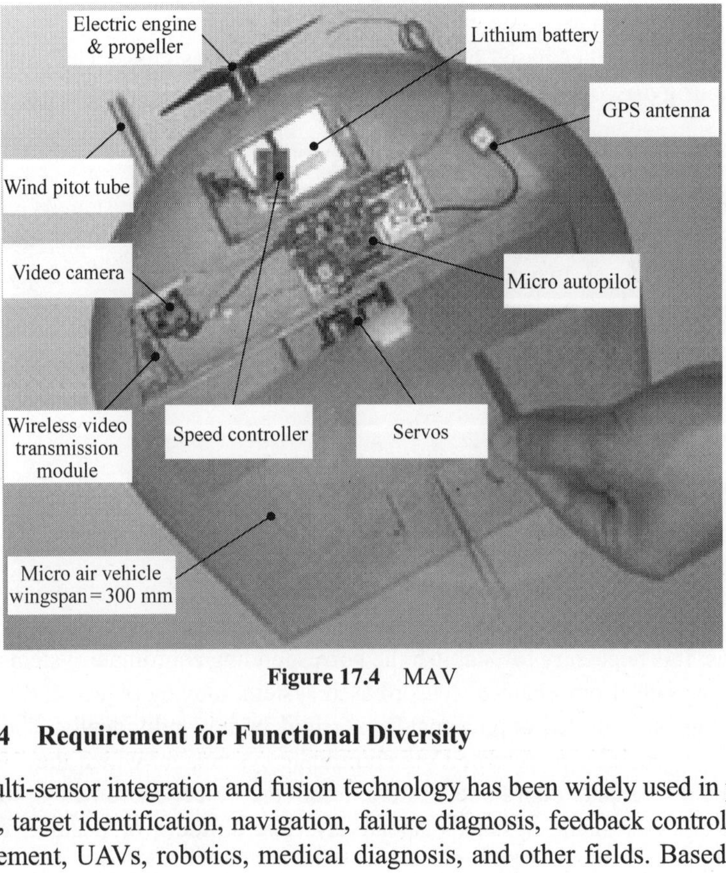

Figure 17.4 MAV

17.1.2.4 Requirement for Functional Diversity

The multi-sensor integration and fusion technology has been widely used in process control, target identification, navigation, failure diagnosis, feedback control, traffic management, UAVs, robotics, medical diagnosis, and other fields. Based on the sensor types, missions, or applications, various kinds of sensor systems can be developed including microelectromechanical sensor-based systems.

In mathematical sense, a multi-sensor system is a type of data collection unit. For example, the set N for the array of sensors S_i, $i=1,2,\ldots,n$, of the same sensitive element A can be expressed as:

$$N = \{S_i, i = 1,2,\ldots,n \setminus \text{sensitive element } A\} \tag{17.1}$$

The set M for many sensors S_{ji} of different sensitive elements, $j=1,2,\ldots,l$, can be expressed as:

$$M = \{M_j, j = 1,2,\ldots,l\} \tag{17.2}$$

where,

$$M_j = \{S_{ji}, i = 1,2,\ldots,n \setminus \text{sensitive element } A_j\}$$

Example 1: If the precision of an individual sensor cannot meet the application requirement, one approach is to select a number of same sensors to form a parallel system and improve the system performance by using a signal processing technology. As reported, the drift stability of the gyroscopes can be improved by using a Kalman filter based on four gyroscope output signals. The combination of the four gyroscopes G_i can be written as:

$$G = \{G_i, i = 1,2,\ldots,4 \setminus \text{sensitive element is the angular velocity}\}$$

Example 2: Consider the MEMS measurement and control system M mentioned before. To determine the attitude and position in a dynamic state, the system consists of: M_1 – 3 magnetometers, M_2 – 3 accelerometers, M_3 – 3 gyroscope, M_4 – altimeter, M_5 – airspeed meter, M_6 – micro-GPS receiver, etc.

$$M = \{M_j, j = 1,2,...,6\}$$

17.1.3 Coordinate Relation of a Microelectromechanical Sensor-Based System

The signal relations in a multi-MEMS sensor integration system include the relation of geometric quantities and that of physical quantities. For spatial geometric relations, it is necessary to establish the corresponding coordinate systems.

The microelectromechanical sensor-based system, moving object, and reference object can be regarded approximately as rigid bodies individually. These rigid bodies are generally represented via coordinate systems on which they are fixed and named a sensing coordinate system, a moving object coordinate system, and a reference coordinate system, respectively. The attitudes or position relations can be obtained from the relations between the coordinate systems. For example, consider an aircraft as the moving object (fixed with airframe coordinates system $OX_3Y_3Z_3$) on which a microelectromechanical sensor-based system module (fixed with module coordinate system $OXYZ$) is installed, and assume the local geographic coordinate system $ONWT$ as the reference coordinate system, as shown in Fig. 17.5.

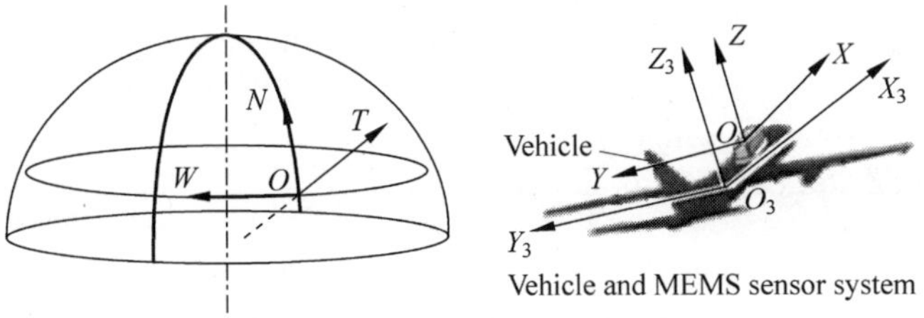

Figure 17.5 Integrated MEMS sensor-based system, moving object, and reference objects and their corresponding coordinate systems

The origin O of the geographic coordinate system is selected at the earth's point on which the moving object is located. The three axes of $ONWT$ are denoted by an ON axis pointing to the North, an OW axis pointing to the West, and an OT axis pointing to the zenith, which constitute a right-handed orthogonal coordinate system. The three axes of the object coordinate system $OX_3Y_3Z_3$ are denoted by OX_3 pointing to the forward direction of the object and OY_3 pointing to the left side of the object, while the three axes constitute a right-handed orthogonal coordinate system. The three rotation angles of $OX_3Y_3Z_3$ related to $ONWT$ are defined as attitude angles of the moving object, namely heading, pitch, and roll angles. Meanwhile, the turning angles of the moving object $OX_3Y_3Z_3$ related to the sensor module $OXYZ$ are represented as measurement errors. For clarifying relationships between $OX_3Y_3Z_3$, $OXYZ$, and $ONWT$, an effective mathematical description method needs to be established.

From a mathematical point of view, $ONWT$, $OXYZ$, and $OX_3Y_3Z_3$ belong to three-dimensional (3D) linear spaces. The transition or transformation relations of three groups are three matrixes, and these transition matrixes or transformation matrixes are reversible. The matrix solution is introduced below.

17.2 Coordinate Transformation and Attitude Measurement in 3D Space

17.2.1 Rotary Coordinate System

The motion of a moving object consists of rotary motion and translational motion, wherein the rotary motion can be regarded as the rotation around a fixed point, which can be expressed by coordinate transformation matrixes (namely, rotary matrixes) between two coordinate systems.

Assume two Cartesian coordinate systems $OXYZ$ and $OX_3Y_3Z_3$ with one origin. $OXYZ$ is taken as the base coordinate system or called as the reference coordinate system, the vehicle coordinate system $OX_3Y_3Z_3$ is formed via three rotations in sequence around the origin O from the coordinate system $OXYZ$. The rotating sequence is: firstly, the coordinate system $OX_1Y_1Z_1$ is formed by rotating angle ψ (heading) around the OZ axis; secondly, the coordinate system $OX_2Y_2Z_2$ is formed by rotating angle θ (pitch) around the OY_1 axis; and finally, $OX_3Y_3Z_3$ is formed by rotating angle γ (roll) around the OX_2 axis. The relationship between $OXYZ$ and $OX_3Y_3Z_3$ is shown in Fig. 17.6.

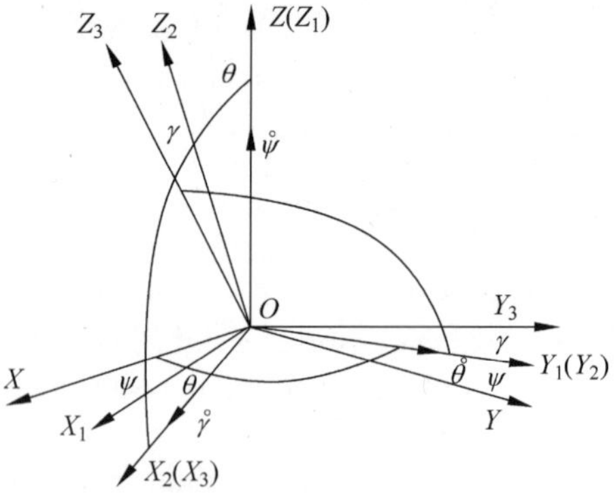

Figure 17.6 Transform relationship between coordinate systems

A vector $\boldsymbol{L}$ shown in Fig. 17.7 can be expressed as $[L_{X3}, L_{Y3}, L_{Z3}]^{\mathrm{T}}$ in the coordinate system $OX_3Y_3Z_3$. Taking the three coordinate axes as the basic axes, it can be expressed as:

$$\boldsymbol{L} = L_{X3}\boldsymbol{X}_3 + L_{Y3}\boldsymbol{Y}_3 + L_{Z3}\boldsymbol{Z}_3 \tag{17.3}$$

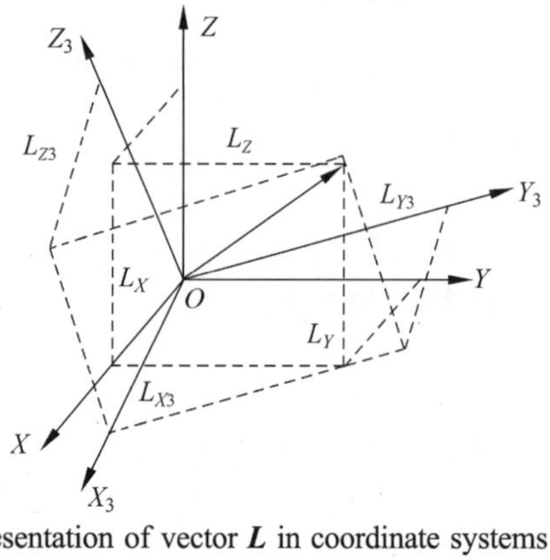

Figure 17.7 Representation of vector $\boldsymbol{L}$ in coordinate systems $OX_3Y_3Z_3$ and $OXYZ$ respectively

The vector $\boldsymbol{L}$ can be expressed as $[L_X, L_Y, L_Z]^{\mathrm{T}}$ in the coordinate system *OXYZ*. Taking the three coordinate axes as the basic axes, this can be expressed as:

$$\boldsymbol{L} = L_X\boldsymbol{X} + L_Y\boldsymbol{Y} + L_Z\boldsymbol{Z} \tag{17.4}$$

The relationship between the coordinate systems can be expressed by the coordinate transformation matrix (also called rotation matrix $\boldsymbol{R}$), shown in Eq. (17.5).

$$\begin{bmatrix} L_{X3} \\ L_{Y3} \\ L_{Z3} \end{bmatrix} = \begin{bmatrix} \cos(X_3,X) & \cos(X_3,Y) & \cos(X_3,Z) \\ \cos(Y_3,X) & \cos(Y_3,Y) & \cos(Y_3,Z) \\ \cos(Z_3,X) & \cos(Z_3,Y) & \cos(Z_3,Z) \end{bmatrix} \cdot \begin{bmatrix} L_X \\ L_Y \\ L_Z \end{bmatrix} \tag{17.5}$$

In which $\boldsymbol{R} = \begin{bmatrix} \cos(X_3,X) & \cos(X_3,Y) & \cos(X_3,Z) \\ \cos(Y_3,X) & \cos(Y_3,Y) & \cos(Y_3,Z) \\ \cos(Z_3,X) & \cos(Z_3,Y) & \cos(Z_3,Z) \end{bmatrix}$ is the rotation matrix, and the elements in this matrix are the direction cosines of the attitude angles; so, it can also be called the direction cosine matrix.

Equation (17.5) can also be expressed by

$$\begin{bmatrix} L_{X3} \\ L_{Y3} \\ L_{Z3} \end{bmatrix} = [\gamma \cdot \theta \cdot \psi] \cdot \begin{bmatrix} L_X \\ L_Y \\ L_Z \end{bmatrix} \tag{17.6}$$

where $[\gamma \cdot \theta \cdot \psi]$ represents the coordinate transformation matrix $\boldsymbol{R}$. The relationships between *OXYZ* and $OX_1Y_1Z_1$, $OX_2Y_2Z_2$ and $OX_1Y_1Z_1$, and $OX_3Y_3Z_3$ and $OX_2Y_2Z_2$ are shown in Fig. 17.8, respectively. The coordinate transformation matrixes corresponding to each rotation are as follows:

$$[\psi] = \begin{bmatrix} \cos\psi & \sin\psi & 0 \\ -\sin\psi & \cos\psi & 0 \\ 0 & 0 & 1 \end{bmatrix}$$

$$[\theta] = \begin{bmatrix} \cos\theta & 0 & -\sin\theta \\ 0 & 1 & 0 \\ \sin\theta & 0 & \cos\theta \end{bmatrix}$$

And

$$[\gamma] = \begin{bmatrix} 1 & 0 & 0 \\ 0 & \cos\gamma & \sin\gamma \\ 0 & -\sin\gamma & \cos\gamma \end{bmatrix}$$

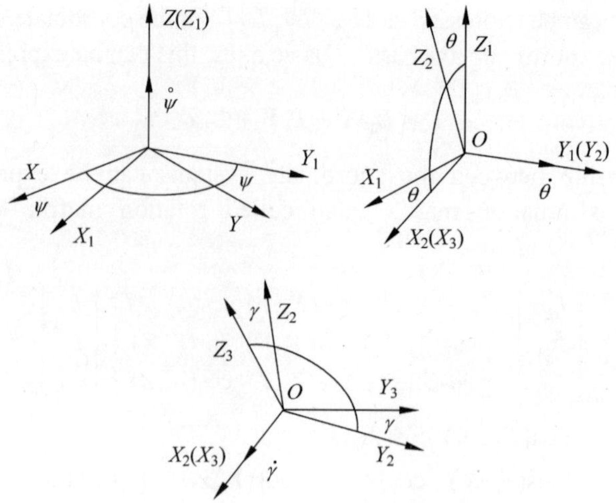

Figure 17.8 Relationship of the coordinate systems

The coordinate transformation matrix between $OXYZ$ and $OX_3Y_3Z_3$ can thus be expressed by:

$$[\gamma\cdot\theta\cdot\psi]=[\gamma]\cdot[\theta]\cdot[\psi]$$

$$[\gamma\cdot\theta\cdot\psi]=\begin{bmatrix}1 & 0 & 0\\ 0 & \cos\gamma & \sin\gamma\\ 0 & -\sin\gamma & \cos\gamma\end{bmatrix}\cdot\begin{bmatrix}\cos\theta & 0 & -\sin\theta\\ 0 & 1 & 0\\ \sin\theta & 0 & \cos\theta\end{bmatrix}\cdot\begin{bmatrix}\cos\psi & \sin\psi & 0\\ -\sin\psi & \cos\psi & 0\\ 0 & 0 & 1\end{bmatrix}$$
$$=\begin{bmatrix}\cos\psi\cos\theta & \sin\psi\cos\theta & -\sin\theta\\ \cos\psi\sin\theta\sin\gamma-\sin\psi\cos\gamma & \sin\psi\sin\theta\sin\gamma+\cos\psi\cos\gamma & \cos\theta\sin\gamma\\ \cos\psi\sin\theta\cos\gamma+\sin\psi\sin\gamma & \sin\psi\sin\theta\cos\gamma-\cos\psi\sin\gamma & \cos\theta\cos\gamma\end{bmatrix}\tag{17.7}$$

Example 1: Suppose that ψ, γ, and θ are all small quantities. and thus we have the approximate relationships: $\cos\psi=\cos\theta=\cos\gamma=1$, $\sin\psi=\psi$, $\sin\theta=\theta$ and $\sin\gamma=\gamma$. The coordinate transformation matrixes can be approximately expressed as:

$$[\psi]=\begin{bmatrix}1 & \psi & 0\\ -\psi & 1 & 0\\ 0 & 0 & 1\end{bmatrix}\quad [\theta]=\begin{bmatrix}1 & 0 & -\theta\\ 0 & 1 & 0\\ \theta & 0 & 1\end{bmatrix}\quad [\gamma]=\begin{bmatrix}1 & 0 & 0\\ 0 & 1 & \gamma\\ 0 & -\gamma & 1\end{bmatrix}$$

$$[\gamma\cdot\theta\cdot\psi]=\begin{bmatrix}1 & \psi & -\theta\\ \theta\gamma-\psi & \psi\theta\gamma+1 & \gamma\\ \theta+\psi\gamma & \psi\theta-\gamma & 1\end{bmatrix}$$

In a practical application, one or two angles of ψ, θ, and γ might be small quantities, the corresponding simplification formula can be deduced.

Example 2: Taking $OX_3Y_3Z_3$ as the reference coordinate system, $OXYZ$ is obtained by rotating the corresponding axes relative to $OX_3Y_3Z_3$ for angles ψ_3, θ_3, and γ_3, respectively. Hence, the following relationship exists:

$$\begin{bmatrix} L_X \\ L_Y \\ L_Z \end{bmatrix} = \begin{bmatrix} \cos(X,X_3) & \cos(X,Y_3) & \cos(X,Z_3) \\ \cos(Y,X_3) & \cos(Y,Y_3) & \cos(Y,Z_3) \\ \cos(Z,X_3) & \cos(Z,Y_3) & \cos(Z,Z_3) \end{bmatrix} \cdot \begin{bmatrix} L_{X3} \\ L_{Y3} \\ L_{Z3} \end{bmatrix}$$

$$[\gamma_3 \cdot \theta_3 \cdot \psi_3] \cdot \begin{bmatrix} L_{X3} \\ L_{Y3} \\ L_{Z3} \end{bmatrix}$$

If the inverse matrix of $[\gamma_3 \cdot \theta_3 \cdot \psi_3]$ exists, the following relations can be proved.

$$\begin{aligned} [\gamma \cdot \theta \cdot \psi] &= [\gamma_3 \cdot \theta_3 \cdot \psi_3]^{-1} \\ &= [\gamma_3 \cdot \theta_3 \cdot \psi_3]^{\mathrm{T}} \end{aligned} \tag{17.8}$$

So the rotation matrix $\boldsymbol{R}$ is an orthogonal matrix.

17.2.2 Sensitive Components of Sensor in Earth Coordinate System

17.2.2.1 Earth's Magnetic Field

The earth can be regarded as a large magnet, which has a fixed spatial magnetic-field distribution. Its surrounding static magnetic field is known as the geomagnetic field. The magnetic poles are not consistent with the two geographical poles. The Geographic North Pole is located on the earth's self-rotating axis, where the longitude lines meet. Beijing is located at latitude 39.9°N, longitude 116.4°E. The Geomagnetic North and South Poles are defined by the internal stable magnetic field of the earth. The Geomagnetic North Pole is located at latitude 74.9°N, longitude 101°W. The Geomagnetic South Pole is located at latitude 67.1°S, longitude 142.7°E. The deviation angle between the geomagnetic axis and the earth's rotary axis is 11.5°. Magnetic dip angle (β) is an angle between the earth's magnetic field vector $\boldsymbol{H}$ and the local horizontal plane. The dip angle varies at different geographic locations on the earth. The magnetic dip angle is 0° on the earth equator and nearly ±90° when approaching the Polar Regions. The magnetic dip angle of Beijing is about 58°. Geomagnetic intensity also changes as location changes. The geomagnetic inductive vector $\boldsymbol{H}$ at the geographic coordinate system ONWT (N- Earth North Pole, W- West, and T- zenith) is shown in Fig. 17.9. The inclination angle α between the horizontal direction of $\boldsymbol{H}$ and the Geographic North Pole is known as magnetic declination. The magnetic declination is caused by nonsuperposition between the Geomagnetic North Pole and the Geographic North Pole. The magnetic declinations differ from location to location. The magnetic declination α at Beijing is approximately –6°.

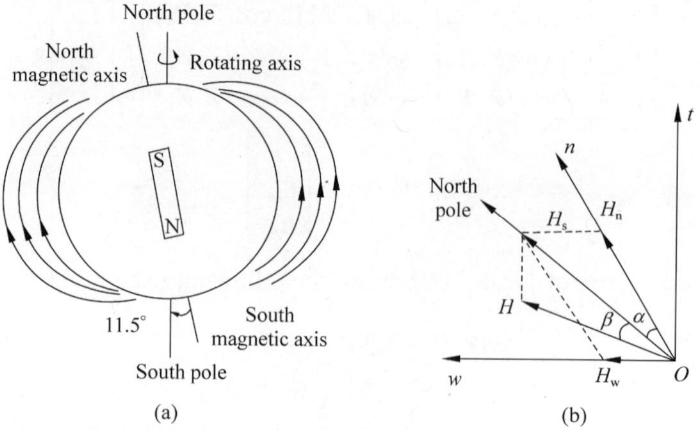

Figure 17.9 Sketch of the geomagnetic inductive intensity, (a) earths magnetic field, (b) geomagnetic inductive intensity components

The geomagnetic vector $\boldsymbol{H}$ can be divided into a horizontal component H_S and a perpendicular component H_T in the geographic coordinate system ONWT. H_S can be further divided into a northern horizontal component H_N and a western horizontal component H_W, namely:

$$\boldsymbol{H} = H_N\mathbf{N} + H_W\mathbf{W} + H_D\mathbf{T} \tag{17.9}$$

17.2.2.2 Earth's Gravity Field

It is assumed that the directions of the coordinate system $OXYZ$ are: OX- magnetic North, OY- West, and OZ- zenith, respectively. The components of the geomagnetic and gravitational fields in the $OXYZ$ coordinate systems are:

$$\begin{bmatrix} x_{m0} \\ y_{m0} \\ z_{m0} \end{bmatrix} = h \cdot \begin{bmatrix} \cos\beta \\ 0 \\ -\sin\beta \end{bmatrix} \tag{17.10}$$

and

$$\begin{bmatrix} x_{g0} \\ y_{g0} \\ z_{g0} \end{bmatrix} = g \cdot \begin{bmatrix} 0 \\ 0 \\ -1 \end{bmatrix} \tag{17.11}$$

where h is the magnitude of $\boldsymbol{H}$, g is the gravity acceleration.

Consequently, the components of the geomagnetic and gravitational fields in $OX_3Y_3Z_3$ are expressed as:

$$\begin{bmatrix} x_{m3} \\ y_{m3} \\ z_{m3} \end{bmatrix} = h \cdot [\gamma \cdot \theta \cdot \psi] \cdot \begin{bmatrix} \cos\beta \\ 0 \\ -\sin\beta \end{bmatrix} \tag{17.12}$$

and

$$\begin{bmatrix} x_{g3} \\ y_{g3} \\ z_{g3} \end{bmatrix} = g \cdot [\gamma \cdot \theta \cdot \psi] \cdot \begin{bmatrix} 0 \\ 0 \\ -1 \end{bmatrix} \tag{17.13}$$

Example 3: The magnetic dip angle β at Beijing is 57°23' while β at Shanghai is 45°. Is there any difference for the directional precision of a mechanical compass at Beijing and Shanghai?

The directional precision of a compass depends on the local magnetic declination rather than the magnetic dip. The component of magnetic intensity in the local horizontal plane depends on the magnetic dip angle. The horizontal component at Shanghai is larger than that at Beijing.

17.2.3 Determination of Attitude Angles by Using Outputs of Sensor Fixed on a Moving Object

Assume that the coordinate system $OX_3Y_3Z_3$ is fixed on a moving object. The triaxial components of sensitive fields along the three axes of the coordinate system $OX_3Y_3Z_3$ can be obtained by sensors (such as magnetometer and accelerometer) mounted along the corresponding axes. Synthesizing Eq. (17.12) and Eq. (17.13), the following formula can be established:

$$\begin{cases} \cos\psi \cdot \cos\theta \cdot \cos\beta + \sin\theta \cdot \sin\beta = x_{m3} / h \\ (\cos\psi \cdot \sin\theta \cdot \sin\gamma - \sin\psi \cdot \cos\gamma) \cdot \cos\beta - \cos\theta \cdot \sin\gamma \cdot \sin\beta = y_{m3} / h \\ (\cos\psi \cdot \sin\theta \cdot \cos\gamma + \sin\psi \cdot \sin\gamma) \cdot \cos\beta - \cos\theta \cdot \cos\gamma \cdot \sin\beta = z_{m3} / h \\ \sin\theta \cdot g = x_{g3} \\ -\cos\theta \cdot \sin\gamma \cdot g = y_{g3} \\ -\cos\theta \cdot \cos\gamma \cdot g = z_{g3} \end{cases}$$

From the equations above, the following formula can be obtained:

$$\gamma = \arctan\frac{y_{g3}}{z_{g3}}$$

$$\theta = -\arctan\left(\frac{x_{g3}}{z_{g3}} \cdot \cos\gamma\right)$$

$$\psi = \arctan\left[\frac{z_{m3}\sin\gamma - y_{m3}\cos\gamma}{x_{m3}\cos\theta + (z_{m3}\cos\gamma - y_{m3}\sin\gamma)\sin\theta}\right] \quad (17.14)$$

These attitude angles are obtained by solving the inverse tangent formula in Eq. (17.14) using the ratio of sensor output data; thus, there is no need to know absolute gravity acceleration g, magnetic induction intensity h, and magnetic dip angle β in advance. To obtain the true azimuth angle corresponding to the geographic North Pole, $\psi + \alpha$ needs to be concerned [11].

Example 4: Attitude algorithms above based on gravitational field and geomagnetic field are adapted to situations in static state and without acceleration of movement. However, for an accelerated motion, the solution has a comparatively large error; and even false information might be brought forth sometimes. If the motion acceleration $a = A\sin\omega t$ exists along the longitudinal axis of a vehicle (namely X_3-axis), how is the attitude angle calculated by using the above algorithm?

According to $\gamma = \arctan\frac{y_{g3}}{z_{g3}}$, $\theta = -\arctan\left(\frac{x_{g3}}{z_{g3}} \cdot \cos\gamma\right)$, a fluctuant acceleration occurs in the output of z_{g3} and thus results in the errors of the roll and the pitch angles. When the roll and pitch angles are zero, the heading angle is free from the motion acceleration, so the calculation result of the heading angle is correct. If the roll and pitch angles are not zero, the calculation of the heading angle ψ is relative to θ and γ; therefore, the error induced by the fluctuant acceleration will occur in the heading angle.

Example 5: Consider to simplify the state value as a level meter: if a triaxial accelerometer is used, the roll angle γ and the pitch angle θ can be calculated without the gravity acceleration value. This can be shown as:

$$\begin{cases} \sin\theta \cdot g = x_{g3} \\ -\cos\theta \cdot \sin\gamma \cdot g = y_{g3} \\ -\cos\theta \cdot \cos\gamma \cdot g = z_{g3} \end{cases}$$

Therefore,

$$\begin{cases} \gamma = \arctan\dfrac{y_{g3}}{z_{g3}} \\ \theta = -\arctan\left(\dfrac{x_{g3}}{z_{g3}} \cdot \cos\gamma\right) \end{cases}$$

If a two-axis accelerometer is used, the value of the gravity acceleration g should be known. According to the following equation, γ and θ can be figured out.

$$\begin{cases} \sin\theta \cdot g = x_{g3} \\ -\cos\theta \cdot \sin\gamma \cdot g = y_{g3} \end{cases}$$

Example 6: Consider to simplify the state as an azimuth indicator. When $\gamma = 0$ and $\theta = 0, \psi$ can be calculated using the two-axis magnetometer without knowledge (value) of the magnetic induction intensity *h*. According to the following equations:

$$\begin{cases} \cos\psi \cdot \cos\beta = x_{m3} / h \\ -\sin\psi \cdot \cos\beta = y_{m3} / h \\ -\sin\beta = z_{m3} / h \end{cases}$$

Therefore,

$$\tan\psi = -y_{m3} / x_{m3}$$

17.3 Attitude Estimation Algorithm of Multi-Sensor System

A direct method for calculating the attitude angles using multi-sensor outputs has been described in the previous section. There exist other algorithms that can be employed to obtain the attitude angles for a moving body [12, 13]. The Kalman filter is proposed, by which the other angles in a dynamic state can be estimated under minimizing the variance of the estimation [14].

(1) The expressions of gravity field, magnetic field, and angular velocity vectors are based on the relationships of the moving object coordinate system and the geographic coordinate system. The gravity field vector and the magnetic field vector have been defined as following.

$$\begin{bmatrix} x_{g3} \\ y_{g3} \\ z_{g3} \end{bmatrix} = g \cdot [\gamma \cdot \theta \cdot \psi] \cdot \begin{bmatrix} 0 \\ 0 \\ -1 \end{bmatrix}$$

$$\begin{bmatrix} x_{m3} \\ y_{m3} \\ z_{m3} \end{bmatrix} = h \cdot [\gamma \cdot \theta \cdot \psi] \cdot \begin{bmatrix} \cos\beta \\ 0 \\ -\sin\beta \end{bmatrix}$$

The rotary vector induced by the self-rotation ω_φ of the earth and the linear velocity V of the moving object in the geographical coordinate can be expressed as:

$$\begin{bmatrix} \omega_N \\ \omega_w \\ \omega_T \end{bmatrix} = \begin{bmatrix} \omega_\phi \cos\lambda + V_{\mathrm{E}}/(R+h) \\ V_{\mathrm{N}}/(R+h) \\ \omega_\phi \sin\lambda + V_{\mathrm{E}}\tan\lambda/(R+h) \end{bmatrix} \tag{17.15}$$

where V_{E} is the motion velocity along the East, V_{N} is the motion velocity along the North, R is the radius of the earth, h is the flying height, and λ is the local latitude. According to the relationships between the moving object coordinate system, the geographic coordinate system, and the inertial coordinate system, the rotation velocity of the moving object coordinate system relative to the inertial coordinate system can be expressed as:

$$\begin{bmatrix} \omega_x \\ \omega_y \\ \omega_z \end{bmatrix} = \begin{bmatrix} \omega_x^c \\ \omega_y^c \\ \omega_z^c \end{bmatrix} - [\gamma \cdot \theta \cdot \psi] \cdot \begin{bmatrix} \omega_{\mathrm{N}} \\ \omega_{\mathrm{E}} \\ \omega_{\mathrm{D}} \end{bmatrix}$$

where $[\omega_x^c \quad \omega_y^c \quad \omega_z^c]^{\mathrm{T}}$ is the measured value of the angular velocity sensor. Define an anti-symmetric matrix of the angular velocity as:

$$[\boldsymbol{\Omega}] = \begin{bmatrix} 0 & -\omega_z & \omega_y \\ \omega_z & 0 & -\omega_x \\ -\omega_y & \omega_x & 0 \end{bmatrix}$$

(2) The differential equation for the direction cosine matrix is

$$\dot{R} = \boldsymbol{\Omega} \cdot \boldsymbol{R} \tag{17.16}$$

Consider the following equation of the direction cosine matrix:

$$\boldsymbol{R} = [\gamma \cdot \theta \cdot \psi] = \begin{bmatrix} r_{11} & r_{12} & r_{13} \\ r_{21} & r_{22} & r_{23} \\ r_{31} & r_{32} & r_{33} \end{bmatrix}$$

$$= \begin{bmatrix} \cos\psi\cos\theta & \sin\psi\cos\theta & -\sin\theta \\ \cos\psi\sin\theta\sin\gamma - \sin\psi\cos\gamma & \sin\psi\sin\theta\sin\gamma + \cos\psi\cos\gamma & \cos\theta\sin\gamma \\ \cos\psi\sin\theta\cos\gamma + \sin\psi\sin\gamma & \sin\psi\sin\theta\cos\gamma - \cos\psi\sin\gamma & \cos\theta\cos\gamma \end{bmatrix}$$

And take the first and third columns of the matrix $\boldsymbol{R}$ to form a state variable vector:

$$\boldsymbol{r} = [r_{11} \quad r_{21} \quad r_{31} \quad r_{13} \quad r_{23} \quad r_{33}]^{\mathrm{T}}$$

Then the state equation can be deduced as

$$\dot{r} = \begin{bmatrix} \boldsymbol{\Omega} & 0 \\ 0 & \boldsymbol{\Omega} \end{bmatrix} \cdot \boldsymbol{r} \tag{17.17}$$

Consider the noise e_r in the state equation, then

$$\dot{r} = \begin{bmatrix} \boldsymbol{\Omega} & 0 \\ 0 & \boldsymbol{\Omega} \end{bmatrix} \cdot \boldsymbol{r} + e_r \tag{17.18}$$

(3) Establish the observation equation as

$$\begin{bmatrix} x_{g3} \\ y_{g3} \\ z_{g3} \\ x_{m3} \\ y_{m3} \\ z_{m3} \end{bmatrix} = \begin{bmatrix} 0 & 0 & 0 & -1 & 0 & 0 \\ 0 & 0 & 0 & 0 & -1 & 0 \\ 0 & 0 & 0 & 0 & 0 & -1 \\ \cos\beta & 0 & 0 & -\sin\beta & 0 & 0 \\ 0 & \cos\beta & 0 & 0 & -\sin\beta & 0 \\ 0 & 0 & \cos\beta & 0 & 0 & -\sin\beta \end{bmatrix} \times \begin{bmatrix} r_{11} \\ r_{21} \\ r_{31} \\ r_{13} \\ r_{23} \\ r_{33} \end{bmatrix} + \begin{bmatrix} e_{xg3} \\ e_{yg3} \\ e_{zg3} \\ e_{xm3} \\ e_{ym3} \\ e_{zm3} \end{bmatrix}$$

where $\boldsymbol{e}_g = [e_{xg3} \quad e_{yg3} \quad e_{zg3}]^{\mathrm{T}}$ and $\boldsymbol{e}_m = [e_{xm3} \quad e_{ym3} \quad e_{zm3}]^{\mathrm{T}}$ are the measurement noises, which are assumed as the white noises, respectively.

Denote

$$\boldsymbol{y} = [x_{g3} \quad y_{g3} \quad z_{g3} \quad x_{m3} \quad y_{m3} \quad z_{m3}]^{\mathrm{T}},$$
$$\boldsymbol{e}_y = [e_{xg3} \quad e_{yg3} \quad e_{zg3} \quad e_{xm3} \quad e_{ym3} \quad e_{zm3}]^{\mathrm{T}}$$

and

$$\boldsymbol{C} = \begin{bmatrix} 0 & 0 & 0 & -1 & 0 & 0 \\ 0 & 0 & 0 & 0 & -1 & 0 \\ 0 & 0 & 0 & 0 & 0 & -1 \\ \cos\beta & 0 & 0 & -\sin\beta & 0 & 0 \\ 0 & \cos\beta & 0 & 0 & -\sin\beta & 0 \\ 0 & 0 & \cos\beta & 0 & 0 & -\sin\beta \end{bmatrix}$$

Then the observation equation can be written as:

$$\boldsymbol{y} = C \cdot \boldsymbol{r} + \boldsymbol{e}_y \tag{17.19}$$

(4) Discretize the state and observation equations

Suppose T is the sampling period, then

$$\Delta \boldsymbol{r}(kT+T)=\begin{bmatrix} \boldsymbol{\Omega}(\omega_{kh})T & 0 \\ 0 & \boldsymbol{\Omega}(\omega_{kh})T \end{bmatrix} \boldsymbol{r}(kT)+\boldsymbol{e}_r(kT)$$

$$\boldsymbol{r}(kT+T)=\boldsymbol{r}(kT)+\Delta \boldsymbol{r}(kT+T)$$

Therefore, the discrete form of the state equation can be written as:

$$\boldsymbol{r}(kT+T)=\begin{bmatrix} I+\boldsymbol{\Omega}(\omega_{kT})T & 0 \\ 0 & I+\boldsymbol{\Omega}(\omega_{kT})T \end{bmatrix} \boldsymbol{r}(kT)+\boldsymbol{e}_r(kT)$$

Define

$$\boldsymbol{F}=\begin{bmatrix} I+\boldsymbol{\Omega}(\omega_{kT})T & 0 \\ 0 & I+\boldsymbol{\Omega}(\omega_{kT})T \end{bmatrix}$$

Then the state equation at time k is written as:

$$\boldsymbol{r}(kT+T)=\boldsymbol{F}\cdot \boldsymbol{r}(kT)+\boldsymbol{e}_r(kT) \tag{17.20}$$

and the observation equation at time k is written as:

$$\boldsymbol{y}(kT)=\boldsymbol{C}\cdot \boldsymbol{r}(kT)+\boldsymbol{e}_y(kT) \tag{17.21}$$

Suppose $\boldsymbol{e}_r(kT)$ and $\boldsymbol{e}_y(kT)$ are the discrete Gauss White Noise arrays, with mean $E\boldsymbol{e}_r(kT)=0$, variance $E\boldsymbol{e}_r(kT)\boldsymbol{e}_r^{\mathrm{T}}(jT)=v\int kj$, mean $E\boldsymbol{e}_y(kT)=0$, and variance $E\boldsymbol{e}_y(kT)\boldsymbol{e}_y^{\mathrm{T}}(jT)=w\int kj$. It will more complex if colored noise is considered[15].

(5) Recursive Algorithm of Kalman Filter

According to the above discrete system model Eq. (17.20) and Eq. (17.21), state variable r could be estimated by the Recursive algorithm of Kalman Filter [8].

Step 1: The initial value $\hat{r}(kT)$ of the state variable is obtained by using several related sensors, and the one-step estimation is

$$\hat{r}(kT+T\mid kT)=F\cdot \hat{r}(kT)$$

Step 2: The covariance matrix $\boldsymbol{P}$ of the one-step prediction error estimation is given by

$$\boldsymbol{P}(kT+T\mid kT)=\boldsymbol{F}\boldsymbol{P}(kT)\boldsymbol{F}^{\mathrm{T}}+\boldsymbol{V}$$

Step 3: The gain matrix $\boldsymbol{K}$ is calculated by

$$\boldsymbol{K}(kT+T)=\boldsymbol{P}(kT+T\mid kT)\boldsymbol{C}^{\mathrm{T}}[\boldsymbol{C}\boldsymbol{P}(kT+T\mid kT)\boldsymbol{C}^{\mathrm{T}}+\boldsymbol{W}]^{-1}$$

Step 4: The one-step prediction value is modified using the gain matrix $\boldsymbol{K}$ and the measurement information y

$$\hat{r}(kT+T)=\hat{r}(kT+T\mid T)+\boldsymbol{K}(kT+T)[\boldsymbol{y}(kT+T)-\boldsymbol{C}\hat{r}(kT+T\mid kT)]$$

Step 5: The current attitude angles are obtained using the modified estimated value of the state variable.

Step 6: The new error covariance matrix $\boldsymbol{P}(kT+T)$ is calculated

$$\begin{aligned}\boldsymbol{P}(kT+T)=&[I-\boldsymbol{K}(kT+T)\boldsymbol{C}]\boldsymbol{P}(kT+T\mid kT)[I-\boldsymbol{K}(kT+T)\boldsymbol{C}]^{\mathrm{T}}\\&+\boldsymbol{K}(kT+T)\boldsymbol{W}\boldsymbol{K}^{\mathrm{T}}(kT+T)\end{aligned}$$

Step 7: The corresponding elements in matrix $\boldsymbol{C}$ are updated using the value of $\boldsymbol{r}(kT+T)$ to continue the next iterative computation and return to step 3. If the moving object is in a steady condition, the iteration would be converged.

(6) Constraint problem

The relationship of trigonometric functions can be expressed as

$$\begin{aligned}r_{11}^2+r_{21}^2+r_{31}^2=1\\r_{13}^2+r_{23}^2+r_{33}^2=1\end{aligned}\tag{17.22}$$

The observation equation can be modified as

$$\begin{bmatrix}x_{g3}\\1\\1\\x_{m3}\\y_{m3}\\z_{m3}\end{bmatrix}=\begin{bmatrix}0&0&0&-1&0&0\\r_{11}&r_{21}&r_{31}&0&0&0\\0&0&0&r_{13}&r_{23}&r_{33}\\\cos\beta&0&0&-\sin\beta&0&0\\0&\cos\beta&0&0&-\sin\beta&0\\0&0&\cos\beta&0&0&-\sin\beta\end{bmatrix}\times\begin{bmatrix}r_{11}\\r_{21}\\r_{31}\\r_{13}\\r_{23}\\r_{33}\end{bmatrix}+\begin{bmatrix}e_{xg3}\\e_{yg3}\\e_{zg3}\\e_{xm3}\\e_{ym3}\\e_{zm3}\end{bmatrix}\tag{17.23}$$

The other recursive algorithm is the same as before.

(7) Determining the attitude angles by using the estimated elements of r

Pitch angle: $\theta=-\arcsin(r_{13})$

$$\text{Roll angle:}\quad \phi=\begin{cases}\arctan(r_{23}/r_{33}), & r_{33}\geqslant 0\\\arctan(r_{23}/r_{33})+\pi, & r_{33}<0\ 且\ r_{23}\geqslant 0\\\arctan(r_{23}/r_{33})-\pi, & r_{33}<0\ 且\ r_{23}<0\end{cases}\tag{17.24}$$

$$\text{Heading angle:}\quad \psi=\begin{cases}\arccos(r_{11}/\cos\theta), & r_{31}\times r_{23}-r_{33}\times r_{21}\geqslant 0\\2\pi-\arccos(r_{11}/\cos\theta), & r_{31}\times r_{23}-r_{33}\times r_{21}<0\end{cases}$$

According to r_{11}, r_{21}, r_{31}, r_{13}, r_{23}, and r_{33}, the moving object attitude angles can be determined.

17.4 Assembly Orthogonal Error Compensation Technology for Sensing System[16]

The 3D sensor module is usually installed on a base plate. Actually, there exists a deviation between the sensor ares and the corresponding base axes. The deviation is called the installation/assembly error which reflects the deviation between the sensor coordinate system $OX_{3'}$ $Y_{3'}$ $Z_{3'}$ and the base coordinate system $OXYZ$, namely

$$\begin{bmatrix} L_{X3'} \\ L_{Y3'} \\ L_{Z3'} \end{bmatrix} = [\gamma_0 \cdot \theta_0 \cdot \psi_0] \cdot \begin{bmatrix} L_X \\ L_Y \\ L_Z \end{bmatrix}$$

where $[\gamma_0 \cdot \theta_0 \cdot \psi_0]$ is also named the deviation matrix. The rotation alignment method based on optical alignment is introduced below, by which the deviation matrix can be measured. The installation/assembly errors of the system can be eliminated through compensation.

Three orthogonally assembled mirrors are installed on the base plate of the 3D multi-sensor module for optical alignment. The three orthogonal axes that are perpendicular to the three orthogonal mirror surfaces constitute a reference coordinate system, denoted by $OXYZ$, which is the base coordinate system. The three sensitive axes of the sensors in the system constitute the sensing coordinate system $OX_3Y_3Z_3$, shown in Fig. 17.10.

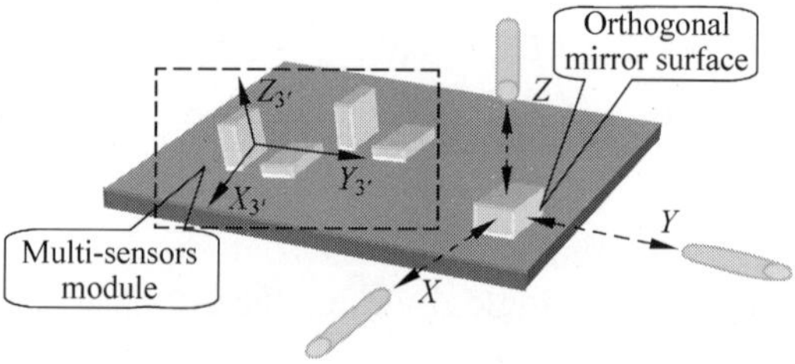

Figure 17.10 3D orthogonal sensing component

In the external environment, the three optical collimators are orthogonally mounted to construct a fixed rectangular coordinate frame ONWT, which is formed by the three collimated light beams. The performance of the proposed method mainly depends on the orthogonality of the 3D optical reference system. Therefore, it is necessary to adjust the three collimators to make the three collimated beams orthogonal each other. After establishing the optical reference system, we can rotate and adjust the circuit board to perform three optical alignments (i.e. X-Y-Z is aligned to N-W-T, T-N-W and W-T-N, in sequence) by beam collimations, as shown in Fig. 17.11[17–19].

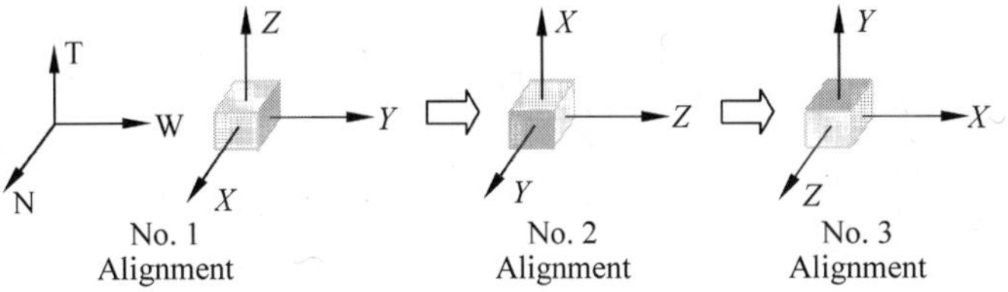

Figure 17.11 Three-step orthogonal alignments

The first alignment is to align the base *X-Y-Z* with N-W-T, where *X* aligns with the North (N), *Y* aligns with the West (W), and *OXYZ* forms the right-handed coordinate system. This can be expressed as:

$$\begin{bmatrix} L_X \\ L_Y \\ L_Z \end{bmatrix} = \begin{bmatrix} L_N \\ L_W \\ L_T \end{bmatrix}$$

Thus, we have

$$\begin{bmatrix} L_{X3'} \\ L_{Y3'} \\ L_{Z3'} \end{bmatrix} = [\gamma_0 \cdot \theta_0 \cdot \psi_0] \cdot \begin{bmatrix} L_N \\ L_W \\ L_T \end{bmatrix} \tag{17.25}$$

The second alignment is to align *Y-Z-X* with N-W-T through two orthogonal rotations, where *Y* aligns with the North, *Z* aligns with the West, and *OXYZ* forms the right-handed coordinate system. It can be expressed as

$$\begin{bmatrix} L_X \\ L_Y \\ L_Z \end{bmatrix} = \begin{bmatrix} L_T \\ L_N \\ L_W \end{bmatrix}$$

$$\begin{bmatrix} L_X \\ L_Y \\ L_Z \end{bmatrix} = [-90 \cdot 0 \cdot -90] \cdot \begin{bmatrix} L_N \\ L_W \\ L_T \end{bmatrix} = \begin{bmatrix} L_T \\ L_N \\ L_W \end{bmatrix}$$

Thus,

$$\begin{bmatrix} L_{X3'} \\ L_{Y3'} \\ L_{Z3'} \end{bmatrix} = [\gamma_0 \cdot \theta_0 \cdot \psi_0] \cdot \begin{bmatrix} L_T \\ L_N \\ L_W \end{bmatrix} \tag{17.26}$$

The third-step alignment is to align *Z-X-Y* with N-W-T through two orthogonal rotations, where *Z* aligns with the North, *X* aligns with the West, and *OXYZ* forms the right-handed coordinate system. It can be expressed as

$$\begin{bmatrix} L_X \\ L_Y \\ L_Z \end{bmatrix} = \begin{bmatrix} L_T \\ L_N \\ L_W \end{bmatrix}$$

$$\begin{bmatrix} L_X \\ L_Y \\ L_Z \end{bmatrix} = [-90 \cdot 0 \cdot -90] \cdot [-90 \cdot 0 \cdot -90] \cdot \begin{bmatrix} L_N \\ L_W \\ L_T \end{bmatrix} = \begin{bmatrix} L_W \\ L_T \\ L_N \end{bmatrix}$$

So,
$$\begin{bmatrix} L_{X3'} \\ L_{Y3'} \\ L_{Z3'} \end{bmatrix} = [\gamma_0 \cdot \theta_0 \cdot \psi_0] \cdot \begin{bmatrix} L_W \\ L_T \\ L_N \end{bmatrix} \tag{17.27}$$

The components of the physical field in the fixed base coordinate system ONWT are expressed as $[H_N, H_W, H_T]^T$. Define $\boldsymbol{H} = \begin{bmatrix} H_N & H_W & H_T \\ H_T & H_N & H_W \\ H_W & H_T & H_N \end{bmatrix}$ as characteristic matrix of the physical field in the coordinate system ONWT. During the three-step alignments, the component expressions (measurements by the triaxial sensor) of the physical field in the sensor coordinate system $OX_3'Y_3'Z_3'$ are defined as $[X_1', Y_1', Z_1']^T$ (first step alignment), $[X_2', Y_2', Z_2']^T$ (second step alignment), and $[X_3', Y_3', Z_3']^T$ (third step alignment), respectively.

Define $\boldsymbol{G} = \begin{bmatrix} X_1' & Y_1' & Z_1' \\ X_2' & Y_2' & Z_2' \\ X_3' & Y_3' & Z_3' \end{bmatrix}$ as the alignment characteristic matrix of the physical field in the $OX_3'Y_3'Z_3'$ coordinate system.

Nonalignment compensation theorem[1]: If a characteristic matrix $\boldsymbol{H}$ of the physical field in the fixed base coordinate system ONWT exists, and $\det(H) \neq 0$,

(1) The deviation matrix Ξ between the sensing coordinate system $OX_3'Y_3'Z_3'$ and the base coordinate system $OXYZ$ can be measured through the three-step orthogonal alignments.

(2) A solution to the linear equation group $\boldsymbol{G} = \boldsymbol{H} \cdot \Xi$ exists. Solve the linear equation group to obtain a deviation matrix Ξ.

The proof is omitted.

The specific solution is given below:

$$\Xi = [\gamma_0 \cdot \theta_0 \cdot \psi_0]^T = \boldsymbol{H}^{-1} \cdot \boldsymbol{G}$$

Denote $\boldsymbol{H}^{-1} \cdot \boldsymbol{G}$ as $\begin{bmatrix} x_{11} & x_{12} & x_{13} \\ x_{21} & x_{22} & x_{23} \\ x_{31} & x_{32} & x_{33} \end{bmatrix}$, and consider

$$[\gamma_0 \cdot \theta_0 \cdot \psi_0]^{\mathrm{T}}$$

$$= \begin{bmatrix} \cos\psi_0\cos\theta_0 & \cos\psi_0\sin\theta_0\sin\gamma_0 - \sin\psi_0\cos\gamma_0 & \cos\psi_0\sin\theta_0\cos\gamma_0 + \sin\psi_0\sin\gamma_0 \\ \sin\psi_0\cos\theta_0 & \sin\psi_0\sin\theta_0\sin\gamma_0 + \cos\psi_0\cos\gamma_0 & \sin\psi_0\sin\theta_0\cos\gamma_0 - \cos\psi_0\sin\gamma_0 \\ -\sin\theta_0 & \cos\theta_0\sin\gamma_0 & \cos\theta_0\cos\gamma_0 \end{bmatrix}$$

Thus

$$\begin{cases} -\sin\theta_0 = x_{31} \\ \tan\psi_0 = \dfrac{x_{21}}{x_{11}} \\ \tan\gamma_0 = \dfrac{x_{32}}{x_{33}} \end{cases}$$

Namely

$$[\gamma_0 \cdot \theta_0 \cdot \psi_0]^{\mathrm{T}} = \begin{bmatrix} \arctan\dfrac{x_{32}}{x_{33}} & -\arcsin x_{31} & \arctan\dfrac{x_{21}}{x_{11}} \end{bmatrix} \tag{17.28}$$

The deviation matrix Ξ can be determined through the optical alignment process presented above. In a practical measurement, the nonorthogonal triaxial component $[X_{3'}, Y_{3'}, Z_{3'}]^{\mathrm{T}}$ that is measured in a sensing coordinate system is transformed into the corresponding orthogonal component $[X, Y, Z]^{\mathrm{T}}$ in the base coordinate axes *OXYZ* through Ξ. Subsequent calculations, such as attitude calculation, can be carried out by using $[X, Y, Z]^{\mathrm{T}}$. By this way, system measurement errors caused by the nonorthogonal assembly/installation of the sensing axes can be eliminated.

$$\begin{bmatrix} X \\ Y \\ Z \end{bmatrix} = \Xi^{-1} \begin{bmatrix} X_{3'} \\ Y_{3'} \\ Z_{3'} \end{bmatrix} \tag{17.29}$$

17.5 Microelectromechanical Sensor-Based Application Systems

With the use of MEMS sensors, the corresponding sensor-based application systems are expected to develop. In this section, we will give a few application examples as follows.

17.5.1 Airspeed Meter[20]

The airspeed meters have been widely applied in the filed of aviation. They have different principle-based types;· for example, hot-wire type, differential pressure type, and rotary type, etc. An airspeed meter based on MEMS differential pressure sensors is introduced in this section. The airspeed can be measured by sensing the dynamic pressure of airflow and the local static pressure. Besides the differential pressure sensor, micro pitot and signal process are also needed to be included in the micro airspeed meter.

Within a certain low-speed range (where air velocity is less than 400 km/h), assuming the incompressibility of air and the momentum theorem, the difference q between the pressure along the airflow direction and the static pressure perpendicular to the airflow direction is proportional to the square of the airflow speed V_A, namely

$$q = \frac{\rho}{2} V_{\mathrm{A}}^2$$

where ρ is the air density at the flying height of the airplane (the ground standard value is1.25 kg/m^3); therefore, the airspeed can be calculated by:

$$V_{\mathrm{A}} = \sqrt{\frac{2q}{\rho}} \tag{17.30}$$

By making a total pressure head and a static pressure hole on the pitot, the total pressure and the static pressure can be detected simultaneously. The holes are connected to two input ends of the differential pressure sensor to measure the dynamic pressure of the airflow. The pitot has a stick structure, with its end in a hemispherical shape, as shown in Fig. 17.12. An airspeed meter should pass through a calibration test to obtain its correction coefficient, which is then stored in its microprocessor.

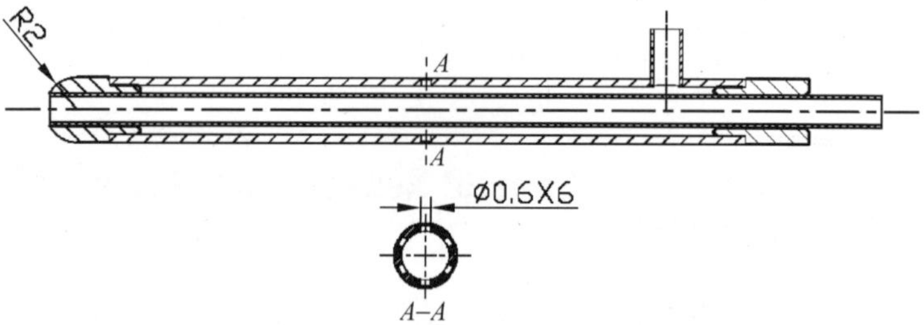

Figure 17.12 A pitot

A calibration test is performed on the airspeed meter in a Test Wind Tunnel, the results of which are shown in Fig. 17.13.

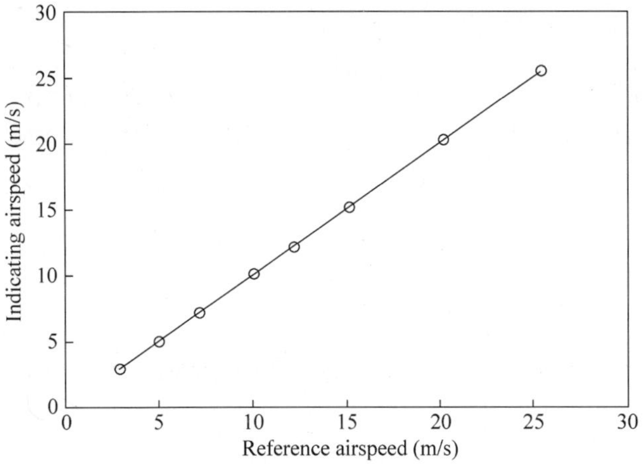

Figure 17.13 Calibration result of an airspeed meter

The integration system with an altimeter and an airspeed meter can be made from a MEMS absolute pressure sensor, a differential pressure sensor, a pitot, an auxiliary circuit, and a microprocessor, the configuration of which is shown in Fig. 17.14.

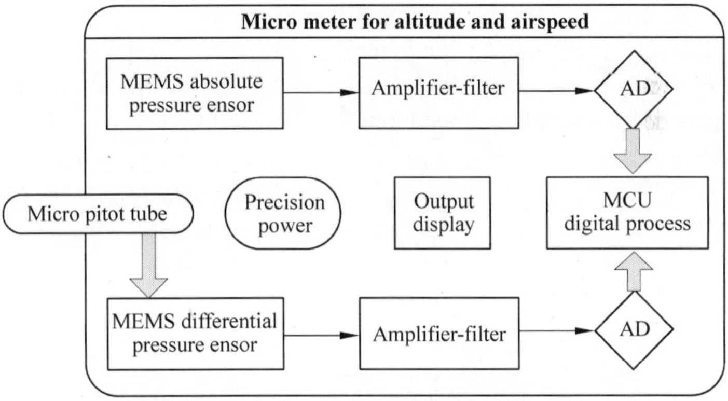

Figure 17.14 Integration of an altimeter and an airspeed meter

17.5.2 Digital Compass

A digital compass is actually a magnetic compass. It gives the information about a moving object's orientation by sensing the earth's magnetic field. It is applied in many fields, such as the North direction, antenna orientation, automobile or aircraft navigation, robot motion control, etc. The magnetic sensors based on the

Hall Effect and the magnetoresistance effect can be adopted [21,22]. When a magnetic compass inclines, an inclining error will occur. This error could be compensated by using accelerometers and a compensated algorithm. The system structure is shown in Fig. 17.15, hereinto, 'm' is the magnetometer; '*a*' is the accelerometer. There are various schemes on the sensor configuration of the magnetic compass: the first and the second schemes in Fig. 17.15 are the azimuth-level detectors; but the third one is a commonly used, simple magnetic compass configuration, namely a horizontal magnetic compass [3].

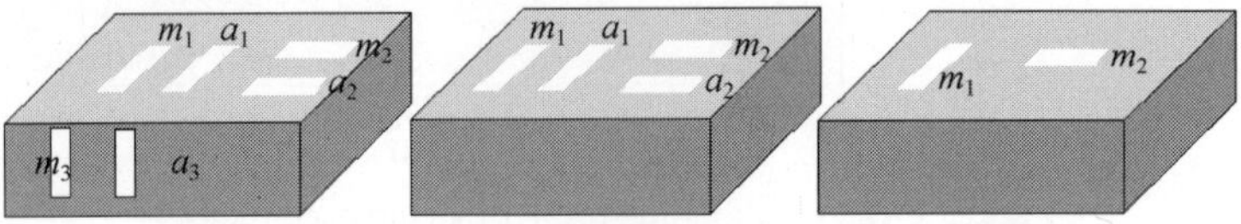

Figure 17.15 Sensor configurations of a digital compass

The azimuth of a simple magnetic compass can be obtained by using the following simple equation:

$$\psi = -\arctan\ (H_Y / H_X) \tag{17.31}$$

Where, H_Y and H_X are the horizontal components of H_{eN} along the *X* and *Y* axes, respectively, measured by the magnetic sensors as shown in Fig. 17.16. The calculation needs to be simplified for reducing the computation load and an effective algorithm should be considered [23, 24].

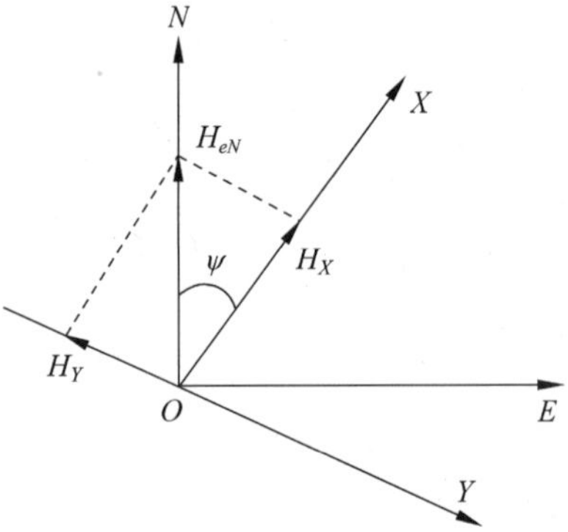

Figure 17.16 Calculation algorithm of azimuth

Besides sensors, the major components of a digital compass include a signal processing circuit, A/D converter, a microprocessor, display, and so on. The composition of the system is shown in Fig. 17.17.

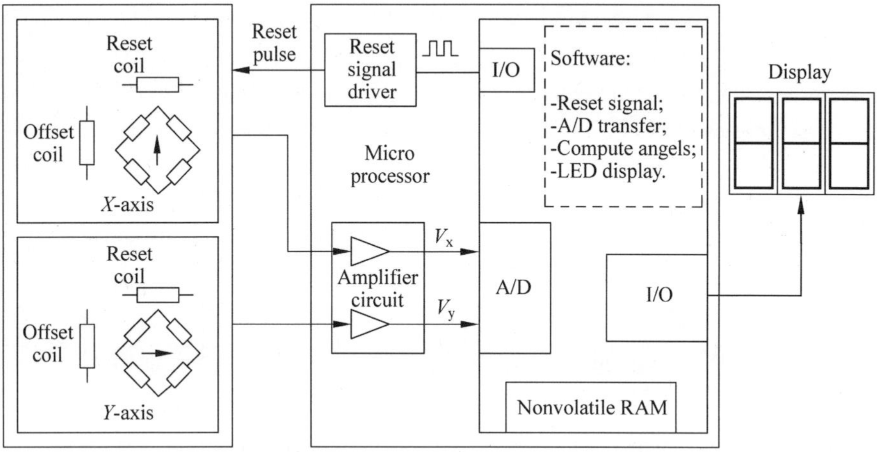

Figure 17.17 Composition of a digital compass

A magnetometer's readout could be influenced by environmental magnetic fields and the temperature in practice. Therefore, a magnetic reset circuit with special SET/RESET functions is necessary to:

(1) eliminate impacts of the external magnetic field on the magnetometer,
(2) maintain the high sensitivity of the magnetometer,
(3) improve the linearity and repeatability of the magnetic measurement,
(4) reduce measurement error from the temperature variation.

In the digital compass calibration, the strong magnetic field must be avoided and a mechanical turntable is adopted, as shown in Fig. 17.18.

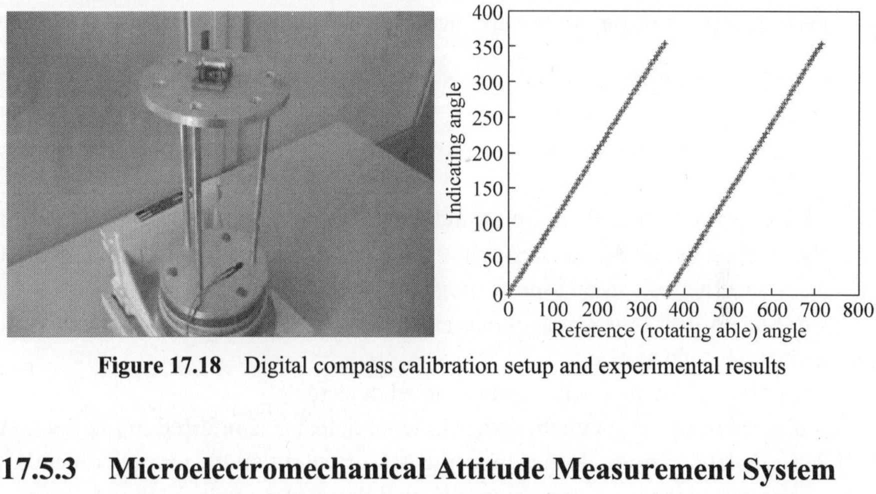

Figure 17.18 Digital compass calibration setup and experimental results

17.5.3 Microelectromechanical Attitude Measurement System

A microelectromechanical attitude measurement system is composed of the triaxial MEMS module of the gyroscopes, the accelerometers, and the magnetometers as shown in Fig. 17.19. The module and display interface are shown in the Fig. 17.20.

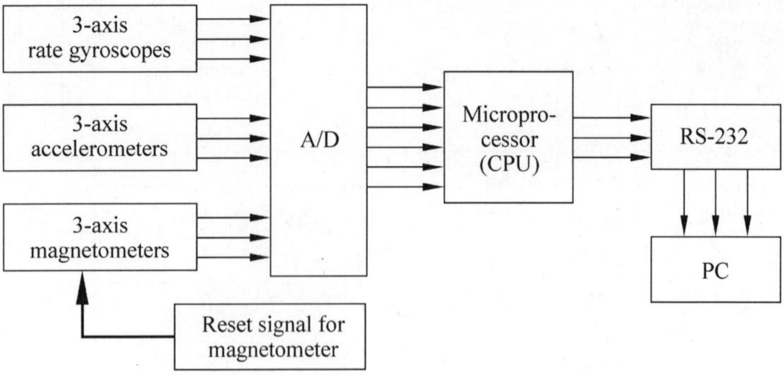

Figure 17.19 Composition of a microelectromechanical attitude measurement system

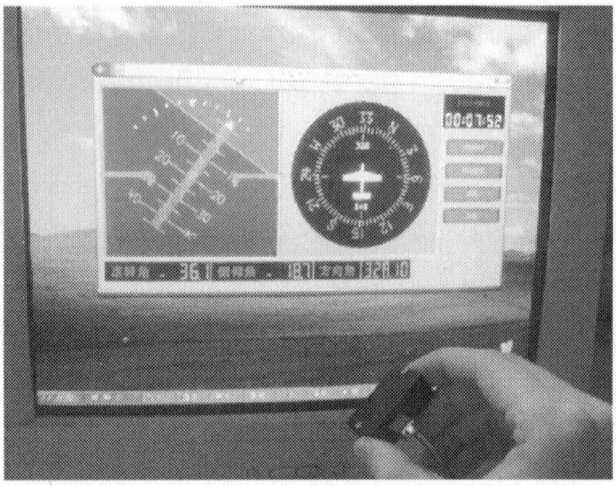

Figure 17.20 Microelectromechanical attitude measurement module and the display interface (see color figure at the end of this book)

The system operating principle is as follows: the angular velocity, acceleration, and magnetic density along the axes *X*, *Y*, and *Z* in the 3D space are measured respectively by using the triaxial sensor module [18, 25]. The analog voltage signals are converted to digital signals by A/D conversion, which will be sent into the CPU through a data bus, then the attitude angles will be obtained and displayed directly or obtained as output through a standard serial communication (or USB interface), which also can be used for real-time attitude control.

According to different signal processing methods and algorithms, the system has various working states:

(1) The state of the magnetic azimuth level detector

The algorithm of the magnetic azimuth level detector is referred in the Section 17.1.3 'Calculate Attitude Angles by using sensor output on the moving object'.

(2) The state of the gyroscope azimuth level detector

The algorithm of the gyroscope azimuth level detector is described in the Section 17.2.

(3) The state of the multi-azimuth level detector

As an example, the two magnetic azimuth level detectors used for measuring the attitude of cervical vertebra are introduced in the next section.

17.5.4 Relationship Between Two Rotation Coordinate Systems, and Application of Cervical Vertebra Attitude Measurement[26]

When the coordinate systems $OX_AY_AZ_A$ and $OX_BY_BZ_B$ of two moving objects rotate into $OX_{A3}Y_{A3}Z_{A3}$ and $OX_{B3}Y_{B3}Z_{B3}$ respectively relative to the base coordinate system *OXYZ*, the corresponding coordinate transformation matrixes of the two rotation coordinate systems are as follows:

$$\boldsymbol{R}_A = [\gamma_A \cdot \theta_A \cdot \psi_A]$$
$$\boldsymbol{R}_B = [\gamma_B \cdot \theta_B \cdot \psi_B]$$

Assume that the coordinate transformation of $OX_{A3}Y_{A3}Z_{A3}$ relative to $OX_{B3}Y_{B3}Z_{B3}$ is $[\gamma_{AB} \cdot \theta_{AB} \cdot \psi_{AB}]$, namely

$$\begin{bmatrix} L_{X_{A3}} \\ L_{Y_{A3}} \\ L_{Z_{A3}} \end{bmatrix} = [\gamma_{AB} \cdot \theta_{AB} \cdot \psi_{AB}] \cdot \begin{bmatrix} L_{X_{B3}} \\ L_{Y_{B3}} \\ L_{Z_{B3}} \end{bmatrix}$$

Then, the following relationship exists:

$$\boldsymbol{R}_A = [\gamma_{AB} \cdot \theta_{AB} \cdot \psi_{AB}] \cdot R_B \tag{17.32}$$

If the matrix $\boldsymbol{R}_B$ could be reversible, the transformation relationship $[\gamma_{AB} \cdot \theta_{AB} \cdot \psi_{AB}] = \boldsymbol{R}_A \cdot \boldsymbol{R}_B^{-1}$ between the two rotation coordinate systems can be calculated.

$$[\gamma_{AB} \cdot \theta_{AB} \cdot \psi_{AB}] = \boldsymbol{R}_A \cdot \boldsymbol{R}_B^{-1} \tag{17.33}$$

This algorithm could be applied to attitude measurement of human cervical vertebra. The medical instrument used for measuring the attitude of the cervical vertebra movement integrates microsensors, microprocessors, and attitude optimization algorithms. This instrument can provide the angle values of head and neck movements in 3D space, including flexion and extension, lateral bending, and rotational movement. For instance, attitude measurement modules A and B are installed on human's head and chest separately, shown in Fig. 17.21. A is used for measuring the head attitude $[\gamma_A \cdot \theta_A \cdot \psi_A]$, B is used for measuring the trunk attitude $[\gamma_B \cdot \theta_B \cdot \psi_B]$, and the calculation of the movement of the head relative to the trunk is obtained by using formula Eq. (17.33). The attitude motion curves are displayed. Through data processing and analysis, the movement range, smooth extent, and malfunction data of the head and neck movements are obtained.

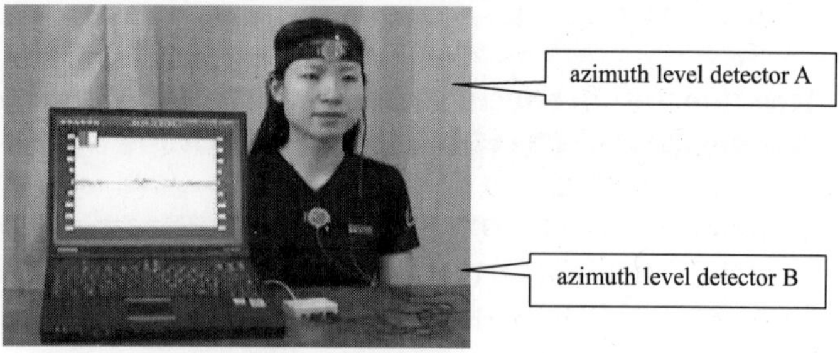

Figure 17.21 Head-neck motion measurement system

17.5.5 Microautopilot

Microautopilot is a composite microsystem integrated with various MEMS sensors, microprocessors (Groups), micro-GPS receivers, FLASH memory, miniature wireless data/image communications, power management, and other components. It can be used in micro-sized, small-sized, and medium-sized UAV navigation and automatic flight control. The hardware structure of the system is shown in Fig. 17.22.

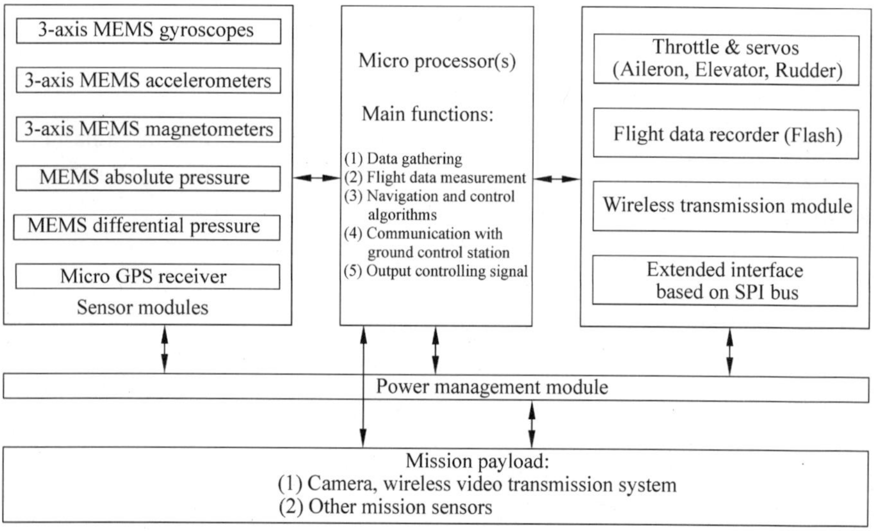

Figure 17.22 Block Diagram of the hardware structure of micro autopilot

The working principle of micro autopilots is as follows: the data from various sensors are collected by the microprocessor. The data includes angular velocity, acceleration, magnetic intensity, absolute pressure, differential pressure, position (latitude and longitude) from a GPS receiver, and speed information of the aircraft. The pitch, roll, and heading angles of the aircraft (detailed algorithm in Section 17.3), the pressure altitude, and the airspeed of the aircraft (detailed measuring principle in Section 17.5.1) are figured out through processing. The latitude and longitude information obtained by a GPS is converted to relative location information. According to a pre-defined flight mission, the micro autopilot controls the actuators on the aircraft, such as accelerator, aileron, elevator, rudder, etc. by using navigation and control algorithms, so as to achieve the autonomous navigation and flight control for the aircraft [2, 27–29].

Data communication between the micro autopilot and a ground station is achieved through a miniature wireless data transmission module.

17.6 Concluding Remarks

Microelectromechanical sensor-based system is an important part of micro/nano technology. It has been extensively applied in fields of industry, agriculture, transportation, communication, environmental monitoring, biomedicine, aerospace and defense, etc. For the detection, identification, tracking or targeting system with high-performance and full-functions, it is generally required to combine multiple types and many of sensors. When the performance and reliability of these microsensors meet the requirements for practical applications, the integration and application of multiple microsensor systems will be put on agenda consequently. They will bring new features, new designs, and new application methods in company with general problems from the multi-sensor integration, fusion, and optimization technology.

Study of microsensor system needs incorporating a MEMS technology with various other science and technologies, such as mathematically and physically modeling, signal processing and data fusion, control theory, neural networks, artificial intelligence technology, and so on. Microsensors are the hardware basis for the application systems. Integrated processing and optimization for output signals will enable systems to obtain more sufficient and more precise, more reliable, and real-time information that meet complex (i.e., both static and dynamic) requirements. It is also indispensable for integrating microsensor-based system with other types of devices in terms of their different applications. For example, integrating micro-inertial sensor-based systems with an image system will present image processing and image recognition issues. The integration of microsensor-based system and wireless communication system will present issues of transmission and interference, etc. 'Sometimes the right combination of tools is the key issue for achieving success' is what it means.

This chapter has synthesized the problems that authors encountered in the recent researches on microsensor applications.

Acknowledgements

Yuning Song, Ting Yu, Lidai Wang, Qiang Wei, Liyang Suo and Xiaoyan Liu also contributed to this chapter.

Reference

[1] Billar B., et al, (1995), Inertial navigation system for a mobile robot. *IEEE Trans. Robotics Autom*, **11**(3): 328 – 342

[2] Savage P. G., (1998), Strapdown inertial navigation integration algorithm design. Part 2: Velocity and position algorithms. *J. Guidance Contr. Dynam,* **21**(2): 208 – 221

[3] Caruso M. J., (2000), Applications of magnetic sensors for low cost compass systems. *IEEE Position Location and Navigation Symposium*: 177 – 184

[4] Gebre E. D., R. C. Hayward, J. D. Powell, (2004), Design of multi-sensor attitude determination systems. *IEEE Trans. Aerospace Electron. Sys.,* **40**(2): 627 – 649

[5] Ruffin P. B., (2008), Progress in the development of gyroscopes for use in tactical weapon systems. In: *Proceedings of SPIE—The International Society for Optical Engineering, Newport Beach*, CA, USA, Mar. 6 – 8, 2 – 12

[6] Gebre E. D., R. C. Hayward, J. D. Powell, (1998), A low cost GPS/Inertial attitude heading reference system (AHRS) for general aviation applications. *IEEE PLANS, Position Location and Navigation Symposium*, 518 – 525

[7] Gebre E. D., G. H. Elkaim, J. D. Powell, B. W. Parkinson, (2000), Gyro-free quaternion-based attitude determination system suitable for implementation using low cost sensors. *IEEE PLANS, Position Location and Navigation Symposium*, 185 – 192

[8] Marins J. L., X. P. Yun, E. R. Bachmann, et al, (2001), An extended Kalman filter for Quaternion-based orientation estimation using MARG sensors. In Proceedings of the 2001 IEEE/RSJ International Conference on Intelligent Robots and Systems, USA, Oct. 29-Nov. 03, 2003 – 2011

[9] Titterton D. H., J. L. Weston, Titterton, (1997), Strapdown Inertial Navigation Technology. Peter Peregrinis Ltd., London, UK, 19 – 57

[10] Grasmeyer J. M. , M. T. Keennon, (2001), Development of the black widow micro air vehicle. In *Proc. AIAA*, Paper AIAA-2001 – 0127

[11] Zhu R., Z. Y. Zhou, X. F. Sun, (2001), MEMS navigation system for general vehicle, IEEE International Conference on Mechatronics and Machine Vision in Practice, Aug. 27 – 29

[12] Wu J., J. B. Su, Y. G. Xi, (2001), Overview of multisensor integration and fusion. *Robot*, **23**(2): 183 – 186

[13] Qu G., et al., (1987), The Principle of Inertial Navigation, Beijing: Aviation Industry Press

[14] Zhou Z. Y., S. S. Xiong, (2001), Basis for Computer Control, Tsinghua Univ., 2

[15] Xiong S. S., Z. Y. Zhou, (2003), Neural filtering of colored noise based on Kalman filter

structure. *IEEE Trans. Instrum. Meas.,* **52**(3): 742 – 747

[16] Zhu R., Z. Y. Zhou, (2002), Optical alignment applied for solving axis-misaligned errors in micro electro-mechanical systems. *Int. J. Nonlinear. Sci.* **3**(SI 3-4): 345 – 348

[17] Chou Y. F, M. H. Hsieh, (1996), Angular alignment for wafer bonding. In Proceedings of SPIE - The International Society for Optical Engineering 2879, Bellingham, WA, USA, Oct. 14 – 15, 291 – 297

[18] Cheng X., Z. Fang, C. Yin, J. Guo, (1996), Adaptive straightness measurement system with dual frequency laser. *Acta Optica Sinica* **16**(10): 1456 – 1459

[19] Beach D. P., J. J. Rodden, (1990), Optical alignment with a beamwalk system, In Proceeding of SPIE—The International Society for Optical Engineering 1304, 94 – 99

[20] Wang L. D., (2005), Research on Micro Air Vehicles Attitude and Airspeed Measurement Control Technique [D], Tsinghua University, China

[21] KMZ52 Magnetic Field Sensor DATA SHEET, (2000), Jun09 Philips Semiconductors

[22] Zhu J. H., Z. Y. Zhou, X. Y. Ye, D. C. Zhang, Y. Hao, T. Li, (2001), Design of micro tunneling magnetometer and research on its fabrication process, *Microfabrication Technol,* **1**: 53 – 56

[23] Liu S. W., J. D. Zhuang, J. C. Hung, H. N. Wang, (1990), Compass deviation analysis and compensation for a three-axis strapdown magnetic heading system. IFAC Symposia Series—Proceedings of a Triennial World Congress v 4 Aug 13 – 17, 471 – 474

[24] Basile G., S. Pirani, M. Rinaldi, S. Varosi, (1996), Novel method for aircraft attitude estimation using magnetic field sensors and dynamic modeling, Southcon Conference Record Jun 25 – 27, 536 – 538

[25] Giurgiutiu V., A. N. Zagrai, (2000), Characterization of piezoelectric wafer active sensors, *J Intell Mater Sys Struct,* **11**(12): 959 – 976

[26] Zhu R., Z. Y. Zhou, (2004), A real-time articulated human motion tracking using tri-axis inertial/magnetic sensors package. *IEEE Trans. Neural Sys. Rehabil. Eng.* **12**(2): 295 – 302

[27] Ruffin P. B., (2000), Progress in the development of gyroscopes for use in tactical weapon systems, In Proceedings of SPIE—The International Society for Optical Engineering, Newport Beach, CA, USA, Mar. 6-8, 2 – 12

[28] Varadan V. K., et al, (2000), High sensitive and wide dynamic range navigation microsystem on a single chip. In *Proceedings of SPIE—The International Society for Optical Engineering*, Melbourne, Australia, Dec. 13 – 15, 134 – 140

[29] Lovren N., J. K. Pieper, (1998), Error analysis of direction cosines and quaternion parameters techniques for aircraft attitude determination. *IEEE Trans. Aerospace Electron. Sys.*, **34**(3): 983 – 989

18 A Surface Micromachined Accelerometer with Integrated CMOS Detection Circuitry

Weijie Yun

Chief Executive Officer, Co-Founder Telegent Systems
E-mail: wyun@telegentsystems.com

Abstract A surface micromachined, capacitive accelerometer described here integrates the mechanical sensing microstructures with CMOS detection circuits. The capacitive sensing structure consists of two polysilicon layers with the sensing and feedback electrodes underneath and the suspended plate as the proof mass. The sensing axis is perpendicular to the substrate. A full capacitive bridge is formed to translate a mechanical displacement signal into an electrical voltage signal. Electrostatic feedback is used to counteract the proof mass displacement due to acceleration. Interdigitated fingers are employed to generate a levitation force using the asymmetrical distribution of electrical fields. A unity gain buffer with low input capacitance is designed to actively drive the ground plane to minimize the parasitic capacitance. A S-D modulation technique is employed as the feedback control loop where the mechanical proof mass is used as the double integrator in the second-order S-D modulator.

Further described is the accelerometer prototype fabrication using a typical double polysilicon surface micromachining process for microstructures and a 3 mm conventional CMOS process for the electronics. The total chip size is 2.5 mm×5 mm. The unity gain buffer has a gain of 0.9 kHz and 500 kHz bandwidth that is limited by the parasitic capacitance from the measurement setup. The gain of the variable gain amplifier (VGA) can vary from unity to 40 and is controlled externally. The accelerometer is first characterized in the open-loop, self-testing mode. The damping coefficient is measured to be 1.2×10^{-3} N/(m/s), which agrees with 1×10^{-3} N/(m/s) from theoretical analysis. The open-loop sensitivity of the accelerometer is 100 mV/g with a 100 mV driving voltage. The stiction of suspended microstructures is observed and various possible solutions are discussed.

Keywords MEMS, accelerometer, surface micromaching, integrated CMOS, detection circuitry

18.1 Introduction

The author describes a surface micromachined, capacitive accelerometer integrated with CMOS detection circuits. A Σ-Δ modulation technique is employed as the feedback control loop where the mechanical proof mass is used as the double integrator in the Σ-Δ loop to provide direct digital output and digital feedback control. Electrostatic feedback is used to counteract the proof mass displacement, and the feedback force is linearly proportional to the pulse density of the feedback pulse train. This configuration provides high sensitivity, intrinsic linearity, and large dynamic range.

The author minimizes the parasitic capacitance and enhances the performance of the device. An input unity-gain buffer with low input capacitance is designed to bootstrap the parasitic capacitance. The chopper stabilization technique is used to eliminate the offset voltage caused by mismatches in the readout electronics. Moreover, the author seeks to minimize nonideal effects due to environmental changes and residual and packaging-induced stress; a dual loop is designed where two identical accelerometers except the proof mass ratio are built side by side and their digital outputs are subtracted.

The accelerometer is fabricated using a surface micromachining process with one structural polysilicon layer for the suspended proof mass. The Modular Integration of CMOS and microStructure (MICS) process is developed that enables the integration of CMOS and microstructure processes in a modular fashion. Tungsten metallization process with $TiSi_2$/TiN diffusion barrier at contacts is developed for the CMOS interconnect. Rapid thermal process (RTP) is developed for phosphosilicate glass (PSG) densification and polysilicon stress annealing. This RTP process is designed to develop low-cost, high-performance accelerometers to stimulating new approaches to the micromechanical sensing element, position sensing structures and interface electronics, and the overall system architecture, as well as to identify basic limits and tradeoffs.

18.2 Background—Literature

Here I review the theory and sensing principals of accelerometers and provide design examples for micromachined accelerometers. Silicon microaccelerometers date to the 1970s[1]. Early research and development focused on exploiting diffused piezoresistors and anisotropic etching technologies that were the basis for silicon diaphragm pressure sensors. Commercial products are now available[2] with the vast majority aimed at high-volume, intermediate performance applications. Capacitive sensing of the proof mass displacement is attractive since it avoids the temperature dependency of piezoresistors. Several prototypes have been reported, with most attempting to achieve high performance through optimized suspensions and highly sensitive interface electronics, at the cost of more elaborate fabrication processes and interface circuitry[3–10]. The driving motivation for development of silicon microfabricated accelerometers has been their potential low cost, due to the application of the batch fabrication processes that revolutionized microelectronics[11, 12].

Surface micromachining has been developed into a competitive technology in the last few years[13–16]. Surface micromachined accelerometers have clear advantages for integrating readout electronics with the mechanical sensing element on the same chip[17–19]. More functionality, such as direct digital output and temperature compensation, can be achieved with little increase in the cost.

Silicon micromachined accelerometers have proven to be competitive for many applications[20–23] for a variety of commercially important reasons. First, they are based on integrated circuit (IC) batch fabrication technology and therefore can be manufactured in large quantities and at a potentially very low cost. Second, they are much smaller and lighter than conventional accelerometers. Third, they weigh much less than their traditional cousins. Finally, they can be 'tuned' for optimal application performance.

I have first discussed the accelerometer theory and the operational principles for open-loop and force-balance accelerometers and then compare their characteristics and performances. Next I have examined various sensing techniques, which are used in microaccelerometers. Further, I have discussed an electrical model for the mechanical portion of the accelerometers.

18.2.1 Accelerometer Theory

The operation principle of an accelerometer is based on the Newton's second law. Upon acceleration, the proof mass (seismic mass) that is anchored on the frame by mechanical suspensions experiences an inertial force

$$F = -ma \tag{18.1}$$

causing a deflection of the proof mass, where a is the frame acceleration. Under certain conditions, the displacement is proportional to the input acceleration $= -m/ka$, where k is the spring constant of the suspension. The displacement can be detected and converted into an electrical signal by several sensing techniques.

From a system point of view, there are two major classes of silicon microaccelerometers: open-loop and force-balanced accelerometers. In an open-loop accelerometer design, the suspended proof mass displaces from its neutral position and the displacement is measured either piezoresistively or capacitively. In a force-balance accelerometer design, a feedback force—typically an electrostatic force—is applied onto the proof mass to counter act the displacement caused by the inertial force. Hence, the proof mass is virtually stationary relative to the frame. The output signal is proportional to the feedback signal.

The first-order behavior of open-loop accelerometers will be described. The stead-state, frequency and transient response will be studied analytically[24–27]. The performance of the force-balance accelerometers will be then considered. The operational characteristics of the two types of accelerometers will be combined and compared. The acceleration along the sensing axis will be assumed and secondary considerations, such as temperature sensitivity, will be neglected.

18.2.1.1 Open-Loop Design

An open-loop accelerometer can be modeled as a proof mass suspended elastically on a frame, as shown in Fig. 18.1. The frame is attached to the object whose acceleration is to be measured. The proof mass moves from its neutral position relative to the frame when the frame starts to accelerate. For any given acceleration, an appropriate proof mass displacement can be determined through the appropriate use of a mechanical suspension and the damping system. In the figure below, capacitive sensing is used. As shown in Fig. 18.1, y and z are the absolute displacements (displacement relative to the earth) for the frame and the proof mass, respectively. The acceleration y is of the interest of measurement. Let x be the relative displacement of the proof mass with respect to the frame. The relative displacement is the difference between the absolute displacements of the frame and the proof mass, or

$$x = z - y \tag{18.2}$$

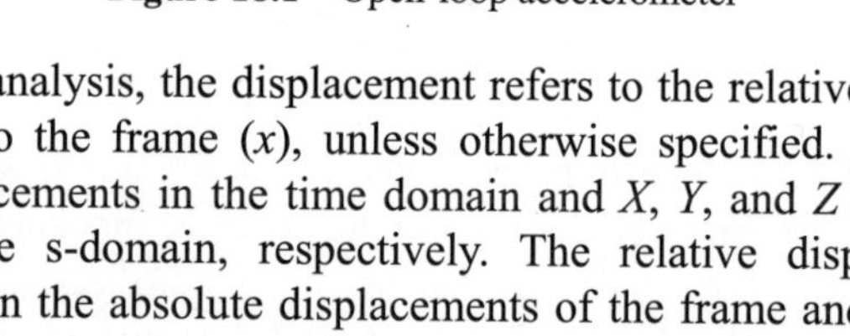

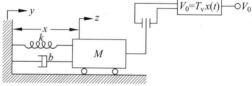

Figure 18.1 Open-loop accelerometer

In the following analysis, the displacement refers to the relative displacement of the proof mass to the frame (x), unless otherwise specified. Here x, y, and z denote the displacements in the time domain and X, Y, and Z are their Laplace transforms in the s-domain, respectively. The relative displacement is the difference between the absolute displacements of the frame and the proof mass, or $x = z - y$. In the following analysis, the displacement refers to the relative displacement of the proof mass to the frame (x), unless otherwise specified. Here, x, y, and z denote the displacements in the time domain and X, Y, and Z are their Laplace transforms in the s-domain, respectively. When the inertial force displaces the proof mass, it also experiences the restoring force from the mechanical spring and the damping force from the viscous damping. The equation of motion of the proof mass can be written as:

$$m\frac{\mathrm{d}^2 z}{\mathrm{d}t^2} = -kx - b\frac{\mathrm{d}x}{\mathrm{d}t} \tag{18.3}$$

where k is the spring constant of the suspension, and b is the damping coefficient of the air and any structural damping. Since the proof mass is usually sealed in the frame, the damping force is proportional to the velocity relative to the frame, rather than to the absolute velocity. Combining Eq. (18.2) and Eq. (18.3), the equation of motion can be obtained:

$$\frac{\mathrm{d}^2x}{\mathrm{d}t^2}+\frac{b}{m}\frac{\mathrm{d}x}{\mathrm{d}t}+\frac{k}{m}x=-\frac{\mathrm{d}^2y}{\mathrm{d}t^2}=-a(t) \tag{18.4}$$

The negative sign indicates that the proof mass displacement is always in the opposite direction of the acceleration. Equation (18.4) can also be rewritten as:

$$\frac{\mathrm{d}^2x}{\mathrm{d}t^2}+2\xi\omega_\mathrm{n}\frac{\mathrm{d}x}{\mathrm{d}t}+\omega_\mathrm{n}^2x=-\frac{\mathrm{d}^2y}{\mathrm{d}t^2} \tag{18.5}$$

where $\overline{\omega}_\mathrm{n}=\sqrt{k/m}$ is the naruralresonantfrequency, and

$\xi=\dfrac{b}{2m\omega_\mathrm{n}}$ is the damping factor.

This is the governing equation for an open-loop accelerometer relating the proof mass displacement and the input acceleration. The performance of an open-loop accelerometer can be characterized by the natural resonant frequency (ω_n) and the damping factor (ξ). The damping is determined by the viscous liquid or the chamber pressure. For silicon microaccelerometers, gas damping is most commonly used and the damping factor is controlled by the chamber pressure and the gas properties. Critical damping is desired in most designs to achieve maximum bandwidth and minimum overshoot and ringing.

The natural resonant frequency is another important parameter in the open-loop accelerometer design. It is designed to satisfy the requirements for the sensitivity and the bandwidth. The natural resonant frequency can be measured either dynamically by resonating the accelerometer or statically by measuring the displacement for a given acceleration. From its definition, the natural resonant frequency can be rewritten as:

$$\omega_\mathrm{n}=\sqrt{\frac{k}{m}}=\sqrt{\frac{a}{x}} \tag{18.6}$$

where a and x are the acceleration and the displacement, respectively. Therefore, the natural resonant frequency can be determined conveniently by measuring the displacement due to the gravitational field. For a constant acceleration, the proof mass is stationaly relative to the frame so that $y=z=0$. Eq. (18.5) becomes

$$\omega_\mathrm{n}^2n=-\frac{\mathrm{d}^2y}{\mathrm{d}t^2}=-a \tag{18.7}$$

Or

$$x = -\frac{m}{k}a \tag{18.8}$$

in a steady state. The sensitivity is determined by the ratio m/k the inverse of the square of natural resonant frequency. Hence, it is desirable to have large proof mass and compliant suspension for high sensitivity.

(1) Frequency response

Frequency response is the accelerometer response to a sinusoidal excitation. Let the frame be in harmonic motion where y is the magnitude of vibration; then, the input acceleration is

$$a(t) = \ddot{y}(t) = -Y\omega^2 \sin \omega t. \tag{18.9}$$

Note that the magnitude of the acceleration is $-Y\omega^2$. The motion governing Eq. (18.5) becomes

$$\ddot{x} + 2\xi\omega_{\mathrm{n}}\dot{x} + \omega_{\mathrm{n}}^2 x = Y\omega^2 \sin \omega t \tag{18.10}$$

The frequency response can be obtained by solving this equation in either the time domain or the s-domain using Laplace transforms. To solve it in the time domain, assuming that the initial velocity and the displacement are both zero, we can transform Eq. (18.10) into s-domain and obtain

$$X(t) = \frac{Y\omega^2}{(s^2 + \omega^2)(s^2 + 2\xi\omega_{\mathrm{n}} s + \omega_{\mathrm{n}}^2)} \tag{18.11}$$

The frequency response in the time domain can be obtained by applying an inverse Laplace transform to Eq. (18.11)

$$x(t) = -\frac{Y\omega^2}{\omega_{\mathrm{n}}^2} \frac{\sin(\omega r - \phi)}{\sqrt{\left(1 - \frac{\omega^2}{\omega_{\mathrm{n}}^2}\right)^2 + \left(2\xi\frac{\omega}{\omega_{\mathrm{n}}}\right)^2}} \tag{18.12}$$

where ϕ is the phase lag and

$$\tan\phi = \frac{2\xi\frac{\omega}{\omega_{\mathrm{n}}}}{1 - \left(\frac{\omega}{\omega_{\mathrm{n}}}\right)^2} \tag{18.13}$$

The sensitivity of an accelerometer can be defined as $S(\mathrm{j}\omega) = \frac{X(\mathrm{j}\omega)}{a(\mathrm{j}\omega)}$. With s

replaced by jω in Eq. (18.11), the frequency response cart be plotted with various damping factors, shown Fig. 18.2. It shows that there are big overshoot and ringing for under-damped accelerometers, and the cut-off frequency for over-damped accelerometers is lower than for critically damped accelerometers. The phase lag 4t can also be plotted for various damping factors, as shown in Fig. 18.3.

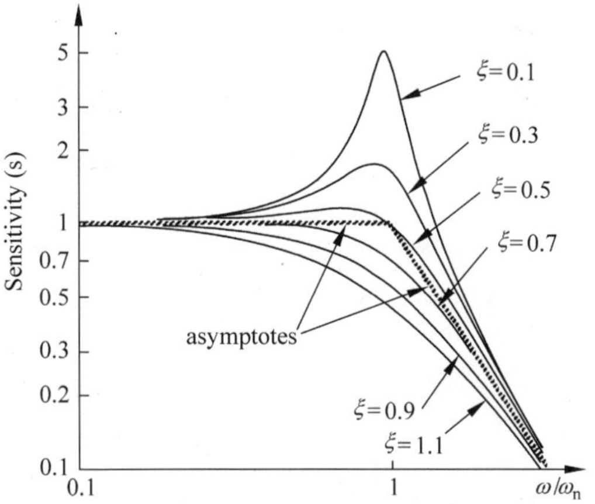

Figure 18.2 Frequency response with various damping factors

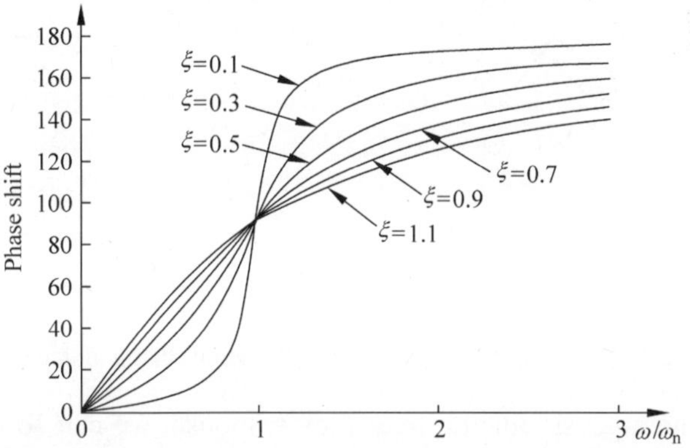

Figure 18.3 Phase shift with various damping factors

At low frequency ($\omega \ll \omega_n$), we obtain $S_0 = -\omega_n^{-2} = -m/k$ from Eq. (18.12), which agrees with the steady-state response Eq. (18.8). At a very high frequency ($\omega \gg \omega_n$), the mechanical spring cannot respond to the high-frequency vibration and relax its elastic energy. Therefore, the frequency for a given acceleration, the proof mass displacement increases. From Eq. (18.12), we can obtain $S(j\omega) = -\omega^2/\omega_n^2$. So the slope of the asymptote is $-\omega^2/\omega_n^2$. at a high frequency.

The accelerometer can also be used to measure velocity and displacement in addition to acceleration, although accelerometers used to measure the velocity have very limited applications. The displacement is proportional to the acceleration when the frequency is below natural resonant frequency, as shown in Fig. 18.4. The accelerometer can be used as a vibrometer (or displacement meter) for frequencies well above the resonant frequency. From Eq. (18. 12), we find that

$$\frac{x(t)}{Y} = -\frac{m}{k}\frac{\omega^2 \sin(\omega t - \phi)}{\sqrt{\left(1-\frac{\omega^2}{\omega_n^2}\right)^2 + \left(2\xi\frac{\omega}{\omega_n}\right)^2}} \tag{18.14}$$

In other words, the response of the vibrometer is the ratio of the vibration amplitude of the proof mass and the amplitude of the applied vibration. At a high frequency ($\omega \gg 0$), the ratio is a constant and is equal to m/k. Figure 18.4 shows the ratio of the proof mass displacement (x) and the frame vibration (y) versus the normalized frequency.

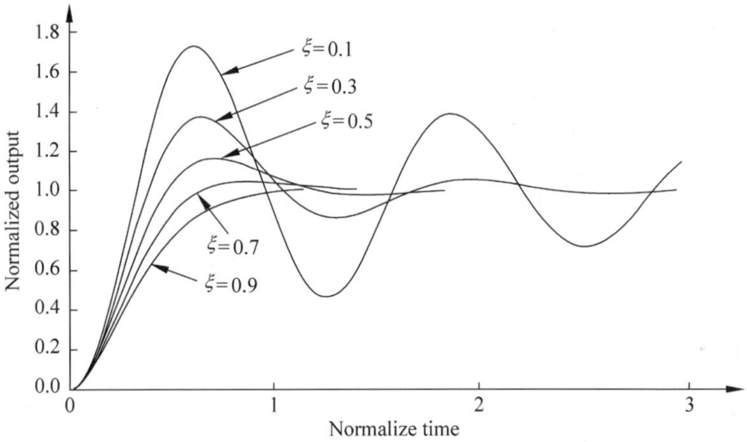

Figure 18.4 Transient response with various damping factors

Similar to the analysis for the frequency response, we can solve Eq. (18.15) using Laplace transform and obtain the transient response in the time domain.

$$x(t) = \frac{m}{k}Y\left(1 - \frac{e^{-\xi\omega_n t}}{\sqrt{1-\xi^2}}\sin\left(\sqrt{1-\xi^2}\,\omega t + \phi\right)\right) \tag{18.15}$$

As shown in Fig. 18.4, the transient response has large over-shoot and ringing if the accelerometer is under-damped. The steady-state displacement is A/ω_n^2.

18.2.1.2 Force-Balance Design

Force-balance accelerometers, also known as closed-loop or servo accelerometers, have some advantages over open-loop designs. The operation of a force-balance accelerometer can be illustrated in Fig. 18.5. The forward path (including sensing and signal detection and amplification) is identical to the open-loop design. Hence, most of the sensing techniques used in open-loop designs are also applicable in force-balance accelerometers. In force-balance designs, the output signal is then used to generate a feedback force onto the proof mass to counteract the displacement due to the acceleration, so the proof mass is 'virtually stationary' and its displacement is negligible. The output is now proportional to the feedback signal, rather than to the proof mass displacement, as in the open-loop design.

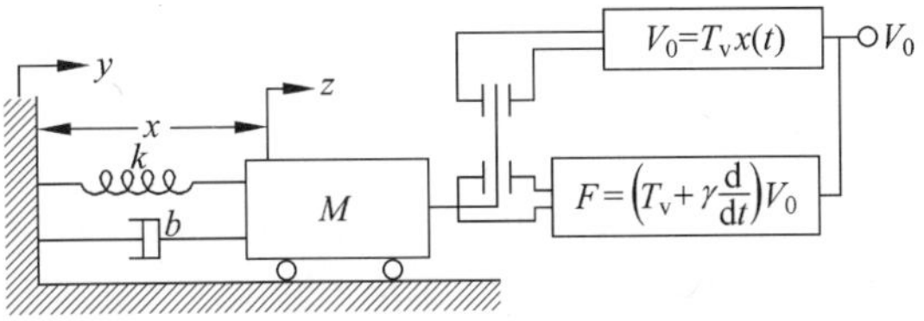

Figure 18.5 Force-balance accelerometer

In many macro-force-balance accelerometers, magnetic feedback is used. Passing the output current through a restoring coil with the magnetic force linearly proportional to the feedback current generates the feedback force. Capacitive sensing and magnetic feedback are often used together to avoid any effect at the sensing node from the feedback signal, known as signal feedthrough. Due to the incompatibility of magnetic materials and coils with IC processes, magnetic feedback is rarely used in silicon accelerometers[28]. Electrostatic feedback has been the most popular technique in recent designs[41]. However, unlike the magnetic feedback where the force is linearly proportional to the feedback current, the electrostatic force is given by:

$$F=-\frac{\partial U_E}{\partial x}=\frac{1C}{2d}V^2 \tag{18.16}$$

where d is the gap between the two electrodes, C is the feedback capacitance, and V is the applied feedback voltage. The feedback force is linearly proportional to the square of the feedback voltage, rather than to the feedback voltage directly. Therefore, this nonlinearity must be corrected to have a linear feedback system. A furthermore difficulty is that electrostatic forces are always contractive—regardless of the polarity of the applied voltage.

There are various techniques to overcome disadvantages (nonlinearity and one-directional force) of the electrostatic feedback. The most common approach is to build two symmetrical feedback electrodes on both sides of the proof mass so that the push-pull force can be generated by changing the magnitudes of the voltage applied to the two electrodes. By applying a differential voltage to the electrodes, the capacitive feedback nonlinearity can be corrected (to first order) and a linear system can be realized[45]. For example, let V be the DC bias voltage and v be the differential feedback voltage applied to the two feedback electrodes, we can have the feedback force:

$$F = \frac{1}{2}C_1 d_1 (V+v)^2 - \frac{1}{2}C_2 d_2 (V-v)^2 = 2C_0 d_0 V v \tag{18.17}$$

when $C_1 = C_2 = C_0$ and $d_1 = d_2 = d_0$. Therefore, with this technique, the feedback force is linearly proportional to the DC bias voltage and the differential feedback voltage. The push-pull feedback force can be generated by changing the polarity of the feedback voltage. Other approaches, such as pulse width modulation (PWM) and pulse density modulation (PDM), can also be employed where the magnitude of the feedback voltage is a constant and the feedback force is proportional to the pulse width and pulse density of the feedback voltage.

18.2.1.3 Steady-State Response

The output of the accelerometer is proportional to the input acceleration:

$$ma = kx + T_f V_0 \tag{18.18}$$

where T_f is the gain in the feedback path, as shown in Fig. 18.5. The electrical feedback force is typically much larger than the mechanical restoring force; thus, the mechanical spring can be neglected in the analysis. Rearranging the equation, we obtain:

$$V_0 = \frac{m}{T} a \tag{18.19}$$

In a force-balance accelerometer design, the proof mass displacement is now the error signal of the feedback system and is determined by the electrical control loop. For a given acceleration, the displacement decreases as the feedback loop gain increases while the steady-state output remains the same. As shown in Eq. (18.19), the output voltage is independent of the amplifier gain in the forward path and is inversely proportional to the gain in the feedback path. Therefore, the steady-state response is independent of the proof mass displacement.

(1) Dynamic response

The force-balance accelerometers can be analyzed similarly to the open-loop accelerometer. We can write the equation of motion as:

$$m\frac{d^2z}{dt^2}=\left(-kx-b\frac{dx}{dt}\right)+\left(-\alpha x-\beta\frac{dx}{dt}\right) \tag{18.20}$$

where $\alpha = T_v \times T_f$, the electrical feedback force per unit displacement (N/m);
$\beta = T_v \times \gamma$, the electrical damping force per unit speed (N/(m/s)).
The first two terms on the right-hand side of the equation are the restoring forces from mechanical suspension and damping. The last two terms are the electric feedback force and are often termed the 'electrical spring' and the 'electrical dumper'. Rearranging the equation, we can obtain

$$\frac{d^2x}{dt^2}+\frac{b+\beta}{m}\frac{dx}{dt}+\frac{k+\alpha}{m}x=-\frac{d^2y}{dt^2} \tag{18.21}$$

Again, the mechanical spring and damping are usually dominated by their electric counterparts and can be neglected in the analysis. Equation (18.21) can be rewritten as:

$$\ddot{x}+2\xi'\omega_0\dot{x}+\omega_0^2x=-y \tag{18.22}$$

where $\omega_0=\sqrt{(k+\alpha)/m}=\sqrt{\alpha/m}$ is the resonant frequency for the feedback system $\xi'=\dfrac{(b+\beta)}{2m\omega_0}=\dfrac{\beta}{2m\omega_0}$ is the electrical damping factor Comparing Eq. (18.4) and Eq. (18.22), it can be observed that the open-loop and force-balance accelerometers have very similar dynamic response when the extra poles and zeros introduced by the electronic feedback are at much higher frequencies than the frequencies of interests. In this case, the analysis for the open-loop accelerometers, such as frequency and transient response, are all applicable to the force-balance accelerometers, except that the resonant frequency and damping are controlled by the electronic feedback control loop. However, there are some subtle differences between the two classes of accelerometers, discussed in the next section.

18.2.1.4 Comparisons

The open-loop and force-balance accelerometers have similar responses to the input acceleration. It can be easily observed from Eq. (18.4) and Eq. (18.22) that both of them are second-order systems. Thus, the analysis for the open-loop accelerometers can be applicable for the force-balance accelerometers. The difference is that the spring constant and damping are determined by the mechanical design in open-loop accelerometers, and the 'electrical spring' and 'electrical dumper' are determined by the electrical feedback system in the force-balance accelerometers. Open-loop accelerometers tend to be low cost and robust for its simplicity. In the force-balance accelerometers, the proof mass displacement signal is sensed and amplified. The output signal is then used to generate a feedback force onto the proof mass to counteract the displacement due to the acceleration. The proof mass is 'virtually stationary' and its displacement is negligible. Thus, the mechanical suspension can be made more compliant so that high sensitivity can be achieved. The dynamic range is usually determined by the linearity of the electronic feedback control.

In the open-loop design, the proof mass deflects from its neutral position upon acceleration and the acceleration is sensed indirectly by the measurement of the displacement. The accelerometer performance is then determined by the mechanical design of the suspension and the damping method. The damping is controlled by the air pressure in the chamber and critical damping is usually desired for maximum bandwidth. To achieve high sensitivity, a compliant suspension is desired for a large displacement. The dynamic range is limited by the linearity of the mechanical spring and a stiffer suspension will improve the linearity by limiting the displacement at the cost of low sensitivity. Therefore, tradeoffs must be made among sensitivity, dynamic range, and bandwidth for open-loop accelerometers.

The detection electronics is usually not the major limiting factor for the sensitivity in the open-loop design. The accuracy is mostly limited by the imperfection in the mechanical suspension, such as hysteresis and the temperature sensitivity in the spring constant. Thus, the mechanical suspension is the key to the open-loop accelerometer designs. These problems lead to the force-balance accelerometers where the mechanical suspension is dominated by the better controlled electrical feedback.

The performance of the force-balance accelerometers is mostly determined by the design of the interface electronics and the servo loop, which can be much better controlled than those in the mechanical system. The feedback design and system partitioning are the keys to the force-balance accelerometer design. Damping for silicon accelerometers is often achieved by squeeze-film dampers, which depend on the gas pressure in the package. It is difficult to achieve a linear damping coefficient due to the compressibility of the gas[43]. The damping coefficient can also be sensitive to the temperature variations. In force-balance designs, the damping factor can be determined by the electrical system.

The force-balance accelerometers provide high sensitivity and large dynamic range, which can be optimized by electronic design. Since the proof mass displacement is negligible, the linearity of the accelerometer is determined by the electronic feedback loop. It is reported that a linearity of 120 dB dynamic range can be achieved[47]. The minimum detectable signal is limited by the noise level at the input, such as the electronic thermal noise, $1/f$ noise, Brownian noise, etc., and the dynamic range is determined by the interface circuitry and the feedback loop. Multiple working ranges can also be achieved by using variable gains in the feedback path[44].

The bandwidth of an open-loop accelerometer is set by the ratio of the spring constant and the proof mass, which has to compromise with the sensitivity. The desired dynamic response of a force-balanced accelerometer can be achieved by tailoring the electronic design, without modifying the mechanical designs. For example, the bandwidth can be doubled by increasing the loop gain by a factor of four. To overwhelm the mechanical properties, it is desirable to have a high gain in the feedback loop, which also increases the bandwidth of the accelerometer. For some applications, accelerometers are operated in a noisy vibrational environment and the signal of interest is in the low frequency spectrum. The force-balance accelerometers may not be well-suited for these applications because the unwanted high-frequency vibration may introduce errors and distortions in low frequencies. Mounting of the accelerometer is also a design consideration. The low cut-off frequency feature of the open-loop accelerometer has now become very attractive for these applications. The high-frequency vibrational noise is conveniently restricted and only the low-frequency signal is measured.

Stability is very critical in the force-balance design, whereas it is not an issue for the open-loop design. Incorporating an active network in the feedback loop often introduces additional poles and zeros that cause phase distortion and time lags in the loop. The accelerometer is then no longer a second-order system. Therefore, the feedback must be carefully designed to ensure the stability of the loop.

18.2.1.5 Sensing Principles: Piezoresistive

Piezoresistive sensing is one of the most popular sensing techniques in accelerometer and pressure sensor designs. In accelerometers, the proof mass displacement causes compressive and tensile stress in different regions along the suspension, which leads to the deformation of lattice, and the resistance of the piezoresistors on the suspension arm will be changed. The acceleration can then be measured by the change in resistance.

The behavior of piezoresistors has been studied extensively and can be accurately modeled[26]. Variation in piezoresistance is related to both longitudinal and transversal stresses in the film. The fractional resistance change is given by[27]:

$$\Delta R / R_0 = \sum_{i=1}^{n} (C_{li}\sigma_1^i + C_{ii}\sigma_1^i) \tag{18.23}$$

where C_{li} and C_{ii} are the longitudinal and transverse ith-order piezoresistive coefficients, and σ_1 and σ_i are the longitudinal and transverse stresses, and $\Delta R / R_0$ is the fractional resistance variations of the piezoresistors.

The third-order polynomial approximation is sufficient for most of the applications. In accelerometer designs, piezoresistors are usually implanted resistors on the suspension. Since piezoresistors are located on the suspension, the longitudinal stress is usually much larger than the transversal stress and the stress level can be controlled by varying their locations along the suspension. Typically, the resistance changes 2% for the maximum proof mass deflection.

Simplicity in signal detection is one of the attractive features in piezoresistive sensing. The Wheatstone bridge is almost exclusively used for piezoresistive sensing, where piezoresistors are used to form the resistive bridge. The output of the Wheatstone bridge has low impedance, and the output voltage can be measured with standard electronic instruments. The full-bridge configuration also rejects the common mode signal, such as higher mode vibration and temperature sensitivity, to first order.

Temperature sensitivity has prevented piezoresistive sensors from applications that require wide temperature ranges. Piezoresistance has a temperature sensitivity of –1%/℃. Although the Wheatstone bridge configuration cancels the temperature sensitivity to first order, accurate modeling and sophisticated electronic compensation are required before they can be used for high-performance applications[28].

18.2.1.6 Sensing Principles: Capacitive

The capacitive sensing technique has clear advantage in terms of the temperature sensitivity compared with the piezoresistive sensing scheme. The temperature coefficient for capacitance is of the order 50 ppm/℃[29], which is significantly lower than 10,000 ppm/℃ in the piezoresistive sensing case. The low temperature sensitivity enables capacitive accelerometers to be widely used in many high-precision applications.

In capacitive accelerometers, one of the two electrodes is the suspended proof mass that deflects with respect to the fixed electrode when it accelerates. The capacitance variation is often used in a capacitive Wheatstone bridge configuration to transduce the displacement into a voltage. Since the outputs of the capacitive bridge are high-impedance nodes, detection circuitry needs to convert the high impedance into low impedance. In addition, the sensing capacitance is typically a few hundred femtofarads (10 – 15 F) to a few picofarads, whereas the parasitic capacitance can be orders of magnitude larger. Therefore, the detection circuitry is much more sophisticated than that in the piezoresistive sensing scheme.

The capacitive Wheatstone bridge is driven by a high-frequency carrier and the acceleration-induced signal is modulated to the carrier frequency, so the bandwidth of capacitive accelerometers can go down to DC. The signal is typically demodulated after amplification to minimize $1/f$ noise contributed by the amplifier.

In open-loop accelerometers, nonlinearity is one of the concerns for the capacitive sensing scheme since the capacitance is inversely proportional to the gap distance between the two electrodes. Although the capacitance is linearly proportional to the overlap area of the two electrodes, it includes fringing fields and tends to be very small. Most accelerometers measure the capacitance variations by the gap. One technique is commonly used to eliminate the nonlinearity problem, in which two fixed electrodes are located symmetrically on each side of the proof mass and formed a pair of differential capacitors. These two differential capacitors can then form a capacitive divider and the first-order output from the capacitive divider is linear with respect to the proof mass deflection. The nonlinearity in the force-balance accelerometers is usually limited by the electronic feedback control due to the negligible deflection of the proof mass.

The fabrication of capacitive accelerometers is similar to that of piezoresistive accelerometers[30–33]. A silicon wafer is etched from the back side (or both sides) to form the suspension and the proof mass. This wafer is then bonded to two capping wafers on both sides. Instead of diffusing piezoresistors on suspensions, capacitive plates are defined on both sides of the proof mass and are aligned with the conductive plates on the capping wafers forming two differential capacitors. Process modifications are needed to contact the electrodes, especially for hermetically sealed cavities.

18.2.1.7 Sensing Principles: Resonant

Silicon micromachined accelerometers were stimulated by the research on devices utilizing push-pull quartz resonant strain gauges in the 1970s[34]. Resonant accelerometers are attractive for their high sensitivity and frequency output. Most of the conventional, high-precision accelerometers are of this type. The structure of resonant accelerometers is quite different from other sensors, as shown in Fig. 18.6. The proof mass is suspended by relatively stiff suspension to prevent a large displacement due to acceleration. Unlike other types of accelerometers, resonators are attached to the proof mass. Upon acceleration, the proof mass changes the strain in the attached resonators, which causes a shift in those resonant frequencies. The frequency shift is then detected by the electronics and the output can be measured easily by digital counters.

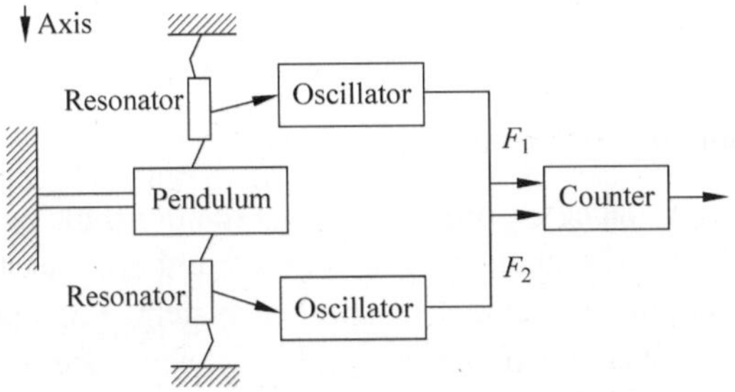

Figure 18.6 Resonant accelerometer

The basic principles of operation for resonant accelerometers have been extensively studied and well understood, but many practical issues still present great challenges to the sensing axis and therefore to accelerometer designers (see Fig. 18.6 above).

For example, the vibration mode of the strain gauges should have high sensitivity to the compressive or tensile axial loads and yet not be close to other modes to minimize mode-jumping. In addition, a high-quality factor for the resonator (high OJ is highly desirable, implying that a low pressure or vacuum ambient is optimum where the quality factor is limited by the structural damping. However, the proof mass and suspensions should be damped to avoid ringing and unwanted frequency noise. Finally, the relative stiff suspensions make packaging-induced stress a problem in corn-pen sating the packaged device. In silicon accelerometers, most of the effort has been focused on the development of force-balance designs. Resonant accelerometers are still in the early stages of research and development. Nevertheless, the use of resonant strain gauges is a competitive approach for high precision sensing and can be developed into a key technology for the inertial grade accelerometers.

18.2.1.8 Electrical Modeling

Modeling provides insight into the system design and makes possible optimization and prediction of performance. It is important to draw analogies between electrical and mechanical systems when analyzing a mixed system, such as accelerometers where the system includes a mechanical proof mass and the electric detection and feedback control. It is convenient that the two systems are transformed into a unified system to use a common analytical and CAD framework. I have first discussed the modeling methodology. Similarities between mechanical and electrical systems have been identified and a force-current analogy between the two systems is derived[35].

Various approaches can be used to analyze and model a physical system. Here I have discussed three basic conceptual steps in analyzing this problem:

(1) Modeling the aspect of the problem of interest (usually in a mathematical form);

(2) Analyzing the model;

(3) Verifying the theoretical results with experiments.

18.2.1.9 Mechanical Modeling

There are various approaches to find analogous relationships between mechanical and electrical systems. The analogy should be natural and intuitive when relating a model in one system to a model in another system. For clarity, symbols arc capitalized for the mechanical system and in lower case for other electrical systems (except RLC) in the following discussion. Thus, $V(t)$ is the velocity and $v(t)$ is the voltage. Comparing the power of the two systems:

$$P_{\text{mech}}(t)=F(t)V(t) \tag{18.24}$$

$$P_{\text{elec}}(t)=v(t)i(t) \tag{18.25}$$

Either voltage or current can be used as the analog of the force when transforming one system into another. However, the force-current analogy (or velocity-voltage analogy) is more convenient than the force-voltage analogy. When the force-current analog is employed, a mechanical model can be directly transformed into an electric circuit model and the configuration remains the same for both systems. By maintaining the same configuration, it means that a junction point in a mechanical model transforms into a junction point in the analogous electric model. This means that instead of summing the force leaving a junction point, we can now sum the currents leaving the analogous electrical junction. On the other hand, if force-voltage analogy is employed in the transformation, the circuit configuration needs to be changed and the transformation process is more complicated.

With force-current as the primary analog, it is relatively easy to derive secondary analogs associating the two systems. For example, in a mechanical system, we have

$$F = M\,\mathrm{d}V/\mathrm{d}t \tag{18.26}$$

We have similar relationship in the electrical system:

$$i = C\,\mathrm{d}v/\mathrm{d}t \tag{18.27}$$

Obviously, mass and capacitance are analogous in the force-current analogy. Similarly, it can be shown that damping (B) and conductance ($1/R$), spring constant (K), and the reciprocal of the inductance (L) are also the 'matching pairs'. Further, more analogies relating the two systems can be found, such as the displacement (X) and the flux (Li) in an inductor, the mechanical momentum (MV), and the electrical charge (Cv) in a capacitor, etc. Table 18.1 shows the variables between the mechanical and electrical systems in the force-current analogy.

Table 18.1 Force-current analog between mechanical and electrical systems

MECHANICAL		ELECTRICAL	
Force		Current	
Velocity		Voltage	
Mass	$F = M\,\mathrm{d}v/\mathrm{d}T$	Capacitor	$i = C\,\mathrm{d}v/\mathrm{d}T$
Friction	$F = BV$	Resistor	$i = i/Rv$
Spring	$F = K\int V(t)\,\mathrm{d}t$	Inductor	$i = 1/L\int V(t)\,\mathrm{d}t$
Displacement	X	Flux	Li
Momentum	MV	Charge	Cv
Kinetic energy	$1/2\ MV^2$	Electric energy	$1/2\ Cv^2$
Potential energy	$1/2\ KX^2$	Magnetic energy	$1/2\ Li^2$
Power	FV	Power	iv

18.2.2 Accelerometer Modeling

As discussed in Section 2.1, an accelerometer can be modeled as a suspended proof mass anchored on a frame. Upon acceleration, there are two mechanical forces acting on the proof mass: the restoring force from the spring and the viscous damping (Fig. 18.7) or it can be modeled with MKL shown in Fig. 18.8.

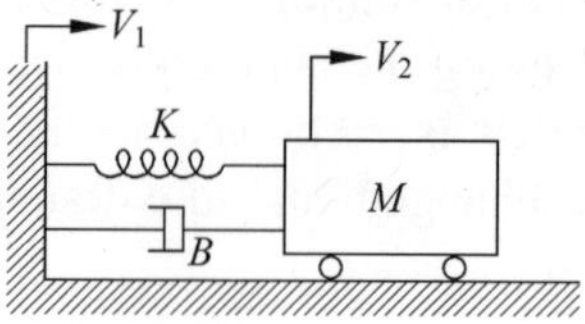

Figure 18.7 Simplified model for an accelerometer

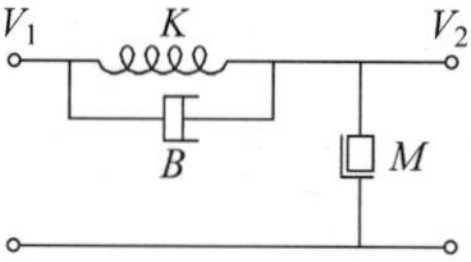

Figure 18.8 Mechanical model for an accelerometer

From D'Alembert's principle, we can sum the velocity at V_2 and obtain:

$$MsV_2 + K1/s(V_2 - V_1) + B(V_2 - V_1) = 0 \tag{18.28}$$

where s is the complex variable. Rearranging the terms, we have:

$$MsV_2 + K1/sV_2 + BV_2 = K1/sV_1 + BV_1 \tag{18.29}$$

where the two terms on the right-hand side of the equation are the input signals, and the left-hand side terms are the response. With the force-current analogy, the mechanical model for the accelerometer in Fig. 18.8 can be transformed into an electrical model directly by replacing *MKB* with *LRC,* without changing the system configuration, as shown in Fig. 18.9. To verify the transformation, we can sum the current at the output node (v_2) using Kirchhoff's current law and obtain:

$$Csv_2 + 1/Ls + 1/R(v_2) = 1/Ls(v_1) + 1/R(v_1) \tag{18.30}$$

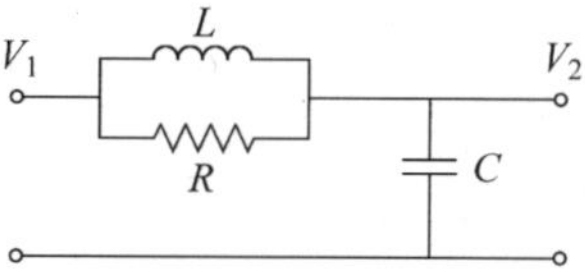

Figure 18.9 Circuit model for the accelerometer

Replacing C, $1/L$, and. l/R in Eq. (18.30) by M, K, and L respectively, Eq. (18.30) becomes Eq. (18.29). Thus, the circuit model shown in Fig. 18.9 is mathematically equivalent to the mechanical model shown in Fig. 18.8, and we have transformed the mechanical system into an electrical system.

18.2.2.1 Noise Analysis

Thermal noise is due to the random fluctuations arising from molecular vibrations. This noise is known as Johnson noise in electrical systems and Brownian noise in mechanical systems. For accelerometers, the proof mass decreases as the devices scale from conventional (macro-) accelerometers to bulk and surface micromachined accelerometers. Thermal noise is inversely proportional to the proof mass; hence, it becomes more important as accelerometers are scaled down. Mechanical thermal noise (Brownian noise) in accelerometer designs will be analyzed first[17]. Electrical noise will also be examined and compared with Brownian noise.

The basic relationship that governs thermal noise analysis is expressed by the Equipartition Theorem[19]: any 'mode' of a system in thermal equilibrium has an average noise energy of $1/2\ k_BT$ where k_B is Boltzmann's constant (1.38×10^{-23} J/K) and T is the absolute temperature (Kelvin). The modes of a system refer to the components in the system energy, which have quadratic terms, such as kinetic energy ($1/2\ mv^2$) and spring potential energy ($1/2\ kx^2$). The Equipartition Theorem leads directly to the analysis of the Brownian noise in an accelerometer design.

The average displacement of the proof mass is given by:

$$1/2\ kx^2 = 1/2\ k_BT \tag{18.31}$$

where k is the spring constant of the suspension and x^2 is the variance of the proof mass displacement.

This relation cannot be used directly to calculate minimum detectable acceleration due to the frequency distribution of the variance of the proof mass displacement. However, the Brownian noise can be calculated by inserting a noise force generator at the same location as each damper in the system. The spectral density of the noise force corresponding to each damper is given by:

$$F_{\mathrm{n}} = \sqrt{4}k_BTb \qquad N/\sqrt{\mathrm{Hz}} \tag{18.32}$$

where F_{n} is the equivalent noise force spectral density and b is the damping coefficient. This result is derived directly from the Equipartition Theorem: a system mode having $1/2\ k_BT$ broadband energy is equivalent to the damper having an associated force generator $\sqrt{4}\ k_BTb$ with spectral density. Due to the thermal noise, the minimum detectable acceleration is given by:

$$a_{\mathrm{n}} = F_{\mathrm{n}}/m = \sqrt{4}\ k_BT\ \omega_{\mathrm{n}}\ (\mathrm{m/s^2})/\sqrt{\mathrm{Hz}} \tag{18.33}$$

where $\omega_{\mathrm{n}} = \sqrt{k/m}$ is the natural resonant frequency and $Q = m\omega_{\mathrm{n}}/b$ is the quality factor. The quality factor can also be measured by the ratio of the resonance frequency to the –3dB bandwidth:

$$Q = f_0 / \Delta f_{-3\text{dB}} \tag{18.34}$$

In vacuum, the quality factor Q is limited by internal damping in the spring and by energy loss through the anchors to the substrate, which is determined by the material property. For polysilicon, Q is at least 50,000 in vacuum[51].

The natural resonant frequency is determined by the bandwidth requirement of the specific application. Therefore, for a given resonant frequency, the minimum detectable acceleration is inversely proportional to the square-root of the accelerometer proof mass. This is the fundamental limit for silicon accelerometers due to the Brownian noise and is independent of the sensing techniques. The signal-to-noise ratio (SNR) can be defined as:

$$S^2 = a^2 / a^2 n = a^2 mQ / 4k_B T\omega_n \tag{18.35}$$

To design a high performance accelerometer, the minimum detectable acceleration must be reduced. From Eq. (18.33) and Eq. (18.35) when the bandwidth requirement is satisfied, the resonant frequency should be minimized by increasing the proof mass and reducing the spring constant. Accelerometers with high Q are also desirable for maximizing the SNR. However, the oscillations near the resonant frequency should be considered in the design.

Let the natural resonant frequency be 100 Hz for simplicity. The proof mass is 1.15×10 kg for a surface micromachined polysilicon plate with a size of $500 \times 500 \times 2\ \mu\text{m}^3$[50]. At room temperature (300 K), the minimum detectable acceleration is $1.7 \times 10^{-17}\ (\text{m/s}^2)/\sqrt{\text{Hz}}$. For a bulk micromachined accelerometer, 1.63 mg is a typical weight for the proof mass [47]. Thus, the minimum detectable open-loop acceleration is $4.5 \times 10^{-9}\ (\text{m/s}^2)/\sqrt{\text{Hz}}$. Equivalent minimum detectable displacements are readily found from the sensitivity to be 1.7×10^{-11} m. These results are summarized in Table 18.2.

Table 18.2 Minimum detectable signals (assuming $\omega = 100$ Hz)

process	size(μm)	mass (kg)	a_n=$a(m/s^2)/\sqrt{\text{Hz}}$	$x_n = m/\sqrt{\text{Hz}}$
surface[31]	$500 \times 500 \times 2$	1.15×10^{-9}	1.7×10^{-7}	1.7×10^{-11}
bulk[28]	$-1{,}000 \times 1{,}000 \times 500$	1.63×10^{-6}	4.5×10^{-9}	4.5×10^{-13}

As mentioned at the beginning of this section, the Brownian noise is less severe in conventional macro-accelerometers. If the proof mass is 0.1 kg and other conditions remain the same, the minimum detectable acceleration due to Brownian motion is $5.75 \times 10^{-11}\ (\text{m/s}^2)/\sqrt{\text{Hz}}$, which is overwhelmed by other noise sources. The analyses above are valid for silicon accelerometers of any configuration. Now, let's examine the Brownian noise in capacitive accelerometers and the noise from the detection electronics. It is assumed that a differential capacitive divider is used to convert the proof mass displacement into a voltage signal, as shown in Fig. 18.10. A MOS buffer amplifier is also used so that the noise current can be neglected[52]. v_{nm}^2 and v_{ne}^2 denote the equivalent noise voltage generators for the mechanical Brownian noise and the electrical noise from detection electronics, respectively.

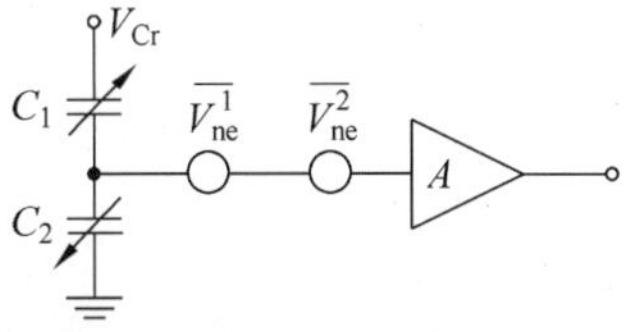

Figure 18.10 Noise analysis for capacitive accelerometer

From capacitive divider, the AC output voltage is:

$$V_0 = \Delta x / 2x_0 v_{\mathrm{dr}} \tag{18.36}$$

where x_0 is the nominal gap of the two capacitors and Δx is the displacement due to the Brownian noise. Note that the areas for the two parallel plate capacitors are assumed to be equal. The output voltage is determined by the ratio of the two capacitances (or the gap ratio), rather than the capacitance variation itself. Hence, it is independent of the area of the capacitors.
The equivalent noise voltage generator is given by:

$$v_{\mathrm{nm}}^2 = X_{\mathrm{n}}^2 / 4X_0^2 V_{\mathrm{dr}}^2 \tag{18.37}$$

In the accelerometer described in this thesis, a full capacitive bridge is used so the equivalent noise variance is double. The equivalent Brownian noise voltage $v_{\mathrm{nm}} = 1.2\ \mu\mathrm{V}/\sqrt{\mathrm{Hz}}$.

The noise voltage for the detection circuit consists of thermal (Johnson) noise and $1/f$ noise. The $1/f$ noise is a low frequency noise and is removed by chopper stabilization; hence, it will not be considered here. The thermal noise for a MOS transistor is given by:

$$v_{\mathrm{ne}}^2 = 4k_B T 2/3g_{\mathrm{m}} \tag{18.38}$$

where the transconductance g_{m} is given by: $g_{\mathrm{m}} = \sqrt{2}\ \mu_{\mathrm{n}} C_{\mathrm{ox}}\ (W/L)(I_{\mathrm{D}})$, where μ is the electron mobility and C_{ox} is the gate capacitance per unit area. For an typical input transistor with $W/L = 100$ and a bias current $I_{\mathrm{D}} = 0.5$ mA, the thermal voltage noise for the input transistor

$$v_{\mathrm{ne}} = 2.22\ \mathrm{nV}/\sqrt{\mathrm{Hz}} \tag{18.39}$$

which is two orders of magnitude lower than the noise voltage due to the Brownian motion. Therefore, the Brownian noise dominates for the case of high-performance microaccelerometers.

18.2.3 Accelerometer Examples

The first silicon micromachined accelerometer dates back to the 1970's[39]. Early research and development focused on exploiting open-loop accelerometers with the piezoresistive sensing technique. Several prototypes have been reported, with most attempting to achieve high performance through optimized suspensions and highly sensitive interface electronics, at the cost of more elaborate fabrication processes and interface electronics[40−43].

The force-balance accelerometers are designed with a feedback actuator that provides a restoring force to the proof mass, so that the movement of the proof mass is negligible in response to inertial forces. Recently, there has been significant interest in this class of accelerometers for both consumer products[45, 46] and high precision applications[47].

Resonant accelerometers are an alternative to achieve high sensitivity and large dynamic range. Commercial resonant accelerometers arc available using chemically milled quartz tuning forks as the resonant strain gauges[48]. For silicon micromachined resonant accelerometers, they have potentials to provide high performance but are still in the early research stage[49].

18.2.3.1 Open-Loop Design

Open-loop accelerometers are the most simple and robust accelerometers and are commonly used for vibration measurement and detonation. The first silicon micromachined accelerometer used bulk micromachining with the piezoresistive sensing technique. A single cantilever is used to suspend the silicon mass and thus the cross-axis sensitivity is determined by the width of the cantilever beam and is relatively poor. In later designs, multiple suspensions are commonly used to reduce the cross-axis sensitivity, to separate the various modes of vibration, as well as to improve its robustness.

An IC Sensors design is a typical example of such device[30−33], where four suspension cantilevers are employed. To further reduce the sensitivity to higher vibration modes, two piezoresistors are diffused on each suspension, one near the frame end and one near the mass end, shown in Fig. 18.11. These eight piezoresistors are connected with two resistors on each arm of a Wheatstone bridge, such that the response to off-axis inputs is suppressed. The wafer is bonded to two wafers providing over-load protection and viscous damping. Due to the large surface of the proof mass and the small gap between the mass and capping wafers, critical damping is achieved through squeeze-film effects. The large temperature sensitivity associated with piezoresistive sensing is the major drawback for piezoresistive accelerometers. Packaging-induced stresses will cause offset and long-term drift in the accelerometer. Thus, the package must have well-matched thermal expansion coefficient with that of silicon. These factors limit the application of piezoresistive accelerometers to a relatively narrow temperature range or requiring extensive temperature compensation and individual calibration. Capacitive sensing is independent of temperature variations and thus capacitive accelerometers are intrinsically superior to piezoresistive accelerometers in terms of the temperature sensitivity.

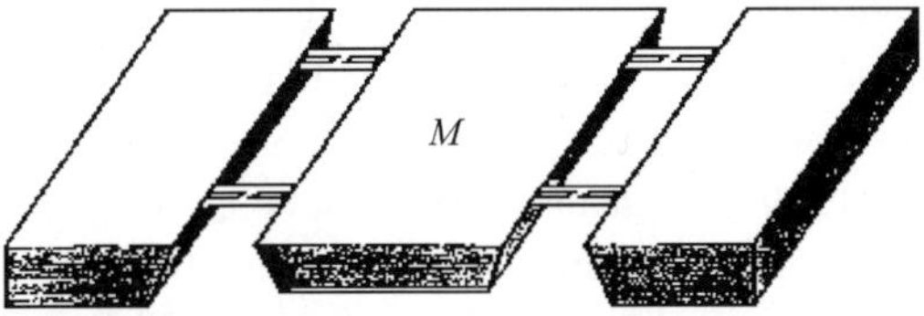

Figure 18.11 Schematic view of IC's accelerometer

In bulk micromachined capacitive accelerometers, one of the two electrodes is the suspended proof mass, which deflects with respect to the fixed electrode upon acceleration.

This capacitor is used in a capacitive bridge to transduce the displacement into an electrical signal. One example of the capacitive accelerometers is the highly symmetrically suspended design from MBB[43], where the proof mass is symmetrically suspended by eight cantilever beams located on both sides of the wafer, shown in Fig. 18.12. All suspension beams are aligned with the diagonal axes of the proof mass to obtain maximum symmetry. Like other capacitive accelerometers, it uses custom CMOS ICs to convert the mechanical signal into an electrical signal. The bulk micromachined accelerometers are typically a few millimeters on each side. The capping wafers form the squeeze film damper and provide over-range protection. Since the capacitance is determined by the gaps of three bonded wafers, the anodic bonding step is critical in determining the yield of the accelerometers. Surface micromachining is an alternative, which offers a smaller chip size and lower cost, since the size of the accelerometer is directly related to the cost of the accelerometer. It also avoids the need for wafer bonding. Motorola has reported a 50 g capacitive accelerometer using surface micromachining techniques for air bag applications[53]. It consists of three polysilicon layers.

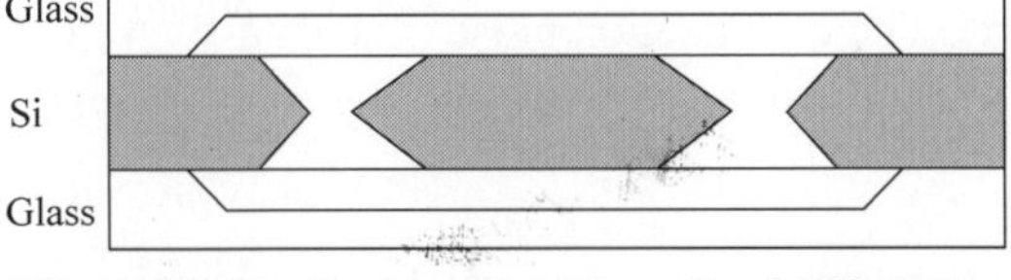

Figure 18.12 Cross-section view of an MBB design

The first and third layers form the upper and lower differential capacitor plates, and the second layer forms the suspended proof mass. A twin-cantilever suspension is used. Limit stops are fabricated from the third polysilicon layer, which overlaps the extensions of the suspension cantilevers. A switched-capacitor readout circuitry is fabricated in a separate CMOS ASIC chip and packaged adjacent to the sensor chip. The accelerometer has an open-loop sensitivity of 0.35 mV/g/V and bandwidth from 10 Hz to 10 kHz.

(1) Force-Balance Design

In force-balance accelerometers, the suspended proof mass deflects in response to the acceleration and this signal (strain or displacement) is sensed, amplified, and fed back to counteract the displacement of the mass due to the input acceleration. Capacitive sensing and electrostatic feedback are almost exclusively used in micromachined accelerometer designs. To achieve navigation grade performance, CSEM has designed a force-balance accelerometer that has Ig-range resolution used for satellite applications. The accelerometer is fabricated using a conventional anisotropic etching of bulk silicon from the both sides, as shown in Fig. 18.13, so that the two cantilever suspensions are aligned with the center of proof mass to reduce the cross-axis sensitivity. It has a cross-axis sensitivity of 0.4%. Two differential capacitors form a capacitor bridge and two operational transconductance amplifiers integrate the charge on these capacitors. The output signal is fed back to balance the proof mass. Since both sensing and feedback are achieved in the analog domain, the requirement for the integrated circuit is very critical. The ASIC chip is a hybrid mounted with the sensor chip. To achieve high resolution without precise circuit components, Σ-Δ modulation techniques are an attractive approach to achieve both high resolution and large dynamic range. 2-*t* modulation has an advantage of intrinsic linearity, process variation insensitivity, and direct digital output, which makes an easy interface with other systems[54, 55]. A second-order Σ-Δ modulator can be used as the feedback loop for the force-balance accelerometer where the mechanical proof mass is used as the double integrator in the forward path[47, 50]. The system block diagram of an accelerometer using this approach is shown in Fig. 18.14. The sensing signal first passes through a unity gain buffer, which is used to drive the active guard electrodes. The lead-lag block is to ensure the stability of the loop. A I-bit quantizer follows to convert the analog signal into a high-frequency, density-modulated pulse train, which is sampled and fed back via a level shifter to null the proof mass position. The decimation filter converts the density-modulated pulse train from the sampler into a digital signal. The clock frequency is much higher than the Nyquist sampling frequency (1,024x). The quantization noise is shaped such that the low-frequency baseband noise is significantly reduced and the high-frequency noise is filtered

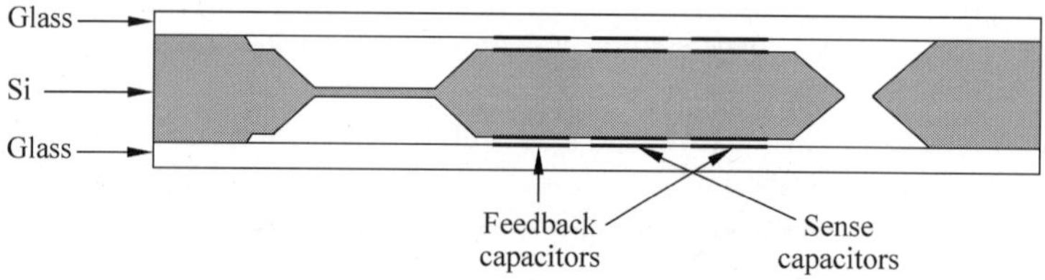

Figure 18.13 CSEM cross-section

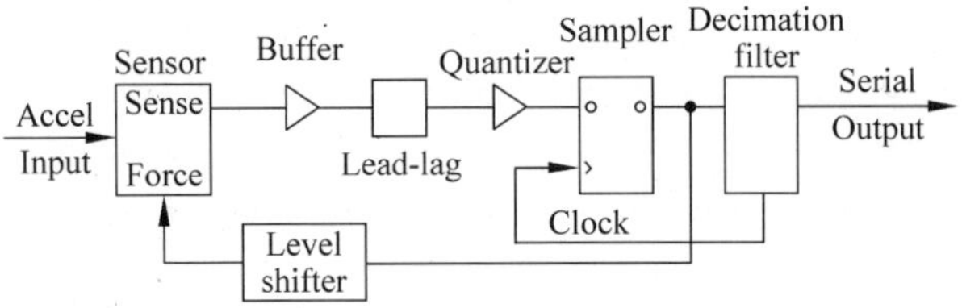

Figure 18.14 Triton's system block diagram

out by the decimation filter. With this modulation technique, a high signal to noise ratio (SNR) and large dynamic range can be achieved without the need for precision components. This accelerometer is reported to have 0.1 g resolution and 120 dB dynamic range[34]. The cross-axis sensitivity is less than 0.001%.

In addition to the complexity of the interface electronics, a bulk micromachining process is used to fabricate this accelerometer that involves 27 lithography steps on five wafer surfaces of the three-bonded wafers. The process complexity reduces yield and increases cost that prevent the accelerometer being used for large volume, low-cost manufacturing. Surface micromachined, force-balance capacitive accelerometers are much simpler in fabrication since only one wafer surface is processed. This fact and the small size of the sensing element make the integration of the sensing and control electronics on the same chip very attractive. Analog Devices, Inc. has reported a major step toward the integration of the sensing element and the sense, control, and interface electronics[40]. This accelerometer uses a polysilicon microstructure process, where polysilicon is deposited and patterned on a sacrificial oxide, to be later freed by etching away the sacrificial oxide in hydrofluoric. Figure 18.15 shows the schematic projection of the sensing elements. The moving plates are suspended by the four tethers; the fixed comb fingers are used for both sensing capacitance change as the plate displaces and for applying the electrostatic restoring force.

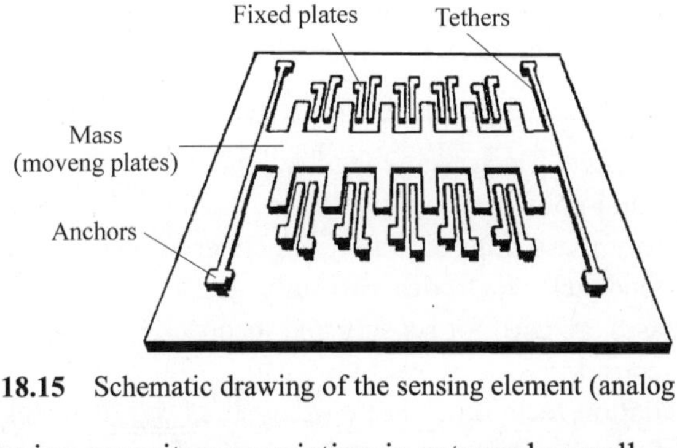

Figure 18.15 Schematic drawing of the sensing element (analog devices)

Since the fringing capacitance variation is extremely small, a Bi-MOS circuit (with 4 μm design rules) is designed for sensing, feedback, and signal conditioning, which is placed around the sensing structures. Two carrier signals, 180° out of phase, are applied to the two adjacent fixed plates, which form the differential capacitors. The capacitance variation is sensed, amplified, demodulated, and filtered. The output signal is fed back to the movable plates to force it back to the equilibrium position. Sophisticated circuitry and precision resistors are used for temperature compensation. A major application for this device, with a range to 50 g, is air-bag deployment.

18.3 Experimental Design: Accelerometer Design

The goals in the design of this accelerometer are to explore new approaches to the micromechanical sense clement, position sensing structure and interface electronics, and the overall system architecture. The system block diagram is shown in Fig. 18.16. The capacitive sensing technique is used in this design to ensure high resolution and low temperature sensitivity. The sensing capacitor consists of an anchored bottom electrode and a suspended proof mass. The sensing axis is perpendicular to the substrate. To reject the common mode noise, a full capacitive bridge is formed to convert the mechanical displacement signal into an electrical voltage. Since the sense capacitor is one-sided, two identical sensing structures are built side by side to form a full bridge. An input buffer with low input capacitance is designed to bootstrap the ground plane to reduce parasitic capacitance and enhance the signal level.

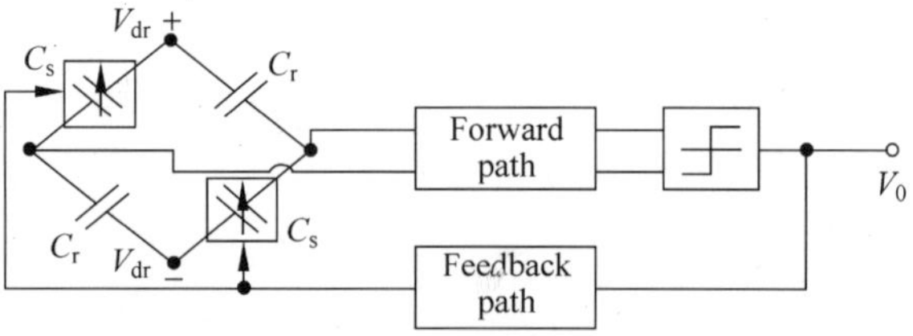

Figure 18.16 System block diagram

A force-balance design is used in this accelerometer to provide high sensitivity and large dynamic range. Electrostatic feedback is used for feedback control. Since there is only structural polysilicon in the design, the feedback electrodes pie located underneath the proof mass. Interdigitated fingers are used to generate a levitation force while the feedback electrodes can only generate a pull-down force. Two separate clock phases are used for sensing and feedback to avoid signal feedthrough from feedback electrodes.

The Σ-Δ modulation techniques are employed as the feedback loop while the mechanical proof mass is used as the double integrator in the forward loop of the second-order Σ-Δ modulator. Its 1-bit digital output is used for the feedback so that the feedback force is linearly (see Fig. 18.16. below) proportional to the density of the pulse train and nonlinearity is eliminated from the electrostatic feedback. The chopper stabilization technique is used to remove the offset voltage in the detection circuit. A dual-loop design is employed where two identical accelerometers except their ratioed mass are built side by side so that the potential drift due to mechanical suspension and packaging-induced stress can be cancelled by subtracting their digital outputs.

18.3.1 Sensing Element

The capacitive sensing microstructure is fabricated using a surface micromachining technique and consists of two layers of *in situ* doped polysilicon with the sensing and feedback electrodes underneath the suspended proof mass. Figure 18.17 shows the schematic top and cross-sectional view of the sensing element. The sensing element is fabricated after the completion of the CMOS process during which the capacitive detection circuitry is fabricated. To passivate the CMOS circuitry from subsequent chemical etching processes, a nitride layer is deposited at the end of the CMOS process, which also serves as the starting layer for the micromachining process. The first *in situ* doped polysilicon layer defines the sensing electrode, the feedback electrodes, and the ground plane. The bottom sensing electrode is 100 μm on each side and is located at the center underneath the proof mass. With 1 μm gap between the suspended proof mass and the bottom electrode, the sensing capacitor has a nominal capacitance of 1 pF. Together with a reference capacitor of the same size, this sensing capacitor is used to form a capacitive bridge that is driven by a high-frequency AC signal.

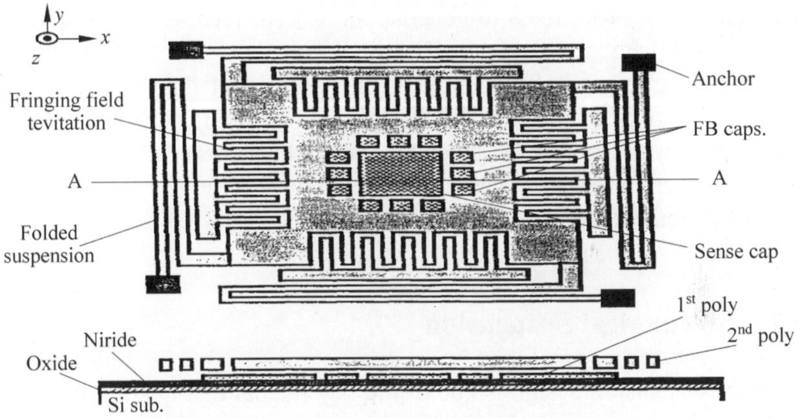

Figure 18.17 Schematic top and cross-sectional views

The twelve feedback electrodes are 25 μm×25 μm each and are located symmetrically round the sensing electrode near the center to avoid exciting higher-mode vibrations. The feedback capacitors are driven by a high-frequency, density-modulated pulse train whose density is directly proportional to the input acceleration. As will be shown later in Section 18.3.3, the feedback signal is a 2-bit digital signal generated from the feedback compensation network. Rather than feeding back a voltage with four levels of amplitudes, the feedback signal is applied to three sets of capacitors and the number of capacitor sets being turned on is controlled by the 2-bit feedback signal. For example, all three sets of capacitors are turned on and connected to a constant feedback voltage V when the feedback control signal is at its highest level. When the feedback signal is at its second highest level, two sets of capacitors will be turned on and connected to VFB and the third set will be grounded. The second polysilicon layer forms the proof mass, the suspensions, and the levitation fingers. The 1 μm sacrificial oxide layer underneath this polysilicon layer is removed after the patterning of the polysilicon so that the polysilicon structures are all suspended above the substrate except at the anchor points. Upon acceleration, the proof mass will deflect from its neutral position and move up or down causing capacitance variations in the sensing capacitor. The capacitance change is translated into a voltage signal by a capacitive bridge.

The sensing axis for this accelerometer is perpendicular to the substrate and the capacitance variations are inversely proportional to the distance between the two electrodes. The acceleration can also be sensed in the directions parallel to the substrate in some designs[56]. However, the thickness of the polysilicon structure is limited to about 3 μm due to the deposition process. The lateral sidewall and fringing field capacitances are usually smaller than the vertical capacitance, where the overlap area can be much larger. In the design of this accelerometer, the feedback electrodes are located underneath the proof mass and can only generate a feedback force pulling the plate downward. This is because the electrostatic force is always attractive regardless of the applied voltage. Adding another polysilicon layer on top of the proof mass to generate an upward feedback force is possible; however, the fabrication is more complicated. To obtain the levitation force without the addition of another layer of polysilicon, interdigitated fingers are used for levitation in this design[57]. With different bias voltages on two opposing sets of fingers, a levitation force can be generated due to the presence of the ground plane underneath, which causes asymmetric distribution of the electrical field. The detailed analysis of this phenomenon will be presented in Section 18.3.4.

18.3.2 Mechanical Suspension

Mechanical suspension design is one of the key factors that greatly influence the accelerometer performance. In force-balance accelerometers, mechanical suspensions should be compliant in the sensitive axis for high sensitivity and still in all other directions so that the cross-axis sensitivity is minimized. They should also be robust to survive shocks and be compact to save silicon area.

Linearity and symmetry are important in accelerometer designs. Accelerometers should have the same response to accelerations in both positive and negative directions along the sensing axis; otherwise, a DC offset will be present at the accelerometer output. For the open-loop accelerometers, the linearity is determined by the suspension design. A double-anchored, quad bean suspension provides better linearity compared with a dual cantilever suspension[58, 59].

Acceleration can be measured capacitively with torsional structures, where an asymmetrically shaped plate is suspended by torsional bars mounted on a pedestal and is free to rotate around the torsion bar axis[60–62]. Due to the asymmetry, the plate is heavier on one side and lighter on the other side. When there is acceleration perpendicular to the substrate, the asymmetry results in rotation of the plate, which causes the capacitance variation between the plate and the sensing electrodes underneath. The two sensing electrodes underneath the torsional plate are driven by a high-frequency carrier signal that applies a constant force pulling the plate downward. This bias force can potentially cause a long-term drift in the accelerometer, as well as nonlinearity in the suspension. Residual stress is one of the major concerns in designing surface micromachined structures. Folded suspensions have the advantage of being nearly free to expand or contract if the residual stress is present. In this accelerometer design, folded suspensions are chosen since it is easy to expand or contact and is stress free. When the proof mass accelerates, it moves up and down like a 'piston'. With an electrostatic feedback, the proof mass remains at its neutral position so that the stress in the suspension is minimized. As shown in Fig. 18.17, the four suspensions are located symmetrically along the four sides of the proof mass and are attached to the four corners of the proof mass to minimize the higher-mode of vibration. It also offers a compliant suspension in a compact area.

To analyze the mechanical properties in details, we can first examine one of the suspension and then the overall suspension. The folded suspension can be divided into four pans, as shown in Fig. 18.18. Note that the folding end L_3 is very rigid and its deflection is negligible. Furthermore, the length and width for L_1 and L_4 are the same so that their spring constants arc identical. Thus, we can calculate the spring constant for the crab-leg L_1 and L_2, which can be approximated by the spring constant of L_1 (as will be shown later). The spring constant for the folded suspension is then half that for the crab-leg suspension.

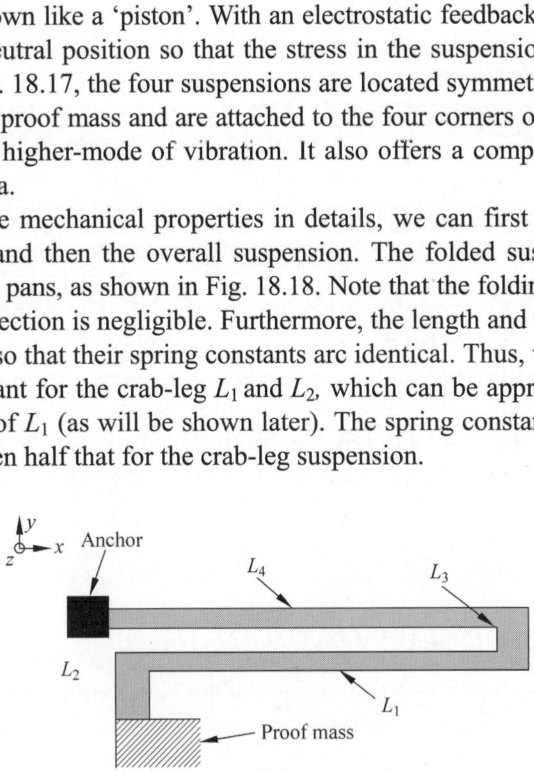

Figure 18.18 Folded suspension

The crab-leg suspension for L_7 and L_2 is shown in Fig. 18.19 below. Since the suspension is made of polysilicon and the area is small, the film thickness r is assumed to be uniform for both L_1 and L_2. The total deflection of the proof mass along the sensing axis (z-axis) consists of deflections of L_1 and L_2, and the torsion of L_j. The spring constant for one of the suspension k_{21} can be calculated and obtained[63, 65, 66]:

$$k_{21} = EW_2(t/L_2)^3/1+W_2/W_2(L_1/L_2)\{(L_1/L_2)^2+12\,1+V_1/1+(W_1/t)2\} \tag{18.40}$$

where k_{21} is the spring constant of each suspension in the z-axis, (the subscript denotes the top suspension's spring constant in z-direction), E is the Young's modular for polysilicon, and v_1 is the Poisson's ratio for polysilicon.

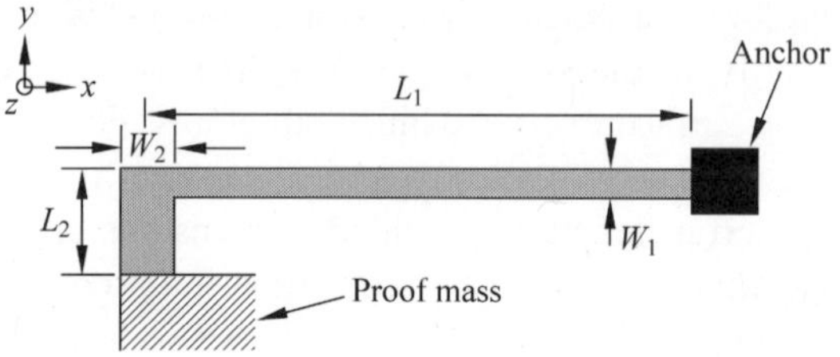

Figure 18.19 Geometry of the crab-leg suspension

Therefore, the total suspension K_2 is the sum of the four suspensions.

$$k_2 = k_{21} \tag{18.41}$$

When $L_2/L_1 \gg 1$, the total spring constant can be derived from Eq. (18.41),

$$k_2 = 4EW_1\,(t/L_1)^3 \tag{18.42}$$

It indicates that the crab-leg suspensions can be approximated by cantilever suspensions with one guided end when $L_1/L_2 \gg$ I. This is because the deflection of L_2 and the moment of inertia of L_1 are negligible when L_1 is much larger than L_2. The spring constant of the folded suspension shown in Fig. 18.19 is then half the spring constant shown in Eq. (18.42). Similar analysis can be used to calculate the spring constants in x and y directions. Taking the suspension on the top as an example, we can get[67, 68]:

$$k_{xt} = 4Et_2W_2^3/L_2^3[1+\{t_2W_2^3L_1/t_1W_1^3L_2\}/4+\{t_2W_2^3L_1/t_1W_1^3L_2\}] \tag{18.43}$$

$$k_{yt} = 4Et_1W_1^3/L_1^3[1+\{t_2W_2^3L_1/t_1W_1^3L_2\}/1+4\{t_2W_2^3L_1/t_1W_1^3L_2\}] \tag{18.44}$$

Therefore, the overall spring constants in the lateral directions can be obtained by adding up the four spring constants.

$$k_x = k_y = k_{xi} + k_{yl} + k_{xb} + k_{yr} = k_{xl} + k_{xb}$$

$$k_x = 8EtW_2^3 / L_2^3[1 + \{W_2^3 L_1 / W_1^3 L_2\} / 1 + 4\{W_2^3 L_1 / W_1^3 L_2\}] \qquad (18.45)$$

The proof mass displacement in the x direction is mostly constrained by the suspensions on the top and bottom of the proof mass (k_{xl} and k_{xb}). Similarly, the displacement in the y direction is constrained by the suspension on the left and right of the proof mass (k_{yl} and k_{yr}). In this design, the flexure L_1 is much longer than the flexure L_2, so Eq. (18.45) can be approximated by:

$$k_x = k_y = 8EiW_2^3 / L_2^3 \qquad (18.46)$$

From Eq. (18.46) and Eq. (18.42), the cross-axis sensitivity can be obtained:

$$k_z / k_x = k_z / k_y = 1/2\, W_1^2 / W_2^3 (L_2 / L_3)^3 \qquad (18.47)$$

The cross-axis sensitivity is determined by ratios of the lengths (L_1 and L_2) and widths (W_1 and W_2). Thus, the cross-axis sensitivity can be minimized by properly choosing the length and width of the suspension. Note that higher mode vibration and rotational displacement are not considered in the analysis.

Folded suspensions are also used in the actual design, as shown in Fig. 18.18, to release any residual stress in the structural polysilicon film. The length of the suspension $L_1 = 450$ μm, $L_2 = 50$ μm, the width $W_1 = 2$ μm, $W_2 = 10$ μm, and the thickness $t = 2$ μm. The Young's modulus of 150 GPa for polysilicon is used. From Eq. (18.40) and Eq. (18.41), the total spring constant is 0.048 N/m and is used in the simulation. With the cantilever approximation, the total spring constant is 0.052 N/m, which gives 7% error.

18.3.3 Capacitive Bridge

The system block diagram of this accelerometer is shown in Fig. 18.20, where two identical sensing capacitors (C_s's) and two reference capacitors (C_r's) of the same value form the capacitive bridge. The capacitance for the sensing and feedback capacitors is 1 pF. Two suspended plates are needed to form a full bridge because the fixed sensing electrode is underneath the proof mass, so the sense capacitor is one-sided. Structures for the reference capacitors are identical to those for the sensing capacitors except that the proof mass of the reference capacitors is fixed

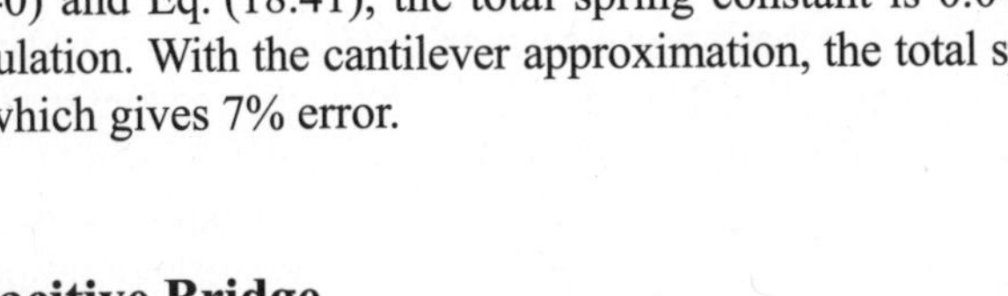

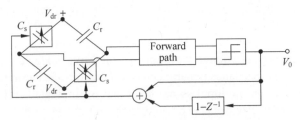

Figure 18.20 Capactive sensing and electrostatic feedback

to the substrate. The bridge is driven by two high-frequency signals with 180° out of phase.

The sensing capacitance is tiny and can easily be overwhelmed by parasitic capacitances that are orders of magnitude larger. In addition to the sensing and reference capacitors, various parasitic capacitors are also present at the input node, which include the feedback capacitors (C_{FB}), the input capacitance to the readout electronics (C_i), and the parasitic capacitance to the ground plane and stray capacitance from interconnect (C_p). The voltage at the input node can be easily derived:

$$V_i(t) = \frac{2X(C_s(t) - C_r) \times V_{dr}(t)}{C_s(t) + C_r + C_p + C_{FB} + C_i} + \frac{C_{FB*} V_{FB}(t)}{C_s(t) + C_r + C_p + C_{FB} + C_i} \tag{18.48}$$

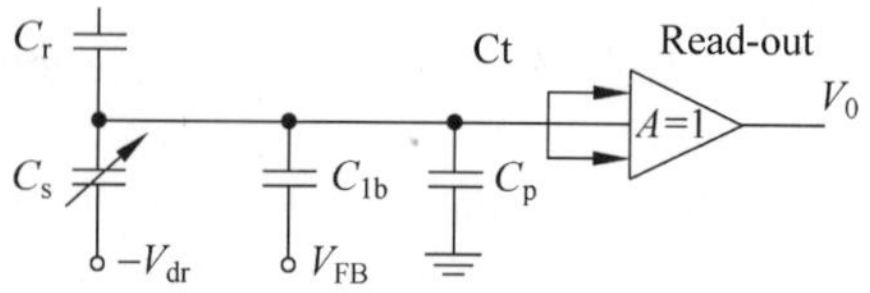

Figure 18.21 Half circuit of the capacitive bridge

The first term on the right-hand side of the equation is the input signal term, and the second term is the feedthrough from the feedback signal. The feedback capacitance (C_{FB}) is about the same as the sensing capacitance (C_s). Due to the large ground plane, the parasitic capacitance (C_p) is about 30 times larger than the sensing capacitance (C_p). The input device for the readout circuit must be of a reasonable size to reduce the noise and offset voltage, which leads to a large input capacitance to the electronics. These parasitic capacitance must be minimized to obtain any measurable signals. An input buffer with low input capacitance is designed to bootstrap the parasitic capacitance, as has been discussed in the next section. The second term in the equation indicates the feedthrough of the feedback signal (V). Since the feedback capacitor is comparable to the sensing capacitor, the feedback signal can significantly distort the input signal.

18.3.4 Input Buffer

The parasitic capacitance can be orders of magnitude larger than the sensing capacitance and must be minimized to measure the capacitance variation caused by the input acceleration. The parasitic capacitance can be bootstrapped with a unity pin buffer, as shown in Fig. 18.22. With this configuration, the voltage of the ground plane tracks the voltage variations of the input node so that the voltage across the parasitic capacitance remains constant. The parasitic capacitance, therefore, will have no effect on the input signal level and is eliminated from Eq. (18.48). The feedback capacitance can also be bootstrapped in the same fashion, connecting the feedback capacitor to tlic buffer output during the sensing phase and to die feedback voltage during the feedback phase. However, the system becomes rather complicated and the feedback capacitance is not bootstrapped in the first version of the design. The signal level is then reduced by 30% compared with the configuration of bootstrapped feedback capacitors.

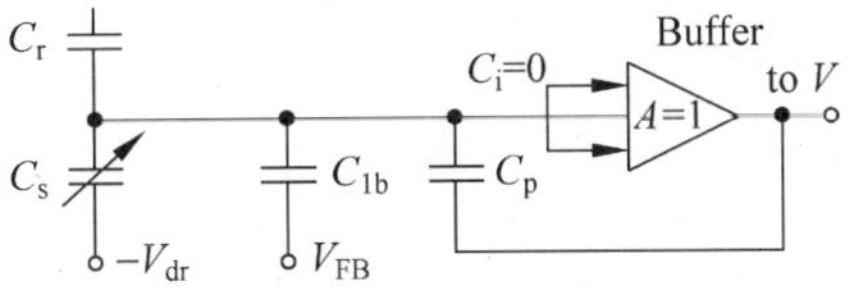

Figure 18.22 Half circuit of the capacitive bridge with bootstrapped substrate

The simplest design of a unity gain buffer is the source follower, which also eliminates the gate-to-source capacitance (C_{gs}). However, this design is not suitable for this application because the DC level of the output is V_{gs} (typically around 1 V) lower than that of the input, which is connected to the proof mass. Note that the ground plane is much larger than the sensing and feedback electrodes. Any voltage difference between the proof mass and the ground plane will cause in a significant electrostatic force on the proof mass causing an offset, or even pulling the proof mass down to the substrate. Therefore, it is essential that the buffer has the same input and output DC level. An input buffer with the same input and output DC level is designed, using large input devices for low noise and mismatch and bootstrapping for low input capacitance. The circuit schematic diagram of this input buffer is shown in Fig. 18.23[69]. The input transistor M_1 is a source follower with the body connected to its own well to eliminate the body effect. The output transistor M_2 has the same W/L as the input transistor. Since the current from the current source on the top is half that from the bottom, M_1 and M_2 have the same current I_{ds}. Since the devices have the same W/L, the gate-to-source voltages (V_{gs}) are identical for both devices so the input and output have the same DC level. Therefore, the output from the buffer can be used to drive the ground plane without exerting any electrostatic force on the proof mass. The input capacitance to the

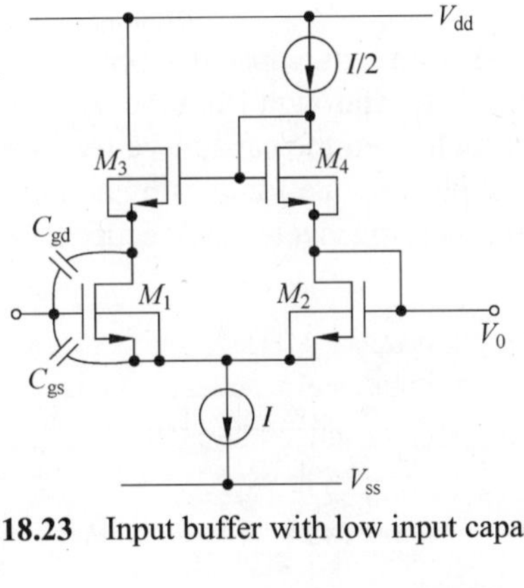

Figure 18.23 Input buffer with low input capacitance

buffer consists of the gate-to-source capacitance (C_{gs}) and the gaze-to-drain overlap capacitance (C_{gd}); the total input capacitance is dominated by C_{gs}.

For noise and matching considerations, large input devices are desired but that would lead to large input capacitance. Although the gate-to-source capacitance (C_{gs}) is largely eliminated by the source-follower configuration, the gate-to-drain capacitor (C_{gd}) is still present at the input node. To obtain minimum input capacitance. M_3 and M_4 are used as batteries to drive the drain of the input device M_1 so that the gate-to-drain capacitor (C_{gd}) is also cancelled.

Computer simulation shows that the input capacitance is 16fF—about 95% reduction in the input capacitance. The buffer is simulated to have a bandwidth of 50 MHz with 1 pF capacitive load. This input buffer is also applicable for other sensors requiring capacitive detection. A VGA follows the buffer to amplify the signal with its gain controlled externally. With this configuration, the parasitic capacitance is reduced substantially. The input signal is now given by:

$$V_i(t) = \frac{2x(C_s(t) - C_r)}{C_s(t) + C_r + C_{FB}} xV_{ar}(t) \tag{18.49}$$

18.3.5 Feedback Design

The electrostatic force between the two capacitive electrodes is proportional to the square of the applied voltage, as shown in Eq. (18.16), and is always attractive regardless of the polarity of the voltage. The feedback force must be linearly related to the accelerometer output signal to achieve a linear system. In most of the bulk micromachined, force-ball.

18.3.5.1 Feedthrough

The signal feedthrough can corrupt the sensing signal and is the major considerations in force-balance accelerometer designs. Since capacitive sensing and capacitive feedback are used in this design, the feedthrough from the capacitive feedback signal can be much larger than the input acceleration signal, as shown in Eq. (18.48), and must be suppressed to measure the input signal. In silicon microfabricated accelerometer designs, capacitive sensing and capacitive feedback are almost exclusively used, and feedthrough from the capacitive feedback is available.

In this design, feedthrough from the capacitive feedback is eliminated by using two nonoverlapping clock phases, one for sensing and one for feedback, as shown in Fig. 18.24. During the sensing cycle, the feedback electrodes are grounded.

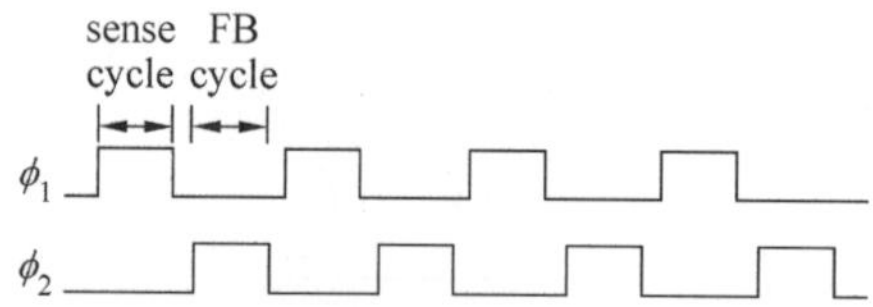

Figure 18.24 Clock diagram

The proof mass displacement is sensed, amplified, and quantized into digital signal. During the feedback cycle, the feedback electrodes are activated and connected to the appropriate feedback voltages. Therefore, the capacitive feedthrough is eliminated with this scheme since the feedback electrodes are grounded during sensing cycles.

18.3.5.2 Fringing Field Levitation

Electrostatic forces can only generate attraction; no repulsive upward force can be generated from the bottom feedback electrodes. One possible solution is to have the electrodes above the proof mass to generate a levitation force. However, this approach requires another layer of structural polysilicon and the topography becomes more complicated. In this design, interdigitated fingers are used to generate the levitation force.

Interdigitated comb structures are an important element in microelectromechanical system, such as lateral resonators, microgrippers, mechanical filters, etc. Due to the presence of the ground plane underneath, a levitation force is generated when a voltage is applied to the fixed electrode fingers[57]. The levitation fingers are located along the four sides of the proof mass. Figure 18.25 shows the cross-sectional view of the three interdigitated fingers and the electrical field distribution. The finger in the middle is attached to the proof mass whose potential is nominally zero, the same as the ground plane. The two outer fingers are the anchored fingers and are biased at a DC level (typically a few volts). Due to the ground plane, there are more electrical field lines terminating on top of the center finger than those terminating on its bottom. This asymmetry in field distribution results a net levitation force induced on the center finger, which is attached to the proof mass. A finite element simulation must be used to quantify this behavior.

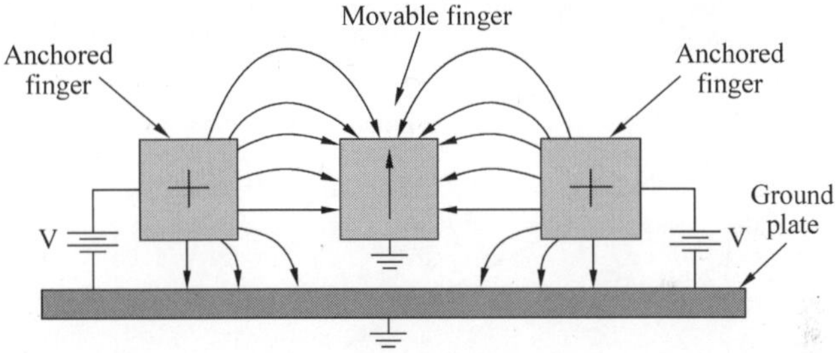

Figure 18.25 Cross-section of interdigitated fingers and electrical field distribution

18.3.5.3 Simulation

Due to the complexity of the electrical field distribution, no analytical solution can be obtained for the vertical levitation force for a particular geometry. The finite element method (FEM) is used to solve the Poisson's equation and model the fringing field distribution[70]. An empirical model for the levitation force is obtained from the FEM simulations.

To model accurately the levitation force, five interdigitated fingers are used in the simulation, as shown in Fig. 18.26. The two outer fingers and the center fingers are attached to the proof mass that is free to move vertically, and the two-shaded fingers are the anchored fingers with a DC bias. Only the levitation force on the central movable finger is calculated. All fingers are 2 μm×2 μm of size, 2 μm apart from each other, and 1 pm above the ground plane. Figure 18.27 shows the levitation force per unit finger length versus the vertical displacement of the proof mass. The neutral position ($z=0$) is defined such that the proof mass fingers are aligned with the anchored levitation fingers (1 μ above the ground plane). For a given bias voltage, the levitation force decreases as the proof mass moves above the neutral position because less electrical field lines terminate on the top of the movable finger and more on the bottom of the movable finger. As the proof mass moves up, there is a point (z_0) at which the levitation force becomes zero. The 'levitation force' will change its sign and become an attractive force when the proof mass elevates above z_0. An empirical model can be established from the simulation and is given by:

$$F=\gamma(z-z_0)LV^2 \tag{18.50}$$

where γ is a fitting parameter. $\gamma=0.096\ \mathrm{N/m^2}V^2$ for the geometry given above, z_0 is the proof mass position where levitation force is zero, L is the total overlapped finger length, and V is the voltage applied.

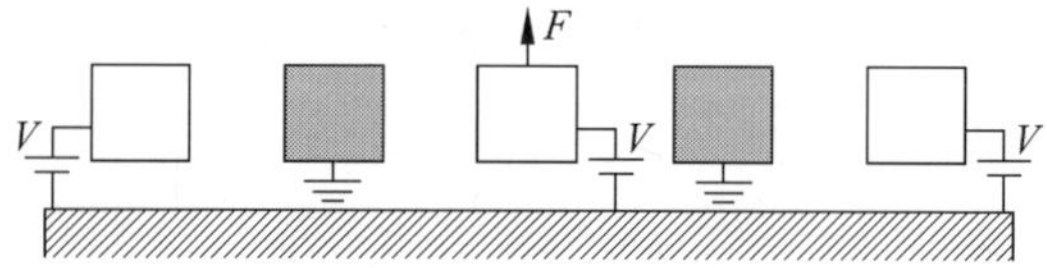

Figure 18.26 Structure used in the simulation

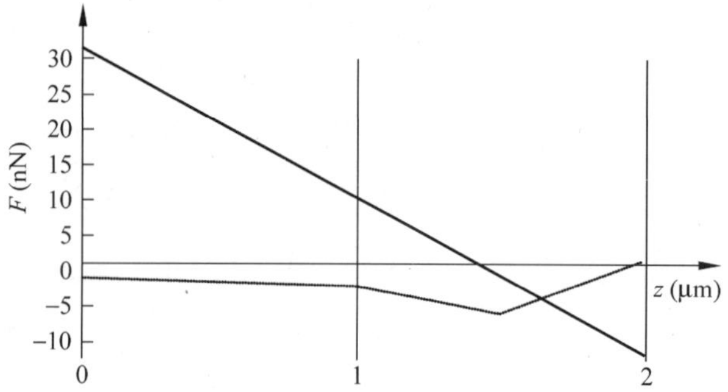

Figure 18.27 Levitation force versus vertical position of proof mass

Note that Eq. (18.50) is only valid in the region shown in Fig. 18.27, which is the region of incres1 for the accelerometer design. The levitation force becomes nonlinear vertical position of the proof mass outside that region. The dash line is the electrostatic force in the lateral direction, which is an indication of the numerical error from the FEM program.

18.3.6 Electromechanical Σ-Δ Modulation

The conventional second-order Σ-Δ modulator consists of two integrators, two summers, and a 1-bit quantizer, as shown in Fig. 18.28. The quantizer converts the sampled analog signal into a digital bit steam that is fed back to the two summers and subtracted from the input.

$$Y(z)=z^{-1}X(z)+e_{\mathrm{n}}(1-z^{-2})^2 \tag{18.51}$$

The transfer function for the modulator is shown in Fig. 18.28.

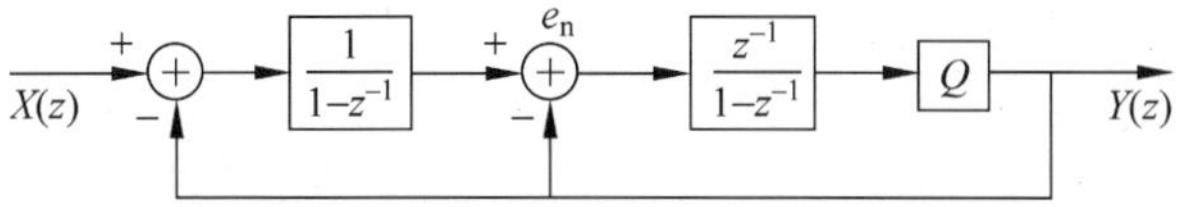

Figure 18.28 Conventional second-order Σ-Δ modulator

where $X(z)$ and $Y(z)$ are the input and output in the z-domain and e_n is noise.

From Eq. (18.51), it can be seen that the quantization noise is shaped by $(1-z^{-1})^2$ of being a white noise, the quantization noise spectrum now becomes:

$$\overline{n_0^2}(f)=e_{\mathrm{n}}^2\left(\sin\pi\frac{f}{f_{\mathrm{s}}}\right)^2=\frac{(\Delta\sigma)^2}{12}\frac{1}{f_{\mathrm{s}}/2}\left(\sin\pi\frac{f}{f_{\mathrm{s}}}\right)^2 \tag{18.52}$$

where $\Delta\sigma$ is the quantization step size, f_s is the sampling frequency, and f is the signal frequency.

The input signal is sampled at a frequency much higher than its Nyquist frequency so that the adjacent samples are correlated with each other. The quantization noise is shaped such that the noise in the baseband is greatly suppressed, as shown in Eq. (18.52). The output spectrum can also be plotted, as shown in Fig. 18.29.

Integrating the noise spectrum in Eq. (18.52), the total noise in the baseband can be obtained as:

$$\overline{n_{\mathrm{tot}}^2}=\int_0^{f_0}\overline{n_0^2}(f)\mathrm{d}f=\frac{(\Delta a)^2}{12}\frac{\pi^4}{5}\left(\frac{f_0}{f_{\mathrm{s}}}\right)^5 \tag{18.53}$$

where f_0 is the signal bandwidth. By filtering the quantization noise at a high frequency with digital filters, high resolution and large dynamic range can be achieved though only a 1-bit quantizer is needed. Therefore, the signal-to-noise ratio increases 15 dB per octave change in the over-sampling ratio.

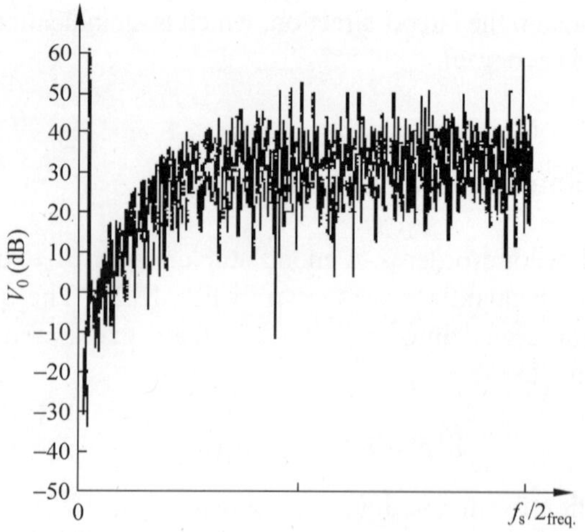

Figure 18.29 Noise shaping of a Σ-Δ modulator

18.3.6.1 Electromechanical Σ-Δ Modulctor

The Σ-Δ modulation technique has several advantages in the feedback control for the force-balance accelerometers. These accelerometers can be configured in such way that the mechanical proof mass is used as the double integrator in the second-order Σ-Δ modulation and the feedback signal is the 1-bit digital bit so-cam. Therefore, the feedback force is linearly proportional to the pulse density that is modulated by the input acceleration.

Let's model the mechanical mass-spring system first. Upon acceleration, an inertial force is exerted on the proof mass of the accelerometer. In addition, two restoring forces are acted on the proof mass: the restoring force from the mechanical suspension and the drag force from the damping. Since the proof mass displacement is measured, the accelerometer can be modeled as shown in Fig. 18.30 where the k and bare the spring constant and the damping coefficient, respectively. For simplicity in the following discussion, the direction of the proof mass deflection is defined as the positive axis.

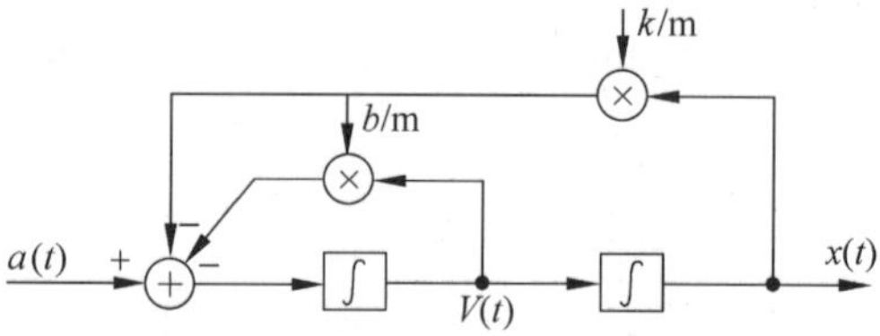

Figure 18.30 Simplified model for the sensing element

The sensing capacitor in the capacitive bridge can be replaced by the model shown in Fig. 18.30. The system block diagram shown in Fig. 18.30 can then be re-drawn as shown in Fig. 18.31. The shaded box represents the sensing capacitor that converts the input acceleration into a displacement of the proof mass in Fig. 18.31. The sense capacitance variation due to the proof mass displacement is then converted into a voltage signal by the capacitive bridge, represented by the next block. This voltage signal is then sampled at a frequency much higher than the Nyquist frequency. The discrete signal is quantized and becomes a digital pulse steam whose density is proportional to the input acceleration. Such digital pulse streams are fed back to the feedback electrodes underneath the proof mass and counteract the proof mass displacement due to the acceleration. Since the feedback signal is a density-modulated pulse train, the feedback force is linearly proportional to the pulse density of the feedback signal.

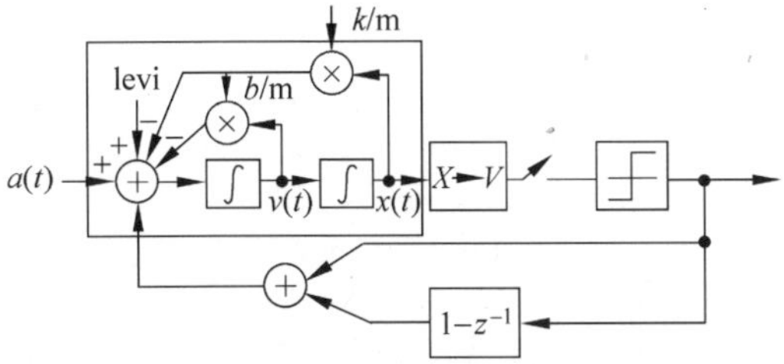

Figure 18.31 Electromechanical Σ-Δ modulator

Comparing Fig. 18.28 and Fig. 18.31, there are many similarities between the two block diagrams. The input signals in both systems are sampled at a frequency much higher than their Nyquist frequencies; both systems have the double integration function in the forward path; both outputs are quantized 1-bit digital pulse train which is fed back and subtracted from the input. However, the realization of the integration is different in the two systems. In the conventional Σ-Δ modulator, the double integration is achieved electronically in the sampled data domain. In the latter case, the double integration is achieved mechanically by the proof mass displacement in the continuous domain. Obviously, the inputs are different: the first system is sampled voltage signal and the second one is continuous mechanical acceleration. Therefore, the second system shown in Fig. 18.31 is called an electromechanical Σ-Δ modulator.

In the conventional Σ-Δ modulator, there is a summer before each integrator and the output signal is subtracted from each node. For an electromechanical Σ-Δ modulator, however, the node between the two integrators represents the velocity of the proof mass and the feedback force cannot be subtracted from the node directly. If the output is only fed back to the summer before the first integrator, the feedback system is unstable because the two poles introduced by the integrators are located at origin in the s-plane. A digital differentiator is designed in the feedback path, which is acting as the 'electrical damping factor'. It introduces a zero in the left-half plane that pulls the two poles at the origin into the left-half plane to ensure the loop stability.

The Σ-Δ modulation technique has several advantages for the force-balance accelerometers. First, the feedback system has intrinsic linearity because the feedback is a 1-bit signal and the magnitude of the feedback force is proportional to the density of the feedback pulses. This property ensures the accelerometer to have large dynamic range. Second, the requirements for the readout circuits are less demanding because the 1-bit quantizer demands only accurate polarity information. This consideration is especially important for integrated accelerometers where the transistor characteristics may be changed due to the sensor process. Lastly, analog-to-digital conversion is done at the sensor level and its digital output makes it easy to interface with rest of the system.

(1) Simulation

Due to the nonlinearity of the quantizer, computer simulation is commonly used to analyze the behavior of the modulator. In the conventional Σ-Δ modulator, all the components are operated in the sampled data domain. In the electromechanical Σ-Δ modulator, however, the mechanical proof mass is in the continuous-time domain, as shown in the shaded box in Fig. 18.31. The electronic detection and feedback are all operated in the sampled data domain. Therefore, a mix-mode simulator has to be developed to simulate the electromechanical system.

A simulation software package is developed to analyze the electromechanical system, based on a program for conventional second-order Σ-Δ A/D[72, 73]. A high-frequency, discrete-time simulation is used to mimic the continuous-time double integrator. The continuous-time double integrator, as shown in the shaded area in Fig. 18.32, is sampled sixteen times faster than the sampling frequency for the quantizer and the feedback, which is operated in the sampled data domain in the practical design. The accelerometer is operated at low pressure so the viscous damping is not included in the simulation, but can be easily added if necessary. Figure 18.33 shows the output spectrum of this accelerometer that shows the proper noise shaping. Figure 18.34 shows the SNR versus the input acceleration. The lower solid line is the SNR for the accelerometer with a 2 μm thick suspension and the top dash line is for 0.5 μm thick suspension. The dynamic range is 75 dB for the current design where the suspensions are made of the same polysilicon layer as the structural polysilicon (2 μm thick). A thinner suspension can be used if large dynamic range is the primary concern. In addition, a 0.5 μm thick suspension with dynamic range of 115 dB can be achieved.

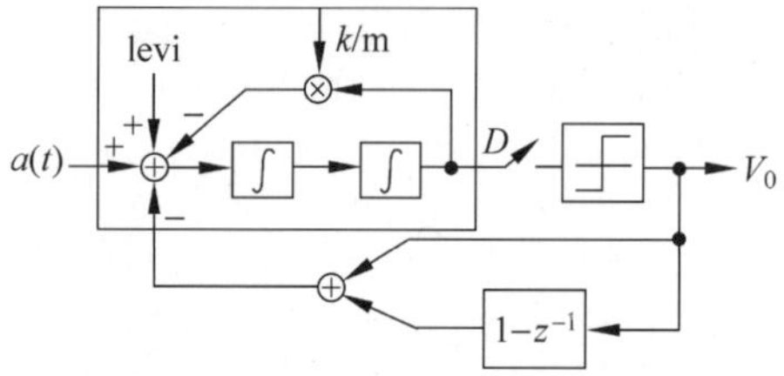

Figure 18.32 Simulation model for electromechanical Σ-Δ modulator

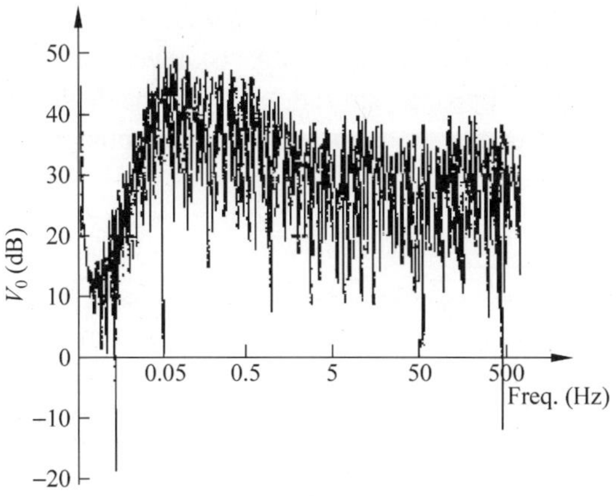

Figure 18.33 Output spectrum

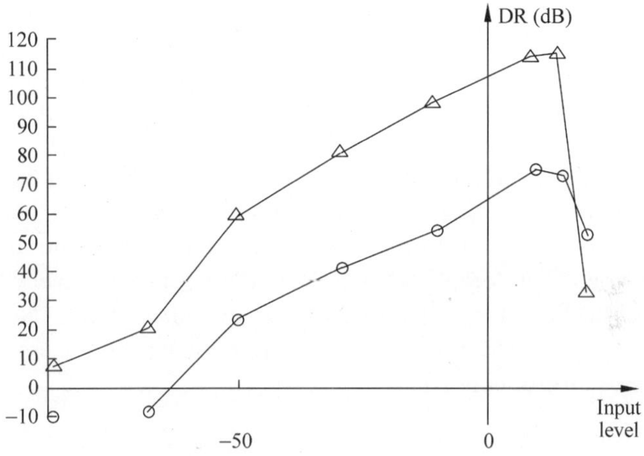

Figure 18.34 SNR versus input level

Practical issues should be considered in this design. Since the output is quantized by a 1-bit quantizer, which only concerns about the polarity of the signal, the accelerometer is very insensitive to the circuit characteristics, such as the amplifier's gain and process variations. However, the offset voltage degrades the accelerometer's performance. Signal levels below the offset voltage cannot be detected and the quantizer will make the wrong decision.

The offset voltage is dominated by the contribution from the unity-gain input buffer and the VGA. The offset voltage of the quantizer is reduced by the gain of the VGA and is negligible at the input. The offset voltage is generated due to mismatches in the input transistors and the current sources. It can be minimized by larger device input buffer and the VGA, which reduces the mismatches.

To further reduce the offset voltage, the chopper stabilization technique is employed in the design, as shown in Fig. 18.35. Since the capacitive bridge is driven by a high-frequency pulse train, the input acceleration signal is modulated to the carrier frequency. The offset voltage is always a DC signal. After the demodulator, the input signal is shifted back to the baseband and the offset voltage is shifted to the carrier frequency. The offset voltage can now be removed by a low pass filter.

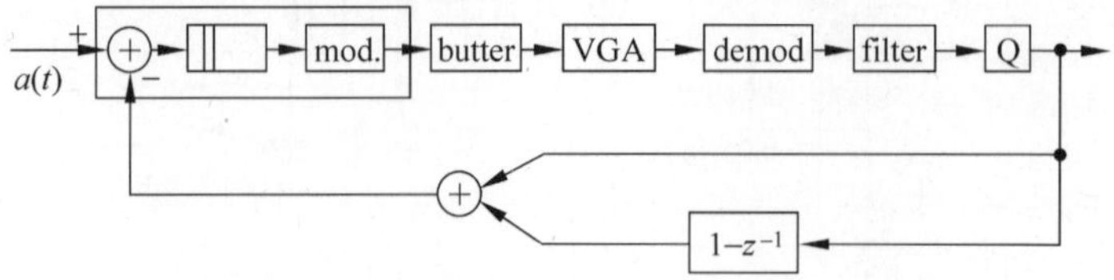

Figure 18.35 System block diagram with chopper stabilization

In practical applications, accelerometers may be operated under harsh environments, such as temperature variation, packaging-induced stress, and electromagnetic interference (EMI). These can cause changes in the sensitivity and the bias of the accelerometers; hence, they need to be minimized in the design.

Two accelerometers can be built side by side to cancel these nonideal effects, as shown in Fig. 18.36. These two accelerometers are identical except that the proof mass in one accelerometer (C_{s^1}'s) is twice the proof mass in the other (C_{s^2}'s) so that one is twice as sensitive as the other one. The environmental changes appear as a common mode signal to the two accelerometers and should affect them in the same fashion. Therefore, these nonideal effects can be cancelled to the first order by subtracting two outputs in the digital domain. Note that the accelerometer is fabricated using surface micromachining, so the area is relatively small and is not a major concern.

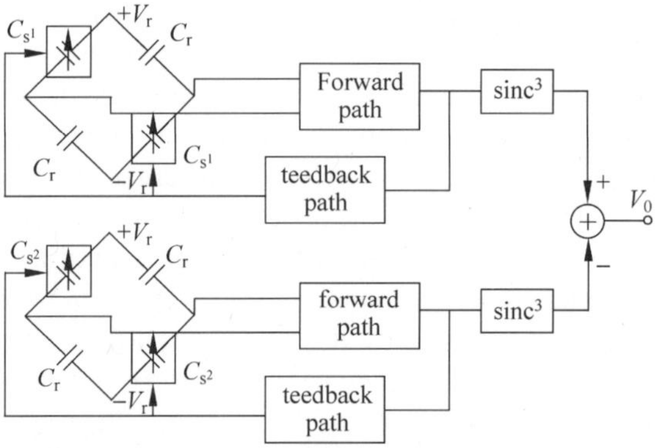

Figure 18.36 Dual-loop design

(2) Implementation

System partitioning is one of the key considerations in implementing integrated sensors. It can include the analog pre-amplifier, the signal conditioning circuitry (such as temperature compensations and voltage regulators), data conversions (such as *A*/*D* converters), and digital signal processing (such as decimation filters). The level of integration must be determined by the specific application. In general, the analog front-end should be bite-grated with sensors on the same chip to minimize the parasitic capacitance and the noise at the input node. System complexity, yield and chip area should be considered when integrating signal conditioning, data convention, and digital signal processing (DSP) with the microsensors on the same chip.

In this design, the accelerometer is implemented with the readout electronics on the same chip. The detection circuitry is implemented in a 3im P-well CMOS process fabricated in Berkeley Microfabrication Laboratory. In the initial run, all the analog detection circuits (including the input buffer, the VGA, the demodulator, and the low pass filter) and the 1-bit quantizer are fabricated on the same chip with the microstructures. The feedback compensation network is operated in the digital domain and is implemented off the chip since the noise is no longer a major concern and integration of the digital feedback circuit with the existing detection circuits is relatively straightforward.

18.4 Fabrication Technology

Fabrication technology for silicon micromachining has developed rapidly and there are two basic silicon micromachining technologies: bulk and surface micromachining. The fabrication technology for micromachining and its integration with IC processes is used as our process. The MICS process is also described. Tungsten metallization is a key innovation in this technology, since it enables high temperature process after completion of the CMOS process.

Surface micromachining has been developed into a competitive technology during the 1980's and 1990's[74–80]. Unlike bulk micromachining, surface micromachining processes materials deposited by low-pressure chemical vapor deposition (LPCVD) or electroplating on the front surface of the wafer. The bulk silicon wafer is used only as a structural support. LPCVD polysilicon and silicon nitride, along with an electroplated metal, are commonly used to build mechanical structures. The sacrificial spacer layer, typically LPCVD oxide, is removed after the structural film is deposited and patterned to release the structure from the substrate. The microstructures are typically a few hundred microns on each side and a few microns thick. The size and thickness of the structures are constrained by the mechanical boundary conditions and the stress field (average and gradient) in the polysilicon film.

Figure 18.37 shows the process flow of a typical surface micromachining process. Surface micromachining usually starts with a thermal silicon dioxide layer and a silicon nitride layer. An *in situ* doped polycrystalline silicon layer, often called polysilicon or poly (Poly1), is deposited that serves as the ground plan[76, 77] or the bottom electrode of the sense and feedback capacitor[79, 80]. A sacrificial PSG is deposited that will be removed later to release the structural polysilicon layer (Poly2) from the substrate. PSO is the best candidate for the sacrificial layer because it etches rapidly in hydrofluoric acid (HF). To have a uniform etch rate, the PSG film is densified by hearing the wafer to 950℃ – 1,100℃ in a furnace or a rapid-thermal annealer[77, 81].

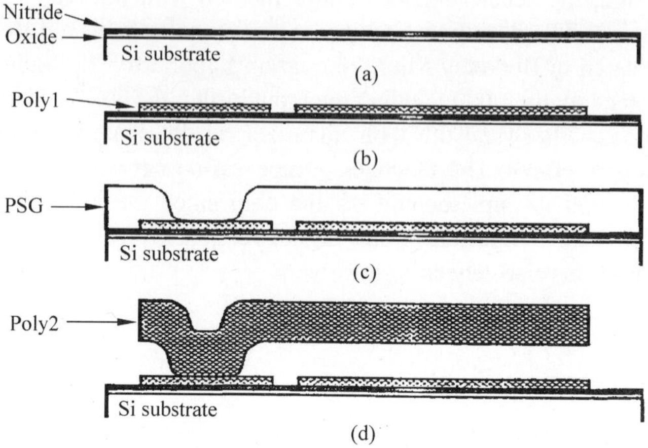

Figure 18.37 Process flow of a typical surface micromachining process

After the PSG is etched, the structural polysilicon layer is deposited. The PSG openings serve as the anchor points for the structural polysilicon layer. Compressive stress and stress gradient are often present in the as-deposited polysilicon film, which can cause the buckling of microbridges and deflection of the cantilever beams. Internal stress in the polysilicon film arises mainly from the thermal coefficient of expansion between the polysilicon film and the substrate and the nucleation and growth of the polysilicon. Furnace annealing is commonly employed to reduce the stress, where the wafers are heated to 1,050℃ for 1 h in nitrogen ambient. Recently, rapid-thermal annealing has also proven effective in reducing the stress in the polysilicon films[82, 84]. A PSO layer is deposited before the stress annealing step so that the polysilicon layer, sandwiched by the PSG layers on the top and bottom, will be annealed symmetrically and the stress gradient will be minimized.

The structural polysilicon film is then etched in the plasma etcher and the wafer is immersed in the HF solution to remove the underlying sacrificial layer, releasing the structure from the substrate. The lateral etch under the structure can be either reaction limited or diffusion limited, which determine the HF etching time[86]. Additional polysilicon structural layers can be added if needed[17, 79, 88]

Surface micromachining process techniques have become a popular technique for microsensors in the last few years. Surface micromachined structures are much smaller than those made by bulk micromachining and take full advantage of high-volume batch processing. Surface micromachined microsensors eliminate the need for wafer bonding and can potentially reduce the packaging cost significantly.

18.4.1 Process Integration

One of the important aspects of surface micromachining is its ability to integrate with standard CMOS. I examined and compare many. The MICS process will be proposed together with a tungsten metallization process. It is possible to integrate surface micromachining processes with conventional IC processes since both technologies process only the front side for the wafer. For surface micromachined capacitive sensors, the sensing capacitances are typically on the order of a few hundred femtofarads. Such tiny capacitances are difficult to detect with off-chip circuitry, where parasitic capacitances are orders of magnitude larger. By putting electronics on the same chip, the detection circuits and signal conditioning circuits can be built right next to the sensing element to enhance the performance of the sensing system. Therefore, process integration of micromachining and IC processes is very desirable for building high-performance and low-cost sensing systems.

Micromachining processes are similar to IC process in several aspects. CMOS processes involve at least 10 lithography steps where the lateral-feature size can be very important. Some processing steps, such as gate and contact patterning, are critical to the functionality and performance of the CMOS circuits. Change in any one of the processing steps will lead to modifications in a number of other steps in the process. In contrast, surface micromachining is relatively simple compared with the CMOS process, usually consisting of two to six processing steps and the feature sizes are much larger than CMOS. The comparison of CMOS and surface micromachining process is listed in Table 18.3.

Table18.3 Comparison of CMOS and surface micromachining processes

Process	CMOS	surface micromachining
Common features	Silicon-based processes Same materials Same etching principles	
Complexity (mask)	>10	2–6
Lateral dimension	<1micron	2–10 micron
Vertical dimension	-lmicron	1–5 micron
Process flow	Standardized	Application specific

In developing a merged CMOS/microstructure fabrication process, several process compatibility issues must be considered, including: ①deposition and anneal temperatures, ②passivation during micromachining etching steps, and ③surface topography. AU the requirements must be satisfied to have a functional process.

Various approaches can be used to integrate the CMOS process with the surface micromachining process. There are three basic approaches to integrate the two processes: the pre-CMOS, mixed, and the post-CMOS microstructural process, as shown in Fig. 18.38. The pre-CMOS approach is to fabricate the microstructures before any CMOS process steps. This approach integrates the two processes modularly without any major modifications. However, due to the vertical dimension of the microstructures, step coverage is a problem for the interconnection between the sensors and the circuitry. Passivation for the microstructure during the CMOS process can also be problematic. Furthermore, the fine-tuned CMOS fabrication sequence, such as gate oxidation, can be affected by the heavily doped structural and sacrificial layers. Therefore, this approach is only used for some special applications[15].

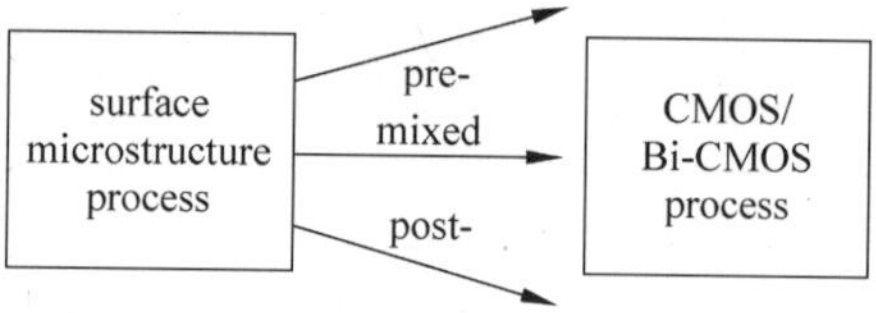

Figure 18.38 Various options for process integration

The most common approach is to interleave the CMOS and micromachining process steps. It has been demonstrated that this approach can be employed to integrate the IC process with either surface or bulk micromachining processes. Since the CMOS process is complex and fine-tuned, any modifications can potentially degrade the performance of the CMOS circuitry. However, merging the two processes can be very time consuming and one process can only be used for one family of products. The last approach is to process the micromachining process after the completion of the CMOS process. The electronic circuit is passivated to protect it from the subsequent micromachining processes. Modifications are not necessary for either the CMOS or micromachining process. This strategy allows the CMOS process to be canted out and completed at an IC foundry, after which the wafers can be sent to another facility for microstructural sensor fabrication. The microstructures can be fabricated as an 'add-on' adjacent to the CMOS circuitry. This process is called Modular Integration of CMOS and microStructure, or MICS, and is conceptualized in Fig. 18.39. Since the author has utilized the MICS process, it has been described in detail. The temperature requirements for the microstructure processes and their effects on the CMOS process as well as the metallization and rapid-thermal annealing processes will be discussed. In later sections, the process flow for the MICS process has been described and the cross-sections after each important step have been shown.

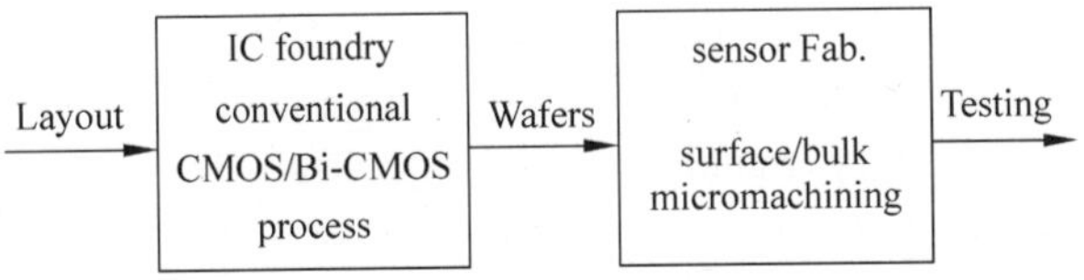

Figure 18.39 MICS process

18.4.2 Temperature Requirements

Robust CMOS circuits that can survive the high-temperature cycles in the subsequent micromachining process steps without degradation is necessary for MICS. Polysilicon as the main structural material of microstructures is the limiting step so CMOS must meet at least this temperature concern. Further the circuitry must be able to survive silicon nitride deposition of 800℃. Table 18.4 shows the deposition temperatures for thin films for the microstructure process, the densification temperature for PSG, and the annealing temperature for polysilicon stress relaxation.

Table 18.4 Temperature requirements

	Temperature	Film/Purpose
Deposition	450℃ 610℃ 650℃ 800℃	LTO/PSG Low-stress poly-doped poly nitride
Anneal	950℃ 1,050℃	PSG densification Poly stress anneal

Traditionally, the PSG is densified in the wet oxygen ambient in a furnace at 950℃ for 30 minutes[89]. Polysilicon stress annealing is typically done by furnace annealing in nitrogen ambient at 1,050℃ for 1 h[77]. Since the p-n junctions begin to migrate at temperatures above 950℃, the CMOS circuitry cannot experience processing steps above this temperature for an extended time without suffering performance degradation. This constraint eliminates furnace processing steps above 950℃ after the completion of the CMOS process. Therefore, other techniques for PSG densification and polysilicon stress annealing are required to replace the furnace processing steps.

18.4.3 Tungsten Metallization

Aluminum metallization must be replaced by an alternative interconnect metallurgy to raise the post-CMOS temperature ceiling higher than 450℃. The simple solution of using a polysilicon layer as the interconnect material is not an option for CMOS process, because of its high resistivity and the need to form contacts to both n and p^+ regions. Due to their high melting points and relatively low resistivity, refractory metals or their suicides are obvious choices for replacing aluminum as the interconnect material. Good adhesion to the substrate during the processing is essential for an interconnect material, which depends on the interfacial bond-strength and on the residual stress in the film. For high-temperature post-CMOS micromachining processing, it is also desirable that the thermal expansion coefficient of the interconnections match that of the silicon substrate.

Of the various candidates, tungsten is attractive because of its low resistivity and relatively low thermal expansion coefficient, which nearly matches that of silicon. Furthermore, tungsten is under extensive development as a VLSI interconnect material for multilevel metallization processes. Although most of the VLSI research has focused on CVD tungsten, DC magnetron sputtering is selected as the deposition technique for the tungsten film to adapt to the equipment available. One problem with tungsten metallization is that tungsten reacts with silicon at about 600℃ to form WSi_2. Therefore, a diffusion barrier layer is needed in the contact holes to retard interfacial diffusion.

A diffusion barrier should have thermodynamic stability as well as low atomic diffusibility for the reacting species. No diffusion barrier completely stops reactions in the contact areas; it only retards the reaction rates. Diffusion barriers provide stability within a time-temperature limit. Increasing the thickness of the barrier will lengthen the time needed for the penetration of reacting species at a given temperature, with the penetration time scaling with the square of the barrier thickness. The barrier thickness is typically limited to around 1,000 Å; thus, the barrier layers have little contribution to the contact resistance. Of course, it is essential for the barrier to form an ohmic contact with both the tungsten and the n^+ and the p^+ regions of the silicon substrate.

A diffusion barrier consisting of $TiSi_2$ and TiN is an attractive combination for this application. Among refractory metal compounds, TiN has been the most studied for barrier applications and has been proven to be an excellent diffusion barrier. A simple self-aligned process has been demonstrated for making this sandwich diffusion barrier from a single deposition of a titanium film. This self-aligned process has been adapted for fabrication of a diffusion barrier suitable for high post-CMOS processing temperatures. In the MICS process, titanium silicide and titanium nitride are formed by DC magnetron sputtering of Ti followed by high-temperature treatments.

18.4.3.1 Rapid Thermal Process

Rapid thermal processing (RTP) plays an important role as the MICS process, by limiting the dopant diffusion and interfacial reaction that would occur in conventional furnace anneals. RTP has several advantages over the conventional furnace process. It reduces the time at high temperature significantly (10 – 120 s), and has a very high-temperature ramp rate (~150 ℃/s)[90]. The processing temperature can be accurately controlled up to 1,100℃. Therefore, RTP plays an important role in high-temperature processing steps in the MICS process, such as PSG densification, diffusion barrier formation, and stress release annealing for tungsten and structural polysilicon.

PSG is the most attractive sacrificial layer in the surface micromachining process because of its fast HF etch rate. However, as-deposited PSO has a very nonuniform etching rate. To have good process control, a PSO densification is needed to improve the etch control in the HF solution. The etch rate in buffered HF can be used as the measure of the densification quality.

Traditionally, PSG is densified at 950℃ for 30 min in wet oxygen ambient in the furnace. As discussed earlier, CMOS circuitry cannot sustain this processing step because of the junction migration. Therefore, rapid thermal annealing is used for densification to replace the furnace densification. Experiments were earned out to characterize the PSG densification using rapid thermal annealing. The wafers coated with PSG are first rapid thermal annealed in nitrogen and then etched in the BHF solution. The etch rate is measured by nanospec. Rapid-thermal annealing at 950℃ for 30 s is used in the MICS process[91].

Compressive stress and stress gradients are often present in the as-deposited polysilicon films due to nucleation and growth of the polysilicon. These can result in the buckling of microbridges and built-in deflection of cantilever beams. The stress level must be reduced to have a useful microstructural material. Conventionally, the film is furnace annealed at 1,050℃ in a nitrogen ambient for an hour. It has been demonstrated that rapid thermal annealing (RTA) can be used to reduced the stress level in the polysilicon film[82, 83]. Experiment has shown that RTA at 1,100℃ for 60 s will reduce the stress level comparable to that achievable by long furnace annealing. Peeling of the films underneath the polysilicon was observed for anneals at 1,100℃. This may be due to the stress and adhesion of the tungsten films and outgas of phosphorus in the PSG layer. The first MICS run uses a 1,000℃ rapid thermal anneal for 60 s.

RTA can also be used to reduce the stress level in the tungsten film. The sputtered tungsten film has a very high intrinsic stress due to the bombardment during the deposition. Because this intrinsic stress is very sensitive to the sputtering conditions, it is difficult to control the stress level consistently. CVD tungsten films have much lower stress levels[92], but are not available in our laboratory at this time. By annealing the film in nitrogen at 950℃ for 30 s, the stress level is reduced from 830 MPa to 450 MPa and the film has much better adhesion to the substrate.

18.4.3.2 Process Description

The initial baseline process is a conventional *P* well CMOS process developed at UC Berkeley Microfabrication laboratory[89]. It uses 3 μm design rules and single-level metal for interconnections, with two polysilicon layers for poly-to-poly capacitors for analog applications. In addition to the accelerometer, the project chip contains six different sensors and actuators including a gyroscope, lateral-resonator oscillators, mechanical filters, lateral actuators, electrostatic voltmeters, and an electrostatic levitated microstructure.

In the CMOS process, all processing steps follow the standard process recipe until the contact etch. The contact etch is one of the most critical processing steps in the CMOS process. An etch-inspect-measure-etch technique is used here for the contact etch. After the contact lithography, a control wafer is etched first to determine the equipment conditions such as the etch rate, selectivity, and uniformity. The oxide on the device wafers is etched SF6 at 850 W at 30 s intervals. These processing steps are repeated until the oxide thickness is measured less than 20 Å. The wafer is then over-etched at 700 W for 20 s, at which conditions the oxide etch rate is lower and the etching selectivity is higher. The contact holes should be white with no color 'rainbows' observable under the optical microscope.

Immediately prior to interconnect metallization, the wafers are etched in 25:1 HF solution for 20 s. This ensures a clean silicon surface for proper ohmic contact. However, undercut of the PSG was observed, which can lead to the step coverage problems for the subsequent metallization. This phenomenon is not consistent and requires further study. The step coverage problem did not occur after the top LTO thickness is reduced to 200 Å.

Figure 18.40 shows the cross-sectional view of the CMOS process after the contact etch. After the contact etch and HF dip, a titanium layer is sputtered at 2 kW in a 20 m Torr argon ambient, with a target film thickness of 1,000 Å. The post-deposition treatment requires that the water be heated by rapid thermal annealing (RTA) to 600℃ in a nitrogen ambient for 30 s. Titanium silicide is formed at the interface of titanium and silicon in the contacts with simultaneous formation of titanium nitride at the surface of the titanium film. Wet etching in a mixture of NH_4:H_2O_2 is then used to remove the selected materials [94].

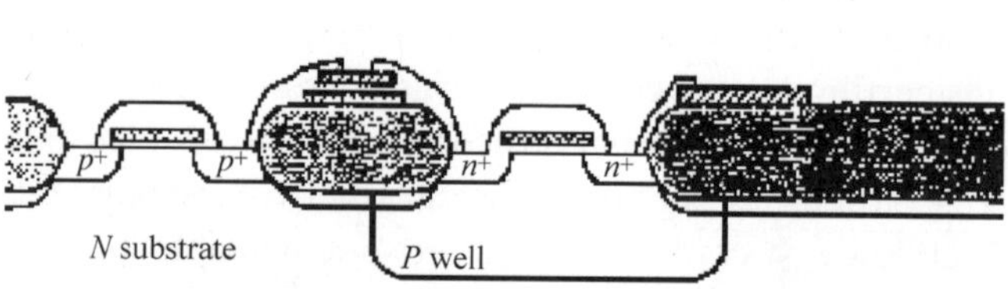

Figure 18.40 CMOS cross-sectional view after contact etch

Finally, 1 μm of tungsten is deposited at 2 kW under 20 m Torr argon chamber pressure and the film is etched in SF_6 plasma. With the $TiSi_2$/TiN diffusion barrier layer, the contacts are found to be ohmic with contact resistance of around $5\times10^{-7}\,\Omega\,cm^{-2}$. The contacts have no noticeable degradation for temperature cycles up to 850℃ for 30 minutes[10, 11].

CVD tungsten can offer very low intrinsic film stress, but the interfacial bonds between the tungsten and the underlying oxide are typically very weak. A 'glue layer', such as TiN and TiW, is commonly used to improve the adhesions for the CVD tungsten. Sputtered tungsten films have strong interfacial bonds due to the atomic bombardment during the deposition. For the same reason, the sputtered tungsten has high stress in the film. The film stress level is very sensitive to the deposition conditions and it is almost impossible to obtain as-deposited low-stress films consistently. The high stress can degrade the adhesion to the substrate causing the peeling of the tungsten film. To reduce the as-deposited stress and prevent delamination, the wafer is annealed by RTA at 950℃ for 30 s in nitrogen ambient after sputter deposition. This anneal can reduce the stress in tungsten film by about 30% – 40%[95]. Figure 18.41 depicts tungsten metallization.

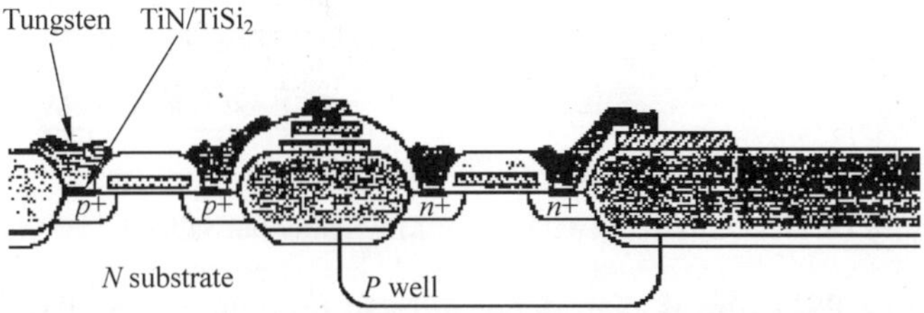

Figure 18.41 CMOS cross-sectional view with tungsten metallization

After the completion of the CMOS process with tungsten metallization, a 3,000-Å LTO is deposited to prevent any exposures of tungsten layer in the nitride tube. The wafer is then encapsulated with a 2,000-Å LPCVD silicon nitride layer to protect the CMOS circuitry from the subsequent etching steps in the micromachining process, as shown in Fig. 18.42. It is important to minimize the furnace temperature overshoot and excess time in the furnace. This nitride layer is also served as the starting layer of the microstructures.

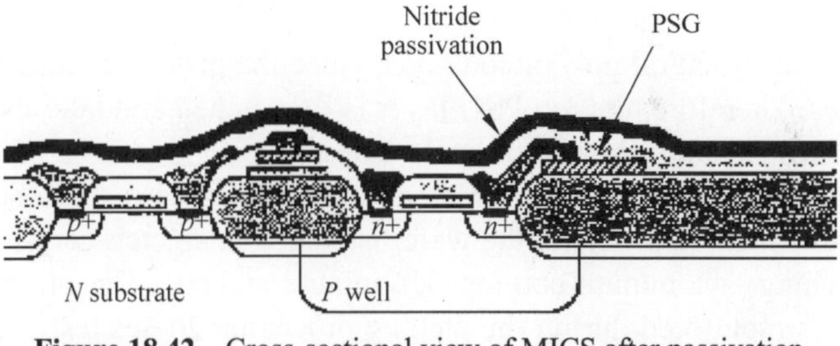

Figure 18.42 Cross-sectional view of MICS after passivation

After etching the contacts in the nitride and oxide layers, the first polysilicon layer in the sensor process is deposited and forms the bottom electrodes for sensing and feedback capacitors, as well as the ground plane. This *in situ* doped polysilicon layer (3,500 Å) is also used as the interconnection between the sensor and the readout circuits. Because of concerns with any possible contamination in the polysilicon tube due to the out-diffusion of the mobile ions in the sputtered tungsten film, this polysilicon layer contacts the capacitor polysilicon layer (or gate polysilicon layer), instead of contacting the tungsten layer directly. These capacitor electrodes are used as 'jumpers' between the first polysilicon and the tungsten layers. This design prevents any tungsten exposure in the polysilicon furnace tube. Figure 18.43 shows the cross-sectional view after the deposition of the first polysilicon layer.

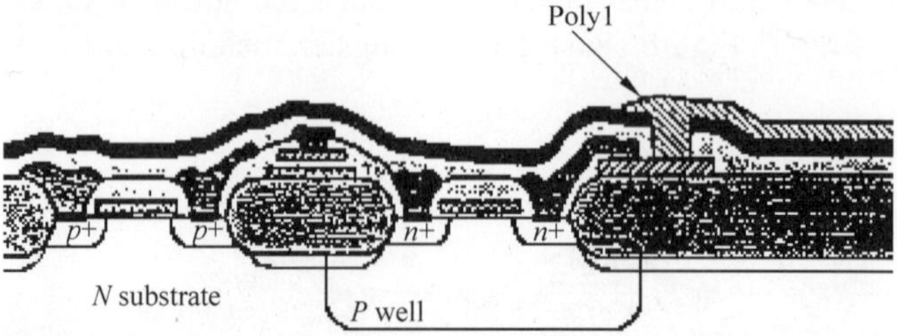

Figure 18.43 Cross-sectional view of MICS after polysilicon deposition

A 1 μm thick PSG film is then deposited and used as the sacrificial layer. To control the etch rate, this layer is densified by rapid-thermal annealing at 950℃ for 30 s in a nitrogen ambient. The second *in situ* doped polysilicon layer (2 μm thick) is then deposited, which later forms the proof mass, the suspensions, and the interdigitated levitation fingers. To minimize the stress gradient in the structural polysilicon layer, a 0.5 μm thick PSG is deposited so that the structural polysilicon is now sandwiched between two PSG layers. The top PSG layer later serves as the masking material during the structural polysilicon etching. The wafer is now annealed by rapid-thermal annealing at 1,000℃ for 60 s in the nitrogen ambient.

Etching of the structural polysilicon in the LAM etcher is demanding, because of its thickness. The photoresist mask is not good enough to obtain vertical sidewalk on the structural polysilicon layer, since the plasma etching takes about 6 – 7 minutes. Therefore, the top PSG layer is first etched and later used as oxide masks for the structural polysilicon etch. Due to the long plasma etch, substrate heating and uniformity can be problematic so special care must be taken. To avoid substrate heating problem, the wafer is etched in an etch-cool-etch fashion: 1 minute etching — 1 minute cooling — 1 minute etching. The plasma chamber temperature is monitored during the etching process and rises less 3℃ with this technique. The wafer is also rotated 180° after every 2 minutes of etching to improve the uniformity. This etching process may not be needed when other plasma etcher is used. Figure 18.44 shows the interdigitated levitation fingers with vertical sidewalls.

Figure 18.44 SEM of levitation fingers with vertical sidewalls

The structural release is accomplished by a buffered HF etch, at which point the structural polysilicon layer is released from the substrate and freely suspended being anchored at the contact points to the first ground polysilicon layer. Release etch in the buffered HF is later proven to leave residues after the etching process, which can cause stiction of the proof mass to the substrate[93]. Concentrated HF is a better choice for a fast etch rate of the PSG layer. The cross-sectional view of the MICS process after the release etches is shown in Fig. 18.45. The wafer is now completed and is ready to be diced and packaged.

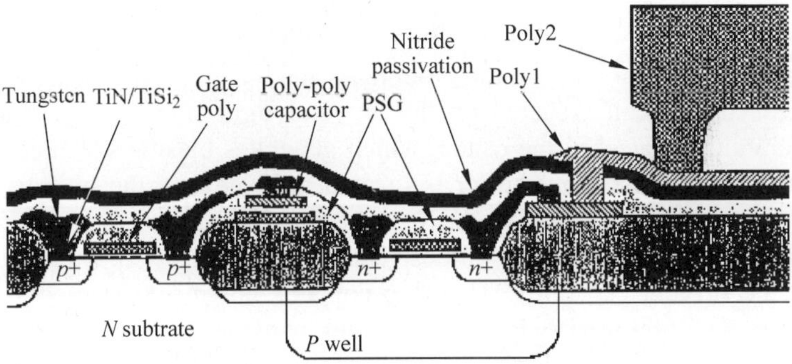

Figure 18.45 Cross-section of the MICS process

18.5 Experimental Results

The accelerometer with the readout electronics is implemented using the MICS process in a 3 μm P-well CMOS process fabricated in Berkeley Microfabrication Laboratory. In the initial run, all the analog detection circuits (including the input buffer, the VGA, the demodulator, and the low-pass filter) and the 1-bit quantizer are fabricated on the same chip with the microstructures. The feedback compensation network is operated in the digital domain and is implemented off chip in the first run.

Figure 18.46 shows the die photo of the accelerometer with the dual-loop design. The accelerometer is laid out in such a way that has the high symmetry to minimize the mismatch. The six square structures around the center of the die are the polysilicon capacitive sensing structures. The two structures on the right are the capacitive sensing structures with full proof mass, and the two on the left are structures with half proof mass. The two structures in the center form the reference capacitors. There are two electrodes underneath each fixed top plate so that four reference capacitors are formed with the two structures.

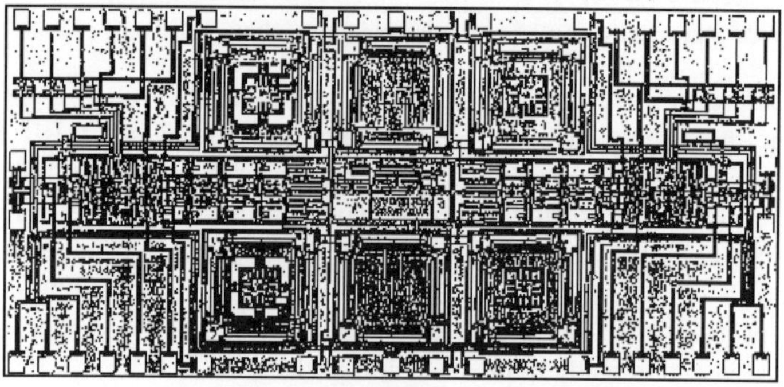

Figure 18.46 Accelerometer die photo

The readout electronics are located in the middle of the device. The detection circuits are identical for both the full proof mass and half proof mass accelerometers. They are symmetrically located on the left and right side of the device. The biasing circuit is placed in the center, which generates biasing voltages for both detection circuits. The input buffer is located right next to the biasing circuits near the center, following the VGA. Next are the demodulator and the low pass filter. The quantizer is located outmost and is followed by an output drive to increase the driving capability. The chip contains about 500 transistors and is about 2.5 mm×5 mm in size. It has 42 bonding pads, most of which are used for inter-stage testing and multiple power supplies. The digital feedback is implemented with off-shelf components on a wire-wrap board.

Scanning electron micrographs (SEM) are used to examine the microstructures. Figures 18.47 and Fig. 18.48 are the SEMs for the capacitive sensing structures with full and half mass, respectively. Since the ratio of the two proof masses is determined by the area and is insensitive to the film thickness variation, it can be controlled and insensitive to process variations. The bottom sensing and feedback electrodes can be vaguely seen from the photographs. The etching holes on the proof mass are 4 pm by 4 pm and are 10 pm apart to reduce the release etching time. The levitation fingers are located along the four edges of the proof mass. The folded suspensions are attached to the four corners of the proof mass. Note that the proof mass is also suspended by four T-shaped fuses on the corners. The folded suspensions are also held by the fuses at its folding end.

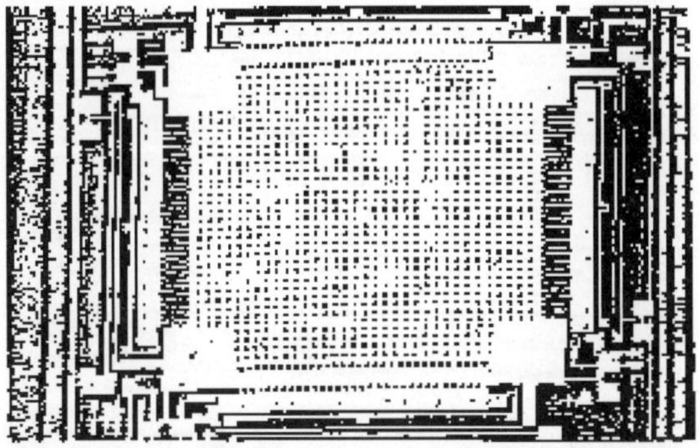

Figure 18.47 SEM of sensing structure with full mass

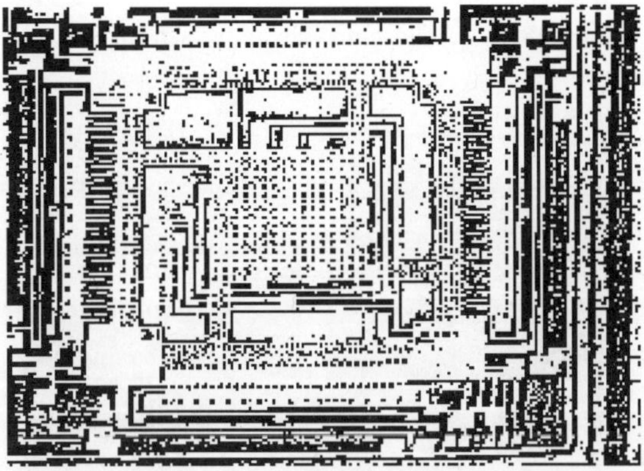

Figure 18.48 SEM of a sensing structure with half mass

Figure 18.49 shows a close-up view of a corner of the proof mass. At the bottom of the photograph, it shows the T-shaped fuse holding a folded suspension. The μm wide, structural polysilicon line between the suspension and anchors of the interdigitated levitation fingers are grounded to avoid any levitation effect on the suspension. The fuse holds the suspension during the release etching process and can be severed by passing a current through the two anchoring pads[96]. Figure 18.50 shows a fuse holding the proof mass before and after it is broken. Packaging is always a challenging step for the sensors. This accelerometer is processed on 4 inch wafers where the dies are 10 mm by 10 mm and are separated by 1 mm wide scribe lines. For a standard IC process, the wafer is first coated with photoresist to avoid the dicing dust deposited directly onto the wafer. The wafer is then glued on special dicing tape and diced through scribe lines on an automatic dicing machine. For micromachined sensors, the packaging process is much more complicated since there are free standing microstructures on the wafer surface. The conventional photoresist coating technique cannot be applied here because the dicing particles on the photoresist may get underneath microstructure when the photoresist is removed.

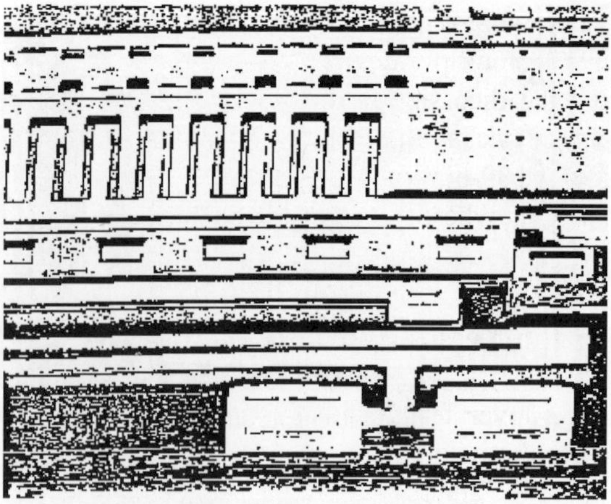

Figure 18.49 A close-up view of the sensing structure

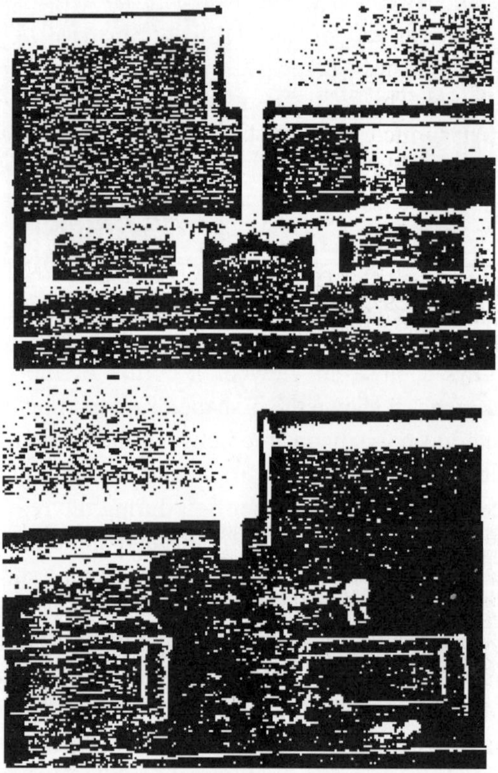

Figure 18.50 Fuse after and before being broken

The wafers are diced manually using a diamond pen for this accelerometer. To dice the wafers manually, apply a moderate pressure with your hand to the top and bottom of the wafer so that the wafer is under stress, and then use a diamond pen to scratch the left and/or right side of the wafer perpendicularly until the wafer cracks. Since there are multiple devices on this run, the wafers are diced along scribe lines so that the dice size is a little larger than 10 mm by 10 mm. The cavity in the regular cc packages is usually 10 mm by 10 mm and cannot be used to package the dice. A 209-pin Pin-Grid-Array (PGA) package made by Kyocera is used for the packaging where the cavity in the package is 15 mm by 15 mm.

18.5.1 Calibration Techniques

The 2 g (or±1 g) turnover test is the simplest technique to measure the DC response for the accelerometers[97]. It produces a 2 g acceleration by turning the device upside down in the gravitation field. This test can be very useful to measure the functionality and sensitivity easily.

A more sophisticated calibration is to use a dividing head where the accelerometer is mounted on a wheel. By rotating the wheel a certain angle (θ) from the vertical direction, the acceleration for the accelerometer equals to $g\cos(\theta)$. Since the gravitational field only varies very slightly throughout the world, it serves as a very stable input source. This test also measures the cross-axis sensitivity of the accelerometer. The dynamic characteristics of an accelerometer can be calibrated on a shaker (or shake table) where the testing accelerometer and a reference accelerometer are mounted on the shaker. The output of the testing accelerometer is compared with that of the reference accelerometer. The accelerometer characteristics, such as sensitivity, linearity, bandwidth, can be measured using this technique. The movement of the shaker can also be measured by laser interferometry. The excited acceleration can then be derived and used to calibrate the testing accelerometer[97].

18.5.2 Electrical and Mechanical Measurement

Various testing circuits and mechanical structures are included on the same chip. The same detection circuitry is implemented without the microstructures and can be used for characterizing circuit performance. The circuit performance is evaluated by wafer-level probing due to the number of connections required to characterize the circuit. A customized probe card is made in Wentworth Laboratory so that all the bonding pads can be accessible at the same time for the testing. The power supply is 5 V for the circuit. The unity gain buffer is measured to have a gain of 0.9, which is limited by the finite output resistance of the current source. The bandwidth is around 500 kHz, which is limited by the parasitic capacitance (–100 pF) from the probes and coaxial cables so the measurement instrument. In the accelerometer design, the input capacitance from the following VGA is around 1 pF and the buffer bandwidth is 50 MHz from SPICE simulation. The input capacitance to tie the buffer is not measured since it is dominated by the parasitic capacitance.

The gain of the VGA is controlled by an external voltage and can be varied from unity to 40. The differential output swing is 1.5 V and the amplifier becomes nonlinear if output swing is larger than that. Figure 18.51 shows a 10 kHz differential input to the buffer (top sine wave) and a 20 mV output at the VGA. The gain is 20 in this case.

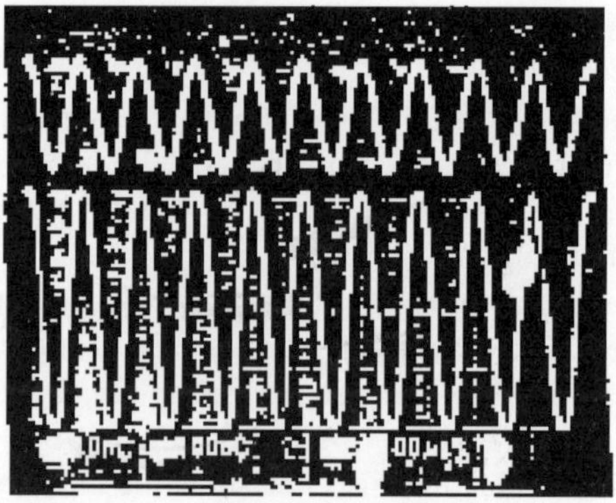

Figure 18.51 Input and output waveforms of the amplifier

The boron dose for the threshold implant is $1.2\times10^{11}/\text{cm}^2$ and is too high such that the PMOS transistor has a threshold voltage of +0.1 V. Thus, the leakage current in CMOS switches is large. The sample-and-hold (S/H) circuit in the demodulator is not functioning due to the large leakage current. The design is implemented off-chip, together with the feedback circuitry, and is tested fully functioning[97].

A floating node is found in the biasing circuit layout, which is used to set up the biasing voltage for the VGA. A focused ion beam technology, also known as microsurgery, is used to reconnect the nodes. The contact holes to the two nodes are opened by the ion beam and then a tungsten layer is deposited that links the two contact holes[100]. Mechanical structures are also built to characterize the mechanical properties of the structural polysilicon. The strain of the polysilicon is found so be around 0.07% measured by a Vernier structure[101].

18.5.3 Accelerometer Measurement—Static Response

The static response of the accelerometer is first characterized in the open-loop self-testing mode. A voltage can be applied to the feedback electrodes and the levitation fingers to generate an electrostatic force exerted onto the proof mass to simulate an acceleration. Since gravitation force and electrostatic force from the bottom sensing electrode pull the proof mass downward, the voltage is applied to the interdigitated fingers to generate a levitation force and feedback electrodes are grounded during the test. Figure 18.52 shows the output voltage versus the levitation voltage at two different driving voltages, V_{dr} of 150 mV and 250 mV. When the levitation voltage is grounded, the proof mass is pulled below the equilibrium position by the gravity and electrostatic force from the sensing electrode giving an offset voltage at the output. The proof mass displacements are 1,500 Å and 2,140 Å for 150 mV and 250 mV driving voltages, respectively. As the levitation voltage increases, the levitation force pulls the plate toward the equilibrium position and the output voltage decreases.

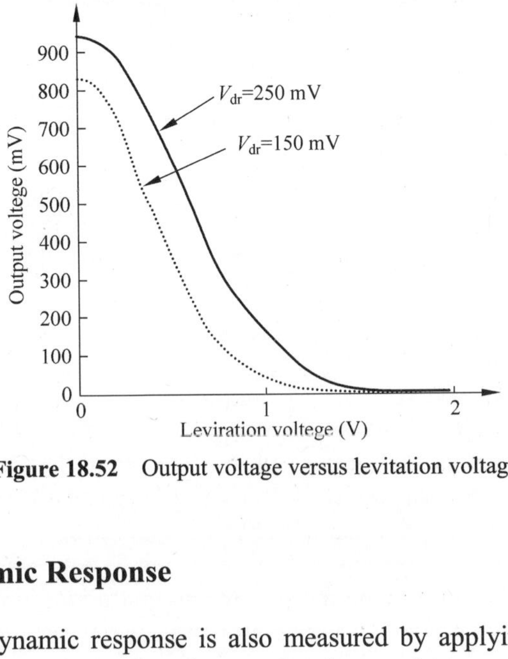

Figure 18.52 Output voltage versus levitation voltage

18.5.4 Dynamic Response

The open-loop dynamic response is also measured by applying a pulse to the feedback or levitation electrode and measuring the transient response at the output. Figure 18.53 shows a digital scope photo of the envelop of the high-frequency sinusoidal output when a 500 ms, 0.5 V pulse is applied to the levitation fingers. Note that the output voltage is modulated to 100 kHz and the pulse is only a 1-Hz signal. The magnitude of the envelop is the output voltage.

The damping coefficient can be obtained by measuring the settling time of the output. The settling time is about 5 ms from the photo, which gives a damping coefficient of 1.2×10^{-3} N/(m/s). The damping coefficient can also be derived from the geometry of the plate. It can be shown that the damping coefficient of a rectangular plate is given by[98]:

$$C_v = \mu f\left(\frac{W}{L}\right)L\left(\frac{W}{d}\right)^3\left(\frac{1}{1+z/d}\right)^{1.5} \tag{18.54}$$

Figure 18.53 Transient response of the accelerometer

where L and W are the length and width of the plate, μ is the viscosity of the air, and $f(W/L)$ is an empirical number depending on the shape of the plate. The plate can be divided into a number of rectangular plates, and the damping coefficient for each place can be calculated using Eq. (18.54). The damping coefficient can be obtained by summing those for each rectangular plate. The theoretical calculation predicts the damping coefficient for the plate to be 1×10^{-3} N/(m/s), which agrees with the experimental measurement.

18.5.5 Turnover Test

The 2 g turnover test is also performed to characterize the DC performance. In the current design, the sensitivity is 100 mV/g at a 100 mV excitation voltage. However, stiction of the proof mass is observed and the board has to be shaken to get it released from the substrate. This phenomenon is not completely understood. It is generally believed that the release etching and drying processes are of the key factors in making a free standing structure. Various approaches have been suggested to reduce or prevent the stiction[97–105]. Dimples are used on the proof mass in this run to reduce the contact area between the die proof mass and the ground plane to minimize surface tension. Methanol, isopropanol, photoresist and acetone mixture, and prolonged Dl water rinsing have separately proven to be an effective treatment for reducing stiction than brief water rinsing.

Surface cleanness is also important to have free standing structures. An NH_4OH/H_2O_2 solution can be used to remove the fluorocarbon residue that could have been responsible for the stiction. In the first MICS run, however, the structures were released in the 5:1 buffered hydrofluoric acid (HF), which was later proven to leave a residue on the etching surface. Concentrated HF should be used to maintain a clean surface after the etching. Device storage should be considered to have free standing microstructures. Ideally, the accelerometer should be sealed in a hermetic package so that it is not affected by the environment. The devices in this run are kept in the room ambient where humidity in the air may cause the stiction. The device should be at least kept in the dehydrated chamber. The charge in the native oxide on the polysilicon structure can also be a factor for the problem due to stiction. Figure 18.54 is a SEM photo that shows fingers attached to the proof mass are clearly above the interdigitated fingers anchored on the substrate. This may be caused by the scanning electron beams that charge up the native oxide layers and pushes the structural polysilicon layer away from the bottom polysilicon ground plane.

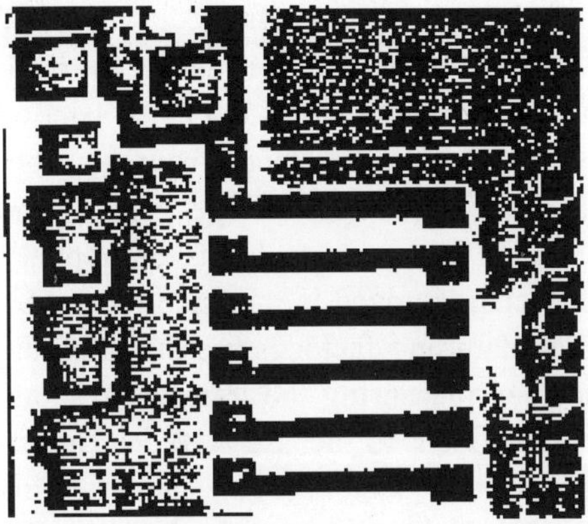

Figure 18.54 SEM with proof mass above its neutral position

18.6 Conclusions and Future Research

I have described a surface micromachined accelerometer integrated with CMOS detection circuits. The surface micromachined, capacitive sensing element is fabricated with one layer of structural polysilicon. The sensing axis for the accelerometer is perpendicular to the substrate. Folded suspensions are used to provide compliant suspensions along the sensing axis and stiff suspension in other directions. The sensing and feedback electrodes are located underneath the proof mass, and interdigitated fingers are used to generate the levitation force. Further improvements on the Σ-Δ modulation technique is used for the feedback control for the accelerometer.

The mechanical proof mass is used as the double integrator in the second-order Σ-Δ modulator. The compensation is achieved in the feedback path in the digital domain. The chopper stabilization technique is used to remove the DC offset voltage. A dual-loop design is proposed to cancel nonideal effects, such as environmental changes and packaging-induced stress. A low-input capacitance buffer is used to bootstrap the ground plane to minimize the parasitic capacitance. The analog front-end is implemented on the same chip with the sensing element, which includes the input buffer, the VGA, the demodulator, and the 1-bit quantizer.

The integrated accelerometer is fabricated in the Berkeley Microfabrication Laboratory. A MICS process is developed to fabricate the accelerometer. A conventional 3 μm *P* well CMOS process is carried out and completed for the detection circuitry. An LPCVD nitride layer is used to passivate the circuit areas to prevent any etching from subsequent processes. The surface micromachined sensing structure is then fabricated next to the electronic circuitry. Tungsten is used as the interconnect material to replace aluminum for CMOS metallization. An RTP is used extensively for the contact diffusion barrier formation, PSG densification, and polysilicon stress annealing.

The detection circuit performance is evaluated by wafer-level probing. The input buffer is measured to have a gain of 0.9 and a bandwidth around 500 kHz, which is limited by the parasitic capacitance from the probes and coaxial cables of the measurement instrument. The voltage gain of the VGA is controlled externally and can be varied from unity to 40. Its differential output swing is 1.5 V.

The accelerometer is characterized in the open-loop mode with a self-test and a 2 g turnover test. The damping factor is measured by applying a pulse to the levitation fingers and then measuring the transient response of the output. The damping factor is determined to be 1.2×10^{-3} N/(m/s), while a theoretical calculation predicts it to be 1×10^{-3} N/(m/s). The open-loop sensitivity for the accelerometer is 100 mV/g determined by the 2 g turnover test. Stiction of the proof mass to the substrate has occurred and has prevented any closed-loop testing.

18.6.1 Future Research

Passivation of the CMOS circuit needs improvement. Systematic experiments should be carried out to have a good understanding of the RTA stress annealing. Polysilicon is the most popular material for surface micromachined microstructures. For accelerometers, a low-mass density makes polysilicon unattractive as the proof mass. One structural polysilicon layer is used in this run to form the proof mass and suspension for process simplicity. The thickness for the proof mass and the suspension are the same; fringing field levitation is used to generate the levitation force. An additional polysilicon layer can be added to have more compliant suspension and better feedback control. A third polysilicon layer could be advantageous for allowing a parallel-plate 'pull-up' capacitor, since the parallel-plate electrostatic force is much larger than the fringing field levitation. Future research into the Σ-Δ modulation technique should be considered since it has shown promises here. More research into differing systems integration techniques such as; more research on MEMS fabrication for integration (i.e MEMS before CMOS, MEMS after CMOS and MEMS in the middle).

References

[1] Roylance L. M., and J. B. Angell, (1979), A batch-fabricated silicon accelerometer. *IEEE Trans. Electron Devices,* **ED-26**: 1911 – 1917

[2] Terry S, (1988) A Miniature Silicon Accelerometer with Built-in Damping. *IEEE Solid Stare Sensor Actuator Workshop*, Hilton Head Island, SC, 114 – 116

[3] Henry A. V., et al, (1989), Accelerometer Systems with Self-testable Features. *Sensors and Actuators,* **20**: 153 – 161

[4] Barth P.W., (1988) A Monolithic Accelerometer with Integral Air Damping and Overrange Protection. *IEEE Solid-State Sensor and Actuator Workshop*, Hilton Head Island, SC, 35 – 38

[5] Rudolf F., (1983), A Micromechanical Capacitive Accelerometer with a two-point Inertial-mass Suspension. *Sensors and Actuators*, **4**: 191 – 198

[6] Wilner L.B., (1988), A High Performance, Variable Capacitance Accelerometer. *IEEE Trans. on Instrumentation and Measurement*, **37**: 303 – 307

[7] Seidel H., et al, (1990), Capacitive Silicon Accelerometer with Highly Symmetrical Design. *Sensors and Actuators A*, **21-A23**: 312 – 315

[8] Aske V.H., (1987), An Integrated Silicon Accelerometer. Scientific Honeywell, 53 – 58

[9] Rudolf F., (1987), Silicon Microaccelerometer.Transducer'87, Tokyo, Japan, 395 – 398

[10] Suzuki S., et al, (1990), Semiconductor Capacitance-type Accelerometer with PWM Electrostatic Servo Technique. *Sensors and Actuators*, **A21-A23**: 316 – 319

[11] Peterson K.E., et al, (1982), *Micromechanical Accelerometer Integrated with MOS on Electron Devices*, **29**: 23 – 27

[12] Muller R.S., (1987), From IC's to microstructures: materials and technologies. *IEEE Micro Robots and Teleoperators Workshop*, Hyannis, MA

[13] Howe R.T., (1987), Resonant microsensors.4th International Cozsference on Solid State Sensors and Actuators, Tokyo, Japan, 843 – 848

[14] Howe R.T., and R.S.Muller, (1984) Integrated Resonant-Microbridge Vapor Sensor. Mt. Elec. Device Mig, 213 – 316

[15] Fan L.S., (1989), Integrated Micromachinery: moving structures on silicon chips. Ph.D. Thesis, Electrical Engineering and Computer Sciences, University of California at Berkeley, Berkeley, CA

[16] Tang W.C., et al, (1989), Laterally driven polysilicon resonant microstructures. *Sensors and Actuators*, **20**: 25 – 32

[17] Payne R.S., and K.A.Dinsmore, (1991), Surface Micromachined Accelerometer A Technology Update. SAE, Detroit, MI, 127 – 135

[18] Ristic L., et al, (1992), Surface Micromachined Polysilicon Accelerometer. IEEE Solid-Stare Sensor and Actuator Workshop, Hilton Head Island, SC, 118 – 122

[19] Yun W., et al, (1992), A Surface Micromachined, Digitally Force-balanced Accelerometer with Integrated CMOS Detection Circuitry. IEEE Solid-State Sensor and Actuator Workshop, Hilton Head Island, SC, 122 – 125

[20] Howe R.T., (1987), Resonant microsensors. 4th International Conference on Soil-State sensors and Actuators, Tokyo, Japan, 843 – 848

[21] Howe R.T., and R.S.Muller, (1984), Integrated Resonant-Microbñdge Vapor Sensor. *Mi. Elec. Device Mig Dcc.,* 213 – 316
[22] Fan L.S., (1989), Integrated Micromachinaly: moving structures on silicon chips. PhD. Thesis, Electrical Engineering and Computer Sciences, University of California at Berkeley, Berkeley, CA
[23] Tang W.C., et al, (1989), Laterally driven polysilicon resonant microstructures. *Sensors and Actuators,* **20**: 25 – 32
[24] Amini A., and M. Trifunac, (1985), Analysis of a Force Balance Accelerometer. *Soil Dynamics and Earthquake Engineering*, **4**(2): 82 – 90
[25] McLaren I., (1974), *Open and Closed Loop Accelerometers.* AGARD Flight Test Instrumentation Series, Edited by W. D. Mace and A. Pool, **6**(160)
[26] Bryzek J., (1985), Modeling Performance of Piezoresistive Pressure Sensors. The 3rd hit. Conf. on Solid-State Sensors and Actuators, 168 – 173
[27] Suzuki K., et al, (1985), Nonlinear Analyses on CMOS Integrated Silicon Pressure Sensor. *IEEE Mt. Electron Devices Meeting,* 137 – 140
[28] Aske V.H., (1987), An Integrated Silicon Accelerometer. *Scientific Honeywell*, 53 – 58
[29] Wise K.D., (1986), Integrated Sensors: Key to Future VLSI Systems. Proc. 6th Senor Symp., 1 – 9
[30] Terry S., (1988), A Miniature Silicon Accelerometer with Built-in Damping. IEEE Solid-State Sensor and Actuator Workshop, Hilton Head Island, SC, 114 – 116
[31] Allen H.V., et al, (1989), Accelerometer Systems with Self-testable Features. *Sensors and Actuators*, **20**: 153 – 161
[32] Barth P.W., (1988), A Monolithic Accelerometer with Integral Air Damping and Over range Protection. IEEE Solid-Stare Sensor and Actuator Workshop, Hilton Head Island, SC, 35 – 38
[33] Peterson K.E., (1982), Silicon as a Mechanical Material. Proceeding of the IEEE, **70**: 417
[34] Albert W.C., (1982), Vibrating Quartz Crystal Beam Accelerometer. ISA In: Instrument Symp., Las Vegas, NV
[35] Lynch W., and J. Truxel, Introductory System Analysis. McGraw-Hill Book Company
[36] Gabrielson T.B., (1991), Fundamental Noise limits in Miniature Acoustic and Vibration Sensors. Mission Avionics Technology Department (Code *5044*), Naval Air Development Center
[37] Sears F.W., and F.L.Salinger, (1975), Thermodynamics, Kinetic Theory, and Statistical Thermodynamics. Addison-Wesley, Reading, MA
[38] Kinel C., (1958), Elementary Statistical Physics. Wiley, New York, NY
[39] Roylance L.M., and B. Angell, (1979), A Batch-fabricated Silicon Accelerometer. *IEEE Trans. Electron Devices,* **ED-26**: 1911 – 1917
[40] Peterson K.E., et al, (1982), Micromechanical Accelerometer Integrated with MOS Detection Circuitry. *IEEE Trans. on Electron Devices,* **29**: 23 – 27
[41] Rudolf F., (1983), A Micromechanical Capacitive Accelerometer with a two-point Inertial-mass Suspension. *Sensors and Actuators*, **4**: 191 – 198
[42] Wilner L.B., (1988), A High Performance, Variable Capacitance Accelerometer. *IEEE Trans. on Instrumentation and Measurement,* **37**: 303 – 307

[43] Seidel H., et al, (1990), Capacitive Silicon Accelerometer with Highly Symmetrical Design. *Sensors and Actuators A*, **21**(1 – 3): 312 – 315

[44] Rudolf F., (1987), Silicon Microaccelerometer.Transducer'87, Tokyo, Japan., 395, 398

[45] Payne R.S., and K.A. Dinsmore, (1991), Surface Micromachined Accelerometer A Technology Update. SAE, Detroit, Ml, 127 – 135

[46] Ristic L.J., et al, (1992), Surface Micromachined Polysilicon Accelerometer. IEEE Solid-State Sensor and Actuator Workshop, Hilton Head Island, SC, 118 – 122

[47] Henrion W., et al,(1990),Wide Dynamic Range Direct Digital Accelerometer. IEEE Solid-State Sensor and Actuator Workshop, Hilton Head Island, SC, 153-157

[48] Meldrum M.A., (1990), Application of Vibrating Beam Technology to Digital Acceleration Measurement. *Sensors and Actuators,* **A21-23**: 377 – 380

[49] Chang S.C., et al, (1990), Resonant-bridge Two-axis Accelerometer. *Sensors and Actuators,* **A21-A23**: 342 – 345

[50] Yun W., et al, (1992), A Surface Micromachined, Digitally Force-balanced Accelerometer with Integrated CMOS Detection Circuitry. IEEE Solid-State Sensor and Acnsasor Workshop, Hilton Head Island, SC, 122 – 125

[51] Tang W.C., et al, (l989), Laterally-driven Polysilicon Resonant Microstructures, IEEE Micro Mechanical Systems Workshop, Salt Lake City, Utah, 53 – 59

[52] Gray P.R., and R.G. Meyer, Analysis and Design of Analog Integrated Circuits. 2nd edition, Wiley

[53] Ristic L.J., et al, (1992), Surface Micromachined Polysilicon Accelerometer. IEEE Solid-Sate Sensor and Actuator Workshop, Hilton Head Island, SC

[54] Candy C., (1986), A Use of Double Integration in Sigma-Delta Modulation. *IEEE Trans. Commun.,* **Com-34**: 72 – 76

[55] Boser B.E., (1988), Design and Implementation of Over sampled Analog-to-Digital Convertera,' Ph.D. Thesis, Department of Electrical Engineering. Stanford University, Stanford, CA

[56] Payne R.S., and K.A. Dinsmore, (1991), Surface Micrornachined Accelerometer A Technology Update. Soc. Auto. Eng. P.242, Detroit, MI, 127 – 135

[57] Tang W.C., et al, (1990), Electrostatically Balanced Comb Dzive for Controlled Levitation. IEEE Solid-State Sensor and Actuator Workshop, Hilton Head Island, SC, 23 – 27

[58] Terry S., (1988), A Miniature Silicon Accelerometer with Built-in Damping. IEEE Solid-Stare Sensor and Actuator Workshop, Hilton Head Island, SC, 114 – 116

[59] Christel L.A., et al, (1991), Vibration Rectification in Silicon Micromachined Accelerometers. Transducer'91, San Francisco, CA, 89 – 92

[60] Boxenhorn B., and P. Greiff, (1990), Monolithic Silicon Accelerometer. *Sensors and Actuators*, **A21-23**: 273 – 277

[61] Boxenhom B., and P. Greiff, (1989), An Electrostatically Rebalanced Micromechanical Accelerometer.AJAA Guidance, Navigation, and Control Conference, Boston, 118 – 122

[62] Cole J.C., (1989), A New Capacitive Technology for Low-cost Accelerometer Applications. *Sensors Expo International*

[63] Young-Ho Cho, personal communication

[64] Roarks R.L., and W.C.Young, (1989), Formulas for Stress and Strain. McGraw-Hill, 6th edition, 100

[65] Popov E.P., (1968), Introduction to Mechanics of Solids.Prentice-Hall, 167

[66] Joseph E. S., and D. M.Larry, (1983), Mechanical Engineering Design. 4th edition, McGraw-Hill, 138

[67] Pisano A. P., and Cho Y.H., (1990), Mechanical Design Issues in Laterally-driven Microstructures. *Sensors and Actuators,* **A21-A23**: 1060 – 1064

[68] Cho Y.H., and A. P. Pisano, (1990), Optimum Structural Design of Micromechanical Crab-leg flexures with Microfabrication Constraints. Symposium on Micro- Mechanical Systems, 1990 ASME Winter Annual Meeting, Dallas, TX

[69] Uehara G.T., personal communication.

[70] Maxwell S., v.4.20, *Ansoft Corp.*, 4 Station Square, 660 Commerce Court Building, Pittsburgh, PA 15219

[71] Candy J.C., and G.C.Temes, (1992), Over sampling Delta-Sigma Data Converters: Theory, Design and Simulation. IEEE Press

[72] Hauser M.W., and R.W. Brodersen, (1986), Circuit and Technology Considerations for MOS Delta-Sigma AID Converters. IEEE Proc. Int. Symp. on Circuit and Systems, 1310 – 1315

[73] Mar M., and R.W. Brodersen, (1992), Design Technique for ASIC Over sampling A/D Converters. VLSI Signal Processing V, edited by k. Yao. et al. IEEE Press, 407 – 416

[74] Howe R.T., (1987), Resonant microsensors.4th International Conference on Soil-Stare sensors and Actuators, Tokyo, Japan, 843 – 848

[75] Howe R.T., and R.S. Muller, (1984), Integrated Resonant-Microbridge Vapor Sensor. *Int. Elec. Device Mrg,* 213 – 316

[76] Fan L.S., (1989), Integrated Micro machinery moving structures on silicon chips. Ph.D. Thesis, Electrical Engineering and Computer Sciences, University of California at Berkeley, Berkeley, CA

[77] Tang W.C., et al, (1989), laterally driven polysilicon resonant microsm2cturcs. *Sensors and Actuators,* **20:**25-32

[78] Payne R.S., and K.A. Dinsmore, (1991), Surface Micromachined Accelerometer. A Technology Update. SAE, Detroit, Ml, 127 – 135

[79] Ristic L.J., et al, (1992), Surface Micromachined Polysilicon Accelerometer', IEEE Solid Stare Sensor and Actuator Workshop, Hilton Head Island, SC, 118 – 122

[80] Yun W., et al, (1992), A Surface Micromachined, Digitally Force-balanced Accelerometer with Integrated CMOS Detection Circuitry. IEEE Solid-Stare Sensor and Actuator Workshop, Hilton Head Island, SC, 122 – 125

[81] Sze S.M., (1981), Physics of Semiconductor Devices.2nd edition, John Wiley

[82] Putty M., et al, (1989), Process Integration for Active Polysilicon Resonator Microstructures. *Sensors and Actuators*, **20**: 143 – 151

[83] Yun W., W.C.Tang, and R.T.Howe, (1989), Fabrication Technologies for Integrated Microdynamic Systems. The Third Toyota Conference: Integrated Micro Motion Systems, Nissin, Aichi, Japan

[84] Yun W., (1989), CMOS Metallization for Integration with Micromachining Processes. MS. Thesis, UC Berkeley, Dept. of EECS

[85] Yun W., et al, (1992), A Surface Micromachined, Digitally Force-balanced Accelerometer with Integrated CMOS Detection Circuitry. IEEE Solid-State Sensor and Actuator Workshop, Hilton Head Island, SC, 122 – 125

[86] Monk D., et al, (1992), A Diffusion/chemical Reaction Model for HF Etching of LPCVD Phosphosilicate Glass Sacrificial Layers. IEEE Solid-State Sensor and Actuator Workshop, Hilton Head Island, SC, 4649

[87] Pister K.S., (1992), Hinged Polysilicon Structures with Integrated CMOS 'flTs. IEEE Solid-State Sensor and Actuator Workshop, Hilton Head Island, SC, 136 – 139

[88] Fedder G.K., et al, (1992), Thermal Assembly of Polysilicon Microactuators with Narrow-Gap Electrostatic Comb Drive. IEEE Solid-Stoic Sensor and Actuator Workshop, Hilton Head Island, SC, 63 – 68

[89] Voros K. and P.K. Ko, (1987), MOS Processes in the Microfabrication Laboratosy. Memorandum No. UCB/ERL M87

[90] Peters L., (1991), Why You Need RTP. Semiconductor International, 71 – 74

[91] Chang, personal communication.

[92] Bustillo, personal communication

[93] Monk D., personal communication.

[94] Giandomenico D., personal communication.

[95] Noworoiski M., personal communication.

[96] Fedder G.K., et al, (1992), Thermal Assembly of Polysilicon Micro actuators with Narrow-Gap Electrostatic Comb Drive. IEEE Solid-S tare Sensor and Actuator Workshop, LIII- ton IIead Island, SC, 63 – 68

[97] IC Sensors Calibrating Your Accelerometer. *Sensors,* April 1992: 29 – 34

[98] Starr B., (1990), Squeeze-film Damping in Solid-State Accelerometers. IEEE Solid-State Sensor and Actuator Workshop, Hilton Head Island, SC, 44 – 47

[99] Ehud Silterstein, personal communication

[100] FibLab, Inc., 1574 Central Pointe Dr., Milpitas, CA

[101] Gary Fedder, personal communication

[102] Guckel H., et al, (1989), Advances in Processing Techniques for Silicon Micromechanical Devices with Smooth Surfaces. International Workshop on Micro Electromechanical Systems, Salt Lake City, UT, 71 – 75

[103] Orpana M., and A.O.Korhonen, (1991), Control of Residual Stress of Polysilicon Thin Films by Heavy Doping in Surface Micromachining. Transthscers'91, San Francisco, CA, 957 – 960

[104] Alley R.A., et al, (1989), The Effect of Release-etch Processing on Surface Microstructure Stiction. International Workshop on Micro Electromechanical Systems, 71 – 75

[105] Mastrangelo C.H., and C.H.Hsu, (1992), A Simple Experimental Technique for the Measurement of the Work of Adhesion of Microstructures. IEEE Solid-S rare Sensors and Actuators Workshop, Hilton Head Island, SC, 208 – 212

[106] Fedder G.K., and R.T. Howe, (1991), Thermal Assembly of Polysilicon Microstructures. IEEE Micro Mechanical Systems Conference, Tokyo, Japan, 51 – 57

19 MEMS in Automobiles

Shih-Chia (Scott) Chang

Smart Sensors and Integrated Microsystems
Department of Electrical & Computer Engineering, Wayne State University
5050 Anthony Wayne Drive, Detroit, Michigan 48202
E-mail address: sc2chang@wayne.edu

Abstract This chapter provides an overview of microelectromechanical system (MEMS)-based commercial products. It also discusses the basic MEMS technologies, including IC technology, MEMSCAD (MEMS computer added design), micromachining, materials, and packaging and testing. The emphasis is on the compatibility issues of the various micromachining and packaging technologies with the special requirements of automotive applications. The fabrication, application, and evolution of the silicon membrane-based pressure transducers, silicon-based micro-accelerometers, and solid-state gyroscopes are described. A variety of driver vision assistance devices, the potential high-volume automotive products, are presented. The paper is concluded with a remark on the upcoming systems that are able to make automobile safer, more fuel efficient, and fun to drive.

Keywords Automotive MEMS-based sensors, MEMS technology, driver vision assistant systems, packaging

19.1 Overview of Automotive MEMS

Sensors and actuators are the essential components for automotive control systems[1–3]. For example, a manifold absolute pressure (MAP) transducer and a manifold air temperature (MAT) have been used to compute the mass airflow rate for the microprocessor-based automotive engine control module. An accelerometer (keep) has been used to detect the sudden speed change of an automobile for airbag deployment in crush protection. The pervasive usage of sensors in automobile is reflected in Fig. 19.1. The method of fabrication and the materials used for the construction of automotive transducers (sensors and actuators) depend very much on the aimed specific applications. For example, oxygen sensors used in engine control have been fabricated using a thick film technology with high temperature ceramics. Although the MEMS-based approach has been attempted,

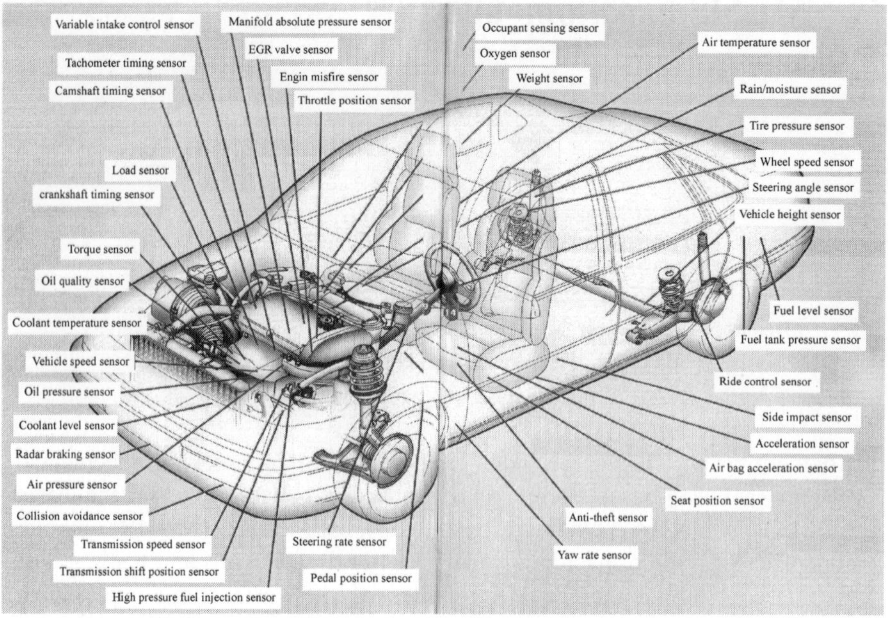

Figure 19.1 Current and future automotive sensors

this approach has never passed the actual performance test because of the harsh environment (high temperature, corrosive chemical species, and soot). However, due to the profound advantages of MEMS technologies, MEMS-based devices have been gradually expanding into the automotive market. In the early stages, the advancement of MEMS technologies and products were mainly driven by the demand of automotive MEMS. This fact is reflected in Table 19.1 that shows the 1998 DARPA data of the MEMS market and major MEMS manufacturers. Tables 19.2 and Table 19.3 show the data of the MEMS market segments for 1996 and 2002, respectively, published by NEXUS in 1998. As shown in the two tables, the early dominance of the automotive MEMS was replaced in the later days by the consumer-related and medical-related MEMS.

The MEMS technology is basically an extension of the IC microfabrication technology. It is a batch process with good process and dimensional control, and therefore, can provide good device-to-device uniformity, produce small (keep)-size devices with high production volume, and lower manufacturing cost. All of these are the essential requirements of the automotive products.

As mentioned earlier, the motivation for the development of automotive MEMS is attributed to the profound advantages of MEMS. The major driving forces for the development of automotive devices (sensors, actuators) are somewhat different from those of other consumer products. They are:

(1) Government regulations

For example, the 1970's pollution control and fuel economy requirements forced

Table 19.1 MEMS Market and Industry Studies (1998 DARPA Data)

Technology Area	Typical Devices / Applications	Companies	Market Baseline ($Millions)	Market 2003 (Est.) ($Millions)
Inertial Measure-ment	Accelerometers, Rate Sensors, Vibration Sensors	TI, Sarcos, Boeing .ADI, EG&G IC Sensors, AMMI, Motorola, Delco,Breed, Systron Donner, Honeywell, Allied Signals	$350–$540	$700–$1,400
Micro-fluidics Chemical Testing/ Processing	Gene Chip, Lab on chip, Chemical Sensors, Flow Controllers , Micronozzles, Microvalves	Battelle, Sarnoff, Microcosm ,ISSYS, Berkeley Microlnstruments, Redwood, TiNi Alloy, Affymetrix, EG&G IC Sensors, Motorola, Hewlett Packard, TI, Xerox, Canon, Epson	$400–$550	$3,000–$4,450
Optical NEMS (MOEMS)	Displays ,Optical Switches ,Adaptive Optics	Tanner, SDL, GE, Sarnoff, Northrop-Grumman, Westinghouse, Interscience, SRI, CoreTek, Lucent, Iridigm, Silicon Light Machines, TI, MEMS Optical, Honeywell	$25–$40	$450–$950
Pressure Measur-ement	Pressure Sensors for Automotive, Medical and Industrial Applications	Goodyear, Delco, Motorola, Ford, EG&G IC Sensors, Lucas NovaSensor, Siemens, TI	$390–$760	$1,100–$2,150
RF Technology	RF Switches, Filters, Capacitors, Inductors, Antennas, Photo Shifters, Scanned Apertures	Rockwell, Hughes, ADI, Raytheon, TI, Aether	(Essentially $0 as of 1998)	$40–$120
Other	Actuators, Microrelays, Humidity Sensors, Data Storage, Strain Sensors, Microsatellite Components	Boeing, Exponent ,HP, Sarcos, Xerox Aerospace, SRI, Hughes, AMMI, Lucas Novasensor, Sarnoff, ADI, EG&G IC Sensors, CP Clare, Siemens, ISSYS, Honeywell, Northrop Grumman, IBM, Kionix, TRW	$510–$1,050	$1,230–$2,470

Table 19.2 MST Markets by Product and App.: 1996 Actual Market Segment Sizes for 1996(in $US millions)—Existing Products

Products/ Applications	IT Peripherals	Medical and Biochemical	Industry and Automation	Tele communication	Automotive Product	Environmental Monitoring	Total Turnover per Product
Read/write heads	4,500						4,500
Inkjet printheads	4,000			400			4,400
Hearing airds		1,150					1,150
Heart pacemakers		1,000					1,000
Pressure sensors		100	350		150		600
In vitor diagnostics		450					450
Chemical sensors		75	75			150	300
Accelerometers			90		150		240
IR imagers			220				220
Gyroscopes	100		50				150
Optical switches				50			50
Total turnover per application	8,600	2,775	785	50	300	150	13,060

Table 19.3 MST Markets by Product and App.: 2002 Predicted Market Segment Sizes for 2002 (in $US millions)—Existing Products

Products/ Applications	IT Peripherals	Medical and Biochemical	Industry and Automation	Tele communication	Automotive Product	Environmental Monitoring	Total Turnover per Product
Read/write heads	12,000						12,000
Inkjet printheads	900			1000			10,000
Hearing airds		2,000					2,000

(Continued)

Products/ Applications	IT Peripherals	Medical and Biochemical	Industry and Automation	Tele communication	Automotive Product	Environmental Monitoring	Total Turnover per Product
Heart pacemakers		3,700					3,700
Pressure sensors		200	600		500		1,300
In vitor diagnostics		2,800					2,800
Chemical sensors						800	800
Accelerometers			130		300		430
IR imagers			800				800
Gyroscopes	240		60		60		360
Optical switches				1,000			1,000
Drug delivery systems		1,000					1,000
Lab on chip		1,000					1,000
Magneto-optical heads	500						500
Miscellaneous							810
Total turnover per application	$21,740	$10,700	$1,590	$2,000	$860	$800	$38,500

NOTE: Figures are for world market (publicly available Source by NEXUS, 1998).

automotive industries to develop oxygen sensor for monitoring of the air-to-fuel ratio, and pressure and temperature sensor for determining the air mass flow rate. The 1980's vehicle safety requirement forced them to develop an accelerometer for airbag deployment. The upcoming (September 2008) regulation on direct tire pressure monitoring systems (TPMS) has been pushing the development of effective power supply system as well as low power consumption transceivers.

(2) Customer demand (competition)

① Fuel economy (pressure and oxygen sensors);

② Safety (accelerometer, gyroscope, tire pressure monitoring systems, night vision, blind spot detection, collision avoidance);

③ Comfort (climate control, entertaining systems);

④ High (keep)-tech image (display);

⑤ Wireless communication (GPS, cell phone, rfMEMS);

⑥ Power demand (MEMS-based relay, electronic cooling).

The following conditions are the essential factors for a successful introduction of MEMS products[4–6].

(1) Existence of starving market segment

For example, the business success of pressure sensors and accelerometer is due to the urgent demand of engine control and airbag deployment.

(2) Convergence of technology

The success of the Analog Devices, Inc.'s (ADI's) microaccelerometer is due to the convergence of surface micromachining and IC technologies.

(3) Systems approach

The developer(keep) and manufacturer should develop the entire MEMS system in a parallel fashion.

(4) Select the fabrication technology that fits in the existing process modules

Delco Electronics' bulk micromachined accelerometer is an extension of their piezoresistive pressure transducer.

19.2 Essence of MEMS Technology

The evolution of MEMS-based devices is closely related to the evolution of MEMS technology. Monolithic integration has been the general trend of MEMS-based devices. Therefore, as the technology advances so is the complication of MEMS-based devices. This is reflected in Fig. 19.2, which shows the evolutions of several MEMS-based devices and the Intel's microprocessors (which follow Moore's Laws). MEMS technology consists of IC technology, MEMSCAD, micromachining techniques, materials, packaging and testing, and interface electronics. Although the mentioned technologies are commonly used for various different MEMS fabrication, there are special requirements and constraints for automotive MEMS. One important concept that needs to be emphasized for the development of MEMS product is: at the very beginning of product development, all the technological aspects mentioned above must be addressed globally rather than summing them up individually at the end. A brief description of the MEMS technology is presented below.

19.2.1 IC Technology

MEMS fabrication generally requires a conventional IC fabrication technology

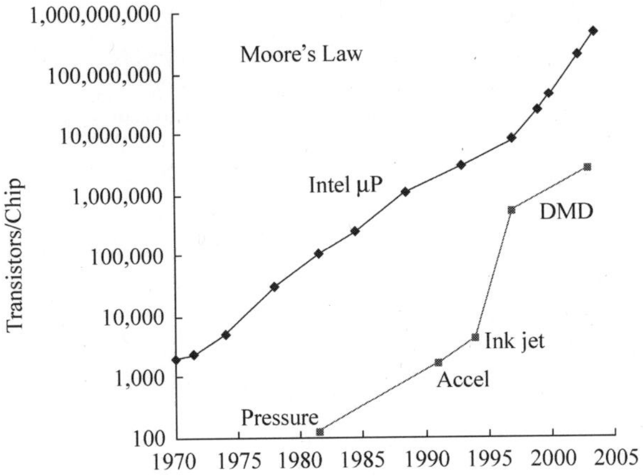

Figure 19.2 The evolution of certain MEMS-based devices and Intel's microprocessor, which follow Moore's Law. The complexity level of the MEMS devices increases as the MEMS technology advances. (courtesy of Kurt Petersen, Trans'05)

plus a MEMS (keep)-specific technology, such as micromachining. If a monolithic integration approach is adopted, both the process and material compatibility issues between the IC and MEMS (keep)-specific fabrication need to be carefully addressed.

19.2.2 MEMS CAD

To help researcher to try out a new concept and to reduce the total time of transferring a device concept into commercial product, computer simulation and modeling have to be carried out first. MEMS (keep)-specific CAD involves moving parts, has to interact with environment, and is most likely three-dimensional (3D).

19.2.3 Micromachining Technology

There are various means to generate 3D structures that the MEMS devices generally require. The selection of a specific micromachining technology depends on the specific product, specific application, and the existing infrastructure of the in-house technology. Further, if an on-chip circuitry is required, process compatibility between micromachining and IC fabrication needs to be carefully considered. For example: in the development of an accelerometer, a surface micromachining technique was selected by ADI, because of the 2D structure and the requirement of an extensive on-chip CMOS circuitry that fits well with ADI's strength in the IC technology. A bulk micromachining/piezoresistive technique was selected by Delco because the required technology was very similar to their existing piezoresistive pressure sensor process module. The most commonly used micromachining techniques are briefly described below:

19.2.3.1 Orientation (keep)-Dependent Wet Chemical Etching[7–9]

The basic etching characteristics of the orientation-dependent wet etching are: slow etch rate for Si⟨111⟩, SiO_2, Si_3N_4; fast etch rate for Si⟨100⟩, and Si⟨110⟩. There are specific etch angles for different crystalline surfaces. Figure 19.3 is the schematics showing the characteristics of the orientation (keep)-dependent etch and an SEM photograph of the bulk (keep)micromachined silicon structure.

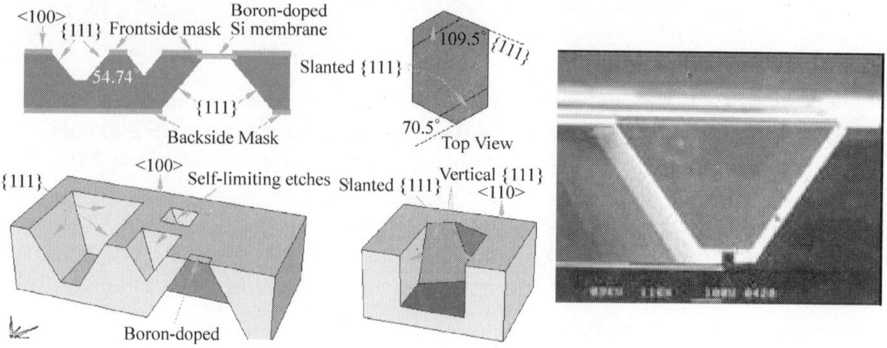

Figure 19.3 Orientation dependent wet chemical etching: Etch-stop: heavy boron diffusion, Etchants:EDP, KOH or TMAH. An SEM photograph of bulk micromachined structure, the bridge was formed by $B^{++}Si$

19.2.3.2 Deep Reactive Ion Etching (DRIE)[10–12]

Several different plasma processes have been experimented for high aspect ratio etching of silicon. The inductively coupled plasma (ICP) etching system with 'Bosch process' (developed by Bosch Research Labs) has been the most commonly used deep trench etching method. In the Bosch process, a cyclic process, consisting of etching and passivation, was employed to achieve high aspect ratios. Figure 19.4 shows DRIE etching mechanism and the SEM pictures of DRIE etched structures.

19.2.3.3 Surface Micromachining[13–15]

This method in general produces structures that are nearly 2D (keep) (thickness of polySi ~2 μm). With a proper choice of etching solution and device materials, the process may be CMOS compatible. Figure 19.5 shows processing steps and an SEM picture of the surface micromachined polySi structure.

19.2.3.4 Microelectroforming[16–18]

The mold formation can be done in different ways, depending on the required accuracy and cost. The general processing steps are shown in Fig. 19.6. In this

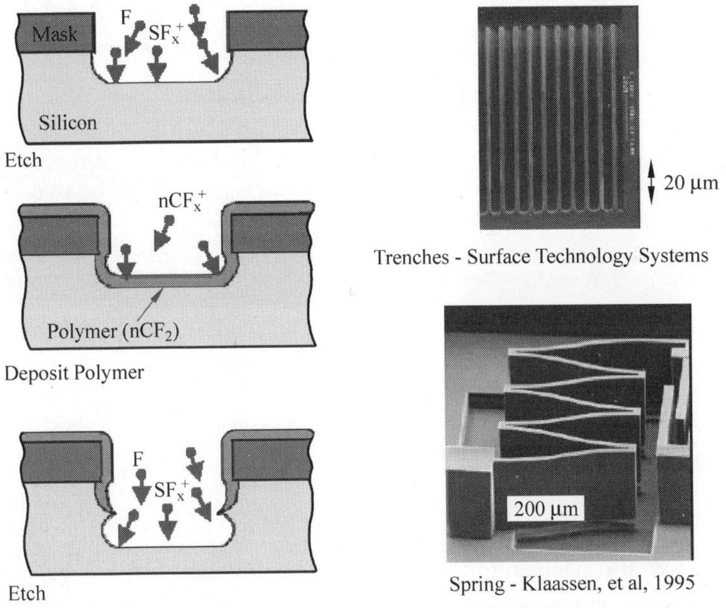

Figure19.4 DRIE with Bosch cyclic etching/passivation process. Examples of Silicon

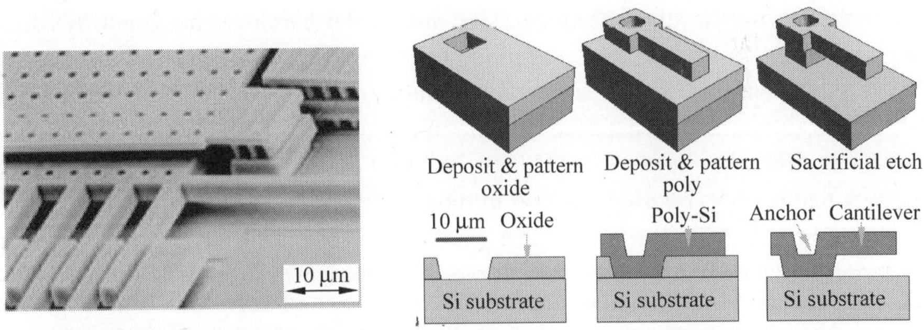

Figure 19.5 Example of surface micromachined structure and the surface micromachining processing steps

particular example, the PMMA (no need to explan) mold is formed lithographically using an X-ray source. If the synchrotron X-ray source is used, a very high aspect ratio mold can be formed. For an automotive MEMS, the minimal feature size may not be very small and hence the mold may be formed by SU8 (a negative photoresist) using a regular mask aligner with the UV light source. Figure 19.6 shows the processing steps of microelectroforming and a SEM picture of the UV (keep)-patterned SU8 structure.

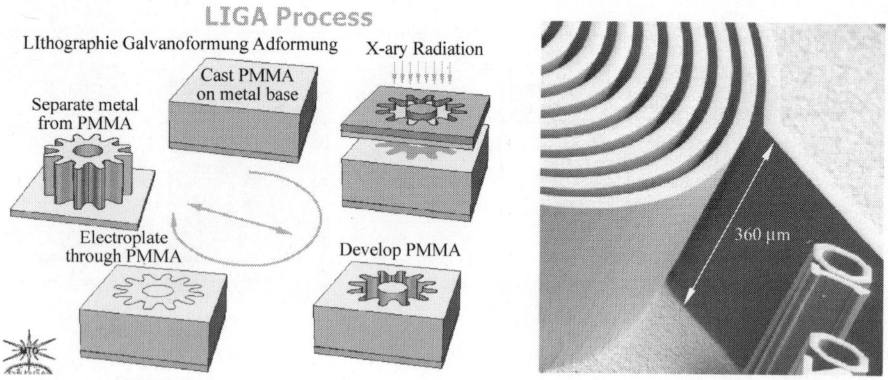

Figure19.6 Processing steps of micro-electroforming with X-ray and an SEM picture of a SU8 microstructure generated by regular UV source

19.2.4 Materials[19, 20]

Compatibility among the various materials used to form a sensor, as well as materials used for packaging, are critical for the successful development of MEMS products. For example, for force-based sensors, stresses induced by a thermal expansion coefficient difference among the various materials used for constructing the device may seriously compromise device performance. This is particularly true for automotive MEMS, due to the harsh environment in which the device has to be operated. For automotive applications, devices may have to face an environment with a temperature ranging from –40℃ – 150℃ or higher. Therefore, in choosing materials for the automotive MEMS devices, one of the important factors to be considered is the thermal expansion coefficient among the various materials to be used. Silicon in most cases is the base material for MEMS devices. Silicon has very attractive mechanical properties compared to other materials as shown in Table 19.4. Table 19.5 shows the physical properties of some transduction materials.

Table 19.4 Physical properties of some materials commonly used for the construction of MEMS devices and other mechanical structures

Material	Yield Strength (10^{10} dyne/cm^2)	Knoop Hardness (kg/mm^2)	Young's Modulus (10^{10} dyne/cm^2)	Density (g/cm^3)	Thermal Conductivity (W/cm℃)	Thermal Expansion (10^{-6}/℃)
Diamond	53	7,000	10.35	3.5	20	1.0
SiC	21	480	7.0	3.2	3.5	3.3
Si	7.0	850	1.9	2.3	1.57	2.33

(Continued)

Material	Yield Strength (10^{10} dyne/cm^2)	Knoop Hardness (kg/mm^2)	Young's Modulus (10^{10} dyne/cm^2)	Density (g/cm^3)	Thermal Conductivity (W/cm℃)	Thermal Expansion (10^{-6}/℃)
Si_3N_4	14	3,486	3.85	3.1	0.19	0.8
SiO_2	8.4	820	0.73	2.5	0.014	0.55
W	4.0	485	4.1	19.3	1.78	4.5
Al	0.17	130	0.70	2.7	2.36	25
Mo	2.1	275	3.43	10.3	1.38	5.0
Iron	12.6	400	1.96	7.8	0.803	12
Steel	4.2	1,500	2.1	7.9	0.97	12
Stainless Steel	2.1	660	2.0	7.9	0.329	17.3
Al_2O_3	15.4	2,100	5.3	4.0	0.5	5.4
TiC	20	2,470	4.97	4.9	3.3	6.4

Table 19.5 Physical properties of some transduction materials

Class	Sub Class	Density (kg/m^3)	Stress (MN/m^2)	Stiffness (GN/m^2)	Strain (%)	Strain Rate (s^{-1})	Power (W/kg)	Energy (kj/m^3)	Life Cycles	Eff (%)
Muscle	Human Heart	1,037	0.35	0.06	40	5	100	0.8	10^9	35
Piezo Electric	Ceramic	7,500	3.5	40	0.09	10	1,000	10	10^8	30
	PVDF	1,780	3	3	0.1	1	100	1	10^6	
SMA	NiTi	6,450	200	78	5	3	1,000	10	10^5	3
Polymer	ger	1,300	0.3	0.1	40	0.1	5	0.4	10	30
	Conducting	1,500	180	5	2	1	1,000	1	10^5	30
Magneto Strictive	rare earth	9,250	70	35	0.2	1	1,000	10	10^5	3
Elector static	polyimide	1,061	0.04	0.01	10	1	10	1	?	20

19.2.5 Packaging and Testing[21, 22]

Packaging and testing together represent a considerable portion of the total cost (can be 50% – 70% of the total cost) of MEMS products. It has been estimated that the cost break down for a MEMS device is roughly 33% silicon content, 33%

package, and 33% test. MEMS packaging is, in general, much more challenging than regular IC packaging. The essential factors related to MEMS packaging are: ①Packaging is usually application specific. ②The device structure is 3D and most likely contains moving parts. ③The system has to interact with the outside world, and hence hermetic sealing or vacuum packaging may be required (for protection, damping control, or achieving a higher quality factor Q and thus higher sensitivity). ④Minimizing the packaging-induced stress that may have detrimental effect on the device's sensitivity and drift. ⑤Mounting accuracy is critical for certain force-based sensors, such as accelerometers, so that an accurate reading can be achieved. ⑥Packaging must be cost effective. For an automotive application, harsh environment (high ambient temperature and humidity; strong mechanical vibration and EMI, electro-mechanical interference) makes the MEMS packaging even more challenging. Figure 19.7 illustrates the environment that automotive devices have to operate in. Figure 19.8 gives the coefficient of thermal expansion for some commonly used packaging materials. The general approach for MEMS packaging consists of 0-level packaging plus the conventional standard IC packaging, as illustrated in Fig. 19.9.

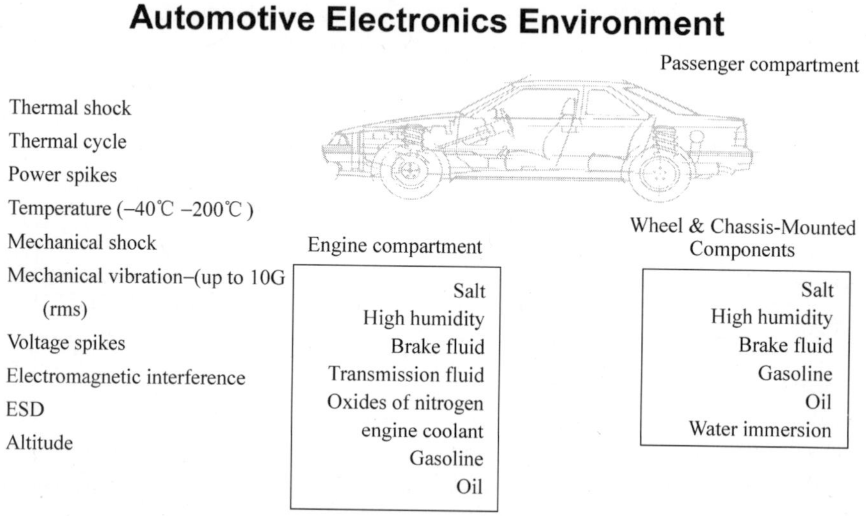

Figure 19.7 Automotive environment that MEMS devices have to operate in. The harsh ambient condition makes automotive MEMS packaging much more challenging than that of other consumer electronic products

Due to the functional requirements, MEMS testing is more complicated than that of regular ICs. It involves the conventional IC testing for the interface electronics (on-chip or off-chip), as well as physical or chemical interface tests. Furthermore, the test is in general application specific. All these factors make the MEMS testing more costly than that of regular ICs.

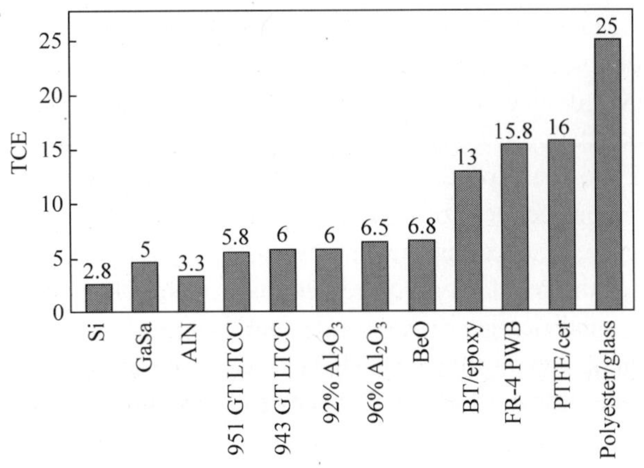

Figure 19.8 Temperature coefficient of thermal expansion for some commonly used packaging materials. (CTE in ppm/℃)

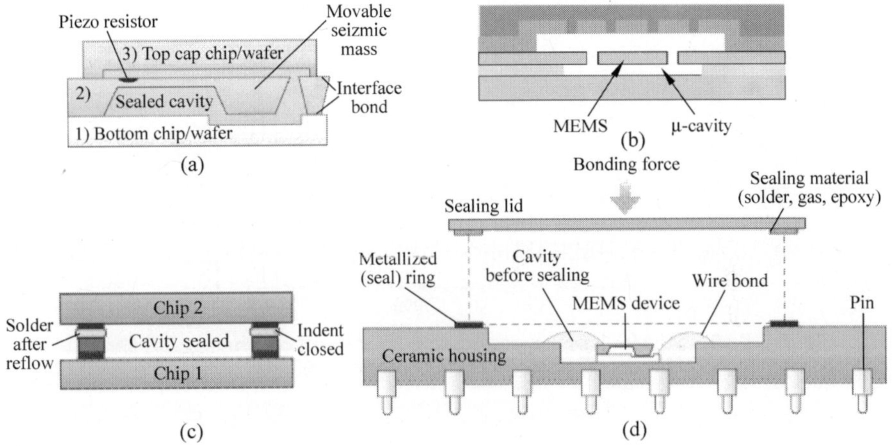

Figure 19.9 MEMS packaging: (a) wafer-to-wafer bonding (0-level packaging); (b) surface micromachining; (c) flip chip packaging and (d) conventional 1-level packaging

The five technical issues described above are directly related to the construction of an MEMS device. Other issues that are not discussed here, such as trimming, interface electronics, system partitioning, yields, and reliability, are also very important for the successful development of the automotive MEMS.

19.3 Automotive MEMS

As discussed earlier, the MEMS devices have very attractive advantages as compared to devices fabricated by more conventional technologies. Yet, there are only a few automotive MEMS devices that are currently being widely used. This is mainly due to the following reasons:

(1) The MEMS devices have to compete with the conventional devices. Since automotive products are usually mass-produced, the manufacturing infrastructures established for the mass production constitute a big investment. Consequently, the new fabrication technologies have to have significant cost and performance advantage to replace the existing technologies.

(2) Because of the reliability requirement, new automotive products have to go through lengthy qualification processes, before they can be mass-produced.

The current mass (keep)-produced, MEMS-based automotive devices are pressure sensor and accelerometer. The solid (keep)-state gyroscope is in the process of emerging as another major automotive MEMS product. Figure 19.10 shows the various MEMS-based sensors produced by Delphi Delco from 1980 to 2000.

In the following sections, pressure sensors, accelerometers, and solid-state gyroscopes have been reviewed.

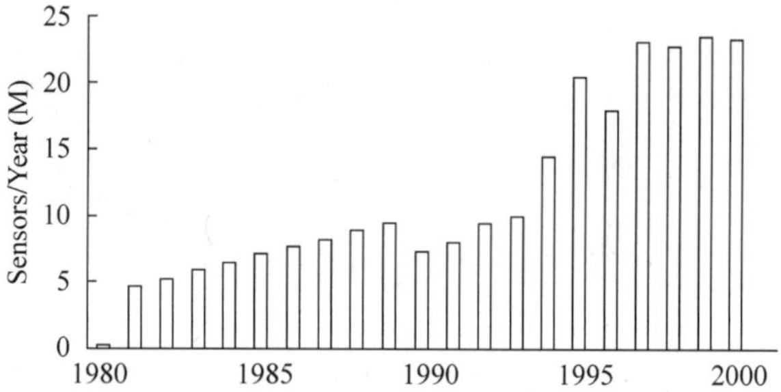

Figure 19.10 MEMS based pressure sensors and accelerometers produced by Delphi Delco from 1980 to 2000

19.3.1 Pressure Sensor[23–26]

Pressure sensors have been used extensively for close to 30 years for automotive applications. They have been used to measure the manifold absolute pressure, barometric absolute pressure, fuel rail fuel and fuel vapor pressure, transmission, brake and HVAC pressure, side airbag crash detection, passenger occupant detection, and tire pressure sensing. The first significant automotive MEMS- based device was the MAP sensor. As mentioned earlier, using the MAP and MAT manifold sensors, the air-to-fuel ratios can be calculated and used for the electronics engine control. The silicon membrane and readout mechanism are the two essential parts of the pressure transducer. The pressure difference between the two sides of the membrane is obtained by measuring the deflection of the membrane. The membrane deflection can be detected by the change in piezoresistance, capacitance, membrane resonant frequency, and optical path length, as shown in Fig. 19.11. For the automotive application, both piezoresistive and capacitive readout schemes have been used. The fabrication of silicon membrane involves etching and etch-stop technologies. The orientation (keep)-dependent wet chemical etch has been used to etch membrane. The etch solutions used are ethylenediamine-pyrocatechol-water (EDP), potassium hydroxide (KOH), or tetramethyl ammonium hydroxide (TMAH). Because of its toxicity, EDP is no longer used in the production line. Due the characteristics of the orientation (keep)-dependent wet chemical etch, the etched profile always has a slope of 54.7° (angle between Si$\langle 111 \rangle$ and Si$\langle 100 \rangle$). Therefore, there is a waste of the silicon material. Recently, a directional plasma etch, DRIE, has been used to create the silicon membrane using SOI wafer, as shown in Fig. 19.12. An etch-stop technique is essential in controlling the thickness of the etched membrane. The magnitude of deflection and the resulting stress in a membrane are strongly dependent on the membrane thickness. Consequently, an accurate control of the membrane thickness is very important for the pressure sensors' performance (the capacitive (keep)-type pressure sensor depends on the

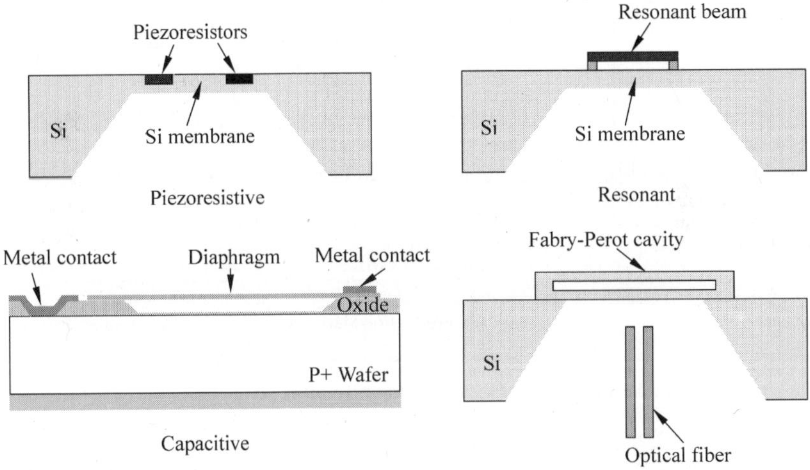

Figure 19.11 Different readout schemes for pressure transducers

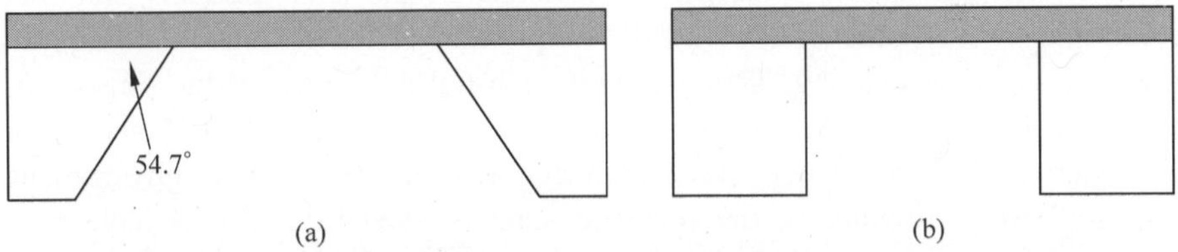

Figure 19.12 Silicon membranes fabricated by using (a) orientation dependent wet chemical etched, and (b) DRIE. With same membrane area the chip size reduction by using DRIE is clearly demonstrated

magnitude of deflection, while the piezoresistive (keep)-type pressure sensor depends on stress). The timed (keep)-etch stop was first used to control the membrane thickness. Due to the variation in the wafer thickness, and the difficulty in accurately controlling the condition of etching solution, the timed-etch stop is not a reliable method. Heavy boron-doped silicon, which has a close-to-zero etch rate in the etching solution, was then used as the etch-stop. There is one major drawback of this technique. Due to the potential boron out diffusion, and the dopant-induced stress, the minimum thickness of the silicon epi-layer (which determines the membrane thickness) has to be larger than 25 μm to obtain a device quality Si epilayer. The constraint in the membrane thickness, in turn, puts a minimum requirement of the membrane area for the desired sensor sensitivity. Currently, an electrochemical etch stop technique (which has no such constraint) is used in the production line. Figure 19.13 illustrates the evolution of Delco's pressure transducers. By adopting new technologies, the device size as well as its cost can be significantly reduced.

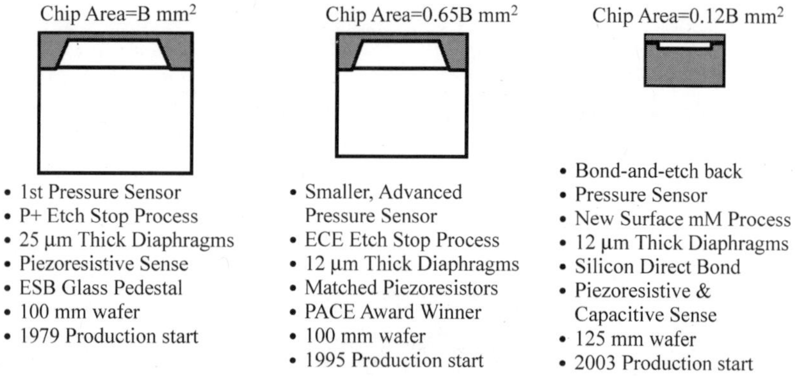

Figure 19.13 The evolution of Delco's pressure sensors. By adopting new fabrication technology, the device size has been significantly reduced

Figure 19.14 shows various pressure transducer products manufactured by Delphi Delco throughout the years. In the earlier products, discrete active and passive components, such as interface electronics, resistors, and thermistors, were used. Pyrex was used for the sensor package. In the later products, interface electronics were made of separate IC chips, and wafer-to-wafer bonding was used for sensor packaging. This new approach not only reduced the sensor unit size, it also resulted in better temperature performance. Figure 19.15 shows the evolution of Motorola's pressure transducer. Due to the potential government-imposed safety regulation, the pressure sensors used in a TPMS have been looming as the next high-volume automotive product. In this application, due to the wide temperature operation range (–40℃ to 200℃), a temperature sensor is required for the determination of the tire pressure. The concern of the energy

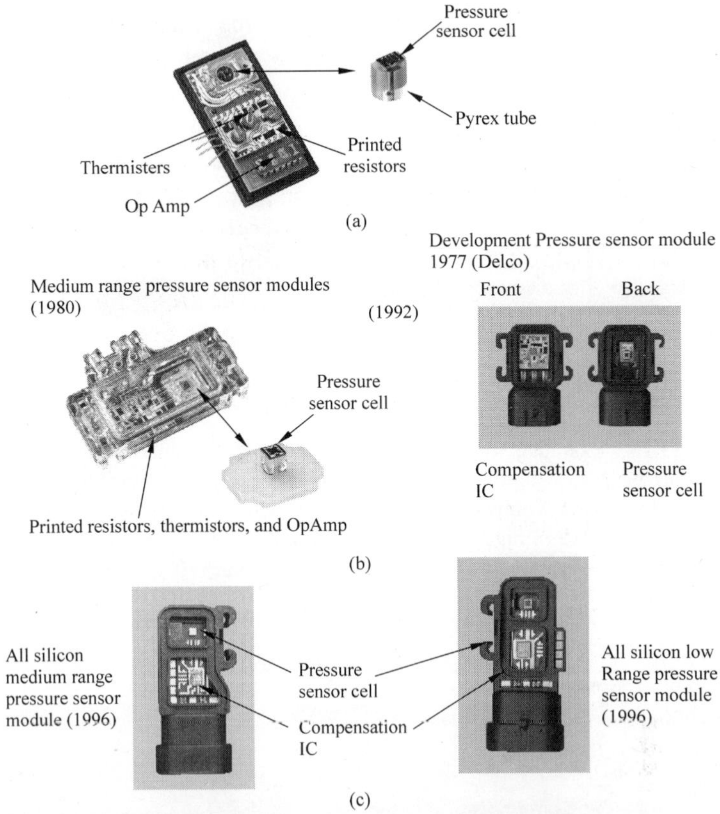

Figure 19.14 Delphi Delco's pressure transducer products for the past 20 years. (a) Development pressure sensor in 1977; (b) Medium range pressure sensors, pyrex was used for sensor package, printed resistors and thermistors, and separate OpAmp were used in the interface electronics; (c) All silicon sensor unit using wafer-to-wafer bonding. Interface electronics is an IC chip

consumption leads to the adoption of a capacitive pressure sensor and a low power consumption transceiver for the transmission and identification of signal from different tire sensing unit. A small (keep)-size, solid-state battery—such as lithium 'coin' cell battery—has been the choice for the energy source by Motorola. There have been active researches on an alternative energy source to power the TPMS, such as micropower generator in harvesting and converting the vehicle vibration kinetic energies into electrical energy. Because the whole TPMS system has to be mounted inside the tires, the TPMS module has a size limitation as well as a mounting position constrain. Figure 19.16 shows the Motorola tire pressure monitoring system.

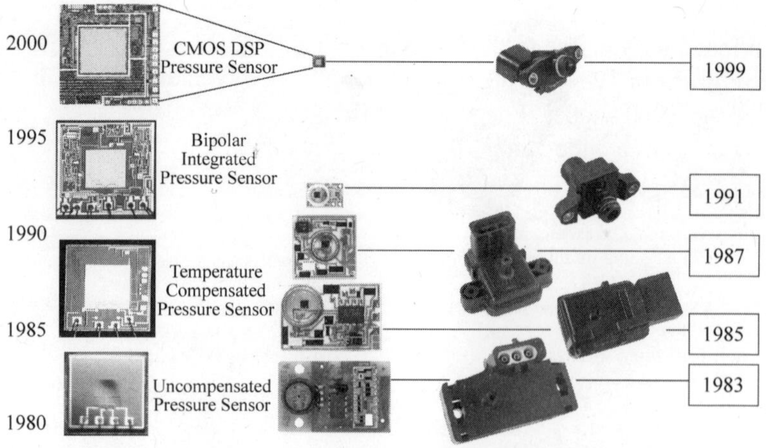

Figure 19.15 Examples of the Motorola manifold absolute pressure (MAP) sensors products from 1980 to the present. The pressure sensors were piezoresistive bulk micromachined. Temperature compensation with CrSi resistors was added. In the later model, CMOS digital signal processor (DSP), and embedded non-volatile memory (NVM) were used to improve the sensor accuracy. (Courtesy of Dr. David Monk of Motorola)

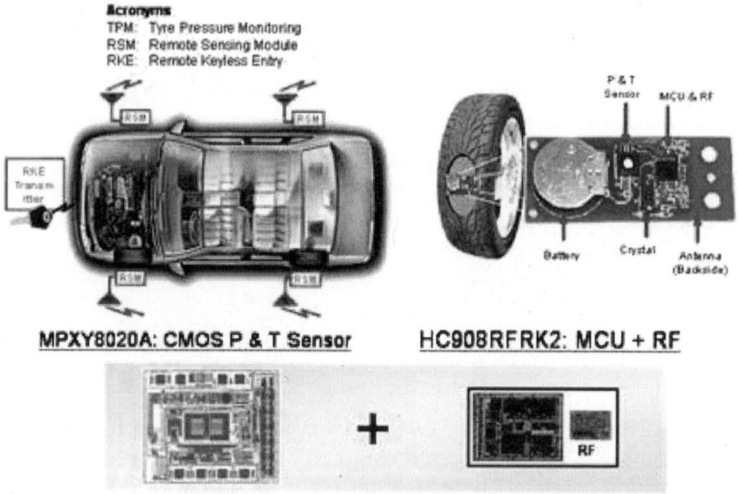

Figure 19.16 One example of Motorola's tire pressure monitor system. The sensor module inside the tire consists of pressure and temperature sensors (MPXY 8000 series), an MCU, and RF output (Motorola HC908RFRK2), and a battery. The module is placed in each tire. A central receiver that is also used for receiving signals for remote keyless entry, receives the signal from each tire, and provides information to a display via CAN bus. (Courtesy of Dr. David Monk of Motorola)

19.3.2 Accelerometer[27–30]

As mentioned before, due to the motor vehicle safety regulation imposed by the US government in 1984, all passenger cars have to have an airbag to protect the driver in the 1990 model. For the safety of vehicle occupancies, the complete system consists of a wide variety of sensors as shown in Fig. 19.17. Among those,

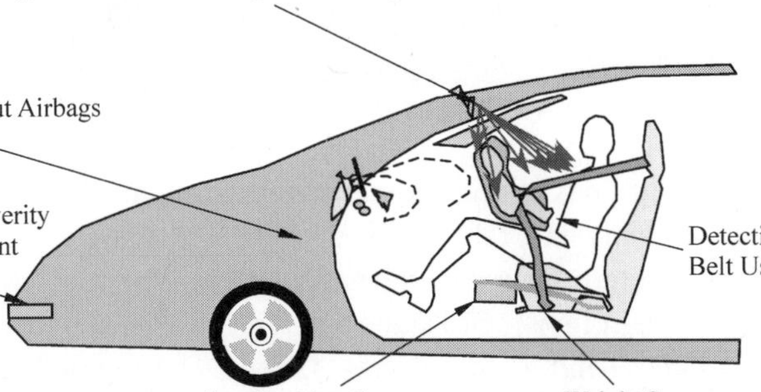

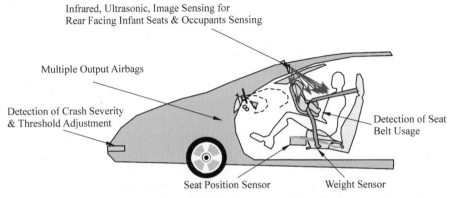

Figure 19.17 Future vehicle occupants' safety system. To make the system 'smart', various sensors have to be used: accelerometer for airbag deployment; seat position and weight sensors for the adjustment of the force and height of the airbag deployment, infrared sensors to detect the position of the occupants

the acceleration sensor to detect the acceleration or deceleration of the car for the deployment of airbag is the most critical one. In the earlier model vehicles, a macroscopic sensing system, 'ball-in-tube', was used to detect the acceleration threshold. In early 1980 s, several companies, such as Analog Devices Inc., Motorola, and Delco Electronics, started producing MEMS-based microaccelerometers. Besides airbag application, accelerometers were used in suspension systems, braking and traction control systems, and navigation. Several different fabrication technologies have been used for the fabrication of microaccelerometers: bulk (keep) micromaching (Delco Electronics), surface micromaching (Analog Devices), thick epi polySi/deep trench etching (Bosch), and the others. Depending on an individual company's manufacturing technology base, different types of accelerometer have been produced: piezoresistive, capacitive, resonant, tunneling, thermal, piezoelectric, optical, acoustic, etc. For automotive applications, piezoresistive and capacitive accelerometers are the two dominant types. The basic characteristics of the piezoresistive and capacitive accelerometers are given below:

Piezoresistive

(1) Device structure, fabrication, and readout circuitry are extended from the technology base used for the piezoresistive (keep)-type pressure sensor;

(2) Low output impedance;
(3) Self-testing can be readily implemented by using thermal actuation;
(4) Lower sensitivity compared with the capacitive (keep)-type accelerometer;
(5) Higher temperature sensitivity.

Capacitive
(1) Simple structure;
(2) High sensitivity;
(3) Low power dissipation;
(4) Low temperature sensitivity;
(5) Good dc response and noise performance;
(6) Low drift;
(7) Susceptible to electromagnetic interference;
(8) High output impedance.

Typical specifications of accelerometers for the automotive and inertial navigation applications are shown in Table 19.5.

The basic structure for a piezoresistive (keep)-type accelerometer is shown in Fig. 19.18. The most important factors that affect the sensitivity of the accelerometer are beam thickness and the proof mass (keep). The piezoresistor is fabricated by boron doping of the silicon. The optimum dosage of the boron and the positioning of the resistor have to be carefully determined.

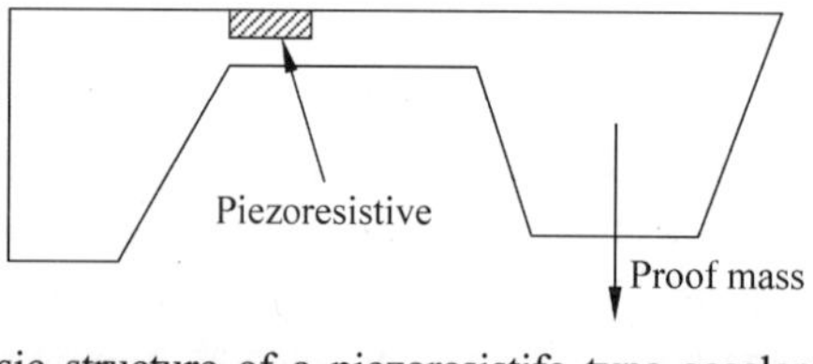

Figure 19.18 Basic structure of a piezoresistife type accelerometer consists of cantilever beam and proof mass. In reacting to the acceleration, the cantilever beam bends introducing stress in piezoresistors and changing its resistance

The major processing steps of the piezoresistive (keep)-type accelerometer are very similar to those used for producing the piezoresistive (keep)-type pressure sensors. The only major modification is the formation of the seismic mass that involves a corner compensation scheme. Both the weight and shape (symmetry) of the proof mass are important to the sensor performance. The weight affects the sensitivity, whereas the shape affects the accuracy of the accelerometer. Delco Electronics decided to manufacture the bulk micromachined, piezoresistive (keep)-type accelerometer for their earlier products, because Delco has the complete production technology infrastructure for piezoresistive pressure sensors. Later on Delco also produced capacitive-type accelerometers. Figures 19.19 and Fig. 19.20 show Delco's early development accelerometer modules and the later accelerometers products.

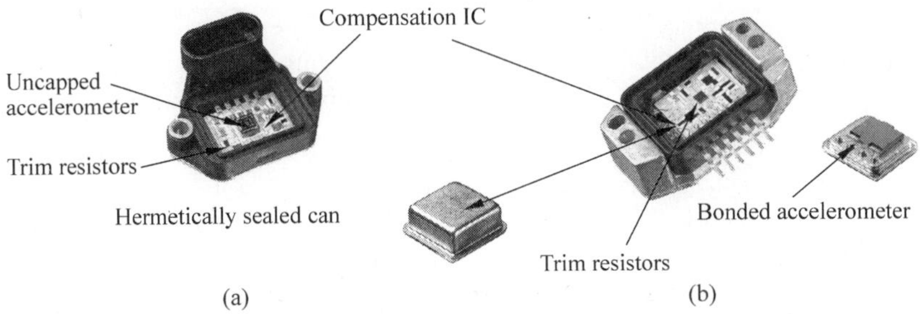

Figure 19.19 (a) Development medium range accelerometer (1988). (b) Early production accelerometer (1994)

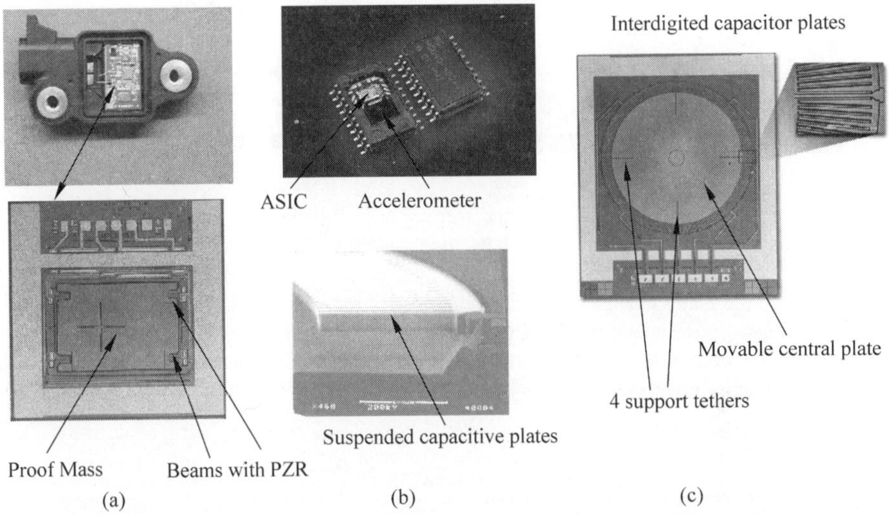

Figure 19.20 Various accelerometers produced by Delco Electronics. (a) High G module, (b) Low G module, and (c) Angular accelerometer

For a capacitive (keep)-type automotive accelerometer, the surface micromachined, polySi (keep)-based acceleration sensor produced by ADI has been the dominant commercial products. The basic sensor structure is a set of interdigited polySi plates. One set of the plates is stationary and the other set of the plates is attached to the proof mass. The movement of the proof mass due to acceleration causes the capacitance between the two sets of plates to change. The quantity of the acceleration was determined by the measured capacitance change. Because of the polySi height limitation (<3 μm), the value of the sensor capacitance change is very low (in the range of femtofarad). An on-chip circuitry for the signal amplification and conditioning are required. Figure 19.21 shows the ADI's polySi surface micromachined acceleration sensing system. By positioning the two sets of acceleration sensors orthogonally, a 2D in-plane sensing is achieved.

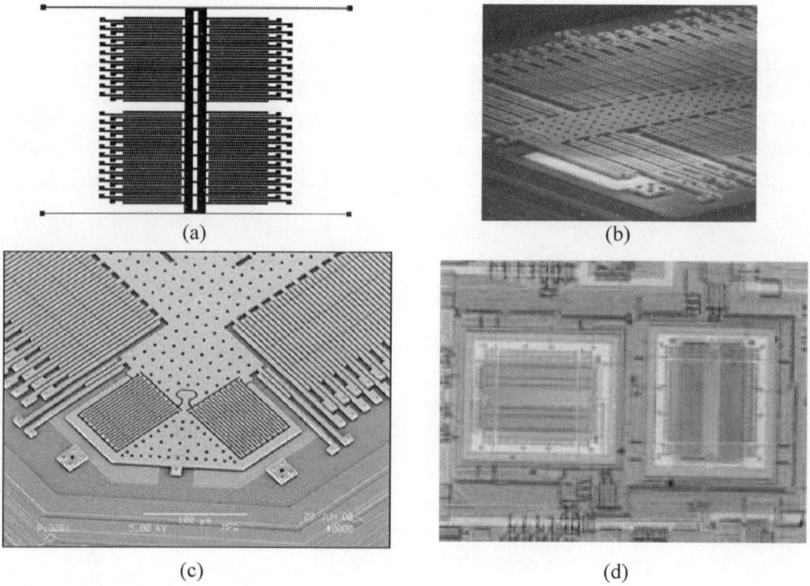

Figure 19.21 Surface micromachined accelerometers produced by ADI. (a) Schematic showing two sets of interdigited plates: one movable, one stationary. The movable plates were attached to the proof mass. When in-plane acceleration happens, the gaps between the plates changes. The value of acceleration was determined by measuring the capacitance change. (b) SEM picture of the sensor structure. (c) Accelerometer for 2-D acceleration sensing. (d) 2-D acceleration sensing system. (courtesy of Dr. K. Chau of ADI)

19.3.3 Solid-State Gyroscope[31–34]

A solid (keep)-state gyroscope that senses the rotational motion has been applied for vehicle stability control and navigational assistance. At this point, the solid-state gyroscope has not yet been widely used in automotive products, but it has the potential to be the next high-volume product in automotive industries. In an automotive application, when the gyro (keep)-sensing system detects a driver losing some degree of control, it will automatically provide stability to help the driver stay on the intended course or avoid a rollover situation. The stability control system automatically applies brakes to any of the four wheels or adjusts the engine speed to help the driver maintain control during over-steer situations or in critical weather conditions, such as wet or snowy roads. There are many different types of solid-state gyroscopes, such as quartz tuning fork (BEI), lateral-drive surface micromachined polySi (ADI), vibratory ring (Delphi, SiliconSense). All of these are based on the Coriolis effect. Different applications of gyroscope require different specifications. Table19.6 shows some essential specifications for the three different grades of gyroscopes. Figure 19.22 illustrates the sensing principle of a vibratory ring gyroscope that was developed at Delphi in collaboration with the University of Michigan. For Delphi's ring gyro, an electrostatic force was used to drive the ring into a resonant vibratory motion. The shifts of the nodal lines were capacitively detected. Two different technologies have been used to fabricate the ring gyros: microelectroforming of nickel and DRIE of silicon. Figure 19.23 shows the SEM pictures of the two differently fabricated ring gyroscopes. Due to the larger thermal expansion coefficient difference between nickel and silicon, the potential fatigue problem associated with the nickel structure, and the difficulty in controlling the electroplating process, electroforming of nickel is not the technology of choice for mass production of force-based (especially resonant type) sensors. Silicon on the other hand is a material with good physical mechanical properties, and silicon processes are well controlled. Consequently, silicon and silicon technology are better suited for the force-based sensors, such as gyroscope.

Table 19.6 Specifications for accelerometers used for automotive and inertial navigation applications

Parameter	Automotive	Navigation
Range	±50 g(airbag) ±2 g(vehicle stability)	±1 g
Frequency range	DC-400 Hz	DC-100 Hz
Resolution	<100 mg(airbag) <10 mg(vehicle stability)	<4 μg
Off-axis sensitivity	<5%	<0.1%
Nonlinearity	<2%	<0.2%
Max.Shock	>2,000 g	>10 g
Temperature range	–40℃ to 125℃	–40℃ to 80℃
TC of Offset	<60 mg/℃	<50 μmg/℃
TC of sensitivity	<900 ppm/℃	<50 ppm/℃

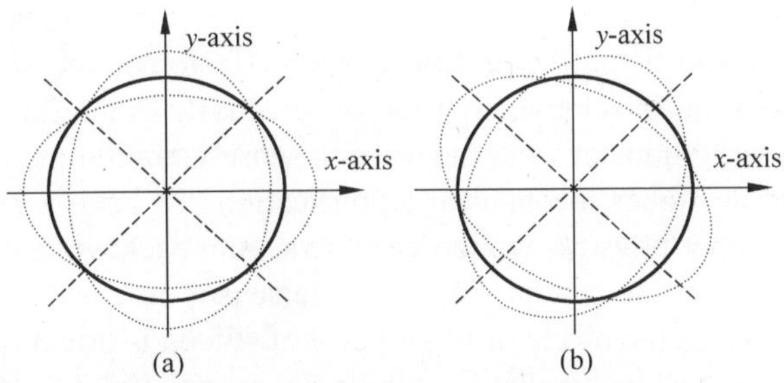

Figure 19.22 Sensing principle of a vibratory ring gyroscope. The ring is driven into elliptical-shape mode that has two nodal diameters (a) When rotational motion happens the nodal lines lag behind the rotation or precess. The angular rotation can be determined by measuring the nodal line shift (b)

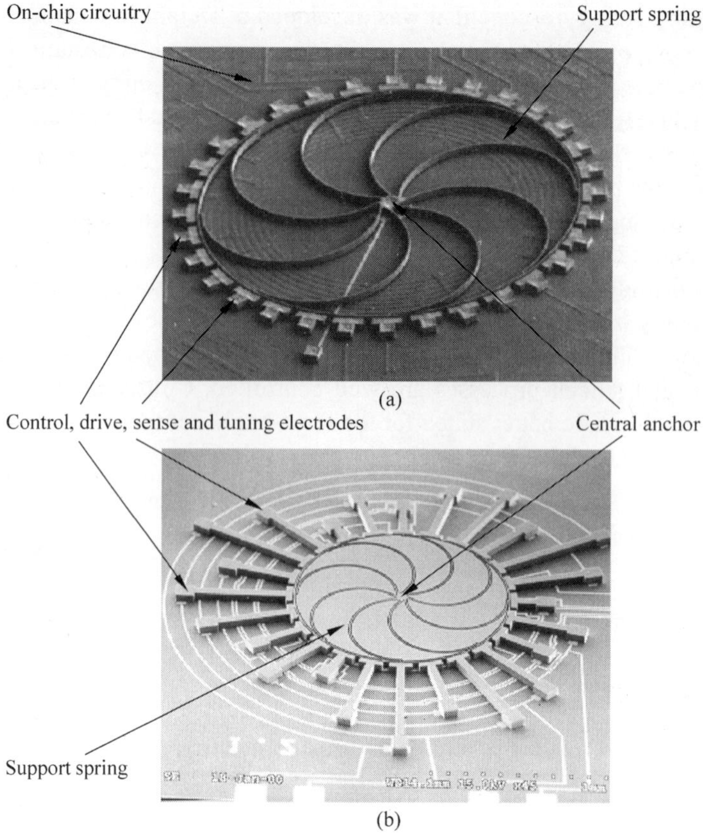

Figure 19.23 Ring gyros fabricated by Delphi. (a) Ring gyro fabricated by electroforming of nickel on silicon substrate. The on-chip ICs were fabricated first, followed by electroforming which was a low temperature process. The minimum feature size was ~ 5 μm, and height of the nickel structure was ~ 20 μm. (b) Ring gyro fabricated by deep plasma trench etch of silicon. The ring gyro in this particular case was bonded on electroded glass plate. The height of the silicon structure was ~30 μm

For a resonant-type ring gyroscope, the matching of resonant frequencies between drive and sense, and a high mechanical quality factor of the sensor structural material are preferred to achieve high sensor sensitivity. A good frequency match facilitates the energy transfer from the drive to sense vibration mode, and a higher Q value results in higher mechanical amplification. To have a higher Q value, materials with proper physical properties and vacuum packaging are desired. One drawback in using single crystal silicon as the sensor structural material for the ring gyroscope is that the mechanical property of silicon is orientation dependent, and hence, its resonant frequency (which is a function of the modulus of elasticity) may also be orientation dependent. Two different approaches have been experimented to avoid the problem. One is to operate the vibratory ring gyroscope at a third harmonic flexural vibration mode as demonstrated by the experimental results shown in Fig. 19.24. The other approach is using ⟨ 111 ⟩ orientated silicon wafer to construct the device as shown in Fig. 19.25. The mechanical properties of silicon in the ⟨ 111 ⟩ oriented wafer are isotropic and hence its resonant frequency is isotropic. Sumitomo Precision Products and BAE Systems have formed the 'Silicon Sensing' company for the manufacturing of inertial sensors. The basic structure of the ring gyro produced by Silicon Sensing is similar to Delphi's ring gyroscope. However, electromagnetically produced force is used to drive and sense ring vibration. Figure. 19.26 shows the packaged ring gyro with permanent magnet in the center, and portion of the sensor structure.

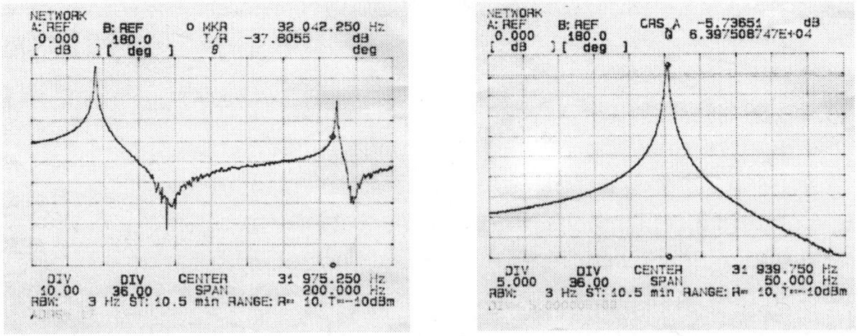

(a) (b)

Figure 19.24 Resonant frequencies of a single crystal ring at $n=3$ flexible vibration mode. The frequency split is ~0.3% as compared to 3% for the $n=2$ vibration mode. The quality factor Q of the ring under a vacuum of 10 mTorr is ~64,000

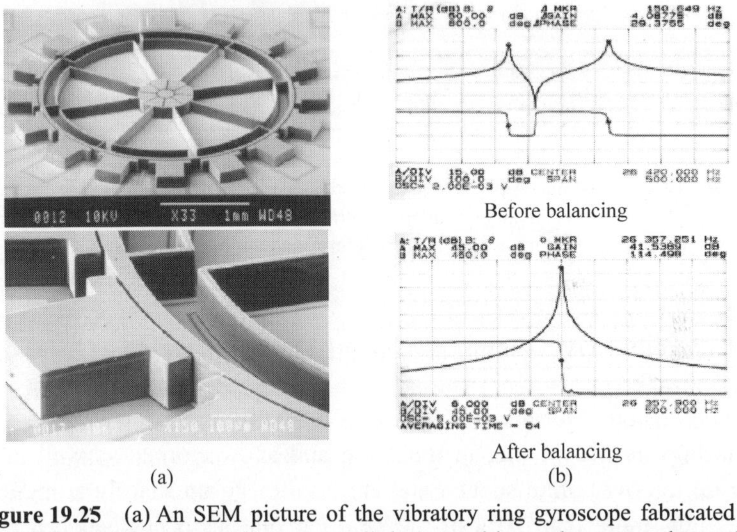

(a) (b)

Figure 19.25 (a) An SEM picture of the vibratory ring gyroscope fabricated in Si⟨ 111 ⟩. (b) The resonant frequency split between drive and sense mode are due to non-perfect of fabrication, and was corrected electrostatically. The quality factor under vacuum was ~12,000. (Courtesy of Prof. K. Najafi of U. of Michigan)

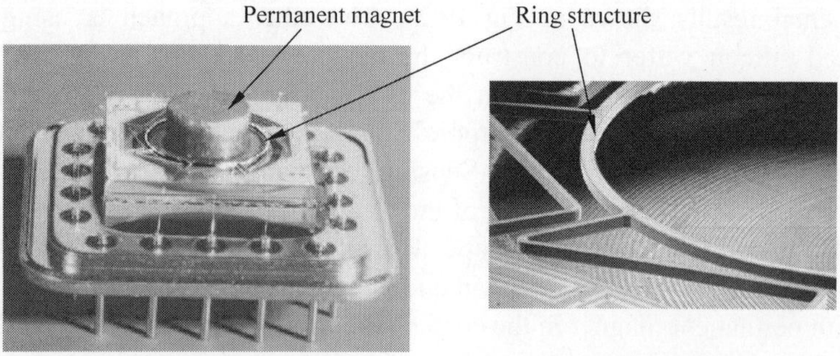

Figure 19.26 Ring gyro produced by Silicon Sensing. Electromagnetic drive and sense were used for sensor operation. (Public available information)

ADI has produced a gyroscope based on their surface micromachined, interdigited capacitive-type accelerometer technology. The sensor consists of two identical moving structures (masses) with sets of interdigited sense fingers (capacitors). The two mass structures are electrostatically driven to an out-of-phase vibratory motion. When rotation happens, the opposite Coriolis forces move the two masses in opposite directions, generating a differential capacitance change between the two structures. Figure 19.27 illustrates the basic sensing principle. Figure 19.28 shows the SEM pictures of ADI's surface micromachined gyroscope. As mentioned before, due to the small sensor capacitance, an elaborate on-chip circuitry is required.

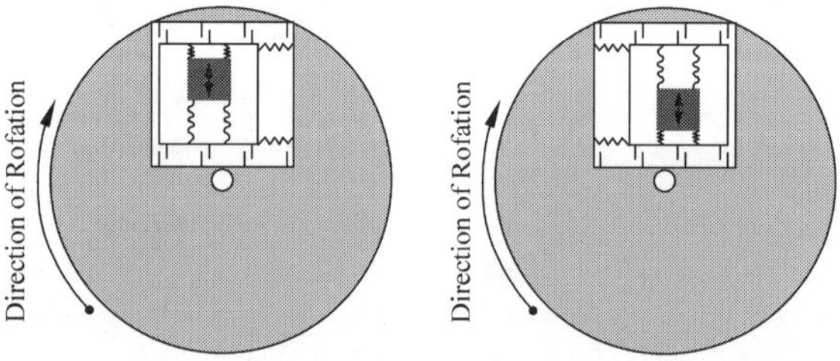

Figure 19.27 The out-of-phase resonating masses are displaced laterally in response to the Coriolis forces. The displacement is determined from the change in capacitance between the sense fingers, which in turn determines the rate of rotation

19.3.4 Automotive Vision Assistant Detector Systems[35–46]

Automotive vision assistant detectors are aimed at improving a driver's vision at night, during the heavy rain, in thick fog and snow storms, as well as during backing up to cover blind spots. Fatal car crashes go up sharply at night. In the Unites States, more than 20% of the fatal car crashes occur between midnight and 6 a.m., though less than 3% of traffic volume is on the roads during that time period. According to the European Commission for the Automobile Industry,

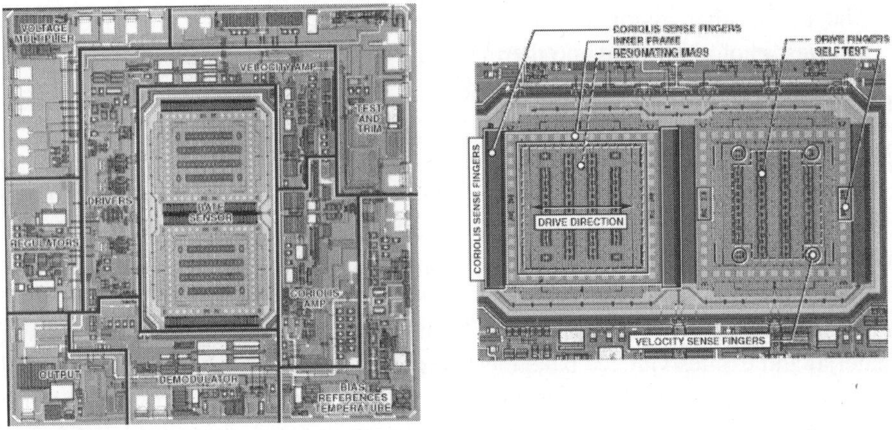

Figure 19.28 Surface micromachined gyroscope produced by Analog Devices Inc. The gyro consists of two identical sensor structures, electrostatically drive to an out-of-phase vibration. Because of low sensor capacitance, elaborate on-chip circuitry is required. (Courtesy of Kevin Chau of ADI)

about 42% of fatal car accidents happen at night, even though there is about 60% less traffic during the night. Also, the US Department of Transportation has reported that 27% of all accidents occur during the vehicle backing up (blind spots), and more than 100 children are backed over and killed every year. All those accidents can be drastically reduced if automobiles are equipped with effective vision assistant detecting systems. The night vision systems have been offered and produced in the past few years by several car companies, such as General Motors, Ford, Toyota, Honda and BMW. However, thus far, they have not been widely accepted. This is mainly due the fact that the systems are pricy (current price of the system is ~$1,000), and they are not driver-friendly enough (current system may distract driver's attention). Figure 19.29 shows the vision enhancement by using Raytheon's 'Night driver' system.

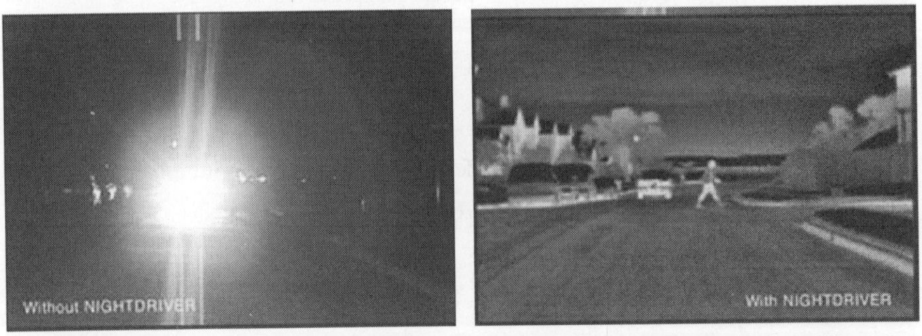

Figure 19.29 Driver's vision difference at night with or without vision assistant device. The night vision system clearly improves driver's vision at night. (www.night driver.com)

The automotive vision assistant sensors can be divided into two different categories: photon infrared and thermal infrared detectors.

19.3.4.1 Photon Infrared Detector[39–41]

The photon infrared detectors are based on the photon-electron interaction (a quantum effect). There are mainly two different kinds of photon infrared detectors: photodiode and quantum-well infrared photodetectors (QWIP). Figure 19.30 illustrates the basic sensing principle and the cross-sectional view of a planar-diffused photodiode. A special light source with a proper wavelength is aimed at objects. The reflected light from the objects impinges on the sensing material and excites valence band electrons to the conduction band of the sensing material, and thus changes the electrical conductance of the sensor material. Since the photon infrared systems are based on photon-induced electron transition, an effective thermal isolation for the sensor structure is not required, and hence the MEMS technology may not be needed. Compared to thermal infrared detectors, photon infrared detectors are faster in response and higher in sensitivity. However, photon infrared detectors may have to be operated in lower temperature to achieve higher quantum efficiency. The cost of cooling equipment and a separate light source may be compensated by the fact that most photon IR (no need to explain) detectors can be fabricated using IC (no need to explain) -compatible processes and easily installed.

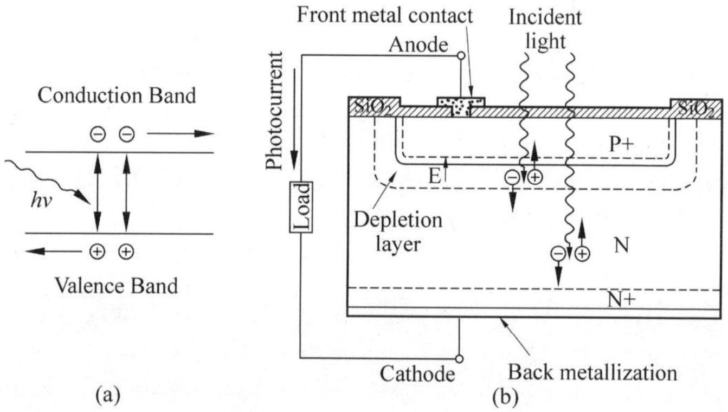

Figure 19.30 Basic operational principle of a photodiode, and the cross sectional schematic of a planar diffused photodiode. (Hamamatsu technical information)

19.3.4.2 Thermal Infrared Detector[42–46]

For thermal infrared detectors, separate light source is not needed. An infrared radiation from objects (e.g., pedestrians, the wavelength is usually in the range of 7 μm – 14 μm) is absorbed by the sensor structure (absorber), and the absorbed heat in the absorber is conductively transferred to the temperature-sensitive sensor material, causing the change of its physical property (e.g., electrical resistance, dielectric constant, etc.).

The thermal infrared sensors can be further divided into several different modes of detection. For automotive vision assistant applications, the most commonly used modes are:

(1) Pyroelectric mode (change of electric polarization),

(2) Bolometric mode (change of electrical conductance or dielectric constant),

(3) Thermoelectric mode (thermocouple).

The basic structure of a thermal infrared sensor is shown in Fig. 19.31. Beside the sensing material, there are two important components of the thermal infrared detector system: absorber and thermal insulator. Both of these are required to achieve high sensitivity of the detector. The MEMS technology (either surface or bulk micromachining) is usually applied to achieve good thermal isolation for the sensor structure. Figure 19.32 shows three different MEMS-based thermal isolation structures.

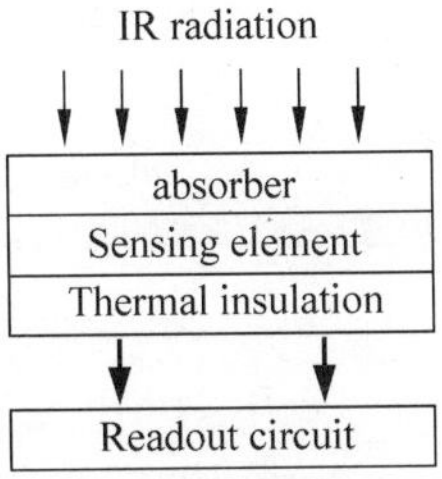

Figure 19.31 Schematic of a thermal infrared sensing system: Absorber is for capturing the light and converting it to heat; thermal insulation is required to improve the sensitivity; a variety of schemes have been used to form the sensing element

The basic characteristics of some IRFPA (IR focal point array) detectors are listed in Table 19.7. The noise equivalent temperature difference (NETD) is an important figure of merit and has been used to measure the sensitivity of an infrared detector. It is defined as the temperature of the black object that produces a signal-to-noise ratio of one. For an automotive vision assistant application, the spectral range is preferably set in the range of 8 – 14 μm. This is due to the fact that warm objects (e.g., human body) emit more radiation in that wavelength range, and atmospheric absorption is relatively low in that band. Furthermore, for a thermal infrared detector, the effective heat absorber (positioned on top of the sensor structure) can be readily formed by commonly used CMOS dielectric materials because the Si-N bonds have vibrational and rotational states with energies lying in that wavelength range.

A variety of infrared vision assistant detectors have been offered by different automotive companies. For example: photon infrared systems by Toyota, Mercedes, and Chrysler; and thermal infrared systems by Honda, BMW, and GM. From market point of view, the important factors for increasing customers' acceptance of the vision assistant systems are the detector performance and price. These two

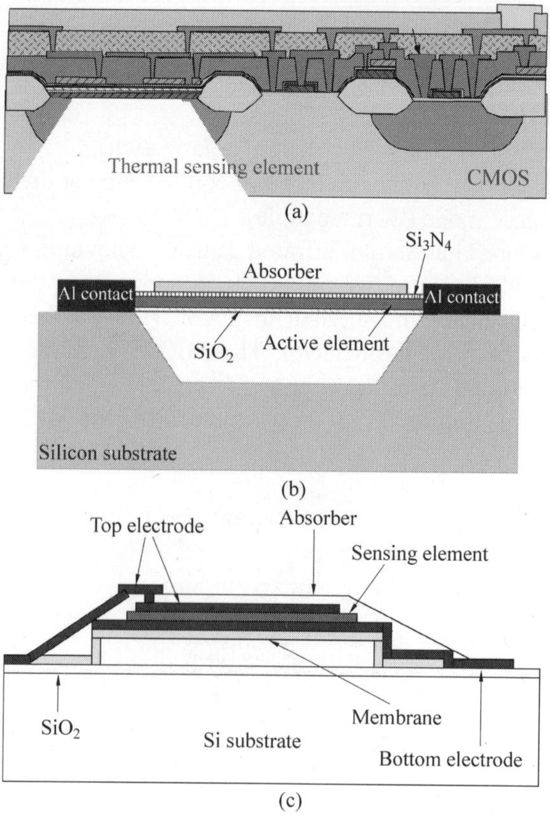

Figure 19.32 Three different MEMS-based thermal isolation schemes: (a) backside bulk orientation dependent wet etch, (b) front side bulk orientation dependent wet etch, and (c) surface micromachining

Table 19.7 Typical requirements for gyroscopes

Parameter	Rate Grade	Tactical Grade	Inertial Grade
Angle Random Walk, °/Öh	0.5	0.05–0.05	0.001
Bias Drift, °/h	10–1,000	0.1–10	<0.01
Scale Factor Accuracy, %	0.1–1	0.01–0.1	<0.001
Full Scale Range, °/sec	50–1,000	>500	>400
Max. Shock, g's	10^3	10^3–10^4	10^3
Bandwidth, Hz	>70	~ 100	~ 100

Table 19.8 Characteristics Comparison of Some Infrared detectors

Detector type	Pixel size (μm)	Sensor material	spectral range(μm)	operating temperature(K)	NETD (mK)
Photodiode	30×30	InSb	1 – 5.5	300	70
Photodiode	40×40	GhCdTe	1 – 4.6	120	10
QWIP	640×480	GaAs/AIGaAs	8 – 19	70	36
Schottky-barrier	17×17	PtSi	3 – 5	300	33
Bolometer	48×48	VOx	8 – 14	300	9 – 60
Bolometer	45×45	aSi	8 – 14	300	56
Pyro	35×35	BST	8 – 14	300	50
Pyro	50×50	PLZT	2 – 14	273 – 313	40
Thermopile	228×220	PolySiAl	8 – 14	300	176

factors are closely related to the science and technology (materials and fabrication) used to build the vision assistant detector systems. To construct a reliable automotive vision assistant system may have to adopt the 'sensor fusion' concept. This is mainly because each individual sensor has its detection limitations; yet, for automotive safety application, the detector has to deal with a pretty complicated environment. A single sensing unit may not be sufficient enough to comprehensively cover the entire situation. For example, it is believed that for detecting blind spots, ultrasonic or radar system is a better technology of choice, while for improving a driver's night vision, the infrared detector will be a better choice. Therefore, multiple sensors (infrared detector and radar) that are complement to each other may have to be 'fused' or 'integrated' to form a reliable driver vision assistant system.

19.3.5 Other MEMS-Based Automotive Devices

Application of (keep) MEMS in automotive (keep) industry has been expanding. The four sensors described above are either being widely used or in the process of becoming a high-volume product. There are many other automotive devices that potentially can be produced by the MEMS technology, such as gas and liquid flow rate sensor, speed sensor, position sensor, and chemical sensors. Two MEMS-based devices that have been actively pursued for the past few years and have the potential of being widely used in automotive industries in the near future are briefly described below:

19.3.5.1 Microswitch and Relay[47]

About 15 – 30 switches and relays with varying current ranges are used in an automobile today. Mechanical relays are bulky and are in general power consuming. Solid-state switches are smaller in size, but are polarity sensitive and have low off-resistance. There have been active researches on the MEMS-based micro-relay attempting to replace both solid-state and mechanical relays. However, so far, no significant advantages have been demonstrated in both cost and performance. Figure 19.33 shows the SEM picture of a micro-relay fabricated at Delphi Research Labs.

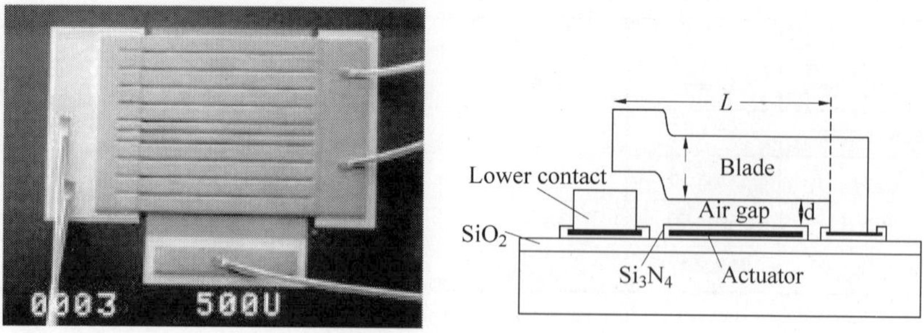

(a) (b)

Figure 19.33 (a) SEM photograph of an all-metal cantilever structured microrelay. (b) Cross-sectional view of the relay

19.3.5.2 MEMS for Wireless Communication[48]

Wireless communication in automobiles is becoming more and more pervasive. The MEMS technology has the potential to reduce the size and power consumption of transceivers. The components in a transceiver that can be produced by the MEMS technology include: voltage tunable high Q capacitor, inductors, resonators, and filter and switch. Figure 19.34 shows: (a) a surface micromachined filter (University of Michigan) and (b) a deep trench etched tunable capacitor (Rockwell).

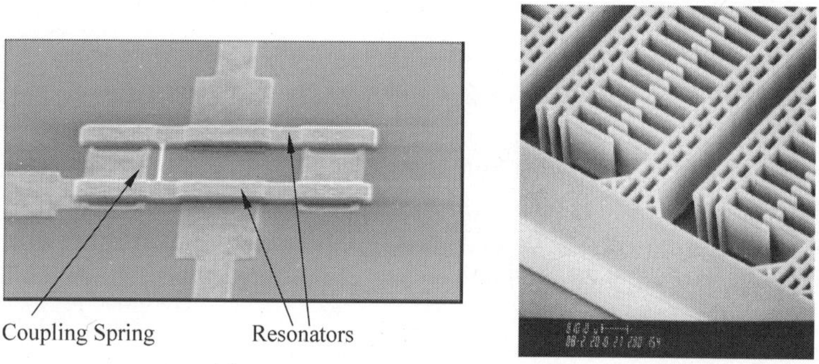

(a) (b)

Figure 19.34 (a) Surface micromachined filter with Q ~7,450 under 10 mTorr vacuum. (Courtesey of Prof. Clark, U. of Michigan). (b) Deep trench etched single crystal silicon tunable capacitor (Rockwell)

19.4 Concluding Remark

The importance of the MEMS technology has been widely recognized. MEMS industries can become a large industry in itself. MEMS are the enabling technology and can facilitate the growth of other industries, such as biomedical, communication, automotive electronics, and aerospace. Further, MEMS are, in general, environmental friendly because of their intrinsic smaller size. This technology uses less material for construction, less energy to operate, and produces less waste. MEMS has fundamentally enhanced and vastly expanded the limits of modern practice of engineering. The successful commercialization of MEMS products requires:

(1) Pool of knowledge and technical abilities: An integrated manufacturing approach where design, material, fabrication, Packaging, and testing have to be developed concurrently to produce reliable and cost-effective products.

(2) Inter-disciplinary and team work:MEMS may involve a wide spectrum of sciences and technologies. Collaboration among universities, government, and industries can facilitate the successful development of the MEMS products.

(3) Customer knowledge and marketing channel. The current and future automotive electronic applications are listed below. Many of the systems require device components (such as sensors and actuators) that can be produced by using the MEMS technology:

Advanced Thermal Comfort System: Comfort controller, remote (keep) engine start-preconditioner, regenerative air filter, electronic compressor control, advanced sensors and actuators;

Advanced Safety Systems:Reliable and cost-effective driver vision assistant systems, adaptive restraint system (smart airbags), integrated adaptive belt-restraint seat modules, optimized modular steering control system, voice-activated controls, autoprofiling-fingerprint ID, passive entry/passive go.

(1) Drive-By-Wire Control Systems Throttle-by-wire, steer-by-wire, brake-by-wire, suspension-by-wire;

(2) Integrated Vehicle E/E Systems

E/E controllers, smart switches, actuators, connectors, sensors, antennas, generators and batteries;

(3) Advanced Energy Systems

Energy generation, control and storage, LiPo battery, 42-volt system, converters/inverters, motors/generators, fuel cells;

(4) Smart Sensors and Actuators

Higher value sensors/actuators, flexible architecture, open systems, virtual and/or sharing sensing;

(5) Mobile Telematics

Mobile media link bus, digital receiver, advanced playbacks/display, two-way communication, adaptive reception, direct broadcast satellite reception, in-vehicle internet and E-mail, passenger video and game systems, personal assistance services, navigation system, premium surround sound system, satellite radio;

(6) Collision Avoidance

Radar and vision sensors, processors and software, warning display, brake, throttle and steering system, adaptive cruise control, driver vision enhancement system, external vehicle sensing aids;

(7) Advanced Engine Management System

Gasoline and diesel direct injection control, hybrid vehicle control, electric vehicle control, and electronic valve actuator/timing, advanced emission sensors and controllers.

The outlook of automotive MEMS can be summarized as follows:

(1) Automotive MEMS have been and will continue to be a major market for MEMS devices.

(2) The advancement of MEMS science and technology will continue to be the major driving force for the improvement of performance and cost of automotive products.

(3) Integration of MEMS and IC's will continue, linking multiple sensors (sensor fusion) with decision-making microprocessor to form a smart sensing system.

With extensive application of the MEMS devices, we may be able to mass produce ideal automobiles having the following characteristics:

Don't Have Accidents
Never Get Lost
Can't Be Stolen
Never Get Caught in traffic Jams
Drive Themselves
Don't Guzzle Gas
Don't Pollute
Never Spin Out of Control
Are Never Out of Touch
Surf the Internet
Never Break Down
Don't have to wait at the toll brooths
Are Very Entertaining

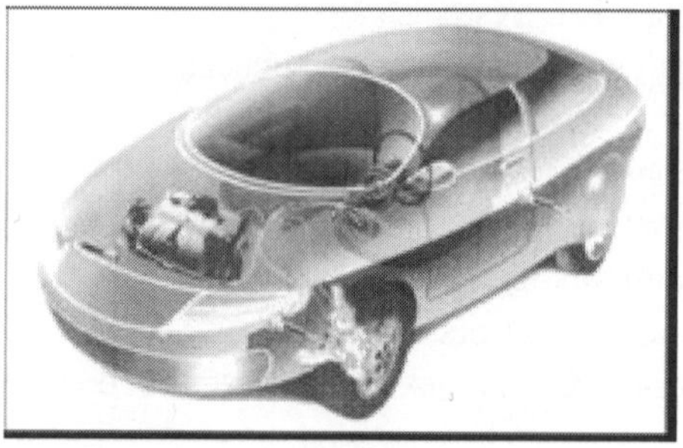

Yet, Are Very User Friendly and Comfortable And, Are Not Expensive!

Acknowledgements

The author would like to thank the following persons for their help in providing valuable materials for this paper: James Logsdon and Bruce Myers of Delco Electronics, David Monk and Jeffrey Burgess of Motorola, Douglas Sparks of ISSYS, Inc., and Michael Putty of Delphi Research Laboratories.

References

[1] Eddy D. S., D. R. Sparks, (1998), Application of MEMS technology in automotive sensors and actuators. *Proc. IEEE*, **86**(8): 1747 – 1755

[2] Fleming W. J., (2001), Overview of automotive sensors. *IEEE Sens. J.*, **1**(4): 296 – 308

[3] Monk D.J., (2002), MEMS physical sensors for automotive applications. In *Proceedings of the ECS Microfabricated Systems and MEMS VI*, Philadelphia, PA, Spring 2002, 43 – 63

[4] Petersen K. E., (2000), Bring MEMS to market. In *Proceedings of Solid-State Sensor and Actuator Workshop*, Hilton Head Island, SC, 60 – 64

[5] Bryzek J., (2001), Increasing probability of a success for high-tech startup companies. In Proceedings of Transducers' 01 Eurosensors XV, Munich, Germany, 4A1.01, 1268 – 1275

[6] Payne R. S., (2001), MEMS commercialization: Slow but steady. In Proceedings of Transducers '01 Eurosensors XV, Munich, Germany, 4A1.04

[7] Williams K. R., R. S. Muller, (1996), Etch rates for micromachining processing. *J. Microelec- tromechan. Sys.*, **5**(4): 256 – 269

[8] Shikida M., K. Sato, K. Tokoro, D. Uchikawa, (2000), Differences in anisotropic etching properties of KOH and TMAH solutions. *Sens. Actuat.*, **80**: 179 – 188

[9] Kovacs G. T., N. I. Maluf, K. E. Petersen, (1998), Bulk micromachining of Silicon. *Proc. IEEE,* **86**(8): 1536 – 1551

[10] de Boer M. J., J. G. E. Gardeniers, h. v. Jansen, E. Smulders, M. J. Gilde, G. Roelofs, J. N. Sasserath, M. Elwenspoek, (2002), Guidelines for etching silicon MEMS structures using fluorine high-density plasmas at cryogenic temperatures. *JMEMS*, **11**(4): 385 – 401

[11] Ayon A. A., R. A. Braff, C. C. Lin, H. H. Sawin, M. A. Schmidt, (1999), Characterization of a time Multiplexed Inductively Coupled Plasma Etcher. *J. ECS.*, **146**(1): 339 – 349

[12] Elwenspoek M., H. V. Jansen, (1998), Silicon micromachining. Cambridge Studies in Semi-conductor Physics and Microelectronics Engineering: 7, Cambridge University Press

[13] Bustillo J. M., R. T. Howe, R. S. Muller, (1998), Surface micromachining for microelectro-machanical systems. *Proc. IEEE,* **86**(8): 1552 – 1574

[14] Nathanson H. C., W. E. Newell, R. A. Wickstrom, J. R. Davis, (1967), The resonant gate transistor. *IEEE Trans. Electron Devices*, **ED-14**: 117 – 133

[15] Payne R. S., S. Sherman, S. Lewis, R. T. Howe, (1995), Surface micromachining: From vision to reality to vision. In *Proceedings of IEEE International Solid-State Circuit Conference*, San Francisco, CA 1995, 164 – 165

[16] Romankiw L. T., (1995), Evolution of the plating through lithographic mask technology. In *Proceedings of the fourth International Symposium on Magnetic Materials, Process and Devices* (Application to Storage & Microelectromechanical Systems MEMS), Chicago, IL, USA 1995, 253 – 272

[17] Becker E. W., W. Ehrfeld, P. A. Hagmann, D. Münchmeyer, (1986), Fabrication of microstructures with high aspect ratios and great structural heights by synchrotron radiation lithography, galvanoforming and plastic moulding (LIGA). *Microelectron. Eng.*, **4**: 34 – 35

[18] Dukovic J. O., (1994), Current distribution & shape change in electrodeposition of thin films for microelectronic fabrication. In *Advances in Electrochemical Science & Engineering*. Edited by Gerischer H, Tobias CW, VCH, New York, 117 – 161

[19] Petersen K. E., (1982), Silicon as a mechanical material. *Proc. IEEE*, **70**(5): 420 – 457

[20] Mehregany M., C. A. Zorman, N. Rajan, C. H. Wu, (1998), Silicon carbide MEMS for harsh environments. *Proc. IEEE*, **86**(8): 1594 – 1610

[21] Sparks D. R., (1998), Component integration and packaging of automotive microsystems. In *Proceedings of Microsystem Symposium*, Delft, The Netherlands 1998, 37 – 45

[22] Ziaie B., N. K. Kocaman, K. Najafi, (1997), A generic micromachined silicon platform for low-power, low-loss miniature transceivers. In *Proceedings of Trnasducers'97*, Chicago, IL 1997, 257 – 260

[23] Clark S. A., K. D. Wise, (1979), Pressure sensitivity in anisotropically etched thin diaphragm pressure sensors. *IEEE Trans. Electron Devices*, **ED-26**(12): 1887 – 1896

[24] Fung C. D., W. H. Ko, (1982), Miniature capacitive pressure transducers. *Sens. Actuat.*, **2**: 321 – 326

[25] Baney W, D. Chilcott, X. Huang, S. Long, J. Siekkinen, D. Sparks, S. Staller, (1997), A comparison between micromachined piezoresistive and capacitive pressure sensors. *SAE Special Publications*, **1311**: 61 – 64

[26] Burgess J., (2003), Tire pressure monitoring: An industry under pressure. *Sensors*

[27] Monk D. J., D. Mladenovic, M. Skaw, (2003), Accelerometer for automotive applications, sensors applications volume 4. In *Sensors for Automotive Applications.* Marek J, Trah HP, Suzuki Y, Yokomori I Ed., VCH, Wiley, 296 – 297

[28] MacDonald G. A., (1990), A review of low cost accelerometers for vehicle dynamics. *Sens. Actuat. A*, **21**(1 – 3): 303 – 307

[29] Aikele M., K. Bauer, W. Ficker, F. Neubauer, U. Prechtel, H. Schalk, H. Seidel, (2001), Resonant accelerometer with self-test. *Sens. Actuat.,* **A-92**: 161 – 167

[30] Core T. A., W. K. Tsang, S. J. Sherman, (1993), Fabrication technology for an integrated surface- micromachined sensor. *Solid State Technol.*, **36**(10): 39 – 47

[31] Krakauer A., (2003), A unique angular-rate-sensing gyro. *Sens. Magazine,* **20**(9): 53 – 58

[32] Putty M.W., K. Najafi, (1994), A micromachined vibrating gyroscope. In *Proceedings of Solid-State Sensor and Actuator Workshop*, Hilton Head Island, SC, 1994, 213 – 220

[33] Newton G. C., (1963), Theory and practice in vibratory rate gyros. *Control Eng.*, 95 – 99

[34] McNie ME, Burdess JS, Harris AJ, Young M (1999) High aspect ratio ring gyroscopes fabricated in [100] silicon on insulator (SOI) material. In Technical Digest IEEE International Conference on Solid-State Sensors and Actuators, Sendai, Japan, 1590 – 1593

[35] Frank R., (2006), Vision sensing enables safer vehicles. *Auto Electronics* January/Februay: 12 – 19

[36] Day J. H., (2007), Peripheral vision. *Auto Electron.* January/February: 10 – 14

[37] Sun Z, G. Bebis, R. Miller, (2006), On-road vehicle detection: A review. *IEEE Trans. Pattern Anal. Machine Intell.*, **28**(5): 694 – 711

[38] Kallhammer J. E., (2006), Imagine: The road ahead for car night vision. *Nature Photonics*, May: 12 – 13

[39] Rogalski A., (2003), Third-generation infrared photon detectors. *Optical Eng.,* **42**(12): 3498 – 3516

[40] Walther M., R. Schmitz, R. Rehm, S. Kopta, F. Fuchs, W. Fleibner, J. Cabanski, J. Ziegler, (2005), Growth of InAs/GaSb short-period superlattices for high-resolution mid-wavelength infrared focal plane array detectors. *J Crystal Growth*, **278**: 156 – 161

[41] Bandara S. V., S. D. Gunapala, D. Z. Ting, J. K. Liu, C. J. Hill, J. M. Mumolo, S. Keo, (2007), Monolithically integrated near-infrared and mid-infrared detector array for spectral imaging. *Infrared Phys. Technol.,* **50**: 211 – 216

[42] Dong L., R. Yue, L. Liu, (2005), Fabrication and characterization of integrated uncooled infrared sensor arrays using a-Si thin film transistors as active elements. *J. Microelectromech. Sys.*, **14**(5): 1167 – 1177

[43] Neli R. R., D. Ioshiaki, J. A. Diniz, J. W. Swart, (2006), Development of process for far infrared sensor fabrication. *Sens. Actuat.*, *A* **132**: 400 – 406

[44] Calaza C., N. Viarani, M. Pedretti, A. Gottardi, A. Simoni, V. Zanini, M. Zen, (2006), An uncooled infrared focal plane array for low-cost applications fabricated with standard CMOS technology. *Sens. Actuat.*, *A* **132**: 129 – 138

[45] Wang S. B., B. F. Xiong, S. B. Zhou, G. Huang, S. H. Chen, X. J. Yi, (2005), Preparation of 128 element of IR detector array based on vanadium oxide thin films obtained by ion beam sputtering. *Sens. Actuat.*, *A* **117**: 110 – 114

[46] Mantese J. V., A. L. Micheli, N. W. Schubring, M. W. Putty, M. P. Thompson, S. C. Chang, J. R. Troxell, L. Oberdier, J. Celinska, C. P. de Araujo, (2007), Enhanced pyroelectric sensitivity using ferroelectric active mode detection. *Appl. Phys. Lett.*, **90**: 113503

[47] Lee H. S., C. H. Leung, J. Shi, S. C. Chang, (2002), Electrostatically actuated copper-blade microrelays. *Sens. Actuat., A* **100**(1): 105 – 113

[48] Nguyen C. T. C., L. P. B. Katrechi, G. M. Rebeiz, (1998), Micromachined devices for wireless communications. *Proc. IEEE,* **86**(8): 1756 – 1768

20 Biochip

Dafu Cui

State Key Laboratory of Transducer Technology, Institute of Electronics,
Chinese Academy of Sciences, Beijing, China
E-mail: dfcui@mail.ie.ac.cn

Abstract In this chapter, both microarray biochip and microfluidic biochip have been introduced. The background, fabrication technology, and detection technology of the microarray chips and microfluidic chips are presented. This chapter emphasizes microfluidic biochips (including sample pretreatment chips, polymerase chain reaction (PCR) chip, capillary electrophoresis (CE) chips, chromatography chips, hybridization chips, immunoassay chips, micro total analytical system) and their technologies. Many different approaches or methods are discussed here, including their advantages and disadvantages. Some of the microfluidic biochips, such as crossflow filtration chip for blood cells separation, porous silicon chip for DNA purification, chamber stationary PCR chip, glass/PDMS/glass sandwich CE chip, and so on, are designed and fabricated in the State Key Laboratory of Transducer Technology, Institute of Electronics, Chinese Academy of Sciences, Beijing, China.

Keywords Microarray, microfluidic, micro total analytical system (μTAS), microelectromechanicalsystems (MEMS)

20.1 Introduction

Biochip is a new powerful all-around technology derived from the combination of modern electronic technology with modern biotechnology, which can integrate many discontinuous steps (e.g., sample pretreatment, biochemical reaction, detection, and so on) together, sized to a 'micro' format with dimensions of several centimeters like an ordinary stamp, and offers a continuous, high-throughput, rapid analysis and detection of biochemical information. The significance of biochip is not only to extend the function, category, and application field of the existing electronic components, but also to bring on a revolution in the electronic industry and biological/medical technology.

Biochip is mainly divided into two categories: microarray chip and microfluidic chip.

A microarray chip is a collection of miniaturized test sites (microarrays) arranged on a solid substrate that permits a number of homologous tests to be performed at the same time to achieve higher throughput and speed, based on a static affinity hybridization technology. A microarray comprises a large number of ordered objects of biological material (DNA, protein, or tissue), printed on a solid substrate (glass, plastic, or silicon chip) in a 'micro' format. Typically, a microarray chip's surface area is no larger than a fingernail. Like a computer chip that can perform millions of mathematical operations in one second, a microarray chip can perform thousands of biological reactions, such as decoding genes, in a few seconds. The most famous is the DNA microarray, which plays an integral role in gene expression profiling. For example, the DNA microarray chips have helped to dramatically accelerate the identification of the estimated 80,000 genes in human DNA, an ongoing worldwide research collaboration known as the Human Genome Project. In addition to genetic applications, protein microarray, cell microarray, and tissue microarray occur, which are being widely used in toxicological, protein, and biochemical research. The gene microarray chip is the first commercialized device, which has proven to be reliable and robust, enabling many new discoveries and breakthroughs over the years.

Microfluidics is the science and technology of systems that process or manipulate small ($10^{-9} - 10^{-18}$ liter) amounts of fluids, using channels with dimensions of tens to hundreds of micrometers. Microfluidics chips, micro total analytical systems (μTAS), or so-called lab-on-a-chip (LOC), enabling a series of complex biochemical analysis, are constructed from various miniaturized biochemical analytical units or microsystems. These units are connected to each other via microchannel nets on a solid substrate (glass, plastic, or silicon chip) in a 'micro' format by means of a microfluid control technology. These microchannel nets are usually fabricated by microelectromechanical systems (MEMS) or other micro-machining technology. Currently the microfluidics chips have various functions, such as driving sample, controlling fluid, separating cell/particle, purifying analyte, PCR amplification, other biochemical reactions, detecting, and so on. These chips can realize exact, rapid, high-throughout tests of inorganic ion, organic ion, protein, nucleic acid, cells, etc. According to different functions and applications, microfluidics chip consists of a sample pretreatment chip, a biochemical reaction chip (PCR chip, hybridization chip, or immunoreaction chip), a separation detection chip (capillary electrophoresis chip or CE chip), and an integrated chip with multifunction.

As a technology, the microfluidic chip first has been used for analysis, which offers so many advantages of using very small quantities of samples and reagents, and carrying out separations and detections with high resolution and sensitivity, low cost, short times for analysis, and small footprints for the analytical devices. Small volumes reduce the time taken to synthesize and analyze a product, and also cut down reagent costs and the amount of chemical wastes. It offers fundamentally new capabilities in the control of concentrations of molecules in space and time.

The microfluidic chip technology will be a practical technology widely used in a number of fields, such as clinical medical diagnosis, drug discovery, environment monitoring, and so on. But it also has few problems and disadvantages: ① It is difficult to integrate all components—the microchannels that serve as pipes, and other structures that form valves, mixers and pumps—that are essential elements of the microchemical 'factories' on a chip. ② Most microfluidic chip systems do not offer the ability of sample preparing and pretreatment. ③ The detection is still commonly accomplished by a microscope located off-chip.

Many developed countries and famous companies (e.g., Agilent, Hitachi, Caliper) have invested huge money in exploiting microfluidics. With the development of microfluidics, a distinct new field of BioMEMS has emerged, which becomes one of the most rapidly developing fields in MEMS.

20.2 Historical Background and Present Condition

The appearance and development of a biochip is combined with the complexity of life phenomena and deep progress in the modern life science on a molecular level. The traditional molecular biology technology can analyze only a single DNA at one time. To reveal the large amount of information including gene and non-gene of human DNA sequence, it is necessary to develop a new technology to study the genome thoroughly. The first DNA array biochip came out in 1996. It utilized microelectronics manufacturing technologies and chemistry synthesis methods to fix thousands and thousands of DNA fragments on a tiny glass, forming a detection probe array that was able to analyze genes simultaneously. This breakthrough greatly accelerated the process of gene sequencing and made the Human Genome Project finish 2 years earlier than estimated. In 2003, it was announced that the Human Genome Project had been completed. At the same time, the commercial DNA chip array with all the human genome, disease-related diagnosis chip, and remedy development chip also came out.

Researchers found that a gene contains only the code of synthetic protein, and the protein is the real entity to execute the life functions. Proteins continually change by interacting with genes. The expression of the proteins can differ in different phases of life cycle. For example, in human the protein types range between hundred thousands and millions: the hypothesis that 'a gene determines a protein' is false. To classify and define the functions and interactions between proteins, there is need for a rapid, precise, and parallel way to analyze the protein. This led to the invention of protein chip, followed by cell chip and organism chip.

In early times, the biochip was mainly a microarray chip. With the development of MEMS and the cross-link of many disciplines, the second-generation biochip evolved: microfluidic chip.

The invention of the microfluidic chip can be traced back to 1975. Terry and his colleague fabricated a micro gas chromatography chip on a silicon wafer that can separate a gas mixture in a few seconds. But there were few responses to this great work. In 1990, Swiss scientist Manz[1] brought out the concept of Micro Total Analysis Systems (μTAS). Since then μTAS has been attracting the attention of the researchers. The concept was brought out in the domain of a new chemical sensor at that time to enhance the analyzing ability of the sensor, and not to reduce its size. But after this concept emerged, people realized that the reduction in size had many benefits. These benefits are proved by various theories and experiments: with the reduction in size, many physical effects could be significantly improved; it is good for analyzing the quality and efficiency; the analyzing speed is increased, the responding delay time is shortened; and the heat dissipation performance is enhanced. Besides these benefits, the reduction in size can also save the reagent, it can reduce the pollution and cost, it can manipulate threshold, and it is portable.

Since 1992, various microfluidic chips have been developed one after the other, mainly focused on the capillary electrophoresis. There are various factors stimulating the development of these chips: the need for analyzing methods and systems, such as gas chromatography, high-performance liquid chromatography, and capillary electrophoresis; the need for detecting biologic and chemical weapons; the exploring of genes; research in high molecule DNA sequencing; and the progress of microelectronics and MEMS. At the same time, μTAS has also promoted the progress in many new disciplines, such as microfluidics, micro heat, and mass transfer. Today, microfluidic chip is the most active area of research, representing the future directions of biologic and chemical analysis instruments: miniaturization, integration, individuation, and application.

These days, microfluidic chips and μTASs are developing in many countries, including China. In recent years, a research team led by D F Cui has done significant work in biochip field, especially in microfluidic chip area, and achieved outstanding results. They have developed capillary electrophoresis microfluidic chip, PCR chip, cell separation chip, cell breaking chip, solid-phase extraction (SPE) chip for purifying DNA, and also piezoelectric micropump for the actuate chip, PCR detection instrument, and DNA computer microfluidic experiment system, etc.

20.3 Microarray Chip

Microarray chips can be divided into several categories, such as gene microarray chip, protein microarray chip, cell microarray chip, tissue microarray chip, and so on, according to the detection targets or functions.

The nucleic acid chip, also called as DNA chip or gene chip (Fig. 20.1), utilizes microscopic arrays (microarrays) of molecules immobilized on solid surfaces for biochemical analysis. Hundreds of thousands of nucleic acid probes with different sequences are immobilized onto designated locations within a microscopic area of a silicon or glass substrate of the chip, creating DNA microarrays. A sample labeled with a fluorescent molecule is hybridized on these DNA microarrays. Following hybridization, the nucleic acid molecules that are not combined with the probes are removed by washing the microarrays. The microarrays are then scanned by activation with lasers at the appropriate wavelength to excite the dye. The relative fluorescence of the dye on each spot is then recorded and a composite image is produced. The relative intensities of each channel represent the relative abundance of the RNA or DNA product in the samples. After the image has been analyzed using software, a quantified result about abundant genes can be achieved, which may rapidly direct correlative researches.

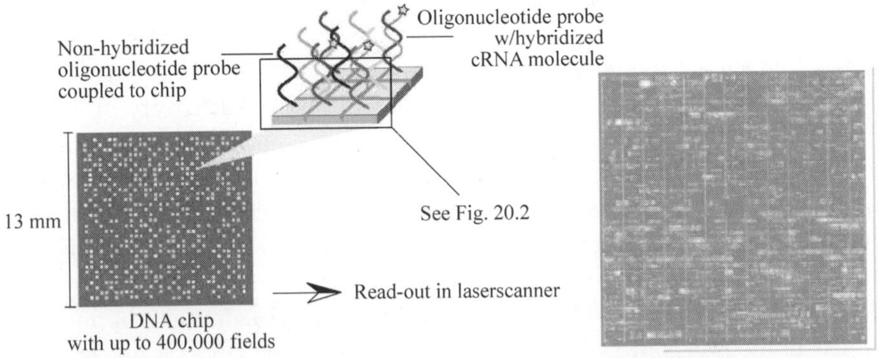

Figure 20.1 Schematic of DNA microarray chip (see color figure at the end of this book)

Complementary DNA chip (cDNA chip) is one type of nucleic acid chip based upon the mutual and specific affinity of the complementary strands of DNA. The array size can range from a small subset of 500 genes to a large pool of 30,000 genes. Once the desired genes are chosen, individual clones for each are obtained by polymerase chain reaction (PCR) amplification. A two-color fluorescent probe hybridization technology is usually used for the cDNA chip. Two different cDNA samples are marked with different fluorescent dyes and mixed completely; then the hybridization is implemented on the same probe spot. Two fluorescent signals representing hybridization of different samples are obtained by using two beams of excited light having different wavelengths. Complex fluorescent-labeled probes allow for simultaneous hybridization and separate detection of the hybridization signals from two or more probes. This in turn allows a very accurate and reliable measurement of the relative abundance of specific sequences in the two complex samples. The cDNA microarray chip can be used to monitor changes in gene expression levels as a result of a variety of metabolic, xenobiotic, or pathogenic challenges from different individuals (the health and patient).

A protein microarray chip is a piece of glass on which molecules of protein or polypeptide with different aminophenol sequence (e.g., various enzyme, receptor or antibody) are affixed at separate locations in an ordered manner, thus forming a microarray. The protein microarray chip can be used for studying high-throughput protein–protein interactions, immunoreactions, ligand reactions, etc. In addition, molecules immobilized on the chip may also represent a nucleic acid, a compound of nucleic acid and protein, a small-molecule substrate for enzyme, and so on.

For the cell microarray chip, cells are used as probes to construct a high-density cell microarray on membranes. Based on the principles of nucleic acid hybridization and protein affinity effect, multi-target molecules in cell samples of different tissues can be studied on the cell microarray chip by means of comparative method. Because cell microarray analyses require only a small amount of medium, one could systematically examine cellular interactions with small molecules, natural products, peptides, antibodies, polysaccharides, and other large molecules, most of which are too difficult or expensive to be synthesized in large quantity. Such systematic phenotypic studies would accelerate the discovery of drug and drug targets. Cell microarrays may also become a powerful tool for medical diagnosis. With the development of microfluidics, cell chips have progressed from cell microarray to cell microfluidic chip (e.g., cell culture chip, cell trapping chip, cell microsorter, cell lysis chip, single cell analysis chip, multi-function cell chip, etc.)[2].

A tissue microarray (TMA) chip allows rapid visualization of molecular targets in thousands of tissue specimens at a time, at the DNA, RNA, or protein level. The principle of TMA analysis is as follows. Cylindrical core biopsies are obtained from up to 1,000 individual, formalin-fixed, paraffin-embedded tissue blocks. These are transferred to a TMA block. Multiple TMA blocks can be generated at the same time. Each TMA block can be sectioned up to 300 times. All the resulting TMA slides have the same tissues in the same coordinate positions. The individual slides can be used for a variety of molecular analyses. Kononen et al.[3] first described their TMA chip in 1988, which could overcome the limitations of conventional techniques and realize a high-throughput analysis of tissue samples. The TMA chips have a number of advantages compared to the conventional techniques: the speed of molecular analyses is increased by more than 100-fold; precious tissues are not destroyed; and a very large number of molecular targets can be analyzed from consecutive TMA sections. Most of the applications of the TMA technology have originated from the field of cancer research. Examples include analysis of the frequency of molecular alterations in large tumor materials, exploration of tumor progression, identification of predictive or prognostic factors, and validation of newly discovered genes as diagnostic and therapeutic targets.

20.4 Fabrication and Detection of Microarray Chip

20.4.1 Fabrication Methods

20.4.1.1 Fabricaiton of DNA Microarray Chip

The DNA microarray chip is also called oligonucleotide microarray chip. Oligonucleotide usually is a short polymeric chain of two to ten nucleotides, at most not more than thirty nucleotides. The fabrication methods of the DNA microarray chip fall into two broad categories: *in-situ* synthesis and printing technology.

An in-situ synthesis is used to synthesize all oligonucleotides probe sequences in situ and then to directly immobilize them on the substrate. Affymetrix firstly created a light-directed in-situ synthesis technology adapting the technique of semiconductor photolithography and the traditional artificial solid-phase synthesis nucleic acid technology. Using fixed mask lithography, oligonucleotide synthesis is achieved by repeated cycles of base additions with different masks for light-directed deprotection of terminal hydroxyl groups. The main steps are shown in Fig. 20.2. First the substrate surface is derivatized with hydroxy groups that are protected by photolabile protecting groups. Light removes protecting groups at defined areas on the array by chosing a suitable photomask every time. Then, the hydroxy groups are coupled with one end of the monomer molecules. The other end of the molecules is specially designed with photolabile protecting groups. Therefore, a high-density array of oligonucleotide probes having desired

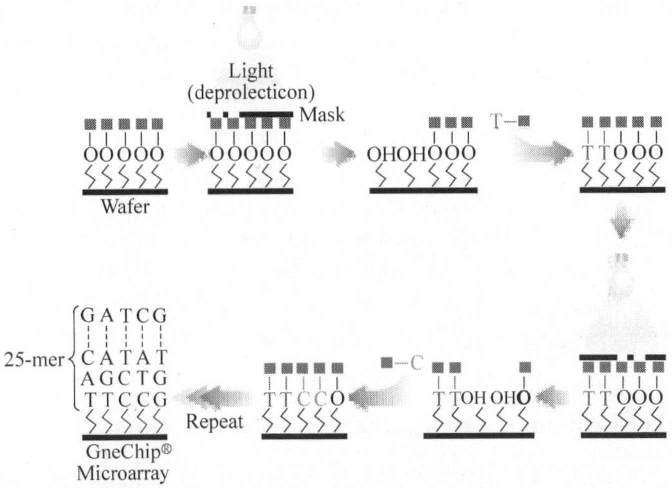

Figure 20.2 Light-directed synthesis strategy used in the manufacture of oligonucleotide microarrays (see color figure at the end of this book)

sequences at a given region is achieved by adjusting the photomask, the category of monomer molecules, and the order of reaction[4, 5]. This method currently allows for the manufacture of very high density (106/cm^2) microarrays. However, current coupling efficiencies impose a limit of ~25 bases per chips.

Incyte Pharmaceuticals[6] manufactures microarrays via an *in-situ* synthetic scheme based on piezoelectric printing of nucleotide precursors and common chemical processing of each nucleotide layer. Minute volumes of 5 ink (4 bases plus catalyst) are delivered from defined locations on the slide similar to 'ink-jet' printing methods. Other steps such as washing, deprotection, polymerization, and so on are the same as those in the traditional solid-phase *in-situ* synthesis technology. The probe length is from 40 nucleotides to 50 nucleotides, having higher coupling efficiency in each cycle than the light-directed *in-situ* synthesis.

20.4.1.2 Fabrication of cDNA Microarray Chip

Reverse transcription PCR (RT-PCR) is used to convert the mRNA transcripts into cDNA made of hundreds of nucleotides. Once the synthetic cDNA samples have been prepared, they are individually spotted, usually in duplicate, onto glass slides in a predetermined array by printing. Printing can be done in one of the three ways: photolithography, mechanical microspotting, or ink jetting. Photolithography uses light to covalently attach the DNA strands to the slide, mechanical spotting uses spotting pins and capillary action to transport DNA, and ink jetting uses an electric current to dispense the appropriate amount of DNA. The ultraviolet cross-linking after the slides have been spotted denatures the DNA and ensures that it remains fixed to the glass surface.

20.4.1.3 Fabrication of Protein Microarray Chip

For protein microarray, a protein molecule may be immobilized on several substrate materials, such as cellulose membrane[7], polyacrylamide gel[8], poly (vinylidene fluoride) (PVDF) membrane[9], glass slide[10], silicon wafer[11], aluminum oxide sheet[12], and so on, by absorbing, covalent bonding, self-assembling, etc.

The protein microarray is manufactured by the deposition of prepared protein by using the mechanical printing system (e.g., MicroGrid Printing System of BioRobotics) or the microliquid dispensation system (e.g., Biomek FX liquid dispenser of Beckman), which are widely used for DNA microarray. Theoretically, protein microarrays can also be fabricated by a method similar to light-directed *in-situ* synthesis technology, which is used for manufacturing DNA microarray. But synthesis of peptides is much more expensive than synthesis of oligonucleotides. Therefore, anyone hardly uses this method.

20.4.1.4 Fabrication of Cell Microarray Chip

Biochemical photolithography technology fabricates cell microarray chips. Protein is patterned on the microelectrode array on which cells are grown and cultured. Thus, the cells are connected to inorganic devices.

20.4.1.5 Fabrication of TMA Chip

Construction of a TMA chip is achieved by acquiring cylindrical core specimens from up to 1,000 fixed and paraffin-embedded tissue specimens and arraying them at a high density into a recipient TMA block. The detailed process of the fabrication is shown in Fig. 20.3. First, core biopsies (0.6 mm diameter, 3 – 4 mm high) are cut from different donor blocks. Then, holes are made in the recipient TMA block (45 mm×20 mm) with regular configuration, a cylindrical core sample is acquired from the donor tissue block, and this core is deposited into the TMA block. This process is repeated with a precision instrument to array hundreds of tissue specimens. Finally, using a microtome, 5 μm sections are cut from the TMA blocks to generate TMA slides for molecular analyses. Up to 300 consecutive sections can be cut from each TMA block. An adhesive-coated tape sectioning system helps transfer the precise locations of the tissue spots in the TMA block onto the microscope slides.

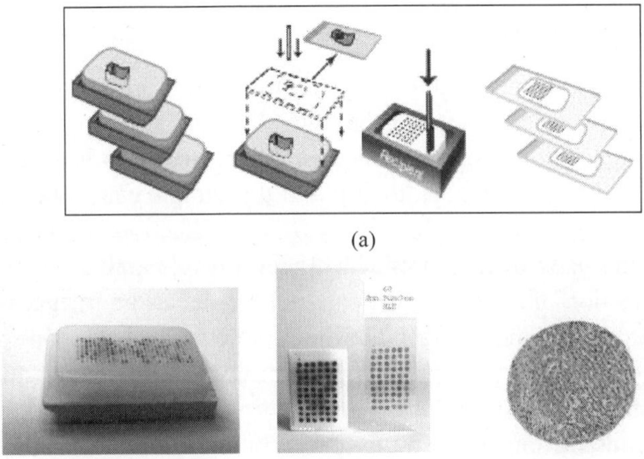

(a)

(b) (c) (d)

Figure 20.3 Schematic of fabricating TMA chip and the pictures of TMA chip, (a) general line of fabricating TMA chip, (b) TMA block, (c) TMA slide, (d) tissue spot in the TMA chip (see color figure at the end of this book)

A single TMA experiment can yield information about the molecular characteristics of up to 1,000 specimens at once. This is in contrast with the conventional analyses, where each slide contains a section of a single tissue. In the latter case, analysis of 1,000 cases would require staining and analysis of 1,000 individual slides.

20.4.2 Detection Methods

Detection technologies for the microarray chip mainly include fluorescence/isotopes detection technology, atomic force microscope (AFM) technology[13], surface plasmon resonance (SPR) technology[14], multi-photon detection (MPD) technology, surface-enhanced laser desorption/ionization (SELDI) technology[15], matrix-assisted laser desorption/ionization time-of-flight/mass spectrometry (MALDI-TOF/MS) technology[16], and so on.

20.4.2.1 Fluorescence/Isotope Detection Technology

Fluorescent dyes and isotopes are used as markers, which are then labeled on samples or biochemical molecules. Finally, the information about biochemical reactions or reaction products on biochips is obtained by detecting these markers.

Fluorescence detection technology is mainly divided into two categories: confocal laser scanning and charge-coupled device (CCD) imaging. The former has higher sensitivity and resolution than the latter, while the detection time of the latter is less. Currently there are several companies, such as Genomic Solutions, Packard, GSI, and Molecular Dynamics, which produce a special fluorescence detector for biochips.

20.4.2.2 AFM Technology

The AFM technology uses a cantilever, usually made from silicon or silicon nitride, with a very low spring constant, on the end of which a sharp tip is fabricated using semi-conductor processing techniques. When the tip is brought close to a sample surface, the forces between the tip and the sample cause the cantilever to bend. This motion can be detected optically by the deflection of a laser beam that is reflected off the back of the cantilever. If the tip is scanned over the sample surface, the deflection of the cantilever can be recorded as an image, which in its simplest form represents the 3D shape of the sample surface. The tip surface may be modified chemically, for example special biological molecule (nucleic acid, protein, etc.) immobilized on the tip. Then the tip is scanned over the surface of the biochip. The interaction between the special biological molecule on the tip and the biological molecule on the biochip bends the cantilever, and therefore the images have information about the tip—biochip interaction. The AFM technology together with the chemical modification is also called chemical force microscopy (CFM).

There are some significant advantages of AFM as an imaging tool in biology when compared with complementary techniques, such as electron microscopy. Not only does AFM achieve molecular resolution but the technique also requires almost no sample preparation and, most importantly, it can be performed under fluids, permitting samples to be imaged in near-native conditions.

20.4.2.3 SPR Technology

SPR is a physical phenomenon that occurs when a polarized light beam is projected through a prism onto a thin metal film (gold or silver). At a specific angle of the projected light, resonance coupling between light photons and surface plasma of the gold can occur since their frequencies match. Because the resonance leads to an energy transfer, the reflected light shows a sharp intensity drop at the angle where SPR is taking place. Resonance coupling of the plasma generates an evanescent wave that extends 100 nm above and below the gold surface. For SPR as an analytical tool, it is most important that a change in the refractive index within the environment of the evanescent wave causes a change in the angle where the sharp intensity drop can be observed. Binding of one biomolecule to another immobilized on top of the sensor chip's gold surface will lead to a change in the refractive index and will be recorded as a change in the reflected light by a detector. This setup enables a real-time measurement of biomolecular interactions, with refractive index changes proportional to mass changes. SPR is considered to be the most sensitive, label-free, full-field, and real-time detection tool. Since BIAcore introduced in 1990 the first commercial SPR machine, BioTul, Texas Instruments, etc. have also begun to manufacture the SPR system. In China, the group of Prof. Cui studied the SPR instrument for years and developed several types of SPR biochemical analytical systems, including single-parameter-type SPR system; two-parameter-type SPR system; and high-throughput, multi-parameter-imaging-type SPR system, which were used by several colleges and institutes.

20.4.2.4 MPD Technology

The multi-photon detection (MPD) technology invented by BioTraces is a highly sensitive radioactive isotope detection technology. This method in combination with a passive shielding technology can evidently reduce the intensity of the background and 10^{-21} mol isotopes can be detected. The quantity of isotope required is sharply cut down, which minimizes the harm to experimenters. In addition, MPD can be used for multi-sample detection by using two or more types of isotopes simultaneously.

20.4.2.5 SELDI Technology

The surface-enhanced laser desorption/ionization (SELDI) technology was invented by Texas Medicine Center in the early 1990's. The detailed process is as follows: trapping and enriching the target protein by protein chip; desorbing the protein from the surface of chip; ionizing the protein; and finally, implementing quality analysis by means of MS or affinity chromatography.

20.4.2.6 MALDI-TOF/MS Technology

Mass spectrometry is a powerful technique for identifying unknowns, studying molecular structure, and probing the fundamental principles of chemistry by measuring the molecular weight of molecules based on the motion of charged particles in an electrical or magnetic field. Visually speaking, mass spectrometry uses a 'hammer' to scrap the analyte molecules into fragments (ions or neuter particle), and then 'weighs' these fragments. The 'hammers' used for the conventional MS are commonly fast atom bombardment (FAB) or electron spray ionization (ESI). The molecular weight of the analyte is less than 10 kDa, and the analyte molecules are usually dissociated into a large number of fragments. But for protein, the molecular weight is usually more than 10 kDa and the structure is more complex. If the protein were dissociated into extensive fragments, it would be difficult to interpret the spectra of MS.

To resolve these problems, the matrix-assisted laser desorption/ionization time-of-flight/mass spectrometry (MALDI-TOF/MS) technology was developed in 1988. MALDI has been demonstrated to have several advantages, including spectral simplicity due to singly charged ions, a high mass range up to 1,000 kDa, low noise levels, high sensitivity up to 10^{-15} mol, little sample consumption, short measurement times, average salt tolerance, and minimal fragmentation. Today a wide variety of samples can be analyzed using MALDI-TOF/MS, including peptides, proteins, synthetic polymers, polypeptides, oligonucleotides, oligosaccharides, drugs, and metabolite systems.

Typically, samples are mixed with an organic compound that acts as a matrix (protonated at acidic pH) to facilitate desorption and ionization of compounds in the sample. The analytic ions are then accelerated by an applied high voltage, separated in a field-free flight tube and detected by MS as an electrical signal at the end of the flight tube.

20.5 Sample Pretreatment Microfluidic Chip

Almost all the biochips require the same first step, that is extraction or isolation of DNA, RNA, or protein from crude biologic samples, before implementing analysis or detection. But in a number of instances, the biologic samples requiring analyses are highly complicated biologic mixtures (e.g., whole blood, urine, saliva, feces, sputum, spinal fluid, lacrimal fluid, tissue biopsies, buccal swabs, cultured cells, and tissue homogenates) or the mixture of biologic sample and impurity (e.g., the mixture of various bacteria and impurity, such as food, dirt, and so on). Except few samples, most crude samples cannot directly react with biochip. For example, whole blood includes various blood cells, blood platelets, plasma etc. The useful protein related to diseases is always less abundant and thus analysis often requires significant preprocessing that involves purification and enrichment before detection. Genomic analysis needs prior cell isolation, cell lysis, and DNA or RNA extraction from whole blood because DNA or RNA is located in white blood cells (WBCs). Sample pretreatment microfluidic chips usually consist of microchannels and microwells; further, it may also include other components such as electrode, heater/cooler, filtration membrane, and so on based on the function of the biochip. Sample pretreatment biochip is one kind of microfluidic chips, which has its own characteristics besides the characteristics of microfluidic chips:

(1) Special application: Different crude samples often require different sample pretreatment biochips; different analytic targets also require different biochips because of various complicated real crude samples.

(2) Diversity owing to diversity of crude samples and analytic targets: Traditional methods of sample pretreatment include liquid-liquid extraction, SPE, and chromatography. For the scale-down, optic, dielectrophoresis (DEP), and magnetic methods have been widely used in sample pretreatment biochip.

(3) Integration: According to the analytic targets and their detection methods, a sample pretreatment step can be integrated with downstream steps of biochemical reactions, analysis, and detection on one microfluidic chip using the MEMS technology, which will realize μTAS capable of reducing contamination and improving the level of automatization during the whole analytic process.

Presently there is no uniform criterion of sorting the sample pretreatment biochip for its own characteristic and rapid development. Based on the principle, sample pretreatment has been divided into filtration chip, SPE chip, membrane separation chip, DEP chip, ultrasonic technique chip, magnetic technology chip, and so on. According to the function, it has been classified into cell/particle separation chip, DNA/RNA extraction chip, protein purification chip, mixing chip, enrichment chip, integration chip, etc.

20.5.1 Particle/Cell Separation Biochip

Separation, sorting, or trapping particles/cells is a sample pretreatment technology, which can be used to obtain homogeneous target particles/cells from a large number of heterogeneous particles/cells. At present, the methods of separation, sorting, or trapping particles/cells based on MEMS technology are as follows:

20.5.1.1 Method of Microfiltration

It is a physical method of separation based on the diversity in size of particles/cells. When a liquid or gas flows through microstructures, such as microposts, tortuous microchannels, comb-type structures, weir structure, sieve, etc., particles/cells with different sizes are separated. The advantages of this method include: simple principle, no requirement of special buffer, and easy integration. However, it also has disadvantages: the process is complex and it requires distinct size difference between the target particle/cells and the other impurities. The major difficulty with the microfilter biochip is the preparation of the filtration microstructures. Techniques of low-pressure chemical vapor deposition (LPCVD), reactive ion etching (RIE), deep reactive ion etching (DRIE), and wet etching were used on a silicon wafer or silicon nitride membrane to fabricate various filtration microstructure arrays or filter membranes. In a different approach, the filtration microstructure array was achieved by molding PDMS material[17], while a nanoporous filtration membrane in a microfluidic device was obtained by micromachining and ion track technology[18].

Based on the flow direction of the fluid, microfiltration includes dead-end filtration mode and crossflow filtration mode. Both can realize solid-liquid separation, solid-gas separation, and separation of particles/cells with different sizes. Wilding et al.[19] designed and fabricated a silicon-glass hybrid microchip containing a series of micropillars or 'weir-type' filters as a cellular trap by means of dead-end filtration, shown in Fig. 20.4. RBCs at rest assumed a biconcave discoid shape with a diameter of ~8 μm and a thickness of ~2 μm and they passed through the microstructure barrier, while larger WBCs with a diameter of more than 10 μm were trapped by them. The WBCs were then used as a DNA source for the microchip-based PCR. But there were problems of clogging or jamming in most of these separation microchips due to dead-end filtration. In this case, the fluidic flow is perpendicular to the filtration structures so that smaller particles pass through the filtration barriers along the fluid; larger particles cannot pass through but build up near the filtration barriers, lead to colloid-cake formation, and finally result in clogging or jamming of channels.

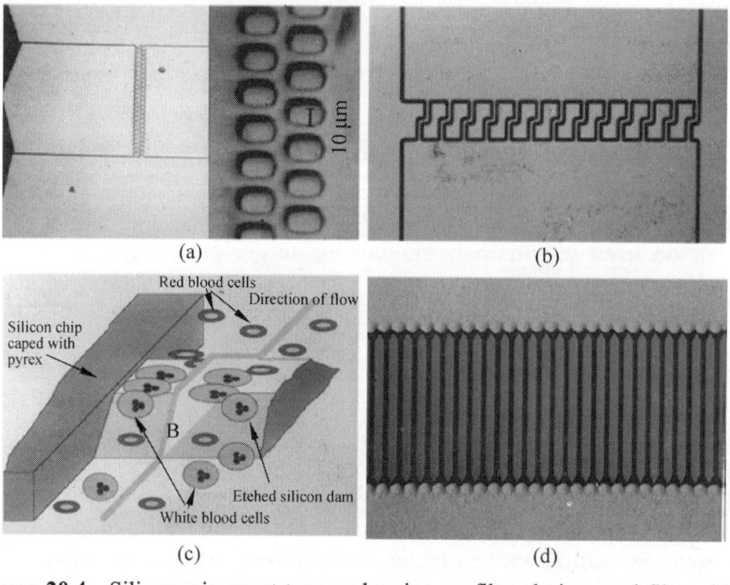

Figure 20.4 Silicon micropost-type and weir-type filter designs and filter chips. (a) Offset array of simple microposts (13×20 μm spaced 7 μm apart). (b) Array of complex microposts (73 μm wide) separated by 7 μm wide tortuous channels spaced 30 μm apart. (c) A 3.5 μm gap between the top of the etched silicon dam and the Pyrex glass cover. (d) Comb-type filter formed from an array of 120 posts (175 μm×18 μm spaced 6 μm apart)

To overcome the clogging of dead-end filtration, crossflow filtration, which allows the bigger particles to stay in a suspended state instead of being deposited, can be used in microfluidic chips. For a crossflow filtration, the flow direct of the fluid is parallel to the filtration structures. High tangential rates are utilized for transporting the permeated smaller particles from the feed stream to the lateral stream through the filtration structures, and the retentate larger particles are still along the feed stream. Therefore, the crossflow filtration can dramatically restrict the problem of clogging or jamming. He et al.[20] used a deep reactive ion etching technology to create a network of intersecting 1.5 μm×10 μm channels in a quartz wafer. When placed at the bottom of reservoirs with a side exit, this channel network behaved as a lateral percolation filter composed of an array of cube-like structures, one layer deep. 5 μm silica particles were filtrated by electro-osmotic flow (EOF) after the fluid was introduced into the microfluidic biochip.

Sethu et al.[17] applied the crossflow filtration with a glass-PDMS hybrid microchip for cell sorting. As shown in Fig. 20.5, the microchip fabricated by simple soft lithographic techniques employs microsieves that exploit the size and shape difference between different cell types to obtain depletion of leukocytes from the whole blood. For the given device design, isolation of ~50% of the inlet RBCs, along with depletion of >97% of the inlet WBCs, was performed by optimizing the flow rate.

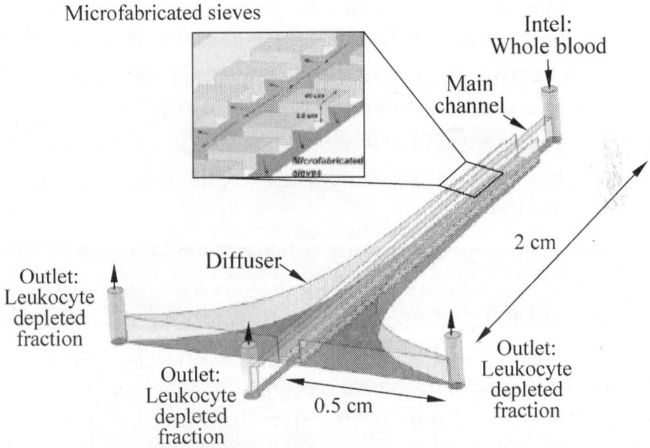

Figure 20.5 Schematic of the diffusive filter for size-based continuous flow fractionation of erythrocytes from whole blood. Insert shows the 40 μm×2.5 μm sieve structure and the arrangement connecting the main channel to the diffuser

Chen and Cui[21] developed a crossflow filtration microfluidic chip capable of separating and collecting plasma, WBC, and RBC at different outlet ports simultaneously, shown in Fig. 20.6(a). Multilevel filtration barriers with different gaps were fabricated by deep reaction ion etching (DRIE) technology. The efficiency of separation was improved by microcentrifugal effect when the arc channel was designed. Also, this group described a micropost array microfluidic chip by using the MEMS technology, shown in Fig. 20.6(b).

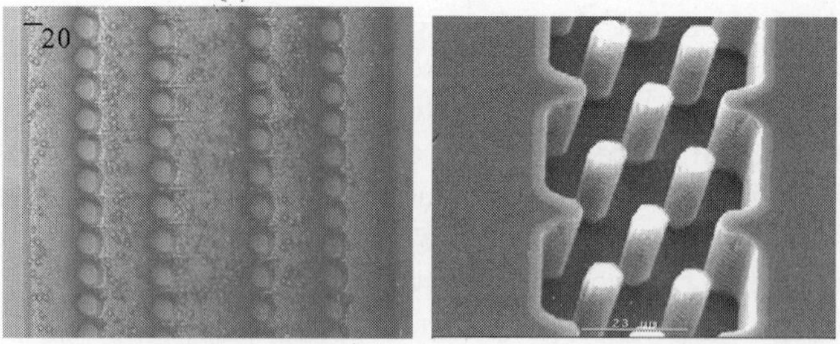

(a) (b)

Figure 20.6 (a) Photograph of multilevel crossflow filtration microchip for blood separation. (b) SEM of micropost array microfluidic chip (see color figure at the end of this book)

20.5.1.2 Dielectrophoresis (DEP) Method

Dielectrophoretic cell separation exploits dielectrophoretic forces that are created on cells when a nonuniform electrical field interacts with the field-induced electrical polarization on the cells. Microelectrode array fabricated on silicon, glass, or polymer substrate by using the MEMS technology produces a nonuniform electric field. Depending on the dielectric properties of the cells relative to their suspending medium, these forces can be either positive or negative and can direct the cells toward strong or weak electrical field regions, where cells with distinct intrinsic dielectric properties can be trapped and collected. The use of dielectrophoresis for cell separation has several potential advantages:

(1) Label-free separations: The intrinsic dielectric properties of a particular type of cells can be used to separate these cells from mixtures when other biomarkers are not available.

(2) Easy miniaturization: The ability to separate cells on a microelectronic chip array enables the development of a chip-scale cell separator.

(3) Automation and integration: The use of an electric field makes it easy to directly interface with conventional electronics for automated control and to integrate with other electric field-based assays.

Huang et al.[22] described two DEP microfluidic chips with 5×5 or 10×10 microelectronic array. Using their microdevice, U937 cells and peripheral blood mononuclear cells were separated into two homogeneous populations before biochemical analysis. The purity of dielectrophoretically separating cells can be greater than 95%. Hu et al.[23] furthered the idea of DEP-activated cell sorting with a glass/polyimide microfluidic chip, shown in Fig. 20.7, for isolating rare target cells from complex mixtures. Rare target cells labeled by marker particles with different dielectric properties were efficiently separated from unlabeled cells. Tagging cells have allowed DEP sorting for rare target cells at rates up to 10,000 cells/s and with enrichment factors of more than 200.

Although the DEP method has been demonstrated as an effective and selective method in concentrating, manipulating, and separating cells and bacteria without

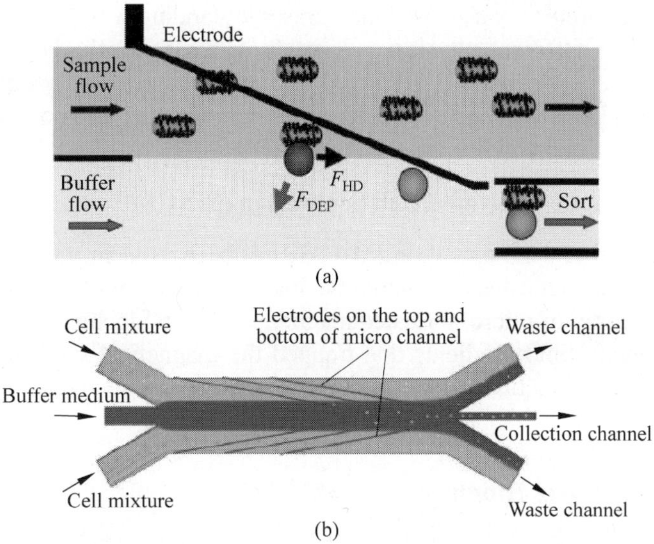

Figure 20.7 DEP-activated cell sorter. (a) The DEP-activated cell sorting concept: Cells entering in the sample stream are only deflected into the collection stream if they are labeled with a dielectrophoretically responsive label. (b) Schematic view of the electrode region of the microchannels with sample and buffer inlets, as well as waste and collection outlets

size difference, it requires special buffers and strong polarization charges in a nonuniform electric field, which might damage cells.

20.5.1.3 Fluorescence Activated Cell Sorter (FACS)

When flow cytometry is combined with cell sorting, the so-called fluorescent activated cell sorters (FACS) are realized. FACS has been miniaturized using integrated pneumatically activated pumps and valves that divert cells into a collection chamber on the basis of their fluorescent properties reported by Quake et al.[24]. They employed multilayer soft lithography technology to create glass/PDMS hybrid microfabricated fluorescent activated cell sorting (μFACS) devices. For the given typical cell sorter chip, cells can be sorted at rates of up to ~40 cells/s with enrichment factors of ~90 and recovery yields between 16% and 50%. Using optical forces instead of mechanical valves to switch the direction of cells, Wang et al.[25] also implemented a μFACS device that permits a slightly higher throughput of ~100 cells/s, with recovery yields above 85% and enrichment factors of up to ~70.

20.5.1.4 Ultrasonic Technique

An acoustic standing wave, of a half wavelength, is maintained within the cavity, and as the particles move through the field, they migrate to the pressure node at the center of the cavity. Based on the acoustic impedances of different materials, Harris et al.[26] designed and fabricated a silicon microfluidic ultrasonic separator.

The group of Laurell[27, 28] also used the ultrasonic standing wave forces to separate particles having different physical properties within microfluidic channel; i.e., lipid vesicles were continuously separated from erythrocytes. Separation efficiency of polyamide spheres was up to 100% using further miniaturization of the separation device under optimal conditions.

20.5.1.5 Magnetic-Activated Cell Separation (MACS)

Magnetic-activated cell separation (MACS) has been used in microfluidic chips based on the magnetic bead technology. Inglis and colleagues[29] designed and fabricated an array of microfabricated magnetic strips in biochip to create a series of high magnetic field gradients that trapped the magnetically labeled cells and altered their flow direction, when the cells flowed over these magnetic strips.

20.5.2 Cell Lysis Biochip

Methods for cell lysis can be divided into mechanical lysis and nonmechanical lysis. Mechanical lysis is realized by nanostructures or by ultrasonic energy. The methods of nonmechanical lysis mainly include thermal lysis, electronic-based lysis, chemical-based lysis, and so on.

20.5.2.1 Mechanical Lysis by Nanostructures

Mechanical lysis using nanostructure filter-like contractions (nano-knives) in microfluidic channels with a pressure-driven cell flow is a useful technique, and can provide nonadulterated cell lysates that can be used for downstream assays. Carlo et al.[30] used nanostructure barbs microfabricated on silicon wafer to disrupt sheep blood cells, shown in Fig. 20.8.

20.5.2.2 Sonication

Sonication is a widely practiced method to rapidly disrupt a variety of cell types. The mechanism in which sonication forces disrupt cells has been proposed to be gaseous cavitation. In this process, pockets of air form from the dissolved gases in a solution and then rapidly collapse to a portion of the original size, creating high pressure and temperature microenvironments that are damaging to cells. Belgrader and co-workers[31, 32] reported a microfluidic system with a minisonicator to lyse spores. Bacillus spores were successfully disrupted in 30 s with the resulting sample in a PCR-compatible form.

20.5.2.3 Electronic-Based Lysis

Electroporation utilizes electric field to create transient or permanent pore (s) on the cell membrane. This phenomenon occurs when sufficient voltage required for dielectric breakdown of the membrane, about 0.2 – 1.5 V, is imposed by an external electric field. Pores can be of two states: reversible electrical breakdown,

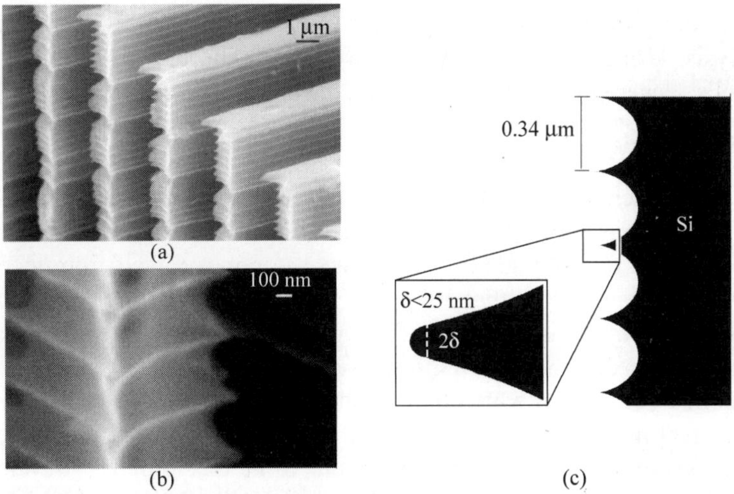

Figure 20.8 (a, b) SEM of the nano-knives are shown. Sharp protrusions are clearly seen as orthogonal scallops meet at corners during the DRIE process. (c) A schematic drawing of the nano-knives is shown describing the geometry. Distance between barbs is ~ 0.34 μm and radius of curvature of tips is below 25 nm

where the pores reseal themselves when the external electric field is removed; and irreversible breakdown, where the damage is permanent.

Based on the phenomenon of electroporation, Gao et al.[33] provided a microfluidic system, where the voltages were applied to perform electrophoretic injection and separation to lyse the cells. For the given design, both cell lysis and capillary electrophoretic (CE) separation were achieved on one single chip, and disruption times were as low as about 40 ms. Lee et al.[34] developed a micromachined cell lysis device with multielectrode pairs to apply electric fields to disrupt cells, shown in Fig. 20.9. By carefully controlling the strength of the electrical field, microfabricated electroporation devices can also reversibly destabilize the cell membrane for gene transfection applications[35].

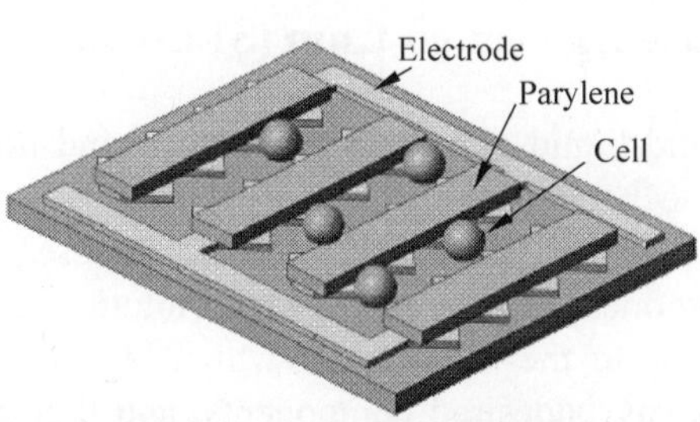

Figure 20.9 Schematic view of cell lysis device

20.5.2.4 Thermal Lysis

Although the thermal lysis is not applicable to proteins analysis because protein molecules denature at high temperature, it is a simple method for releasing DNA for analysis. Using the heater of PCR in microfluidic biochips, E. coli [36] and cheek cells[37] were thermally lysed during the initial stages of PCR.

20.5.2.5 Chemical-Based Lysis

Chemical approaches mostly utilize lysis buffer with reagents, such as SDS, Triton X-100, and protein enzyme K, to solubilize the lipid membrane. However, the use of surfactant requires additional treatment to remove itself from the sample. Another main drawback is that although chemical methods are widely used for extraction of DNA, it is not ideal if the prime concern is integrity of protein. Chen and Cui[17] designed and fabricated a sandwich flow microfluidic biochip with a coiled channel on which blood cells were rapidly damaged by using the lysing reagent mixture of guanidine and Triton X-100. Furthermore, combining chemical lysis with crossflow filtration and SPE, this group[38] developed an integrated sample pretreatment biochip, shown in Fig. 20.10, on which WBCs were separated from whole blood; then the WBCs were damaged, DNA was released, and finally PCR-amplifiable DNA was extracted.

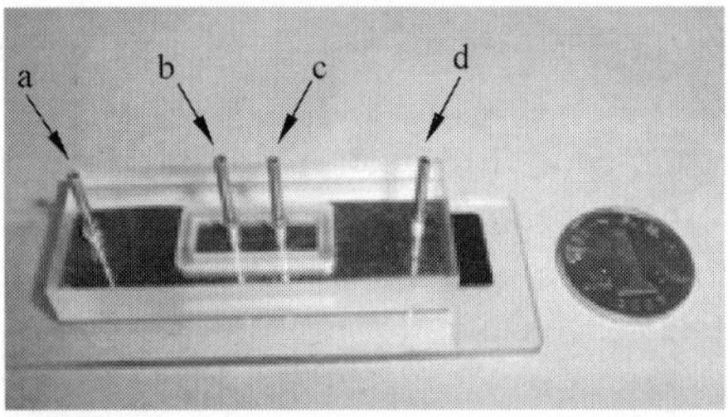

Figure 20.10 Photograph of a sample pretreatment biochip: a. Inlet of whole blood, b. Outlet of red blood cells, c. Inlet of buffers, d. Outlet of waste and DNA (see color figure at the end of this book)

20.5.3 Solid Phase Extraction Chip (SPE-Chip)

A combination of solid-liquid extraction technology and liquid chromatography technology with chip technology (SPE-chip) occurs, which is a sample pretreatment method of micro solid-phase extraction (μSPE) that uses a solid phase and a liquid phase to isolate one type of analyte from a solution. The general procedure is to load a solution onto the SPE phase, which is immobilized or fabricated within chips, wash away undesired components, and then wash off the desired analytes with another solvent into a collection tube. Compared with traditional SPE and solid-phase microextraction (SPME), SPE-chip has many advantages: ① miniaturization, which could treat a nanoliter sample with less consumption of reagents and less contamination; ② high extraction efficiency, e.g., 70% – 80%

recovery of DNA and approximately 87% removal of the protein from a cell lysate; ③ wide application foreground with various SPE phases; ④ simple, rapid, and automatic procedure, which can be integrated into the μTAS.

The SPE phase is one of the most important factors with regards to effects of the SPE-chips. Three types of SPE phases are reported: open tubular type, bead type, and monolithic column type. For the open tubular type, SPE phase is just coated on the inner walls of the microchannel, not filling it, which has advantages of easier fabrication and lower column pressure, and disadvantages of little surface area, lower load capability, and unsteady coating phase. For bead type, beads in the SPE phase are packed into the microchannel using grid microstructure[39], weir microstructure[40], or microchannel-based 'keystone effect'[41], shown in Fig. 20.11. The bead SPE phase can be flexible, and the load capability is significantly improved. But the procedure of packing beads is more complex, the uniformity of SPE phase is unstable and there might be higher back pressure. For monolithic column type, the SPE phase is directly fabricated as or after the formation of microchannel, which has advantages of good uniformity, low back pressure, huge surface area, and so on.

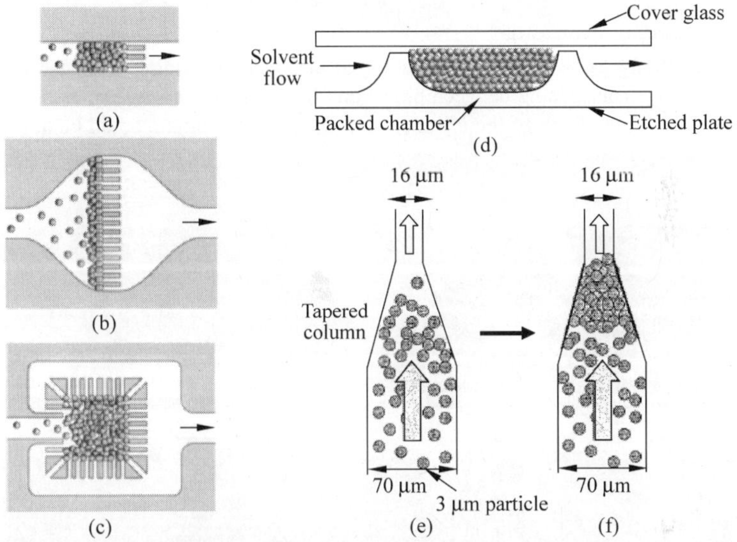

Figure 20.11 Schematicof grid microstructure (a–c)[39], weir microstructure (d)[40], microchannel-based 'keystone effect'(e, f)[41]

Presently, SPE-chip is already being used to extract, purify, and enrich coumarin, peptide, tetrapeptide, protein, DNA, or RNA. As a preface to chip-based DNA extraction, Landers's group[42] established a μSPE system in a capillary packing with silica resin where PCR-suitable genomic DNA was directly extracted from human WBCs, whole blood, or cells in culture. This effort was followed by the work of the same group[43] in which a sol-gel method was used to immobilize the bare silica beads in a microchannel for DNA extraction. Extraction efficiency with this SPE phase of monolithic column type averaged >80%, with λ-phage DNA showing efficiencies >90% for some chips. Cady et al.[44] used deep reactive ion etching or reactive ion etching silicon to generate pillar structures with adequate surface area as solid-phase matrix for DNA extraction. One device with microfabricated pillars with an increase in surface area of 300% – 600% is shown in Fig. 20.12. For this chip, the binding capacity for DNA was approximately 82 ng/cm^2 and approximately 87% of the protein was removed from the cell lysate. However, the increasing surface area was limited and the problems of clogging could not be completely solved.

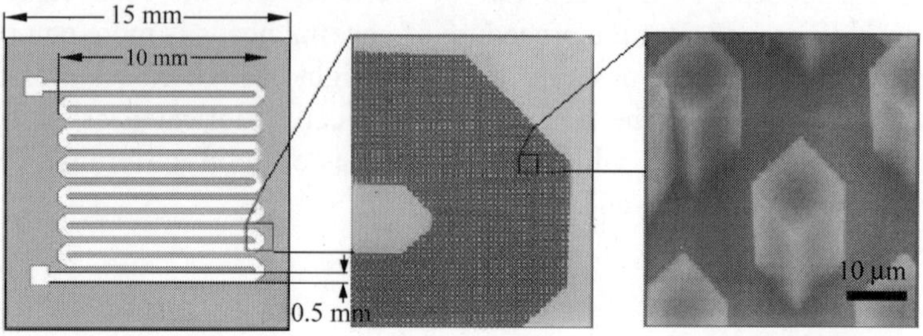

Figure 20.12 Schematic representation of channels containing microfabricated silica pillars. The spacing between pillars and the pillar width was kept constant at 10 μm, while the depth of the channels and height of the pillars could be adjusted between 20 μm and 50 μm

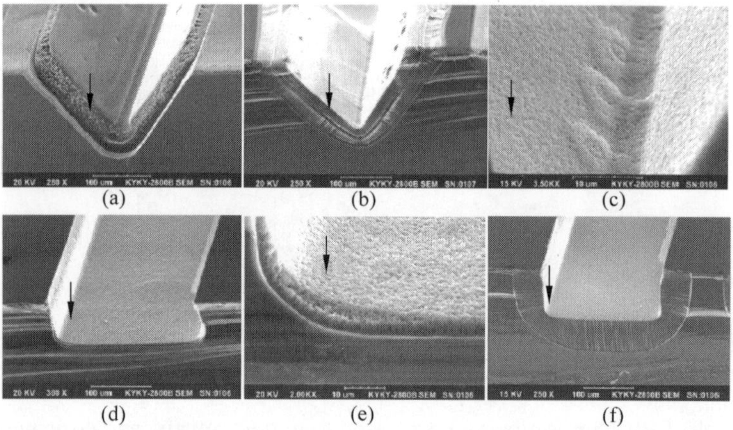

Figure 20.13 SEM micrographs of porous channels anodized in 30% HF electrolyte for 15 min. (a) Porous V-type channels anodized at 30 mA/cm^2; (b) Porous V-type channels anodized at 80 mA/cm^2; (c) The higher magnification image of porous V-type channels anodized at 80 mA/cm^2; (d) Porous rectangle channels anodized at 30 mA/cm^2; (e) The higher magnification image of porous rectangle channels anodized at 30 mA/cm^2; and (f) Porous rectangle channels anodized at 80 mA/cm^2

Chen and Cui[45] developed an SPE chip using porous silicon with a large surface area as the solid-phase matrix for adsorption DNA. SEM pictures of the porous silicon channel are shown in Fig. 20.13. The pore size of porous rectangular channel anodized under optimal conditions has been determined in the range of 20 to 30 nm, and surface area is approximately 400 m^2/g by using the BET technology. Thus the surface area to volume of porous microfluidic chip is approximate 300 m^2/cm^3, which is thousands of times more than that of the nonporous one. For the optimal SPE chip, 49.5 ng PCR-amplifiable DNA was extracted from per microliter of whole blood under optimal conditions in 15 min, which was approximately twofold compared with commercial kits.

20.5.4 Other Extraction Biochips

20.5.4.1 Solid-Phase Reversible Immobilization (SPRI)

Solid-phase reversible immobilization is similar to SPE, which extracts analyte by: absorbing analyte on the solid-phase matrix, washing the undesired impurity, and eluting the purified analyte under certain conditions. The difference between SPRI and SPE is that the analyte is absorbed specially on the solid-phase matrix for SPRI, while it is nonspecially for SPE. The SPRI technology has higher sensitivity for purification, but elution step usually requires longer time and more rigorous conditions. In addition, the solid-phase matrix generally needs to be chemically modified. The SPRI-chip technology has the same problem of matrix preparation and immobilization. Xu et al.[46] used photoactivated polycarbonate (PC) to fabricate DNA extraction chip based on SPRI. An immobilization bed for the DNA purification was produced by exposing a posted microchannel to UV radiation, which induced a surface photooxidation reaction, resulting in the production of carboxylate groups, which could absorb DNA specially.

20.5.4.2 Magnetic Technology

Magnetic technology, which can be easily used in microfluidic system, has already been exploited for extraction of mRNA. Harrison's group[47] demonstrated mRNA capture in a microfluidic chip device using paramagnetic oligo-d_T beads and magnetic trapping to capture and then release the beads. Using Drosophila melanogaster (fruit fly) DNA, they were able to capture ~2.8 ng of total mRNA from 0.85 μg of total RNA (tRNA) and as much as 34 ng of total mRNA was estimated to be captured from 10 g of tRNA.

20.5.4.3 Liquid/Liquid Extraction (LLE)

LLE is another alternative method for extraction and purification widely used in conventional sample pretreatment and describes the physical process by which a compound (or a mixture of compounds) is transferred from one liquid phase to another. Reddy and Zahn[48] generated dual inlet and three inlet microfluidic systems based on organic–aqueous liquid (phenol) extraction, which could be used for purifying DNA directly from cells (Fig. 20.14).

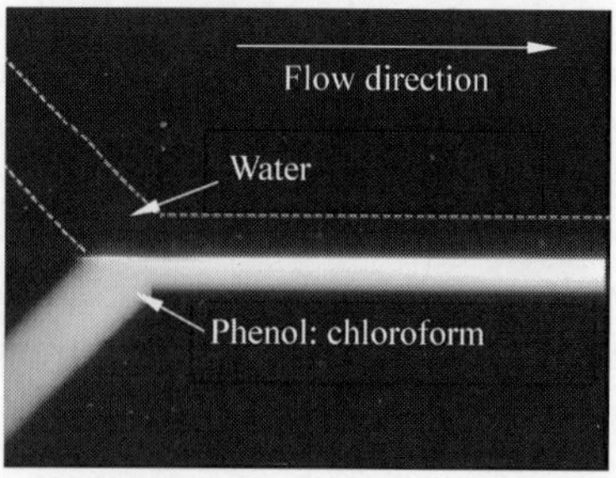

Figure 20.14 Co-infusion of water and phenol:chloroform solution showing a stable stratified flow profile

20.5.5 Mixing Biochip

In a typical microfluidic device, viscosity dominates flow and, as a result, the Reynolds number is low and the flow is laminar. Therefore, the mixing of two or more fluid streams in microfluidic devices is by virtue of diffusion, which is a slow process. On the other hand, in microfluidic devices, such as LOC, it is very important to mix two or more reagents together. Based on structures, micromixers can be categorized as using either active or passive mixing methods.

In earlier period, Kamholz et al.[49] and Ismagilov et al.[50] demonstrated two simple passive micromixers of T-type and Y-type, shown in Fig. 20.15. Some passive mixers reduce the diffusion path between fluid streams by splitting and recombining to enhance mixing. Liu et al.[51] described a passive chaotic micromixer with 3D serpentine-type channels.

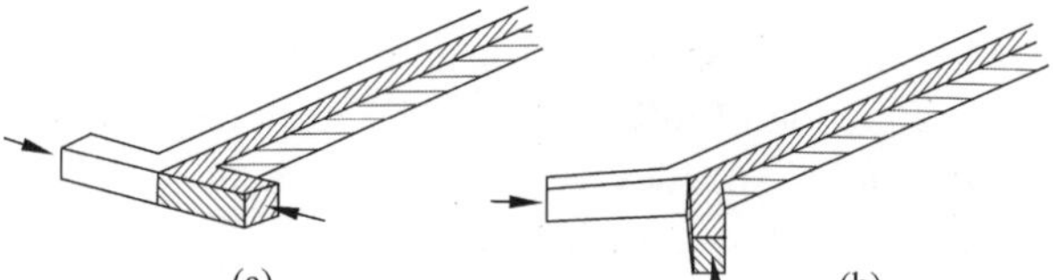

Figure 20.15 Schematic of (a) T-type and (b) Y-type micromixer

Stroock et al.[52] designed and fabricated a herringbone micromixer by the means of chaotic advection at low Reynolds numbers. A series of herringbone ridges placed at the bottom of the channel to create two counter-rotating vortices enhanced the mixing. Howell et al.[53] furthered this idea and provided a new microfluidic mixer consisting of a rectangular channel with grooves placed at the top and the bottom, shown in Fig. 20.16, having improved mixing efficiency.

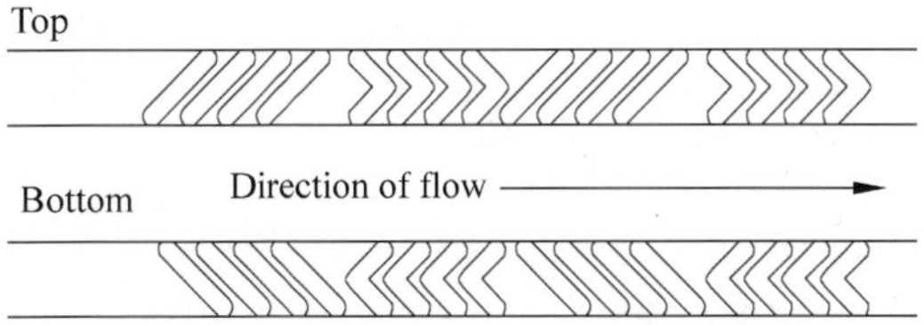

Figure 20.16 Schematic of a herringbone micromixer

Most active micromixers enhance mixing by stirring flow using exterior energy, including acoustic disturbance[54], pressure field disturbance[55], magnetohydrodynamic disturbance[56], and so on. Active micromixers are particularly suitable for chamber mix; however, most active micromixers are complex to fabricate and require an external power source, and the quantity of heat produced during mixing might destroy some biological samples, cells, enzymes, or proteins.

20.6 PCR Biochip

Polymerase chain reaction (PCR) is a method in molecular biology that is used to produce millions of copies of a specific DNA sequence. There are three basic steps in PCR. First, the target genetic material must be denatured; that is, the strands of its helix must be unwound and separated by heating to 90℃ – 96℃. The second step is hybridization or annealing, in which the primers bind to their complementary bases on the now single-stranded DNA. The third is DNA synthesis by a polymerase. The result is two new helixes in place of the first, each composed of one of the original strands plus its newly assembled complementary strand. To get moreDNA, these steps can be repeated. The amounts will double every time. Each cycle takes only 1 – 3 min, so repeating the process for just 45 min can generate millions of copies of a specific DNA strand. PCR requires a machine that can control these temperature variations; thus, the heater, cooler, and their operation mode are very important for amplification efficiency of PCR.

However, conventional PCR instruments usually achieve a ramping rate of about 1℃/s – 2℃/s in the temperature range relevant for PCR, where a complete PCR analysis needs approximately 1 – 2 h. Fortunately, since the introduction of the first PCR chip, all kinds of PCR microfluidic technologies have facilitated DNA amplification with much faster rates as the result of smaller thermal capacity and larger heat transfer rate between the PCR sample and temperature-controlled components, which have advantages of small sizes, fast ramping rates, low cost, high integration, and so on.

The reported PCR biochips fall into three broad categories. In the first, a chamber stationary PCR biochip was described by Northrup et al.[57] in 1993 (Fig. 20.17), where a microwell cavity structure acts as an appropriate PCR reaction chamber fabricated by using silicon anisotropic wet etching. An amplification of 20 cycles was carried out in a 50 μL microwell, fourfold faster than in a conventional PCR device, along with a much lower consumption of power.

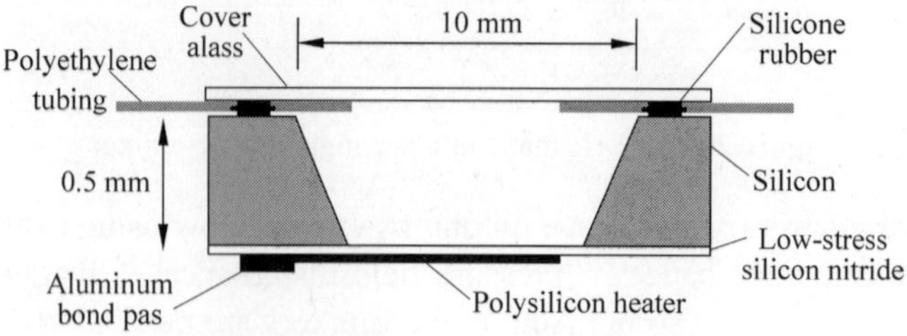

Figure 20.17 Northrup's PCR chip

The group of Prof. Cui[58] designed and fabricated a chamber stationary PCR biochip, shown in Fig. 20.18(a). The size of the biochip was 4 mm×8 mm, the size of the reaction chamber was 2 mm×4 mm×0.3 mm, and the volume of PCR reaction was approximately 2 μL. By means of pulse width modulation (PWM) technology, the same group developed a miniaturized heat cycler system matching with above PCR biochip with the heating rate of 15℃/s, cooling rate of 10℃/S, shown in Fig. 20.18(b). A standard hepatitis B (HB) testing reagent test was successfully realized by using this PCR biochip and its miniaturized system.

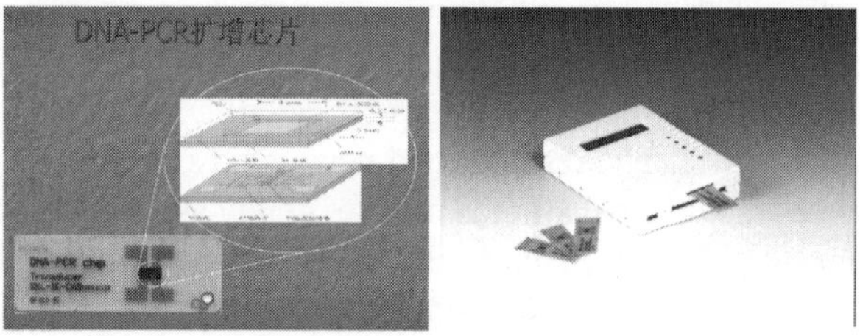

(a) (b)

Figure 20.18 (a) DNA-PCR chip, (b) a miniaturized heat cycler system (see color figure at the end of this book)

By means of thin-film technology in combination with MEMS technology, the group of Cui[59] reported an integrated PCR biochip with temperature sensor, where a novel thermoelectric layer was splashed on the back side of the chamber, according to Peltier model, to control the temperature of the chamber, shown in Fig. 20.19. The processes of heating and cooling were easily switched by changing the direction of the current.

To improve the PCR throughput and reduce the analysis time as well as the required labor (due to the introduction of a robot to inject the sample), multi-chamber stationary PCR microfluidics on a single chip was explored by Daniel et al.[60].

The second class of PCR biochip is flowthrough PCR microfluidics chip. Kopp et al.[61] developed a serpentine rectangular channel based flowthrough PCR

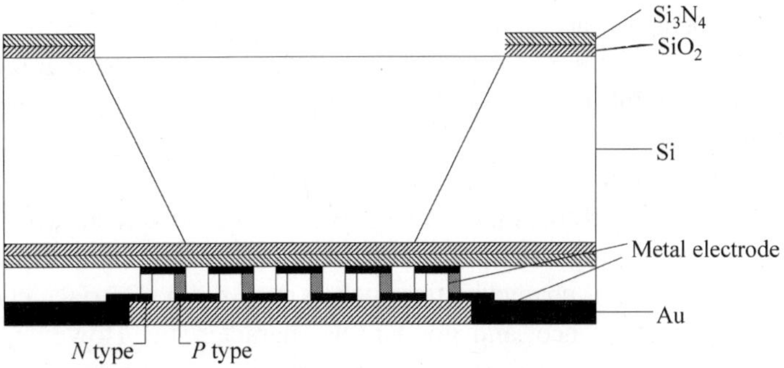

Figure 20.19 Schematic of PCR-chip integrated with thermoelectric material

microfluidics chip, shown in Fig. 20.20. The channel passed 20 times through three temperature zones of 95℃, 60℃, and 77℃, respectively. With flow rates between 5.8 nL/s and 72.9 nL/s, the transition time between two temperatures was less than 100 ms and the total amplification time was between 18.8 min and 1.5 min. The current flowthrough PCR chips have a higher rate of heating cycle.

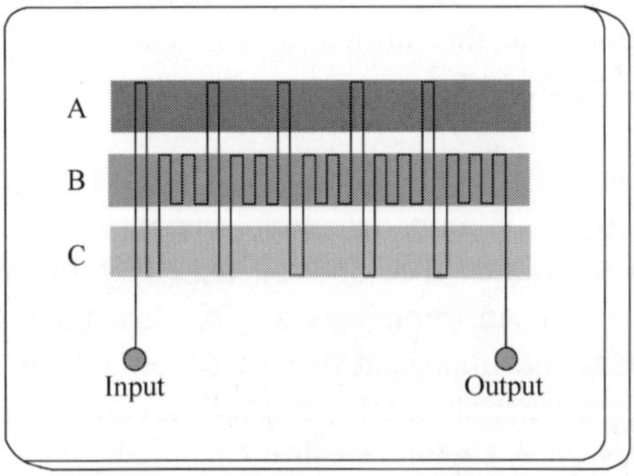

A 95℃ -melting B 77℃ -extension C 60℃ -annealing

Figure 20.20 Schematic of a microfluidic chip for flowthrough PCR. Three well-defined zones are kept at 95℃, 77℃, and 60℃ by means of thermostated copper blocks

The third class of PCR biochip is similar to the second one, except for the difference that the PCR reaction solution is fixed and three modules having different temperatures successively running are used to heat the solution[62].

Suitable substrate material is one of the most important factors that influence PCR microfluidics. From the 1990 s to date almost all PCR microchambers (or microchannels) were constructed from silicon as the substrate because the standard photolithography and chemical etching techniques could be used conveniently and effectively for silicon material to produce the microfluidic networks. In addition, the silicon material has superior thermal conductivity, allowing for very fast ramping times. Furthermore, the various metal film heaters and sensors are easily patterned on its surface so as to provide a high degree of integration. However, silicon as a substrate material for the PCR chamber also has disadvantages. First, the bare silicon inhibits the PCR reaction by reducing the amplification efficiency and even may not exhibit any amplification reaction at all. Second, the high conductivity of silicon proves to be problematic when applying high voltages necessary to induce electroosmotic flow (EOF). Third, the silicon substrate is not transparent, often limiting the application of real-time optical detection. Glass possesses some beneficial characteristics such as well-defined surface chemistries, superior optical transparence, and good EOF characteristic. However, the PCR microfluidics made from silicon or glass material are not disposable due to the higher cost of fabrication.

Although no single substrate material can offer a preferable solution to all these restrictions including cost, ease of fabrication, disposability, biocompatibility, optical transparence, etc., polymers might show their superiority over silicon/glass and become the very promising substrate materials for PCR microfluidics. In only 4 years or 5 years, about ten categories of polymers, including polydimethylsiloxane (PDMS), polycarbonate (PC), polymethylmethacrylate (PMMA), polyimide (PI), polyethylene, terephthalate (PET), SU-8, poly(cyclic olefin), and epoxy, have been successfully applied to the fabrication of PCR microfluidics and they are also believed to have a perfect future as the substrate materials of choice for PCR microfluidics.

There are many methods of detection of PCR amplification products for PCR microfluidics. The most common detection scheme is off-line or on-line CE separation of the PCR product (see above), usually followed by laser-induced fluorescence detection or, in some cases, EC detection. Fluorescence-based detection is a powerful and important detection method for PCR microfluidics. Real-time detection is another alternative method. It can be realized by kinetically measuring the fluorescence signals resulting from the interaction between the fluorescent dye/probes and the increasing amount of double-stranded DNA, where one can observe the yields of the PCR process as soon as they reach the detection threshold, rather than waiting till all the cycles necessary for the total PCR process have been completed. Taylor et al.[63] made use of real-time detection technology to monitor the PCR reaction in the microchamber etched in a silicon wafer. Belgrader et al.[64] designed and fabricated a portable real-time detector for PCR microfluidics. For the given PCR chip, the volume of reaction was 25 μL, and the detection time for *Hemochroma-Tosis* was just approximately 20 min.

The PCR microfluidics is the main component of the μTAS, and presently, partially integrated PCR microfluidics are increasingly being developed, including the integration of PCR with CE, DNA microarray hybridization, and/or sample preparation, respectively, on single microfluidic devices. Water et al.[65] reported an integrated biochip including cell lysis, PCR amplification, and capillary electrophoresis. To take advantages of the superiority of PCR microfluidics and DNA microarrays, a highly integrated microfluidic device has been developed on a PC wafer smaller than a credit card, which is capable of extracting and concentrating nucleic acids from milliliter aqueous samples and performing microliter chemical reactions, serial enzymatic reactions, metering, mixing, and nucleic acid hybridization.

Besides the integration of PCR microfluidics with CE or microarray hybridization, the function of sample preparation has also been integrated into these devices to circumvent the possible inhibition of amplification or the success of PCR analytical instruments by chemical interference. Cepheid company produced an integrated biochip comprising sample pretreatment, PCR reaction, and fluorescence detection, shown in Fig. 20.21, which would be applied widely with the least contamination.

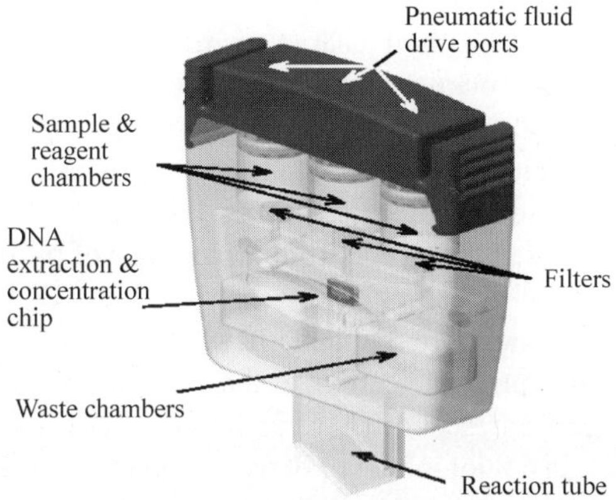

Figure 20.21 Integrated PCR chip with sample pretreatment

20.7 Capillary Electrophoresis Microfluidic Chip

20.7.1 Structure and Development

Capillary electrophoresis microfluidic chip (CE microchip) is a microcolumn separation technique that can separate target analytes on the basis of differences in electrophoretic mobility, via the application of high electric fields (several hundreds of V/cm) by using micro channels in glass, quartz, silicon, or polymer chips. Micro capillary electrophoresis (CE) chips fabricated by micromachining technologies have been widely used in analyzing biological molecules such as proteins and DNA samples. The analyzing technique using micro CE has several advantages over conventional large-scale counterparts, including high separation efficiency, miniaturization, low sample/reagent consumption, and high detection limit.

Briefly, CE chip consists of an injection channel intersecting with a separation channel fabricated on each device. The injection channel connects the sample) and sample waste, while separation channel connects the buffer and buffer waste. Electrical contacts are established on the CE chip by inserting Pt wires into the reservoirs or by micromachining microelectrodes at the bottom of the reservoirs. Several potentials are applied in the different channels to force the solution to flow and design well-defined sample plugs. The first capillary electrophoresis (CE) chip employed a T-injector design. Then some CE chips included cross- and double-T injectors. Pinched injection, gated injection, and floating injection have been also developed for the generation of well-defined plugs in various analytical applications.

Various modes of CE chip can be used depending upon the characteristics of sample mixture to be separated. Capillary zone electrophoresis (CZE) separates charged compounds based on their charge to mass ratio (electromobility), and micellar electrokinetic chromatography (MEKC) can separate both charged and neutral compounds based on differential partitioning into a moving micelle pseudophase (hydrophobicity). Capillary isoelectric focusing (CIEF) separates proteins and peptides based on their isoelectric points (p*I* values). Capillary gel electrophoresis is often used for sized-based separations of protein and DNA.

Many different types of detectors can be interfaced to CE chips. Most organic molecules contain a chromophore that absorbs in the UV region from 195 to 254 nm; therefore, UV absorption detection is the most commonly used detection method. Laser-induced fluorescence (LIF) is the most sensitive detection method but analytes must contain a fluorophore or derivatization is required. Other detection modes used in conjunction with CE include MS or conductivity measurement.

Most CE microchips have been fabricated from silicon or glass substrates using well-established semiconductor technology[66]. However, the fabrication process is expensive, time-consuming, and labor-intensive. Alternatively, polymer substrates, including PDMS[67], polycarbonate[68], and polymethylmethacrylate (PMMA)[69], are promising materials for building microchips. As an excellent microchip material, PDMS has shown a number of advantages over other polymer materials: PDMS microchips can be easily replicated and produced by rapid prototype approaches to low cost, so it is widely used to fabricate all kinds of microchip for different applications. The excellent optical transparency (from 230 nm to 700 nm wavelength) of PDMS has been exploited to integrate different elements in the optical detection and fabricate PDMS microoptical element. One of the most important advantages of PDMS microchips is that PDMS replica allows for a simple and reversible sealing with many planar substrates, thus removing the constraints of elaborate bonding procedures.

Liu and Cui[70] developed a rigid glass/PDMS/glass sandwich CE microchip by thin-casting method, shown in Fig. 20.22. For the given microchip, a thin PDMS membrane with microfluidic networks was sandwiched between top and bottom glass plates. Compared to the previously reported PDMS microchip, the rigid PDMS sandwich microchip without any plasma oxygen process could withstand higher internal pressures and showed better heat-dissipation properties. In addition, the PDMS sandwich microchip provides a user-friendly rigid interface just like glass microchip, so it is easier to fix microtubes for microfluidic transport, and this provided a substantial advantage for microchip sealing and transporting.

Figure 20.22 SEM of the rigid glass/PDMS/glass sandwich CE microchip

Capillary array electrophoresis for massive parallelization of electrophoresis has also been demonstrated. Shi et al.[71] developed 96-channel radial capillary electrophoresis chip, which had separation channels (100 μm wide and 50 μm deep) with 200 μm twin-T injectors, shown in Fig. 20.23. For the given chip, detection

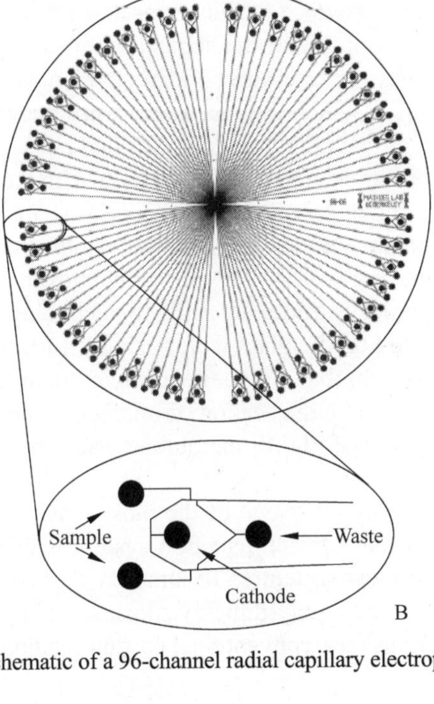

Figure 20.23 Schematic of a 96-channel radial capillary electrophoresis microplate

was performed using a laser-excited galvoscanner and 96 different DNA samples could be injected, separated, and detected in less than 8 min. Paegel et al.[72] presented a microfabricated electrophoretic bioprocessor for DNA sequencing, sample desalting, template removal, preconcentration, and CE analysis. This highly integrated device has been optimized so as to have as many as 384 separate lanes for capillary array electrophoresis on a single chip[73].

Recently two-dimensional liquid-phase separation has been conducted on-chip, which extends the application of CE chip. A MEKC/CE was reported by Rocklin et al.[74]. The first-dimensional MEKC separation was followed by a second-dimensional CE separation to separate the tryptic digests of cytochrome c, β-lactalbumin, and ribonuclease A.

20.7.2 Integrated CE Chip

One of the more significant advantage of microfluidic chip is the ability to integrate multiple analytical steps onto a single device, leading to the development of the so-called 'lab-on-a-chip' or 'micro total analytical system'.

Joshua et al.[75] integrated high-voltage electrodes for electrophoresis into a polymer layer that was able to be reversibly bound to glass microchips for electrophoretic separations. By using the liquid precursor to the polymer polydimethylsiloxane (PDMS), platinum electrodes and reservoirs were positioned prior to solidification, providing a simple and flexible method for electrode interface construction. The interface functioned as an electrofluidic interface between the high-voltage power supply and the separation channel and, when reversibly sealed to an etched glass plate, it served as a cover plate establishing a hybrid PDMS–glass microchip in which the electrodes were directly integrated into the device. The versatility of this chip was demonstrated not only by separating DNA fragments in a novel buffer sieving matrix, but also with the molecular diagnostic analysis of a variety of DNA samples for Duchenne muscular dystrophy and cytomegalovirus (CMV) infection, using both microchip interface configurations.

Liu and Cui[76] also reported a poly(dimethylsiloxane) (PDMS) microchip integrated with platinum electrodes by MEMS technology. Since high-voltage electrodes were integrated on the glass wafer using lift-off process, the microchip was a friendly-to-use system that did not need any extra mechanical apparatus for electrode insertion. To improve the sealing of microchip and ensure the uniformity of microchannel material, one PDMS membrane was formed on glass wafer with electrodes.

Optical detection technology is one of the most sensitive methods in CE chip detection. However, current optical detection system is expensive and has large volume and complex optical structure. To simplify the optical detection system, Chabinyc et al.[77] fabricated a poly(dimethylsiloxane) (PDMS) with an integrated optical detection system using a conventional casting method. The microavalanche photodiode detector (APD) was embedded in PDMS and the multimode optical fiber used for coupling excitation light into the microchannel. However, these integrated optical-fiber PDMS microchips, fabricated using conventional casting method, were very soft due to the elastomeric nature of PDMS. Thus, special care should be taken on the course of their experimental operation. Moreover, to avoid PDMS microchannel distortion from rigid optical fiber, the distance of optical fiber was generally kept 50 – 100 μm away from the separation microchannel, which resulted in an additional excitation light beam expansion and lowered the separation efficiency.

Liu and Cui[78, 79] developed an integrated PDMS sandwich microchip (Fig. 20.24) whose optical fiber could directly contact with the separation microchannel, and a thin-casting method was used for fabricating it. In this integrated PDMS sandwich microchip, the soft PDMS membrane replica with optical fiber was sandwiched between the rigid glass plates, which not only showed rigid characteristics just like glass microchip, but also efficiently avoided the distortions of integrated optical-fiber PDMS membrane replica. In addition, a portable CE chip detection system with a small, low-power, and inexpensive blue LED for inducing fluorescence has been also developed[80].

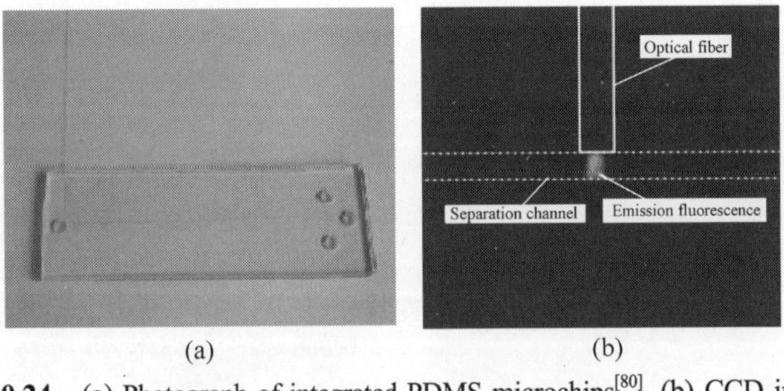

Figure 20.24 (a) Photograph of integrated PDMS microchips[80]. (b) CCD images of fluorescent emission at the intersection region of microchannel and optical fiber[81] (see color figure at the end of this book)

Jackson et al.[81] developed a glass CE chip, which fully integrated electrochemical detection and high-voltage electrodes, and was designed for use with a portable system. The use of microfabrication techniques to integrate permanent electrodes into the chip minimized the number of manual operations required for operation and reduced difficulties associated with variability in electrode placement and geometry. A portable power supply for the chip detection has been developed.

20.7.3 Application

As an emerging technology, CE chip is finding its way into the field including home medical care, field detection of bioterrorism compounds, analysis of materials on NASA space missions, and so on.

Electrophoretic sizing of nucleic acids is a dominating application in CE chips. Negligible Joule heating and very small, well-defined sample plugs result in diffusion-limited separations and superior performance compared with slab-gel and conventional capillary electrophoresis. Rapid, high-resolution on-chip separations have been demonstrated for oligonucleotides, for RNA and DNA fragments, and in genotyping and sequencing applications.

In 1992, Manz and Harrison published the first article about CE microfluidic chip. Since then DNA electrophoresis chip became the mainstream of research which was used for medical diagnoses. Lee et al.[82] fabricated a PMMA electrophoresis chip based on the hot imprinting technology, on which the PCR products of HCV virus were separated and detected. Liu and Cui[78] developed integrated PDMS sandwich CE microchip, on which DNA markers were effectively separated and detected (Fig. 20.25).

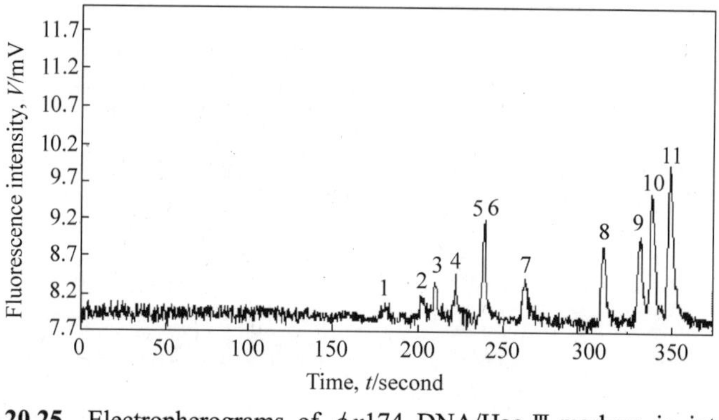

Figure 20.25 Electropherograms of $\phi x174$ DNA/Hae Ⅲ markers in integrated PDMS microchip. (1. 72 bp, 2. 118 bp, 3. 194 bp, 4. 234 bp, 5. 271 bp, 6. 281 bp, 7. 301 bp, 8. 603 bp, 9. 892 bp, 10. 1078 bp, 11. 1353 bp)

Emrich et al.[83] microfabricated a 384-lane capillary array electrophoresis chip that was utilized for massively parallel genetic analysis with a four-color rotary confocal fluorescence scanner. For the given CE chip, simultaneous genotyping of 384 individuals for the common hemochromatosis-linked H63D mutation in the human HFE gene was implemented in only 325 s.

DNA sequencing is an extremely challenging separation task, as very high resolving power is required for accurate base calling. After successful demonstration of single-channel sequencing chips, the group of Mathies[84] developed a 96- line bioprocessor that enabled ultrafast, high-throughput DNA sequencing in microfabricated radial capillary array electrophoresis fluidic circuit format, equipped with a robotic fluid dispensing and a four-color rotary confocal fluorescence scanner. Utilize either straight or specially designed, folded separation channels, the system generated read lengths of 500 bases in <25 min and represented perhaps the next generation of DNA sequencing platform.

Explosives were analyzed by MEKC on a CE chip with indirect LIF detection[85]. Cy7 was added to the BGE to achieve indirect fluorescence detection when excitation was provided by a near-IR diode laser operating at 750 nm. EPA 8330 mixture containing 14 explosives could be analyzed at ppm level in less than 1 min in a 65 mm long separation channel. Ten peaks corresponding to trinitrobenzene, dinitrobenzene, trinitrotoluene, tetryl, 2,4-DNT, 2,6-DNT, 2-amino-4,6-DNT, and 4-amino-2,6-DNT were obtained when 2-, 3-, and 4-nitrotoluene were not resolved and nitramines HMX and RDX showed rather high detection limits.

Detection of life on Mars requires definition of a suitable biomarker and development of sensitive compact instrumentation capable of performing *in situ* analyses. The group of Mathies[86] developed an integrated CE chip for amino acid analysis of Mars because amino acids are the dominant chemical component of carbon-based life on earth, they are very resistant to decomposition, and amino acid chirality is a well-defined biomarker. The state-of-the-art CE chip consisted of channels etched by photolithographic techniques and a microfluidic pumping system sandwiched into a four-layer disk four inches in diameter, with the layers connected by drilled channels. The tiny microfabricated valves and pumps were created from two glass layers with a flexible polymer (PDMS or polydimethylsiloxane) membrane in between, moved up and down using a pressure or vacuum source. To move this analysis to the field, they developed the Mars Organic Analyzer (MOA), a portable organic amine analysis system that consists of a compact instrument and this multi-layer CE microchip. The prototype of microfabricated organic analyzer and CE chip are showed in Fig. 20.26.

(a)

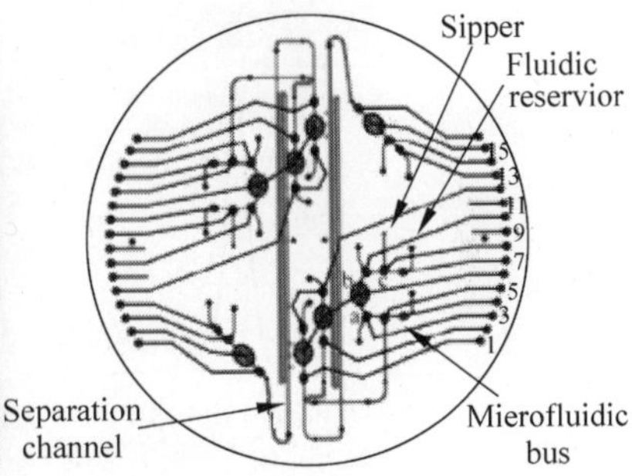

(b)

Figure 20.26 (a) Prototype of microfabricated organic analyzer. (b) Integrated microfluidic chip in MOA. (see color figure at the end of this book)

20.8 Chromatography Chip

20.8.1 Gas Chromatography

Gas chromatography system includes injector system, carrier gas system, column, temperature control system, detector, and auto control/data processing system. Researchers mainly focus on the minimization of injector system, column, and detector on the way of the minimization of gas chromatography system.

The fabrication of micro chromatography column is no longer a difficult problem using the techniques of microelectronics and microfabrication. Lehmann et al.[87] used silicon and glass as the substrate to fabricate a 2 m long column on an area of 20 mm×25 mm, and the cross section was 27 μm×70 μm. Frye-Mason and his team[88] fabricated a 1 m long column on the silicon wafer using the deep reactive ion etching (DRIE) technology. For the given chip, the cross section of the column was 40 – 100 μm wide, 300 – 400 μm deep, and the whole column was in spiral shape and on a 1 cm^2 silicon wafer.

D F Cui and his team fabricated the column on a 3 inch silicon wafer using deep reactive ion etching technology. The thick of the silicon wafer was 500 μm; the column was 6 m in length, 100 μm in depth, and 100 μm in width; and the cross section was rectangular. The column was etched on the front side of the silicon wafer using deep reactive ion etching technology (Figs. 20.27(a) and (b)). After the

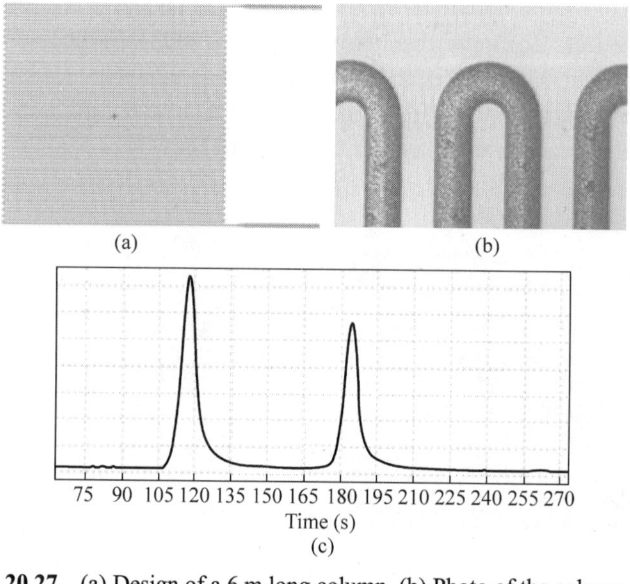

Figure 20.27 (a) Design of a 6 m long column. (b) Photo of the column corner under the microscope. (c) Chromatogram of a 6 m long column (see color figure at the end of this book)

etching, the column was bonded with Pyrex 7,740 glass using anode bonding technology. The gas flow was into the inlet, through the 6 m long 'S'-shaped column and out of the column. Column temperature was 25℃, carrier gas was He, detector was FID, the mixture gas for separation was benzene and toluene, sample was 5 μL, inject method was expelling air, split ratio was 1:500. The chromatogram is shown in Fig. 20.27(c).

20.8.2 Liquid Chromatography

The ideal minimization of liquid chromatography includes on-chip pump, on-chip injector, on-chip column, and on-chip detector. When these parts are connected, the dead volume is small and it can enhance the column efficiency. Minimized liquid chromatography was used to study some of the initial theoretical work on scale-down devices, which was published as early as the 1950s — for example, by van Deemter et al.[89] on packed-column liquid chromatography. These papers led to the development of commercial gas chromatographs using capillaries with micrometer diameters, and liquid chromatographs with micrometer-scale particles for the stationary phase.

On-chip chromatographic separations have been attempted by trapping coated beads within a microchannel network, or using *in situ* microfabricated or polymerized beds. Micromachining technology provides a route to high-efficiency micro- and nanovolume liquid chromatography columns, which is simpler and probably more reproducible than the conventional packed column approach. Based on the ease with which millions of submicrometer-size structural features are micromachined into silicon wafers in the production of computer chips, hundreds of columns will be possibly fabricated on a single wafer.

With the development of MEMS and the cross-link of many disciplines, integrated liquid chromatography (LC) chips emerged because of their significant advantages over conventional systems. However, they were very challenging to build due to the high complexity of LC systems and the need for high-level integration of many discrete microfluidic devices. He et al.[90] developed an integrated ion liquid chromatography chip, including column, frits/filters, injector, and conductivity detector, on which separation and detection of anions in water (~25 ppm) were successfully achieved. The detection limit was estimated to be 1 ppm for the common anions.

20.9 Microfluidic Hybridization and Immunoassay Biochips

Hybridization reaction or immunoreaction is often used for analytical detection and assay in the fields of molecular biology, life sciences, environmental science, and so on. The earlier form of these reactions is microarray chip: some microarray chips entered commercial market several years later. With the development of MEMS technology, fluidics and biotechnology, microfluidic hybridization and immunoassay biochip has appeared.

20.9.1 Microfluidic Hybridization Biochip

Using microfluidic chip, solid-phase DNA hybridization has been carried out between the probes immobilized on glass microchannels and their complementary oligonucleotides by continuously flowing reagents through the microchannels. Hybrid time could be shortened from hours to minutes.

Wang et al.[91] designed and fabricated a PMMA microfluidic chip with four spots of DNA probes for detection of low-abundance point mutation in the K-ras gene. Aminated 24 mer DNA probes were immobilized via glutaraldehyde linkage on the amine groups on the surface of PMMA microchannel. Hybrid time was reduced from 3 h in a conventional array to less than 1 min in the microfluidic chip.

DNA hybridization has been carried out on beads. For instance, Fan et al.[92] made use of target-bearing paramagnetic polystyrene beads to realize DNA hybridization in microchannels. Simultaneous interrogations of four DNA targets consecutively by five probes were achieved in eight microchannels within the microfluidic chip. DNA targets (25 – 50 mer) were immobilized on paramagnetic beads either by interaction between the streptavidin-coated beads and biotinylated DNA targets (25 – 30 mer) or by base pairing between $(dT)_{25}$ oligonucleotide beads and poly-A-tailed target DNA.

DNA hybridization was also conducted after PCR. Integrated microfluidic chip system including DNA hybridization and PCR was designed by Anderson et al.[93] and Liu et al.[94], which has been illuminated in the next section.

20.9.2 Microfluidic Immunoassay Biochip

Immunoassay involves the use of the highly specific antibody–antigen interaction for assay of the antigen or the antibody, which is generally classified into the homogenous and the heterogeneous formats. Thus there are two types of immunoassay biochips. For homogenous immunoassay, the reaction is carried out in solution. So capillary electrophoresis chip technology is usually used to separate and detect the products of the immunoreaction. Cheng et al.[95] designed and fabricated a multichannel microfluidic system for homogeneous immunoassay by using affinity capillary electrophoresis. Simultaneous immunoassays for ovalbumin and anti-estradiol were performed on a six-channel microfluidic chip within 60 s. In another report[96], a glass microfluidic chip consisting of a precolumn reactor, a CE separation channel, and a postcolumn reactor was used for an electrochemical enzyme immunoassay. While the precolumn reactor was used for the binding of mouse IgG by the ALP-labeled antibody (goat anti-moused IgG), the postcolumn reactor was used for the enzymatic conversion of the ALP substrate, 4-aminophenyl phosphate (APP). Amperometic detection of APP was achieved using a carbon ink electrode.

One form of heterogeneous immunoassay is called enzyme-linked immunosorbent immunoassay (ELISA), which can be conducted in microfluidic biochip. Ko et al.[97] described a PMMA microfliuidic chip for electrochemical immunoassay. Horse spleen ferritin (antigen) was attached to the DTSSP layer which had been self-assembled on the gold electrode deposited on the PMMA plate. Then a 100 μg/mL solution of anti-horse ferritin (rabbit serum) was added. A secondary anti-rabbit antibody (HRP-linked) was introduced. A substrate (4-CN) was finally added which was converted into a precipitated product. A reduction in the electrode surface was caused by the precipitate and then recorded in the electrochemical current. Lai et al.[98] designed and fabricated a PMMA compact disk (CD) biochip used for ELISA with 24 sets of assays, shown in Fig. 20.28. A centrifugal force was generated when the disk was spun, and this force was employed for liquid pumping. The LOD of rat IgG is found to be 5 mg/L, which is adequate for IgG analysis (1 – 100 mg/L) in hybridoma cell cultures. The whole procedure took only 200 s to complete in a microwell biochip.

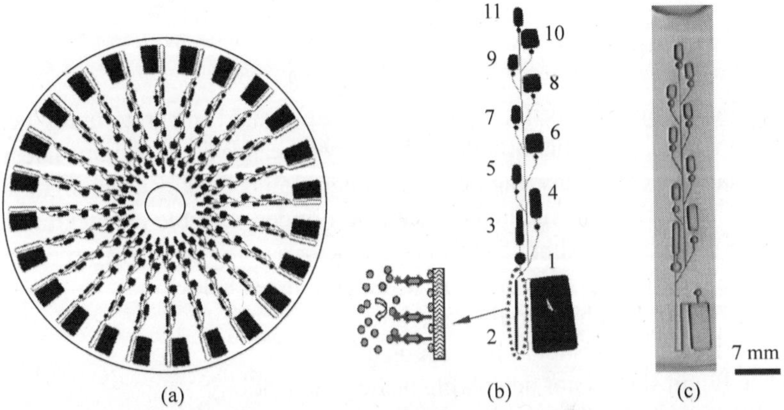

Figure 20.28 Schematics of (a) a CD-ELISA design with 24 sets of assays, (b) a single assay, (1, waste; 2, detection; 3, first antibody; 4, 6, 8, 10, washing; 5, blocking protein; 7, antigen/sample; 9, second antibody; and 11, substrate), and (c) photo of a single assay (see color figure at the end of this book)

Fluorescent immunoassay was also conducted at a microscale. Linder et al.[99] reported a PDMS microfluidic chip for immunoassay of IgG. The IgG was labeled by the fluorescent Cy5. The antibody–antigen binding (signal), background, and nonspecific binding were accomplished simultaneously in the microfluidic biochip by fluorescence measurement.

Recently, several companies including ACLARA, Agilent, Caliper, and Cepheid are invested in researching on microfluidic immunoassay biochips and their systems. Some commercial immunoassay biochips have been developed.

20.10 Micro Total Analysis System

Micro total analysis system (μTAS), also called Lab-on-a-Chip, uses the MEMS technology to fabricate micro biochemical analyzing cell and system on the surface of solid chip. It can detect and measure large amounts of inorganic ions, organic matters, proteins, nucleic acids, and other biochemical ingredients quickly and precisely. It is a newly developed biochemical detection technology based on microelectronics, biotechnology and many other areas. Actually it is a micro-biochemical analyzing instrument for the integration of three main steps: sample processing, biochemical analyzing reaction, and detection of results on a single microchip. It has many advantages such as low cost, high throughput, analyzing process automation, fast analysis, less consumption of the reagent, and easy integration. It can be widely used in biomedicine, remedy filtration, food sanitation, environment inspection and many other areas. It takes the lead in the future trends of analyzing instruments: minimization and integration.

20.10.1 Introduction

A real 'Micro Total Analysis' microfluidic chip should integrate many cells of multiple functions, using microfluidic technology to realize the continuity, integration and automation of the analyzing process. Integration is the key problem of μTAS. According to integration methods, it can be divided into blend integration and whole chip integration. Although the design methods of integrated chip design are various, the requirements are the same which are listed below:

(1) The flow in the chip should be steady.

(2) The dead volume should be minimized.

(3) The liquid should not be volatile or flow unbending.

(4) The mixture should be uniform to prevent formation of bubbles.

(5) The material should be consistent, should not pollute the environment, and should not restrain reaction or lead to degradation.

(6) The fluid should not interfere with signal collection.

(7) The signal-to-noise ratio should be high.

(8) There should be proper disposal of the wasted fluid and chip.

Considering its performance and structural features, blend integration uses separate parts to construct μTAS. This integration method is bottom-up, connecting various separated chips of multiple functions on the board of a micro platform. It does not need to be integrated on a single chip, so it is easy to be fabricated, though large in size, but low in cost and high in quality. This kind of chip is not mature enough in application, it needs exterior detection system such as optical detection instruments, and it is confined in the laboratory, so the cost is high.

Whole chip integration is using top-down design method. First design the requirements of the chip performance, and then design the structure and fabricating process. It integrates the flowing, heating, and detecting function to achieve integration and intelligentization.

Recently, μTAS is not 'micro' enough, and far from 'total'. The integration level is low. For example, many μTAS do not contain sample preprocessing function. The realization of the entire whole integrated chip still needs many years of research and development. What is more, it needs to reduce cost for spread application.

20.10.2 Application

Mathies and his team[100] reported a DNA analyzing chip integrated PCR amplification and capillary electrophoresis in 1996 for the first time, which could complete the PCR amplification of the 268 bp β-protein and capillary electrophoresis in 20 min. In 1998, Cheng et al. [101] developed a micro total analysis chip, which can complete sample fabrication, biochemical detection and result detection in sequence. The system can separate *E. coli* from the mixture of *E. coli* and blood cells. After concentration the cell is broken on the chip, the nucleic acid is released, and then hybridization is detected.

In the same year, Burns and his colleague[102] reported a nanoliter DNA μTAS integrating several operating steps, shown in Fig. 20.29. This chip included injector, mixer, heater, capillary electrophoresis separating channel, diode detector, and connecting channels. The diode detector was fabricated on the silicon wafer, and a filter layer was deposited on the wafer surface which prevented the excitement of ultraviolet light. The heater and electrode were fabricated on the surface side by side. The glass with capillary net and tiny cells etched on the surface was bonded with silicon wafer. The design of the flow system is fine, it can precisely operate the sample and reagent at nanoliter level, and rapidly implement PCR in the temperature control cavity. In the electrophoresis separation and detection system, it can rapidly implement DNA separation and detection. This system adopted separate cells to execute different DNA analyzing and processing functions. Each cell was connected with microflow channels that were fabricated using micro-fabrication technology. All the cells were fabricated on a single silicon wafer. It laid the foundation of the design and fabrication of this type μTAS in the future.

In 2000, Anderson and his colleague[93] in Affymetrix Ltd. invented an HIV chip, including RNA distilling, RT-PCR, Nest-PCR, DNA tagging, hybridizing, and elution steps, that was able to implement multi-biological processes for various

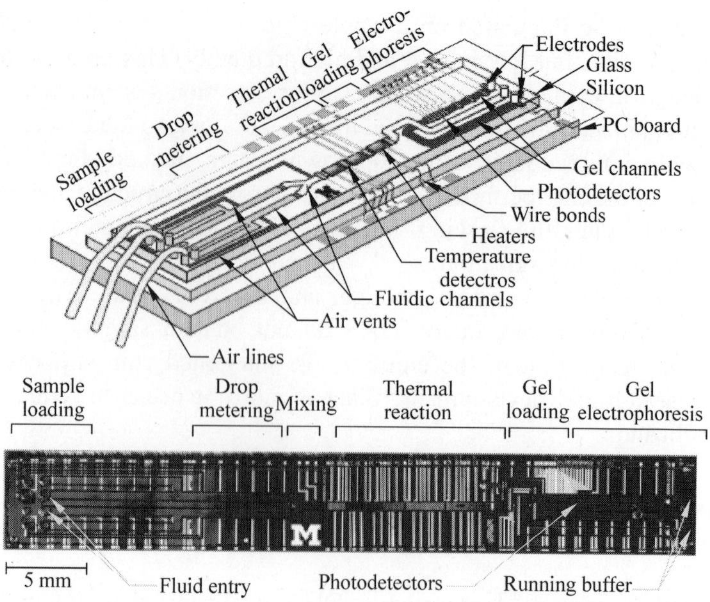

Figure 20.29 Schematic and photograph of an integrated device with a nanoliter liquid injector, a sample mixing and positioning system, a temperature-controlled reaction chamber, an electrophoretic separation system and fluorescence detectors. The device is capable of measuring aqueous reagents and DNA containing solutions, mixing the solutions together, amplifying or digesting the DNA to form discrete products and separating and detecting those products (see color figure at the end of this book)

kinds of samples (e.g., genomic DNA, tRNA, serum, cell lysates, and so on) such as extraction and enrichment, nucleic acid amplification reaction, restriction digestion, detection of concentration, mixing, hybridization, etc.

In 2004, Motorola Labs[94] developed a fully integrated biochip device that consisted of microfluidic mixers, valves, pumps, channels, chambers, heaters, and DNA microarray sensors, shown in Fig. 20.30, which was able to perform DNA analysis of complex biological sample solutions. For the given system, sample preparation (including magnetic bead-based cell capture, cell preconcentration and purification, and cell lysis), PCR, DNA hybridization, and electrochemical detection were performed in this fully automated and miniature device.

In 2005, Pal et al.[103] reported a microfluidic chip system integrated with a valve, temperature sensor, heater, PCR, and CE separation, shown in Fig. 20.31, which was able to carry out DNA detection. Now the cost of the chip is 7 dollar. If the chip size becomes smaller, the cost might be reduced to less than 1 dollar.

Mathies et al.[104] reported another microfluidic system used for measuring DNA sequence, shown in Fig. 20.32. It was a glass–PDMS hybridized microfluidic chip, integrating heat circulation, sample purification, and capillary electrophoresis functions, which included a 250 nL microreactor, an affinity purification micropool, high-performance capillary electrophoresis separation channels, pneumatic valves,

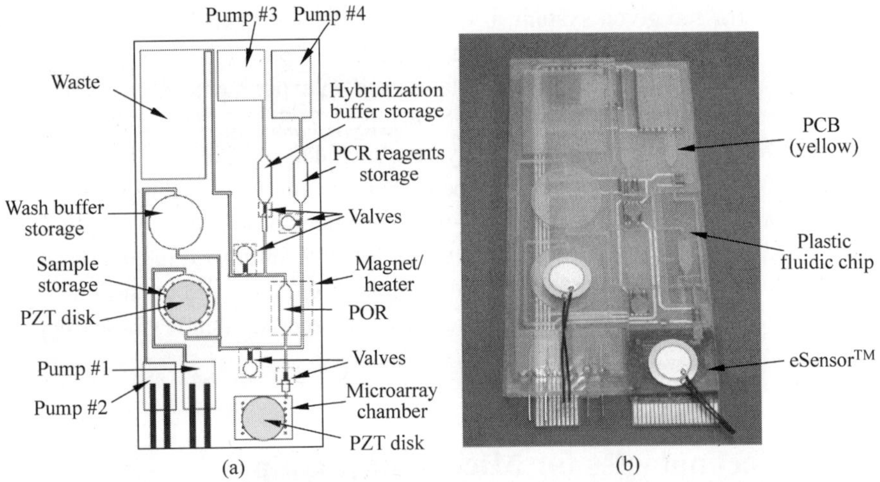

Figure 20.30 (a) Schematic of the plastic microfluidic chip. Pumps 1-3 are electrochemical pumps, and pump 4 is a thermopneumatic pump. (b) Photograph of the integrated device that consists of a plastic fluidic chip, a printed circuit board (PCB), and a Motorola eSensor microarray chip (see color figure at the end of this book)

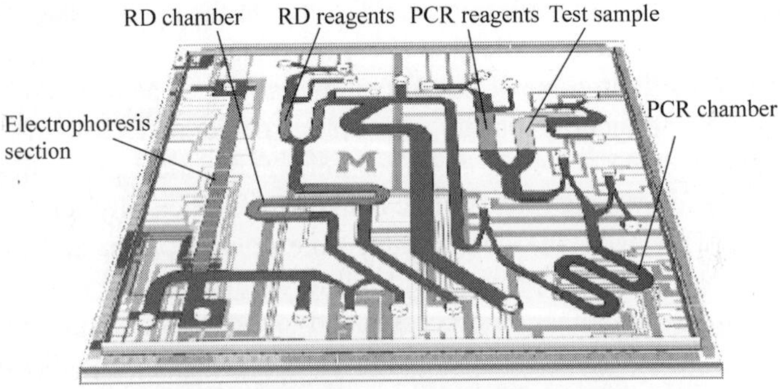

Figure 20.31 Schematic of integrated microfluidic chip (see color figure at the end of this book)

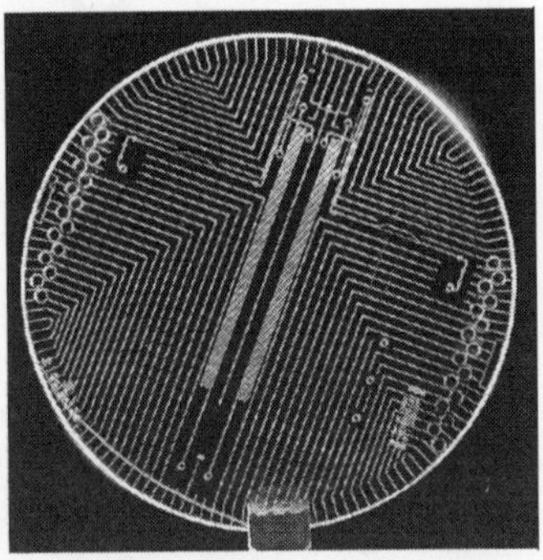

Figure 20.32 Integrated microfluidic chip system for sequencing (see color figure at the end of this book)

and pumps. For the given system, it only needs 1 fmol DNA template to do the Sanger DNA sequence measuring experiment.

The group of Prof. Cui designed and fabricated an experimental DNA computing system, as a typical example of the mixed-type μTAS, for the Bio-X Center of Shanghai Jiao Tong University. The system included a mixer for DNA sample fabricated by MEMS technology, an electrochemical microarray chip for detecting computational solution, a pint-sized self-made magnetic bead separator, a peristaltic pump for driving fluid, and a 24-way valve for controlling fluid. For the given system, 16 samples of DNA, NaOH solution, and buffers could be automatically sampled, injected, driven, and controlled by a microcomputer via USB, leading to an intact mixed-type μTAS.

20.11 Technologies for Microfluidic Chip

20.11.1 Substrate Material for Microfluidic Chip

Substrate material is a carrier for microfluidic chip. In the initial stage, silicon wafer is chosen to fabricate microfluidic chip using the mature semiconductor technology. But there are some limitations of the silicon material such as its unendurable high voltage, opacity, and incompatibility with optical detection technology.

Glass materials have excellent electroosmotic and optical properties; and they are very suitable for making microfluidic chip owing to their physical and chemical characteristics. However, the complexity, time consumption, and high cost of etching and photolithograph processing limit its application.

Hereafter, simply manufacture processes and low-cost macromolecule polymers were gradually used as substrate material. Currently, polydimethylsiloxane (PDMS) – a representative of the organic macromolecule polymer–has already become the focus of research, showing exceedingly ideal material characteristics:

(1) Good insulation property and high voltage resistibility: PDMS has been extensively used for manufacturing capillary electrophoresis microfluidic chips.

(2) High thermal stability: PDMS is suitable for processing various biochemical reaction chips.

(3) High biological compatibility and gas permeability: PDMS can be used for culturing cells.

(4) Perfect optical property: PDMS can be used in various optical detection systems.

(5) Low flexibility modulus: PDMS is suitable for processing microfluidic control devices, such as pump membrane. Furthermore, PDMS can be compatible with Si, Si_3N_4, SiO_2, and glass, and thus it becomes a popular material for microfluidic chip, besides macromolecule polymers such as polymethylmethacrylate (PMMA), polycarbonate (PC), etc.

20.11.2 Processing Technology for μTAS Chip

Processing technology for μTAS chip originates from microelectronic technology, but differs from the silicon integrated circuit processing technology. Microfluidic channels are generally wider and deeper, and the processing precision requisition is comparatively lower. The processing materials of the μTAS chip are already developed from silicon into glass, quartz, and organic polymer. Besides the traditional photolithograph technology and etching technology, the processing technologies such as molding technology, imprinting technology, LIGA technology, and laser ablation technology are also commonly used.

20.11.2.1 Processing Technology for Si/Quartz/Glass Chip

The processing technology of μTAS chip is mainly by means of MEMS technology, which is combined IC integrated circuit technology (including photoetching, oxidation, adulteration, diffusion, evaporation, cathode sputtering, wet etching, plasma etching, etc.) with micromechanical technology, and increases anisotropy and isotropy corrosion of monocrystalline silicon, DRIE, X-ray lithography, electroplating, thick film (SU-8), LIGA, silicon–glass and silicon–silicon bonding. According to the difference of radiation source, photolithograph can be classified into optic beam exposure, electron beam exposure and ion beam exposure. In case of optic beam exposure, ultraviolet beam is usually used as the light source for manufacturing microfluidic chip. Etching technology mainly includes DRIE and wet chemical etching. Bonding technology including high-temperature bonding and electrostatic bonding plays a key role in microfluidic chip manufacture. At present, these technologies are widely used for fabricating microfluidic chips based on silicon, glass, and quartz substrate.

As described above, both glass and quartz materials have good chemical inertness, biologic compatibility and perfect optical property; therefore, they are suitable for manufacturing the microfluidic chip based on their physical and chemical characteristics. Glass and quartz substrate chip have similar technology; only the etching methods are slightly different. Jacobson et al.[105] used wet etching technology to fabricate a capillary electrophoresis microfluidic chip on glass substrate. HF/HNO_3 and HF/NH_4F are common etching agents. To improve the smoothness of the etched channels, HF wet etching can be implemented in an ultrasonic bath[106]. HF etching glass or quartz is isotropic; hence, the etched channel is often trapezoid or semi-circle in appearance.

20.11.2.2 Processing Technology for Macromolecule Polymer Chip

There are all kinds of macromolecule polymers for microfluidic chip, and their physical and chemical properties are highly different. Thus the microprocessing technology shows diversity, which mainly includes molding, imprinting, LIGA, laser ablation, and soft lithographic methods.

(1) Molding

The procedure of molding is as follows. Firstly, the convex positive mold is fabricated by photolithograph or other technology. Then the liquid macromolecule polymer is cast. Finally the macromolecule polymer is peeled from the mold and the replica of microfluidic net is obtained after the macromolecule polymer solidifies. Microfluidic chip is sealed to form closed channels by bonding this replica with other macromolecule polymer replica. Molding is a direct casting technology. The group of DF Cui developed a casting technology for PDMS material. Liquid PDMS was directly cast onto the glass or macromolecule rigid replica to form PDMS thin membrane or thick membrane (even of several tens of or hundreds of micrometer thick), and then bonded with another rigid replica. The research group also developed PDMS sandwich electrophoresis chip, cell separation chip, DNA purification chip, and so on. The technology resolves the problems of PDMS. The PDMS membranes fabricated by direct casting method are too soft and of lower sealing intensity to be conveniently used. Moreover this technology involves a new method to manufacture high-strength room-temperature packaging and low-cost microfluidic chip.

Materials of low viscidity and low solidification temperature are suitable for microfluidic chip by means of molding, such as PDMS, polycarbonate, poly(methyl methacrylate) (PMMA), polystyrene, nitrocellulose, poly(ethylene), poly(tetrafluoroethylene), etc. According to the applied material, the molding technology can be classified into injection molding, compression molding, hot embossing and, soft lithography.

(2) Imprinting

Imprinting technology is a method that also needs a mold to fabricate the chip. Imprinting technology uses higher-mechanical-strength silicon or metal as the positive mold, softens the solid macromolecule polymer at a high temperature, and presses it to form a pattern. PMMA and PC macromolecule polymer are usually used to fabricate microfluidic chip by means of imprinting technology. Compared with the molding, imprinting technology is fast, but the repeatability of the microchannel is worse and the microchannel is more easily distorted. Moreover, the manipulation condition is relatively rigorous.

(3) LIGA Technology

LIGA process initiated in Germany has been rapidly developed. LIGA is the acronym for German words of Lithographie, Galvanoformung, and Abformung. This processing technology can achieve high aspect ratio of the 3-D structure by utilizing synchrotron radiation X-ray lithography combined with electroforming and casting technology. Among the three technologies, casting technology is compatible with traditional IC technology, which can be integrated with micromechanical systems and microelectronic systems. The process suitable for batch production becomes one of the most popular technologies in the field of MEMS. The LIGA can not only process multiple metals, plastics, and ceramics, but also obtain hundreds of micron depth and high aspect ratio of the microstructure, which has been widely used, not only for manufacturing micro-gear, micro-motor, microaccelerometer, microfluidic meter, etc, but also for processing micromechanical system in special fields, such as micro-robot and micro-operating table.

(4) Laser Ablation

Laser ablation processing is a new micromachining technology. The process is as follows: a pulsed excimer laser breaks the covalent bond of the long-chain polymer, and then degrades the macromolecule polymer, forming the decomposed polymer fragment and eventually obtaining the ablation processing pattern. The laser beam is according to the design; the computer CAD compiles the data, and the microholes and microchannels with all sorts of shapes and sizes can be obtained by controlling the position of laser along *x–y* direction. The special characteristics of the technology include small heat damage, vertical channel, and exactly desired depth of the channel. The technology is also called noncontact processing technology. Several materials are suitable for laser ablation method: PMMA, polystyrene, nitrocellulose, etc.

20.11.3 Liquid Pumping and Controlling Technology in μTAS

Liquid pumping technology is an important aspect in microfluidic chip system, which can be classified into mechanical and nonmechanical pumping system.

Mechanical pumps used in μTAS are mainly classified into piezoelectric micropump, electrostatic micropump, electromagnetism micropump, and heat driving micropump. In general, these kinds of pumps have valves, and their advantage is that they can drive almost any sort of liquid. But the driving liquid shows pulse state instead of continuous state. Among these pumps, piezoelectric micropump having advantages of simple structure, large dynamics, high electrostatic pump frequency, fast response, and low consumption, has been widely used. The group of DF Cui developed a piezoelectric micropump, which could fill itself and has excellent properties (Fig. 20.33). A maximum flow of 3.1 mL/min and 29.5 mL/min was reached for water and air, respectively, and a maximum output pressure of 16 kPa was obtained.

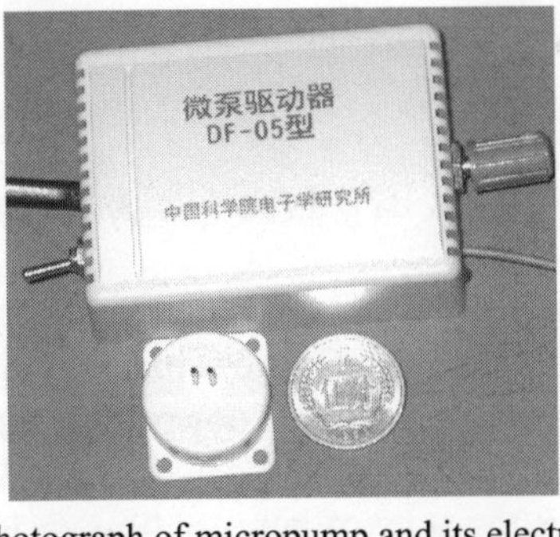

Figure 20.33 Photograph of micropump and its electrical source driver

Nonmechanical pump usually belongs to valveless pumps, which mainly includes electroosmosis pump, heat bubble pump, electrolytic pump, etc., Compared with the mechanical pump, this sort of pumps can be easily manufactured without any mobile components. Thus they are more suitable for miniature integration.

The critical component of the microfluidic control component is the microvalve, which controls the flow of liquid and the mixture of reagents. Microvalves can be of various kinds, including active valves and passive valves. Recently, some passive valves are being manufactured based on surface tension and capillarity, which will make microvalve integration easily in chips.

20.11.4 Packaging, Integration and Storage Technology for μTAS Chip

There are some serious problems in the practical applications of μTAS chips that should be resolved, such as packaging, integration, and storage.

μTAS chips need corresponding electronic circuits and fluidic networks, and the packaging should be safe and reliable with regard to these two functions. Packaging is certainly capable of separating these two kinds of signal lines which are different in nature. Electronics connections should be insulated by epoxy without any exposure, while the interfaces of liquid connections should be open and flow fluently.

The storage of reagents and biologic chips is also important. Unlike microelectronic components, a majority of biologic molecules are apt to lose their activity. So a certain condition and operation criterion should be carefully considered for the demand. For example, enzymes require a low-temperature storage condition. The possible methods involve:

(1) Infusing reagents after assembling the chip, and using physical and chemical methods to conserve, such as dehydration, cooling, freezing, and desiccation. This method operates conveniently, but the liquid reagents are prone to volatilize.

(2) Infusing the reagents and sample just before analysis to avoid volatilization of the liquid reagents. But this method needs much more volume of reagents. The correlative researches are still going on.

20.11.5 Special Problems in μTAS Chips

The development and application of μTAS chips relate to microhydrodynamics, materials technology, biology, medicine, microelectronics and so forth, thereby they are difficult to realize. When scaling down, operating and controlling liquid in chips become different compared with the normal conditions. The flow of liquid in microchips often shows the state of laminar flow instead of turbulent flow. So the flow of multiple liquids will not interfere with each other. This characteristic sometimes is good, but may bring troubles on occasion. For instance, laminar flow does not work when the mixed sample is needed. At the same time, the surface characteristics, such as hydrophobicity, hydrophilicity, conductivity, etc, usually become the main factors that affect the flow of liquid. This leads to difficulties in design and material choice of chip.

When research and manufacturing of microfluidic medicinal diagnosis chips, sensitivity should be paid more attention. Because the bulk of chip diminishes greatly, the requirement for sensitivity of the sensor is enhanced much more. There are 200 leukocytes in 50 nL blood, while the quantity of HIV in whole blood is less than 400 virions per milliliter. So the dimensions of the chip should be moderate rather than extremely small.

The portability of μTAS chips requires not only microchips, but also pint-sized, portable sensors and power supplies. Currently μTAS chips have some problems, such as nonstandard fabrication process, high cost, and so on, which are in the laboratory phase. In order to realize practicality and industrialization of μTAS chips, the cost should be cut down much more, and the fabrication technique and operation flow should be standardized accordingly.

20.11.6 Detection Technique for Microfluidic Chips

The structure of μTAS chip decides the particularity of its detection technology. Compared with traditional detection instruments, μTAS chips require higher sensitivity, faster response speed, parallel analysis capability, and portability. Recently, many detection technologies based on different principles have been used in microfluidic chips, such as optical and electrochemical detection, mass spectrum, and so forth.

20.11.6.1 Optical Detection

Optical detection is the method that is the most widely used in microfluidic chip with the advantages of high sensitivity and good practicability. In addition, the sensors need not contact the analyzed object directly. Laser-induced fluorescence (LIF) is one of the most sensitive detection methods at present. The sensitivity level can be achieved at 10^{-9} mol/L to 10^{-12} mol/L. For some high-fluorescence-efficiency molecules, the detection capability can reach the level of a single molecule. So it is the only detector that has been used in merchandised microfluidic chip systems. But these kinds of detection equipments are expensive and big, and do not match with the microsized microfluidic chip extremely. Therefore, the popularization and application is limited to a certain extent. It is reported that a fluorescence detection system is integrated into the microfluidic chip system.

Recently, there are some reports about the research of chemical luminescence and electrochemical luminescence detection. L'Hostis et al.[107] detected dextrose and cocaine by utilizing electrochemical luminescence. DNA was fixed in the glass channel and detected by chemical luminescence reaction catalyzed by enzymes[108]. The instrument and measurement are simpler compared with the above optical detection method (such as LIF, etc.) because of no extra lamphouse. So it is more apt to integrate into microchip system, and has better application future.

20.11.6.2 Electrochemical Detection

The detection system based on electrochemical detection principle is considered as the most easily integrated system for chips. The reason is that the manufacturing techniques of microelectrodes and microfluidic chips are quite compatible and mass production is practical. Electrochemical detection has many advantages such as high sensitivity, selectivity, specificity, etc. In addition, electrochemistry detection is not influenced by optical path and sample turbidity; it only needs small volumes of sample. A few peripheral equipments are able to realize quick detection. There are mainly three methods: ampere, voltage, and conductance detection.

In 1998, Woolley et al.[109] used electrochemical detection (EC) technology to construct a capillary electrophoresis (CE) microfluidic chip in which the segments of DNA and products of PCR were separated and detected. Later, Wang et al.[110] reported another CE chip with EC, which had a lower detection limit. Gawron et al.[111] described a CE chip based on carbon by means of double-electrode detection. Weber et al.[112] reported a PMMA CE chip using voltage detection. Electrode detection of single-chain DNA decorated with polymer has also been reported[113]. Moreover, a CE-EC chip given by Martin et al.[114] was fabricated utilizing PDMS and using double electrodes to detect.

20.11.6.3 Mass spectrum Detection

As an important method in biochemical analysis, mass spectrum detection technique can give basic structural and quantitative information about biomolecules in sample compositions. It shows immense potential in microfluidic chip detection technology. Li and Zhang[115, 116] utilized microprocessing technique to fabricate microfluidic chip, in which combination CE with an electronozzle mass spectrum chip was used to detect albumen and polypeptide. Deng et al.[117] employed nanometer-level electronozzle to detect microcarnitines in urine. This method makes integration simple in chips, and application foreground is very wide. However, the limitation of mass spectrum detection is the problem of the interface between mass spectrograph and microfluidic chip.

20.11.6.4 Nonlabel Detection

Recently, nonlabel detection has developed fast, which can directly detect changes in physical and chemical parameters caused by reactions. This not only operates simply but also makes detection simultaneously and online. The most representative technique is the surface plasma resonance (SPR), which has been applied universally. The group of Prof. Cui independently designed an SPR angle modulation biochemical analyzer. It had a spread modulation range (40℃ – 70℃), high accuracy (0.001℃), high sensitivity (10^{-12} mol/L), and wide refractive index measure scope (1.04 – 1.47). Both liquid and gas samples were detected by means of SPR. The temperature of reaction pool was controllable and adjustable. The temperature was as high as 95℃, which could satisfy the requirement of DNA amplification. The system was intellectualized to a great extent and had been already merchandised. Furthermore, the same group has invented high-throughput, multi-parameter image SPR biochemical analyzer, which can realize biochip multi-sample quantitative parallel detection, shown in Fig. 20.34.

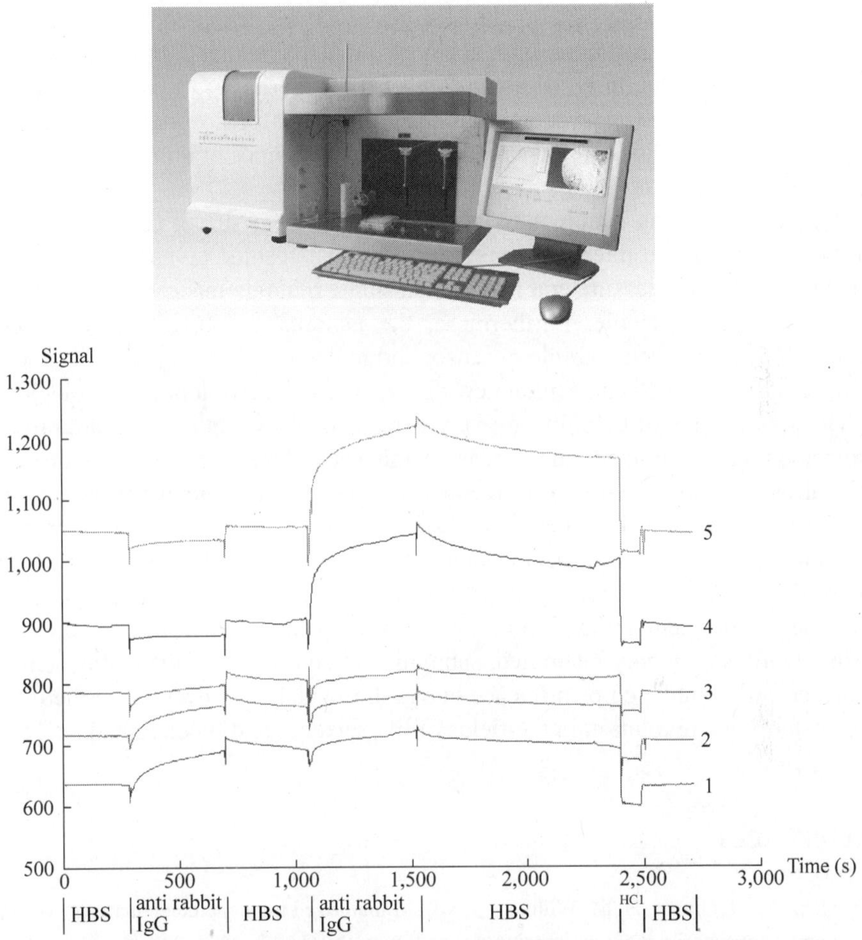

Figure 20.34 Photograph of SPR biochemical analyzer (top) and the SPR testing result (bottom) (see color figure at the end of this book)

In addition, some new detection methods have been developed: ellipsometry and polarized light (EPL), light-addressable potentiometric sensor (LAPS), ion-sensitive field effect transistor (ISFET), surface acoustic wave (SAW), quartz crystal microbalance (QCM), cantilever girder, and so on.

20.12 Perspectives

The biology chip technology based on MEMS has the capability to analyze automatically and process quickly, efficiently, and parallely, which fundamentally changes the mode and efficiency of the traditional biochemical analysis. It is believed that μTAS chip will highly improve and become widely popularized with the development of new processes and techniques in the near future. For instance, a portable 'lab on a chip' is going to be designed to monitor the physical status. Even the remote diagnoses will be realized through wireless communication technology. Biology chip systems are likely to take the place of human operation so as to become the stock apparatus of hospitals and research organizations. In addition, they may turn into the necessities of domestic healthcare in the near future.

Rapidly developing nanometer and MEMS technology drives the development of biochips. Further micromachining of biochips results in nanometer chips, which can directly measure and manipulate single biologic macro molecule at the level of single molecule. Furthermore, the nanometer robot, dosage system, molecule tracking system, biology sensor and molecule executer are in the course of development, which can exploit new directions for the development of biochips.

The applications of biochips are very extensive. They can be used not only in molecule biology, biomedicine, disease diagnosis and treatment, exploitation and utilization of medicament, crop breeding and melioration, biochemistry weapon monitoring, judicatory judgment, and food sanitation monitor, but also in creature evolution and origin, new species identification, and so forth. It is assumed that the profound revolution arising from biochips in these fields will greatly shorten the time people spend on exploring life and bring people numerous resources.

In a word, as a highly integrated, subminiature and intellectualized biochemical analyzer, microfluidic chips influence human life widely and deeply. Furthermore, they can bring a revolution in the fields of life sciences and biochemical analysis.

References

[1] Manz A., N. Graber, H. M. Widmer, (1990), Miniaturized total chemical analysis systems: a novel concept for chemical sensing. *Sens. Actuat. B*, **1**(1 – 6): 244 – 248

[2] El-Ali J., P. K. Sorger, K. F. Jensen, (2006), Cells on chips. *Nature*, **442**(27): 403 – 411

[3] Kononen J., L. Bubendorf, A. Kallioniemi, M. Barlund, P. Schraml, S. Leighton, J. Torhorst, M. J. Mihatsch, G. Sauter, O. P. Kallioniemi, (1998), Tissue microarrays for high-throughput molecular profiling of tumor specimens. *Nature Med.*, **4**(7): 844 – 847

[4] Fodor S. P., J. L. Read, M. C. Pirrung, L. Stryer, A. T. Lu, D. Solas, (1991), Light-directed, spatially addressable parallel chemical synthesis. *Science*, **251**: 767 – 773

[5] Pease A. C., D. Solas, E. J. Sullivan, M. T. Cronin, C. P. Holmes, S. P. Fodor, (1994), Light-generated oligonucleotide arrays for rapid DNA sequence analysis. *Proc. Natl. Acad. Sci. USA*, **91**: 5022 – 5026

[6] Hughes T. R., M. Mao, A. R. Jones, J. Burchard, M. J. Marton, K. W. Shannon, S. M. Lefkowitz, M. Ziman, J. M. Schelter, M. R. Meyer, S. Kobayashi, C. Davis, H. Dai, Y. D. He, S. B. Stephaniants, G. Cavet, W. L. Walker, A. West, E. Coffey, D. D. Shoemaker, R. Stoughton, A. P. Blanchard, S. H. Friend, P. S. Linsley, (2001), Expression profiling using microarrays fabricated by an ink-jet oligonucleotide synthesizer. *Nat. Biotechnol.*, **19**: 342 – 347

[7] Roda A., M. Guardigli, C. Russo, P. Pasini, M. Baraldini, (2000), Protein microdeposition using a conventional ink-jet printer. *BioTechniques*, **28**(3): 492 – 496

[8] Guschin D., G. Yershov, A. Zaslavsky, A. Gemmell, V. Shick, D. Proudnikov, P. Arenkov, A. Mirzabekov, (1997), Manual manufacturing of oligonucleotide, DNA, and protein microchips. *Anal. Biochem.*, **250**: 203 – 211

[9] Büssow K., D. Cahill, W. Nietfeld, D. Bancroft, E. Scherzinger, H. Lehrach, G . Walter, (1998), A method for global protein expression and antibody screening on high-density filters of an arrayed cDNA library. *Nucl. Acids Res.*, **26**(21): 5007 – 5008

[10] Zhu H., M. Bilgin, R. Bangham, D. Hall, A. Casamayor, P. Bertone, N. Lan, R. Jansen, S. Bidlingmaier, T. Houfek, T. Mitchell, P. Miller, R. A. Dean, M. Gerstein, M. Snyder, (2001), Global analysis of protein activities using proteome chips. *Science*, **293**: 2101 – 2105

[11] Mooney J. F., A. J. Hunt, J. R. McIntosh, C. A. Liberko, D. M. Walba, C. T. Rogers, (1996), Patterning of functional antibodies and other proteins by photolithography of silane monolayers. *PNAS*, **93**: 12287 – 12291

[12] FitzGerald S. P., J. V. Lamont, R. I. McConnell, E. O. Benchikh, (2005), Development of a high-throughput automated analyzer using biochip array technology. *Clin. Chem.*, **51**(7): 1165 – 1176

[13] Frisbie C. D., (1994), Functional group imaging by chemical force microscopy. *Science* **265**: 2071 – 2074

[14] Markey F., (1999), What is SPR anyway? *Bio Journal*, **1**: 14 – 17

[15] Merchant M., S. R. Weinberger, (2000), Recent advancements in surface-enhanced laser desorption/ionization-time of flight-mass spectrometry. *Electrophoresis*, **21**(6): 1164 – 1177

[16] Sinclair B., (1999), MALDI-TOF goes mainstream: laser desorption mass spectrometers for multisample analysis. *The Scientist*, **13**(12): 18

[17] Sethu P., A. Sin, M. Toner, (2006), Microfluidic diffusive filter for apheresis (leukapheresis) *Lab Chip*, **6**: 83 – 89

[18] Metz S., C. Trautmann, A. Bertsch, Ph. Renaud, (2004), Polyimide microfluidic devices with integrated nanoporous filtration areas manufactured by micromachining and ion track technology. *J. Micromech. Microeng.*, **14**: 324 – 331

[19] Wilding P., L.J. Kricka, J. Cheng, G. Hvichia, M. A. Shoffner, P. Fortina, (1998), Integrated cell isolation and polymerase chain reaction analysis using silicon microfilter chambers. *Anal. Biochem.*, **257**: 95 – 100

[20] He B., L. Tan, F. Regnier, (1999), Microfabricated filters for microfluidic analytical systems. *Anal. Chem*, **71**: 1464 – 1468

[21] Chen X, D. F. Cui, C. C. Liu, H. Li, (2008), Microfluidic chip for blood cell separation and collection based on crossflow filtration. *Sens. Actuat. B*, **130**: 216 – 221

[22] Huang Y., S. Joo, M. Duhon, M. Heller, B. Wallace, X. Xu, (2002), Dielectrophoretic cell separation and gene expression profiling on microelectronic chip arrays. *Anal. Chem.*, **74**: 3362 – 3371

[23] Hu X.Y., P. H. Bessette, J. R. Qian, C. D. Meinhart, P. S. Daugherty, H. T. Soh, (2005), Marker-specific sorting of rare cells using dielectrophoresis. *Proc. Natl Acad. Sci. USA*, **102**: 15757 – 15761

[24] Fu A. Y., H. P. Chou, C. Spence, F. H. Arnold, S. R. Quake, (2002), An Integrated microfabricated cell sorter. *Anal. Chem.*, **74**: 2451 – 2457

[25] Wang M. M., E. Tu, D. E. Raymond, J. Mo Yang, H. Zhang, N. Hagen, B. Dees, E. M. Mercer, A. H. Forster, I. Kariv, P. J. Marchand, W. F. Butler, (2005), Microfluidic sorting of mammalian cells by optical force switching. *Nature Biotechnol.*, **23**: 83 – 87

[26] Townsend R. J., M. Hill, N. R. Harris, N. M. White, (2004), Modelling of particle paths passing through an ultrasonic standing wave. *Ultrasonics*, **42**: 319 – 324

[27] Coakley W. T., J. J. Hawkes, M. A. Sobanski, C. M. Cousins, J. Spengler, (2000), Analytical scale ultrasonic standing wave manipulation of cells and microparticles. *Ultrasonics*, **38**: 638 – 641

[28] Edwards T., B. K. Gale, A. B. Frazier, (2001), Microscale purification systems for biological sample preparation. *Biomed. Microdev.*, **3**: 211 – 218

[29] Goubault C., J. L. Viovy, J. Bibette, (2003), Capture of rare cells by magnetic filaments. In 7th International Conference on Miniaturized Chemical and Biochemical Analysts Systems, 239 – 242

[30] Carlo D. D., K. H. Jeong, L. P. Lee, (2003), Reagentless mechanical cell lysis by nanoscale barbs in microchannels for sample preparation. *Lab Chip*, **3**: 287 – 291

[31] IchikP T., Y. Sugiyama, S. Kase, Y. Horiike, (2003), Surface micromachined hollow microneedle array integrated on a microfluidic chip. In 7th International Conference on Miniaturized Chemical and Biochemical Analysts Systems, 1025 – 1026

[32] Taylor M. T., P. Belgrader, B. J. Furman, F. Pourahmadi, G. T. A. Kovacs, M. A. Northrup, (2001), Lysing bacterial spores by sonication through a flexible interface in a microfluidic system. *Anal. Chem.*, **73**: 492 – 496

[33] Gao J., X. F. Yin, Z. L. Fang, (2004), Integration of single cell injection, cell lysis, separation and detection of intracellular constituents on a microfluidic chip. *Lab Chip*, **4**: 47 – 52

[34] McClain M. A., C. T. Culbertson, S. C. Jacobson, N. L. Allbritton, C. E. Sims, J. M. Ramsey, (2003), Microfluidic devices for the high-throughput chemical analysis of cells. *Anal. Chem.*, **75**: 5646 – 5655

[35] Lee S. W. , Y. C. Tai, (1999), A micro cell lysis device. *Sens. Actuat. A,* **73**: 74 – 79

[36] Waters L. C., S. C. Jacobson, N. Kroutchinina, J. Khandurina, R. S. Foote, J. M. Ramsey, (1998), Microchip device for cell iysis, multiplex PCR amplification, and electrophoretic sizing. *Anal. Chem.*, **70**: 158 – 162

[37] He Y., Y. H. Zhang, E. S. Yeung, (2001), Capillary-based fully integrated and automated system for nanoliter polymerase chain reaction analysis directly from cheek cells. *J. Chromatogr. A*, **924**: 271 – 284

[38] Chen X, D. F. Cui, C. C. Liu, H. Li, J. Chen, (2007), Continuous flow microfluidic devices for cell separation, cell lysis and DNA purification. *Analytica Chimica Acta*, **584**(2): 237 – 243

[39] Oleschuk R. D., L. L. Shultz-Lockyear, Y. Ning, D. Jed Harrison, (2000), Trapping of bead-based reagents within microfluidic systems: on-chip solid-phase extraction and electrochromatography. *Anal. Chem.*, **72**: 585 – 590

[40] Andersson H., W. van der Wijngaart, P. Enoksson, G. Stemme, (2000), Micromachined flow-through filter-chamber for chemical reactions on beads. *Sens. Actuat. B*, **67**: 203 – 208

[41] Ceriotti L., N. F. de Rooij, E. Verpoorte, (2002), An integrated fritless column for on-chip capillary electrochromatography with conventional stationary phases. *Anal. Chem.*, **74**: 639 – 647

[42] Tian H., A. F. Hühmer, J. P. Landers, (2000), Evaluation of silica resins for direct and efficient extraction of DNA from complex biological matrices in a miniaturized format. *Anal. Biochem.*, **283**: 175 – 191

[43] Wolfe K. A., M. C. Breadmore, J. P. Ferrance, M. E. Power, J. F. Conroy, P. M. Norris, J. P. Landers, (2002), Toward a microchip-based solid-phase extraction method for isolation of nucleic acids. *Electrophoresis*, **23**: 727 – 733

[44] Cady N. C., S. Stelick, C. A. Batt, (2003), Nucleic acid purification using microfabricated silicon structures. *Biosen. Bioelectron.*, **19**: 59 – 66

[45] Chen X., D. F. Cui, C. C. Liu, H. Li, (2007), Microfabrication and characterization of porous channels for DNA purification. *J. Micromech. Microeng.*, **17**(1): 68 – 75

[46] Xu Y. C., B. Vaidya, A. B. Patel, S. M. Ford, R. L. McCarley, S. A. Soper, (2003), Solid-phase reversible immobilization in microfluidic chips for the purification of dye-labeled DNA sequencing fragments. *Anal. Chem.*, **75**: 2975 – 2984

[47] Jiang G. F., D. Jed Harrison, (2000), mRNA isolation in a microfluidic device for eventual integration of cDNA library construction. *Analyst*, **125**: 2176 – 2179

[48] Reddy V., S. Yang, J. D. Zahn, (2005), Interfacial stabilization of organic–aqueous two-phase microflows for a miniaturized DNA extraction module, Organic/aqueous two phase microflow for biological sample preparation. *J. Colloid Interface Sci.*, **286**: 158 – 165

[49] Kamholz A. E., P. Yager, (2002), Molecular diffusive scaling laws in pressure-driven microfluidic channels: Deviation from one-dimensional Einstein approximations. *Sens. Actuat. B*, **82**: 117 – 121

[50] Ismagilov R. F., A. D. Stroock, P. J. A. Kenis, G. M. Whitesides, H. A. Stone, (2000), Experimental and theoretical scaling laws for transverse diffusive broadening in two-phase laminar flows in microchannels. *Appl. Phys. Lett.*, **76**: 2376 – 2378

[51] Liu R. H., M. A. Stremler, K. V. Sharp, M. G. Olsen, J. G. Santiago, R. J. Adrian, H. Aref, D. J. Beebe, (2000), Passive mixing in a three-dimensional serpentine microchannel.

Microelectromech. Syst., **9**(2): 190 – 197

[52] Strock A., S. K. Dertinger, G. M. Whitesides, A. Ajdari, (2002), Patterning flows using grooved surfaces. *Anal. Chem.*, **74**(20): 5306 – 5312

[53] Howell P. B., D. R. Jr. Mott, S. Fertig, C. R. Kaplan, J. P. Golden, E. S. Oranb, F. S. Ligler, (2005), A microfluidic mixer with grooves placed on the top and bottom of the channel. *Lab Chip*, **5**: 524 – 530

[54] Yaralioglu G. G., I. O. Wygant, T. C. Marentis, B. T. Khuri-Yakub, (2004), Ultrasonic mixing in microfluidic channels using integrated transducers. *Anal. Chem.*, **76**: 3694 – 3698

[55] Glasgow I., N. Aubry, (2003), Enhancement of microfluidic mixing using time pulsing. *Lab Chip*, **3**(2): 114 – 120

[56] Lu L. H., K. S. Ryu, C. Liu, (2002), A magnetic microstirrer and array for microfluidic mixing. *J. Microelectromech. Syst.* **11**: 462 – 469

[57] Northrup M. A., M. T. Ching, R. M. White, R. T. Watson, (1993), DNA amplification with a microfabricated reaction chamber. In Proceedings of IEEE International Conference on Solid-State Sensor and Actuators. 924 – 926

[58] Zhao Z., Z. Cui, D. F. Cui, S. H. Xia, (2003), monolithically integrated PCR biochip for DNA amplification. *Sens. Actuat. A*, **108**(1 – 3): 162 – 167

[59] Zhao Y, Q., D. F. Cui, (2006), PCR-Chip integrated with thermoelectric temperature control. *Rare Metal Mater. Eng.*, **35**(suppl. 3): 313 – 314

[60] Daniel J. H., S. Iqbal, R. B. Millington, (1998), Silicon microchambers for DNA amplification. *Sens. Actuat. A*, **71**: 81 – 88

[61] Kopp M. U., A. J. de Mello, A. Manz, (1998), Chemical amplification: Continuous-flow PCR on a chip. *Science*, **280**: 1046 – 1048

[62] Liu J., M. Enzelberger, S. Quake, (2002), A nanoliter rotary device for polymerase chain reaction. *Electrophoresis*, **23**:1531 – 1536

[63] Taylor T. B., E. S. Winn-Deen, E. Picozza, T. M. Woudenberg, M. Albin, (1997), Optimization of the performance of the polymerase chain reaction in silicon-based microstructures. *Nucl. Acids Res.* **25**: 3164 – 3168

[64] Belgrader P., S. Young, B. Yuan, M. Primeau, L. A. Christel, F. Pourahmadi, M. A. Northrup, (2001), A battery-powered notebook thermal cycler for rapid multiplex real-time PCR analysis. *Anal. Chem.*, **73**: 286 – 289

[65] Waters L. C., S. C. Jacobson, N. Kroutchinina, J. Khandurina, R. S. Foote, J. M. Ramsey, (1998), Microchip device for cell lysis, multiplex PCR amplification, and electrophoretic sizing. *Anal. Chem.*, **70**: 158 – 162

[66] Manz A., D. J. Harrison, E. M. J. Verpoorte, J. C. Fettinger, A. Paulus, H. Ludi, H. M. Widmer, (1992), Planar chips technology for miniaturization and integration of separation techniques into monitoring systems. *J. Chromatogr.*, **593**: 253 – 258

[67] McDonald J. C., M. L. Chabinyc, S. J. Metallo, J. R. Anderson, A. D. Stroock, G. M. Whitesides, (2002), Prototyping of microfluidic devices in poly(dimethylsiloxane) using solid-object printing. *Anal. Chem.*, **74**: 1537 – 1545

[68] Henry A. C., T. J. Tutt, M. Galloway, Y.Y. Davidson, C. S. McWhorter, S. A. Soper, R. L. McCarley, (2000), Surface modification of poly(methyl methacrylate) used in the fabrication of microanalytical devices. *Anal. Chem.*, **72**: 5331 – 5337

[69] Liu Y., D. Ganser, A. Schneider, R. Liu, P. Grodzinski, N. Kroutchinina, (2001), Microfabricated polycarbonate CE devices for DNA analysis. *Anal. Chem.*, **73**: 4196 – 4201
[70] Liu C. C., D. F. Cui, H. Y. Cai, X. Chen, Z. X. Geng, (2006), An rigid Poly(dimethyl siloxane) sandwich electrophoresis microchip based on thin-casting method. *Electrophoresis*, **27**(14): 2917 – 2923
[71] Shi Y., P. C. Simpson, J. R. Scherer, D. Wexler, C. Skibola, M. T. Smith, R. A. Mathies, (1999), Radial capillary array electrophoresis microplate and scanner for high-performance nucleic acid. *Anal. Chem.*, **71**:5354 – 5361
[72] Paegel B. M., S. H. I. Yeung, R. A. Mathies, (2002), Microchip bioprocessor for integrated nanovolume sample purification and DNA sequencing. *Anal. Chem*, **74**: 5092
[73] Emrich C. A., H. J. Tian, I. L. Medintz, R. A. Mathies, (2002), Microfabricated 384-lane capillary array electrophoresis bioanalyzer for ultrahigh-throughput genetic analysis. *Anal. Chem.*, **74**: 5076
[74] Rocklin R. D. , R. S. Ramsey, J. M. Ramsey, (2000), A microfabricated fluidic device for performing two-dimensional liquid-phase separations. *Anal. Chem.*, **72**(21): 5244 – 5249
[75] Sanders J. C., M. C. Breadmore, P. S. Mitchell, J. P. Landers, (2002), A simple PDMS-based electro-fluidic interface for microchip electrophoretic separations. *Analyst,* **127**(12): 1558 – 1563
[76] Liu C. C., D. F. Cui, (2005), Design and fabrication of PDMS electrophoresis microchip with integrated electrodes. *Microsyst. Technol.*, **11**(12): 1262 – 1266
[77] Chabinyc M. L., D. T. Chiu, J. C. McDonald, A. D. Stroock, J. F. Christian, A. M. Karger, G. M. Whitesides, (2001), An integrated fluorescence detection system in Poly(dimethylsiloxane) for microfluidic applications. *Anal. Chem.*, **73**(18): 4491 – 4498
[78] Liu C. C., D. F. Cui, H. Y. Cai, B. Su, X. Chen, H. N. Wang, Z. X. Geng, (2006), An integrated PDMS electrophoresis microchip with LED induced fluorescence detection. *Rare Metal Mater. Eng.*, **35**(12): 315 – 318
[79] Liu C. C., D. F. Cui, X. Chen, (2007), Development of an integrated direct-contacting optical-fiber microchip with LED-induced fluorescence detection. *J. Chromatogr. A*, **1170**: 101 – 106
[80] Su B., D. F. Cui, C. C. Liu, X. Chen, (2006), Fabrication of microfluidic fiber chip detection system. *Rare Metal Mater. Eng.*, **35**(12): 325 – 326
[81] Jackson D. J., J. F. Naber, T. J. Roussel, M. M. Crain, K. M. Walsh, R. S. Keynton, R. P. Baldwin, (2003), Portable high-voltage power supply and electrochemical detection circuits for microchip capillary electrophoresis. *Anal. Chem.*, **75**(14): 3311 – 3317
[82] Lee G. B., S. H. Chen, G. R. Huang, W. C. Sung, Y. H. Lin, (2001), Microfabricated plastic chips by hot embossing methods and their applications for DNA separation and detection. *Sens. Actuat. B*, **75**(1 – 2): 142 – 148
[83] Emrich C. A., H. Tian, I. L. Medintz, R. A. Mathies, (2002), Microfabricated 384-lane capillary array electrophoresis bioanalyzer for ultrahigh-throughput genetic analysis. *Anal. Chem.*, **74**(19): 5076 – 5083
[84] Medintz I. L., B. M. Paegel, R. A. Mathies, (2001), Microfabricated capillary array electrophoresis DNA analysis systems. *J. Chromatogr. A*, **924**(1 – 2): 265 – 270

[85] Wallenborg S. R., G. B. Christopher, (2000), Separation and detection of explosives on a microchip using micellar electrokinetic chromatography and indirect laser-induced fluorescence. *Anal. Chem.*, **72**(8): 1872 – 1878
[86] Renzi R. F., J. Stamps, B. A. Horn, S. Ferko, V. A. VanderNoot, J. A. A. West, R. Crocker, B. Wiedenman, D. Yee, J. A. Fruetel, (2005), Hand-held microanalytical instrument for chip-based electrophoretic separations of proteins. *Anal. Chem.*, **77**(2): 435 – 441
[87] Lehmann U., O. Krusemark, J. Müller, A. Vogel, D. Binz, P. Krippner, C. J. Schmidt, (2001), Micro machined analytical gas chromatograph with a plasma polymerised stationary phase. *Proc. Sens.*, **2**: 487 – 492
[88] Frye-Mason G., R. Kottenstette, P. Lewis, E. Heller, R. Manginell, D. Adkings, G. Dulleck, D. Martinez, D. Sasaki, C. Mowry, C. Matzke, L. Anderson, (2000), Hand-held miniature chemical analysis system (μchemlab) for detection of trace concentrations of gas phase analytes. Van den Berg A, et al. (eds). *Micro Total Anal. Sys:* 229 – 232
[89] van Deemter J. J., F. J. Zuiderweg, A. Klinkenberg, (1956), Longitudinal diffusion and resistance to mass transfer as causes of nonideality in chromatography. *Chem. Eng. Sci.*, **5**: 271 – 289
[90] He Q., C. Pang, Y. C. Tai, T. Lee, (2005), An integrated ion liquid chromatography chip with conventionally-packed separation column. *Center for Embedded Network Sensing.* Jan. 1 Paper 466
[91] Wang Y., B. Vaidya, H. D. Farquar, W. Stryjewski, R. P. Hammer, R. L. McCarley, S. A. Soper, Y. W. Cheng, F. Barany, (2003), Microarrays assembled in microfluidic chips fabricated from poly(methyl methacrylate) for the detection of low-abundant DNA mutations. *Anal. Chem.*, **75**:1130 – 1140
[92] Fan Z. H., S. Mangru, R. Granzow, P. Heaney, W. Ho, Q. Dong, R. Kumar, (1999), Dynamic DNA hybridization on a chip using paramagnetic beads. *Anal. Chem.*, **71**: 4851 – 4859
[93] Anderson R. C. , X. Su, G. J. Bogdan, J. Fenton, (2000), A miniature integrated device for automated multistep genetic assays. *Nucl. Acids Res.*, **28**(12): e60
[94] Liu R. H., J. Yang, R. Lenigk, J. Bonanno, P. Grodzinski, (2004), Self-contained, fully integrated biochip for sample preparation, polymerase chain reaction amplification, and DNA microarray detection. *Anal. Chem.*, **76**: 1824 – 1831
[95] Cheng S. B., C. D. Skinner, J. Taylor, S. Attiya, W. E. Lee, G. Picelli, D. J. Harrison, (2001), Development of a multichannel microfluidic analysis system employing affinity capillary electrophoresis for immunoassay. *Anal. Chem.*, **73**(7): 1472 – 1479
[96] Wang J., A. Ibanez, M. P. Chatrathi, A. Escarpa, (2001), Electrochemical enzyme immunoassay on microchip platforms *Anal. Chem.*, **73**: 5323 – 5327
[97] Ko J. S., H. C. Yoon, H. Yang, H. B. Pyo, K. H. Chung, S. J. Kim, Y. I. Kim, (2003), A polymer-based microfluidic device for immunosensing biochips. *Lab Chip* **3**: 106 – 113
[98] Lai S., S. Wang, J. Luo, L. J. Lee, S. T. Yang, M. J. Madou, (2004), Design of a compact disk-like microfluidic platform for enzyme-linked immunosorbent assay. *Anal. Chem.*, **76**: 1832 – 1837
[99] Linder V., E. Verpoorte, W. Thormann, N. F. de Rooij, H. Sigrist, (2001), Surface biopassivation of replicated poly(dimethylsiloxane) microfluidic channels and application

to heterogeneous immunoreaction with on-chip fluorescence detection. *Anal. Chem.*, **73**: 4181 – 4189

[100] Woolley A. T., D. Hadley, P. Landre, A. J. deMello, R. A. Mathies, M. A. Northrup, (1996), Functional integration of PCR amplification and capillary electrophoresis in a microfabricated DNA analysis device. *Anal. Chem.*, **68**(23): 4081 – 4086

[101] Cheng J., E. L. Sheldon, L. Wu, A. Uribe, L. O. Gerrue, J. Carrino, M. J. Heller, J. P. O'Connell, (1998), Preparation and hybridization analysis of DNA/RNA from *E. coli* on microfabricated bioelectronic chips. *Nature Biotechnol.*, **16**(6): 541 – 546

[102] Burns M. A., B. N. Johnson, A. N. Brahmasandra, K. Handique, J. R. Webster, M. Krishnan, T. S. Sammarco, P. M. Man, D. Jones, D. Heldsinger, C. H. Mastrangelo, D. T. Burke, (1998), An integrated nanoliter dna analysis device. *Science*, **282**: 484 – 487

[103] Pal R., (2005), An integrated microfluidic device for influenza and other genetic analyses. *Lab Chip*, **5**: 1024 – 1032

[104] Blazej R. G., P. Kumaresan, R. A. Mathies, (2006), Microfabricated bioprocessor for integrated nanoliter-scale Sanger DNA sequencing. *Proc. Natl. Acad. Sci. USA*, **103**: 7240 – 7245

[105] Jacobson S. C., L. B. Koutny, R. Hergenröder, A. W. Moore, J. M. Ramsey, (1994), Microchip capillary electrophoresis with an integrated postcolumn reactor. *Anal. Chem.*, **66**: 3472 – 3476

[106] Hofmann O., D. Che, K. A. Cruickshank, U. R. Mueller, (1999), Adaptation of capillary isoelectric focusing to microchannels on a glass chip. *Anal. Chem.*, **71**(3): 678 – 686

[107] L'Hostis E., P. E. Michel, G. C. Fiaccabrino, D. J. Strike, N. F. de Rooij, M. Koudelka-Hep, (2000), Microreactor and electrochemical detectors fabricated using Si and EPON SU-8. *Sens. Actuat. B*, **64**: 156 – 162

[108] Cheek B. J., A. B. Steel, M. P. Torres, Y. Y. Yu, H. Yang, (2001), Chemiluminescence detection for hybridization assays on the flow-thru chip, a three-dimensional microchannel biochip. *Anal. Chem.*, **73**: 5777 – 5783

[109] Woolley A. T., K. Q. Lao, A. N. Glazer, R. A. Mathies, (1998), Capillary electrophoresis chips with integrated electrochemical detection. *Anal. Chem.*, **70**: 684 – 688

[110] Wang J., B. Tian, E. Sahlin, (1999), Micromachined electrophoresis chips with thick-film electrochemical detectors. *Anal. Chem.*, **71**: 5436 – 5440

[111] Gawron A. J., R. S. Martin, S. M. Lunte, (2001), Fabrication and evaluation of a carbon-based dual-electrode detector for poly(dimethylsiloxane) electrophoresis chips. *Electrophoresis*, **22**: 242 – 248

[112] Weber G., M. Johnck, D. Siepe, A. Neyer, R. Hergenroder, (2000), In Proceedings of micro total analysis systems. Kluwer Academic Publishers, Dordrecht, The Netherlands, 383 – 386

[113] Ontko A. C., P. M. Armistead, S. R. Kircus, H. H. Thorp, (1999), Electrochemical detection of single stranded DNA using polymer modified electrodes. *Inorg. Chem.*, **38**:1842 – 1846

[114] Martin R. S., A. J. Gawron, S. M. Lunte, C. S. Henry, (2000), Dual-electrode electrochemical detection for poly(dimethylsiloxane)-fabricated capillary electrophoresis microchips. *Anal. Chem.*, **72**: 3196 – 3202

[115] Li J., P. Thibault, N. H. Bings, C. D. Skinner, C. Wang, C. L. Colyer, D. J. Harrison, (1999), Integration of microfabricated devices to capillary electrophoresis-electrospray mass spectrometry using a low dead volume connection: application to rapid analyses of proteolytic digests *Anal. Chem.*, **71**: 3036 – 3045

[116] Zhang B., H. Liu, B. L. Karger, F. Foret, (1999), Microfabricated devices for capillary electrophoresis-electrospray mass spectrometry *Anal. Chem.*, **71**: 3258 – 3264

[117] Deng Y. Z., J. Henion, J. J. Li, P. Thibault, C. Wang, D. J. Harrison, (2001), Determination of Carnitines in Human Urine *Anal. Chem.*, **73**: 639 – 646

21 Micro/Nano Technologies and Their Biological and Medical Applications

Chun-Wei Huang and Gwo-Bin Lee

Department of Engineering Science, Tainan Cheng Kung University
E-mail: gwobin@mail.ncku.edu.tw

Abstract Recently, biomedical or biological micro/nano electromechanical systems (Bio-MEMS/NEMS) have been extensively explored in a wide variety of biomedical applications. These systems realized by micro/nano fabrication techniques comprising micropumps, microvalves, microfilters, micromixers, microchannels, microsensors, and microreactors are also referred to as micro-total-analytical-systems (μTAS) or lab-on-a-chip (LOC). Crucial processes including sample pretreatment, transportation, reaction, mixing, separation, and detection can be performed on a single chip. Various biosamples such as bloods, urines, cells, pathogens, proteins, DNA, or RNA can be used to perform the processes including cell culture, cell sorting and counting, cell lysis, DNA/RNA extraction, purification, amplification, separation, detection, and pathogen detection. In this chapter, these technologies have been reviewed to demonstrate their important biomedical or biological applications in a variety of fields, such as biological and chemical analysis, point-of-care diagnosis, clinical and forensic analysis, molecular diagnosis, drug discovery, and disease detection.

Keywords DNA, cell counting, cell sorting, molecular diagnosis, immunoassay, electrochemical detection

21.1 Introduction

In the past two decades, the micro-electro-mechanical-systems (MEMS) technology has attracted considerable interest and made a substantial impact on a variety of fields due to the increasing popularity of using silicon micromachining techniques for fabricating microsensors and microactutators[1]. The foundation of MEMS technology is the capability to fabricate miniature sensing and moving devices using integrated circuits (IC) manufacturing technologies and unique micromachining techniques. In other words, MEMS are integrated devices or systems consisting of electrical and mechanical components with a characteristic scale ranging from the sub-micron meter to millimeter level. Furthermore, the size of the miniature devices has been recently reduced to the nanometer scale; thanks to nanotechnology. Due to the advent of micromachining techniques and nanotechnology, a unique opportunity to fabricate miniature devices or systems for biological applications to realize the concept of bio-micro-electro-mechanical-systems (Bio-MEMS) has become feasible. Such microsystems for biomedical and biological applications are also referred to as micro-total-analytical-systems (μTAS) or lab-on-a-chip (LOC), which can integrate all functional microdevices for sample pretreatment, reaction, separation, and detection on a single chip[2]. Bio-MEMS is generally defined as the devices or systems that are constructed using micromachining technologies for pretreatment, delivery, manipulation, separation, and analysis of a small amount of biological and chemical entities. As an emerging technology, it has become increasingly prevalent and has addressed a crucial need in a wide variety of biological and medical applications such as drug delivery, health monitoring, clinical therapies, and health care maintenance. Compared to other large-scale devices fabricated using traditional manufacturing techniques, Bio-MEMS devices or systems offer several advantages, including compactness in size, high sensitivity and resolution, low cost due to batch fabrication and sample consumption, the ability to incorporate other functional microdevices on the same substrate to increase their functionality and reliability, and the capability to perform many experiments in multiple microchannels in parallel and simultaneously.

MEMS devices and systems have been fabricated using a variety of materials. Among them, silicon is one of the most popular materials used in micromachining and MEMS since it possesses superior mechanical properties especially suitable for a variety of sensing applications, for example, accelerometers and gyroscopes. These silicon-based microfabrication techniques can be briefly divided into three major categories, including ① bulk micromachining, ② surface micromachining, and ③ lithographie galvanoformung abformtechik (LIGA) processes[3]. The detailed processes usually involve the following steps, including thin-film deposition, photolithography, etching, and substrate bonding. These processes are relatively mature for producing microdevices; however, there are some disadvantages to use these techniques, especially for biological and medical applications. Firstly, silicon is not biocompatible, which hinders its practical applications in the field of biology and medical science. Secondly, the relatively high cost of the silicon chip also limits its applications in these fields since the dimensions of the Bio-MEMS chip usually are several centimeters. Thirdly, the photolithography process requires clean-room facilities and expensive equipment, and most chemicals used are toxic to biosamples. Besides, biological samples are strictly banned from clean room facilities, which are originally designed only for microelectronics applications[4]. Lastly, surface modifications for introducing specific chemical functionalities or ligands for biological applications are not easily performed using silicon-based materials[5].

Alternatively, glass is becoming more popular recently for fabricating microdevices for biological and medical applications. Various microfluidic devices have been fabricated on different glass substrates for μTAS applications, such as capillary electrophoresis (CE) and electrochromatography. It provides advantages over other materials, such as high resistance to mechanical stress and chemicals, relatively low cost, a large optical transmission range, and high electrical insulation. Besides, the techniques for surface treatment of functional groups on a glass substrate for biological and medical applications are relatively mature. It is believed that glass-based microfluidic devices for biological and medical applications will still remain popular in the near future.

Recently, many biomedical microdevices use polymeric materials, such as polydimethylsiloxane (PDMS), polymethyl methacrylate (PMMA), polycarbonate (PC), isobornyl acrylate (IBOA), and polyimide (PI)[6]. Polymers are relatively inexpensive and can be used in disposable devices, thus circumventing stringent sterilization-upon-reuse requirements. Furthermore, polymers can exist in a hard, glassy state or a soft, rubbery state, a distinctive characteristic that is not present in the MEMS structures based on silicon or glass[7]. For example, a technique called 'soft lithography' was reported, which is more suitable for biological applications[8]. A soft elastomeric material was used for pattern transfer in this technique. These soft lithographic techniques commonly use polydimethylsiloxane (PDMS) since this material has the appropriate properties. It is highly biocompatible, optically transparent, permeable to gases, elastomeric, and durable. For example, cells have been successfully cultivated on a PDMS surface and the surface properties can also be readily modified[9]. A μTAS comprising several functional devices for sample pretreatment, transportation, reaction, mixing, separation, and detection on a small chip can now be realized by combining functional microfluidic components manufactured by specific Bio-MEMS techniques. The concept of a μTAS was first raised and demonstrated in the early 1990s[2]. Since then, microdevices and microsystems to realize the concept of the μTAS have been extensively investigated. In general, a μTAS combines various microfluidic devices to form a functional microsystem for measurement and analysis of biomedical samples. For example, a microsystem for fast detection of infectious pathogens can be realized on a single microchip by using this technology[10]. Traditionally, biological laboratory processes, medical examinations, or biochemistry analyses usually involve complicated, time-consuming, and labor-intensive procedures. Besides, all these expensive, dedicated pieces of equipment take up valuable laboratory space. Microfabrication techniques can be used to miniaturize the instrument required for these traditional analysis processes. The functional microdevice components including micropumps, microvalves, microfilters, micromixers, microchannels, and microsensors can be integrated into a single chip to automate these processes. For instance, a microfluidic cell culture system comprising microheaters, a micro-temperature sensor, micropumps, microvalves, microchannels, a cell culture area, and several reservoirs was reported for automatic cell culturing[11]. The traditional manual cell culture processes for human lung cancer cells (A549) can be realized by using this microfluidic chip automatically. It is envisioned that automatic microfluidic systems using micro/nanotechnologies can replace tedious procedures performed in routine laboratories if the mass-production issue can be properly addressed. This chapter is therefore aimed at briefly reviewing the biological and medical applications using micro/nanotechnologies, including DNA/RNA extraction and purification, nucleic acid amplification, DNA separation and detection, DNA manipulation, cell culture, counting and sorting, and disease diagnosis using several methods.

21.2 Biological and Medical Applications

21.2.1 DNA/RNA Extraction and Purification

It is an essential process for bioanalysis to extract and purify deoxyribonucleic acid (DNA) or ribonucleic acid (RNA) from either clinical substances or a mixture of cytoplasm and lysing solution. Numerous microdevices using different approaches have been reported in the literature for DNA/RNA extraction and purification by using electric field, membranes, solid-phase extraction, or magnetic beads. One of the most popular and direct methods for DNA sample preparation is to use electrokinetic forces since the molecules are negatively charged in a water-based solution. For instance, an integrated DNA trapping and extraction microchip based on electrophoresis, using periodically crossed electric fields in a micropillar array, was reported. The DNA extraction microchip, integrated with a micropillar array, microchannels, nanogap entropic barriers, loading and unloading windows, was fabricated by a 3-mask microfabrication process and can extract DNA successfully[12]. The use of electrophoretic, alternating current (AC) electroosmotic, and dielectrophoretic (DEP) forces for trapping a variety of biological entities (from the nanometer to micrometer range) was demonstrated. Various biological objects in a large range of sizes, including Escherichia coli (E. coli) bacteria, λ-phage DNA, and single-stranded DNA fragments have been successfully purified. For example, E. coli were also separated from a mixture containing human blood cells by means of dielectrophoretic forces and then subjected to electrical lysis followed by proteolytic digestion on a single microfabricated chip[13]. The lysate containing a spectrum of nucleic acids including RNA, plasmid DNA, and genomic DNA was further processed by electronically enhanced hybridization on separate bioelectronic chips[14]. Alternatively, a microchip device for DNA extraction was constructed based on electrostatic interaction between surface amine groups and DNA molecules. The amount of DNA extracted from whole blood was approximately 10 ng with a recovery ratio of 27% – 40%[15].

Another approach to performing DNA/RNA extraction and purification is to use membranes. Liquid membrane extraction is an efficient technique for the extraction of ions from the analyte with the characteristics of high ion flux and high selectivity. For example, a microdialysis membrane was sandwiched between two microchips having micromachined serpentine channels. Efficient desalting was demonstrated for both DNA and protein samples, which were ready for electro-spray ionization (ESI) mass spectrometer (MS) applications[16, 17]. The microdialysis system was also used to perform online monitoring of clinical substances[18]. An integrated microsystem for rapid DNA analysis, which couples a compact thermal cycling device based on dual Peltier elements and analysis by micro-CE, was also developed. The use of a microfabricated porous membrane structure provides additional DNA sample extraction and purification, allowing reduced numbers of thermal cycles for polymerase chain reaction (PCR) and enabling complete DNA analysis within 20 min[19].

Alternatively, the solid-phase extraction method was also widely explored for DNA/RNA extraction and purification. The principle of solid-phase extraction is based on the partition of an analyte between the sample matrix and the coating on a fused-silica surface. The coated surface can be directly immersed into the sample or placed into the headspace above the sample, where the analytes of interest are extracted. Therefore, it is an easy-to-handle sample pretreatment method that combines sample clean-up, concentration, and introduction into the separation system. For example, a silica-based, solid-phase extraction system for a microchip platform was utilized in a variety of genetic analysis applications, such as DNA sequencing. The extraction procedure utilized is based on adsorption of the DNA onto bare silica[20]. Similarly, a solid-phase extraction by using silica beads, which were packed into glass microchips, was also reported. The beads were immobilized with a sol-gel to provide a stable and reproducible solid phase onto which the DNA could be adsorbed[21]. Photo-activated polycarbonate (PC) was also used for purification of dye-labeled, terminator sequencing fragments using solid-phase reversible immobilization (SPRI) prior to gel electrophoretic sorting of these DNA molecules[22].

The extraction and purification of RNA/DNA molecules using magnetic beads performed on a microfluidic chip is becoming popular recently. The major advantage of the magnetic separation technique for chemical analysis and biotechnology is the ease to manipulate bio-molecules, which are immobilized on magnetic beads. These beads are commercially available and their tailor-made coatings with specific molecules such as antibodies, antigens, hormones, DNA, and RNA are easily attained. By adopting magnetic bead separation techniques[23, 24], rapid, efficient, and user-friendly processes can be achieved in separating appropriate particles from diluted suspensions and isolation of complexes existing in clinical samples[25, 26]. With this approach, the extraction of DNA/RNA molecules has been successfully demonstrated. For example, messenger RNA (mRNA) isolation for the purpose of complimentary DNA (cDNA) library construction was performed in a microfluidic chip device using paramagnetic oligo-dT beads. The simple Y-intersection flow design can mix beads and the mRNA sample efficiently. Then a magnetic trapping method was used to separate these beads from the mixture.

The detection limit for the rare bicoid gene of Drosophila Melanogaster was estimated to be approximately 2.8 ng total mRNA from 0.85 mg of total RNA (tRNA) by using the microchip[27].

21.2.2 Nucleic Acid Amplification

21.2.2.1 Microfluidic Systems for PCR

PCR is a well-recognized technique for nucleic acid amplification. Based on the proper selection of specific primers, PCR can perform fast nucleic acid amplification *in vitro* to produce a large quantity of a target nucleic acid sequence. The specific primers are single-stranded DNA molecules of about 20 – 30 nucleotides, which are specifically designed to flank two ends of the target genome. Theoretically, the concentration of a certain segment of double-stranded DNA could be doubled during a thermal cycling process involving three different temperatures[28]. Typically, PCR utilizes temperatures in the range of 90℃ – 95℃ for denaturing of the double-stranded DNA, 50℃ – 65℃ for hybridization of the primers, and 70℃ – 75℃ for DNA extension. A schematic diagram of the PCR thermocycling is shown in Fig. 21.1. The concentration of a certain segment of the double-stranded DNA can be amplified by using such a thermal cycling. PCR-related

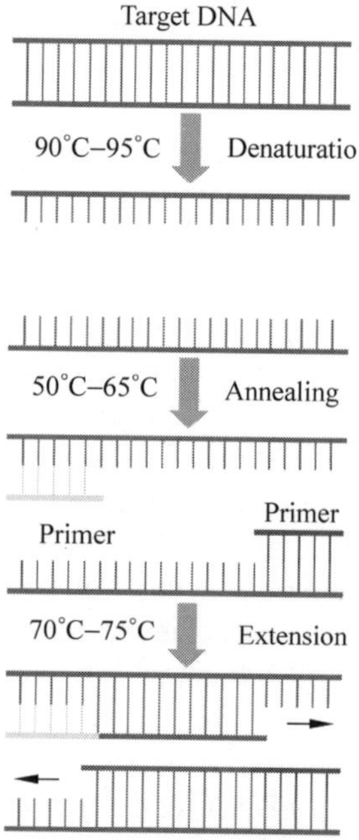

Figure 21.1 Schematic diagram of polymerase chain reaction (PCR) thermocycling. The procedure comprises three steps involving denaturation, annealing, and extension of DNA (see color figure at the end of this book)

techniques are crucial for the detection, quantification, and sequencing of DNA molecules. Micromachined PCR chips have a number of significant advantages, including disposability, low consumption of reagents and samples, portability, low power consumption, low cost, and the potential for automation and integration. Especially, their low thermal inertia accelerates the DNA amplification process. The compactness of the micro-PCR chips and systems may make it feasible for point-of-care applications.

The micro-PCR chips can be classified by their substrate materials. They are generally fabricated on either silicon or glass. Silicon is popular for micro-PCR chips due to the mature silicon micromachining techniques, which allow one to fabricate microheaters and microsensors on the same substrate[29, 30]. It also has good thermal conductivity to perform thermocycling. However, it is relatively expensive when compared with other substrates. Alternatively, silica-based substrates (glass and fused silica) are electrically insulating and thermally conductive. Micro-PCR chips using metal resistors as microheaters or micro-temperature sensors can be fabricated on these substrates[19, 31]. Furthermore, electrokinetic manipulations of reagents and the integration of other devices such as microreactors, electrophoretic separation channels, and optical detection devices in a single device are feasible. For example, integrated silicon-based PCR reactors and glass capillary electrophoresis (CE) chips to form an integrated microfluidic chip for DNA analysis were reported[29]. This platform combines the rapid thermal cycling capabilities of micro-PCR devices with the high-speed DNA separations provided by microfabricated CE chips. The PCR chamber and the CE chip were directly linked through a photolithographically fabricated channel filled with a hydroxyethylcellulose sieving matrix. A monolithic integrated DNA analysis system comprising microfluidic valves and vents, PCR amplification chambers, and CE separation channels was also microfabricated in a glass sandwich structure[31]. Valves and hydrophobic vents provide precise sample loading into the 280 nl PCR chambers that are ready for nucleic acid amplification.

Alternatively, polymers with a higher transition temperature can also be utilized for micro-PCR application. Several polymeric materials have been reported for the micro-PCR chips including PC[32], polyimide[33], PMMA[34], and polydimethylsiloxane (PDMS)[35]. Although their lower thermal conductivity makes them less efficient for thermal cycling and Joule heat removal during an on-chip electrophoretic separation process, the relatively low-cost and high biocompatibility of many polymeric materials still make them quite popular for micro-PCR applications. For example, a serpentine-shaped microreactor using PC material for PCR applications was reported[32]. Not only does it allow for a rapid operation and a high efficiency, but it also provides a high detection sensitivity and specificity for amplification of specific genes. A polyimide-based micro-PCR chip using an infrared (IR)-mediated temperature control scheme was also demonstrated[33]. The developed polyimide-based PCR chip has several advantages including a high breakdown voltage (~1,500 kV/cm), an optical transmission in the useful IR range in which the IR-mediated thermocycling can be performed, and a high glass transition temperature (350℃).

In addition to their classification by material types, the micro-PCR chips can also be divided into two categories: stationary-chamber type[29, 30] or continuous-flow type[36, 37], depending on if the samples are stationary or moving inside the reaction channels. The stationary-chamber micro-PCR chip is directly derived from the thin-wall tube, which is usually used in a conventional PCR instrument to amplify nucleic acids. For example, Lagally et al. reported a stationary-chamber micro-PCR chip utilizing a platinum resistor as a heater and using a thermocouple to measure temperature inside the stationary reaction chamber. Nevertheless, the temperature field inside the reaction chamber is not uniform, which may affect the amplification efficiency of the PCR process[31]. The issue regarding the temperature field non-uniformity inside a PCR chamber can be tackled by utilizing a new heater design[38, 39]. An accurate temperature was maintained within a PCR chamber by means of a predictive control system that operates in conjunction with a neural network. When the system was powered by a portable 9 V battery, the developed system was capable of increasing the temperature in the chamber at a rate of 20.5℃/s and decreasing the temperature at 7℃/s over a working range of 50℃ – 95℃. The capability of the developed system in performing the detection of infectious diseases was verified using a portable system to successfully detect the species-specific gene and the antimicrobial resistant determinant, respectively, in Salmonella.

In contrast, the continuous-flow micro-PCR chips allow the DNA samples to continuously flow through a serpentine microchannel integrated with three reaction regions where the temperatures required for denaturization, annealing, and extension are well controlled. Continuous-flow PCR devices have also been extensively explored[36, 37]. Several constant-temperature zones together with microchannels containing flow-through DNA samples is analogous to an electronic amplifier and relies on the movement of samples through thermostated temperature zones on a glass microchip. The input and output of material (DNA) is continuous, and amplification is independent of input concentration. Therefore, the cross-contamination in a continuous-flow format is significantly alleviated when compared with the situation in a stationary-tube PCR format[36].

Recently, a circulating PCR chip utilizing multiple-membrane activation was reported[40]. DNA amplification was performed while the sample was continuously driven through three chambers with a triangular layout, each equipped with a thermal control module. Instead of using a pneumatic micropump to drive the fluids continuously inside the microchannel, the three membranes were used to control the movement of the DNA samples, which allows one to precisely control the stepwise movement of DNA samples. In addition to the inherent advantages of the traditional continuous-flow PCR chip, without the need for heating and cooling processes, it provides a new design that allows the users to arbitrarily adjust the timing ratios and cycle numbers using multiple-membrane activation.

The size of the circulating PCR chip is also relatively small when compared to previous devices due to the reciprocating triangular layout. Experimental results showed that detection of genes for two pathogens, Streptococcus pyogenes (*S.* pyogenes, 777 bps) and Streptococcus pneumoniae (*S.* pneumoniae, 273 bps), can be successfully amplified using the circulating PCR chip. The minimum number of the thermal cycles to amplify the DNA-based *S.* pyogenes for slab gel electrophoresis is 20 cycles with an initial concentration of 42.5 pg/μL. Experimental data also indicates that the detection limit of the *S.* pyogenes is 4 pg/μL.

21.2.2.2 Reverse-Transcription Polymerase Chain Reaction

Reverse-transcription polymerase chain reaction (RT-PCR) is another process for amplifying RNA. The RT-PCR chip performs two reaction processes: ① a reverse transcription reaction to synthesize the cDNA from the RNA molecules, and ② a PCR reaction to further amplify the specified region of the synthesized cDNA template. RT-PCR can be used for detection of an RNA virus (such as hepatitis C virus (HCV)[41] or for mass production of cDNA for further biomedical applications. With RNA as the template for RT-PCR, the first strand of cDNA has to be synthesized firstly by a set of an artificial primer and a designated enzyme. Secondly, the cDNA is then used as the template for any subsequent PCR process. Finally, millions of DNA fragments are duplicated by repeated use of Taq DNA polymerase. The continuous development of MEMS and microfabrication techniques has facilitated many advances in the micro-RT-PCR chips. The micro-RT-PCR chips can also be categorized into a stationary type and a continuous-flow type. For example, a stationary micro-RT-PCR system was developed for molecular diagnosis of microorganisms automatically[38]. A portable chip-based RT-PCR system for amplification of specific nucleic acids and detection of RNA-based viruses has been successfully demonstrated. On-chip micropumps/microvalves and two identical micro-temperature control elements were integrated to conduct automatic detection of RNA viruses. Two RNA-based viruses, including dengue virus type-2 and enterovirus 71 (EV) 71 were amplified and detected by the developed micro-RT-PCR system. The micro-RT-PCR chips can be further integrated with a sample pretreatment device. For example, by using antibodies-conjugated to superparamagnetic beads, a microsystem was capable of detecting viruses with a higher sensitivity and specificity when compared with traditional biological diagnosis methods using an RNA extraction kit[42, 43]. The target viruses were first captured by the conjugated antibodies on the magnetic beads, and were enriched using a magnetic field generated by micro electromagnets or permanent magnets. Two different types of viruses including dengue virus serotype 2 and enterovirus (EV) 71 were tested for this developed integrated system that can perform mixing, incubation, purification, transportation, and nucleic acid amplification of the RNA-based virus.

For a continuous-flow micro-RT-PCR chip, RNA samples are moving inside microchannels during the entire nucleic acid amplification process. For instance, a micro-RT-PCR chip was reported to quantitatively detect tumor viruses[44]. Test sample reservoirs, RT-PCR meanders, and CE separation channels were integrated on an SU-8 based microchip. The integrated system exhibits high efficacy for heat transfer and superior sensitivity to precisely control the required reaction temperatures in all heated zones of the micro-RT-PCR chip.

21.2.2.3 Digital-Microfluidic PCR

Surface tension is a well-known dominant force used to manipulate droplets in the micrometer scale. One of the approaches to actuate microdroplets is to generate a surface tension gradient that modulates the droplet wettability on the surface. By utilizing surface tension gradient actuation, the motion of the microdroplets can be well controlled without movable components. Droplet-based microfluidic systems can handle and manipulate discrete droplets rather than a continuous stream, which are usually referred as ‘digital microfluidics’[45, 46]. These discrete droplets (in air or in liquid) can be manipulated on an open channel with pre-patterned microelectrodes. There are several advantages to digital microfluidics, when compared with continuous-flow systems, including excellent controllability of droplets, no need for pumps/valves and channels, precise control of sample volumes, and high integration with other microfluidic components. There are two popular schemes for digital microfluidics including ultrasonic actuation (e.g. surface acoustic waves (SAW))[47], and electro-wetting-on-dielectric (EWOD), which is more popular[48–50]. By using the EWOD effect, most microfluidic operations can be carried out using discrete microdroplets with less Joule heating. They also permit excellent control of the fluid flow since they can be reconfigured simply by reprogramming the sequence of potentials applied to the electrodes. For example, an ingenious concept for an addressable microliquid handling technique was reported[46]. Four fundamental fluidic operations including creating, transporting, cutting, and merging of droplets can be demonstrated. Therefore, it is quite straightforward to integrate an EWOD device and a micro-PCR chip to perform a digital-microfluidic PCR process. For example, a hydrophobic/hydrophilic structure to overcome the integration issue of the EWOD-based chip with the on-chip PCR was developed. The integrated microfluidic chip was capable of performing EWOD-based sample/reagent creation, merging, mixing, and transportation as well as amplifying DNA samples. Then the on-chip micro-temperature control comprising of microheaters and a micro-temperature sensor was used for the PCR process. Besides, the developed chip only used an operation voltage of 12 V_{RMS} for digital microfluidic actuation and 9 V for temperature sensing and heating. The capability of the developed chip was demonstrated by successfully duplicating a detection gene for Dengue Ⅱ virus[51].

21.2.3 DNA Separation and Detection

21.2.3.1 Microcapillary Electrophoresis Chips

Electrophoretic separation is a crucial method for separating ionized compounds such as DNA, amino acids, and proteins. Comparing with slab-gel or traditional CE separation techniques, micro-CE chips fabricated by using micromachining techniques possess many advantages including higher separation efficiency, compactness, less sample and reagent consumption, lower applied voltage, and higher detection limit[52]. The common substrates used for the micro-CE chips include silicon, glass, and various plastic materials. Silicon wafers are used due to their IC microfabrication process compatibility. Glass-based CE chips are popular since they provide advantages over other materials such as a high resistance to mechanical stress and chemicals, a large optical transmission range, and a high electrical insulation. Moreover, both silicon-based and glass-based microchannels can be chemically modified to change their surface properties by using mature surface modification techniques[53]. However, sealing silicon-based or glass-based microchannels usually involves a high-temperature bonding process, which can be time-consuming and costly. Recently, plastic CE chips have become increasingly popular due to their low cost and relative ease to mass produce thus making them disposable. PMMA, PC, polypropylene (PP), and PDMS are the most popular polymer materials for plastic CE chips. The corresponding mass-production methods including hot-embossing, injection molding and casting[54], ultraviolet (UV)-initiated polymerization[55] and heat- and UV-initiated polymerization[56] for PMMA-based chips were also reported in the literature.

Chip bonding is an important issue for the micro-CE chips. Several methods to seal plastics-based microchannels including glue bonding[57], solvent bonding[58], thermal bonding[59], oxygen plasma bonding[60], and laminated films[61] have been reported. However, these methods have different disadvantages. For example, glue leakage can easily clog microchannels, making it detrimental to the CE separation process. Solvent bonding requires a specific formulation for plastic substrates and more importantly, may change the surface property of the CE chips. Thermal bonding, being a relatively time-consuming process, is not suitable for mass production of CE chips. Oxygen plasma bonding is suitable only for PDMS substrates and does not work well for other plastics such as PMMA or PC. Currently, a new packaging method using a polyethylene/thermoplastic elastomer (PE/TPE) film to seal an injection-molded CE chip made of either PMMA or PC materials was presented. The packaging was performed at atmospheric pressure and at room temperature, which is a fast, easy, and reliable bonding method to form a sealed CE chip for chemical analysis and biomedical applications. A mixture of an amplified antibiotic gene for Streptococcus pneumoniae and ϕx-174/Hae Ⅲ DNA markers were successfully separated and detected by using these developed CE chips[62].

A typical micro CE chip has a cross-shape channel with four reservoirs at the end of each channel for sample, waste, or buffer solutions. One of the channels is for sample injection and another for sample separation. These four reservoirs also provide access for the electrodes for high-voltage input. As a high voltage is applied in the injection channel, the sample will be driven electrokinetically and moved across the intersection of the cross channels. With appropriate switching off of this voltage and applying another high voltage on the separation channel, a small amount of sample will be injected into the separation channel. With the existence of a high electric field, samples will be moved and separated subsequently. An optical or electrochemical detection method can also be applied at the end of the separation channel to detect separated sample fragments. For example, separation of fluorescence-labeled oligonucleotides, ranging in size from 10 bps to 25 bps, can be successfully separated within 45 s using a 3.8 cm separation channel[63]. Separation of longer DNA fragments has also been demonstrated. For example, DNA fragments (70 – 1,000 bps) were successfully separated in 120 s using hydroxypropyl cellulose (HPC) as a sieving matrix[53].

21.2.3.2 Capillary Electrophoresis Chips with Online Optical Detection Functions

The detection technique commonly associated with the use of micro CE chips is known as laser-induced fluorescence (LIF) detection. With this technique, the samples are labeled with a particular fluorescein, and the fluorescence signals induced by a laser source are then detected as the samples flow through the downstream region of the separation channel. However, the conventional LIF technique utilizes a bulky optical detection apparatus comprising a microscope and various delicate light coupling components. Therefore, the advantages provided by the miniaturization of the micro CE chips are somewhat lessened. Hence, the integration of miniature optical detection systems with micro CE chips has attracted considerable interest, which can provide the means of realizing the separation and online detection of bio-samples. Several approaches toward integrating micro CE chips with optical detection devices have been reported, including using optical fibers[64], liquid-core waveguides[65], solid-core waveguides[66], leaky waveguides[67], and optical waveguides[68].

Typically, integrated waveguides were fabricated by surface micromachining techniques using nitride/oxide or doped oxide/oxide as the waveguide structures[68]. However, the size of the fabricated optical waveguide was limited by the thin-film deposition process and may not meet the requirement for larger flow-channel applications. It is also a time-consuming and highly skill-intensive process to couple the detection light into the planar optical waveguide. An optical leaky waveguide device was fabricated in fused silica using wet chemical etching and bonding techniques[67]. However, the optical loss in the waveguide can be an issue because of the leaky operating mode. The micro-CE chips integrated with optic fibers for absorbance detection are very straightforward and can provide good optical connection between microfluidic chips and the optical equipments[64]. However, their approach included a time-consuming manual alignment process such that its practical applications may be limited. A high reflective index organic solvent was filled into a channel buried in silica substrates to form a liquid-core optical waveguide[65]. However, the performance of the waveguide was affected by the surface roughness of the etched channel and the small refractive index difference at the core/wall interface. Recently, a simple and reliable method to embed etched optic fibers in glass-based microchip devices was reported[66]. A photograph of the micro CE chip is shown in Fig. 21.2. A simple method to couple/connect the detection light source between the microchip and peripheral equipments such as laser light sources and optical sensors was also developed.

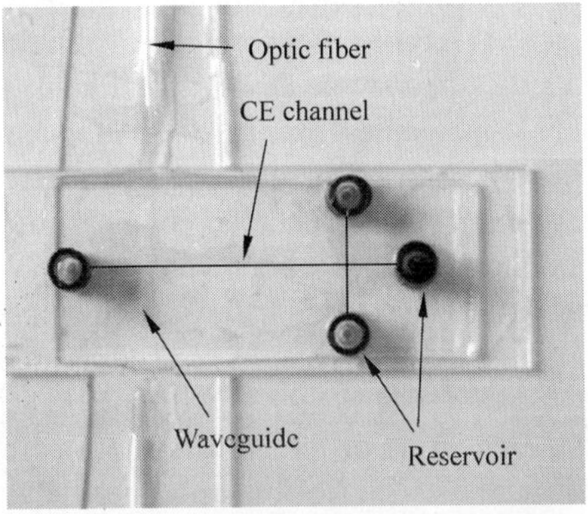

Figure 21.2 A micro-capillary electrophoresis chip integrated with buried optical waveguides on glass substrates for on-line detection of bio-analytical samples. Etched optic fibers were directly inserted into a waveguide channel for connection of a light signal between microfluidic devices and peripheral optical sensors[66] (© 2003 ELSEVIER)

Nevertheless, it should be noted that after coupling into the microchip, both the light source and the fluorescence light signals are attenuated and can be relatively weaker than using traditional methods. To solve these problems, a microlens was used to focus both the light source beam and the fluorescence light, which can successfully enhance the performance of the micro CE chips[69]. A two-dimensional (2D) optical lens on a PDMS substrate was reported. The intensity of the detection light can be enhanced effectively by using a microlens with an appropriate curvature[70]. Recently, a plastic micro CE chip capable of performing multiple-wavelength fluorescence detection by means of multimode optic fiber pairs embedded downstream of the separation channel was demonstrated[71]. The fluorescence signals can be enhanced by positioning micro focusing lens structures at the outlets of the excitation fibers and at the inlets of the detection fiber, respectively. Similarly, a micro CE chip integrated with a controllable microlens using moving-wall structures to enhance the excitation and detection signal from a LIF system was also reported[72]. It is envisioned that a micro CE chip integrated with the optical detection devices can be utilized for fast separation and online detection of DNA and protein samples.

21.2.4 DNA Manipulation

The mechanical properties of DNA play a key role in cellular functions, including folding, regulation, recombination, replication, and transcription[73]. DNA, with a diameter of 2 nm, presents a randomly coiled conformation, which is hard to examine under a microscope. Therefore, manipulating a single DNA molecule is usually performed after it is fluorescence-labeled. Two basic functions, involving stretching and rotating of DNA molecules form the foundation for the investigation of the biophysical properties of a single DNA molecule[74]. For this purpose, tools to manipulate the DNA molecules are in great demand. Typically, a DNA manipulation platform is composed of three components, a DNA manipulator, specific end anchoring, and force transducers to measure the magnitude of the applied forces. Several methods have been reported in the literature as DNA manipulators including optical tweezers[75], flexible microneedles[76], atomic force microscopes (AFM)[77], magnetic tweezers[78], receding meniscus approaches[79], hydrodynamic force[80], and electrically driven methods[81, 82]. Among these manipulators, the optical tweezers or the AFM system is relatively complex and requires expensive instruments. The flexible microneedle is not yet commercially available and is usually custom-made. Moreover, the force curve of the optical tweezers, the stiffness of the flexible microneedle, and the spring constant of the AFM probe must be precisely calibrated in advance to get precise measurement of the physical properties of the DNA molecules. The receding meniscus approaches present a molecular combing process to stretch a single DNA molecule on the substrates. In this approach, surface tension forces are so dominant that the DNA molecule can sustain greater stretching forces if the molecule is held chemically at one end. However, it is difficult to accurately calibrate the applied force by using this approach. Nevertheless, molecular combing is still useful to determine a polymer length of DNA molecules.

Recently, a MEMS-based DNA manipulation method using an electric field has attracted considerable interest. The electrically driven field method can be classified into two categories: electrophoresis[82] and the DEP approach[81]. At the single-molecule level, both techniques must be realized by using microscale[83] or nanoscale[82] devices. For example, a new nanofluidic channel device integrated with nanopillar structures for separating long DNA molecules was demonstrated. The device enables fast sizing and sorting of long polymers compared with pulsed-field gel electrophoresis[84].

Alternatively, using a continuous hydrodynamic flow is a more convenient approach to investigate the rheological properties of a single DNA polymer including conformation and relaxation, because a shear force with various strengths can be easily generated by changing the flow patterns. For example, various types of shear forces in elongational flows were generated to observe a series of conformation changes in a single DNA molecule[80]. They characterized the relaxation time for DNA molecules and investigated the relationship between the shear strength and the extension length of DNA. Especially, a hydrodynamic flow can be coupled with other techniques such as optical and magnetic tweezers to provide versatile functionalities[85].

However, it is quite important to know the full mechanical responses while investigating the mechanical properties of single DNA molecules. Using either hydrodynamic or electrical forces, the DNA molecule can be only stretched to the entropic region (< 5 pN) due to the lack of anchoring on the polymer free end. Recently, a micromachined magnetic DNA manipulation platform for stretching and rotating the single DNA molecule was developed[74]. The essential technologies including localized DNA immobilization, micromagnetic device fabrication, and microfluidics were integrated into the platform. The three-dimensional (3D) magnetic tweezers (as shown in Fig. 21.3) consisting of microelectromagnets and a ring-trap structure can generate sufficient magnetic force to extend the DNA molecule in excess of the whole contour length to investigate its entropic and elastic regions (5 – 65 pN). The important elastic modulus of DNA has been found to be 453 pN at a low ionic strength. This result reveals that DNA becomes more susceptible to elastic elongation at a low ionic strength due to electrostatic repulsion[86]. In addition to the magnetic tweezers, the methods basing on the gravity balance[85] and hydrodynamic drag[87] have also been reported to investigate DNA stretching.

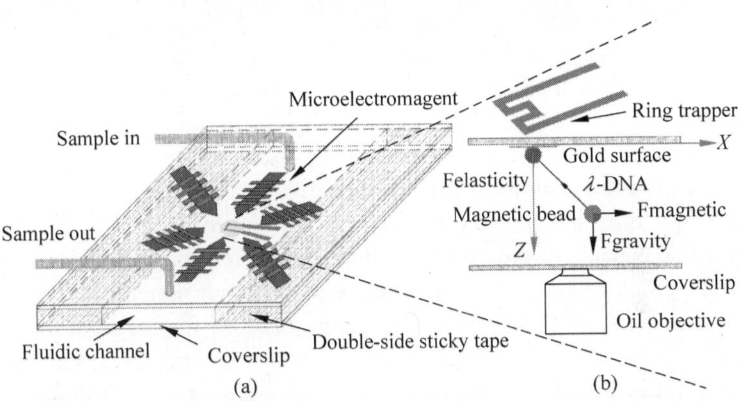

Figure 21.3 (a) Schematic illustration of magnetic tweezers integrated with microelectromagnets, a ring trapper, a fluidic channel, and a gold-patterned surface. (b) Tethered-DNA magnetic bead was in equilibrium under the action of the magnetic force, DNA elastic force, and gravity[86] (© 2006 IOP) (see color figure at the end of this book)

21.2.5 Cell Culture, Counting and Sorting

21.2.5.1 Cell Culture Chips

Conventional cell culture techniques usually require large numbers of cell culture areas, bulky incubators, large fluid volumes, and expensive human labor and other specialized equipment. While culturing cells *in vitro*, a number of variables can affect a cell's phenotype, including contamination, degree of confluence, presence of cell-to-cell adhesion, and seeding density. Moreover, *in vivo* cells can be reorganized in different ways in response to the surrounding microenvironment spatially and temporally, which may complicate the cell behavior. Alternatively, the microfluidic technology may facilitate the study of cell behavior *in vitro* since it provides tools for creating *in-vivo*-like microenvironments. More importantly, microfluidic devices/systems are especially suitable to perform biological experiments at the cellular level because the physical size of microchannels within these devices is commensurate with the cellular length scales. Cell culture using microfluidic devices has attracted considerable interest recently and may make a substantial impact on cell biology research. Several interesting approaches for culturing various types of cells have been demonstrated. For example, eukaryotic and insect cells such as Listeria innocua[88], E. Coli[89], and Spodoptera frugiperda, (Sf9)[90] have been successfully cultured using microfluidic chips. Some microsystems have further been used for culturing of mammalian cells. For instance, mouse embryos[91, 92], hepatocytes[93], endothelial cells[94], nerve cells[95], axons[96], muscle cells[97], human colon cells[98], cardiac myocytes[99], Human carcinoma (HeLa) cells[100], human lung cancer cells (A549)[11], and neural stem cells[101] have been demonstrated by using cell culture chips.

According to the method of the medium supply, the cell culture microsystems can be divided into two categories: static[11] and perfusion-based[97] micro cell culture systems. For most types of conventional static cell cultures, the culture medium is literally supplied in a batch-wise manner. For instance, the culture medium is replaced manually and periodically in a common static culture. Not only does it suffer from a contamination risk, but it also results in a fluctuating and unsteady culture environment. Conversely, perfusion-based bioreactors are capable of not only keeping the culture system sterile during the entire culture period but also capable of providing a culture system for continuous nutrient supply and waste removal, hence keeping the culture environment more stable[102]. However, the constant flow poses a challenge because the medium must be pre-warmed (for mammalian cells) and pre-equilibrated with specific gas compositions. Reliable fluidic control is particularly paramount for perfusion-based cell differentiation studies because the differentiation processes are biochemically delicate and they can take several days to complete[97].

Furthermore, most of the existing research exploits conventional 2D cell culture systems, where cells are cultured as a monolayer on a substrate surface.

Standard 2D culture conditions are poor mimics of the *in vivo* environments. In mammalian tissues, cells connect not only to each other, but also to a support structure called the extracellular matrix (ECM), which contains proteins, such as collagen, elastin, and laminin, that give tissues their mechanical properties and help organize communication between cells embedded within the matrix. Receptors on the surface of the cells, in particular a family of proteins called the integrins, anchor cells to the ECM, and also determine how the cells interpret biochemical cues from their immediate surroundings where they are discovering patterns of gene expression and other biological activities that more closely mirror what happens in living organisms. Therefore, three-dimensional (3D) microcell culture systems were reported to tackle this issue. For example, a perfusion-based, micro-3D cell culture platform for high-throughput cell culture using a microfluidic technology was reported[103]. The micro cell culture platform can maintain homogenous and stable culture environments, as well as provide pumping of multiple mediums and efficient cell/agarose (scaffold) loading functions, allowing realization of more precise and high-throughput cell culture-based assays. Furthermore, as a demonstration case study, a 3D culture of oral cancer cells was successfully performed, showing that the cell viability remained as high as 98% during a 48 h cell culture. As the result of miniaturization, this perfusion-based 3D cell culture platform not only provides a well-defined and stable culture condition, but also greatly reduces the sample/reagent consumption and the need for human intervention.

21.2.5.2 Cell Sorting and Counting Chips

Flow cytometry is a popular method for high-throughput analysis of suspended cells, bacteria, and other microorganisms. Typically, fluorescence-labeled cells or particles are hydrodynamically focused by surrounding sheath flows into a narrow stream to pass through a region where fluorescence emission or scattered light is collected by several sophisticated optical detection instruments[104]. In the past decade, dye synthesis and a high-speed data analysis technology have exerted synergistic effects on improving the flow cytometry technology and have brought this powerful analytical tool into routine clinical and laboratory use in the field of gene diagnosis[105], transfusion medicine[106], bacteria analysis[107], clinical hematology diagnosis[108], DNA molecular sizing[109], environmental microbial sensing[110], and various applications for identifying cell samples[111]. In addition to the functions of cell detection and counting, flow cytometers also allow the separation and the collection of cells or particles for sample purification process[112].

Although conventional flow cytometry systems provide rapid and reliable capabilities for cell counting and sorting, delicate optical components including focused laser beams, various optical detection/filtering devices, and complicated control circuits make the system relatively bulky and expensive[113]. Such drawbacks of the conventional flow cytometers result in the increasing demand for a compact cellular analysis system. Therefore, there is a great need for micro flow cytometer to provide precise analysis and characterization of biological samples, such as cells, organelles, and microorganisms[81]. Basically, micro flow cytometer chips could be fabricated onto several types of substrates, such as glass[114], silicon[115], and polymers[116], so that advantages including a lower cost, a more compact size, and being disposable to avoid contamination could be invoked.

The microfluidic technology has shown a great potential in miniaturizing flow cytometry[113]. By utilizing a microfluidic system, high-speed particles or cell sample flows can be first focused hydrodynamically[117] or electrokinetically[118] by using neighboring sheath flows and then flowed individually past incident focused laser beams. Scattered light or induced fluorescence signals at different wavelengths for each individual cell can be collected through in-line optical detection systems. Detected optical signals can be collected by a series of optical components and processed by using a data analysis system to investigate both biomedical and functional properties of the cell samples. For micro flow cytometers, the prefocused cell samples are usually sorted into collection chambers by using microfluidic devices, such as flow switches[119], DEP electrodes[120], or electromagnetic devices[121]. Such a combination of a microfluidic focusing/switching module, integrated optics, and control electronics in the micro flow cytometers provides a promising platform to measure the characteristics and the distribution of a cell sample population. Recently, a micro flow cytometer integrated with micropumps to generate the required hydrodynamic forces for flow focusing and cell transportation was also reported[122]. A cell counting/sorting system, as shown in Fig. 21.4, with integrated micropumps and microvalves to generate hydrodynamic forces was developed, so that the miniature self-contained flow cytometers are feasible for handling small amounts of sample fluids with high precision.

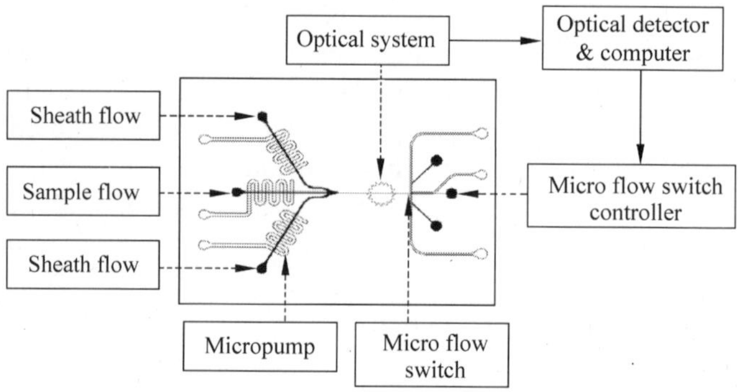

Figure 21.4 Schematic illustration of the microfabricated automatic flow cytometry chip. The cell counting/sorting system integrated with several essential components including a micromachined flow cytometer chip device, an optical detection system and a data-analysis and control system to achieve the functions of cell sample injection, optical signal detection, and cell collection[122] (© 2006 IOP)

21.2.6 Disease Diagnosis

21.2.6.1 Molecular Diagnosis of Pathogens

Molecular biology has been a powerful technology for pathogen detection. The main focus of molecular biology is the study of DNA, RNA, and proteins and the mechanisms by which genetic information (DNA) replicates, mutates, recombines, and affects the phenotype (expressed characteristics) of an organism. It usually involves the processes of sample pretreatment, cell lysis, DNA/RNA extraction, nucleic acid amplification, separation, and detection for traditional molecular diagnosis. There are numerous microchips and microsystems for performing pathogen detection using molecular diagnosis techniques. For example, an integrated plastic microfluidic device was reported for bacterial detection and identification[123]. The device, made from poly(cyclic olefin) with integrated graphite ink electrodes and photo-patterned gel domains, can accomplish DNA amplification, microfluidic valving, sample injection, on-column labeling, and separation. Two types of bacteria, E. coli O157 and Salmonella typhimurium, were successfully detected to demonstrate its capability based on amplification of their unique genes. The detection limit can be as low as about six copies of the target DNA. Another example using a fully automated microfluidic system for the DNA amplification process by integrating an electroosmotic pump, an active electrokinetically driven micromixer, and an on-chip temperature control system was reported[124]. In this integrated chip, the cell lysis was initially performed in a micro cell lysis reactor. Extracted DNA samples, primers, and reagents were then driven electroosmotically into a mixing region where they were mixed by the active micromixer. The homogeneous mixture was then thermally cycled in a micro-PCR chamber to perform DNA amplification. Experimental results showed that the integrated device can successfully automate the sample pretreatment operation for DNA amplification, thereby delivering significant savings in time and effort. Another integrated micro-RT-PCR system was also reported for automatic molecular diagnosis of microorganisms[42, 43]. By using antibodies-conjugated to superparamagnetic beads, the developed system can detect viruses with higher sensitivity and specificity when compared with traditional biological diagnosis methods. The target viruses were first captured by the conjugated antibodies on the magnetic beads, and were enriched using a magnetic field generated by microelectromagnets or permanent magnets. With this approach, the virus can be purified and concentrated first; then the virus RNA was extracted and transcripted to cDNA, followed by a nucleic acid amplification process using a micro-RT-PCR module. The integrated microfluidic chip can successfully perform the specific detection of two different types of viruses: Dengue virus serotype 2 and Enterovirus (EV) 71.

The detection of amplified nucleic acid products is commonly achieved by electrophoretic separation incorporated with a LIF detection system, which can be easy to accomplish with the use of fluorescent intercalating dyes. These similar online LIF systems can be used for pathogen detection when implemented on a micro CE chip. The commonly used fluorescent dyes include CY-5, YOYO-1, ethidium bromide (EtBr), Rhodamine 6G, and flourescein isothiocyanate (FITC)[125]. For an online LIF detection, a simple and reliable method to embed etched optical fibers in the glass-based microchip devices was reported. A simple method to couple/connect a detection light source between a microchip and peripheral equipment, such as laser light sources and optical sensors was also developed. The ϕx-174 Ⅲ DNA markers were used to evaluate the injection and separation performance of the developed micro-CE device[126]. This CE chip can be further integrated with a micro-PCR module for fast diagnosis of pathogens[127]. The developed microfluidic chip was capable of automatically performing DNA/RNA amplification, electrokinetic sample injection and separation, and online optical detection of the nucleic acid products. A photograph of the integrated microfluidic chip is shown in Fig. 21.5. The functionality of the microfluidic device was demonstrated through its successful application to the DNA-based bacterial detection of Streptococcus pneumoniae and the RNA-based detection of Dengue-2 virus. Microfluidic devices using real-time nucleic acid sequence based amplification (NASBA) for detection of artificial human papilloma virus 16 sequences were also reported with a sensitivity limit of 10^{-6} μM[128]. Similarly, an integrated microfluidic device capable of performing a variety of genetic assays was also developed. The device integrates fluidic and thermal components, such as heaters, temperature sensors, and addressable valves, to control two

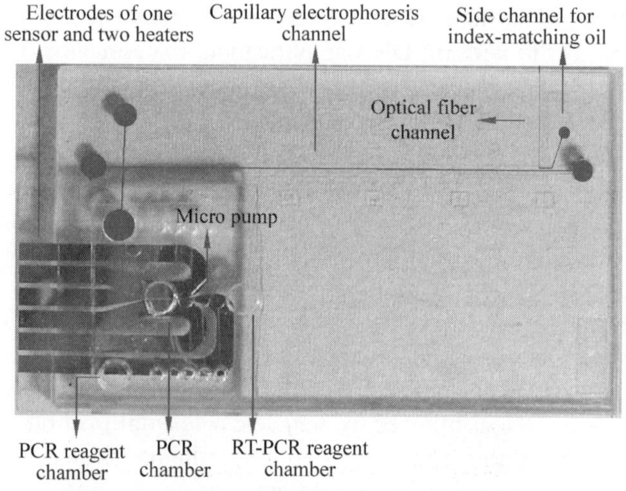

Figure 21.5 A photograph of the integrated microfluidic chip capable of performing DNA/RNA (ribonucleic acid) amplification, electrophoretic separation, and online optical detection of DNA samples[127] (© 2006 WILEY-VCH Verlag GmbH & Co.) (see color figure at the end of this book)

nanoliter reactors in series followed by an electrophoretic separation module[129]. The sequence-specific hemagglutinin A subtype for the A/LA/1/87 strain of influenza virus has been successfully identified.

In addition to the on-chip LIF devices, micro CE systems with integrated electrochemical sensors have been microfabricated on glass substrates for pathogen detection. For example, photolithographic patterning of the working electrode just outside the exit of the electrophoretic separation channel provides a high-sensitivity, electrochemical detection with minimal interference from the separation electric field[130]. By using this microsystem, a 159-bp amplicon from Salmonella was successfully detected.

21.2.6.2 On-Chip Immunoassay

Methods to conjugate target antigen/antibodies have also attracted considerable interest for disease diagnosis. Among the existing immunological assays for disease detection, enzyme-linked immunosorbent assay (ELISA) is one of the most popular diagnostic methods due to its simplicity and high sensitivity[131]. The principle of ELISA is schematically illustrated in Fig. 21.6. In principle, ELISA employs an enzyme label for detection of antibody-antigen complexes formed in a solid phase. The detection of antibody-antigen complexes is based on the enzyme catalytic activity of an appropriate colorless substrate to give a colored product, whose intensity is measured by the optical density. The on-chip ELISA for disease diagnosis has been widely explored. For example, the immunoassay in a microfluidic format by quantifying anti-HIV-1 antibodies in the serum of HIV-1-infected patients was reported. This immunoassay is inexpensive and can be operated with minimal human intervention. Experimental data showed that comparable performance can be achieved when compared with a bench-top format in clinical laboratories[132]. A microfluidic fluorescent immunoassay (FIA) to detect the concentration of antibodies in human serum containing HIV was also reported[133]. A micro analytical platform integrating photopolymerized cross-linked polyacrylamide gels within a microfluidic device for performing electrophoresis-based immunoassays was developed. A competitive immunoassay was also developed for detection of tetanus toxin C-fragment[134].

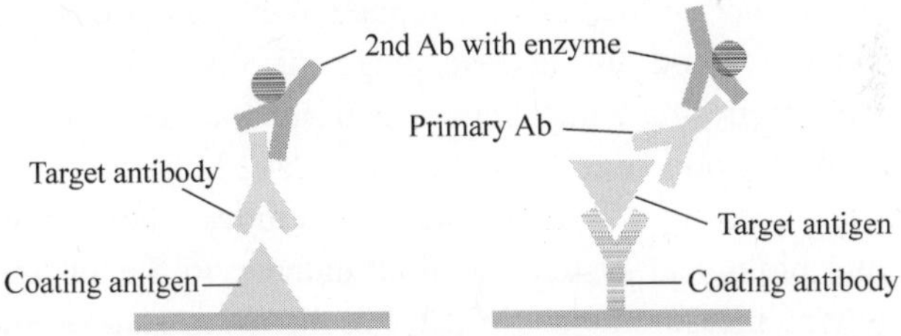

Figure 21.6 A schematic illustration of the operating principle of an enzyme-linked immunosorbent assay (ELISA) (see color figure at the end of this book)

More self-contained integrated microfluidic devices for fast diagnosis of diseases using an immunoassay were also reported. For example, an integrated chip with microvalves and micropumps to detect two diseases, the hepatitis C virus and syphilis, using an ELISA-like assay was developed[135]. The chip adopts a new design called 'spider-web' micropumps to increase the pumping rate and to improve the uniformity of flow rates inside multiple microchannels. Another electrokinetically controlled heterogeneous immunoassay microchip for multiple analyte detection was reported[136, 137]. Multi-antigen immobilization was accomplished by adsorbing the antigen molecules onto a PDMS-coated glass slide. Immobilized lysate antigen of E. coli O157: H7 at different concentrations was successfully detected with a detection limit of 3 μg/mL. The assay also possessed an excellent specificity. Using a similar method, an immuno-PCR technique for detecting the Cry1Ac toxin was also developed. In the assay, anti-Cry1Ac antibodies were covalently bound to a reporter DNA chain via a linker molecule. A high sensitivity and selectivity has been observed[138].

Polymer beads are useful for immunoassays because they can dramatically increase the surface area in a small fluid volume, and when dispersed, speed up incubation times by reducing the diffusion distances. Very rapid turnover times can be obtained if the beads are pretreated with antibodies or antigens. This strategy also provides for highly reproducible control of the antibodies being delivered to a microchannel[139]. Magnetic beads are also popular for microfluidic immunoassays. For instance, a microfluidic system with three integrated functional devices for pumping, mixing, and separation was developed. By using antibody-conjugated magnetic beads, the developed system can be used to purify and enrich virus samples such that the subsequent detection of viruses can be performed with a higher sensitivity. The developed system was used to successfully perform the purification and enrichment of Dengue viruses[42, 43]. Another bead-based microfluidic device was demonstrated to achieve rapid and sensitive ELISA with quantum dots as the labeling fluorophore for virus detection. A marine iridovirus has been successfully detected[140].

21.2.6.3 On-Chip Electrochemical Detection

In addition to the detection methods mentioned above, electrochemical detection is another popular method for disease diagnosis. Electrochemical techniques are promising for their simplicity, high sensitivity (particularly with the use of modified electrodes), good selectivity, fast response, long-term stability, ease of handling, and the possibility of fabricating electrodes small enough for direct implantation into biological systems without damage to the surrounding tissues for real-time *in vivo* measurements[141]. Electrochemistry can be employed to get information about biochemical reactions, morphology, physical, chemical, and electric properties. The rapid and accurate detection of electrolyte concentrations in biological fluids, for example blood or urine. is popular for diagnosing various bio-indicators associated with diseases[142]. Due to the biological fluids being relatively complicated, the materials of electrodes for electrochemical detection must have a high selectivity for sensing different bio-indicators. Some issues will influence the sensitivity and reproducibility of the electrochemical sensors. For example, the surface of the electrodes may absorb some organisms while the electrodes soak in solution, the slow reaction response on the surface of the electrode, and the detection limit of the electrodes to electroactive species[143]. There are several popular methods to fabricate chemically modified electrodes, including adsorption, covalent binding, carbon paste electrodes, and polymerization[144]. Electrochemical sensing devices for biological and chemical analysis have been explored for different applications, including multi-function detection[145, 146], point-of-care diagnosis[147], clinical and forensic analysis[148, 149], molecular diagnosis, and drug discovery[150, 151] by using a microfabrication technology.

The applications of electrochemical detection integrated with the microfluidic technology have been widely explored. For example, a microfluidic device with an all-solid-state potentiometric biosensor array was developed[152]. The sensor array included a pH indicator and potassium and calcium ion-selective microelectrodes. The developed device provided a convenient way to measure the concentration of hydrogen, potassium, and calcium ions. A microfluidic system for detecting morphine using a combination of a molecularly imprinted polymer and electrochemical sensing techniques was developed[153]. A monomer, called 3,4-ethylenedioxythiophene (EDOT), was mixed with morphine molecules through an electropolymerization process on a sensing electrode. Similarly, an integrated microfluidic chip capable of detecting the concentration of albumin in urine was also reported[154]. The albumin in urine was also detected by measuring the difference in peak currents between a bare reference electrode and an albumin-adsorption electrode using electrochemical detection techniques. A microfluidic system capable of blood sample collection, real-time electrochemical measurement of glucose concentration, and automatic insulin injection was also reported[151]. Compared with separate glucose monitoring and insulin injection platforms, the integrated system has a potential for online monitoring of glucose concentration and precise injection of proper doses of insulin. A microfluidic device integrated with a micro-reactor and glucose- and lactate-sensing microelectrodes in a dual channel was fabricated for *in vivo* monitoring. The device was used to study the suppression of chemical crosstalk and the effect of L-AA, and demonstrated the quantitative continuous *in vivo* monitoring of the variation in the concentrations of glucose and lactate in a rat brain stimulated with veratridine[155]. These electrochemical microfluidic systems provide a powerful platform for disease diagnosis.

21.3 Conclusions and Future Prospective

The concept of a μTAS can be realized by the utilization of microfabrication techniques. Traditional biological laboratory processes, medical examinations, or biochemistry analyses can now be performed by using the integrated microsystems automatically. The integrated microchip comprising micropumps, microvalves, microfilters, micromixers, microchannels, microsensors and microreactors can carry out the processes including sample pretreatment, transportation, reaction, mixing, separation, and detection on a single chip. The microsystems can deal with various biosamples such as blood, urine, cells, pathogens, proteins, DNA, and RNA. Crucial processes including cell culture, cell sorting and counting, cell lysis, DNA/RNA extraction, purification, amplification, separation, detection, pathogen detection, and biochemical analysis of toxin, drugs, and body fluids can be realized on these microsystems. μTAS can be applied in a variety of fields, such as biological and chemical analysis, point-of-care diagnosis, clinical and forensic analysis, molecular diagnosis, drug discovery, and disease detection. Moreover, rapid detection methods for clinical diagnosis by using micro/nano technologies are in great need. Bio-MEMS devices or systems offer advantages, including compactness in size, high sensitivity and resolution, low cost and sample consumption, and the ability to integrate sequential possesses, that demonstrate their superiority for biological and medical applications. However, despite the rapid development of on-chip analysis for biological and medical applications, these microdevices and microsystems still cannot be used for practical applications until the mass-production and reliability issues have been properly addressed.

Acknowledgements

The authors gratefully acknowledge the financial support provided to this study by the Taiwan Science Council.

References

[1] Petersen K., (1982), Silicon as a mechanical material. *Proc. IEEE Electron. Devices* **70**: 420 – 457

[2] Manz A., N. Graber, H. M. Widmer, (1990), Miniaturized total chemical analysis systems: a novel concept for chemical sensing. *Sens. Actuat. B* **1**: 244 – 248

[3] Mandou M. J., (2001), *Fundamentals of Microfabrication: The Science of Miniaturization*, 2nd ed., CRC Press, Boca Raton

[4] Folch A., M. Toner, (2000), Microengineering of cellular interactions. *Annu. Rev. Biomed. Eng.* **2**: 227 – 256

[5] Kane R., S. Takayama, E. Ostuni, D. E. Ingber, G. M. Whitesides, (1999), Patterning proteins and cells using soft lithography, *Biomaterials*, **20**: 2363 – 2376

[6] Whitesides G. M., E. Ostuni, S. Takayama, X. Jiang, D. E. Ingber, (2001), Soft lithography in biology and biochemistry. *Annu. Rev. Biomed. Eng.* **3**: 335 – 373

[7] Ziaie B., A. Baldi, M. Lei, Y. Gu, R. A. Siegel, (2004), Hard and soft micromachining for BioMEMS: review of techniques and examples of applications in microfluidics and drug delivery, *Adv. Drug Deliv. Rev.,* **56**: 145 – 172

[8] Xia Y., G. M. Whitesides, (1998), Soft lithography. *Annu. Rev. Mater. Sci.*, **28**: 153 – 184

[9] Park T. H., M. L. Shuler, (2003), Integration of cell culture and microfabrication technology. *Biotechnol. Prog.*, **19**: 243 – 253

[10] Liao C. S., G. B. Lee, J. J. Wu, C. C. Chang, T. M. Hsieh, C. H. Luo, (2005), Micromachined polymerase chain reaction system for multiple DNA amplification of upper respiratory tract infectious diseases. *Biosen. Bioelectron*, **20**: 1341 – 1348

[11] Huang C. W., G. B. Lee, (2007), A microfluidic system for automatic cell culture. *J. Micromech. Microeng.*, **17**: 1266 – 1274

[12] Yi S., K. S. Seo, Y. H. Cho, (2005), A DNA trapping and extraction microchip using periodically crossed electrophoresis in a micropillar array. *Sens. Actuat. A*, **120**: 429 – 436

[13] Wong P. K., C. Y. Chen, T. H. Wang, C. M. Ho, (2004), Electrokinetic bioprocessor for concentrating cells and molecules. *Anal. Chem.*, **76**: 6908 – 6914

[14] Cheng J., E. L. Sheldon, L. Wu, J. P. O'Connell, (1996), Channel-less separation of bioparticles on a bioelectronic chip by dielectrophoresis. United States Patent No. 6129828

[15] Nakagawa T., T. Tanaka, D. Niwa, H. T. Osaka, T. Matsunaga, (2005), Fabrication of amino silane-coated microchip for DNA extraction from whole blood. *J. Biotechnol.*, **116**: 105 – 111

[16] Xu N., Y. Lin, S. A. Hofstadler, D. Matson, C. J. Call, R. D. Smith, (1998), A microfabricated dialysis device for sample cleanup in electrospray ionization mass spectrometry. *Anal. Chem.*, **70**: 3553 – 3556

[17] Xiang F., Y. Lin, J. Wen, D. W. Matson, R. D. Smith, (1999), An integrated microfabricated device for dual microdialysis and on-line ESI-Ion trap mass spectrometry for analysis of Complex biological samples. *Anal. Chem.*, **71**: 1485 – 1490

[18] Böhm S., W. Olthuis, and P. Bergveld, (1998), A μ-TAS based on microdialysis for on-line monitoring of clinically relevant substances. Proc. Micro Total Analysis Systems, **1**: 31 – 34

[19] Khandurina J., T. E. McKnight, S. C. Jacobson, L. C. Waters, R. S. Foote, J. Ramsey, (2000), Integrated system for rapid PCR-based DNA analysis in microfluidic devices. *Anal. Chem.*, **72**: 2995 – 3000

[20] Wolfe K. A., M. C. Breadmore, J. P. Ferrance, M. E. Power, J. F. Conroy, P. M. Norris and J. P. Landers, (2002), Toward a microchip-based solid-phase extraction method for isolation of nucleic acids. *Electrophoresis*, **23**: 727 – 733

[21] Breadmore M. C., K. A. Wolfe, I. G. Arcibal, W. K. Leung, D. Dickson, B. C. Giordano, M. E. Power, J. P. Ferrance, S. H. Feldman, P. M. Norris, J. P. Landers, (2003), Microchip-based purification of DNA from biological samples. *Anal. Chem.,* **75**: 1880 – 1886

[22] Xu Y. C., B. Vaidya, A. B. Patel, S. M. Ford, R. L. McCarley, S. A. Soper, (2003),

Solid-phase reversible immobilization in microfluidic chips for the purification of dye-labeled DNA sequencing fragments. *Anal. Chem.*, **75**: 2975 – 2984

[23] Choi J. W., K. W. Oh, (2002), An integrated microfluidic biochemical detection system for protein analysis with magnetic bead-based sampling capabilities. *Lab Chip,* **2**: 27 – 30

[24] Lien K. Y., J. L. Lin, C. Y. Liu, H. Y. Leid, G. B. Lee, (2007), Purification and enrichment of virus samples utilizing magnetic beads on a microfluidic system. *Lab Chip*, 7: 868 – 875

[25] McConnell S. J., T. Dinh, M. H. Le, D. G. Spinella, (1999), Biopanning phage display libraries using magnetic beads vs. polystyrene tubes. *Biotechniques*, **26**: 208 – 210

[26] Tsai-Wu J. J., H. T. Su, W. H. Fang, H. H. Wu, (1999), Preparation of heteroduplex DNA containing a mismatch base pair with magnetic beads. *Ann. Biochem.*, **1**: 127 – 129

[27] Jiang G., D. J. Harrison, (2000), mRNA isolation in a microfluidic device for eventual integration of cDNA library construction. *Analyst*, **125**: 2176 – 2179

[28] Kanagawa T., (2003), Review: bias and artifacts in multitemplate polymerase chain reactions (PCR). *J. Biosci. Bioeng.*, **96**: 317 – 323

[29] Woolley A. T., D. Hadley, P. Landre, A. J. deMello, R. A. Mathies, M. A. Northrup, (1996), Functional integration of PCR amplification and capillary electrophoresis in a microfabricated DNA analysis device. *Anal. Chem.*, **68**: 4081 – 4086

[30] Northrup M. A., B. Bentt, D. Hadley, P. Landre, S. Lehew, J. Richards, P. Stratton, (1998), A miniature analytical instrument for nucleic acids based on micromachined silicon reaction chambers. *Anal. Chem.*, **70**: 918 – 922

[31] Lagally E. T., P. C. Simpson, R. Mathies, (2000), A Monolithic integrated microfluidic DNA amplification and capillary electrophoresis analysis system. *Sens. Actuat. B*, **63**: 138 – 146

[32] Yang J. N., Y. J. Liu, C. B. Rauch, R. L. Stevens, R. H. Liu, R. Lenigk, P. Grodzinski, (2002), High sensitivity PCR assay in plastic micro reactors. *Lab Chip*, **2**: 179 – 187

[33] Giordano B. C., E. R. Copeland, J. P. Landers, (2001), Towards dynamic coating of glass microchip chambers for amplifying DNA via the polymerase chain reaction. *Electrophoresis*, **22**: 334 – 340

[34] Lee D. S., S. H. Park, K. H. Chung, T. H. Yoon, S. J. Kim, K. Kim, Y. T. Kim, (2004), Bulk-micromachined submicroliter-volume PCR chip with very rapid thermal response and low power consumption. *Lab Chip* , **4**: 401 – 407

[35] Yu X. M., D. C. Zhang, T. Li, L. Hao, X. H. Li, (2003), 3-D microarrays biochip for DNA amplification in polydimethylsiloxane (PDMS) elastomer. *Sens. Actuat. A*, **108**: 103 – 107

[36] Kopp M. U., A. J. de Melloo, A. Manz, (1998), Chemical amplification: Continuous-flow PCR on a chip. *Science*, **280**: 1046 – 1048

[37] Zhang Q. T., W. H. Wang, H. S. Zhang, Y. L. Wang, (2002), Temperature analysis of continuous-flow micro-PCR based on FEA. *Sens. Actuat. B*, **82**: 75 – 81

[38] Liao C. S., G. B. Lee, H. S. Liu, T. M. Hsieh, C. H. Luo, (2005), Miniature RT-PCR system for diagnosis of RNA-based viruses. *Nucl. Acids Res.*, **33**: 1 – 7

[39] Hsieh T. M., C. H. Luo, G. B. Lee, C. S. Liao, F. C. Huang, (2006), A micromachined low-power-consumption portable PCR system. *J. Medical. Biolog. Eng.*, **26**(1): 43 – 49

[40] Wang C. H., Y. Y. Chen, C. S. Liao, T. M. Hsieh, C. H. Luo, J. J. Wu, H. H. Lee, G. B. Lee,

(2007), Micromachined flow-through polymerase chain reaction chips utilizing multiple membrane activations. *J. Micromech. Microeng.*, **17**: 367 – 375

[41] Lin Y.C., M. Y. Huang, K. C. Young, T. T. Chang, C. Y. Wu, (2000), A rapid micro-polymerase chain reaction system for hepatitis C virus amplification. *Sens. Actuat. B*, **71**: 2 – 8

[42] Lien K. Y., W. C. Lee, H. Y. Lei, G. B. Lee, (2007), Integrated reverse transcription polymerase chain reaction systems for virus detection. *Biosens. Bioelectron.*, **22**: 1739 – 1748

[43] Lien K. Y., J. L. Lin, C. Y. Liu, H. Y. Leid, G. B. Lee, (2007), Purification and enrichment of virus samples utilizing magnetic beads on a microfluidic system. *Lab Chip*, **7**: 868 – 875

[44] Tsai N. C., C. Y. Sue, (2006), SU-8 based continuous-flow RT-PCR bio-chips under high-precision temperature control. *Biosens. Bioelectron.*, **22**: 313 – 317

[45] Pollack M. G., R. B. Fair, A. D. Shenderov, (2000), Electrowetting-based actuation of liquid droplets for microfluidic applications. *Appl. Phys. Lett.*, **77**: 1725 – 1726

[46] Cho S. K., H. , C. J. Kim, (2003), Creating, transporting, cutting, and merging liquid droplets by electrowetting-based actuation for digital microfluidic circuits. *J. MEMS*, **12**: 70 – 80

[47] Guttenberg Z., H. Müller, H. Habermüller, A. Geisbauer, J. Pipper, J. Felbel, M. Kielpinski, J. Scribaa, A. Wixforth, (2005), Planar chip device for PCR and hybridization with surface acoustic wave pump. *Lab Chip*, **5:** 308 – 317

[48] Welters W. J. J., L. G. J. Fokkink, (1998), Fast electrically switchable capillary effects. *Langmuir*, **14**: 1535 – 1538

[49] Decamps C., J., De Coninck, (2000), Dynamics of Spontaneous Spreading under Electrowetting Conditions. *Langmuir*, **16**: 10150 – 10153

[50] Quinn A., R. Sedev, J. Ralston, (2003), Influence of the Electrical Double Layer in Electrowetting. *J. Phys. Chem. B*, **107**: 1163 – 1169

[51] Chang Y. H., G. B. Lee, F. C. Huang, Y. Y. Chen, J. L. Lin, (2006), Integrated polymerase chain reaction chips utilizing digital microfluidics. *Biomed. Microdev.*, **8**: 215 – 225

[52] Harrison D. J., K. Fluri, K. Seiler, Z. H. Fan, C. S. Effenhauser, A. Manz, (1993), Micromachining a miniaturized capillary electrophoresis-based chemical analysis system on a chip. *Science*, **261**: 895 – 897

[53] Woolley A. T., R. A. Mathies, (1994), Ultra-high-speed DNA fragment separations using microfabricated capillary array electrophoresis chips. Proc. Natl. Acad. Sci. USA, **91**: 11348 – 11352

[54] Becker H., C. Gärtner, (2000), Polymer microfabrication methods for microfluidic analytical application. *Electrophoresis*, **21**: 12 – 26

[55] Muck A. J., J. Wang, M. Jacobs, G. Chen, M. P. Chatrathi, V. Jurka, Z. Vborn, S. D. Spillman, G. Sridharan, M. J. Schöning, (2004), Fabrication of poly(methyl methacrylate) microfluidic chips by atmospheric molding. *Anal. Chem.*, **76**: 2290 – 2297

[56] Xu G., J. Wang, Y. Chen, L. Zhang, D. Wang, G. Chen, (2006), Fabrication of poly(methyl methacrylate) capillary electrophoresis microchips by in situ surface polymerization. *Lab Chip*, **6**: 145 – 148

[57] Huang Z., J. C. Sanders, C. Dunsmor, H. Ahmadzadeh, J. P. Landers, (2001), A method for UV-bonding in the fabrication of glass electrophoretic microchip. *Electrophoresis*, **22**: 3924 – 3929

[58] Wang J., M. Pumera, M. P. Chatrathi, A. Escarpa, R. Konrad, A. Griebel, W. Dörner, H. Löwe, (2002), Towards disposable lab-on-a-chip: Poly(methylmethacrylate) microchip electrophoresis device with electrochemical detection. *Electrophoresis,* **23**: 596 – 601

[59] Lee G. B., S. H. Chen, G. R. Huang, W. C. Sung, Y. H. Lin, (2001), Microfabricated plastic chips by hot embossing methods and their applications for DNA separation and detection. *Sens. Actuat. B*, **75**: 142 – 148

[60] Wu Z. Y., N. Xanthopoulos, F. Reymond, J. S. Rossier, H. H. Girault, (2002), Polymer microchips bonded by O_2-plasma activation, *Electrophoresis*, **23**: 782 – 790

[61] Roberts M. A., J. S. Rossier, P. Bercier, H. Girault, (1997), UV laser machined polymer substrates for the development of microdiagnostic systems. *Anal. Chem.*, **69**: 2035 – 2042

[62] Huang F. C., Y. F. Chen, G. B. Lee, (2007), CE chips fabricated by injection molding and polyethylene/thermoplastic elastomer film packaging methods. *Electrophoresis*, **28**: 1130 – 1137

[63] Effenhauser C. S., A. Paulus, A. Manz, H. M. Widmer, (1994), High-speed separation of antisense oligonucleotides on a micromachined capillary electrophoresis device. *Anal. Chem.*, **66**: 2949 – 2953

[64] Liang Z. H., N. Chiem, G. Ocvirk, T. Tang, K. Fluri, D. J. Harrison, (1996), Microfabrication of a planar absorbance and fluorescence cell for integrated capillary electrophoresis devices. *Anal. Chem.*, **68**: 1040 – 1046

[65] Grewe M., A. Gross, H. Fouckhardt, (2000), Theoretical and Experimental investigations of the optical waveguiding properties of on-chip microfabricated capillaries. *Appl. Phys. B*, **70**: S839 – S847

[66] Lin C. H., G. B. Lee, S. H. Chen, G. L. Chang, (2003), Micro capillary electrophoresis chips integrated with buried SU-8/SOG optical waveguides for bio-analytical applications. *Sens. Actuat. A*, **107**: 125 – 131

[67] Grosse A., M. Grewe, H. Fouckhardt, (2001), Deep wet etching of fused silica glass for hollow capillary optical leaky waveguides in microfluidic devices. *J. Micromech. Microeng.*, **11**: 257 – 262

[68] Mogensen K. B., N. J. Petersen, J. Hûbner, J. P. Kutter, (2001), Monolithic integration of optical waveguides for absorbance detection in microfabricated electrophoresis. *Electrophoresis*, **22**: 3930 – 3938

[69] Roulet J. C., R. Völkel, H. P. Herzig, E. Verpoorte, (2001), Fabrication of multilayer systems combining microfluidic and microoptical elements for fluorescence detection. *J. MEMS*, **10**: 482 – 491

[70] Camou S., H. Fujita, T. Fujii, (2003), PDMS 2D optical lens integrated with microfluidic channels: principle and characterization. *Lab chip*, **3**: 40 – 45

[71] Hsiung S. K., C. H. Lin, G. B. Lee, (2005), Micro-capillary electrophoresis chip with micro-focusing-lens utilizing multi-wavelength detection for bio-analytical applications. *Electrophoresis*, **26**: 1122 – 1129

[72] Hsiung S. K., G. B. Lee, (2007), A controllable micro-lens structure for bio-analytical applications. Proc. The 20th Internal Conference on Micro Electro Mechanical Systems, **2**: 763 – 766

[73] Strick T., J. Allemand, V. Croquette, D. Bensimon, (2000), Twisting and stretching single DNA molecules. *Prog. Biophys. Mol. Biol.*, **74**: 115 – 140

[74] Chiou C. H., G. B. Lee, (2005), A micromachined DNA manipulation platform for the stretching and rotation of a single DNA molecule. *J. Micromech. Microeng*, **15**: 109 – 117

[75] Chu S., (1991), Laser manipulation of atoms and particles. *Science*, **253**: 861 – 866

[76] Cluzel P., A. Lebrun, C. Heller, R. Lavery, J. L. Viovy, D. Chatenay, F. Caron, (1996), DNA: an extensible molecule. *Science*, **271**: 792 – 794

[77] Shivashankar G. V., A. Libchaber, (1997), Single DNA molecule grafting and manipulation using a combined atomic force microscope and an optical tweezers. *Appl. Phys. Lett.*, **71**: 3727 – 3729

[78] Strick T., J. F. Allemand, D. Bensimon, A. Bensimon, V. Croquette, (1996), The elasticity of a single supercoiled DNA molecule. *Science*, **271**: 1835 – 1837

[79] Bensimon D., A. J. Simon, A. Chiffaudel, V. Croquette, F. Heslot, D. Bensimon, (1994), Alignment and sensitive detection of DNA by a moving interface. *Science*, **265**: 2096 – 2098

[80] Perkins T. T., D. E. Smith, S. Chu, (1997), Single polymer dynamics in an elongational flow. *Science*, **276**: 2016 – 2021

[81] Washizu M., O. Kurosawa, I. Arai, S. Suzuki, N. Shimamoto, (1995), Applications of electrostatic stretch-and-positioning of DNA. *IEEE Trans. Ind. Appl.*, **31**: 447 – 456

[82] Han J., H. G. Craighead, (1999), Entropic trapping and sieving of long DNA molecules in a nanofluidic channel. *J. Vac. Sci. Technol., A* **17**: 2142 – 2147

[83] Namasivayam V., R. Larson, D. T. Burke, M. A. Burns, (2002), Electrostretching DNA molecules using polymer-enhanced media within microfabricated devices. *Anal. Chem.*, **74**: 3378 – 3385

[84] Cabodi M., S. W. P. Turner, H. G. Craighead, (2002), Entropic recoil separation of long DNA molecules. *Anal. Chem.*, **74**: 5169 – 5174

[85] Haber C., D. Wirtz, (2000), Magnetic tweezers for DNA micromanipulation. *Rev. Sci. Instrum.*, **71**: 4561 – 4570

[86] Chiou C. H., Y. Y. Huang, M. H. Chiang, H. H. Lee, G. B. Lee, (2006), New magnetic tweezers for investigation of mechanical properties of single DNA molecules. *Nanotechnology*, **17**: 1217 – 1224

[87] Gosse C., V. Croquette, (2002), Magnetic tweezers: Micromanipulation and force measurement at the molecular level. *Biophys., J.* **82**: 3314 – 3329

[88] Gómez R., R. Bashir, A. Sarikaya, M. R. Ladisch, J. Sturgis, J. P. Robinson, T. Geng, A. K. Bhunia, H. L. Apple, S. Wereley, (2001), Microfluidic biochip for impedance spectroscopy of biological species. *Biomed. Microdev.*, **3**:201 – 209

[89] Chang W. J., D. Akin, M. Sedlak, M. R. Ladisch, R. Bashir, (2003), Poly(dimethylsiloxane) (PDMS) and silicon hybrid biochip for bacterial culture. *Biomed. Microdev.*, **5**: 281 – 290

[90] Walker G. M., M. S. Ozers, D. J. Beebe, (2002), Insect cell culture in microfluidic channels. *Biomed. Microdev.*, **4**: 161 – 166

[91] Beebe D. J., G. A. Mensing, G. M. Walker, (2002), Physics and applications of microfluidics in biology. *Annu. Rev. Biomed. Eng.*, **4**: 261 – 286

[92] Raty S., E. M. Walters, J. Davis, H. Zeringue, D. J. Beebe, S. L. Rodriguez-Zax, M. B. Wheeler, (2004), Embryonic development in the mouse is enhanced via microchannel culture. *Lab Chip*, **4:** 186 – 190

[93] Powers M. J., K. Domansky, M. R. Kaazempur-Mofrad, A. Kalezi, A. Capitano, A. Upadhyaya, P. Kurzawski, K. E. Wack, D. B. Stolz, R. Kamm, L. G. Griffith, (2002), A microfabricated array bioreactor for perfused 3D liver culture. *Biotechnol. Bioeng.*, **78**: 257 – 269

[94] Borenstein J. T., H. Terai, K. R. King, E. J. Weinberg, M. R. Kaazempur-Mofrad, J. P. Vacanti, (2002), Microfabrication technology for vascularized tissue engineering. *Biomed. Microdev.*, **4**: 167 – 175

[95] Moriguchi H., Y. Wakamoto, Y. Sugio, K. Takahashi, I. Inoue, K. Yasuda, (2002), An agar-microchamber cell-cultivation system: flexible change of microchamber shapes during cultivation by photo- thermal etching. *Lab Chip*, **2**: 125 – 130

[96] Taylor A. M., M. Blurton-Jones, S. W. Rhee, D. H. Cribbs, C. W. Cotman, N. L. Jeon, (2005), A microfluidic culture platform for CNS axonal injury, regeneration and transport. *Nat. Meth.*, **2**: 599 – 605

[97] Tourovskaia A., X. Figueroa-Masot, A. Folch, (2005), Differentiation-on-a-chip: a microfluidic platform for long-term cell culture studies. *Lab Chip*, **5**: 14 – 19

[98] Stangegaard M., S. Petronis, A. M. Jørgensen, C. B. V. Christensen, M. Dufva, (2006), A biocompatible micro cell culture chamber (μCCC) for the culturing and on-line monitoring of eukaryote cells. *Lab Chip*, **6**: 1045 – 1051

[99] Kaji H., M. Nishizawa, T. Matsue, (2003), Localized chemical stimulation to micropatterned cells using multiple laminar fluid flows. *Lab Chip*, **3**: 208 – 211

[100] Hung P. J., P. J. Lee, P. Sabounchi, R. Lin, L. P. Lee, (2004), Continuous perfusion microfluidic cell culture array for high-throughput cell-based assays. *Biotechnol. Bioeng.*, **89**: 1 – 8

[101] Chung B. G., L. A. Flanagan, S. W. Rhee, P. H. Schwartz, A. P. Lee, E. S. Monuki, N. L. Jeon, (2005), Human neural stem cell growth and differentiation in a gradient-generating microfluidic device. *Lab Chip*, **5**: 401 – 406

[102] Wu M. H., J. P. G. Urban, Z. Cui, Z. F. Cui, (2006), Development of PDMS microbioreactor with well-defined and homogenous culture environment for chondrocyte 3-D culture. *Biomed. Microdev.*, **8**: 331 – 340

[103] Huang S. B., M. H. Wu, Z. F. Cui, Z. Cui, J. L. Lin, G. B. Lee, (2007), A perfusion-based micro 3-D cell culture platform. Proc. The 14th International Conference on Solid-state Sensors, Actuators and Microsystems, **2**: 767 – 770

[104] Chung C. M., S. K. Hsiung, G. B. Lee, (2007), A micro flow cytometer chip incorporated with micro-pumps/micro-valves for multi-wavelength cell counting and sorting. *Jpn. J. Appl. Phys.*, **46**: 3126 – 3134

[105] Hughes M. P., H. Morgan, (1999), Measurement of bacterial flagellar thrust by negative dielectrophoresis. *Biotechnol. Prog.*, **15**: 245 – 249

[106] Greve B., G. Valet, A. Humpe, T. Tonn, U. Cassens, (2004), Flow cytometry in transfusion medicine: development, strategies and applications. *Transfus. Med. Hemother.*, **31**: 152 – 161

[107] Gunasekera T. S., P. V. Attfield, D. A. Veal, (2000), A flow cytometry method for rapid detection and enumeration of total bacteria in milk. *Appl. Environ. Microbiol.*, **66**: 1228 – 1232

[108] Brown M., C. Wittwer, (2000), Flow cytometry: principles and clinical applications in hematology. *Clin. Cham.*, **46**: 1221 – 1229

[109] Agronskaia A., J. M. Schins, B. G. Grooth, J. Greve, (1999), Two-color fluorescence in flow cytometry DNA sizing: identification of single-molecule fluorescent probes. *Anal. Chem.*, **71**: 4684 – 4689

[110] Gruden C., S. Skerlos, P. Adriaens, (2004), Flow cytometry for microbial sensing in environmental sustainability applications: current status and future prospects FEMS. *Microbiol. Ecol.*, **49**: 37 – 49

[111] Edwards B. S., T. Oprea, E. R. Prossnitz, L. A. Sklar, (2004), Flow cytometry for high-throughput, high-content screening. *Current Opin. Chem. Bio.*, **8**: 392 – 398

[112] Horan P. K., L. L. Wheeless, (1977), Quantitative single cell analysis and sorting. *Science*, **198**: 149 – 157

[113] Huh D., W. Gu, Y. Kamotami, J. B. Grotberg, S. Takayama, (2005), Microfluidics for flow cytometric analysis of cells and particles. *Physiol. Meas.*, **26**: R73 – R98

[114] Lee G. B., C. H. Lin, G. Chang, (2003), Micro flow cytometers with buried SU-8/SOG optical waveguides. *Sens. Actuat. A*, **103**: 165 – 170

[115] Altendorf E., E. Iverson, D. Schutte, B. Weigl, T. Osbom, R. Sabeti, P. Yager, (1996), Optical flow cytometry utilizing microfabricated silicon flow channels. *Proc. SPIE*, **2678**: 267 – 276

[116] Chung S., S. J. Park, J. K. Kim, C. Chung, D. C. Han, J. K. Chang, (2003), Plastic microchip flow cytometer based on 2- and 3-dimensional hydrodynamic flow focusing. *Microsystem Tech.*, **9**: 525 – 533

[117] Huh D., Y. C. Tung, H. H. Wei, J. B. Grotberg, S. J. Skerlos, K. Kurabayashi, S. Takayama, (2002), Use of air-liquid two-phase flow in hydrophobic microfluidic channels for disposable flow cytometers. *Biomed. Microdev.*, **4**: 141 – 149

[118] Kruger J., K. Singh, A. O'Neill, C. Jackson, A. Morrison, P. O'Brien, (2002), Development of a microfluidic device for fluorescence activated sorting. *J. Micromech. Microeng.*, **12**: 486 – 494

[119] Fu L. M., R. J. Yang, C. H. Lin, Y. J. Pan, G. B. Lee, (2004), Electrokinetically driven micro flow cytometers with integrated fiber optics for on-line cell/particle detection. *Anal. Chim. Acta*, **507**: 163 – 169

[120] Lin C. H., G. B. Lee, L. M. Fu, B. H. Hwey, (2004), Vertical focusing device utilizing dielectrophoretic force and its application on microflow cytometer. *J. MEMS*, **13**: 923 – 932

[121] Lemoff A. V., A. P. Lee, (2003), An AC magnetohydrodynamic microfluidic switch for micro total analysis systems. *Biomed. Microdev.*, **5**: 55 – 60

[122] Yang S. Y., S. K. Hsiung, Y. C. Hung, C. M. Chang, T. L. Liao, G. B.A. Lee, (2006), cell counting/sorting system incorporated with a micro fabricated flow cytometer chip. *Meas. Sci. Technol.*, **17**: 2001 – 2009

[123] Koh C. G., W. Tan, M. Q. Zhao, A. J. Ricco, Z. H. Fan, (2003), Integrating polymerase chain reaction, valving, and electrophoresis in a plastic device for bacterial detection. *Anal. Chem.*, **75**: 4591 – 4598

[124] Lee C. Y., G. B. Lee, J. L. Lin, F. C. Huang, C. S. Liao, (2005), Integrated microfluidic systems for cell lysis, mixing/pumping and DNA amplification. *J. Micromech. Microeng.*, **15**: 1215 – 1223

[125] Sun Y., Y. C. Kwok, (2006), Polymeric microfluidic system for DNA analysis. *Anal. Chim. Acta*, **556**: 80 – 96

[126] Lin R., D. T. Burke, M. A. Burns, (2003), Selective extraction of size-fractioned DNA samples in microfabricated electrophoresis devices. *J. Chromatogr. A*, **1010**: 255 – 268

[127] Huang F. C., C. S. Liao, G. B. Lee, (2006), Integrated microfluidic chips for DNA/RNA amplification, electrophoresis separation and on-line optical detection. *Electrophoresis*, **27**: 3297 – 3305

[128] Gulliksen A., L. A. Solli, K. S. Drese, O. Sorensen, F. Karlsen, H. Rogne, E. Hovig, R. Sirevag, (2005), Parallel nanoliter detection of cancer markers using polymer microchips. *Lab Chip*, **5**: 416 – 420

[129] Pal R., M. Yang, R. Lin, B. N. Johnson, N. Srivastava, S. Z. Razzacki, K. J. Chomistek, D. C. Heldsinger, R. M. Haque, V. M. Ugaz, P. K. Thwar, Z. Chen, K. Alfano, M. B. Yim, M. Krishnan, A. O. Fuller, R. G. Larson, D. T. Burke, M. A. Burns, (2005), An integrated microfluidic device for influenza and other genetic analyses. *Lab Chip*, **5**: 1024 – 1032

[130] Woolley A. T., K. Lao, A. N. Glazer, R. A. Mathies, (1998), Capillary electrophoresis chips with integrated electrochemical detection. *Anal. Chem.*, **70**: 684 – 688

[131] Gosling J. P., (1990), A decade of development in immunoassay methodology. *Clinical Chem.*, **36**: 1408 – 1427

[132] Sia S. K., V. Linder, B. A. Parviz, A. Siegel, G. M. Whitesides, (2004), An integrated approach to a portable and low-cost immunoassay for resource-poor settings. *Angew. Chem., Int. Ed.*, **43**: 498 – 502

[133] Jiang X. Y., J. M. K. Ng, A. D. Stroock, S. K. W. Dertinger, G. M. J. Whitesides, (2003), A miniaturized, parallel, serially diluted immunoassay for analyzing multiple antigens. *Am. Chem. Soc.*, **125**: 5294 – 5295

[134] Herr A. E., D. J. Throckmorton, A. A. Davenport, A. K. Singh, (2005), On-chip native gel electrophoresis-based immunoassays for tetanus antibody and toxin. *Anal. Chem.*, **77**: 585 – 590

[135] Wang C. H., G. B. Lee, (2005), Automatic bio-sampling chips integrated with micro-pumps and micro-valves for disease detection. *Biosens. Bioelectron.*, **21**: 419 – 425

[136] Gao Y. L., G. Q. Hu, F. Y. H. Lin, P. M. Sherman, D. Q. Li, (2005), An electrokinetically-controlled immunoassay for simultaneous detection of multiple microbial antigens. *Biomed. Microdev.*, **7**: 301 – 312

[137] Gao Y. L., F. Y. H. Lin, G. Q. Hu, P. M. Sherman, L. Dongqing, (2005), Development of a novel electrokinetically driven microfluidic immunoassay for the detection of Helicobacter pylori. *Anal. Chim. Acta*, **543**: 109 – 116

[138] Allen R. C., S. Rogelj, S. E. Cordova, T. L. Kieft, (2006), Immuno-PCR method for detecting Bacillus thuringiensis Cry1Ac toxin. *J Immunol. Methods*, **308**: 109 – 115

[139] Choi J. W., K. W. Oh, (2002), An integrated microfluidic biochemical detection system for protein analysis with magnetic bead-based sampling capabilities. *Lab Chip*, **2**: 27 – 30

[140] Liu W. T., L. Zhu, Q. W. Qin, Q. Zhang, H. H. Feng, S. Ang, (2005), Microfluidic device as a new platform for immunofluorescent detection of viruses. *Lab Chip*, **5**: 1327 – 1330

[141] Diab N., J. Oni, W. Schuhmann, (2005), Electrochemical nitric oxide sensor preparation: A comparison of two electrochemical methods of electrode surface modification. *Bioelectrochemistry*, **66**: 105 – 110

[142] Schwarz M. A., P. C. Hauser, (2001), Recent developments in detection methods for microfabricated analytical devices. *Lab Chip*, **1**: 1 – 6

[143] Suzuki H., T. Hirakawa, S. Sasaki, I. Karube ,(2000), An integrated module for sensing pO_2, pCO_2, and pH. *Anal. Chimica Acta*, **405**: 57 – 65

[144] Bard A. J., (2001), Electrochemical method. In *Fundamentals and Applications,* 2nd ed., John Wiley & Sons, New York, 465

[145] Beebe D., M. Wheeler, H. Zeringue, E. Walters, S. Raty, (2002), Microfluidic technology for assisted reproduction. *Theriogenology*, **57:** 125 – 135

[146] Lin C. F., G. B. Lee, C. H. Wang, H. H. Lee, W. Y. Liao, T. C. Chou, (2006), Microfluidic pH-sensing chips integrated with pneumatic fluid-control devices. *Biosen. Bioelectron*, **21**: 1468 – 1475

[147] Tudos A. J., G. A. J. Besselink, R. B. M. Schasfoort, (2001), Trends in miniaturized total analysis systems for point-of-care testing in clinical chemistry. *Lab Chip,* **1**: 83 – 95

[148] Bange A., H. B. Halsall, W. R. Heineman, (2005), Microfluidic immunosensor systems. *Biosens. Bioelectron.*, **20**: 2488 – 2503

[149] Verpoorte E., (2002), Microfluidic chips for clinical and forensic analysis. *Electrophoresis*, **23**: 677 – 712

[150] Rudolph A. S., J. Reasor, (2001), Cell and tissue based technologies for environmental detection and medical diagnostics. *Biosens. Bioelectron.*, **16**: 429 – 431

[151] Huang C. J., C. H. Wang, Y. H. Chen, T. C. Chou, G. B. Lee, (2007), Integrated microfluidic systems for automatic glucose sensing and insulin injection. *Sens. Actuators B*, **122**: 461 – 468

[152] Liao W. Y., C. H. Weng, G. B. Lee, T. C. Chou, (2006), Development and characterization of an all-solid-state potentiometric biosensor array microfluidic device for multiple ion analysis. *Lab Chip*, **6**: 1362 – 1368

[153] Weng C. H., W. M. Yeh, K. C. Ho, G. B. Lee, (2007), A microfluidic system utilizing molecular imprinting polymer films for amperometric detection of morphine. *Sens. Actuat. B*, **121**: 576 – 582

[154] Huang C. J., C. C. Lu, T. Y. Lin, T. C. Chou, G. B. Lee, (2007), Electrochemical albumin sensing system utilizing microfluidic technology. *J. Micromech. Microeng.*, **17**: 835 – 842

[155] Kurita R., K. Hayashi, X. Fan, K. Yamamoto, T. Kato, O. Niwa, (2002), Microfluidic device integrated with pre-reactor and dual enzyme-modified microelectrodes for monitoring in vivo glucose and lactate. *Sens. Actuat. B*, **87**: 296 – 303

22 Microfluidic Platforms for Lab-On-A-Chip Applications

Stefan Haeberle[1], Daniel Mark[1], Felix von Stetten[1,2], and Roland Zengerle[1,2]

[1] HSG-IMIT. Institute for Micromachining and Information Technology, Wilhelm-Schickard-Straße 10, 78052 Villingen-Schwenningen, Germany

[2] Laboratory for MEMS Applications, Department of Microsystems Engineering - IMTEK, University of Freiburg, Georges-Koehler-Allee 106, 79110, Freiburg, Germany
E-mail: zengerle@imtek.de

Abstract We review microfluidic platforms that enable the miniaturization, integration, parallelization, and automation of biochemical assays[1]. Nowadays, there is an unmanageable variety of alternative approaches that can do this in principle. Here, we focus on those kinds of platforms only that allow performance of a set of microfluidic functions-defined as microfluidic unit operations-that can be easily combined within a well-defined and consistent fabrication technology to implement application-specific biochemical assays in an easy, flexible, and ideally monolithic way.

The microfluidic platforms discussed in the following sections are capillary test strips, also known as lateral flow assays, the 'microfluidic large-scale integration' approach, centrifugal microfluidics, the electrokinetic platform, pressure-driven droplet-based microfluidics, electrowetting-based microfluidics, SAW driven microfluidics, and, last but not the least, 'free scalable non-contact dispensing'. The microfluidic unit operations discussed within these platforms are fluid transport, metering, mixing, switching, incubation, separation, droplet formation, droplet splitting, nL and pL dispensing, and detection.

Keywords Microfluidic platforms, microfluidics, lab-on-a-chip, unit operations

22.1 Introduction: The Need for Microfluidic Platforms

The impact of microfluidic technologies in the academic world has dramatically increased during the last few years. This is quite remarkable since microfluidics is not a product that a consumer wants to buy. Microfluidics should be merely considered as a toolbox, which is needed to develop innovative new products in the life sciences area. As a consequence, the most important customer for microfluidic know-how and technologies is the research community itself, developing new products and solutions in different application areas such as biotechnology, diagnostics, and medical or pharmaceutical.

The history of microfluidics dates back to the early 1950s, when efforts to dispense small amounts of liquids in the nano- and subnanoliter ranges were taken for providing the basics of today's ink-jet technology[2]. In terms of fluid propulsion within microchannels of submillimeter cross section, the year 1979 set a milestone when a miniaturized gas chromatograph (GC) was realized on a silicon wafer[3]. The first high-pressure liquid chromatography (HPLC) column device, fabricated using Si-Pyrex technology, was invented by Manz et al[4]. By the end of the 1980s, the first microvalves[5] and micropumps[6, 7] based on silicon micromachining had also been invented. During the following years, several silicon-based analysis systems were presented[8, 9]. All these examples represent microfluidic systems since they enable the precise control of the decreasing fluid volumes on the one hand and the miniaturization of the size of a fluid-handling system on the other hand.

Another important aspect of microfluidics is the exploitation of effects and phenomena that can be utilized only in microdimensions. Smaller channel dimensions drastically increase the surface-to-volume ratio and thus surface-related phenomena like laminar flow, capillarity, fast thermal response, and electrokinetics gain influence. These effects can be used in microfluidic systems to enhance the performance of analytical procedures, e.g. by decreasing diffusion limited or temperature controlled reaction times. Therefore, in 1990, Manz et al[10] proposed the concept of miniaturized total chemical analysis systems (TAS) based on the unique conditions in the microdomain. Today, this approach is also known as micro total analysis systems (micro-TAS) or laboratories on a chip (LOC) as proposed by Harrison et al in 1992[11].

Following this micro-TAS or LOC approach, the first applications that emerged in the field of analytical chemistry were based on the electroosmotic flow (EOF) to pump liquids into small microcapillaries and on electrophoretic (EP) separation to distinguish sample components[11–13]. These developments in the early 1990s drastically increased the academic and commercial interest in microfluidic technologies. This trend continues until today as described in a recent comment on the proliferation of microfluidics in literature and intellectual property, which claims that 581 of 770 microelectromechanical systems (MEMS)-related papers published in 2003 dealt with microfluidics[14].

So far, a manifold of LOC systems have been developed for diverse applications, e.g., for DNA analysis[15], DNA amplification (polymerase chain reaction, PCR)[16, 17], proteomics[18, 19] and sample pre-treatment[20]. Recent general reviews on the whole field of LOC systems can be found in[21–23]. The enormous impact of microfluidic LOC technologies also becomes obvious by the large number of recently published books. They either cover the whole field of microfluidics[24, 25] or focus on the engineering[26] or applications of microfluidic systems[27–30]. Moreover, journals exclusively dedicated to the field of micro- and nanofluidics (Microfluidics and Nanofluidics, Springer) or LOC systems (Lab on a Chip, Royal Society of Chemistry) exist today.

During the last two decades, thousands of researchers spent a lot of time in developing new microfluidic components for fluid transport, fluid metering, fluid mixing, valving, and concentration and separation of molecules within miniaturized quantities of fluids. Today, many different types of micropumps are being described in publications[31–34], many different types of mixers[35, 36] and many different types of microvalves[37] are known, and nearly no standards are defined in terms of interconnections. This seems to be the right time to raise the question whether we really need more of such components. In our opinion, for exploring the huge potential of different applications in the LOC field, a component-based microfluidic approach is much too slow and the R&D effort much too expensive. In addition, the best performance you can get out of such a component-oriented solution will be far behind what you can get in an 'integrated system approach' or in other words a 'microfluidic platform approach'. Therefore, we think that the described practice of assembling discrete components like valves and pumps, at least in the field of LOC applications, belongs to the past and we do not expect it to continue in the future. In our view, the research community really needs validated and easy-to-operate microfluidic platforms. These offer an adequate number of microfluidic unit operations that can be easily combined to build application-specific microfluidic systems. In addition, those systems should be producible by a standardized cost-efficient technology.

Before we describe the power of the microfluidic platform concept further, we describe an example of an application-specific integrated system, representing a unique engineering solution to a unique technical problem. It can thus be regarded as the opposite to a microfluidic platform based on easily combinable, universal microfluidic unit operations. The 'electronic fountain pen'[38] is a good example of a discrete microfluidic solution. It can be regarded as the first fully functional, highly integrated, miniaturized and self-sustaining microdosage system of its kind, operating under real-world conditions. The main components are a liquid level sensor, a microvalve and a bubble, and a particle-tolerant fluidic system. The pen has been optimized with respect to minimum energy consumption. It contains a programmable application-specific integrated circuit (ASIC) and is powered by two standard watch batteries, ensuring operation over a period of 2 years, under standard conditions. The electronic fountain pen perfectly fulfils the requirements of its specific application. For any other application in the field of microdosage, or more generally in the field of microfluidics, however, the specific know-how of developing such a system is only of very limited value and every development of this kind always starts from scratch again. This causes significant costs and time, involving high economic risk. Although we expect that this kind of development makes sense for a few selected tasks in diverse fields of applications, in the future also, it is quite clear that this approach will not succeed for LOC systems.

What is needed for these applications, in contrast to unique solutions, is a microfluidic platform. Very similar to the ASIC industry in microelectronics, which provides validated elements and processes to make electronic circuitries, a dedicated microfluidic platform comprises a reduced set of validated microfluidic elements. These elements have to be able to perform the basic fluidic unit operations required within a given application area. Such basic fluidic unit operations are, for example, fluid transport, fluid metering, fluid mixing, valving, and separation or concentration of molecules or particles (see Table 22. 1). The collection of fluidic unit operations needed for diagnostic applications may have only little overlap with the collection needed for pharmaceutical applications[39] or for applications in microreaction technology[40]. In some cases, detection methods will also belong to the basic set of microfluidic operations, and in other cases they will not. Nevertheless, in all cases the user of a platform has to be able to readily combine the elements within a given platform to implement an assay for diagnostic applications or to screen for new compounds in pharmaceutical applications.

Table 22.1 Common features of microfluidic platforms

Microfluidic unit operations	Fabrication technology
• Fluid transport • Fluid metering • Fluid valving • Fluid mixing • Separation • Concentration / amplification / accumulation • Detection / readout • Reagent storage • Incubation • …	Validated manufacturing technology for the whole set fluidic unit operations (prototyping and mass fabrication) Seamless integration of different elements • Preferably in a monolithic way • Or by a well-defined easy packaging technique

More important than providing a totally complete set of fluidic unit operations within a platform is the fact that all elements have to be producible by a well-established fabrication technology. Furthermore, all elements of a platform have to be connectible, ideally in a monolithically integrated way or at least by a well-defined, ready-to-use interconnection and packaging process. If a platform allows a seamless and simple integration of different fluidic elements in a monolithic way, e.g., without sophisticated additional packaging techniques, this provides a significant advantage compared with other platforms. Thus, thinking about microfluidic platforms involves also at least one validated fabrication technology to create complete systems out of the elements. This results in a definition of a microfluidic platform as follows.

A microfluidic platform provides a set of fluidic unit operations, which are designed for easy combination within a well-defined fabrication technology. A microfluidic platform allows the implementation of different application-specific (bio-)chemical processes, automated by microfluidic process integration.

This chapter is intended to give an overview of microfluidic platforms that have been developed so far. Thus, we will focus only on platforms for LOC applications, being aware that there are also other possible fields of applications for microfluidic platforms like micro process engineering or microdosage systems. However, also in the field of LOC systems, we cannot cover all the microfluidic platforms that are known from literature. Furthermore, this chapter is not intended to assess the different platforms by their value to the industry or to the research community. We rather want to stress the microfluidic platform concept by the use of some examples that are the most sophisticated today and thus clarify the strength of the approach.

22.2 Capillary Driven Test Strips

22.2.1 Lateral Flow Assays

Test strips or 'lateral flow assays', as they are also called, have been well known in the diagnostic field since the 1960s, representing the 'state-of-the-art' technology with billions of units being produced at the lowest costs. Although this can be regarded as the most successful microfluidic platform for LOC applications in terms of the number of commercialized products (e.g., diabetes testing, pregnancy testing), hardly any publication exists from a microfluidic point of view, and this is despite the fact that the complexity of test strips varies from a single fleece (i.e., non-woven material featuring high capillarity) for pH measurement, for example, to very complex and also partially microstructured configurations of multiple fleeces that enable the implementation of more complex tests like immunoassays.

The platform relies on capillary forces, an effect that becomes more and more important when scaling down fluidic channels, since the capillary pressure difference

$$\Delta p_\theta = \frac{2\sigma}{r}\cos\theta \qquad (22.1)$$

scales with the inverse of the capillary radius r. The capillary pressure difference appears across the liquid gas interface of surface tension σ and contact angle θ. For hydrophilic contact angles $0 < \theta < 90°$ (partially wetting), the pressure within the liquid phase exceeds the pressure within the gas phase, leading to a further wetting of the capillary. For hydrophobic contact angles $180° > \theta > 90°$ (partially non-wetting), the meniscus withdraws.

An important phenomenon when dealing with capillary driven liquid flows is 'contact line pinning'. It causes the sudden stop of the proceeding meniscus at edges that represent a geometrical singularity. This has to be taken into account when designing microfluidic structures on the capillary driven test strip platform, since no additional pressure is available to overcome this stop. On the other hand, however, this mechanism can be used to control the course of capillary liquid motion on the platform.

22.2.2 Unit Operations

The basic principle of the platform is passive liquid transport via capillary forces within the capillaries of a fleece or a microstructured layer. The liquid samples are loaded into a start reservoir from where they penetrate the underlying fleeces. Another method, especially applied in patient self-testing applications, is the direct capillary filling of the strip from the sampling point. For blood diagnostic assays, for example, the test strip is directly contacted with the blood spilled out of the finger tip that has been previously pricked with a lancet. Within these test strips, the whole blood sample is first filtered in a separation fleece, holding back the blood cells[41], as depicted in the exemplary immunoassay test strip in Fig. 22.1. The separation fleece is placed directly underneath the start reservoir into which the blood sample is applied.

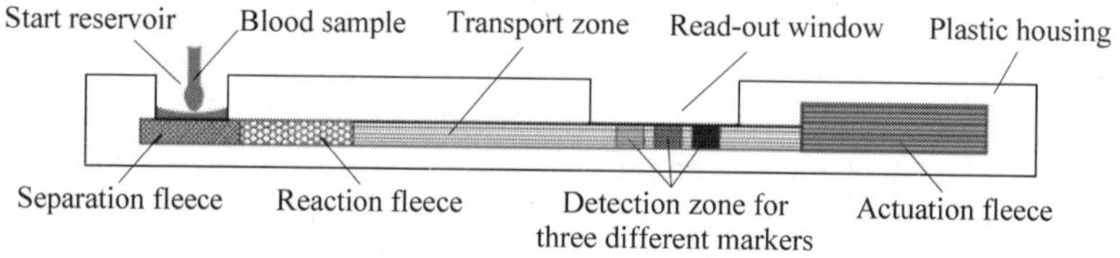

Figure 22.1 Simplified cross section of a typical capillary driven immunoassay test strip

Typically, reagent storage is carried out in terms of dried reagents that have been pre-deposited into the fleeces during fabrication. Dissolving these reagents is done by incubating the liquid in a reaction fleece. Therefore, different zones within the test strip, exhibiting different wetting properties, are required. The dry reagent is placed in a micro-chamber featuring, for example, a pillar structure and a low contact angle for fast priming (see Fig. 22.2). The propagation of the liquid meniscus is slowed down as soon as it reaches the subsequent area with an increased contact angle and, consequently, a reduced capillary force. The area with increased contact angle thus acts as a 'time gate'. The time for the dissolution of the dry reagent is set by the length of the time gate and ends as soon as the liquid reaches the next zone featuring a decreased contact angle, speeding up the flow again.

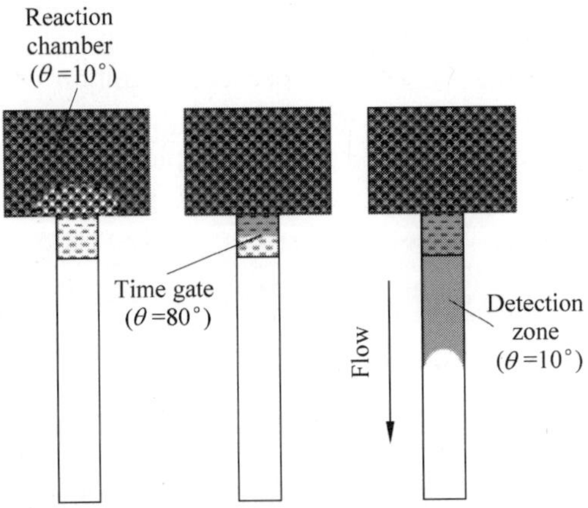

Figure 22.2 Schematic realization of a certain incubation time on the capillary driven test strip platform. The liquid flow is throttled within the time gate of reduced wettability (θ = 80°), thus leading to an extended period of time for reaction within the reaction chamber. Consequently, the dried reagents can be dissolved completely before the liquid proceeds along the detection zone

Metering of liquids is an important unit operation for quantitative assays. Within a test strip, metering is achieved by the defined volumes of the fleeces and microstructures. The liquid flow stops automatically, as soon as the actuation fleece (Fig. 22.1) is fully wetted with liquid. This way, the amount of liquid that has passed the detection zone is well defined. However, in order to have optimum sensitivity, a maximum volume of labeled sample should pass the detection zone. Therefore, the capillarity of the input zone (separation and labeling fleece) should be lower than the capillarity of the actuation fleece, ensuring a complete drainage of the sample into the actuation fleece before the liquid propulsion terminates. The only thing that has to be ensured is that the start reservoir is initially filled with enough sample liquid, i.e., the volume of the complete test strip, to ensure the proper function of the strip.

The results from a test strip assay are mostly read out by optical markers. Since the concentration of these markers within the sample liquid is potentially small, they have to be accumulated within the detection zone. The sample volume passes the detection zone with an adequate flow rate, ensuring the non- diffusion limited binding of the marked sample molecules to the immobilized capture molecules in the detection zone. A remarkable signal is gained after a sufficient sample volume has passed the immobilized molecules. Besides fluorescent markers, which require a test strip reader with some optical components, the reading of assay results with the naked eye is also possible. This is of interest for all applications, where an inexpensive and fast readout is required. A signal that is readable by the naked eye is produced by binding small gold or latex particles to the detection molecule, which accumulate at the detection zone and color it. However, only clear and binary signal-generating assays, such as pregnancy tests, are capable of using the readout by eye. Some assays are also read out using electrochemical mechanisms. The glucose concentration of a blood sample is determined by measuring the electrical charge generated during the enzymatic oxidation of glucose to gluconic acid, for example. The test strip reader applies an external electric potential and measures the current, which is a function of the generated numbers of electrons.

22.2.3 Application Examples

A huge number of assays have been developed on the capillary test strip platform during the past 40 years and have been mainly published in clinical diagnostics and immunological journals. Here, the reader will only be encouraged not to lose sight of the gold-standard microfluidic platform in terms of costs and already implemented LOC applications.

Several applications based on the test strip platform have been shown recently, especially for the population of developing countries that do not have access to state-of-the-art clinical laboratories[42]. Especially, purely disposable test carriers, which do not need any electricity for carrying out the test and can be read out visually, are meant for this field of application. Rapid immunochromatographic strip (ICS) tests for sexually transmitted infections like gonorrhea and syphilis have been successfully implemented on the test strip platform. Moreover, test strips for the detection of Legionella bacteria from environmental cooling tower samples, substituting the need for running an agarose gel after the standard PCR have been shown[43]. The multiplex-nested PCR is performed within a standard thermal cycler and the results are subsequently read out in a lateral flow assay via colloidal gold labeling and visual inspection. This makes the complex and error-prone readout via an agarose gel obsolete.

22.2.4 Strengths and Challenges of the Platform

The possibility of performing an automated on-site measurement using an inexpensive and small disposable test strip, combined with the simple actuation principle that does not need any energy supply, gives the platform a huge potential for point-of-care and patient self-testing applications. Besides simple binary tests, more complex immunoassay protocols have been implemented recently. Thus, the test strip platform is setting a benchmark in terms of costs and integrated, automated assay implementation for all microfluidic platforms discussed within this chapter.

Drawbacks of the platform certainly arise from its simplicity. Assay protocols within capillary driven systems follow a fixed process scheme, imprinted in the microfluidic channel design. Purely passive liquid propulsion by capillary forces cannot be influenced actively once the process is started. As a consequence, the exact timing of the assay steps depends on variations in viscosity and surface tension of the sample. Other crucial unit operations are metering and incubation, the accuracy of which is limited, and mixing, which cannot be accelerated on the test strip platform. Therefore, the precision of the assay result for example is in the order of 10%, which is not likely to be sufficient for future challenges in the implementation of more complex diagnostic assays.

A further critical point is the long-term stability of the wetting properties inside the fleeces or microstructures. Usually, the materials are plasma treated or coated by an additional layer to ensure the desired contact angle and thus wetting behaviors. These coatings or surface activations have to be stable at different temperatures and over a long period of time as they define the test strip lifetime.

22.3 Microfluidic Large-Scale Integration (LSI)

Many pressure-driven microfluidic components and systems have been presented in the past and are commercialized today[44]. Within this section, one of the most prominent and interesting pressure-driven platform concepts is discussed. The microfluidic large scale integration (LSI) platform arose together with a novel fabrication technology for microfluidic channels, called soft lithography. Using this technology, the monolithic fabrication of all necessary fluidic components within one single elastomer material (PDMS) became possible, similar to the silicon-based technology in microelectronics. PDMS (polydimethylsiloxane) is an inexpensive yet powerful material, offering several advantages compared to silicon or glass. It is an inexpensive, rubber-like elastomer with good optical transparency and biocompatibility. It can be structured using the soft lithography technique based on replication molding on micromachined molds. It was first used by the group of George Whiteside for the fabrication of optical devices[45] and stamps for chemical patterning[46, 47]. Thereafter, microfluidic devices were manufactured using the PDMS technology[48–52]. A general and detailed up-to-date view of the use of PDMS for different fields of applications can be found in[53].

Since then, however, PDMS has been used as a merely passive material for the construction of microfluidic channels only. The strength of the technology became obvious when the group of Stephen Quake expanded the technology toward the multilayer soft lithography (MSL) process[54, 55]. With this technology, several layers of PDMS can be hermetically bonded on top of one another, resulting in a monolithic, multilayer PDMS structure. Today, this technology is being promoted by the company Fluidigm Corporation, USA[56].

22.3.1 Unit Operations on the Platform

Based on the high elasticity of PDMS, the basic microfluidic unit operation is a valve made of a planar glass substrate and two layers of PDMS on top of each other. The lower elastomer layer contains the fluidic ducts and the upper elastomer layer features pneumatic control channels. To make a microfluidic valve, a pneumatic control channel crosses a fluidic duct as depicted in Fig. 22.3, left. A pressure p applied to the control channel squeezes the elastomer into the lower layer, where it blocks the liquid flow. Owing to the small size of this valve, of the order of $100\times100\ \mu m^2$, a single integrated fluidic circuit can accommodate thousands of valves. Compared with the development in microelectronics, this approach is called microfluidic LSI[57].

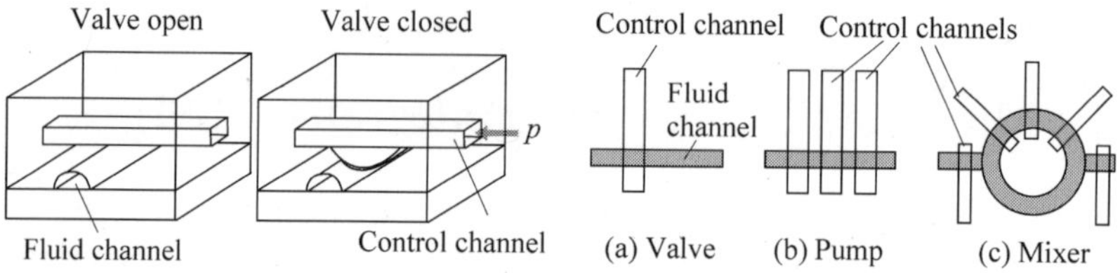

Figure 22.3 Construction of the main unit operations on the multilayer PDMS-based LSI platform. The NanoFlex™ valve as depicted on the left can be closed by applying a pressure p to the control channel. Therefore, microfluidic valves (a), peristaltic pumps (b), and mixing structures (c) can be designed

The valve technology called 'NanoFlex™' is the core technology of the complete platform. Placing two such valves at the two arms of a T-shaped channel, for example, creates a fluidic switch for the routing of liquid flows between several adjacent channels. Liquid transport within the fluid channels can be accomplished by use of external pumps, while the PDMS multilayer device works merely passively, controlling the externally driven liquid flows with the integrated valves. In addition, an integrated pumping mechanism can be achieved by combining several microvalves and actuating them in a peristaltic sequence (Fig. 22.3(b)). Moreover, mixing can be achieved by using the above-described pumping mechanism (Fig. 22.3(c)) by the subsequent injection of the liquids into the fluidic loop through the left inlet (right outlet valve is closed). Later, the inlet and outlet valves are closed and the three control channels on the orbit of the mixing loop are displaced by a peristaltic actuation scheme, leading to a circulation of the mixture within the loop[55]. Thus, the liquids are mixed and later flushed out of the mixer by a washing liquid. By using this mixing scheme, increase of the reaction kinetics of surface binding assays by nearly two orders of magnitude has been demonstrated[58].

The key feature to tap the full potential of the LSI approach is the multiplexing technology, allowing the control of N fluid channels with $2\log_2 N$ control channels only. Based on this principle, a microfluidic storage device with 1,000 independent compartments of approximately 250 pL volume and 3,574 microvalves has been demonstrated[55].

Based on the multiplexer principle, metering of liquid volumes can be achieved by crossed fluid channels and a set of microvalves. First, the liquid is loaded into the central fluid channel, addressed by the multiplexer (see Fig. 22.4). Later, the valves between the different chambers are closed and thus the continuous liquid plug within the fluid channel is segmented into several equal-sized (if the chambers all have the same dimensions) liquid compartments.

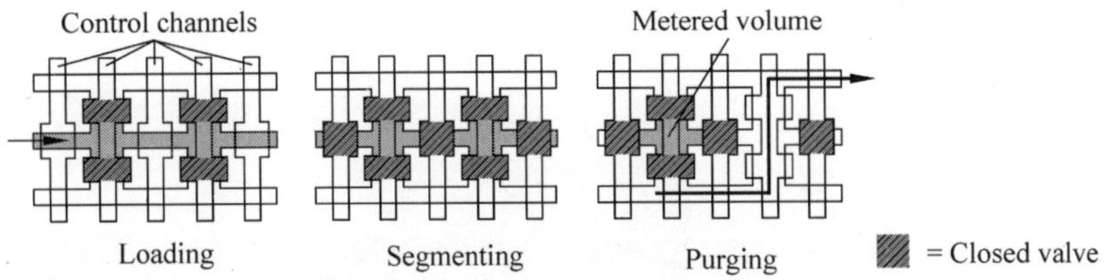

Figure 22.4 Using crossed fluid channels, liquid metering is possible on the microfluidic LSI platform. In the first loading step, a certain fluid channel is addressed using the multiplexer structure and filled with liquid. In the second step, the liquid within this channel is segmented by closing the valves between the chambers. In the last step, fluid that should not be kept is purged via two additional fluid channels on both sides of the metering channel

During the last step, a washing liquid is pumped through the system, addressed to the fluid channel right next to the metering fluid line. All chambers that should not contain a metered volume of the initial liquid after the metering process are now purged vertically since the vertical valves to the two neighboring channels are now open. As a result, a metered liquid volume remains in designated metering chambers.

22.3.2 Application Examples

One promising application on the LSI platform is protein crystallization based on the free interface diffusion method (FID)[59]. The method is based on the counter-diffusion of two liquid phases, namely the protein solution and the precipitant solution, at their contact interface (see Fig. 22.5). During the diffusion process, the concentration profile changes and crystal growth is initiated as soon as the appropriate conditions are met. Within the small dimensions of the microfluidic crystallization structure, a stable interface between the two liquids can be accomplished, ensuring diffusion-based mixing between the two phases only. The crystallization experiments are performed in parallel within 48 unit cells on the microfluidic LSI chip, facilitating 144 different simultaneous crystallization reactions while consuming 3.0 mL of protein solution only[60, 61]. The protein crystallization technology on the LSI platform has been commercialized by the company Fluidigm (Topaz® technology).

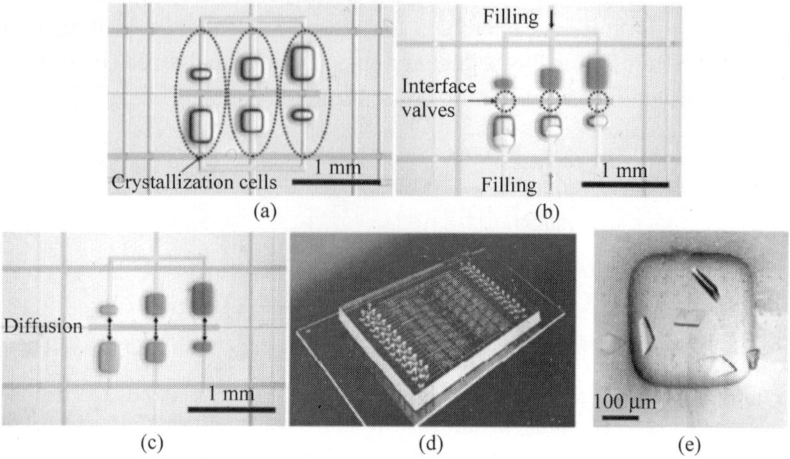

Figure 22.5 Microfluidic realization of a FID protein crystallization assay, based on the LSI platform[61]. One unit cell consists of three crystallization cells for crystallization with different mixing ratios (a). They are initially filled with liquid while the central interface valve is closed (b). Later, the interface valve is opened to allow diffusive mixing between the coupled chambers (c). The chip (d) consists of 48 cells for protein crystallization. An example for a protein crystal grown in the LSI chip is depicted on (e)

A second application example of the microfluidic LSI platform is the extraction of nucleic acids from a small number of cells[62, 63]. For the extraction of DNA from a cell suspension, the cell membrane has to be destroyed first (lysis of the cell). Later, the DNA is specifically separated from the residual cell constituents within the solution. This extraction protocol is completely implemented on the microfluidic platform using the basic unit operations for valving, metering, mixing, and switching of fluids. Purified genomic DNA from as little as 28 bacterial cells (*E. coli* culture) could be successfully isolated on the platform. This corresponds to an increase in sensitivity of this process by three to four times compared to that of conventional methods[40]. Based on this technology, a nucleic acid processor for complete single-cell analysis is under way[64–66].

22.3.3 Strengths and Challenges of the Platform

The microfluidic LSI platform certainly has the potential to become one of the foremost microfluidic platforms for highly integrated applications. It is a flexible and configurable technology that stands out owing to its suitability for LSI. The PDMS fabrication technology is comparably inexpensive and robust and it can be used to fabricate disposables. Reconfigured layouts can be assembled from a small set of validated unit operations, and design iteration periods for new chips are of the order of days. Some of the system functions are hardware defined by the fluidic circuitry but others, like process sequences, can easily be programmed from outside.

Limitations of the platform are related to the material properties of PDMS: for example, chemicals that are not inert to the elastomer cannot be processed, and elevated temperatures such as in microreaction technology are not feasible. Moreover, the implementation of applications in the field of point-of-care diagnostics, where a handheld device is often required, seems not to be beneficial using the LSI platform. The external pressure sources and valves have to be shrunk to a smaller footprint, which is technically feasible, but the costs would be higher in comparison with other platform concepts.

22.4 Centrifugal Microfluidics

The approach of using centrifugal forces to process samples and reagents dates back to the end of the 1960s[67, 68]. At that time, centrifugal analyzers had first been used to transfer and mix a series of samples and reagents in the volume range from 1 μL up to 110 μL into several cuvettes followed by spectrometric monitoring of reactions and real-time data processing. At the beginning of the 1990s, the company Abaxis[69] developed the portable clinical chemistry analyzer[70, 71]. The system consists of a plastic disposable rotor for processing the specimen, dried reagents pre-loaded to the cartridge, and an analyzer instrument for actuation and readout. A new generation of centrifugal devices emerged from the technical capabilities offered by microfabrication and microfluidic technologies[72–75]. Length scales of the fluidic structures in the range of a few hundred micrometers allow parallel processing of up to one hundred units assembled on a disk. This enables a high throughput of many tests by highly parallel and automated liquid handling. In addition, the new opportunities arising from the miniaturization of the centrifugal fluidics cut down assay volumes to less than 1 μL. In particular, fields such as drug screening, where precious samples are analyzed, benefit from the low assay volumes. A review of the theory of the centrifugal microfluidic platform and applications on the platform has been published recently[76].

The basic concept of centrifugal microfluidics is the transport of fluids within a rotating channel by means of the centrifugal force. For a module rotating with an angular frequency $\omega = 2\pi\nu$, the centrifugal force density

$$f_{\omega} = \rho\omega \cdot (\omega \times r) \tag{22.2}$$

acts on a fluid of mass density ρ, at a radial position r. This pumping force is directed radially outward, thus driving the liquid plugs toward outer diameters as long as they possess a net radial plug length. Besides the liquid properties, the radial position and the rotational speed define the pumping force and thus the liquid handling actuation. This eases the parallelization of several identical microfluidic structures being placed on one rotating substrate at different angles, but the same radial position. Although these structures experience the same centrifugal force, they still operate independently from each other, thus making this scheme of parallelization very robust.

The substitution of pressure-generating pumping devices by the pulse-free centrifugally initiated fluid flow enables complex liquid handling processes within a completely passive microstructure. Without any moving part, the rotating modules called disks can be fabricated using cost-efficient microfabrication technologies for plastics, like injection molding. These processes can be replicated from the audio compact disk industry, where microstructure polymer disks have been injection molded for the past several decades. Low-cost disposable disks combined with a non-disposable rotary drive and detecting unit build the modular centrifugal microfluidics platform.

22.4.1 Unit Operations on the Platform

Liquid transport is initiated by the radial outward-directed centrifugal force f_{ω}, which can be scaled over a wide range by the frequency of rotation ω together with the flow resistance of the fluidic channels. Small flow rates of the order of nL/s, as well as high throughput continuous flows up to 1 mL/s[77] can be generated. So, scaling of flow rates over six orders of magnitude and independent of the chemical composition, ionic strength, conductivity, or pH value of the liquid can be accomplished, opening up a wide range of possible applications.

Liquid valves can basically be constructed by three different microfluidic structures on the centrifugal platform, as depicted in Fig. 22.6. A very simple valve can be realized with a sudden expansion of a microfluidic channel, for example into a bigger reservoir (a). The valving mechanism of this capillary valve is based on the energy barrier for the breaking of the meniscus, which is pinned at the sharp corner. This barrier can be overcome under rotation by the centrifugal pressure load of the overlying liquid plug[73]. For a given liquid plug position and length, i.e., for a given set of geometric parameters, the valve can be influenced by the frequency of rotation only, leading to a critical burst frequency ω_c, above which such valve structures forward the liquid. Another possibility to stop the liquid flow within a channel is local hydrophobic coating of the channel walls (b). Moreover, this valve is opened as soon as the rotational frequency exceeds the critical burst frequency ω_c. A third method is based on a hydrophilic U-shaped siphon channel, wherein the two liquid-gas interfaces are levered at high frequencies of rotation (c). Below a critical frequency ω_c, however, the right meniscus proceeds beyond the bend, thus generating a net radial length allowing the centrifugal force to drain the complete liquid from the siphon.

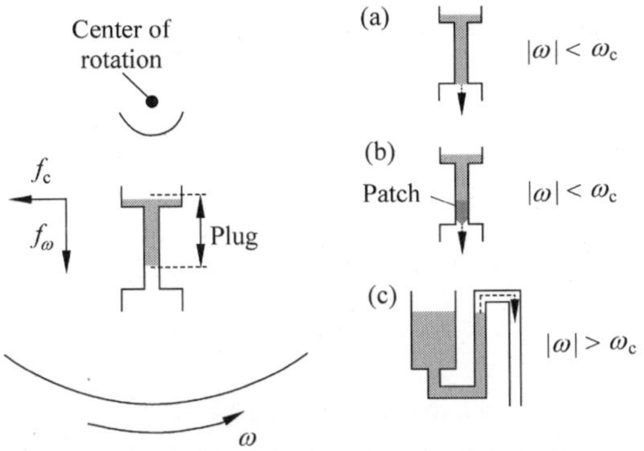

Figure 22.6 Principal centrifugal approach and schematic sketch of the three valving techniques on the centrifugal platform. (a) Geometric capillary valve, (b) Hydrophobic valve, and (c) Hydrophilic siphon valve

An alternative approach to the control of liquid flows on the centrifugal platform is followed by the company SpinX Technologies, Switzerland[78]. A laser beam individually opens fluidic interconnects between different channel layers on a plastic substrate (virtual laser valve, VLV). This enables an online control of the liquid handling process on the rotating module for adjusting metered volumes and incubation times within a wide range. For this reason, the SpinX platform works with a standardized fluidic cartridge that is not custom made for each specific application, but can be programmed just before the measurement, or even online during a running process.

By placing one of the above-mentioned valves at the outer end of a chamber and an overflow channel at the inner end, a metering structure is realized[79]. The metered liquid portion is directly set by the volume capacity of the chamber. Owing to the high precision of microfabrication technologies, small coefficients of variation (standard deviation/mean value), e.g., a CV < 5% for a volume of 300 nL[80] and also metered volumes of only 5 nL have been achieved[81]. By arranging several metering structures interconnected via an appropriate distribution channel, simple aliquoting structures can be realized[82].

These structures split a sample into several defined volumes, enabling the conduction of several assays (with different volumes) from the same sample simultaneously. Different mixing schemes have been proposed for the centrifugal platform. Considering mixing of continuous liquid flows within a radially directed rotating channel, the perpendicularly directed Coriolis force f_c (Fig. 22.6) automatically generates a transverse liquid flow[77, 83, 84]. A continuous centrifugal micromixer, utilizing the Coriolis stirring effect, showed an increasing mixing quality toward very high volume throughputs of up to 1 mL/s per channel[77]. Besides the mixing of continuous liquid flows, the homogenization of discrete and small liquid volumes within microchambers is also of importance, especially when analyzing small sample volumes (batch mode mixing). One possibility to enhance the mixing is the active agitation of the liquid within a mixing chamber by inertia-related shear forces, induced by a fast change of the sense of rotation (shake-mode mixing)[79]. This method leads to reduced mixing times of the order of several seconds, compared with several minutes for pure diffusion-based mixing. A further downscaling of mixing times below one second using magnetic microparticles located in the mixing chamber has also been demonstrated[85].

For routing (switching) of liquids, a switch that uses the transverse Coriolis force to guide liquid flows between two outlets at the branching of an inverse Y-shaped channel has been invented[86]. Depending on the sense of rotation, the Coriolis force is either directed to the left or to the right, guiding the liquid stream into one of two downstream reservoirs at the branching. An improved version of Coriolis-based switching operates on individual droplets and enables switching of small flow rates of 160 nL/s only at low frequencies down to a few Hz[87]. Another method for liquid routing, based on different wetting properties of the continuative channels, has been reported by Gyros AB, Sweden[88]. The liquid stream is initially guided toward a radial channel, exhibiting a hydrophobic patch at the beginning. Therefore, the liquid is deflected into another, not hydrophobic, channel next to the radial one.

For high frequencies of rotation, the approaching liquid possesses enough energy to overcome the hydrophobic patch and is therefore routed into the radial channel[89].

A common sample preparation step in many analytical protocols is the extraction of plasma from a whole blood sample (separation). Since blood plasma is less dense than white and red blood cells, it can be found in the upper phase, the supernatant, after sedimentation in the artificial gravity field under rotation. The spatial extraction of the plasma obtained from the cellular pellet can be done via a capillary extraction channel that branches from the sedimentation chamber at a radial position where only plasma is expected[71]. Another method uses a pre-separation of the cellular and plasma phases during the sample flow through an azimuthally aligned channel of just 300 μm radial width[90]. The obtained plasma fraction is thereafter split from the cellular components by a decanting process (see Fig. 22.7, left). The whole extraction proceeds as follows. Initially, a raw blood sample is metered to a fixed volume defined by an overflow channel next to the outlet of the inlet chamber (metering). Subsequently, the metered sample is forwarded via the drain channel to the decanting structure. Within the drain channel, the blood is pre-separated with the plasma phase flowing on top of the cellular phase. The two joint streams separate when they enter the decant chamber. The denser cellular phase sinks outward while the less dense plasma phase stays on top. When the decant chamber is entirely filled, pure plasma in the supernatant overflows into a plasma chamber (Fig. 22.7, right). The course of separation concludes when the entire blood sample has been transported from the metering chamber into the decant and the plasma chamber, respectively. The extracted plasma volume is defined by the chamber geometries and can therefore be directly forwarded to further downstream processes e.g., by a capillary duct.

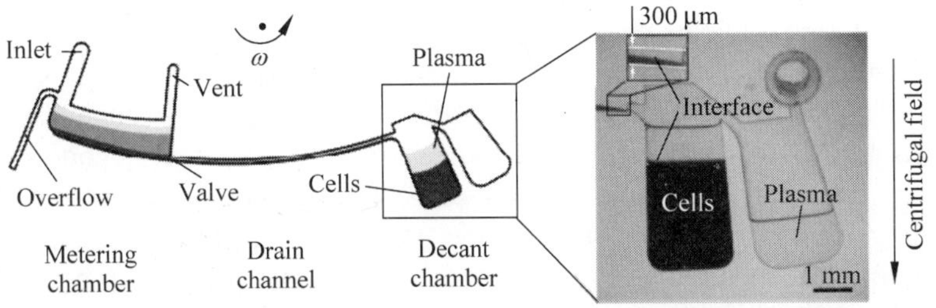

Figure 22.7 Left: Flow scheme of the decanting structure for plasma extraction from a raw blood sample; Right: Purified plasma is decanted into a separate reservoir while the cellular pellet is retained at the bottom of the decant chamber (adopted from[90])

This centrifugal flow separation technique extracts 2 μL of plasma from a raw blood sample that is initially metered to 5 μL. Typical separation times of 20 s could be achieved for moderate spinning frequencies of 40 Hz. The residual cell concentration in the bulk plasma is less than 0.1%.

22.4.2 Application Examples

Madou et al from the University of California, Irvine, showed a series of capillary valves to perform enzyme-linked immunosorbent assays (ELISAs) on the centrifugal platform[91]. The different assay liquids are contained in reservoirs connected via valves of different burst frequency to the reaction chamber. The capillary valves are opened subsequently by increasing the frequency of rotation. It could be shown that the centrifugally conducted assay has the same performance in terms of detection range as the conventional method on the 96-well plate, while having advantages over the conventional method such as less reagent consumption and shorter assay time.

Gyros AB, Sweden[88], uses a flow-through sandwich immunoassay at nanoliter scale to quantify proteins within the Gyrolab Workstation. Therefore, a column of pre-packed and streptavidin-coated microparticles is integrated in each of 112 identical assay units on the microfluidic disk. Each unit has an individual sample inlet and a volume definition chamber that leads to an overflow channel. Defined volumes (200 nL) of samples and reagents can be applied to the pre-packed particle column. The laser-induced fluorescent (LIF) detector is incorporated into the Gyrolab Workstation. Using this technology, multiple immunoassays have been carried out to determine the imprecision of the assay result. The day-to-day (total) imprecisions (CV) of the immunoassays on the microfluidic disk are below 20%[92]. The assays were carried out within 50 minutes while, in comparison, the traditional ELISA in a 96-well plate typically takes a few hours, with sample volumes of a few hundred microliters. A fully integrated colorimetric assay for the determination of the alcohol concentration in human whole blood has been shown on the centrifugal Bio-Disk platform[80]. After loading the reagents into the reagents reservoir, a droplet of untreated human blood obtained from a finger tip is loaded into the inlet port of the microstructure. To enforce rapid mixing within the reaction chamber, the sense of rotation is frequently reversed every 10 s, leading to a homogeneous mixture (shake-mode mixing). Thus, an enzymatic reaction is initiated, changing the color of the mixture depending on the alcohol concentration. After sedimentation of the residual blood cells, the absorbance is monitored in real time via a laser beam that is reflected into the disk plane on integrated V-grooves[93]. By using this automated assay and readout protocol, the concentration of alcohol in human whole blood could be determined within 150 seconds itself. The results are comparable to common point-of-care tests. Only a minute blood volume of just 500 nL was required. In addition, a protein crystallization assay has been demonstrated on the centrifugal microfluidic platform, as depicted in Fig. 22.8[81]. First, a defined volume of the protein solution is dispensed into the protein inlet and transported into the crystallization chamber. Next, the pre-loaded precipitant is metered under rotation and transferred into the crystallization chamber as soon as the hydrophobic valve breaks. In the last step, the pre-loaded oil is released at a still higher frequency and placed on top of the liquid stack within the crystallization chamber, to prevent evaporation. The successful crystallization of proteinase K and catalase could be demonstrated.

22.4.3 Strengths and Challenges of the Platform

The modular setup of the system with inexpensive and disposable plastic cartridges is certainly one major advantage of the centrifugal microfluidic platform. The cost-efficient fabrication predominantly originates from the simple and passive microfluidic elements that can easily be combined in a monolithic way within the same fabrication process. These elements allow the implementation of all needed unit operations to perform complex assay protocols in an automated way. Owing

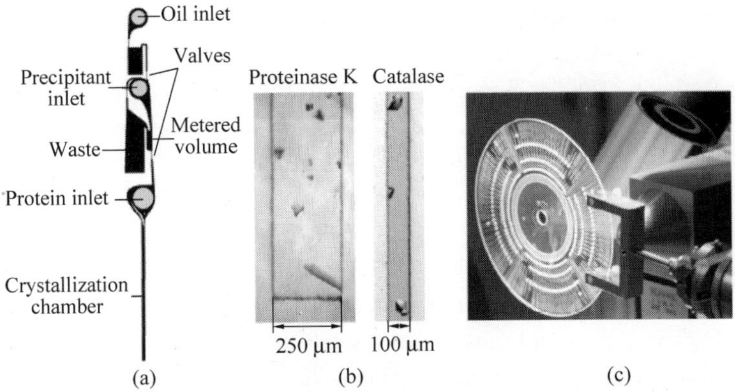

Figure 22.8 Microfluidic realization of a free interface diffusion (FID) protein crystallization assay, based on the centrifugal microfluidic platform (a)[81]. The three liquids (protein, metered precipitant, oil) are subsequently transported into the crystallization chamber triggered by hydrophobic valves. Two examples of protein crystals are depicted in the middle (b). The complete microfluidic disk (c) enables up to 100 crystallization experiments in parallel (picture shows readout in the X-ray beamline)

to the rotational symmetry of the disks, a high degree of parallelization can be achieved. All processes are controlled by the frequency of rotation of one single macroscopic rotary engine. In addition, the centrifugal microfluidic platform can be easily applied to a wide range of different applications due to the fact that it allows scaling of the pulse-free flow rates by six orders of magnitude.

As soon as any additional actuation or sensing function is required on the module while it is rotating, things become tricky from a technical point of view if a contact-free interface is not applicable. The platform also lacks flexibility compared with others that allow online programming of fluidic networks within one piece of hardware that fits all. Most of the logic functions, as well as their critical frequencies, are permanently imprinted into the channel network.

22.5 Electrokinetic Platforms

Electrokinetic pumping and particle manipulation principles are based on surface forces and become feasible actuation methods in the microdimension due to the increased surface-to-volume ratio. This advantage combined with the simple setup of electrokinetic systems, which basically consist of microfluidic channels and electrodes, explains the early advent of microfluidic LOC applications based on the electrokinetic platform. These applications focused on the analysis of chemical compounds via electrophoretic separation within microchannels (capillary electrophoresis, CE)[11–13, 94].

22.5.1 Unit Operations on the Platform

Fluid propulsion (fluid transport) on the electrokinetic platform is based on the movement of the liquid layer right at the interface to the solid phase (electric double layer) initiated by an external voltage (Fig. 22.9(a)). Standard channel materials for electrokinetic actuation are silicon or glass, which possess negatively charged surfaces thus causing a surplus of positively charged liquid molecules in the double layer close to the channel walls. As soon as an electric potential is applied along the channel, the positively charged liquid molecules are attracted by electrostatic forces and thus move toward the negative electrode. As a result of the viscous coupling, the bulk liquid is dragged by the moving layer and a planar velocity profile (***v***) evolves. This is a major difference compared with the parabolic velocity profile of pressure-driven flows. Consequently, a rectangular shaped liquid plug with limited dimensions along a microchannel gets increasingly widened within a pressure-driven flow, while it keeps its original flat shape within an EOF. Thus, sample dispersion is drastically reduced in electroosmotic flows, making it the method of choice for chromatographic analysis.

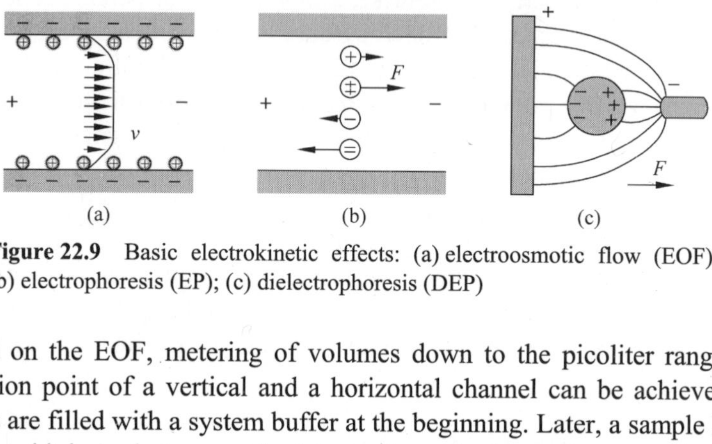

Figure 22.9 Basic electrokinetic effects: (a) electroosmotic flow (EOF); (b) electrophoresis (EP); (c) dielectrophoresis (DEP)

Based on the EOF, metering of volumes down to the picoliter range at the intersection point of a vertical and a horizontal channel can be achieved. Both channels are filled with a system buffer at the beginning. Later, a sample liquid is injected and it is made to cross the intersection point by applying a voltage to the vertical channel (see Fig. 22.10(a)). Subsequently, the flow is stopped and an electric field applied to the horizontal channel causes a liquid flow of the buffer, which displaces the small plug at the junction and thus meters a volume corresponding to the dimensions of the intersection area. This method is used within capillary electrophoresis tests for the injection of the sample into the separation channel.

The mixing of two co-flowing streams can be demonstrated on the electrokinetic platform by applying an alternating current (AC) voltage to a pair of coplanar meandering electrodes configured parallel to the channel[95]. A mixing time of 0.18 s, which is 20-fold faster than diffusion, has been reported. Moreover, complete process schemes comprising cell lysis, mixing, and DNA amplification based on fluid propulsion by EOF have been demonstrated[96].

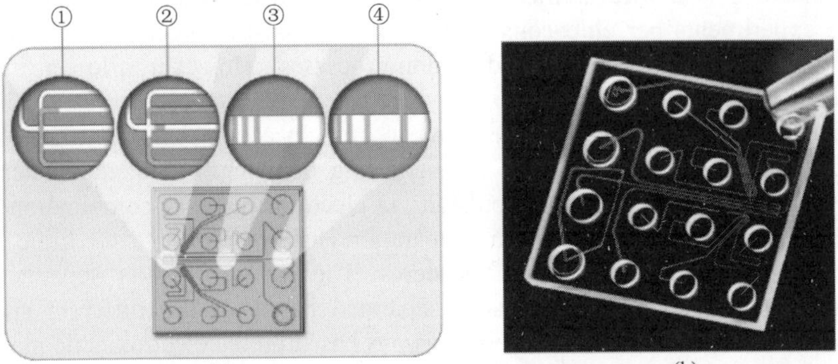

(a) (b)

Figure 22.10 Microfluidic realization of capillary electrophoresis analysis on the electrokinetic platform[103]. After the sample has been transported to the junction area ①, it is metered by the activated horizontal flow and injected into the separation channel ②. Therein, the sample components are electrophoretically separated ③ and read out by their fluorescence signal ④. The complete microfluidic CE chip is depicted on the right (© Agilent Technologies, Inc. 2000–2009)

Besides electroosmosis, other effects also occur within the electric field if the liquid contains electrically charged particles or molecules (Fig. 22.9(b)). They are attracted by one of the electrodes, depending on their charge and valence, and consequently move toward the electrode in a stationary surrounding liquid. The velocity of the molecule depends on its charge and size and enables the distinction between different species. This effect is called electrophoresis (EP) and is used for chromatographic separation.

A modification of electrophoresis is free-field electrophoresis, which enables the continuous separation of a mixture according to charge with subsequent collection of the sample band of interest[97]. Therefore, the electric field is applied perpendicular to the superposed pressure-driven flow within a broad and flat microchamber. While passing this extraction chamber, the species contained in the sample flow are deflected, depending on their charge, and thus exit the chamber through one of several outlets. The third electrokinetic effect is based on the temporary charging of intrinsically uncharged particles within an AC electrical field. This can either be a time-changing or a locally changing electrical signal, i.e., non-uniform electric field, as depicted in Fig. 22.9(c). This effect is applied in many fields, e.g., for the controlled separation and trapping of sub-micron bioparticles[98], for the fusion of cells[99], or the separation of metallic from semiconducting carbon nanotubes[100].

22.5.2 Application Examples

Capillary electrophoresis systems were the first micro-TAS and emerged from the analytical chemistry field at the end of the 1990s[11–13, 94]. They arose from the idea that chemical measurements within sub-millimeter reaction vessels enable more experiments per chip consuming less (expensive) reagents within shorter reaction times (due to the faster diffusion processes). However, a lower limit of the reaction vessel dimensions exists since the number of molecules within the sample would vanish when downscaling too far. In conclusion, the 10 – 100 μm dimensional scale appears to be an interesting domain for miniature chemical analysis systems[101]. Liquid propulsion via electroosmosis in combination with the injection of a sample plug into a separation channel represents the basic setup of capillary electrophoresis (CE) systems. The sample is later separated by electrophoresis, leading to spatially separated bands of the different species within the sample (Fig. 22.10). Today, assays based on the electrokinetic platform that use CE are commercially distributed by Caliper Life Sciences, Inc.[102] and Agilent Technologies[103] for DNA and protein analysis.

22.5.3 Strengths and Challenges of the Platform

The electroosmotic actuation of liquid flows enables pulse-free pumping without any moving part. Additionally, no dispersion occurs in the EOF flow and thus sample plugs are not broadened during chromatographic separation. These two advantages are the reason for the successful application of capillary electrophoresis for DNA and protein quantification. Miniaturization of electrophoretic analysis enables the automation and parallelization of tests with small dead volumes, thus reducing the required amount of sample. Furthermore, higher voltages can be used for the separation and the dissipation of heat is increased when compared to macroscopic systems due to the higher surface-to-volume ratio. Overall, miniaturized electrophoresis enables the fast and efficient analysis of biomolecules. Drawbacks of the technology can be seen in the need for high-performance detection technologies due to the reduced volumes and thus reduced signals. Moreover, technical problems arise in capillary electrophoresis systems due to pH gradients, streaming currents that counteract the external electric field and gas bubbles that can occur due to electrolysis at the electrodes. In addition, high voltages are needed that can hardly be generated in, for example, mobile handheld devices.

22.6 Droplet-Based Microfluidic Platforms

The principal idea behind droplet-based or digital microfluidic systems is the use of single droplets as reaction confinements for biological assays or chemical reactions. Interfacial and surface tensional forces enable the precise generation and spatial stabilization of these droplets. Since the droplets are kept isolated within an immiscible surrounding fluid like air or oil, lateral dispersion (Taylor dispersion) can be avoided while moving the droplets to different locations. A multitude of parallel screening reactions, each consuming only a minute amount of reagent is enabled inside several small-sized droplets on the platform. Droplet-based microfluidic systems can be fundamentally divided into two basic setups, the channel-based and the planar surface-based approach as described in Fig. 22.11. The channel-based systems are mostly pressure driven with the droplet generation and manipulation relying on actuation via liquid flows within closed microchannels. On the planar surface-based platforms, droplets can be arbitrarily moved in two dimensions representing planar programmable LOCs. They are actuated by electrowetting on dielectrics (EWOD) or surface acoustic waves (SAW) respectively.

Approach	Schematic sketch	Description
Channel based	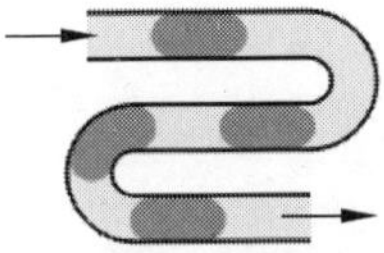	- Liquid flow driven actuation (pressure driven) - Simultaneous motion in 1 dimension - Droplet movement defined by geometry - Closed microchannels
Surface based	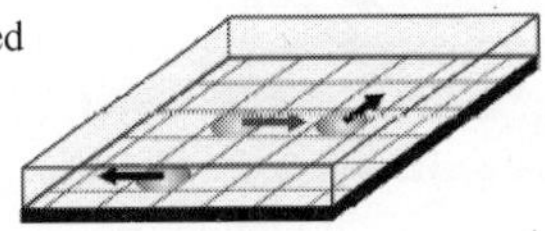	- Actuation by SAW or EWOD - Individual motion in 2 dimensions - Arbitrary droplet movement on surface - Planar, (open) surface - Online control of assay protocol

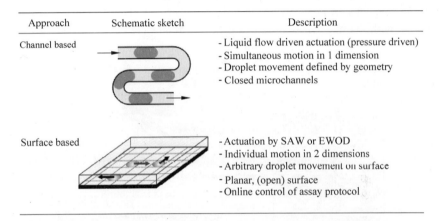

Figure 22.11 Description of the two basic setups for droplet-based microfluidic platforms

22.6.1 Pressure-Driven Unit Operations and Applications

The pressure driven, droplet-based platform relies on a two-phase fluid flow through the microchannels. The two immiscible phases are dispersed into each other so that a sample fluid (e.g., aqueous solution) forms plugs of a certain length, separated by the carrier fluid (e.g., oil) along the channel. This flow scheme is called segmented flow; since the size of the inner-phase droplet exceeds the cross-sectional dimensions of the channel, leading to squeezed fluid plugs. The two-phase flow is pumped throughout the channels by an externally applied pressure.

The most elementary unit operation on the pressure-driven, droplet-based platform is the initial generation of the droplets. This step can also be considered as metering, since the liquid volumes involved in the latter reaction within the droplet are defined during the droplet formation process. Two different microfluidic structures have been reported for a controlled droplet generation, namely, flow-focusing structure[104, 105] and the T-shaped junction[106]. The formation of double emulsions, e.g., water-in-oil-in-water (W/O/W), has been shown in a serial arrangement of T-junctions[107] or within more complex interleaved microcapillaries arrangements[108] also. The size of the droplet is influenced by the channel dimensions and the strength of the shear forces at the channel junction (higher shear forces lead to smaller droplets) for both droplet formation mechanisms.

To use droplets inside channels as reaction confinements, the different liquid streams have to be loaded into the droplets first. A method to combine three different sample liquid streams by a sheath flow arrangement with subsequent injection as a common droplet into the carrier fluid has been shown by the group of Rustem F. Ismagilov at the University of Chicago, USA[109]. Different concentrations and ratios of two reagent sub-streams plus a dilution buffer merge into one droplet and perform an on-chip dilution[110]. The mixing ratios can be adjusted by the volume flow ratio of the three streams (see also Fig. 22.12(a)).

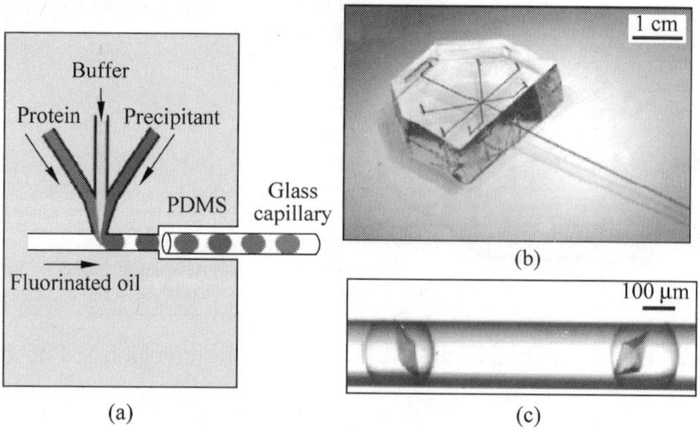

Figure 22.12 Microfluidic realization of a protein crystallization assay, based on the pressure-driven droplet-based platform[111]. The protein and precipitation solutions are continuously injected into one droplet of adjustable volume (a) and later transported into a glass capillary for crystallization (b). Recirculating flows inside the droplets enhance mixing and induce the crystallization process (c)

Using a combination of two opposing T-junctions connected to the same channel, the formation of droplets of alternating composition has been demonstrated[112]. This method can be used for protein crystallization or indexing within the continuous flow screening experiments on the droplet-based platform, for example. By use of a similar technique, the injection of an additional reactant into a liquid plug moving through the channel at an additional downstream T-junction has also been demonstrated[113]. Not only liquid chemical reagents but also other components like cells have been loaded into droplets as reported in[114]. Therefore, a flow-focusing device has been used with an aqueous cell suspension as the sample phase flowing through the central channel. The merging of different sized droplets possessing different velocities to form single droplets is also feasible as shown in[109]. In the same study, the controlled splitting of droplets at a channel branching point has been demonstrated. Using a similar method, the formation of droplet emulsions with controlled volume fractions and drop sizes has been realized[115].

Mixing inside the droplets can be accelerated by a recirculating flow due to shear forces induced by the motion along the stationary channel wall[116]. This effect is even more pronounced if two liquids of differing viscosities are mixed within the droplet, as reported in[117]. Based on the recirculation flow, a mixing scheme for the pressure-driven, droplet-based platform has been proposed using wound microchannels[118]. Within each channel curvature, the orientation between the phase pattern in the droplet and the direction of motion is changed so that the inner recirculation leads to a stretching and folding of the phases. Under favorable conditions, sub-millisecond mixing can be achieved and has been employed for the multi-step synthesis of nanoparticles, for example[113]. A detailed and theoretical description of this mixing effect is given in[119]. Besides the mixing within liquid droplets dispersed into another liquid carrier phase, mixing within the carrier phase can also be accelerated by a segmented flow. The injection of gas bubbles into a continuous liquid stream forming a segmented gas-liquid flow has been described by the group of Klavs Jensen at the MIT[120, 121]. The gas bubbles are introduced into the liquid flow and they initiate recirculation flows within the liquid segments in between due to the motion along the channel wall. The gas bubbles can be completely separated from the liquid stream using a planar capillary separator after the reaction is complete. Using this technology, the synthesis of colloidal silica particles has been demonstrated[122]. Another microfluidic mixing scheme based on a gas- liquid segmented flow uses an additional repeated separation and recombining of the channel[123].

The incubation time of the reagents combined inside a droplet at the injection position can easily be calculated at a certain point of observation from the traveling distance of the droplet divided by the droplet velocity. Thus, the incubation time can be monitored, time resolved, by simply scanning along the channel from the injection point to more downstream positions.

This is a unique feature of the platform and enables the investigation of the kinetics of chemical reactions of the order of only a few milliseconds[110]. On the other hand, incubation times of the order of a week for storing applications have been demonstrated[124]. This is enabled by the droplet compartments that are separated by the carrier fluid, which prevents evaporation and diffusion. Using this approach, several 60 nL liquid droplets containing one or more cells were generated within a microfluidic chip and later flushed into a Teflon capillary tube for cultivation. The cell densities were still as high as in conventional systems after 144 hours of growth within the droplets.

Additional unit operations based on charged droplets and electric fields have been added to the droplet-based, pressure-driven platform by David A. Weitz and his associates[125]. Using dielectrophoresis, the sorting of single drops out of a droplet train (switching) at rates up to 4 kHz has been shown, for example[126]. The pressure-driven, droplet-based technology enriched with electric field-based unit operations is currently commercialized by the company RainDance Technologies, Inc., USA[127].

Protein crystallization has been implemented on the pressure-driven, droplet-based platform by Ismagilov and his associates[111, 128]. Droplets from three liquids, namely the protein solution, a buffer, and the precipitant, are dispersed into the oil carrier phase (Fig. 22.12). The precipitant concentration inside the droplet is adjusted via the buffer and precipitant flow rate, respectively. Thus, different concentrations are generated and transferred into a glass capillary for subsequent X-ray analysis[129]. Non-specific protein adsorption to the liquid- liquid interface can be suppressed by adding certain surfactants to the carrier phase[130]. The effect of mixing on the nucleation of protein crystallization has been investigated by combining the described crystallization structure with a winding mixing channel[131]. Fast chaotic mixing has been found to be favorable for the formation of well-formed proteins within the droplets[132]. Besides the described method for crystallization, an alternative process in which the concentration within one droplet is changed over time has been demonstrated[111, 133]. In this case, a carrier liquid that enables diffusion between the droplets, i.e., a water-permeable liquid, is selected. Alternating droplets of protein and precipitant on the one hand and a high-concentration salt solution on the other hand are generated using two opposing droplet-generation structures[112]. Water diffuses through the oil carrier phase from the low salt concentration, i.e., protein-containing droplet, to the high concentration droplet. This steadily increases the concentration within the protein-containing droplet until suitable crystallization conditions are achieved.

Recent developments on the pressure-driven, droplet-based platform aim at high-throughput screening applications. Therefore, a large number of droplets, each containing a different reagent, are separated and surrounded by a fluorinated carrier fluid within a microcapillary. In order to prevent coalescence during possibly long storing times, a gas bubble is injected between the droplets as an additional separation phase[134]. Based on this three-phase liquid-liquid-gas system, reliable and high-throughput screening assays can be performed, which could be an alternative for well plates in the future[135].

22.6.2 Electrowetting-Driven Unit Operations and Applications

The electrowetting (EW) effect was first described by Gabriel Lippmann in 1875, while recent developments were initiated in the early 1990s by introducing the idea of using thin insulating layers to separate the conductive liquids from the metallic electrodes in order to eliminate electrolysis (described in a recent review paper on electrowetting,[136]). This paved the way for the application of the EW effect as a liquid propulsion principle for LOC systems.

The electrowetting-on-dielectric (EWOD)[137] technology is based on the principle of a liquid droplet placed between two electrodes covered with insulating dielectric layers. An applied voltage between the two electrodes changes the contact angle (Fig. 22.13(a)). Thus, EWOD can be simply described as a tool to control the contact angle of conductive liquids[138]. Using the EWOD setup, a microfluidic actuation method for moving droplets has been published by Michael G. Pollack and his associates from the Duke University, Durham[139], and Chang-Jin (C. J.) Kim from the University of California, Los Angeles (UCLA)[140] in 2000. A schematic cross section of an EWOD actuator is depicted in Fig. 22.13(b). Several individual addressable control electrodes are located on the bottom of the device to control the droplet path. They are typically arranged in two-dimensional (2D) arrays. An additional hydrophobic layer (mostly Teflon®) is applied to the insulator surface to enhance the droplet movement. A common ground electrode replaces the extended electrode for contacting of the liquid droplet.

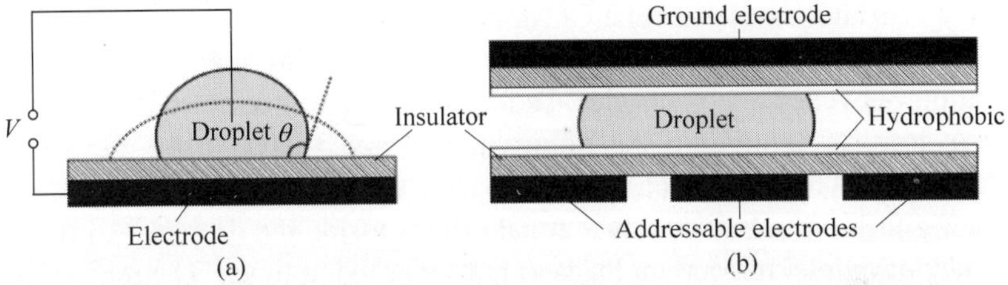

Figure 22.13 (a) The electrowetting principle. If a voltage V is applied between a conductive liquid and an electrode separated by an insulating layer, the contact angle θ of the liquid/solid interface can be decreased. (b) Schematic sketch of the electrowetting actuation of liquid droplets. Several individual addressable control electrodes (bottom) are used to locally change the contact angle and thereby initiate a droplet movement

The droplet, which is enclosed between the two electrode plates, features a sufficient volume to cover parts of two addressable electrodes at all times. If a voltage is applied to one of the control electrodes covered by the droplet, the contact angle at this part of the droplet is reduced, initiating a movement of the droplet along the paths given by the activated pads.

Since the path of the droplets is determined by the pattern of electric fields, the EWOD-driven, droplet-based platform is easily programmable. This allows an operator to perform different assays, to be run by different programs on the same piece of hardware. Besides aqueous solutions, several other liquids, like organic solvents, ionic liquids, aqueous surfactants solutions[141], and also biological fluids, like whole blood, serum, plasma, urine, saliva, sweat, and tears[142], have been successfully transported on the EWOD droplet-based platform. The dispensing, i.e., initial metering unit operation, is probably the most critical on the EWOD-driven, droplet-based platform. Metered droplets can be formed from an on-chip reservoir in three steps[142]. First, a liquid column is extruded from the reservoir by activating a series of electrodes adjacent to it. Second, once the column overlaps the electrode on which the droplet is to be formed, all the remaining electrodes are turned off to form a neck in the column. The reservoir electrode is then activated during the third, final step to pull back the liquid and break the neck completely to form a droplet. Using this droplet-metering structure, droplets of 20 nL volume could be generated with a standard variation below 2%[142]. Since the droplet dispensing is a crucial step for the performance and accuracy of all assays on the EWOD platform, additional measures for a controlled liquid metering like on-chip capacitance measurement of volume control[143] or the use of numerical methods for the design of EWOD structures[144] have been proposed.

In addition, the merging of droplets on three linearly aligned EWOD electrodes has been presented by contacting two initially separated droplets on a single electrode[145]. Together with droplet generation from a reservoir and the droplet transport along electrode arrays, the controlled merging and splitting of droplets complete the four fundamental fluidic operations considered essential in building digital microfluidic systems for LOC applications[146].

The most basic type of mixing within droplets on the EWOD platform is an oscillation between two electrodes. Before this active mixing scheme is applied, the two droplets containing the liquids to be mixed have to be merged into a single droplet. This coalesced droplet is later moved along the electrodes in an oscillating fashion to induce advectional effects inside the droplet. An increasing frequency of droplet movement leads to reduced mixing times. The mixing process can be further accelerated by oscillating over a longer linear electrode array. The shortest mixing time for two 1.3 μL droplets in linear oscillation on 4 electrodes was about 4.6 s[147]. In another study, the mixing times could be further reduced to less than 3 s using 2D arrays[148].

Different readout schemes for biochemical assays have been applied to the EWOD-driven, droplet-based platform. Colorimetric, enzymatic assays that are important for diagnostic applications have been successfully implemented and glucose concentration measurements on several biological fluids (serum, plasma, urine, and saliva) with comparable results could be performed[142]. The microfluidic chip layout for the colorimetric glucose assay is depicted in Fig. 22.14, featuring reservoirs, injection structures (metering), and a network of electrodes for droplet transport, splitting, and detection.

As an example, the use of an EWOD system for the automated sample preparation of peptides and proteins for matrix-assisted laser desorption/ionization mass spectrometry (MALDI-MS) has been reported[149]. In this study, standard MALDI-MS reagents, analytes, concentrations, and recipes have been demonstrated to be compatible with the EWOD technology, and mass spectra comparable to those collected by conventional methods were obtained. A recent comprehensive review of the EWOD platform can be found in[150].

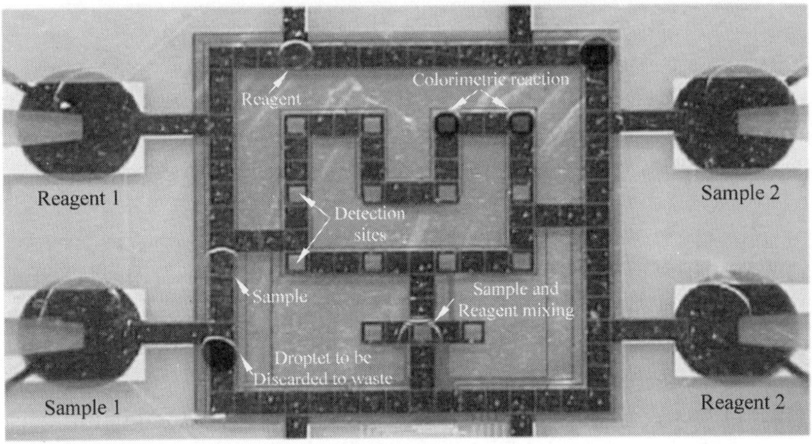

Figure 22.14 Integrated LOC architecture for a colorimetric glucose assay, based on the droplet-based EWOD platform. Four reservoirs with injection elements are connected to an electrode circuit, where the droplets are mixed, split, and transported to detection sites for readout[142]

An alternative actuation principle for surface-based droplet manipulation, which does not require a second electrode in contact with the droplet, is based on dielectrophoresis. The basic unit operations, like droplet generation, movement, metering, and merging, by using this alternative actuation have been demonstrated recently[151, 152].

22.6.3 Surface Acoustic Wave-Driven Unit Operations and Applications

An alternative to the EW-based transport of droplets on a plane surface has been proposed by Achim Wixforth and his associates at the University of Augsburg, Germany[153]. The approach is based on surface acoustic waves (SAW), which are mechanical waves with amplitudes of typically only a few nanometers. These waves are generated by a piezoelectric transducer chip (e.g., quartz) fabricated by placing interdigital electrodes (interdigital transducer, IDT) on top of a piezoelectric layer. Liquid droplets situated on the hydrophobic surface of the chip can be moved by the SAWs if the acoustic pressure exerted on the liquid droplet is high enough as depicted in Fig. 22.15[154]. The actuation of small amounts of liquids of viscosities extending over a large range (from 1 – 1,000 mPa s) has been shown[155]. This approach is also sometimes referred to as 'flat fluidics' because no cover or slit is required, unlike in the EWOD approach. Today, this technology is being promoted by the company Beckman Coulter, Inc., (formerly Advalytix, Germany)[156].

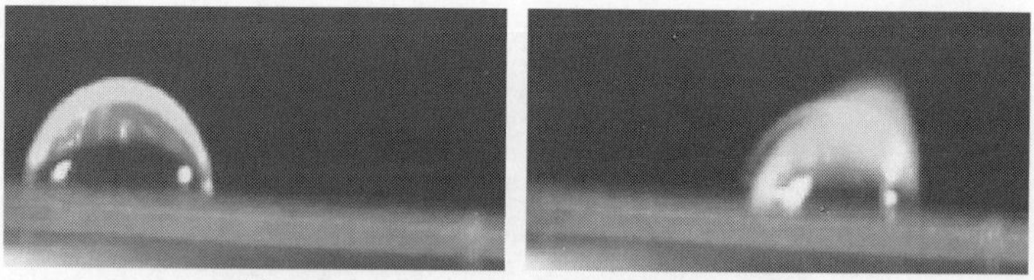

Figure 22.15 Side view of an approximately 50 nL droplet on the hydrophobic surface (contact angle of about 90°) of a piezoelectric substrate. (a) Resting droplet, (b) The droplet is 'hit' by a SAW impinging from the left, resulting in a momentary asymmetry of the wetting angles of the droplet[154]

Metering is accomplished by placing patches of different wetting properties onto the surface. A liquid droplet is moved over a small hydrophilic 'metering spot' via surface acoustic waves, leaving behind a small metered liquid portion. In addition, aliquoting has been shown by moving the initial droplet over a hydrophobic/hydrophilic chessboard zone. Since the transport of a droplet depends non-linearly on the droplet size, the initial droplet of larger volume is constantly moved forward, while small, picoliter-sized droplets remain on the hydrophilic parts of the wetting pattern[153].

Mixing presents a system-inherent unit operation on the SAW-driven, droplet-based platform. A droplet placed on the substrate and then getting hit by a SAW experiences an internal streaming due to the vibrating forces of the wave. If the amplitude is not large enough for droplet movement, the liquid inside the droplet is efficiently 'stirred' while its position on the substrate is retained.

For some assay protocols, incubation steps at elevated temperatures are also required, e.g., for a PCR amplification. Therefore, the liquid plug is placed above a micro-heating element on the substrate surface. However, since the nanoliter-sized droplet possesses a high surface-to-volume ratio, the liquid volume decreases rapidly due to evaporation. Hence the aqueous liquid plug is covered with an oil plug having a smaller contact angle. This covered droplet can still be moved via SAW on the substrate surface. By using this technology, a PCR assay (amplification) within a 200 nL droplet enclosed in mineral oil was performed with an online monitoring of the DNA concentrations and provided a sensitivity of 0.1 ng[157].

22.6.4 Strengths and Challenges of the Platform

General advantages of droplet-based microfluidics are the small liquid volumes of the droplets, reducing reagent, and sample consumption, thus paving the way for high-throughput screening applications. Additionally, the batch mode operation scheme within the nanoliter to microliter-sized droplets represents a consistent further development of the classic assay protocols in well plates, for example.

The pressure-driven approach combines these advantages with high-throughput capabilities in a quasi-continuous operational scheme. The completely enclosed liquid droplets furthermore allow the incubation and storage of liquid assay results over a long period of time without evaporation. However, the microfluidic functionality is fixed by the channel design and cannot be adopted during an assay, for example.

In contrast, the surface-based actuation schemes (EWOD and SAW) result in high flexibility since liquid processing paths can be freely programmed. In addition, the simple setup without any moving parts can be fabricated very cost- efficiently by using standard lithographic processes.

In the case of the EWOD principle for droplet actuation on the planar surface, the electrical change of the contact angle depends on the liquid properties and could cause electrolysis, while the SAW principle allows easier adaption to the liquid properties. Evaporation of liquid and the long-term stability of the hydrophobic and hydrophilic surface coatings are the major drawbacks of the surface-based techniques.

22.7 Free Scalable Non-Contact Dispensing

The free scalable non-contact dispensing platform allows delivery of liquids as free-flying droplets onto planar substrates (e.g., microarrays), conventional containers, such as well plates, or any other target. This approach is closest to the traditional laboratory routine, which is based on conducting assays via successive pipetting steps, manually or by automated laboratory equipment (pipetting robot). Within these fields, the dispensing of droplets of different volumes (pL to mL), from a single or up to thousands of channels in parallel, with different pitch sizes and an individual controllability is required. We focus here on the simultaneous dispensing of a large number of different reagents in parallel and disregard non-contact printing technology in general (for an overview of ink-jet printing technologies, see[2]). The three highlighted operating principles all use a very similar fluidic geometry that can be fabricated based on the same fabrication technology as described in the following section.

22.7.1 Unit Operations on the Platform

One functional unit of the free scalable non-contact liquid dispensing platform is based on the combination of a reservoir for holding the liquid, a nozzle chamber with a nozzle, from which the liquid is dispensed, and a capillary channel connecting reservoir and nozzle chamber. Depending on the arrangement of these components, as well as the actuation principle, liquid volumes from several tens of picoliters to several microliters can be dispensed. Arranging several units on a so-called dosage chip enables the dispensing of up to thousands of different liquids in parallel and has been demonstrated at a pitch ranging from several hundreds of micrometers to several millimeters. Three different actuation schemes based on the same geometrical arrangement, namely the dispensing well plate (DWP)[158, 159], the TopSpot®[160, 161], and the TopSpot® Vario[162] technology are depicted in Fig. 22.16.

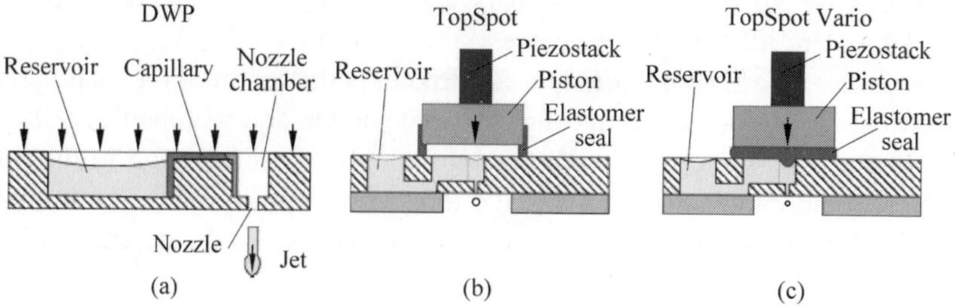

Figure 22.16 (a) DWP: Pressure-based actuation for dispensing from 10 nL up to several mL; (b) TopSpot®: Pressure-based actuation for dispensing volumes in the lower nL range; (c) TopSpot® Vario: Direct displacement principle via an elastomer for dispensing of volumes from 100 – 1,400 pL

The non-contact dispensing process strictly speaking represents two unit operations, liquid metering on the one hand, and liquid transfer on the other. The metered liquid volume is delivered as a free-flying droplet or a jet in a non-contact manner to any substrate, receiving vessel or the reservoir of another dispensing unit. The volume of this liquid portion is determined by the nozzle geometry and the external actuation mechanism.

The DWP principle is based on the complete drainage of the liquid volume within the nozzle chamber. The micro-machined nozzle chamber is filled with liquid from the reservoir by capillary forces via the capillary channel between two dispensing events. The total liquid contained in the nozzle chamber is dispensed by applying a pneumatic pressure of 30.80 kPa for 3.10 ms. Since this pressure pulse is applied on the liquid-air interface of the nozzle chamber and the reservoir simultaneously, no pressure gradient evolves along the capillary channel and thus no backflow of liquid from the nozzle chamber to the reservoir is observed. The dosed volume is hardly affected by the liquid properties like viscosity, density, and surface tension but by the geometry of the nozzle chamber only, making this dispensing method very robust.

The TopSpot® principle also relies on a pneumatic pressure pulse which, in this case, has a sub-millisecond width. Such a short pneumatic pressure pulse can only be generated by compression of an enclosed gas volume. Therefore, an assembly of a piezo-stack actuator driving a piston into a closed actuation cavity above the nozzle chambers is used. The pressure pulse acts equally on all nozzle chambers within the pressurized actuation cavity and causes the simultaneous ejection of single droplets out of each nozzle. The droplet volume is typically of the order of 1 nL for a 50 μm nozzle. This is, in contrast to the DWP principle, just a small fraction of the nozzle chamber volume. The exact droplet volume depends on the liquid properties, the actuation parameters, and the nozzle dimensions[163].

In contrast to the pneumatic technologies described so far, the TopSpot® Vario principle uses the direct displacement of an incompressible but easily deformable elastomer for actuation.

The elastomer inlay replaces the air volume in the setup (see Fig. 22.16(c)) and is displaced into the nozzle chambers by the piston movement if the piezo stack is actuated. A well-defined volume of liquid in the nozzle chamber is displaced by the elastomer and a droplet of corresponding volume is ejected out of the nozzle. This direct displacement principle allows independent control over the droplet volume and the droplet speed. The tunable volume of the droplets ranges from 100 – 1,400 pL (1.4 nL) for a 50 μm nozzle.

Furthermore, temperature-initiated amplification using the PCR method can be conducted within the cavities of the platform[164]. Therefore, the dispensing chip is sealed and mounted between an upper and lower heating plate, which perform a certain temperature cycle between three temperatures (94℃, 53℃, and 72℃). This process is similar to the common PCR cycling within standard well plates. For the microcavities within the PCR slides, however, the upper heating plate too has to change the temperature according to the cycling sequence in order to avoid temperature gradients within the PCR solution. When the cycling is finished, the PCR product (amplified DNA) can be dispensed in nanoliter portions into a microliter plate for further processing, onto a microarray for detection, or into another dispensing chip.

22.7.2 Application Examples

One unique feature of all the three described dispensing principles is the possibility of arranging a multitude of them in parallel with a free scalable pitch of the nozzle chambers and reservoirs. The capillary channel that connects these two substructures accomplishes the format conversion from a reservoir pitch of a few millimeters (enabling the filling of the dispensing chip using standard pipetting robots) to the pitch of the nozzle of a few hundred micrometers, as required for the fabrication of microarrays for example. A DNA microarray is an ensemble of microscopic DNA spots attached to a flat solid surface forming an array of different well-known capture molecules (probes) at well-defined positions. The probes on the surface react with a complex mixture of molecules (sample) during the hybridization phase of a microarray experiment. The sample molecules are equipped with fluorescent markers for subsequent detection in a fluorescent readout device. One technical solution to fabricate these microarrays is based on the TopSpot® technology, a first application of the free scalable non-contact dispensing platform[165, 166].

The key advantage of the non-contact dispensing platform for microarray fabrication is the easy-to-perform passive format conversion within the system. The reservoirs on top of the printhead are arranged at a pitch of 2.25 mm, corresponding to the pitch of 384 well plates, enabling filling with standard laboratory equipment, e.g., pipetting robots. Several microliters of liquids can be loaded into each of the reservoirs, which is enough for several thousand dispensing events without the need for refilling. Each reservoir is connected to a certain nozzle chamber in the middle of the printhead via a capillary channel (Fig. 22.17). The liquids are transported simply by capillary forces to the nozzle chamber and stop at the nozzle until a pressure pulse is applied. The nozzles are arranged in an array of 500 μm pitch on the backside of the printhead, defining the later spot positions on the microarray. The typical coefficient of variation (CV) of spot diameters on the microarray is measured to be below 1% for a single dispensing unit and smaller than 1.5% between all nozzles of a printhead for all relevant printing buffers used[166]. Using the TopSpot® technology, protein microarrays as well as living cell microarrays have been fabricated[167].

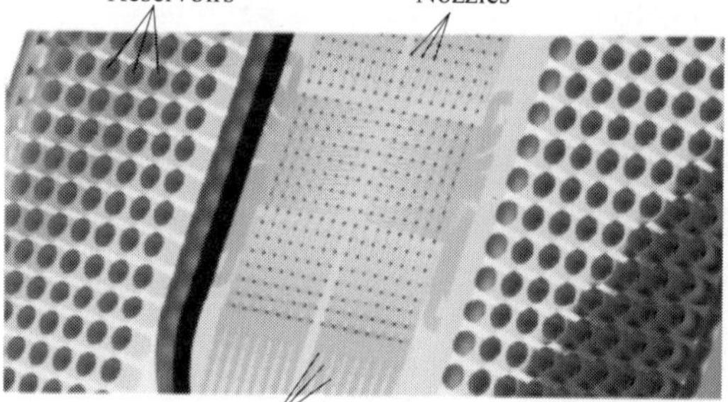

Figure 22.17 The TopSpot® technology combines the unit operations of reagent storage (in top side inlet reservoirs), liquid transport (through capillary channels), metering, and transfer via a free-flying droplet through the micronozzle as soon as the piezostack is actuated. The depicted TopSpot® 384 printhead features 384 dispensing units enabling the contact-free transfer of 384 different liquids onto planar substrates (microarrays)

A method for the simultaneous and contact-free dispensing of typically 50 nL liquid jets into micro well plates or onto flat substrates has been realized on the dispensing platform. The so-called dispensing well plate principle (Fig. 22.16(a)) uses a set of dispensing units, arranged according to the well plate format, each featuring a liquid reservoir, a capillary channel, and a nozzle chamber. All dispensing units are actuated in parallel by applying a pressure pulse on top of the dispensing chip, initiating the simultaneous and complete drainage of all nozzle chambers through the nozzle. As a result, an array of individual spots is delivered to another well plate. After switching off the driving pressure, the nozzle chambers refill again from the reservoirs via the capillary channels. Since the reservoir contains a liquid volume that is much larger than the nozzle chamber volume, many dispensing events can be performed before the chip has to be refilled. This enables the fast replication of a certain well plate loading into other plates (compound reformatting), or the addition of nanoliter volumes to plate-based assays. The reproducibility (coefficient of variation) of the mean dosage volume has been reported to be better than 3%[168]. Based on this principle, a kinase assay based on 100 μM rhodamine substrate with a total assay volume as low as 200 nL has been demonstrated[169].

22.7.3 Strengths and Challenges of the Platform

The wide range of dispensing volumes from 0.1 nL of the TopSpot® Vario up to 1,000 nL for the DWP using the same basic geometric building blocks is certainly the main advantage of the free scalable non-contact dispensing platform. The three dispensing principles can easily be combined on one flat substrate with or without the reformatting by capillary channels and be actuated in a highly parallel mode of operation.

However, the fabrication costs of the dispensing chips have to be reduced in the future, and also making disposable printheads possible, in order to avoid laborious washing procedures. Since the cost reduction is not possible in silicon micromachining (no potential in downscaling of the footprint of the dispensing chips or printheads), microfabrication technologies for polymers like injection molding or hot embossing are probably the most promising alternatives. Today, this technology is being promoted by the company BioFluidix, Germany[170].

22.8 Conclusion

The various examples of microfluidic platforms given in the previous sections indicate that the idea of the platform is already being researched by many groups within the microfluidics community. They not only work on individual components fabricated in diverse technologies but also focus on the combination of validated fluidic unit operations by simple, proven technologies. This approach allows the design and fabrication of application-specific systems easily and will lead to a paradigm shift from a component- and technology-based research to a system-oriented approach. The platforms will allow the microfluidics community to discard the present-day device-oriented research in order to face the next challenge: the flexible and cost-efficient design of hundreds to thousands of different applications that might be accessible by using the full potential of microfluidic platforms without always having to start from scratch.

A good indicator of the growing interest in microfluidic platform technologies can be also seen in the remarkable number of spin-off companies that arose during recent years trying to commercialize LOC products based on microfluidic platform concepts. Some of them have been mentioned within this review paper, but there are many more in business already[171]. A few are likely to emerge in the near future too.

References

[1] Haeberle S., and R. Zengerle, *Lab on a Chip*, 2007, **7**(9): 1094 – 1110

[2] Le H. P., (1998), *Journal of Imaging Science and Technology*, **42**(1): 49 – 62

[3] Terry S. C., J. H. Jerman, and J. B. Angell, *IEEE Transactions on Electron Devices*, 1979, **26**(12): 1880 – 1886

[4] Manz A., Y. Miyahara, J. Miura, Y. Watanabe, H. Miyagi, and K. Sato, *Sensors and Actuators, B: Chemical*, 1990, **1**(1 – 6): 249 – 255

[5] Shoji S., M. Esashi, and T. Matsuo, *Sensors and Actuators*, 1988, **14**(2): 101 – 107

[6] Van Lintel H. T. G., F. C. M. Vandepol, and S. Bouwstra, *Sensors and Actuators*, 1988, **15**(2): 153 – 167

[7] Gass V., B. H. Vanderschoot, S. Jeanneret, and N. F. de Rooij, *Sensors and Actuators, A: Physical*, 1994, **43**(1 – 3): 335 – 338

[8] Arquint P., M. Koudelkahep, B. H. Vanderschoot, P. van der Wal, and N. F. de Rooij, *Clin. Chem.*, 1994, **40**(9): 1805 – 1809

[9] Verpoorte E., A. Manz, H. Ludi, A. E. Bruno, F. Maystre, B. Krattiger, H. M. Widmer, B. H. Vanderschoot, and N. F. de Rooij, *Sensors and Actuators, B: Chemical*, 1992, **6**(1 – 3): 66 – 70

[10] Manz A., N. Graber, and H. M. Widmer, *Sensors and Actuators, B: Chemical*, 1990, **1**(1 – 6): 244 – 248

[11] Harrison D. J., A. Manz, Z. H. Fan, H. Ludi, and H. M. Widmer, *Analytical Chemistry*, 1992, **64**(17): 1926 – 1932

[12] Effenhauser C. S., A. Manz, and H. M. Widmer, *Analytical Chemistry*, 1993, **65**(19): 2637 – 2642

[13] Manz A., D. J. Harrison, E. M. J. Verpoorte, J. C. Fettinger, A. Paulus, H. Ludi, and H. M. Widmer, *Journal of Chromatography*, 1992, **593**(1 – 2): 253 – 258

[14] Kamholz A. E., *Lab on a Chip*, 2004, **4**, 2: 16N – 20N

[15] Burns M. A., B. N. Johnson, S. N. Brahmasandra, K. Handique, J. R. Webster, M. Krishnan, T. S. Sammarco, P. M. Man, D. Jones, D. Heldsinger, C. H. Mastrangelo, and D. T. Burke, *Science*, 1998, **282**(5388): 484 – 487

[16] deMello A. J., *Nature*, 2003, **422**(6927): 28 – 29

[17] Kopp M. U., A. J. de Mello, and A. Manz, 'Chemical Amplification: Continuous-Flow PCR on a Chip', in *Science*, 1998, 280: 1046 – 1048
[18] Lion N., T. C. Rohner, L. Dayon, I. L. Arnaud, E. Damoc, N. Youhnovski, Z. Y. Wu, C. Roussel, J. Josserand, H. Jensen, J. S. Rossier, M. Przybylski, and H. H. Girault, *Electrophoresis*, 2003, **24**(21): 3533 – 3562
[19] Marko-Varga G., J. Nilsson, and T. Laurell, *Electrophoresis*, 2003, **24**(21): 3521 – 3532
[20] de Mello A. J., and N. Beard, *Lab on a Chip*, 2003, **3**(1): 11N – 19N
[21] Auroux P. A., D. Iossifidis, D. R. Reyes, and A. Manz, *Analytical Chemistry*, 2002, **74**(12): 2637 – 2652
[22] Reyes D. R., D. Iossifidis, P. A. Auroux, and A. Manz, *Analytical Chemistry*, 2002, **74**(12): 2623 – 2636
[23] Vilkner T., D. Janasek, and A. Manz, *Analytical Chemistry*, 2004, **76**(12): 3373 – 3385
[24] Li P. C. H., Microfluidic Lab-on-a-Chip for Chemical and Biological Analysis and Discovery. Boca Raton: Taylor & Francis Group, 2006
[25] Nguyen N. T., and S. T. Wereley, Fundamentals and Applications of Microfluidics, Boston: Artech House Books, 2002
[26] Geschke O., H. Klank, and P. Telleman, Microsystem Engineering of Lab-on-a-ChipDevices, Weinheim: WILEY-VCH, 2004
[27] Andersson H., and A. van den Berg, Lab-on-Chips for Cellomics, Micro and Nanotechnologies for Life Science, Dordrecht: Kluwer Academic Publishers, 2004
[28] Oosterbroek R. E., and A. van den Berg, (2003), Lab-on-a-Chip: Miniaturized systems for (bio)chemical analysis and synthesis, Amsterdam, NL: Elsevier Science
[29] Tay F. E. H., Microfluidics and BioMEMS Applications, Boston: Kluwer AcademicPublishers, 2002
[30] Urban G. A., BioMEMS, Berlin: Springer, 2006
[31] Shoji S., and M. Esashi, *Journal of Micromechanics and Microengineering,* 1994, **4**(4): 157 – 171
[32] Laser D. J., and J. G. Santiago, *Journal of Micromechanics and Microengineering*, 2004, **14**(6): R35 – R64
[33] Woias P., *Sensors and Actuators, B: Chemical*, 2005, **105**(1): 28 – 38
[34] Gravesen P., J. Braneberg, and O. S. Jensen, *Journal of Micromechanics and Microengineering*, 1993, **3**(4): 168 – 182
[35] Nguyen N. T., and Z. G. Wu, *Journal of Micromechanics and Microengineering*, 2005, **15**(2): R1 – R16
[36] Hessel V., H. Lowe, and F. Schonfeld, *Chemical Engineering Science*, 2005, **60**(8 – 9): 2479 – 2501
[37] Oh K. W., and C. H. Ahn, *Journal of Micromechanics and Microengineering*, 2006, **16**(5): R13 – R39
[38] Waibel G., J. Kohnle, R. Cernosa, M. Storz, M. Schmitt, H. Ernst, H. Sandmaier, R. Zengerle, and T. Strobelt, *Sensors and Actuators, A: Physical*, 2003, **103**(1 – 2): 225 – 230
[39] Dittrich P. S., and A. Manz, *Nature Reviews Drug Discovery*, 2006, **5**(3): 210 – 218
[40] Hessel V., and H. Lowe, *Chemical Engineering & Technology*, 2003, **26**(1): 13 – 24

[41] Clark T. J., P. H. McPherson, and K. F. Buechler, *Point of Care*, 2002, **1**(1): 42 – 46
[42] Yager P., T. Edwards, E. Fu, K. Helton, K. Nelson, M. R. Tam, and B. H. Weigl, *Nature*, 2006, **442**(7101): 412 – 418
[43] Horng Y.-T., P.-C. Soo, B.-J. Shen, Y.-L. Hung, K.-Y. Lo, H.-P. Su, J.-R. Wei, S.-C.Hsieh, P.-R. Hsueh, and H.-C. Lai, *Water Research*, 2006, **40**(11): 2221 – 2229
[44] Micronics, Inc. (www.micronics.net), Micronit Microfluidics BV (www.micronit.com), Micralyne (www.micralyne.com), i-STAT (www.abbottpointofcare.com), microfluidic ChipShop GmbH (www.microfluidicchipshop.com), and thinXXS Microtechnology AG (www.thinxxs.de)
[45] Xia Y. N., E. Kim, X. M. Zhao, J. A. Rogers, M. Prentiss, and G. M. Whitesides, *Science*, 1996, **273**(5273): 347 – 349
[46] Xia Y. N., and G. M. Whitesides, *Annual Review of Materials Science*, 1998, **28**: 153 – 184
[47] Xia Y. N., and G. M. Whitesides, *Angewandte Chemie-International Edition*, 1998, **37**(5): 551 – 575
[48] Effenhauser C. S., G. J. M. Bruin, A. Paulus, and M. Ehrat, *Analytical Chemistry*, 1997, **69**(17): 3451 – 3457
[49] Delamarche E., A. Bernard, H. Schmid, B. Michel, and H. Biebuyck, *Science*, 1997, **276**(5313): 779 – 781
[50] Fu A. Y., C. Spence, A. Scherer, F. H. Arnold, and S. R. Quake, *Nature Biotechnology*, 1999, **17**(11): 1109 – 1111
[51] Hosokawa K., T. Fujii, and I. Endo, *Analytical Chemistry*, 1999, **71**(20): 4781 – 4785
[52] Duffy D. C., J. C. McDonald, O. J. A. Schueller, and G. M. Whitesides, *Analytical Chemistry*, 1998, **70**(23): 4974 – 4984
[53] Sia S. K., and G. M. Whitesides, *Electrophoresis*, 2003, **24**(21): 3563 – 3576
[54] Unger M. A., H. P. Chou, T. Thorsen, A. Scherer, and S. R. Quake, *Science*, 2000, **288**(5463): 113 – 116
[55] Quake S. R., and A. Scherer, *Science*, 2000, **290**(5496): 1536 – 1540
[56] Fluidigm Corporation, USA (www.fluidigm.com)
[57] Thorsen T., S. J. Maerkl, and S. R. Quake, *Science*, 2002, **298**(5593): 580 – 584
[58] Chou H. P., M. A. Unger, and S. R. Quake, *Biomedical Microdevices*, 2001, **3**(4): 323 – 330
[59] Salemme F. R., *Archives of Biochemistry and Biophysics*, 1972, **151**(2): 533 – 539
[60] Hansen C. L., E. Skordalakes, J. M. Berger, and S. R. Quake, *Proceedings of the National Academy of Sciences of the United States of America*, 2002, **99**(26): 16531 – 16536
[61] Hansen C., and S. R. Quake, *Current Opinion in Structural Biology*, 2003, **13**(5): 538 – 544
[62] Hong J. W., V. Studer, G. Hang, W. F. Anderson, and S. R. Quake, *Nature Biotechnology*, 2004, **22**(4): 435 – 439
[63] Hong J. W., and S. R. Quake, *Nature Biotechnology*, 2003, **21**(10): 1179 – 1183
[64] Marcus J. S., W. F. Anderson, and S. R. Quake, *Analytical Chemistry*, 2006, **78**(9): 3084 – 3089
[65] Liu J., C. Hansen, and S. R. Quake, *Analytical Chemistry*, 2003, **75**(18): 4718 – 4723
[66] Marcus J. S., W. F. Anderson, and S. R. Quake, *Analytical Chemistry*, 2006, **78**(3): 956 – 958

[67] Burtis C. A., N. G. Anderson, J. C. Mailen, C. D. Scott, T. O. Tiffany, and W. F. Johnson, *Clin Chem*, 1972, **18**(8): 753 – 761

[68] Anderson N. G., *Science*, 1969, **166**(3903): 317 – 324

[69] www.abaxis.com, accessed 2006

[70] Schembri C. T., V. Ostoich, P. J. Lingane, T. L. Burd, and S. N. Buhl, *Clin. Chem.*, 1992, **38**(9): 1665 – 1670

[71] Schembri C. T., T. L. Burd, A. R. Kopfsill, L. R. Shea, and B. Braynin, *Journal of Automatic Chemistry*, 1995, **17**(3): 99 – 104

[72] Madou M., and G. J. Kellogg, *Proc. SPIE Systems and Technologies for Clinical Diagnostics and Drug Discovery*, 1998, **3259**: 80 – 93

[73] Duffy D. C., H. L. Gillis, J. Lin, N. F. Sheppard, Jr., and G. J. Kellogg, *AnalyticalChemistry*, 1999, **71**(20): 4669 – 4678

[74] Ekstrand G., C. Holmquist, A. E. Örlefors, B. Hellman, A. Larsson, and P. Andersson, 'Microfluidics in a Rotating CD', in Proceedings of Micro Total Analysis Systems (mTAS 2000), 311 – 314

[75] Madou M., J. Lee, S. Daunert, S. Lai, and C.-H. Shih, *Biomedical Microdevices*, 2001, **3** (3): 245 – 254

[76] Madou M., J. Zoval, G. Y. Jia, H. Kido, J. Kim, and N. Kim, *Annual Review of Biomedical Engineering*, 2006, **8**: 601 – 628

[77] Haeberle S., T. Brenner, H. P. Schlosser, R. Zengerle, and J. Ducrée, *Chemical Engineering & Technology*, 2005, **28**(5): 613 – 616

[78] www.spinx-technologies.com, accessed 2006

[79] Steigert J., M. Grumann, T. Brenner, K. Mittenbühler, T. Nann, J. Rühe, I. Moser, S. Haeberle, L. Riegger, J. Riegler, W. Bessler, R. Zengerle, and J. Ducrée, *Journal of the Association for Laboratory Automation (JALA)*, 2005, **10**(5): 331 – 341

[80] Steigert J., M. Grumann, T. Brenner, L. Riegger, J. Harter, R. Zengerle, and J. Ducrée, *Lab Chip*, 2006, **6**(8): 1040 – 1044

[81] Steinert C. P., J. Mueller-Dieckmann, M. Weiss, M. Roessle, R. Zengerle, and P. Koltay, 'Miniaturized and Highly Parallel Protein Crystallization on a Microfluidic Disc', in *Proceedings of 20th International Conference on Micro Electro Mechanical Systems (MEMS 2006)* Kobe, Japan: 2007, 561 – 564

[82] Zoval J. V., and M. J. Madou, *Proceedings of the IEEE*, 2004, **92**(1): 140 – 153

[83] Ducrée J., S. Haeberle, T. Brenner, T. Glatzel, and R. Zengerle, *Microfluidics and Nanofluidics*, 2005, **2**(2): 97 – 105

[84] Ducrée J., T. Brenner, S. Haeberle, T. Glatzel, and R. Zengerle, *Microfluidics and Nanofluidics*, 2006, **2**(1): 78 – 84

[85] Grumann M., A. Geipel, L. Riegger, R. Zengerle, and J. Ducrée, *Lab on a Chip*, 2005, **5**(5): 560 – 565

[86] Brenner T., T. Glatzel, R. Zengerle, and J. Ducrée, *Lab on a Chip*, 2005, **5**(2): 146 – 150

[87] Haeberle S., L. Naegele, R. Zengerle, and J. Ducrée, 'A Digital Centrifugal Droplet Switch For Routing of Liquids', in Proceedings of the 10th International Conference on Miniaturized Systems for Chemistry and Life Sciences (μTAS 2006) Tokyo, Japan: 2006, 570 – 572

[88] www.gyros.com, accessed 2006

[89] US Patent, G. Ekstrand and T. Thorsen, 'Liquid Router', US 2005/0141344 A1, 2005

[90] Haeberle S., T. Brenner, R. Zengerle, and J. Ducree, *Lab on a Chip*, 2006, **6**(6): 776 – 781

[91] Lai S., S. Wang, J. Luo, L. J. Lee, S. T. Yang, and M. J. Madou, *Anal. Chem.*, 2004, **76**(7): 1832 – 1837

[92] Honda N., U. Lindberg, P. Andersson, S. Hoffman, and H. Takei, *Clin Chem.*, 2005, **51**(10): 1955 – 1961

[93] Grumann M., J. Steigert, L. Riegger, I. Moser, B. Enderle, K. Riebeseel, G. Urban, R. Zengerle, and J. Ducree, *Biomedical Microdevices*, 2006, **8**(3): 209 – 214

[94] Harrison D. J., K. Fluri, K. Seiler, Z. H. Fan, C. S. Effenhauser, and A. Manz, *Science*, 1993, **261**(5123): 895 – 897

[95] Sasaki N., T. Kitamori, and H. B. Kim, *Lab on a Chip*, 2006, **6**(4): 550 – 554

[96] Lee C. Y., G. B. Lee, J. L. Lin, F. C. Huang, and C. S. Liao, *Journal of Micromechanics and Microengineering*, 2005, **15**(6): 1215 – 1223

[97] Raymond D. E., A. Manz, and H. M. Widmer, *Analytical Chemistry*, 1994, **66**(18): 2858 – 2865

[98] Morgan H., M. P. Hughes, and N. G. Green, *Biophysical Journal*, 1999, **77**(1): 516 – 525

[99] Zimmermann U., and J. Vienken, *Journal of Membrane Biology*, 1982, **67**(3): 165 – 182

[100] Krupke R., F. Hennrich, H. von Lohneysen, and M. M. Kappes, *Science*, 2003, **301** (5631): 344 – 347

[101] Ramsey J. M., S. C. Jacobson, and M. R. Knapp, *Nature Medicine*, 1995, **1**(10): 1093 – 1096

[102] Caliper Life Sciences, USA (www.caliperls.com, accessed 2007)

[103] Agilent Technologies, USA (www.agilent.com, accessed 2007)

[104] Anna S. L., N. Bontoux, and H. A. Stone, *Applied Physics Letters*, 2003, **82**(3): 364 – 366

[105] Joanicot M., and A. Ajdari, *Science*, 2005, **309**(5736): 887 – 888

[106] Nisisako T., T. Torii, and T. Higuchi, *Lab on a Chip*, 2002, **2**(1): 24 – 26

[107] Okushima S., T. Nisisako, T. Torii, and T. Higuchi, *Langmuir*, 2004, **20**(23): 9905 – 9908

[108] Utada A. S., E. Lorenceau, D. R. Link, P. D. Kaplan, H. A. Stone, and D. A. Weitz, *Science*, 2005, **308**(5721): 537 – 541

[109] Song H., J. D. Tice, and R. F. Ismagilov, *Angewandte Chemie-International Edition*, 2003, **42**(7): 768 – 772

[110] Song H., and R. F. Ismagilov, *Journal of the American Chemical Society*, 2003, **125**(47): 14613 – 14619

[111] Zheng B., J. D. Tice, L. S. Roach, and R. F. Ismagilov, *Angewandte Chemie-International Edition*, 2004, **43**(19): 2508 – 2511

[112] Zheng B., J. D. Tice, and R. F. Ismagilov, *Analytical Chemistry*, 2004, **76**(17): 4977 – 4982

[113] Shestopalov I., J. D. Tice, and R. F. Ismagilov, *Lab on a Chip*, 2004, **4**(4): 316 – 321

[114] He M. Y., J. S. Edgar, G. D. M. Jeffries, R. M. Lorenz, J. P. Shelby, and D. T. Chiu, *Analytical Chemistry*, 2005, **77**(6): 1539 – 1544

[115] Link D. R., S. L. Anna, D. A. Weitz, and H. A. Stone, *Physical Review Letters*, 2004, **92**(5): 054503

[116] Tice J. D., H. Song, A. D. Lyon, and R. F. Ismagilov, *Langmuir*, 2003, **19**(22): 9127 – 9133

[117] Tice J. D., A. D. Lyon, and R. F. Ismagilov, *Analytica Chimica Acta*, 2004, **507**(1): 73 – 77

[118] Song H., M. R. Bringer, J. D. Tice, C. J. Gerdts, and R. F. Ismagilov, *Applied Physics Letters*, 2003, **83**(22): 4664 – 4666

[119] Bringer M. R., C. J. Gerdts, H. Song, J. D. Tice, and R. F. Ismagilov, *Philosophical Transactions of the Royal Society of London Series A: Mathematical Physical and Engineering Sciences*, 2004, **362**(1818): 1087 – 1104

[120] Gunther A., S. A. Khan, M. Thalmann, F. Trachsel, and K. F. Jensen, *Lab on a Chip*, 2004, **4**(4): 278 – 286

[121] Gunther A., M. Jhunjhunwala, M. Thalmann, M. A. Schmidt, and K. F. Jensen, *Langmuir*, 2005, **21**(4): 1547 – 1555

[122] Khan S. A., A. Gunther, M. A. Schmidt, and K. F. Jensen, *Langmuir*, 2004, **20**(20): 8604 – 8611

[123] Garstecki P., M. A. Fischbach, and G. M. Whitesides, *Applied Physics Letters*, 2005, **86**: 24

[124] Martin K., T. Henkel, V. Baier, A. Grodrian, T. Schon, M. Roth, J. M. Kohler, and J. Metze, *Lab on a Chip*, 2003, **3**(3): 202 – 207

[125] Link D. R., E. Grasland-Mongrain, A. Duri, F. Sarrazin, Z. D. Cheng, G. Cristobal, M. Marquez, and D. A. Weitz, *Angewandte Chemie-International Edition*, 2006, **45**(16): 2556 – 2560

[126] Ahn K., C. Kerbage, T. P. Hunt, R. M. Westervelt, D. R. Link, and D. A. Weitz, *Applied Physics Letters*, 2006, **88**: 2

[127] RainDance Technologies, USA (www.raindancetechnologies.com)

[128] Zheng B., L. S. Roach, and R. F. Ismagilov, *Journal of the American Chemical Society*, 2003, **125**(37): 11170 – 11171

[129] Yadav M. K., C. J. Gerdts, R. Sanishvili, W. W. Smith, L. S. Roach, R. F. Ismagilov, P. Kuhn, and R. C. Stevens, *Journal of Applied Crystallography*, 2005, **38**: 900 – 905

[130] Roach L. S., H. Song, and R. F. Ismagilov, *Analytical Chemistry*, 2005, **77**(3): 785 – 796

[131] Chen D. L., C. J. Gerdts, and R. F. Ismagilov, *Journal of the American Chemical Society*, 2005, **127**(27): 9672 – 9673

[132] Zheng B., C. J. Gerdts, and R. F. Ismagilov, *Current Opinion in Structural Biology*, 2005, **15**(5): 548 – 555

[133] Zheng B., J. D. Tice, and R. F. Ismagilov, *Advanced Materials*, 2004, **16**(15): 1365 – 1368

[134] Zheng B., and R. F. Ismagilov, *Angewandte Chemie-International Edition*, 2005, **44**(17): 2520 – 2523

[135] Chen D. L. L., and R. F. Ismagilov, *Current Opinion in Chemical Biology*, 2006, **10**(3): 226 – 231

[136] Mugele F., and J. C. Baret, *Journal of Physics-Condensed Matter*, 2005, **17**(28): R705 – R774

[137] Lee J., H. Moon, J. Fowler, T. Schoellhammer, and C. J. Kim, *Sensors and Actuators, A: Physical*, 2002, **95**(2 – 3): 259 – 268

[138] Mugele F., A. Klingner, J. Buehrle, D. Steinhauser, and S. Herminghaus, *Journal of Physics-Condensed Matter*, 2005, **17**(9): S559 – S576

[139] Pollack M. G., R. B. Fair, and A. D. Shenderov, *Applied Physics Letters*, 2000, **77**(11): 1725 – 1726

[140] Lee J., and C. J. Kim, *Journal of Microelectromechanical Systems*, 2000, **9**(2): 171 – 180

[141] Chatterjee D., B. Hetayothin, A. R. Wheeler, D. J. King, and R. L. Garrell, *Lab on a Chip*, 2006, **6**(2): 199 – 206

[142] Srinivasan V., V. K. Pamula, and R. B. Fair, *Lab on a Chip*, 2004, **4**(4): 310 – 315

[143] Ren H., R. B. Fair, and M. G. Pollack, *Sensors and Actuators B-Chemical*, 2004, **98**(2 – 3): 319 – 327

[144] Berthier J., P. Clementz, O. Raccurt, D. Jary, P. Claustre, C. Peponnet, and Y. Fouillet, *Sensors and Actuators, A: Physical*, 2006, **127**(2): 283 – 294

[145] Pollack M. G., A. D. Shenderov, and R. B. Fair, *Lab on a Chip*, 2002, **2**(2): 96 – 101

[146] Cho S. K., H. J. Moon, and C. J. Kim, *Journal of Microelectromechanical Systems*, 2003, **12**(1): 70 – 80

[147] Paik P., V. K. Pamula, M. G. Pollack, and R. B. Fair, *Lab on a Chip*, 2003, **3**(1): 28 – 33

[148] Paik P., V. K. Pamula, and R. B. Fair, *Lab on a Chip*, 2003, **3**(4): 253 – 259

[149] Wheeler A. R., H. Moon, C. J. Kim, J. A. Loo, and R. L. Garrell, *Analytical Chemistry*, 2004, **76**(16): 4833 – 4838

[150] Fair R. B., *Microfluidics and Nanofluidics*, 2007, **3**(3): 245 – 281

[151] Gascoyne P. R. C., J. V. Vykoukal, J. A. Schwartz, T. J. Anderson, D. M. Vykoukal, K. W. Current, C. McConaghy, F. F. Becker, and C. Andrews, *Lab on a Chip*, 2004, **4**(4): 299 – 309

[152] Schwartz J. A., J. V. Vykoukal, and P. R. C. Gascoyne, *Lab on a Chip*, 2004, **4**(1): 11 – 17

[153] Wixforth A., *Superlattices and Microstructures*, 2003, **33**(5 – 6): 389 – 396

[154] Wixforth A., C. Strobl, C. Gauer, A. Toegl, J. Scriba, and Z. von Guttenberg, *Analytical and Bioanalytical Chemistry*, 2004, **379**(7 – 8): 982 – 991

[155] Beyssen D., L. Le Brizoual, O. Elmazria, and P. Alnot, *Sensors and Actuators, B: Chemical*, 2006, **118**(1 – 2): 380 – 385

[156] www.advalytix.de

[157] Guttenberg Z., H. Muller, H. Habermuller, A. Geisbauer, J. Pipper, J. Felbel, M. Kielpinski, J. Scriba, and A. Wixforth, *Lab on a Chip*, 2005, **5**(3): 308 – 317

[158] Koltay P., R. Steger, B. Bohl, and R. Zengerle, *Sensors and Actuators, A: Physical*, 2004, **116**(3): 483 – 491

[159] Koltay P., J. Kalix, and R. Zengerle, *Sensors and Actuators, A: Physical*, 2004, **116**(3): 472 – 482

[160] de Heij B., C. Steinert, H. Sandmaier, and R. Zengerle, *Sensors and Actuators, A: Physical*, 2003, **103**(1 – 2): 88 – 92

[161] de Heij B., M. Daub, O. Gutmann, R. Niekrawietz, H. Sandmaier, and R. Zengerle, *Anal. Bioanal. Chem.*, 2004, **378**(1): 119 – 122

[162] Steinert C. P., I. Goutier, O. Gutmann, H. Sandmaier, M. Daub, B. de Heij, and R. Zengerle, *Sensors and Actuators, A: Physical*, 2004, **116**(1): 171 – 177

[163] Gutmann O., R. Niekrawietz, R. Kuehlewein, C. P. Steinert, B. de Heij, R. Zengerle, and M. Daub, *Sensors and Actuators, A: Physical*, 2004, **116**(2): 187 – 194

[164] Kaack R. M., A. Jung, M. H. Wenz, R. Zengerle, and M. Daub, 'PCR-slide: A modular and cascadable platform for DNA sample processing with integrated nanoliter dosage', in Proceedings of IEEE-MEMS 2004

[165] Gutmann O., R. Niekrawietz, R. Kuehlewein, C. P. Steinert, S. Reinbold, H. B. De, M. Daub, and R. Zengerle, *Analyst*, 2004, **129**(9): 835 – 840

[166] Gutmann O., R. Kuehlewein, S. Reinbold, R. Niekrawietz, C. P. Steinert, H. B. De, R.Zengerle, and M. Daub, *Biomed. Microdevices*, 2004, **6**(2): 131 – 137

[167] Gutmann O., R. Kuehlewein, S. Reinbold, R. Niekrawietz, C. P. Steinert, B. de Heij, R. Zengerle, and M. Daub, *Lab on A Chip*, 2005, **5**(6): 675 – 681

[168] Steger R., B. Bohl, R. Zengerle, and P. Koltay, *Journal of the Association for Laboratory Automation*, 2004, **9**(5): 291 – 299

[169] Steger R., C. Mehne, N. Wangler, M. Heckele, R. Zengerle, and P. Koltay, 'Drop in Drop Nanoliter Kinase Assay Made with Hot Embossed Disposable Multi Channel Dispenser', in Proceedings of the 10th International Conference on Miniaturized Systems for Chemistry and Life Sciences (μTAS 2006) Tokyo, Japan: 2006, 999 – 1001

[170] www.biofluidix.com

[171] Haber C., *Lab on a Chip*, 2006, **6**(9): 1118 – 1121

Development and Prospects

23 Development and Prospects

Richard S. Muller[1], Wolfgang Menz[2], Masayoshi ESASHI[3], and Geoff Beardmore[4]

[1] University of California, Berkeley, Founding Director, Berkeley Sensor & Actuator Center (BSAC), IEEE/ASME Journal of Microelectromechanical Systems
E-mail: muller@eecs.berkeley.edu, r.muller@ieee.org

[2] IMTEK (Institute for Micro System Technology), University of Freiburg, Germany
E-mail: menz@imtek.uni-freiburg.de

[3] The World Premier International Research Center Initiative for Atom Molecule Materials, Tohoku University, Sendai, 980-8579, Japan
E-mail: Esashi@cc.mech.tohoku.ac.jp

[4] Myriad Technology, Shandon House off Noverton Avenue Prestbury, Cheltenham Glos GL52 5DB, UK
E-mail: geoff@myriad-technology.com

Abstract This chapter includes 4 separate sections that were written by the prestigious scholars, Professor Richard S. Muller (University of California-Berkeley, USA), Professor Wolfgang Menz (University of Freiburg, Germany), Professor Masayoshi Esashi (Tohoku University, Japan), and Geoff Beardmore (Myraid Technology, UK). They shared their years of experience mainly in the development of MEMS and micro-nano technology, gave an overview of the history, development, and prospect of MEMS. Although from different perspectives, the prospect for MEMS is promising.

Keywords MEMS, micro- nano technology, development and prospects

23.1 Microsystems Technologies: MEMS and NEMS

The integrated circuit (IC) is certainly one of the foremost inventions of the 20th century, an invention that has profoundly influenced the development of human society. Since its invention, fifty years of ever-increasing sophistication in IC design and technology has made complex information processing commonplace in the design of engineering systems. For these engineering systems to be useful, however, they must typically do more than process information; they need to have reliable means for information accession as well as reliable end-effect actuation.

The engineering field that is now widely known as microelectromechanical systems (MEMS) became established in the 1980s to provide these necessary input-output functions with the same efficiency and economy as is achieved in producing integrated circuits. The broad goal of MEMS engineers remains to bring the essential functions of sensing and actuation to the levels of reliability and economy that have been achieved by integrated circuits. As the name MEMS implies, the resulting systems are to be 'tiny' (micro), and to have electrical as well as non-electrical, typically mechanical components. Potential uses for MEMS are huge in number and have applications covering essentially the entire range of human and societal endeavors, from astronomical observations to zoological experiments.

With this huge range of potential applications comes the need for a commensurate range in design techniques, materials, methods, and practices, widening significantly the design parameters beyond those employed regularly to build ICs. As a consequence, for example, progress in the area known as 'inertial MEMS' (in which microaccelerometers and microgyroscopes are already commercial developments) cannot be readily adapted to face the problems associated with MEMS in biological systems and for medical applications. There often is cross-fertilization, as for example in the microfluidics area, between the commercially successful ink-jet pumping and valving systems and some bioMEMS applications, but considerable research is necessary for success. Integrated-circuit technologies, established to solve interconnect and packaging problems and to provide accurate silicon-crystal orientation techniques for etching, metallization, and bonding have contributed excellent foundations on which to build MEMS technologies. It seems clear that much is still to be discovered using these sources along with technologies that are associated with the widening array of materials that are being investigated for MEMS. The best, most inventive minds will continue to be challenged for many years.

23.1.1 Micro- and Nano-Technologies

To speak clearly about MEMS and its challenges, it is of value to consider the vocabulary used to describe the field in the ever-increasing research literature that describes it. Microsystems, microelectronics, and microelectromechanical systems are three terms that have all been in general use for years and their common prefix micro means, in these three instances, tiny or very small. 'Micro' in these cases carries no reference to a specific length scale and should not be associated, for example, with one micrometer in length. The word, 'nanotechnology' is not so precisely defined. Some authors use the term to describe a means to produce systems or elements in which physical dimensions are defined and controlled on the billionth of a meter-, or nanometer-, length scale. This definition does not distinguish nanotechnology from MEMS and its relative- terms as described above. Nanotechnology by this definition is, nonetheless, an area in which highly productive research is ongoing at laboratories and industrial sites throughout the world. Success and great market rewards both in microelectronics and in the growing MEMS area are driving research on nanometer-scale devices, and more-and-more frequently engineers in this area are describing their work as nanoelectromechanical systems or NEMS.

An alternative definition for nanotechnology is to use the term for processes that assemble materials on a molecular scale to build a structural element or system of elements to a specific design. This process could effectively allow researchers to gain direct manipulative control of chemical and biological processes on a molecular scale. Only a few instances are on record of demonstrated success for nanotechnology in this sense, and these instances are limited to one-of-a-kind examples, despite nearly a decade of focus on this area. Nanotechnology as a description of molecular assembling appeals most to the popular press and to the general public since the long-term impacts of success could result in revolutionary changes in society. This second definition for nanotechnology ('engineering structures by manipulation on a molecular scale') has frequently been lumped with the first definition, stated above, (engineering structures on a nanometer scale). This lumping-together causes substantial confusion that pervades discussions about nanotechnology reported to and by government agencies, professional societies, industry, and academia.

An example of nanotechnology as molecular assembly is the technology of carbon and carbon-compound nanotube materials. Spurred by potential uses for these materials in computing, displays, and biomedical research, as well as by the 1996 Nobel Prize to Kroto, Smalley, and Curl for the discovery of these molecular forms of carbon, researchers foresee the possibility of a revolutionary impact in their engineering applications. Clearly, however, this research is at a much earlier state in its development than that of MEMS carried out for structures smaller than micrometers and significant breakthroughs will be required for large-scale commercial applications of molecular assembly processes to take shape.

23.1.2 Silicon Micromachining

We have already remarked on the link between ICs and MEMS and, in fact, described the carry-over of technologies from the IC-world to that of MEMS. Some basic MEMS ideas had already surfaced early in the IC era. In its first decade (the 1960s), a group of researchers at the Pittsburgh Westinghouse research laboratory constructed a metal beam using the silicon planar process and resonated the beam driving it with Coulombic forces. Metal beams had, in the same decade, been fabricated at Bell Laboratories for the purpose of automating the manufacture of integrated circuits in a process known as beam-lead technology.

During this time frame, focus remained strong on electronic-circuit development, however, and the idea that grew into MEMS can be seen to have its origins in the developments of inertial sensing elements (accelerometers) and ink jets in the late 1970s and early 1980s. Kurt Petersen, then an engineer at IBM attracted to the micromechanical world by research on ink jets, wrote a review paper detailing the many innovative ways that researchers were beginning to use 'silicon as a mechanical material.'

Most of the applications cited by Peterson built on etch technologies in the single-crystal substrate material for ICs that could be harnessed using the planar process to configure useful mechanical structures in a process called substrate micromachining. In this same time frame, however, advances in silicon processing that were aimed at improving the performance and yield of CMOS circuits had provided mastery of low-pressure chemical-vapor-deposition (LPCVD) procedures to produce well-engineered films of polycrystalline silicon. At the University of California, Berkeley, Roger Howe took the bold step of tailoring these films to function as mechanical beams, and to build them in a single-batch-process with electronic circuits. Success in this project led to a whole new type of silicon micromachining which took on the name, surface micromachining.

23.1.3 New Materials, New Technologies

As we have seen, making IC processes do double-duty to produce both electrical and non-electrical components is very advantageous. If the processes can be interleaved they can become the basis for a highly successful commercial product (e.g., micro-accelerometers). If, however, the non-electrical components are not produced by IC processes, the design engineer needs always to keep in mind that MEMS inevitably have interfaces with one or more integrated circuits. Hence, non-silicon technologies must continuously be configured to assure a compatibility with IC processing as a design goal, even as operational constraints for enhanced material properties are required. A partial list of material properties that might be very useful in MEMS includes: compatibility with biological environments, special properties, e.g., those needed to produce optical lenses or to be active magnetically, as piezoelectrics or ferroelectrics; resistance to high stresses; stability in harsh and high-temperature environments; and the ability to be configured into robust high-aspect-ratio structures. Finding candidates that have characteristics in any categories on this list is at the heart of MEMS research extending the knowledge frontier far beyond the boundaries established for the IC world.

Figure 23.1 shows recent work in which technologies for polymer deposition (based on ink-jet developments) have been mated with surface micromachining to produce an array of identical optical lenslets that produce point images at their focal planes when they are illuminated by a plane wave. By tailoring the mechanically resonant properties of the polycrystalline silicon supports for the lenses, it is possible to vibrate one lens in the array at a time. This ability is very useful if the lens array is made part of a wavefront-aberration sensor for use in adaptive optics, for example. The figure indicates the compatible fabrication of a non-IC technology element (the lens) in a surface- micromachined technology that makes use of mechanically resonant structures, driven by IC-driver circuits and IC-photonic sensor circuits.

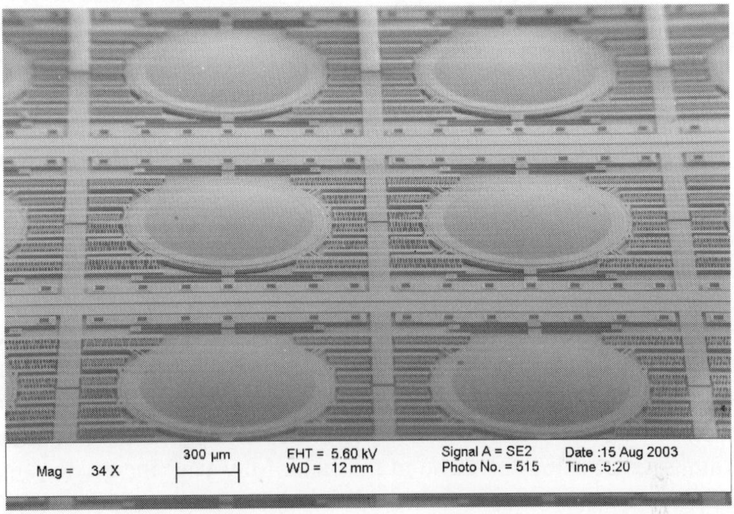

Figure 23.1 Array of lenses made of optically transmissive polymerizing material deposited using ink-jet-like technology and positioned on a uniquely addressable polycrystalline-silicon-carriage array allowing individual lenses to be selectively driven into resonance[1]

Materials that are not usually used in IC processes but that are actively being researched for MEMS applications include those with magnetic, piezoelectric, ferroelectric, or shape-memory properties. Actuating forces for valve closures and motor drives, for example, are drawing attention to the advantages materials on this list would bring to MEMS. Other MEMS developments for optical devices, biological purposes, chemical-process controls, high-temperature applications, and in other hostile environments, will inevitably establish the need for an even broader range of materials. It is a task for design engineers to characterize and test these materials when they are produced by technologies suitable for MEMS. Studies that address fundamental mechanical properties (e.g., Young's modulus, fatigue strength, residual stress, internal friction, and the engineering physics of long-term reliability, frictional effects, and wear) confront any design that employs new materials.

23.1.4 Computer-Aided Design

Rapid development in the IC industry has been aided by the establishment of a foundry infrastructure that ensures the reliability of processes and that permits competitive evaluation of alternative IC designs. The MEMS field is more complicated because of its broad range of applications and the concomitantly large number of alternative materials and technologies. With time, however, it seems clear that there will evolve a limited number of 'standard' materials-technologies sets that will form a basis for MEMS 'foundry' operations. These foundries will, in turn, support the growth of MEMS from the prototype and low-volume commercial level to the volume-driven, low-cost commercial level. The development of a MEMS foundry-technology base, along with CAD methods that exercise it will ensure that MEMS products can be manufactured at competitive rates and would enable the entry of small, innovative companies to target the many areas in which MEMS offers new capabilities.

23.1.5 Conclusions

These brief remarks have emphasized the view of their author: MEMS has come a long way, but its journey and development will persist beyond the working years of anyone presently engaged in the field. Many struggles, challenges, and new problems lie ahead, but clearly so do many achievements, successes, innovations and enormous satisfaction for those in the field. May you, the reader, be among those who share in these advancements of our engineering world!

23.2 Some Considerations of MEMS in the Past and the Future

23.2.1 Introduction

Microelectronics is considered the most successful technology in the history of mankind. The influence on our society is profound but the final outcome is still not yet foreseeable in all the consequences. The scientific and commercial success stimulated the motivation to explore the possibilities of this technology beyond the boundaries of electronics and into the fields of physics, chemistry, biology, and medicine to open up a new world of applications with hitherto unequalled properties. Hence the micro system technology was born. This new born child had many fathers and therefore had many different names. In the Asian countries the name 'micro machine technology' is preferred, whereas in

Europe 'micro system technology (MST)' is popular. In international literature the acronym MEMS (micro electro mechanical systems) is mostly used.

It is necessary to have a closer look at the basics of microelectronics to find out the reason behind the tremendous success of microelectronics. The obvious way would be to compare it with some of the traditional technologies such as manufacturing of steel or transportation. In these examples the empirical development is prevalent and reaching back several millennia. Innovations were protracted and achieved on a purely empirical basis. The technical skills were handed over from generation to generation. Only since the last century further improvements were backed up by scientific theoretical findings. What happened in comparison to this in microelectronics?

23.2.2 Comparison to Microelectronics

To evaluate this new technology it seems necessary to explore the underlying 'philosophy' of microelectronics, in other words, to define the 'recipe of success' of microelectronics in order to be able to compare it to other traditional technologies. Four objectives can be highlighted which are the basics of microelectronics and thus the basics of MEMS too.

Objective 1

The background of microelectronics is not empirical but strictly born out of theoretical physics. The findings in quantum physics, quantum electro dynamics and solid state physics enabled the development of the first transistor. This is the general difference between microelectronics and to all other technologies known before.

Objective 2

The design of an integrated circuit is done almost exclusively by computer. The design in the traditional trial and error approach, to find an optimum solution, is not feasible in microelectronics for economical reasons. The developmental steps must already be performed on the computer using extensive design and simulation tools. This is the second topic of the new approach.

Objective 3

In manufacturing the design data of a product have to be transferred onto the work piece. In microelectronics the transference of geometrical data is done by optical means. The advantage of this method is the lack of wear and tear, and therefore there is no deterioration of geometrical accuracy at products in mass fabrication.

During imaging, the so called photolithography, the geometrical structure to be transferred onto the work piece can be reduced in size and is limited only by the wavelength of the light used in the process step and by the inaccuracies of the optical system. Photolithography had the biggest technological influence on microelectronics, apart from the production of the basic material, the silicon single crystal. This single crystal is provided as a 'wafer', i.e. a disk of several inches in diameter and fractions of a millimeter thick.

Objective 4

By reducing the structures to the sub-micrometer level, the packing density per square unit of the components that were deposited onto the work piece is increased manifold as compared to what any conventional technologies of transfer would allow. Therefore, despite increase in processing costs, the costs for the single element can be greatly reduced. In addition to the cost effectiveness, miniaturization brings with it a considerable advantage in terms of quality. Integrated circuits are generally measured by their function density and their speed of switching. Through miniaturization, the electrical connections within the circuit are correspondingly shortened, which has a direct effect on the speed of signal processing.

Due to the higher packing density of the building elements on the wafer, millions of structure elements experience exactly the same process on subsequent processing. This results in less amount of scattering during processing. Processes which, in the course of development, became more expensive are compensated for by the minimum costs of producing thousands or millions of building elements on one single wafer. Due to lower process scattering and higher yield the processes in turn can be described and simulated more precisely. Therefore the assumptions, which can be made with the software tools to design the circuit, are more accurate and more realistic which results in a positive feedback in the design routine. The manufacture of millions of components with ever decreasing unit costs is the most important prerequisite for the successful market penetration, and is also a significant asset of MEMS for the fabrication of sensor arrays. Batch fabrication therefore, is considered to be the fourth objective in microelectronics.

The same basic concepts of microelectronics also apply to microstructure technology. For the latter, it is of great advantage to take advantage of the enormous technological know-how made available by microelectronics. Even if some of the processes have to be newly developed, essentially it is largely possible to build on the theoretical and technological basis, that have evolved with microelectronics. On the other hand, the close relationship between microstructure technology and microelectronics carries with it the danger of bias towards silicon as the favored material for MEMS.

Silicon is an outstanding material for many applications, especially for its electronic properties, but for many MEMS applications, especially micro-actuators, it is less suited. During the initial phase of enthusiasm about the potential of the new technology, the general aim was to integrate microelectronics and micro systems into one monolithically system. For economical as well as for manufacturing reasons this trend became obsolete very soon. Hybridization is considered the best compromise between functional density and manufacturing costs today.

Hybridization also frees the MEMS from the stilling influence of silicon technology. There is no question about the value of silicon for the necessary signal processing. But many applications call for materials other than silicon as a construction materials. Polymers for example have a wide range of properties which can be used for MEMS. This potential has not yet been fully appreciated. This is especially true in the cases of liquid crystal polymers (LCP) as well as swelling gels present in new actuator principles which could be brought to use for medical and other applications.

Metallic structures are important for applications when large forces or torques for actuators are in demand. Electroplating enables such structures, but the range of metals is very limited. Research work is done on micro-electro-discharge machining (μEDM) as well as micro-electro-chemical machining (μECM). With these technologies the manufacture of micro components from high performance steel are possible.

23.2.3 The Systems Approach to MEMS

Up to now many research organizations over the world worked on micro structure technologies and presented impressive micro components. However the true asset of MEMS is the potential to manufacture whole systems. If one evaluates the 'success story' of microelectronics once more, then it becomes obvious that the commercial success started with the development of microprocessors, giving rise to entire system developments. MEMS in the final presentation incorporates sensors, actuators, signal processing, and interfaces. Consequently this system is enabled to 'feel' the environment, to react upon certain situations, to communicate with the outside world, to perform self-tests, and - if necessary - to initiate repair routines. The true potential of MEMS will come to the fore, when autonomous and intelligent systems come to the market.

Systems on the other side do need considerable effort in manufacturing. There are different structuring technologies involved in addition to complex packaging, simulation and testing tasks to be performed. A small or medium sized company would overstress their development potential by covering the full range of activities necessary to fabricate micro systems. A means to overcome this problem could be the modular concept in MEMS. Certain functional blocks such as power supplies, drivers, sensor arrays, or other subsystems can be used in various other systems with little or no alterations. Therefore, these subsystems or modules should be made available by specialized suppliers. This would reduce some of the developmental load from the shoulders of the system manufacturer. The supplier could fabricate modules and modify those modules according to the needs of the customer by introducing minor changes to the hardware- or the software. Such multi-functional modules are already under development in different research laboratories. The difficulty of putting these modules on the market arises from the fact that there is a lack of standardization with regard to the interfaces of the modules. The system manufacturer needs a competitive selection of modules from different suppliers to be able to choose from. The international standardization is a task to be performed by the industry involved in MEMS activities.

23.2.4 Future Applications

How will MEMS develop in the future? The most prevalent problem for the successful proliferation of MEMS is the need for cost effective means of large, medium sized and small scale fabrication. Hybridization and modular system may solve some of the problems, but concerns related to manufacturing is a matter which has to be tackled by the industry. The industry in turn is dependent on the market, and the market has not yet fully appreciated the potential of MEMS. Obviously there are some applications, such as air bag systems, navigation systems, telecommunication systems to name a few, which have gained acceptance and popularity, but the overwhelming penetration of the market with MEMS products has not yet happened. Too many companies are still hesitant to take up MEMS, too little industrial developers think about MEMS products. In 10 years from now, it is the author's firm conviction that there are products on the market, which nobody even thinks about today. The real commercial success of microelectronics started with the development of the personal computer. For MEMS we need a similar successful business idea.

The question is now, how can academia help to prepare this nascent field. First of all it is necessary to show the superiority of a system as compared to individual components. A predominant task to achieve significant improvements on system performance is to optimize the internal computing power. The advanced micro system should be able to perform internal failure tests, should be able to replace faulty components as well as redundant components. The system should be able to make complex decisions and communicate in an intelligent way with a master computer or with other micro systems.

With distributed micro systems a significant improvement in the new quality of problem solving could be brought about. Some examples should elucidate this statement: Wearable distributed micro systems could give novel insights over body interdependencies such as eye ball pressure versus stress factors found in the blood, or distributed systems in environmental application could detect pollutions and even locate the hidden source of this pollution. Distributed systems on airplanes and other complex machinery could detect weak parts prior to malfunction and could give advice for cost effective maintenance on time.

Looking further into the future, we could think of a highly intelligent, well organized and autonomous 'super system' of many distributed micro systems which can be developed in a similar way as known from nature. One intriguing example would be to find out how the management in a colony of ants or bees does work. One can consider a single ant as a micro system with limited capabilities but with the ability to communicate with other micro systems. These natural micro systems, put together by the thousands, are enabled to build a highly organized and complex society without the presence of a 'master ant' among them. Such a super system should be far superior to the sum of all the individual micro systems put together. It could be an exciting research project to define a concept of communication that would lead to such an evolved super system.

MEMS is an exciting 'philosophy' to help cover new fields of applications and has the potential of solving problems in an unparalleled approach, never achieved before by other technical means. Nature is our teacher and we are well advised to follow nature's concepts.

23.3 History, Experience and Vision on Micromachining and MEMS

23.3.1 Introduction

Micromachining is an extension of IC technology that is used in three-dimensional fabrication based on photolithography, deep etching, wafer bonding and so on. MEMS (Micro Electro Mechanical Systems) are fabricated using micromachining and play important roles as value added key components in various systems. The history of MEMS, my experience with MEMS and my vision on micromachining and MEMS will be described in the following paragraphs/chapters/sections.

23.3.2 History and Our Experience

The history of micromachining and MEMS is shown in Table 23.1, in which each reference number[2–11] is indicated,where all reference numbers are indicated. We can see review papers[12, 13], special issues[14, 15] and a book [16] on the early stages of this technology. Special exhibition of historical MEMS samples and memorable papers was held for commemorating the 10th anniversary of Transducers'99 held in Sendai.

We have been studying micromachining since 1971 and our experiences are shown in Fig. 23.2. My interests have been regarding the practical applications of MEMS. Technologies developed with MEMS are overlapping each other and new areas are being explored, driven by emerging applications. Required process technologies such as deep RIE[17] have been developed and the basic problems found during research such as electrical breakdown[18] have been studied.

Table 23.1 History of micromachining and MEMS

19th century	Photofabrication
1954	Piezoresistive effect (Bell Telephone Lab., USA)[2]
1962	Anisotropic etching
1962	Semiconductor diaphragm pressure sensor (Honeywell, USA)[3]
1967	Resonant gate transistor (Westinghouse, USA) [Surface micromachining][4]
1968	Anodic bonding (Mallory, USA)[5]
1969	Selective etching depending on impurity concentration
1975	Integrated gas chromatography (Stanford Univ., USA) [Sensor + Actuator][6]
1981	1st Transducer meeting in Boston
1991	Surface micromachined integrated accelerometer (Analog Devices, USA)[7]
1992	Deep reactive ion etching (Bosch, Germany)[8]
1993	Digital micro mirror device for projection display (Texas Instruments, USA)[9]
1995	Plasma activated low temperature bonding[10]
2005	Silicon MEMS resonator for clock and frequency reference (SiTime, USA)[11]

Basic process technologies are indicated by underline.

MEMS packaging, integrated MEMS, sophisticated MEMS, small size MEMS, disposable MEMS and MEMS materials have been our areas of concern, as has been discussed in the subsequent paragraphs.

Packaging is important because cost and reliability of MEMS devices depend on the packaging. Wafer level packaging using anodic bonding of silicon and glass which have electrical feedthroughs was developed[19] and applied to integrated capacitive pressure sensors (JTECT, Japan) as shown in Fig. 23.3[20] and to capacitive vacuum sensor (Canon Anelva, Japan) by making vacuum cavity[21]. MEMS relays (Advantest, Japan) have also been fabricated using the wafer level packaging technology and applied in the latest LSI testers[21]. The integration of capacitance detection circuit is effective not only for capacitive sensors[7, 20], but also effective for arrayed MEMS. The arrayed MEMS are employed as digital micro mirror device (DMD), which are used for projection displays[9] as well as ink jet printer heads. Furthermore,,RF MEMS finds effective use as MEMS resonator[11] as well as in disposable devices where it is used as wireless integrated immunosensor[22]. Both monolithic integrated MEMS called SoC (System on Chip) MEMS and hybrid integrated MEMS called SiP (System in Package) MEMS have been developed. One example of our SiP MEMS is multi-probe data storage device [23] in which glass with high density electrical feedthroughs is used to make electrical interconnection from the array MEMS to the control IC chip. Control ICs are indispensable for such arrayed MEMS; however monolithic integration of MEMS and circuits is difficult to achieve in many cases.

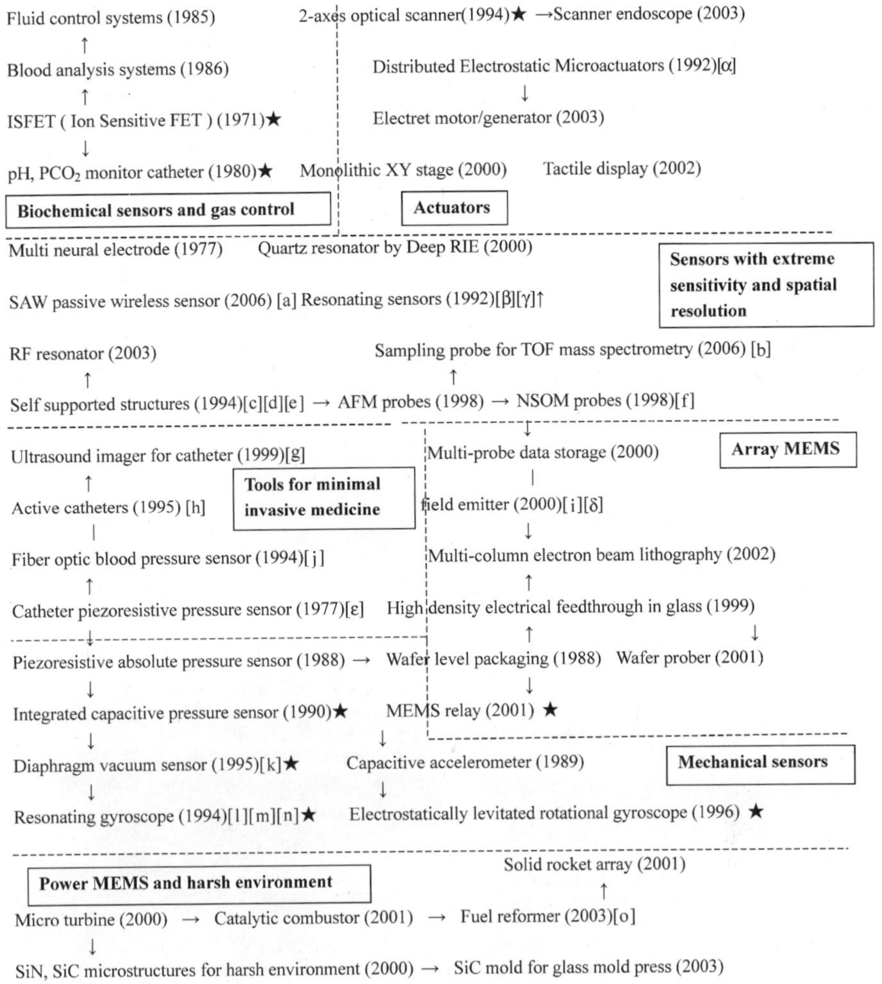

o Developed process technologies

[a] Selective etching of $LiNbO_3$, [b] PZT thin film, [c] Self supported Si nanostructures (1997), [d] Nano-wire growth by field evaporation (1997), [e] Diamond micro/nanostructures (2002), [f] Nano-apertures (1999), [g] PZT structures (1998), [h] Batch assembly (1999), [i] Selective growth of CNT (Carobon Nano Tube) (2000), [j] Laser CVD & etching (1992), [k] Vacuum packaging (1993), [l] Deep RIE (1992), [m] XeF_2 etching (1996), [n] Galvanic etch stop (1996), [o] Trench refill (2002)

o Studied basic problems

[α] Electrical breakdown in narrow gap (2000), [β] Q factor of thin resonator (1999), [γ] Distortion of p^{++} Si (1995), [δ] Stabilization of CNT electron field emitter (2004), [ε] Instability of piezoresisor (1983)

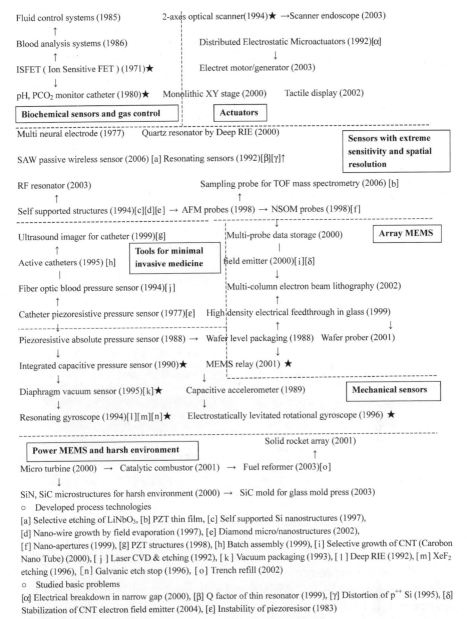

Figure 23.2 Historical flow of our research, Round blanket means the presented year (★ Commercialized)

Highly sophisticated MEMS devices can be fabricated. Silicon rotational gyroscope (Tokyo Keiki, Japan) has been developed for the purpose of motion control and navigation[25]. The principle and the photograph are shown in Fig. 23.4. A silicon ring of 1.5 mm in diameter, which is electrostatically levitated by high

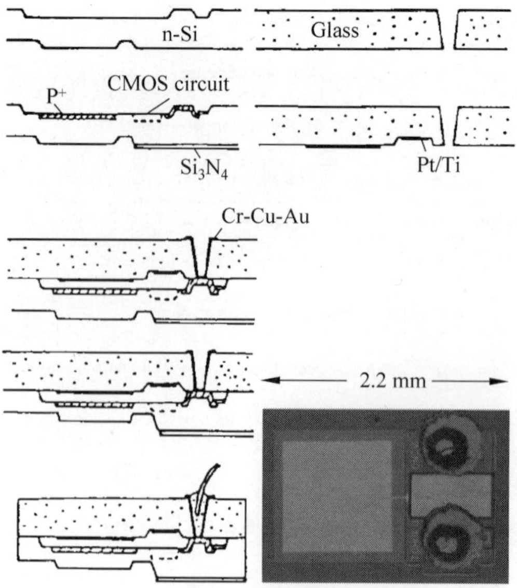

Figure 23.3 Wafer level packaging for integrated capacitive pressure sensor

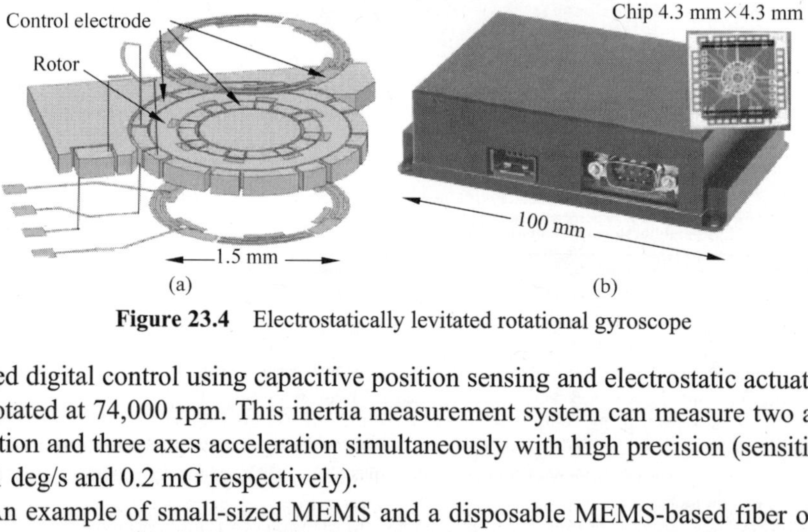

Figure 23.4 Electrostatically levitated rotational gyroscope

speed digital control using capacitive position sensing and electrostatic actuation, is rotated at 74,000 rpm. This inertia measurement system can measure two axes rotation and three axes acceleration simultaneously with high precision (sensitivity 0.01 deg/s and 0.2 mG respectively).

An example of small-sized MEMS and a disposable MEMS-based fiber optic pressure sensor having a small diameter, which is used as a catheter in blood vessel is shown in Fig. 23.5 [26]. Packaging also plays an important role in such catheters in order to make reliable assembly at a reduced cost for making disposable use possible[27]. By taking advantages of the micro/nano structures, extreme sensitivity and spatial resolution could be achieved—for example with SPM (Scanning Probe Microscope) probes.

By combining micromachining with different materials such as SiC, MEMS application can be extended to harsh environments such as in molds used for

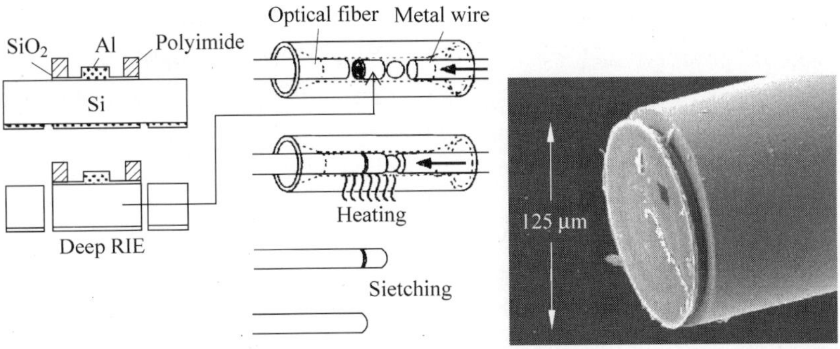

Figure 23.5 Small diameter fiber optic pressure sensor

glass press molding[28]. This takes advantage of the hardness of the SiC at high temperature. The fabrication process and the photograph of the SiC mold are shown in Fig. 23.6. Other materials, such as carbon-based materials (CNT, diamond) and piezoelectric materials (PZT, $LiNbO_3$) are also utilized in MEMS.

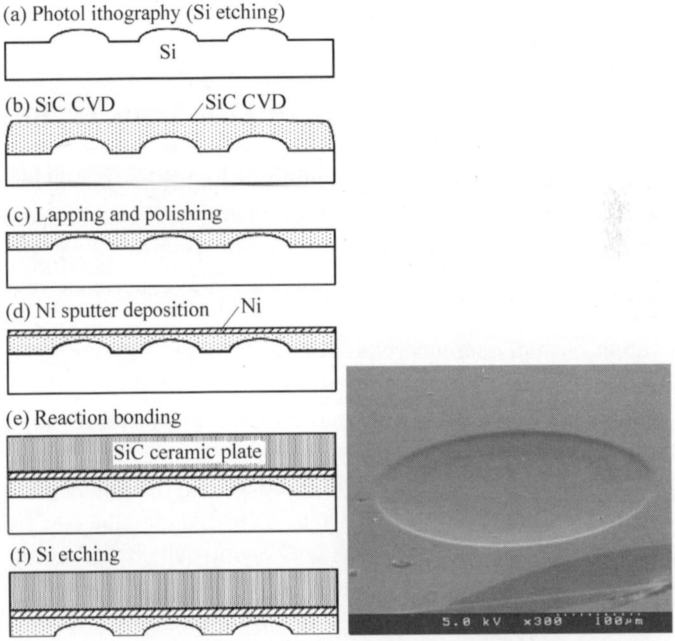

Figure 23.6 SiC for glass press molding

23.3.3 My Vision

MEMS are used in different ways such as key components in systems in the form of MEMS relay in LSI tester[21], in disposable medical devices as catheters[26], in high-volume products such as MEMS resonators[11] and in small-volume devices such as the SiC mold used in glass press molding[28]. MEMS technology is interdisciplinary in nature and is based on micro-fabrication, mechanics, electronics, optics, materials and so on. The efficient development of MEMS is invariably reliant on access to knowledge in various fields due to the fragmented nature of MEMS. Integrated MEMS (MEMS + circuit) have the potential of developing value added LSI (Large Scale Integration) system for the semiconductor industry. The integration of MEMS calls for excellent mechanical properties and advanced features; in addition to the fine size of CMOS LSI. The so-called post-Al surface micromachining by which the MEMS is fabricated at low temperature after the Al metallization process has also been studied[29].

Each MEMS device needs its own fabrication processes and hence it is difficult to standardize the fabrication processes. The inability to standardize the fabrication processes causes difficulties- especially for small-volume production. Business models which use expensive equipments and environments based on efficient open collaborations are required to launch MEMS in the commercial market.

23.4 Not Nearly Enough…Past Experience and Future Predictions for Emerging Micro-Nano Technologies

A leading entrepreneur, who had founded about five highly successful and profitable MEMS companies during his long career, was once asked what he had learnt over this period. He replied ‘Not nearly enough…’. He went on to say that as far as his experience was concerned, it seemed like the same experience repeated itself five times.

My own career has not been nearly as successful, but I can certainly empathise with him, and relate his comments to my own experiences of more than 40 years of working in this area. The older I get, the more I realise how limited my knowledge is, and unlike traditional technologists and scientists of earlier times, the micro and nano-technologists of the future will only be able to assimilate an increasingly smaller proportion of the total knowledge available on their subjects. This suggests that an increasing level of specialisation will occur, which will bring about the real risk of some of the traditional engineering wisdoms and pragmatisms being lost altogether. These wisdoms were gained by exposure to a wide range of engineering disciplines over many years, and often used to complement specialized theoretical knowledge.

For this reason, my contribution will not focus on any particular aspect of the technology or science as other contributors have done, but will attempt to present an eclectic and highly personal summary of just a few of the ‘guidelines’ that I have used over the years to help overcome my lack of detailed knowledge of this rapidly growing area. The rationale behind adopting such an approach is that all technologies have a finite 'shelf life' before they are replaced with newer ones, but the basic wisdoms and experiences usually survive them, and can invariably be adapted to the newer technologies and processes which displace them. I leave it to the reader to adapt these thoughts to their own particular situation as appropriate.

Also, at the risk of being proved very wrong, I will also try to give the reader my own personal vision for the future of micro-nano technologies (MNT).

I do not claim that all my views and comments are original. Some are well known and have been used regularly, often intuitively, by experienced engineers in many different disciplines, and others are peculiar to micro-nano technologies. All have had a particular significance throughout my own work, and those who were older and wiser at the time passed many on to me.

23.4.1 Background Influences

My own background relates predominantly to the aerospace and defence industries, where I worked for 41 years before leaving to run my own micro-nano consultancy company- Myriad Technology. My experience is therefore principally in Microengineering and Micromachines rather than traditional silicon MEMS. When I first began my career in this area, none of the current terminologies had been defined, and so my colleagues and I simply regarded our work as nothing but ultra high precision electro-mechanical engineering. This has probably influenced my thoughts over the years and perhaps has led me to take a somewhat broader view of these emerging technologies than what others have. I started researching and developing micro engineered inertial sensors for the first time in 1965, and helped to successfully bring a number of these products and their associated production processes into series production. Later I had the task of finding out how the newer silicon-based MEMS technologies could be applied across the entire range of company products. For the products I personally worked on, the transition from 'conventional' to Micro engineering-based technology increased the reliability of our inertial sensors by a factor of at least 80, and the performance by over a thousand times. They also allowed at least one completely new product to be developed that could not have been produced at all using conventional technologies. Not bad for a technology that was initially regarded with suspicion by some senior production staff because the specialised production techniques we developed did not produce bins full of oily swarf!

Looking back over my early years, the one thing that stands out is that the total product life cycle of the technology I worked on (from the start of the research & design process to the final sensor coming out of service) was at least 40 years and could eventually reach 50 years. Again, not a bad record for what at that time was to become the emerging technology of Micro-engineering, and perhaps a good omen for the emerging technologies of the future, though as I will point out later, 'engineered obsolescence' will be an important feature of the business models employed by many of the high-volume consumer products that would use MNT technologies in the future.

23.4.2 Basic Wisdoms

These then, are in my view, some basic wisdom that inexperienced engineers may choose to ignore at their own peril.

The Fundamental Laws Still Apply

Never forget that the basic laws of physics, chemistry, engineering and economics still apply to micro-nano technologies. It is surprising to find out how many people believe these emerging technologies somehow confer immunity from the fundamental constraints that traditional engineers have been struggling to overcome for centuries. While it is true that some of these laws may need to be interpreted in a different way, and that their relative effect will often be related to the scale of the item of interest, they are still highly relevant to all stages of design, manufacture and performance.

All Engineering is a Continuum

Despite the multitude of different definitions and acronyms, all engineering is essentially a continuum, from the Great Wall of China to the smallest molecular level device. While it is true that a small number of natural phenomena only occur at certain critical dimensions (e.g. photonic effects), 'macro', 'micro', 'nano' etc. are convenient man-made divisions based on arbitrary definitions. At product level, there is almost always an interface between macro and micro and micro and nano, and very few micro or nano devices exist as usable products in their own right.

It Has All Been Done Before!

This is of course an exaggeration, but you should not assume that all new features of emerging technologies are really completely new. Chemists can justifiably claim that they have always worked in the realms of Nanotechnology, watchmakers have produced micro-machines for hundreds of years and optical engineers have worked with tolerances in the range of 1/100 of a micron for a similar period of time. Almost all the basic process concepts now applied to MNT were developed for conventional engineering long before they were 're-discovered' for silicon; for example: electro deposition, chemical etching, photolithography, ion etching and many such concepts. Even the latest sacrificial layer techniques for fabricating complex 3D microstructures were well known to the ancient Egyptians and Chinese as the lost-wax process. The fundamental principles of all logical devices, upon which modern electronics is based, were well known to early engineers in Victorian England, who used them to design mechanical signalling and points switching mechanisms for their railways. The lesson here is that the past is a rich source of 'original' ideas and concepts for the newly emerging micro-nano engineers.

The 50-Year Technology Cycle

History teaches us that really major technology opportunities on this scale only occur about once every 50 years. Gunpowder, steam power, electronics and microelectronics are examples of emerging destructive technologies that changed almost every aspect of our lives. The MNT revolution is only the latest in this line and will not be the last. Being still relatively young, it offers almost unlimited opportunities for young Engineers beginning their careers. More importantly, the pattern of history suggests that the really major commercial applications in this latest technical revolution will occur over the next 25 years.

23.4.3 Experience—The 50-Year Course

While I was Visiting Professor in Microtechnologies at one of the UK's largest Universities, there was much debate as to whether or not it was possible to teach 'experience', and thereby allow students to become proficient micro and nano engineers as soon as they graduate. When asked if he thought experience could be taught, one of my mature students paused for a moment and replied 'Yes, but it's a 50-year course…'. I would qualify that statement and say that it is at least 66 years and I am still learning. My late father Tom Beardmore, also an Engineer, would have insisted it was at least 95 years!

My experience in the industry and my observations from many hundreds of problem solving and design projects handled by under- graduate and post-graduate students is that very few engineering ventures fail because young engineers do not understand the basic science or technology. They tend to fail for a wide variety of less tangible reasons that older Engineers often refer to as 'lack of experience'.

The following is a fairly random selection of just some of the things I have learnt, often the hard way, and some of the words of wisdom that I have picked up over the years. It is by no means exhaustive, but I hope that at least some of it will eventually be of use to the reader, even if they are already aware of the rest.

Check if you are using the Appropriate Technology

Only use micro and nano technology if it is appropriate to the design or application. There is no point, and is often dangerous, in imposing an emerging-technology solution if a much simpler and proven technology will do just as well. Be prepared to mix and integrate MEMS, Nano and conventional engineering to produce an optimum device or product. Your customer will rarely care how your product works—he cares only about the fact that it does work after all. Unfortunately, any new technology, especially micro and nano technology, tends to be regarded by politicians, pundits and the public alike as the *'Silver Bullet'* that will solve all the problems in the world, whereas the reality is that each new technology hardly ever makes more than an incremental contribution to the overall scheme of things, and in hindsight, will almost always be found to have created additional problems in its wake, which other emerging technologies will then be expected to solve. Ignore the hype and think of MNT as just another useful tool hanging on the wall of your workshop, and you will not go far wrong.

Understand the Relation between Size and Force

For a new student studying micro-nano technologies for the very first time, I would recommend that they plot unit force against unit volume for a range of different types of force such as gravity, electrostatic, thermal, electromagnetic, surface tension etc. on the same sheet. Understanding this simple graph and the significance of the different gradients and crossover points is the key to understanding the design and operation of most microsystems.

Consider the Effect of Relative Tolerances

Strange as it may seem, the relative tolerances achievable by most current MEMS fabrication and machining processes compare very poorly with those routinely achieved in conventional high precision engineering over the last half century. For example, 1-micrometer tolerance on a typical MEMS structure of say 200 micrometers length has a tolerance/size ratio of 1/200, whereas a 2.5 micrometer tolerance on a 25 mm dimension (typical of many conventional aerospace and automotive components) has a corresponding ratio of only 1/10,000. Champions of MEMS technology are quick to point out that most MEMS fabrication processes produce highly consistent and repeatable dimensions, and that the nominal dimensions are therefore unimportant. For some applications, having all the dimensions identical from device to device may be more important than working to an exact size; but where absolute dimensions are critical, as in a mechanically tuned vibrating structure for example, this may necessitate additional and costly trimming of individual components. Having 10 million identical parts is not of much use if they are all identically wrong!

Don't Waste Time and Money Re-proving Established Principles

I have observed a number of major projects fail because they began by building experimental devices that re-demonstrated existing principles and knowledge, often at a larger scale. Such endeavors use up precious time and funding and, if the resulting device is too far removed from what the market finally requires, the 'customer', or those financing the project may not be able to visualise the finished product and may loose interest. My approach has always been to accept existing knowledge and design as close as possible to the final size and architecture as required from the very beginning. Even if this first attempt does not work too well, you will learn far more by tackling the problems early on than by approaching the final size/design incrementally. The earlier you encounter problems in the design-phase as you go about building and testing processes; the easier it will be to correct them.

Breaking the Rules

There is a theory that progress can only be made in technology and engineering by breaking the existing rules and standards. The trick is to do this in a controlled and systematic manner.

Beware of the Incremental Erosion of your Initial Design Concept

Many innovative designs for new products start with a bold technical concept and ambitious goals generated by either an individual or a small design team as the creators are not hampered by the realities of having to put them into practice at this stage, and in any case will have all too frequently underestimated the difficulty of achieving them. As research and development proceeds and the device is made ready for production, and more and more people become involved, there is a real risk of loosing sight of these original design concepts as a result of incremental technical changes to the design, and the constant need to reduce costs. In cases where other partners or an international consortium is involved, 'democratic' decisions and the need to incorporate the needs and ideas of each participant can also, if not firmly managed, contribute to a dilution of the original innovative ideas. Whatever the reason, the design risks being compromised.

Always Design in a Healthy Safety Margin—Always have a 'Plan B'

The marines have saying: '…No margin—No Mission'. Experienced designers always allow a healthy design margin wherever possible. It is of no consequence whether your design is a Victorian Viaduct or the latest MNT system—manufacturing variations and customers have an annoying habit of eating away at your margins, whether they are performance, environmental capability, reliability or life. Theoretical results and advanced computer modelling are no substitutes for common sense and intuition born out of hard experience. Take the old engineers view that if it can happen, it will happen, and then apply the well known and basic law of engineering (attributed to a Mr. Söd) that if it can happen, it will happen to your design! Resist all pressures to optimise a design to the extent that your original design margins are eroded. The need to reduce weight, cost, or size, coupled with over enthusiastic implementation of 'value engineering' concepts can turn a fundamentally good design into a marginal one. If you think this is an exaggeration, consider how many product recalls are reported in the press, or how many serious engineering failures are still caused by design failures, despite all the design tools that are now available to the design team.

Take Advantage of Parallel Technology

Most MNT technology develops at an approximately steady and predictable rate across the world because everyone has access to the same pool of background knowledge upon which all kinds of progress is based. However, major leaps in a particular area of technology can be achieved when an individual recognises a different technology developed in an entirely different field and applies or adapts it to his particular problem. In my own field of micro engineered inertial sensors, the big breakthrough for us was made some 40 years ago, when my colleagues and I suddenly realised that a material developed for shot blast nozzles combined with process techniques already used for thin film electronic circuits could be adapted to manufacture ultra high precision mechanical parts of tolerances of about 1/20 of a micron. Likewise, all early MEMS fabrication processes borrowed from the existing fabrication methods and materials perfected for the microelectronics industry.

Simple Solutions Often Solve Complex Problems

In an ideal world, all problems would be analysed in detail, extensive simulations and tests will be carried out, and the results will be used to define an elegant solution that will in turn reflect a total understanding of the original problem and its causes. It is possible that future engineers and technical specialists will live in a perfect world, but neither my colleagues nor I ever did. Whatever your own version of an AOG situation is (AOG = 'Aircraft on Ground' = ££££ $$$$) there will be tremendous pressure to come up with a solution fast and get the programme back on track. Under these conditions, programme managers and production directors don't really care about what caused the problem—they just demand a solution. Engineers have always solved complex vibration problems in conventional structures by using very simple trial-and-error damping measures long before finite element analysis and 3D modelling software were available, and numerous MEMS devices, for all their sophistication and refinement, rely on a judicious blob of silicone adhesive or such similar materials as a compliant interface between them and the real world. In at least one production crisis that the writer was involved in, we were unable to identify the exact cause of the problem without holding up production to complete many months of testing in order to systematically eliminate the exact cause or causes. Breaking all the rules, we decided to introduce over a dozen simultaneous improvements to the manufacturing process. Which, if at all any, of these cured the problem we never knew, but the problem went away and this 'scattergun' approach to problem solving, though inelegant, was certainly cost effective in that particular case. The motto here is that you sometimes have to solve the problem first and then try to work out how you solved it later.

Know When to Compute and When to Cut

For every project, there is an optimum point in the design and development cycle when the theoretical work should stop and trial hardware manufacture should start. This point will be different for every project, but the foundry costs and timescales associated with micro-nano fabrication mean that this is an area more critical than most. Again, Engineers of the Victorian era recognised the need to freeze the design process and start cutting metal at the right time. While modern analytic tools allow the MEMS designer to have a very good understanding of his design prior to fabrication, it is still important to recognise that calculations and modelling will only take you so far, and there is no substitute to producing a prototype and evaluating its performance. The difference between modelling predictions and experimental performance will generally increase as dimensions get smaller, and for a highly complex product with many fabrication steps, judging this point can appreciably influence the overall development cost and time to market.

Parts That Look Visually Good Perform Better

In many Microsystems, parts that look visually 'good' with sharply defined edges, straight sides and smooth finishes have been found to perform better than dimensionally identical parts that measure the same but look less well formed. Various workers have noted this effect, and I can confirm it from experiences with my own production designs of micro engineered inertial sensors. It is particularly evident in very complex electro-mechanical assemblies containing large numbers of individual parts and features, and probably reflects the inability of current metrology and analytic methods to take into account the *cumulative* second and third order effects of local geometric and material imperfections at this scale.

Symmety of Design

As a general rule, always aim for symmetry in your design where at all possible, and even if the available theory indicates that this is not necessary. If it '...offends the eye' as I was told during my apprenticeship, go back to the drawing board (or your CAD station as appropriate). Regardless of scale, technology or product type, apart from just looking good, physical design symmetry often confers many hidden benefits ranging from structural and thermal stability to balanced forces and predictable behaviour. It can also simplify and speed up theoretical analysis and computer simulation.

Failure is Rarely Due to a Single Cause

In a production device, my experience suggests that the failure of a well-designed electro-mechanical system is rarely due to a single cause. It is much more likely to be a combination of factors that have conspired to produce a single, and sometimes catastrophic, failure. Often this failure is found to have been preceded by an almost imperceptible change in parameters over a lengthy period of time. For high volume production runs, standard statistical process control techniques can be used to minimise this risk, but for small volumes involving stages that are difficult to fully automate and monitor, it can be a problem. One particular case I investigated was caused due to minute changes in differential expansion brought about by *improvements* in material quality. Similarly, most of the failures that I have investigated have been due to very simple causes rather than complex technology issue—, with differential expansion and thermal stress playing a major role in over 80% of the cases, and tooling or handling damage involved in many of the remaining cases.

Most Failures and Disasters are Preceded by Warning Signs That are Ignored

It is very rare, both in nature, everyday life and particularly in engineering and science, for either a disaster or a serious failure to occur entirely unexpectedly and unannounced. Post mortems and hindsight usually show that all the signs were there well before hand, but they were either not recognised as such or simply ignored. Investigations often show in retrospect that otherwise sound initial designs were subsequently compromised by a reduction in safety margins arising out of sub-standard materials, poor workmanship or below par repairs, and also by maintenance failures and minor changes or modifications whose knock-on and cumulative effects were not recognised or predicted. For most products, the skill and knowledge level of those involved will inevitably change at each stage of the product life cycle, starting from research and development staff at the beginning, through the production chain to the repair and maintenance personnel towards the end. There is a risk that the fundamental theory and reasons behind critical aspects of the design will be overlooked, and that subsequent changes or process modifications will conflict with these. In large organisations, the original design team may not be directly involved in subsequent design or process decisions. While this risk is probably very much less for an individual MNT device than a conventional product or system, large-scale integration of different MNT devices into composite host products may mean that this may no longer be the case in the near future.

'Rogue' Test Results will Tend to be Ignored for as Long as Possible

Human nature being what it is, there is an inherent desire in all of us to ignore or dismiss any test results that do not fit in with our preconceived expectations or theoretical predictions. I have observed this time and time again in both new and experienced engineers, who use all manner of euphemisms to justify their dismissal when writing their reports. In many cases, there are genuine reasons why data should be discarded, but sometimes it masks an underlying problem that warrants a far closer examination, however inconvenient and disruptive this may be to the programme. A particular case I recall is that of laboratory tests carried out on a particular design of flexure suspension system, where so called 'rogue' points around the null masked an inherent non-linearity that had not been identified at the analytic stage.

Factors Limiting Performance

For nearly all MEMS sensing and measuring devices, and probably for other devices as well, performance will ultimately be dictated by temperature stability, zero point stability and the likes, rather than by scale factor and resolution alone. As dimensions get smaller, molecular and other noise effects start to play an increasing role in the overall error band of the output signal. While some of the above can be limited by good design, there is an implied limit to size if a really high performance is required, and this in turn suggests that it will not be possible to emulate the reducing cost of Microelectronics with die size for certain classes of MEMS products. Small may be beautiful, but it may also be problematic.

If it Looks Right ... it is Right

This adage has proved a good and reliable 'rule-of-thumb' to generations of Engineers. In conventional macro-scale engineering, if the proportions of a component look correct to the experienced eye, this is usually a good indication that the design is sound. This is a useful 'reality check' to carry out after you have done the calculations. It is especially useful if sophisticated computer design software has been used and visibility of the analysis process has been lost as a result. However, it follows from the force vs. volume plot referred to above that the optimum relative proportions or aspect ratio of mechanical elements in particular are often very different to those we are familiar with in the larger world. Many micro-nano structures are noticeably more slender than their traditional counterparts because gravitational forces become insignificant at very small dimensions, decreasing rapidly as the volume of the structure decreases. To a conventionally trained engineer, these will look incorrect and too fragile. Recognising these differences, and more importantly, understanding the reasons behind them, is important. It allows the experienced designer to quickly carry out a visual check on a very complex design generated by mathematical analysis or by a computer design programme. While the design software may perform correctly, it is highly dependent on boundary conditions and other user inputs, and the ability to judge the overall appearance of the design is a useful art to acquire.

My personal experience has been that if the overall design concept is right, most of the detailed design will be reasonably straightforward, with different design features complementing each other and 'clicking into place' as design and development proceeds. Conversely, if, as a designer, you have to fight every single feature and repeatedly compromise your design goals and performance specification, then it is probably time to reconsider the original concept.

Get Organised! ...

My late uncle, not an Engineer but a very successful hotelier, greeted his staff every morning with the cry 'Get organised!...' Only many years later did I realise the significance of this instruction. During my University work, I found a dramatic difference between the abilities of the younger undergraduates to successfully complete micro-technology design projects and those of the mature students who had already spent time in industry. Typically, the latter would immediately organise themselves into effective teams and work out a strategy for solving the problem with the resources available while the former would waste much time in the early stages of a project due to lack of organisation and often struggle to complete it in the available time, even though they eventually begin to work in a structured and effective manner. Personal and collective organisation is even more important in micro and nano technology than in traditional engineering because design, fabrication, packaging and testing are inextricably linked to a far greater extent than is hitherto known. While large organisations tend to impose a highly structured approach to design and fabrication upon their employees (sometimes to the extent that is stifles creativity), young engineers of the future are more likely to find themselves working in much smaller entrepreneurial start-up companies, whose successes will depend entirely on the personal attributes of their employees. While all this may seem obvious to the reader, I am in no doubt that good organisation is the key to successfully completing a complex and challenging MNT project. The armed forces of most countries have different ways of expressing this vital prerequisite for successfully completing a strategic operation and achieving an objective (few of which could be repeated here!), but the overall message is the same; if you fail to plan, you plan to fail.

Beware of 'Specification Creep'

This is a classic marketing problem that can, if not recognised in time, adversely affect the karma of the design engineer, who is inevitably to be found at the bottom of the corporate decision chain. Customers, clients and even your own marketing department will always press for performance or environmental specifications to be increased after the initial specification has been agreed upon—either to meet new situations, create a larger market share or to compensate for performance deficiencies in another part of a larger system into which the MNT device will be integrated. As one engineer was heard remarking ruefully, '... they don't just keep moving the goal posts, they carry them away and bury them'. As an example, I quote the case of an innovative very low cost sensor that was developed as a non-repairable component for short life applications. It easily met all the original specifications, but customers pressed for more and more performance and longer life for use in other applications. The marketing department, sensing an even larger market share and reluctant to say no, pressed the designer to improve the product, Design changes gave increased performance and life, but the cost also increased accordingly, and customers therefore expected devices to be repairable if they failed. The result was a product that was no longer financially viable in the lowest cost applications for which it was originally intended, and could not compete with the new emerging sensors that eventually displaced it.

Be not the first on which the new are tried, nor yet the last to cast the old aside

This advice was originally attributed to the medical profession, but it is equally applicable in the rapidly emerging field of micro-nano technologies. New manufacturing technologies, processes and materials bring both benefits and risks, and if you are paid to design products using these technologies, your paymasters or shareholders will not be happy if you make a wrong choice on this front. Also, recognise from the start that MNT design is different from conventional design. In conventional designs, in general terms, a final decision on the manufacturing processes can often be deferred until a later stage whereas for an MNT product intended for volume production, the entire research, design, development and manufacturing process has to be considered and specified from the very start, and manufacturing methods have to be taken into account at every stage in the R&D cycle. Concurrent engineering is no longer a recommended and trendy option; it is a necessity.

The Second Mouse...

There is a well known English saying that '...it's the early bird that gets the worm', —but don't forget that it is also the *second* mouse that gets the cheese! In technological terms, the first company to develop a new product may get the credit for being an innovator, but those that follow are often in a better position to exploit the application commercially. Few patents are so strong and comprehensive to be able to totally block those who are determined to follow, and the need to find a way around existing patents is in itself one of the principal drivers of innovation for young engineers.

Multi-Partner International Projects – the Real Advantage

The advantages of these are invariably over stated in order to persuade government and international bodies to provide funding for these socially and politically desirable ventures. To me they rarely seem to represent an efficient use of resources, but are often viewed as essential for commercial and marketing reasons. Their real undeclared advantage as far as the young design engineer is concerned is that they tend to be less liable to sudden cancellation than projects funded by a single company, or even by a single nation. There is nothing so soul destroying as working on an interesting project that gets cancelled for financial or political reasons.

Money has the Power to Change the Most Inflexible Customer Specification

No, I am not talking about bribery and corruption, but the way a technically inferior product can displace a superior one with better performance if the price differential between them is great enough, or if a financial 'deal' involving other issues can be negotiated by the supplier of the lower performance device. If the financial saving is great enough, the pressure to redesign the final application to accept what were previously regarded as components not meeting the minimum purchase specification will become impossible to resist. This has happened twice in my career, so it is possible it could also happen during yours.

How Many Miracles?

As a final 'reality check' on your design, always ask the question: 'How many miracles do we need to get this thing to work?' As a general rule of thumb, if the answer is more than one, it's back to the drawing board!

23.4.4 Predicting the Future

Prior to the new millennium, I completed a survey of people not involved in micro-nano technology and asked them what products they wanted to be developed in the next century. The results were surprising. None of these products corresponded to those that the technologists were at that time predicting that they would be developed. They did however reflect many of the concepts predicted by writers of science fiction, and with basic human desires that could be traced back over many centuries. The top six products the general public wanted to have were, in no particular order as follows:

(1) A universal real-time language translator
(2) A personal flying 'chariot'
(3) Super-human powers of vision, hearing, situation awareness etc.
(4) An instant world-wide personal communicator
(5) A personal medical diagnostic and repair device
(6) A fully autonomous humanoid robot servant/companion/guard.

In every case, each of these futuristic products will only be realised by the massively large-scale integration of micro-nano technologies with advanced conventional scale engineering.

Many different visions for the future have been put forward by contemporary workers in MNT, and the only certainty is that we are all probably wrong, but some predictions will be closer than others. My personal views, based on the survey I referred to above and also based upon my experiences in industry and academia as a whole, are as follows:

(1) Future products will need to integrate many different MEMS and nano devices and materials in a single unit in order to meet the functional expectations of the market. There are probably very few simple MEMS products left to be developed. The OEM market for simple single-function devices such as accelerometers and pressure sensors will continue to develop, but the final products will need to incorporate many different functions and technologies within a common shell or package.

(2) As a direct consequence of the above, 'packaging', but in particular 'intelligent' product-level packaging, will become increasingly important and will

define many different applications and markets for both mass produced and custom made devices.

(3) Micro-nano technologies will lead to highly reliable products that never wear out or break down in the conventional sense. (A British comedy film, 'The Man in the White Suit', made many decades ago, predicts one of the consequences of this situation, and is well worth watching if you can locate it) This means that the business model of the future is likely to be based on rapid obsolescence, with products needing to be replaced only because they become technically out of date or unfashionable. This in turn suggests that the opportunity to establish a very large second and perhaps even a third user market exists, allowing the benefits of MNT to flow rapidly down to developing and third world countries at a cost they can afford.

(4) Just because a new application will become technically feasible in the future, does not necessarily mean it will definitely happen. In the 1940's, it was widely predicted that future technology would allow everyone to have his or her own personal helicopter for everyday transport and leisure. The technology does exist now, and small two seated helicopters are available; but for very obvious practical and financial reasons, the mass ownership and use of these has not happened and probably never will. Despite this, a 'flying chariot' is still seen by many people as a highly desirable future product that they would like to own.

(5) The long tradition of 'over-selling' new technology will continue, but despite this, novel concepts will always take longer to reach the market than initially predicted.

(6) There will be a fusion of micro-nano and biotechnologies that will raise serious ethical questions and public debate in many countries.

(7) Those who have no idea of the scale of the facilities and the sheer number of process steps required to make even the very simplest of micro robots, are likely to continue to predict a future where the entire earth is covered with 'grey goo' or self replicating micro and nano robots that are out of control. I suspect they will be proved wrong.

(8) Very large-scale fabrication facilities and foundries will disappear gradually and will be replaced by specialist mini fabs and micro factories, which can rapidly and economically respond to a fast changing market and unexpected technical opportunities.

(9) The ultimate product that embodies all micro-nano technologies will eventually be the fully autonomous humanoid robot, whose performance and price are such that every family in the developed world would own at least one of them. The true realisation of this product (as traditionally depicted in films and literature) is probably at least one human generation away, but the potential market for such a device is virtually unlimited.

(10) Like all preceding technologies, these new technologies would also be misused in ways that do not benefit mankind. With each new discovery, people will ask the same three questions they have always asked on such occasions:

Can I play with it? Can I fight with it? How can I make money out of it?

This then, is my personal vision of the future, but I imagine that if you were able to jump into a micro engineered time machine, travel into the distant future, and ask one of the Engineers who had created it, as to what he had learnt in the process, his reply would still be *'Not nearly enough ...'*

References

[1] Choo H., R. S. Muller, (2006), Adressable microlens array to improve dynamic range of Shack-Hartmann sensors, *IEEE/ASME Journal of Microelectromechanical Systems*, **15**(6): 1555 – 1567

[2] Smith C.S., (1954), Piezoresistance effect in germanium and silicon, *Physical Review*, **94**: 42 – 49

[3] Tufte O., W.Chapman and D.Long, (1962), Silicon diffused-element piezoresistive diaphragms, *J. of Applied Physics*, **33**: 3322 – 3327

[4] Nathanson H.C., W.E.Newell, R.A.Wickstrom and J.R.Davis, The resonant gate transistor, *IEEE Trans. on Electron Devices*, **ED-14**: 117 – 133

[5] Wallis G., and D.I.Pomerantz, (1969), Field assisted glass-metal sealing, *J. of Applied Physics*, **40**: 3946 – 3949

[6] Terry S.C., J.H.Jerman and J.B.Angell, (1979), A gas chromatographic air analyzer fabricated on a silicon wafer, *IEEE Trans. on Electron Devices*, **ED-26**: 1880 – 1886

[7] Goodenough F., (1991), Airbags boom when IC accelerometer sees 50G, Electronic Design, Aug.**8**: 45 – 56

[8] Larmer F., A.Schilp: Method of anisotropically etching silicon, German Patent DE4241045C1, USA patent 4855017 and 4784720

[9] Hornbeck L.J., (1995), Digital light processing and MEMS: timely convergence for a bright future, Micromachining and Microfabrication'95 SPIE, 3 – 20

[10] Farrens S.N., J.R.Dekker, J.K.Smith and B.E.Roberds, (1995), Chemical free room temperature wafer to wafer direct bonding, *J. Electrochem. Soc.*, **142**: 3949 – 3955

[11] Petersen K., (2005), A new age for MEMS, Digest of Technical Papers, *Transducers'05*, 1 – 4

[12] Nathanson H.C., and J.Guldberg, (1975), Topologically structured thin films in semiconductor device operation, in *Physics of Thin Films* vol.8 (ed. G.Hass) New York Academy Press, 251 – 333

[13] Peterson K., (1982), Silicon as a mechanical materials, *Proc. of the IEEE*, **70**: 420 – 457

[14] Meindle J.D., and K.D.Wise (ed.), (1979), Special issue on solid-state sensors, actuators and interface electronics, *IEEE Trans. on Electron Devices*, **ED-26**(1): 1861 – 1983

[15] Wise K.D. (ed), (1998), Special issue on integrated sensors, microactuators and microsystems (MEMS), *Proceedings of the IEEE*, **86**(8): 1531 – 1787

[16] Fung C., et.al., (1985), Micromachining and micropackaging of transducers, Elsevier

[17] Takinami M., K.Minami, and M. Esashi, (1992), High-speed directional low-temperature dry etching for bulk silicon micromachining, Technical Digest of the 11th Sensor Symposium, 15 – 18

[18] Ono T., D. Y. Sim and M.Esashi, (2000), Micro-discharge and electric breakdown in a micro-gap, *J. Micromech. Microeng.*, 10: 445 – 451

[19] Esashi M., (1994), Encapsulated micro mechanical sensors, Microsystem Technologies, 1: 2 – 9

[20] Matsumoto Y., and M.Esashi, (1992), An integrated capacitive absolute pressure sensor, Electronics and Communications in Japan, Part 2, **76**: 93 – 106

[21] Miyashita H., and Y.Kitamura, (2005), Micromachined capacitive diaphragm gauge, Anelva Technical Report, 11: 37 – 40

[22] Nakamura et.al., (2004), Development of RF MEMS switch, Advantest Technical Report, 22: 9 – 16

[23] Ishikawa T., T.S.Aytur and B.E.Boser, (2005), A wireless integrated immunosensor, Complex Medical Eng. 2005 (CME2005), Kagawa 2005: 943 – 946

[24] Murakoshi T., Y.Endo, K.Fukatsu, S.Nakamura and M.Esashi, (2003), Electrostatically levitated ring-shaped rotational-gyro/accelerometer, *Jpn. J. Appli. Phys.*, 42: 2468 – 2472

[25] Lee D.W., T.Ono, E.Abe and M.Esashi, (2002), Microprobe array with electrical interconnection for thermal imaging and data storage, *J. Microelectromechanical Systems*, 11: 215 – 219

[26] Totsu K., Y.Haga and M.Esashi, (2005), Ultra-miniature fiber-optic pressure sensor using white light interferometry, *J. Micromech. Microeng.*, 15: 71 – 75

[27] Esashi M., and T.Matsuo, (1978), Integrated micro multi ion sensor using field effect of semiconductor, *IEEE Transactions on Biomedical Engineering*, **BME-25**: 184 – 192

[28] Min K.-O., S.Tanaka and M.Esash, (2004), Glass press mold fabricated by SiC APCVD, SiC-SiC bonding and silicon lost molding, Proc. of the 21th Sensor Symposium, 473 – 478

[29] Lagos M.A., et.al., (2005), Processing of MEMS gyroscope on top of CMOS ICs, 2005 Intnl. Solid State Circuits Conf.(ISSCC), 88 – 89

Index Color Figures

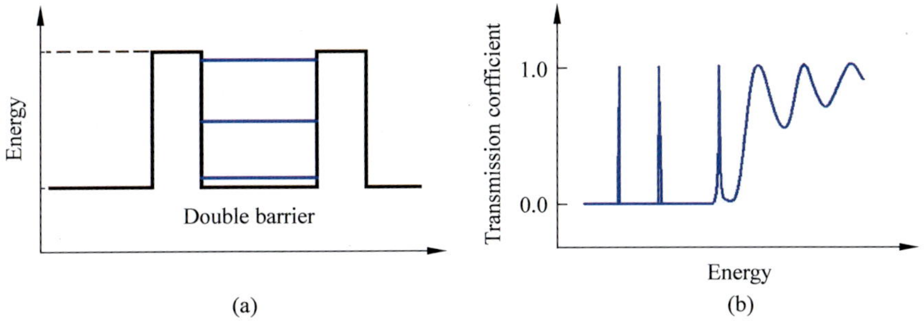

Figure 1.5[29] (a) energy band diagram of a single-well double-barrier quantum system, (b) quantum tunneling probability as function of energy

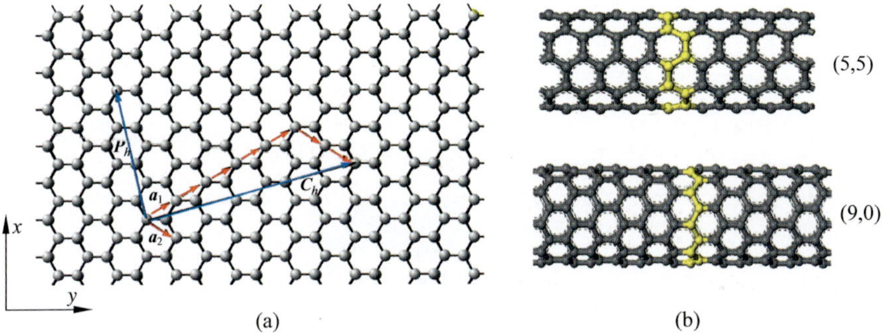

Figure 1.10[41] (a) Structure of graphene, (b) Two different CNT structures

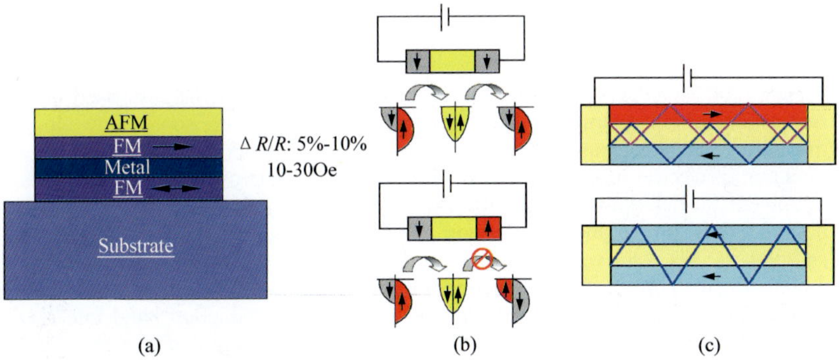

Figure 1.12 GMR[47]: (a) structure, (b) energy band structure and electron population, (c) high resistive and low resistive states

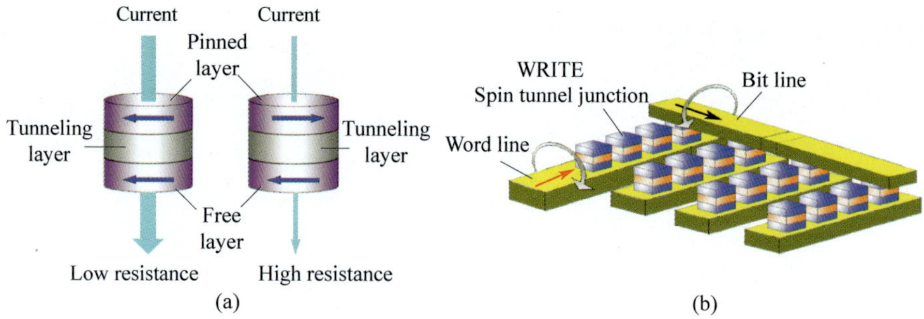

Figure 1.13[49, 50] (a) TMR, (b) MRAM

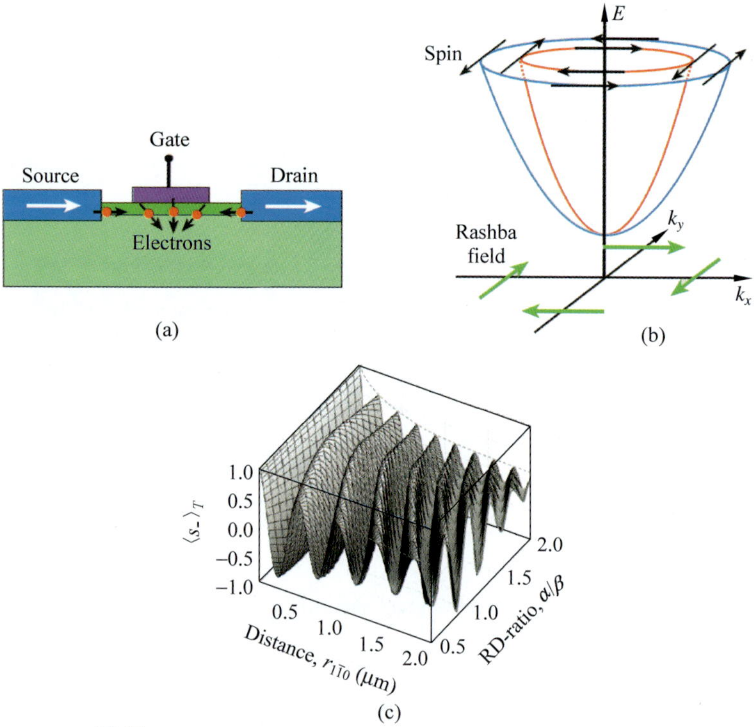

Figure 1.14[51, 52] (a) The spin-FET conceived by Datta and Das is based on a semiconductor heterostructure. Electrons (red) injected from the source flow along the indium-arsenide channel (green) and are detected at the drain. The gate voltage produces an electric field in the growth direction of the heterostructure, which leads to a magnetic field known as the Rashba field. Since this field is perpendicular to both the electric field and the transport direction, the spin of the injected electron can precess. The gate voltage on the transistor controls the Rashba field, thereby modulating the current. (b) The energy of the electrons as a function of momentum, *k*. The Rashba field (green) splits the electrons in the conduction band into two sub-bands that are distinguished by the orientation of their spins. For a give field direction, the two spin-states have slightly different momenta. (c) Spin polarization component $\langle s_- \rangle_T$, with respect to source-drain distance r_{110}, and RD-ratio calculated at Eds = 3.0 kV/cm

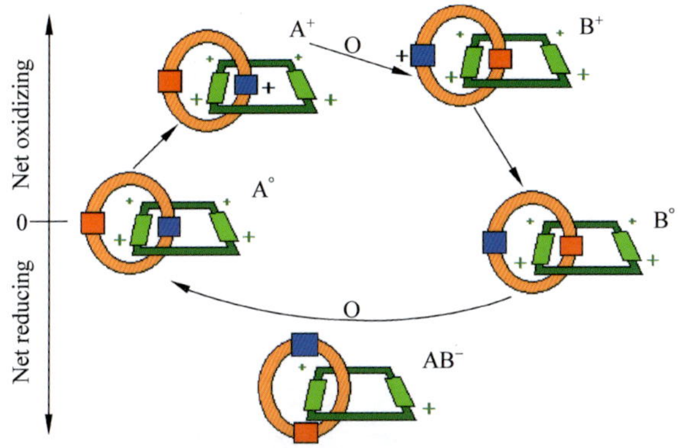

Figure 1.17 The write and rewrite process of binary information using catenane[65]

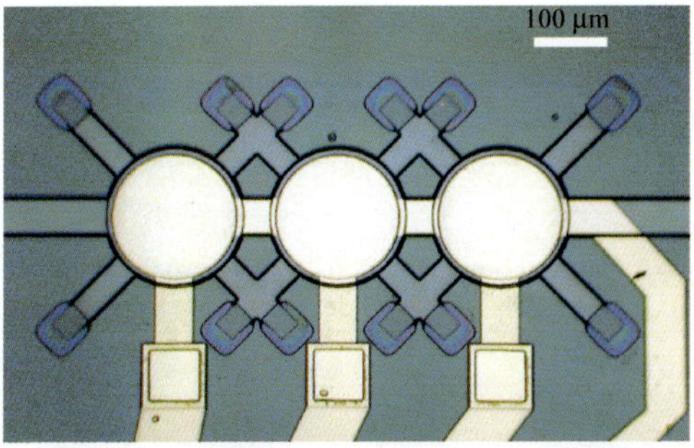

Figure 2.3 A surface-micromachined peristaltic pump[9] with a transverse dimension ~ 3 μm

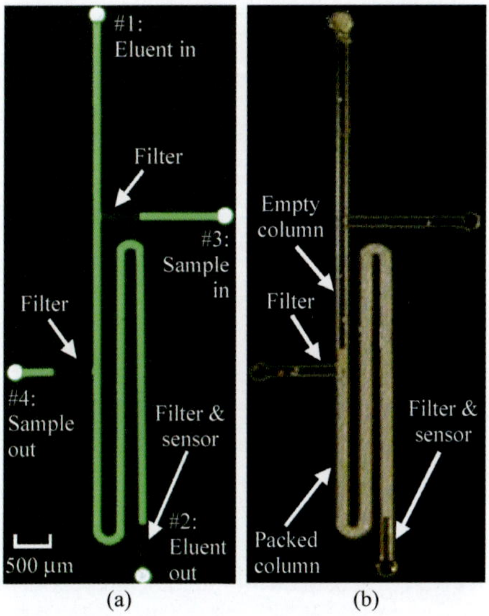

Figure 2.8 An ion-exchange liquid chromatography device with column length of 1 cm

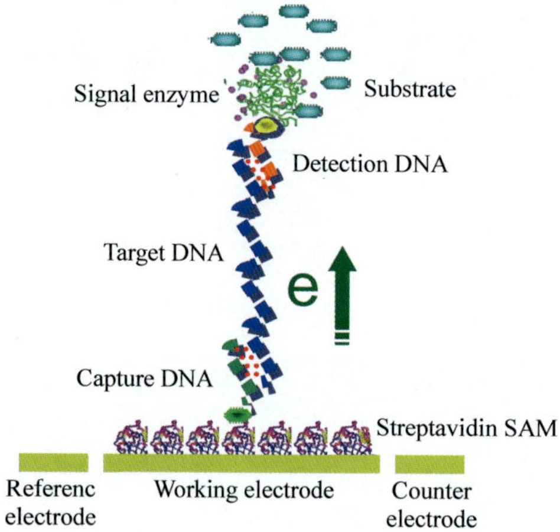

Figure 2.9 A schematic of electrochemical DNA detection

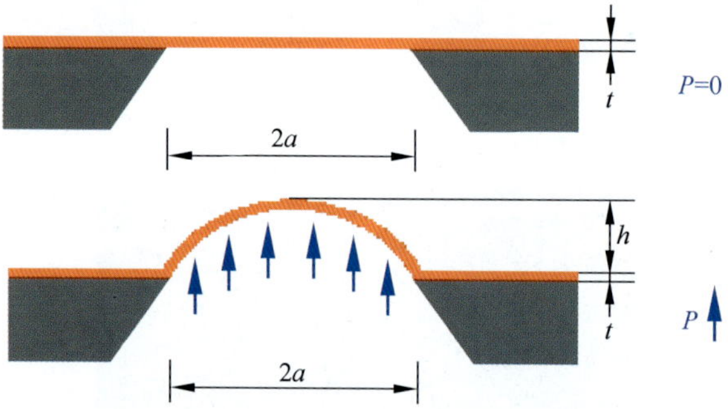

Figure 3.8 Schematic of the bulge test

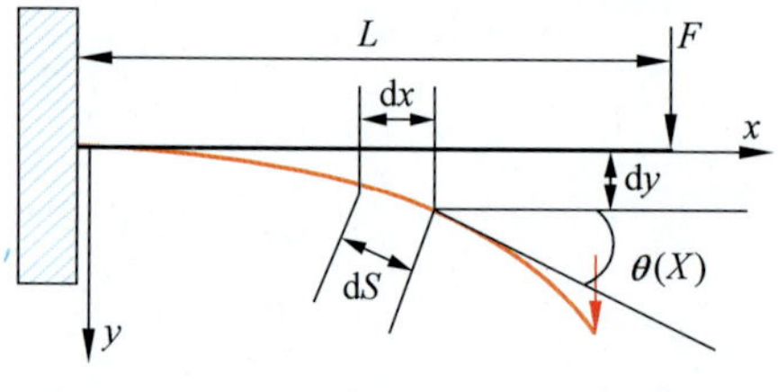

Figure 3.11 Schematic of micro beam bending test

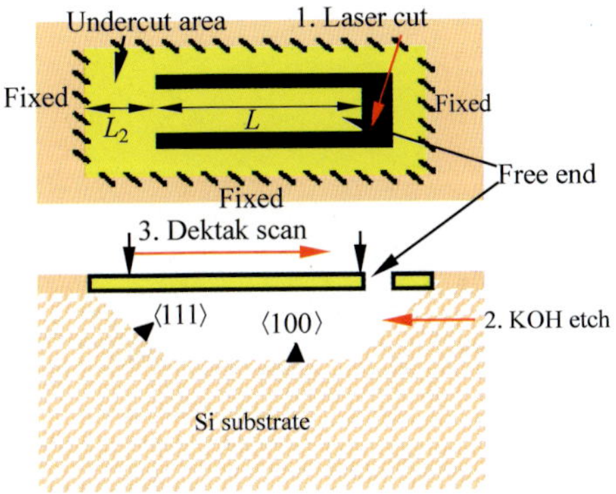

Figure 3.12 Sample preparation process flow of beam bending test[15]

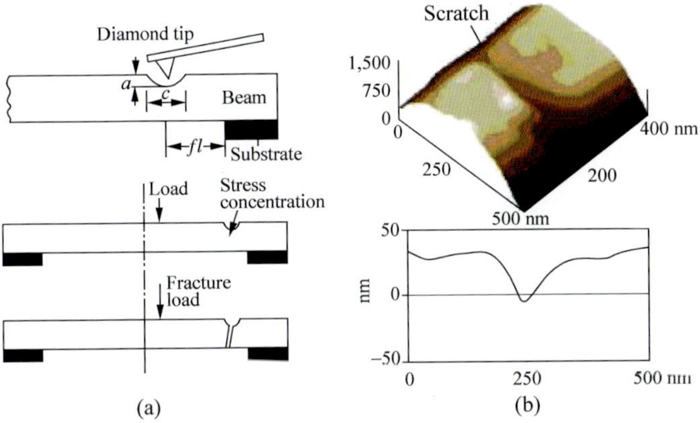

Figure 3.13 The method to generate a crack of known geometry and to measure the K_{1c}

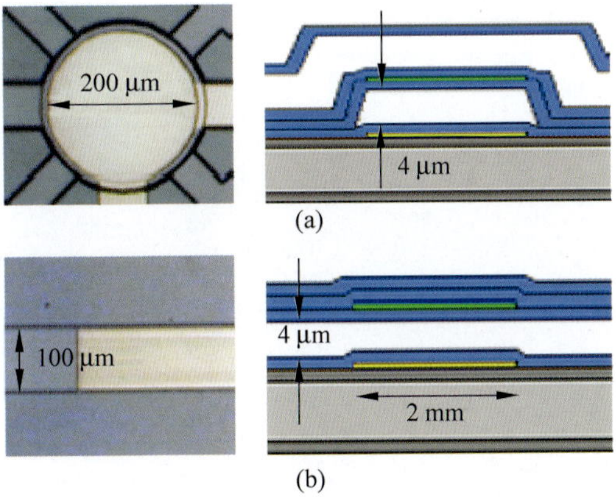

Figure 3.22 A capacitive pressure sensor

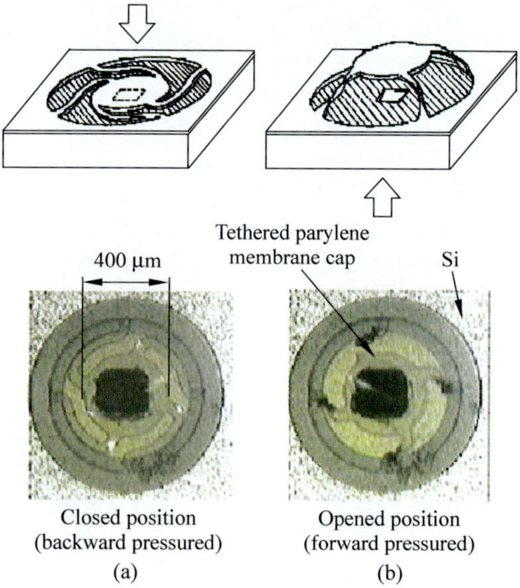

Figure 3.23 Tethered Parylene Plate Check Valve

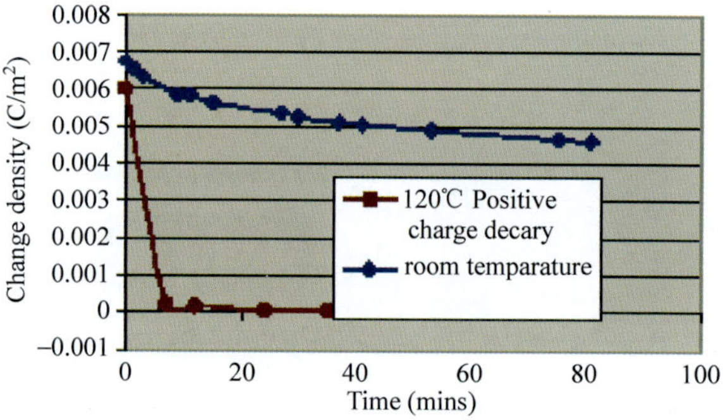

Figure 3.25 Positive charge decays at room temperature and 120℃

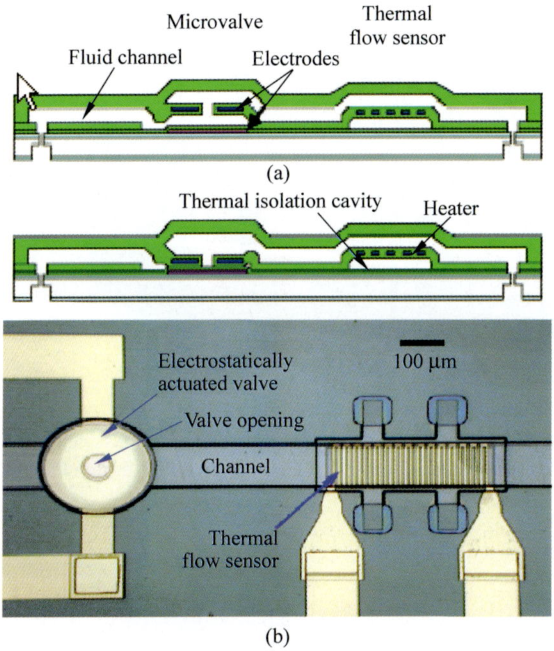

Figure 3.26 Integrated micro mass flow controller

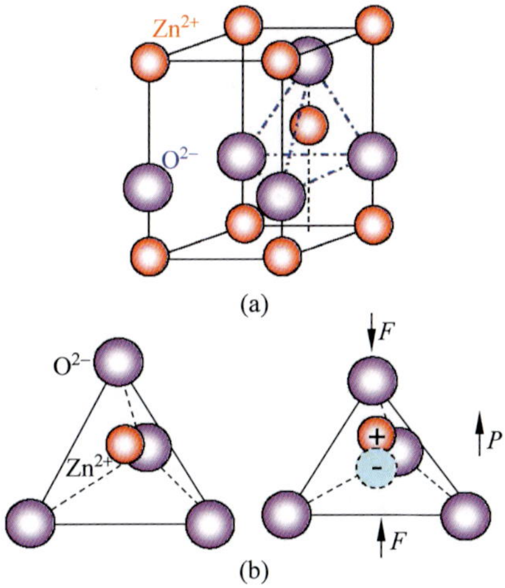

Figure 4.1 (a) Wurtzite structure model of ZnO. (b) The tetrahedral coordination of Zn-O and the corresponding Polarization of ions under stress

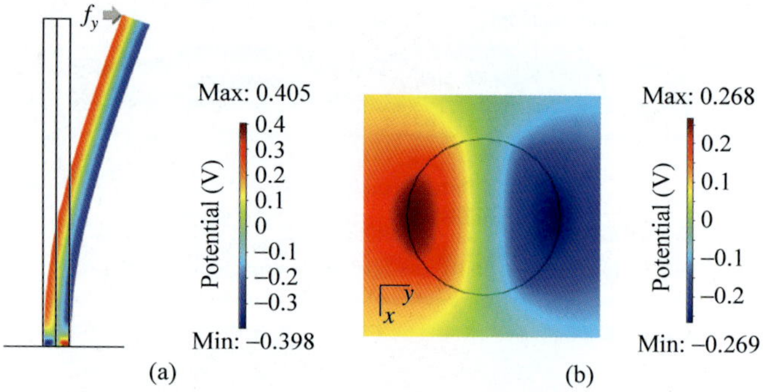

Figure 4.2 Potential distribution for a ZnO nanowire with $d = 50$ nm, $l = 600$ nm at a lateral bending force of 80 nN. (a) and (b) are side and cross-sectional (at $z = 300$ nm) output of the piezoelectric potential in the NW given by finite element calculation

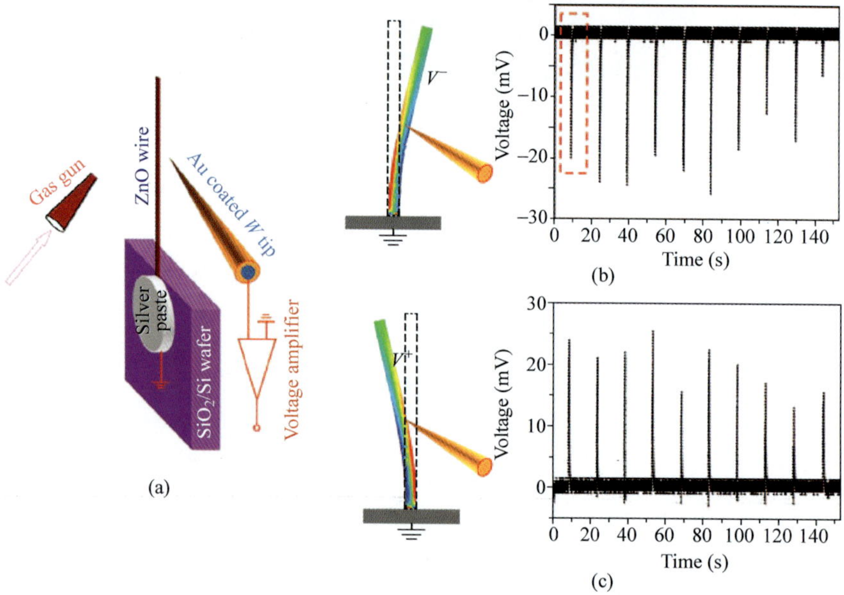

Figure 4.3 (a) Schematic experimental set-up for detecting the surface potential. (b) By placing a metal tip at the right-hand side and blowing Ar pulses at the left-hand side, negative voltage peaks of 0 – 25 mV were observed once the pulse was on. (c) By quickly pushing and releasing the wire at the right-hand side by a metal tip, a positive voltage peak of 0 – 25 mV was observed for each cycle of the deflection

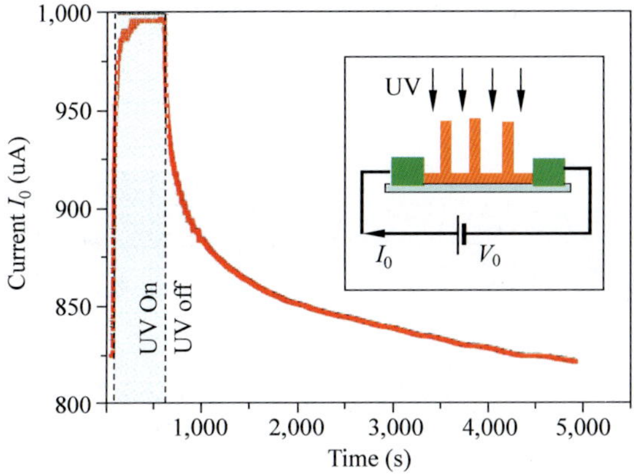

Figure 4.4 Response of the current transported through a thin ZnO film with NWs on top when it is subjected to UV illumination. The inset is the measurement set-up

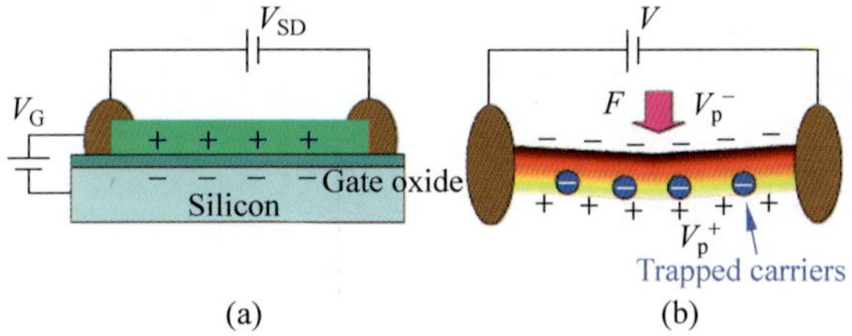

Figure 4.5 (a) Schematics of conventional field-effect transistors (FETs) using a single nanowire/nanobelt. (b) The principle of the piezoelectric field-effect transistor (PE-FET)

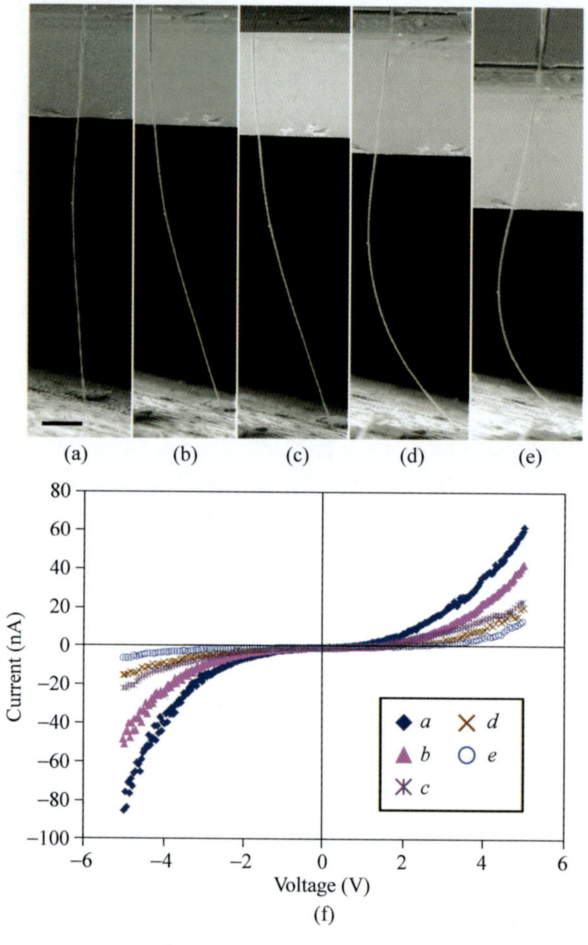

Figure 4.6 (a – e) SEM images with the same magnification showing the five typical bending cases of the ZnO nanowire; the scale bar represents 10 ím. (f) Corresponding $I \sim V$ characteristics of the ZnO nanowire for the five different bending cases. This is the $I \sim V$ curve of the piezoelectric field effect transistor (PE-FET)

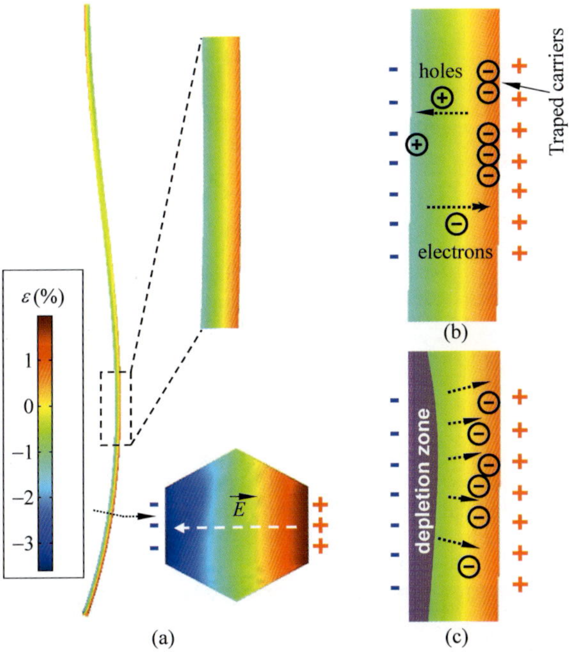

Figure 4.7 Schematic diagrams showing the mechanisms responsible for the conductance change. (a) A finite element simulation of the strain distribution along the ZnO nanowire when it is bent. (b) The carrier trapping effect. (c) The creation of a charge depletion zone

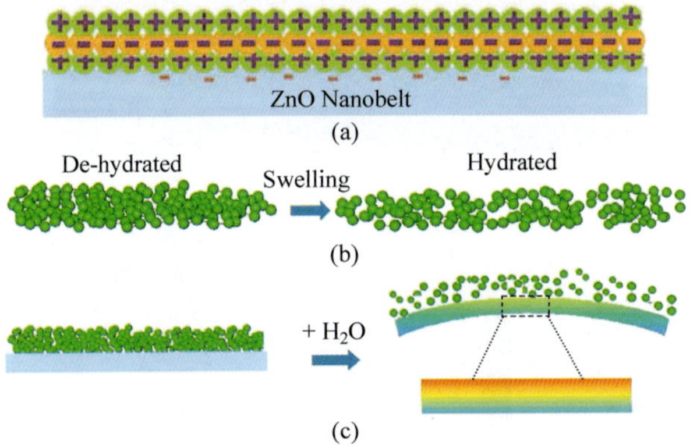

Figure 4.9 (a) Schematic illustration of multilayer deposition of different polymers onto the ZnO NB surface. The green dots represent positively charged PDADMAC. The orange dots represent the negatively charged PNIPAM. (b) The volume of the polymers increases significantly upon hydration. (c) Schematic illustration of ZnO NB deformation upon polymer swelling and the consequently generated piezoelectric fields across the ZnO NB

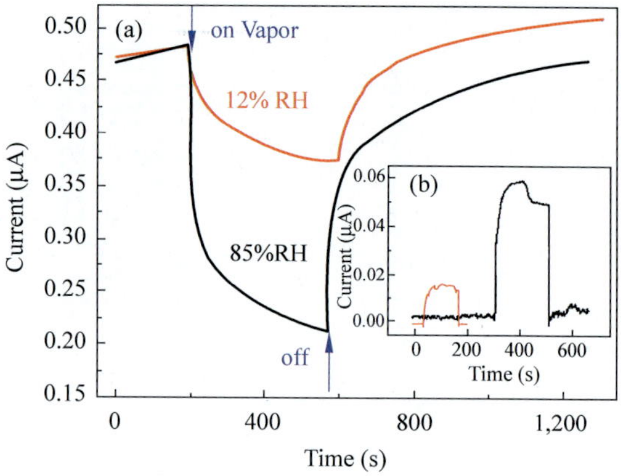

Figure 4.10 (a) IV responses of the PNIPAM polymer functionalized devices upon exposure to 85% (black curve) and 12% (red curve) relative humidities. (b) Current response of an uncoated ZnO NB upon exposure to 85% relative humidity (black) and the polymer (red), showing that neither of them individually is responsible for the reduction of current in (a)

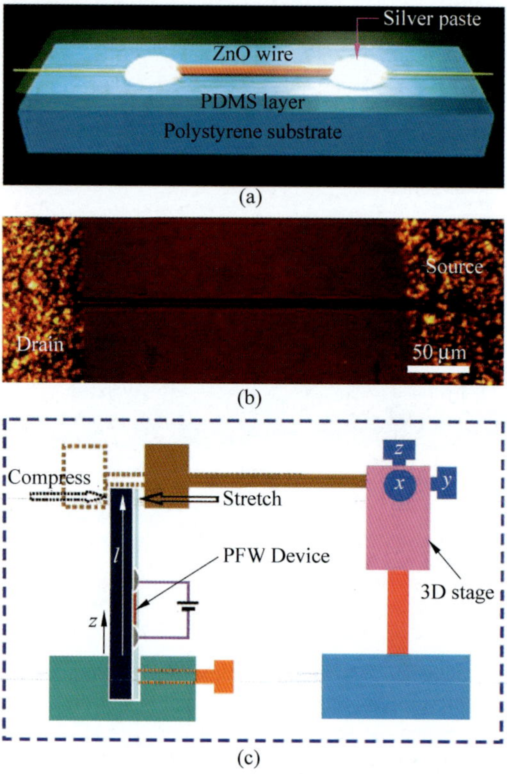

Figure 4.11 (a) Schematic of a single ZnO PFW-based strain sensor device. (b) Optical image of a strain sensor device. (c) Schematic of the measurement system to characterize the performance of the sensor device

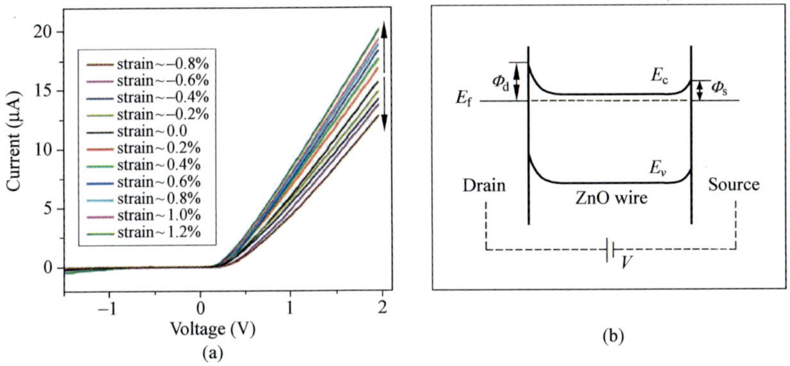

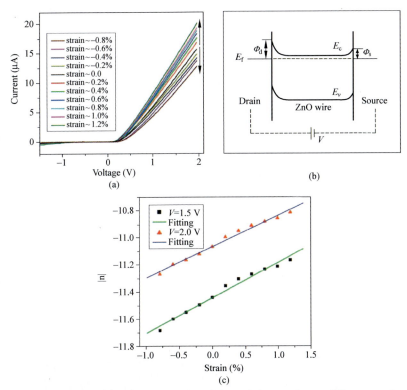

Figure 4.12 (a) Typical $I\sim V$ characteristics of the sensor at different strain. (b) Energy band diagram illustrates the asymmetric Schottky barrier heights at the source and drain contacts of a NW, where the offset by the applied drain-source voltage V was not included, for easy discussion. (c) Logarithm plot of the current (in unit of ampere) at fixed bias of $V = 1.5$ V and 2.0 V as a function of strain

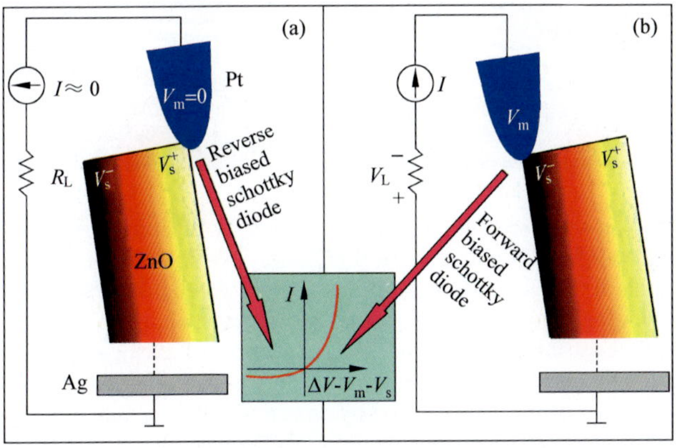

Figure 4.13 Schematic diagram showing the metal-semiconductor contacts between the AFM tip and the ZnO N with reverse (a) and forward (b) biased Schottky rectifying behavior

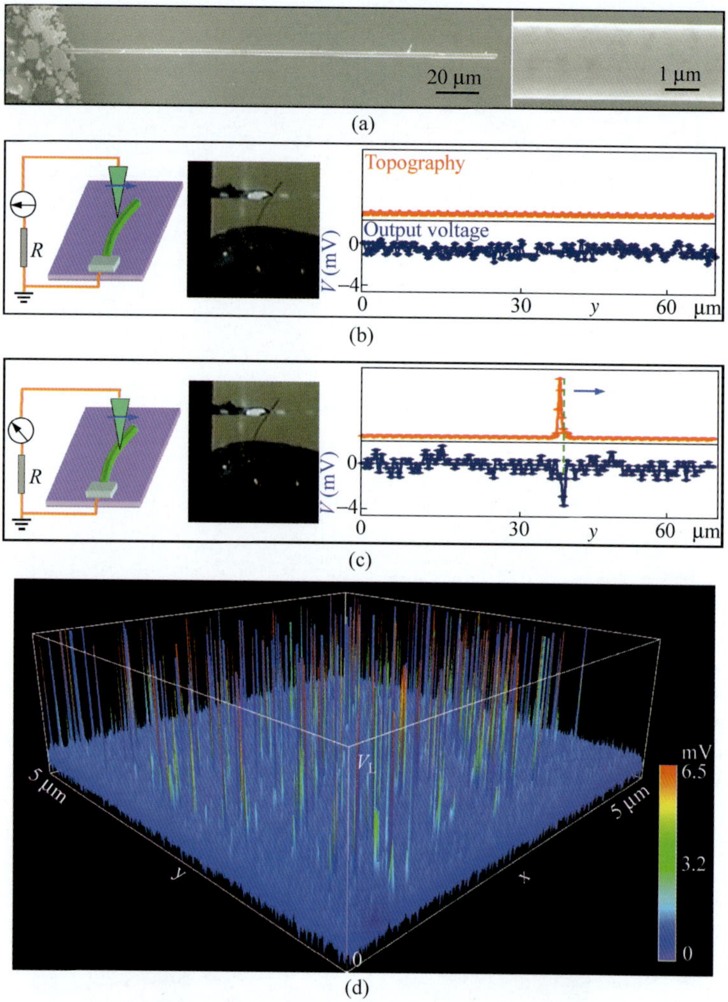

Figure 4.14 In situ observation of the process for converting mechanical energy into electric energy by a piezoelectric ZnO wire. (a) SEM images of a ZnO wire with one end affixed on a silicon substrate. (b, c) Two characteristic snapshots and the corresponding topography (red curve) and output voltage (blue curve) images when the tip is scanned across the middle section of the wire. The schematic illustration of the experimental condition is shown at the left hand side, with the scanning direction of the tip indicated by an arrowhead. (d) Output voltage image map of ZnO NW arrays when they are deformed by a conductive AFM scanning

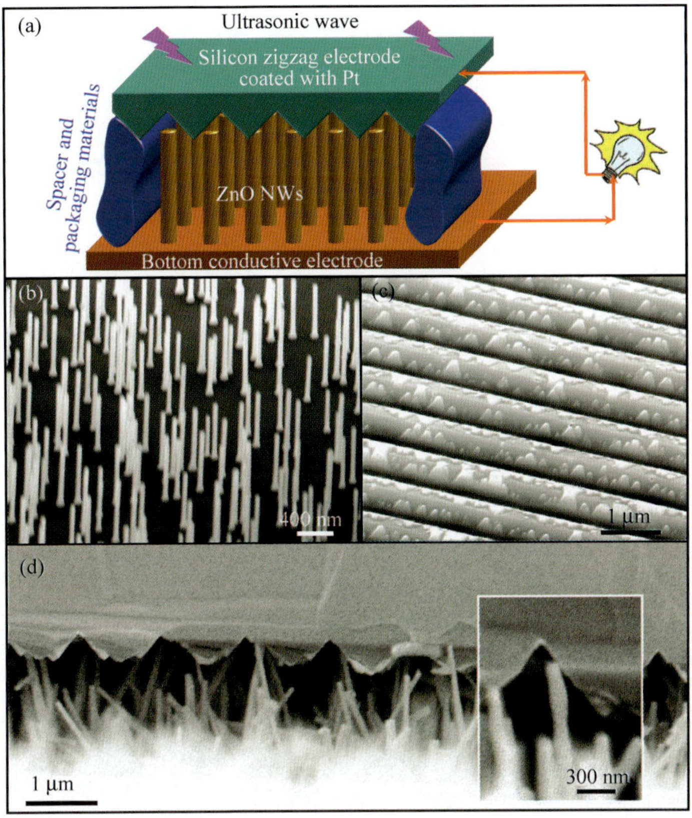

Figure 4.15 Nanogenerators driven by an ultrasonic wave. (a) Schematic diagram showing the design and structure of the nanogenerator. (b) Low-density aligned ZnO NWs grown on a GaN substrate. (c) Zigzag trenched electrode coated with Pt. (d) Cross-sectional SEM image of the nanogenerator; Inset: A typical NW that is forced by the electrode to bend

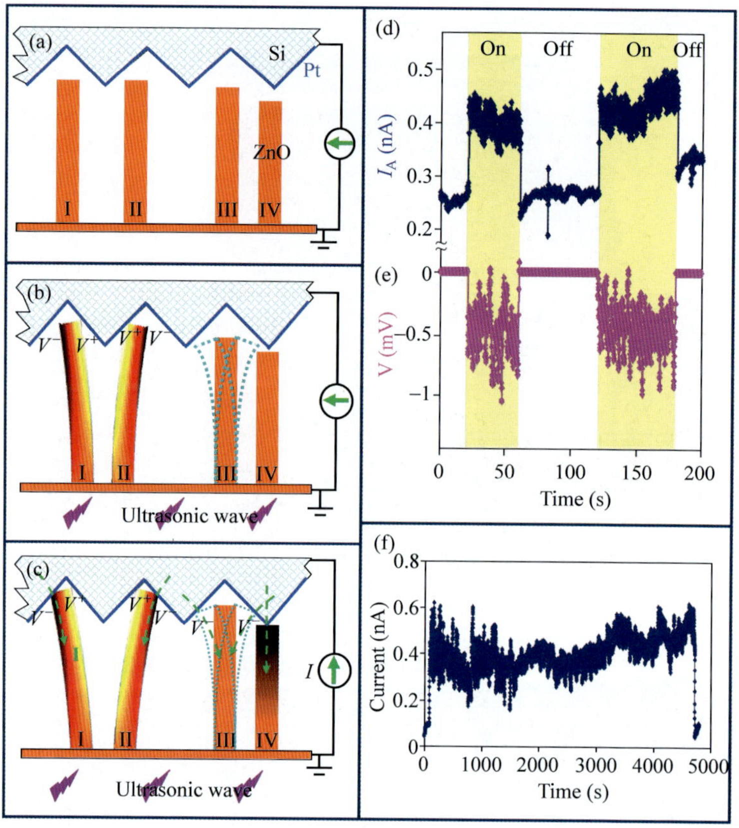

Figure 4.16 (a to c) The mechanism of the nanogenerator driven by an ultrasonic wave. (d, e) Current and voltage measured on the nanogenerator, respectively, when the ultrasonic wave was turned on and off. (f) Continuous current output of the nanogenerator for an extended period of time

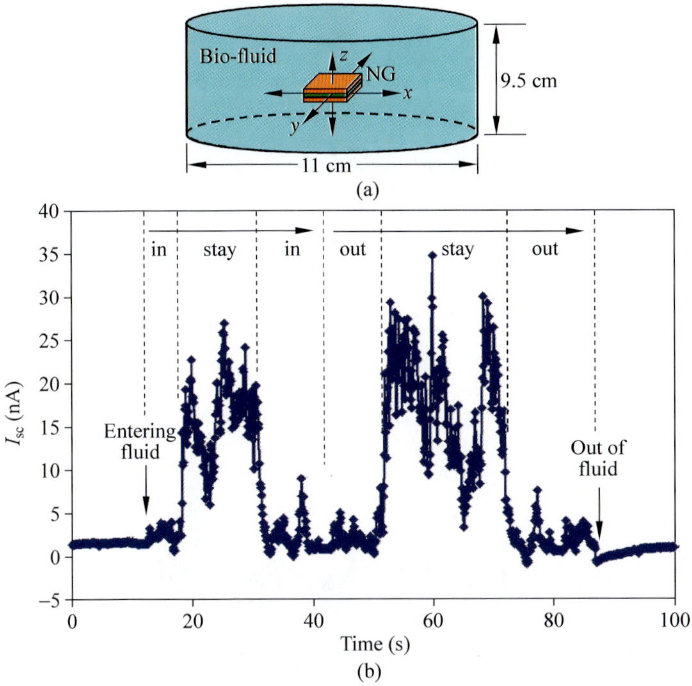

Figure 4.17 Enhanced output power by seeking the strong local intensity of the ultrasonic waves. (a) Schematic of the NG's position and moving directions inside a biofluid. (b) Short-circuit current signal measured during the movement of NG along the z direction (from water surface to the bottom and then back to the surface)

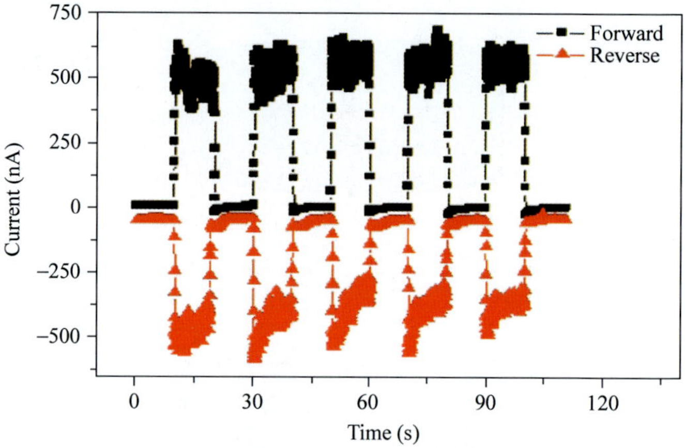

(a)

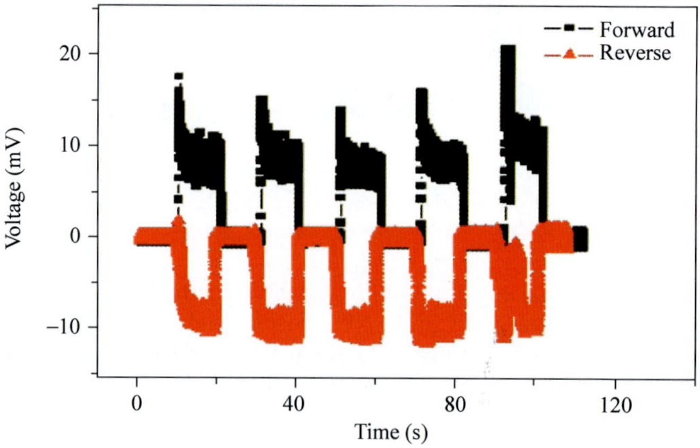

(b)

Figure 4.18 Performance of a high-output NG when periodically excited by an ultrasonic wave. (a) Closed circuit current output and (b) open circuit voltage output measured at forward polarity (dark line) and reversed polarity (red line) connection with the measurement system

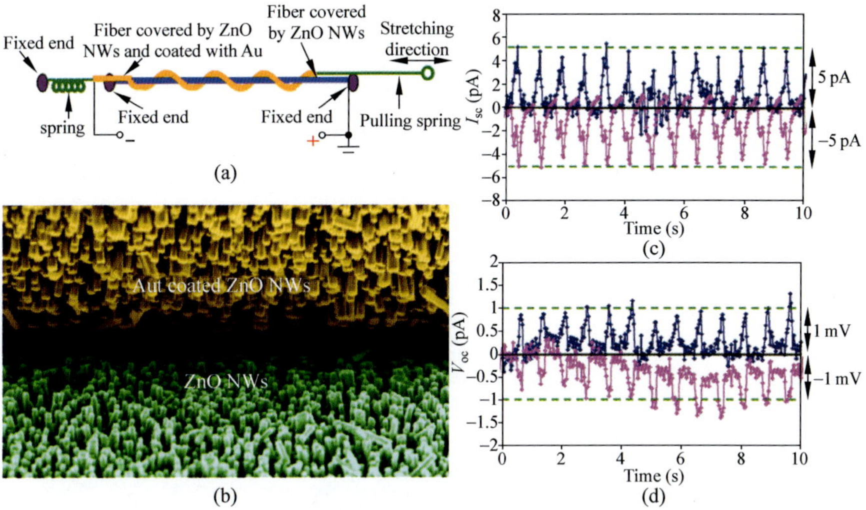

Figure 4.19 (a) Schematic experimental set-up of the fiber-based NG. (b) SEM image at the 'teeth-to-teeth' interface of two fibers covered by NWs with/without gold. (c, d) Isc and Voc of a double-fiber NG

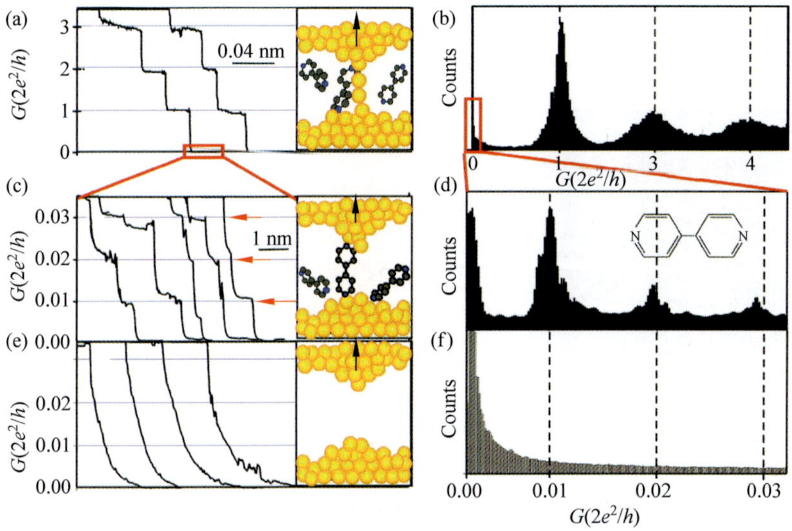

Figure 5.5 (a) conductance of a gold contact formed between a gold STM tip and a gold substrate decreases in quantum steps near multiples of G_0 as the tip is pulled away from the substrate; (b) a corresponding conductance histogram constructed from 1,000 conductance curves as shown in (a); (c) when the contact shown in (a) is completely broken, a new series of conductance steps appears if 4,4' bipyridine molecules are present in the solution. The steps are due to the formation of the stable molecular junction between the tip and the substrate electrodes; (d) a conductance histogram obtained from 1,000 measurements as shown in (c); (e) −(f) In the absence of molecules, no such steps or peaks are observed within the same conductance range. From Ref. [14]. Reprinted with permission from American Association for the Advancement of Science (AAAS)

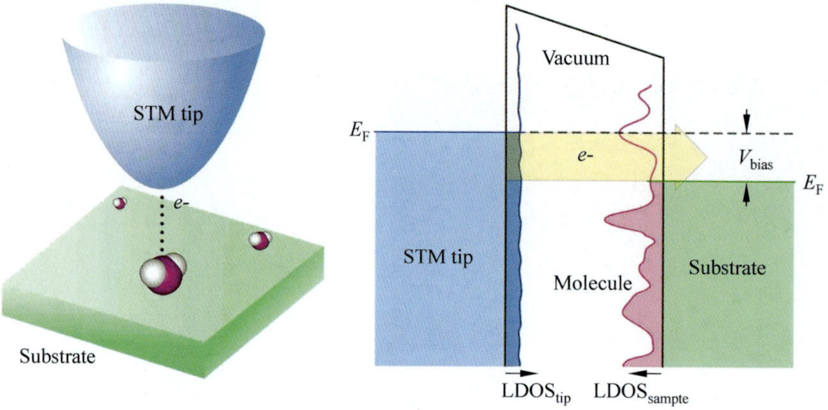

Figure 5.7 (a) Schematic view of single molecules chemisorbed on a substrate detected with an STM tip. (b) Schematic diagram of the STM tip with a constant DOS to probe the single adsorbed molecule with a featured DOS. The Fermi level of the adsorbed molecule is on the same energy of E_F of the substrate upon adsorption

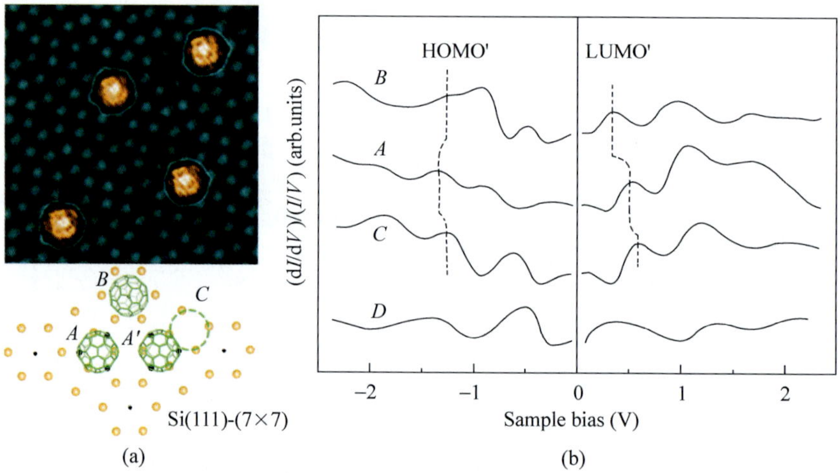

Figure 5.8 (a) STM image of individual C_{60} molecules adsorbed on a Si(111)-7×7 surface (upper) and the three adsorption sites. (b) d*I*/d*V* spectra measured over the three types of molecules and on a bare silicon surface (*D*)

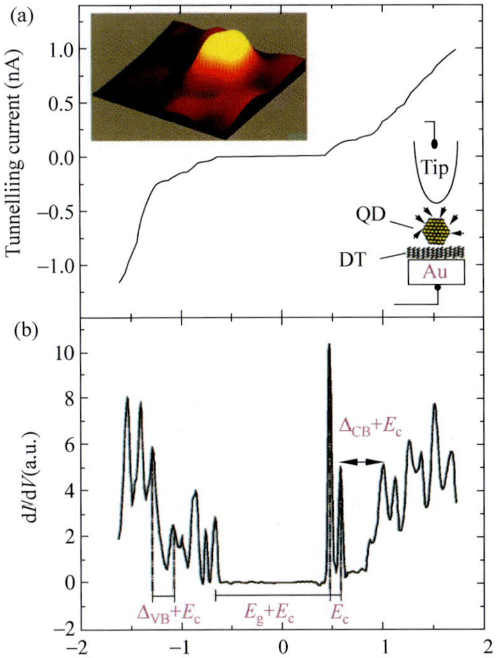

Figure 5.10 (a) STM topographic image of an InAs quantum dot and the tunneling $I\sim V$ characteristic, exhibiting single-electron tunneling effects. A schematic of the STM-based DBTJ system is also shown; (b) The tunneling conductance spectrum, dI/dV. Reprinted with permission from Macmillan Publishers Ltd: Nature (Ref.[25]), copyright 1999

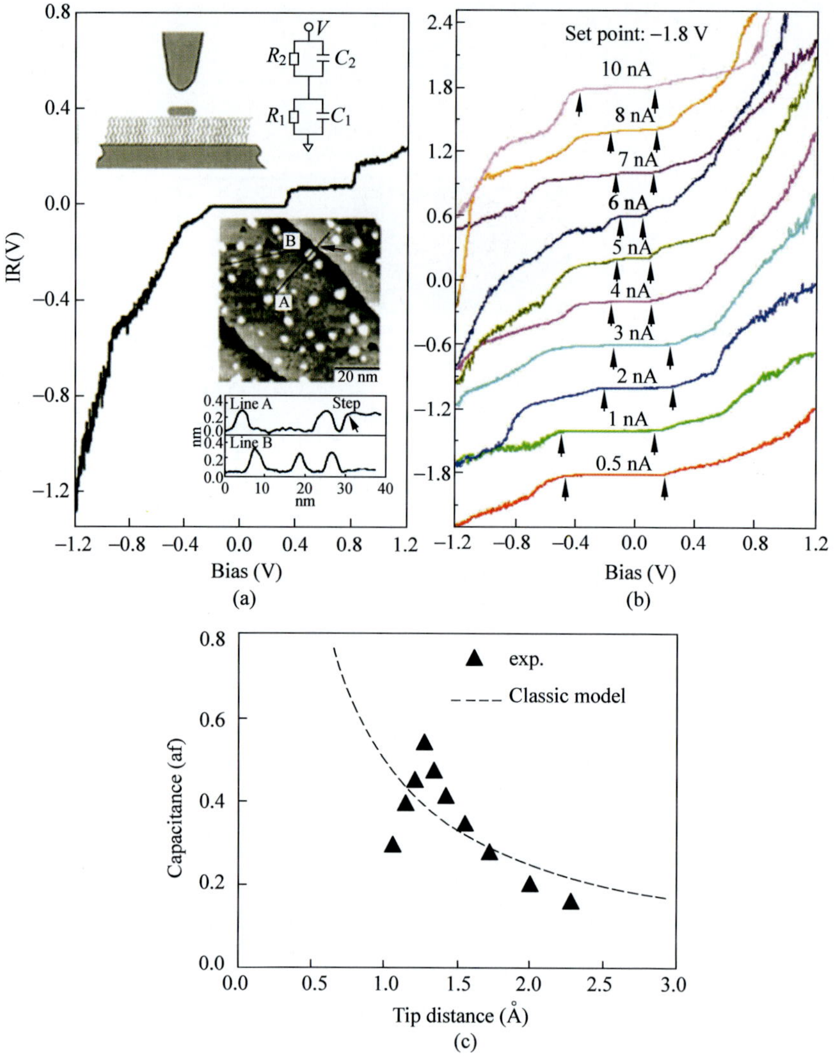

Figure 5.12 (a) a typical $I\sim V$ curve showing clearly the Coulomb blockade and Coulomb staircases. Inserts show the schematic of the DBTJ system consisting of a 2D nanoparticle and a typical STM image, (b) a series of $I\sim V$ curves taken at 5 K for a 4 nm Au cluster at different set point tunneling current. The CB width is indicated by arrows for each $I\sim V$ curve. The curves are shifted vertically for clarity, (c) the deduced capacitance C of the tip-cluster nanojunction as a function of tip-cluster separation d

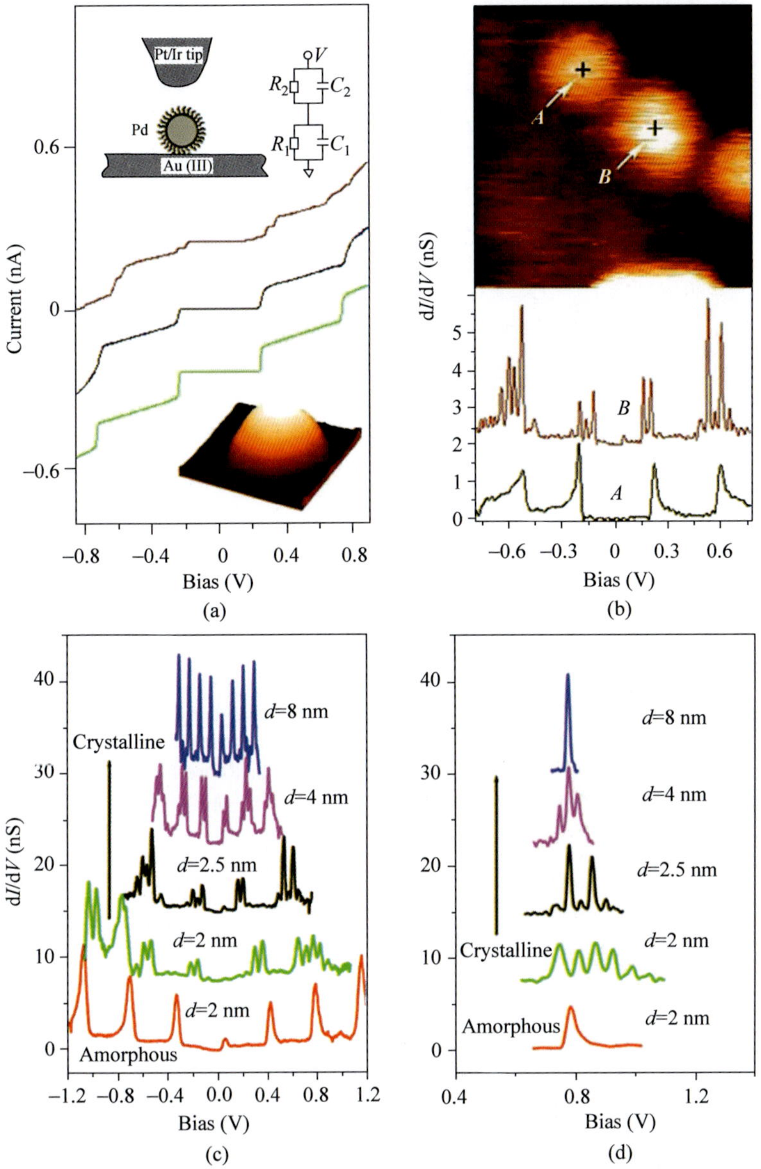

Figure 5.13 (a) curves 1 and 2 are typical $I \sim V$ curves for c-Pd and a-Pd particles, each about 2 nm in diameter. Curve 3 is a fitting curve using the orthodox theory by assuming the DOS is a constant. The top inset is a schematic of the STM DBTJ. The bottom inset is a $6 \times 6\ \text{nm}^2$ STM image, showing a Pd nanoparticle; (b) up panel: An STM image showing an a-Pd particle A and a c-Pd particle B; Down panel: dI/dV spectra acquired on particle A and particle B, respectively; (c) dI/dV spectra of c-Pd particles and an a-Pd particle. For clarity, curves are shifted vertically; (d) comparison of fine spectral features of the second CB steps for various particle size. Peaks are shifted in voltage coordinate

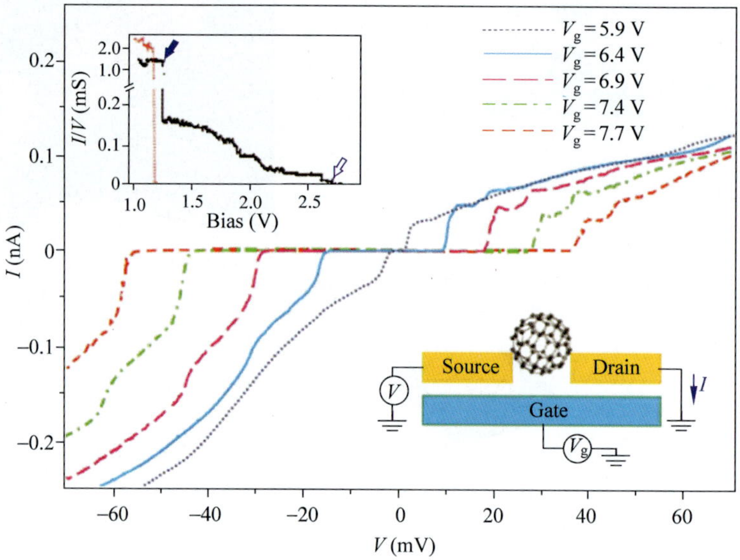

Figure 5.14 $I \sim V$ curves obtained from a single-C_{60} transistor at $T = 1.5$ K. Five $I \sim V$ curves taken at different gate voltages are shown. Upper inset: A large bias was applied between the electrodes while the current through the connected electrode was monitored (black solid curve). Lower inset shows an idealized diagram of a single C_{60} transistor formed by the electromigration method. Reprinted with permission from Macmillan Publishers Ltd: Nature (Ref. [32]), copyright 2000

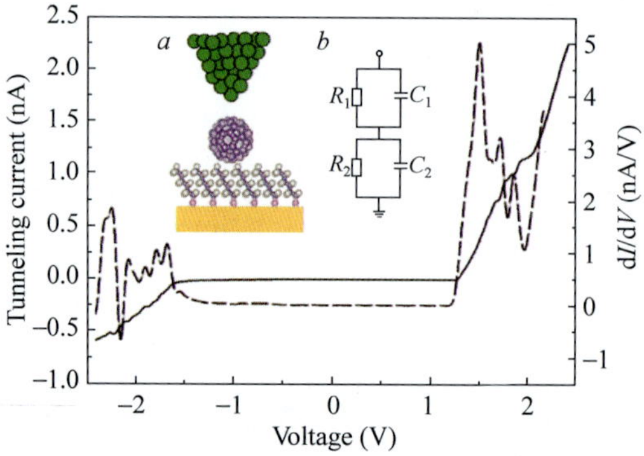

Figure 5.15 Scanning tunneling spectroscopy of a single C_{60} molecule in a DBTJ system. Dashed line is the dI/dV curve; solid line is the $I \sim V$ characteristic curve. (a and b) represent schematics of the DBTJ system and the corresponding equivalent circuit diagram

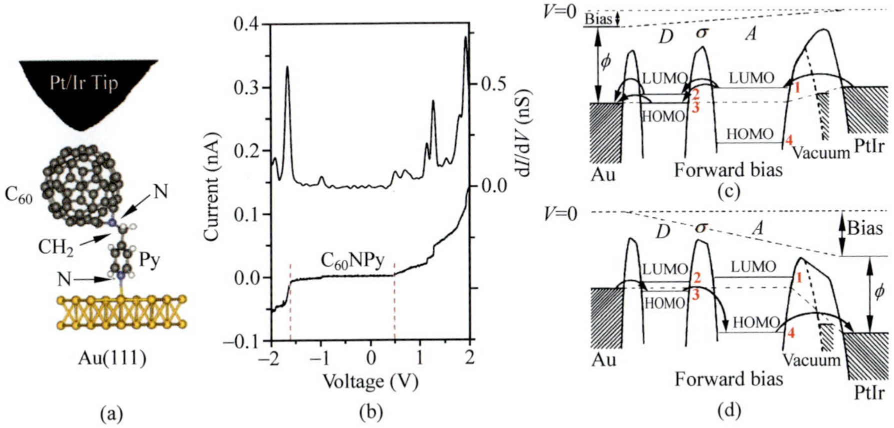

Figure 5.17 (a) Schematic drawing of the model of the C_{60}NPy on Au(111) surface. (b) *I-V* curve and its numerical d*I*/d*V* spectrum for C_{60}NPy measured at 5 K taken at a sample bias voltage of 2.0 V and a set-point current of 0.2 nA. (c), (d) Schematic drawings of the electron transport in C_{60}NPy for (c) forward bias and (d) reverse bias. The vacuum barriers in dashed lines denote the barriers at a higher feedback current

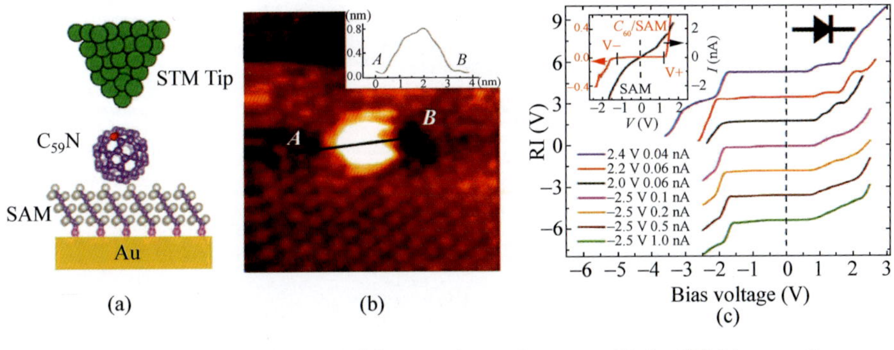

Figure 5.18 (a) the diagram of the experimental system. (b) the STM image of an isolated C_{59}N adsorbed on thiol SAM at 5 K. Inset shows line profile along the line AB. (c) a set of *I*~*V* curves for individual C_{59}N molecules measured at 5 K and at various setting parameters. The inset shows the *I*~*V* curves for the SAM substrate and individual C_{60} for comparison

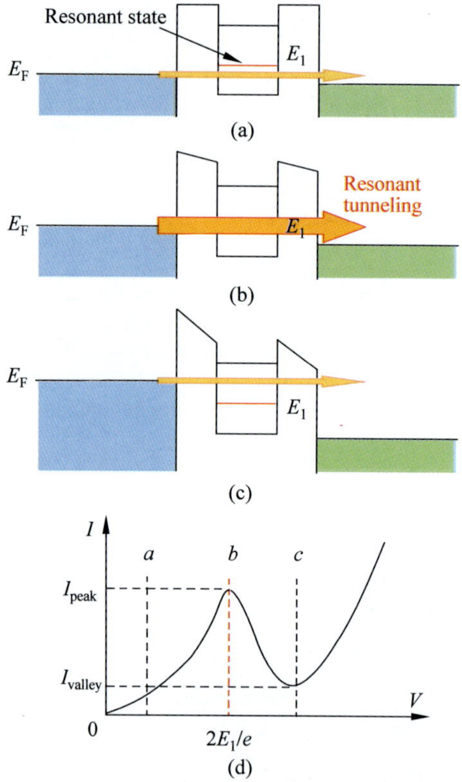

Figure 5.19 Schematic energy diagram (a, b, c) of the NDR effect in a DBTJ. (d) Schematic $I \sim V$ characteristics

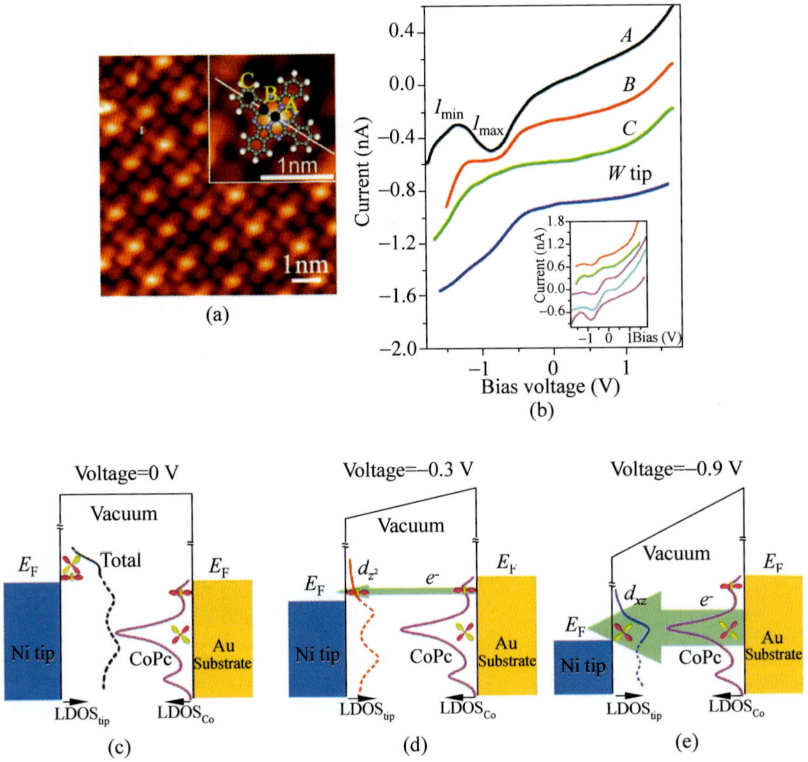

Figure 5.23 (a) An STM image of CoPc monolayer on a Au(111) surface. The inset in (a) is a magnified molecule image with a superimposed CoPc ball-stick sketch. (b) $I \sim V$ curves measured with the Ni tip over sites A, B, and C (marked in the inset of (a)), and with the W tip over site A. The inset in (b) shows results of five different Ni tips over site A. (c−e) The d orbitals of the Ni tip, (c) at the zero bias, not matching any of the Co orbitals, hence no current; (d) at −0.3 eV, interacting with the d_{z^2} orbitals of the Co atom, generating weak tunneling current; (e) at −0.9 V, matching the $d_{xz(yz)}$ orbitals of the Co atom, resulting in the strong NDR effect

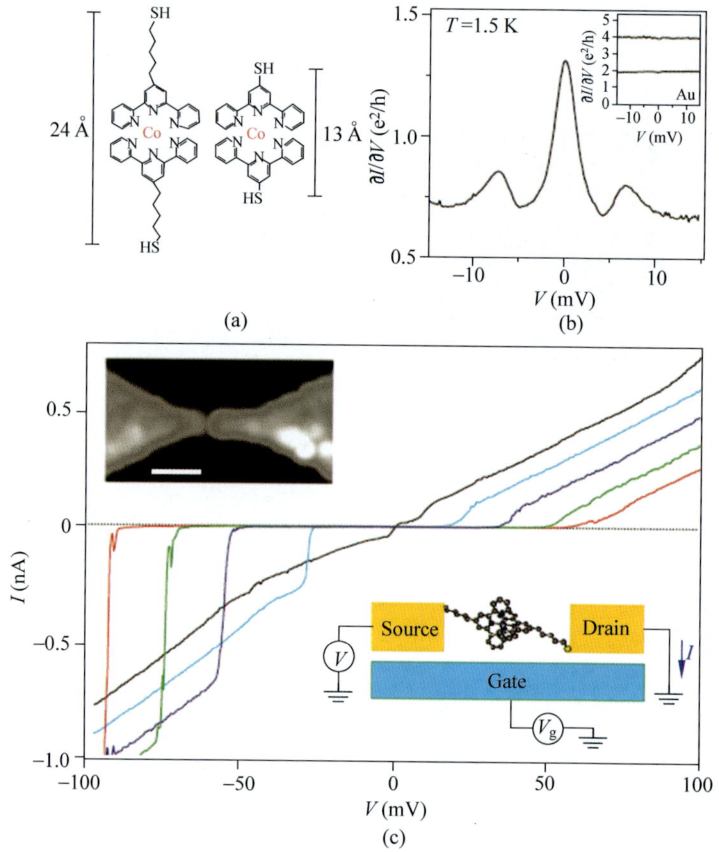

Figure 5.25 (a) Structure of $(Co(tpy\text{-}(CH_2)_5\text{-}SH)_2)^{2+}$ and $(Co(tpy\text{-}SH)_2)^{2+}$. (b) Differential conductance of a $(Co(tpy\text{-}SH)_2)^{2+}$ device at 1.5 K showing a Kondo peak. The inset shows dI/dV plots for bare gold point contacts for comparison. (c) $I \sim V$ curves of a $(Co(tpy\text{-}(CH2)_5\text{-}SH)_2)^{2+}$ single-molecule transistor at different gate voltages showing a Coulomb blockade behavior. Upper inset: A topographic atomic force microscope image of the electrodes with a gap (scale bar, 100 nm). Lower inset, a schematic diagram of the device. Reprinted with permission from Macmillan Publishers Ltd: Nature (Ref. [55]), copyright 2002

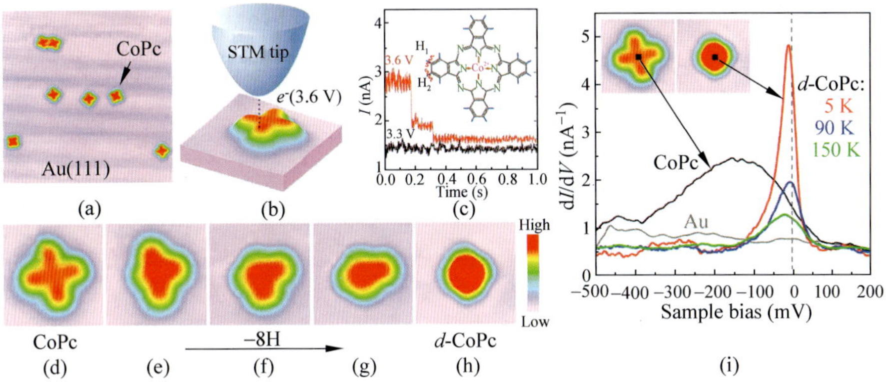

Figure 5.26 (a) individual CoPc molecules adsorbed on Au(111) surface. (b) diagram of the dehydrogenation induced by the tunneling electrons. (c) current traces during two different voltage pulses on the brink of one lobe. Inset shows the molecular structure of CoPc and the two hydrogen atoms to be pruned off in each one lobe. (d) – (h) STM images of a single CoPc molecule during each step of the dehydrogenation process, from (d) an intact CoPc to (h) a d-CoPc. The color scale represents apparent heights, ranging from 0 Å (low) to 2.7 Å (high). (i) dI/dV spectra measured directly over center Co atoms of *d*-CoPc showing strong Kondo resonances near the Fermi level. Two spectra for CoPc and bare Au surface are presented for comparison

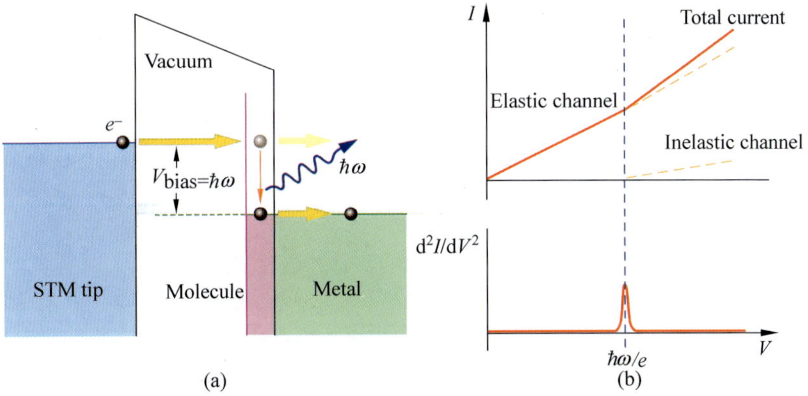

Figure 5.27 (a) Schematic energy diagram of IETS. (b) I–V and d^2I/dV^2 characteristics of IETS

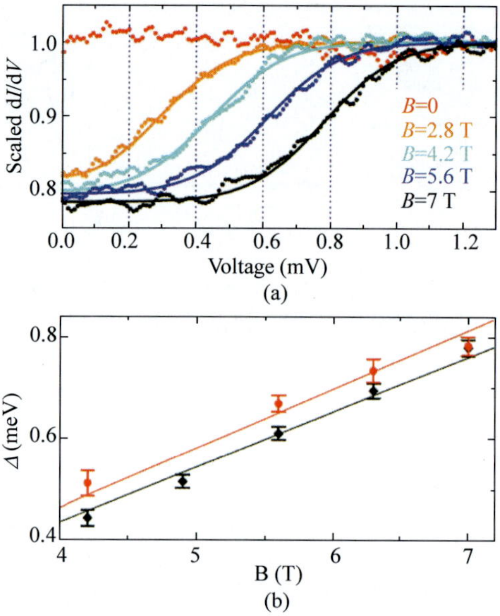

Figure 5.28 (a) conductance spectra (points) for an isolated Mn atom on oxide at different magnetic fields. (b) magnetic field dependence of the Zeeman energy Δ. Black points are extracted from the fits in (a), and red points were taken on a Mn atom near the edge of an oxide patch. Linear fits (black and red lines) constrained to $\Delta=0$ at $B=0$ yield g values of 1.88 and 2.01, respectively. From Ref. [62]. Reprinted with permission from AAAS

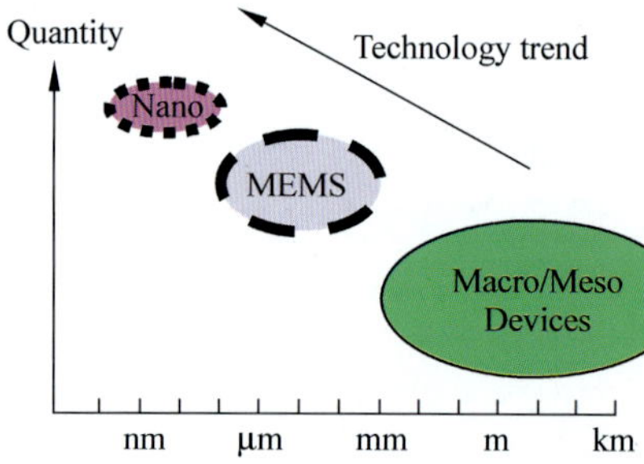

Figure 6.1 The size ranges for various devices and the technology trend

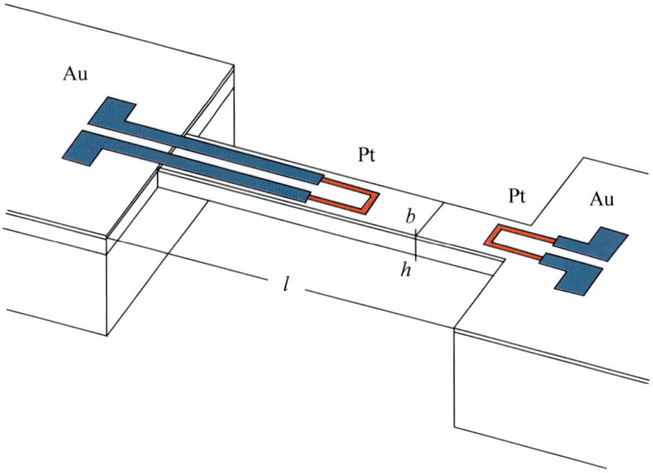

Figure 7.5 Schematic of a beam resonator

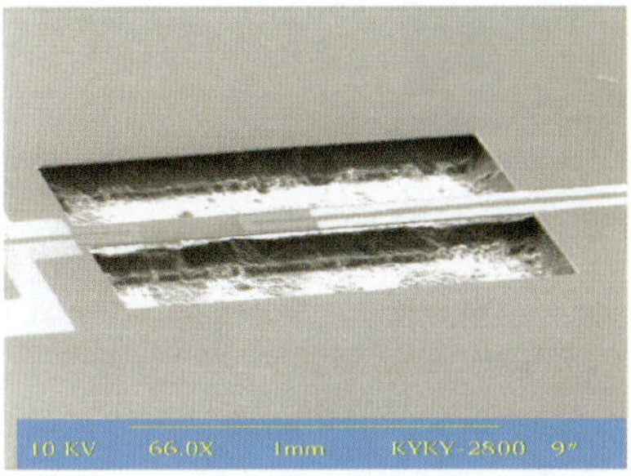

Figure 7.6 SEM photograph of a SiN beam resonator

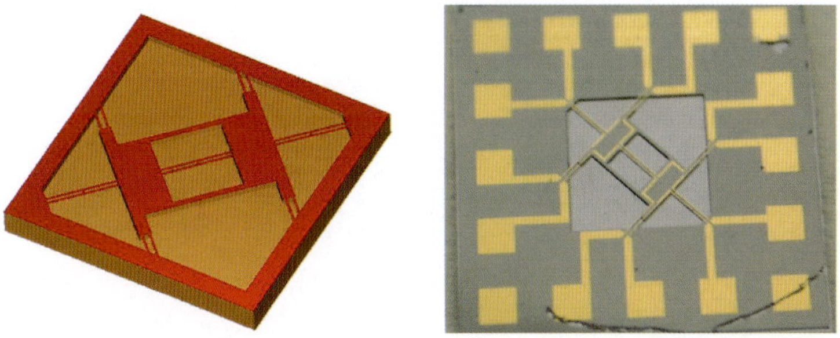

(a) (b)

Figure 7.8 Schematic (a) and photograph (b) of an electromagnetically excited resonant pressure sensor

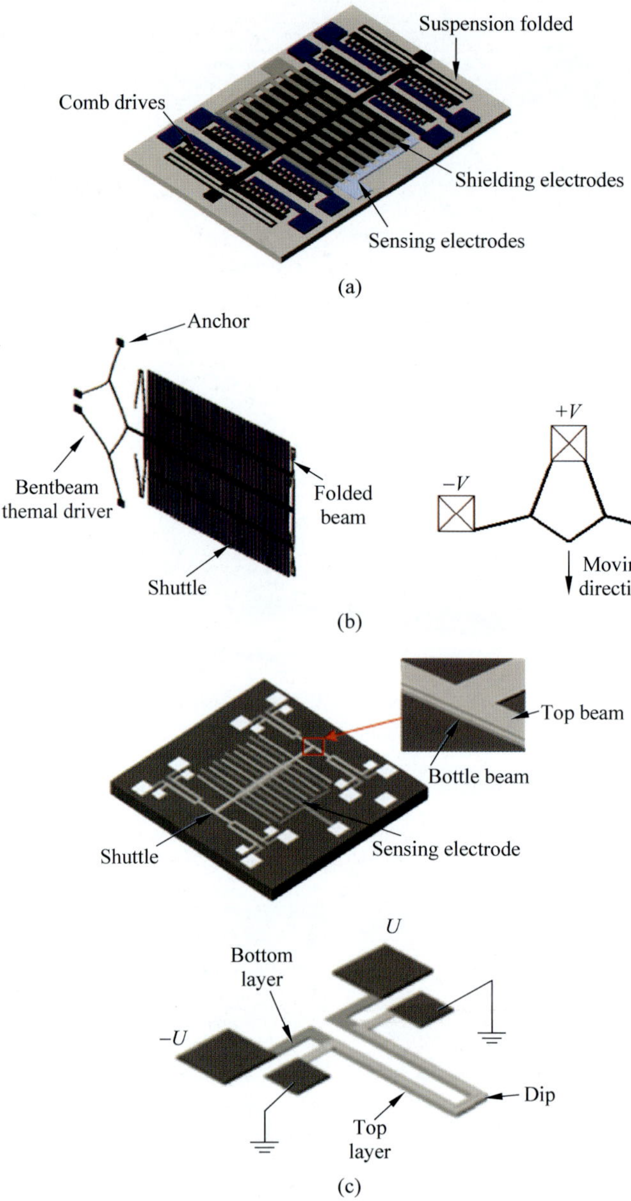

Figure 7.15 The schematic structure of the EFS (a) electrostatic comb-driven lateral vibration type (b) thermally driven lateral vibration type (c) thermally driven vertical vibration type

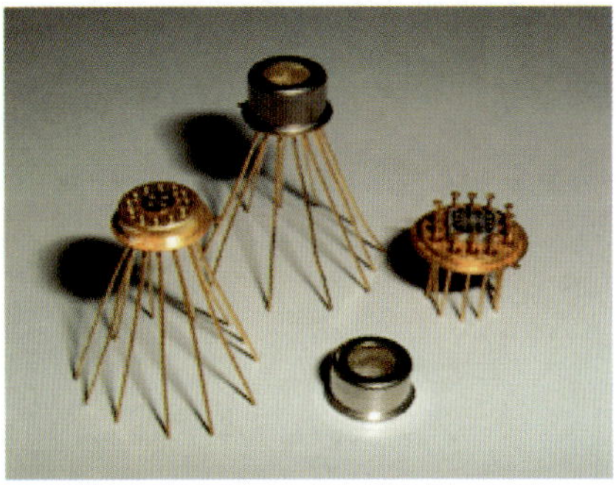

Figure 7.23 Encapsulated microgas sensor array

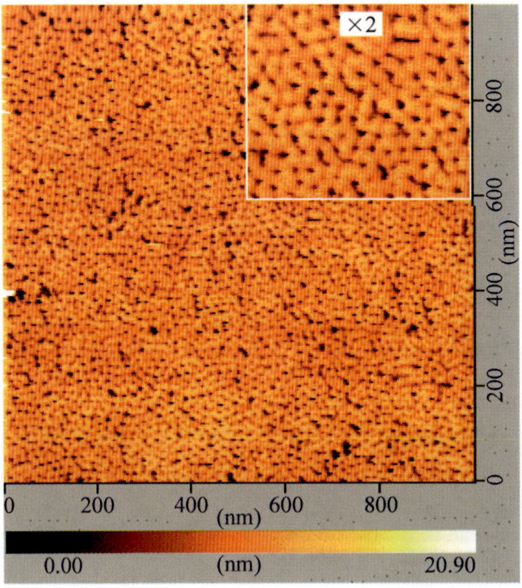

Figure 7.30 AFM image of the open-pore mesoporous TiO_2 thin film

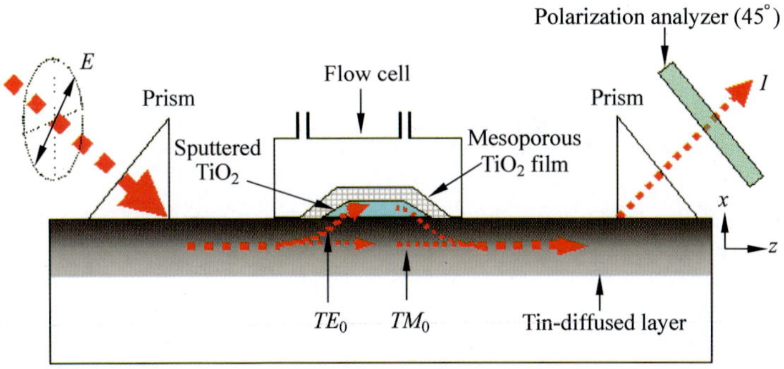

Figure 7.31 Single-beam PI sensor constructed with the planar composite waveguides

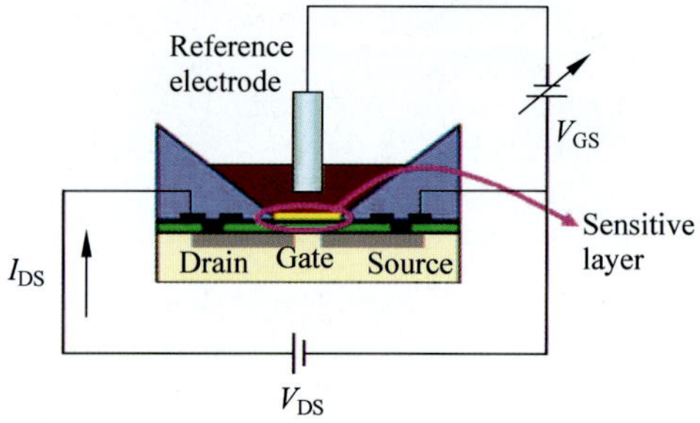

Figure 7.37 Schematic diagram of an ISFET

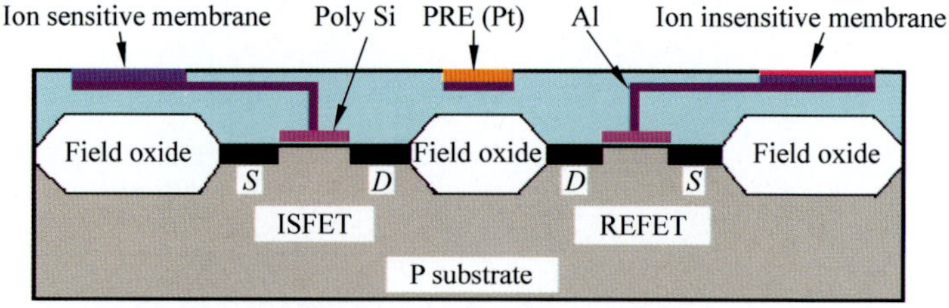

Figure 7.38 Schematic diagram of the differential pH sensor

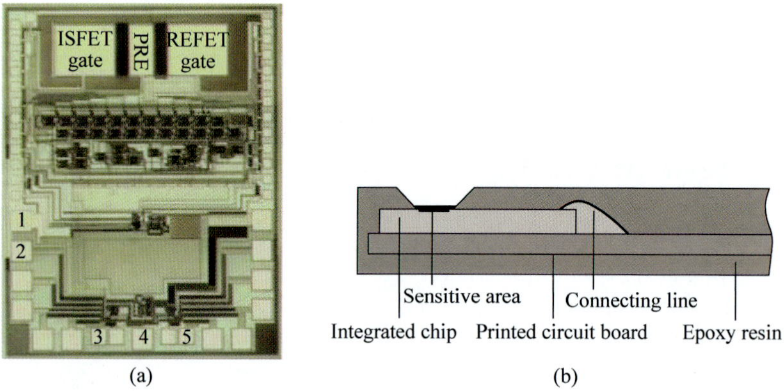

Figure 7.39 (a) Photograph of the chip and (b) schematic diagram of the encapsulated chip

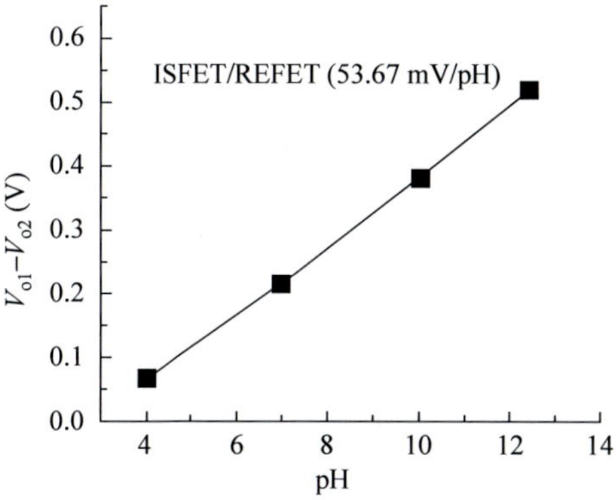

Figure 7.40 Sensitivity of ISFET

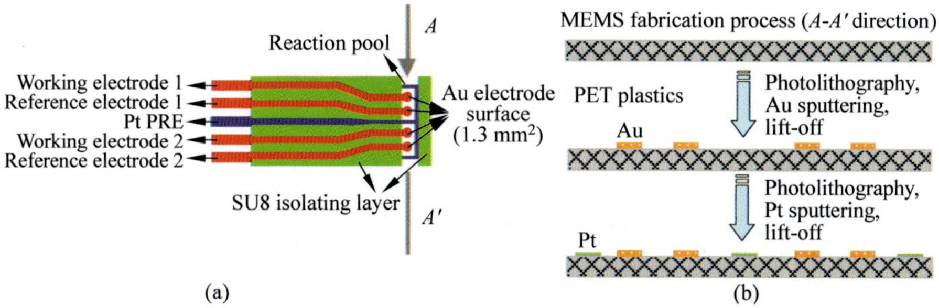

Figure 7.42 Schematic diagrams of (a) the electrode chip of the immunosensor and (b) the MEMS fabrication process

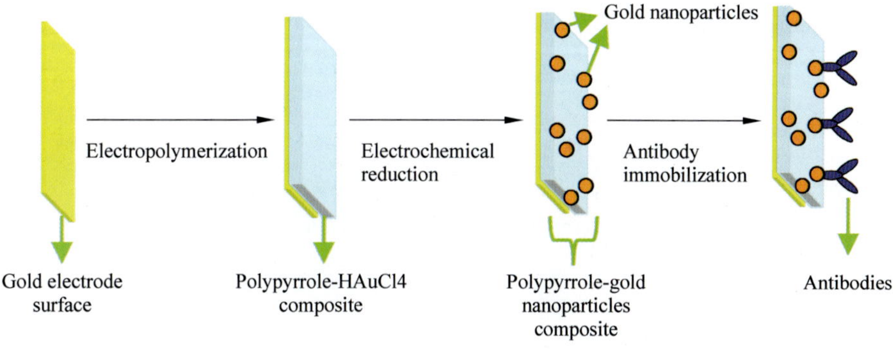

Figure 7.43 Schematic diagrams of the electrochemical synthesis of PPy-AuNPs composite and the antibody immobilization strategy

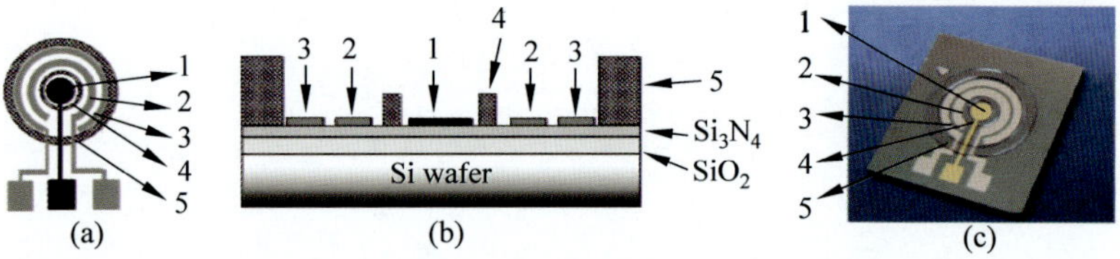

1. Working electrode (Au); 2. Counter electrode (Pt); 3. Reference electrode (Pt);
4. Immuno-reaction pool (SU-8); 5. Electrochemical reaction pool (SU-8).

Figure 7.47 Structural design of the microelectrode (a) top view; (b) cross section view; (c) Photograph of the micro immunosensor (8 mm × 8 mm)

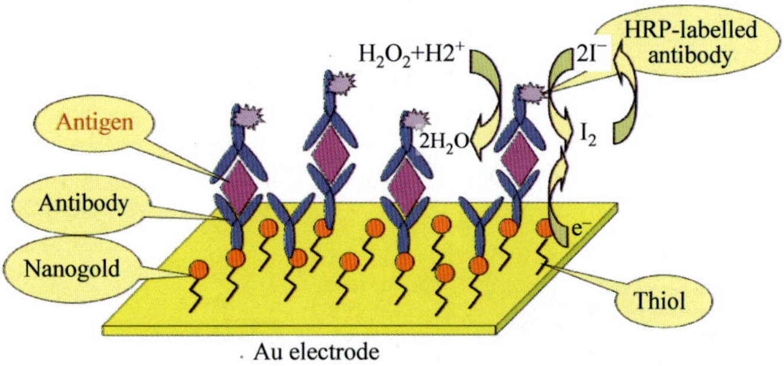

Figure 7.48 Antibody immobilization strategy: using nanogold and PA for the orientation-controlled immobilization of antibody with mixed SAMs technologies

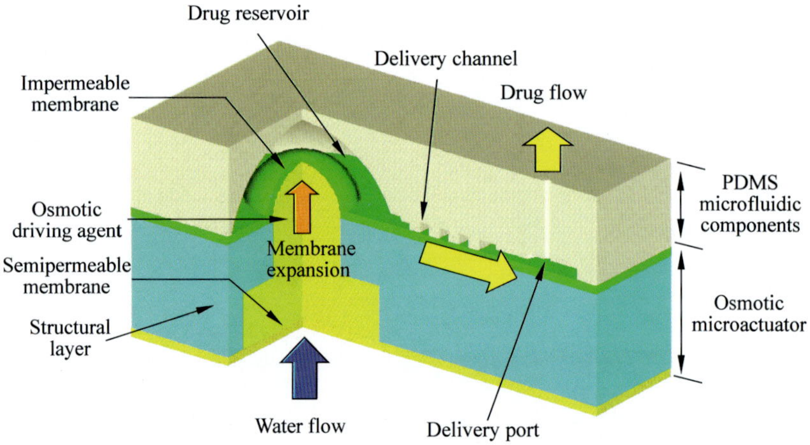

Figure 8.5 A schematic diagram of the micro drug delivery system

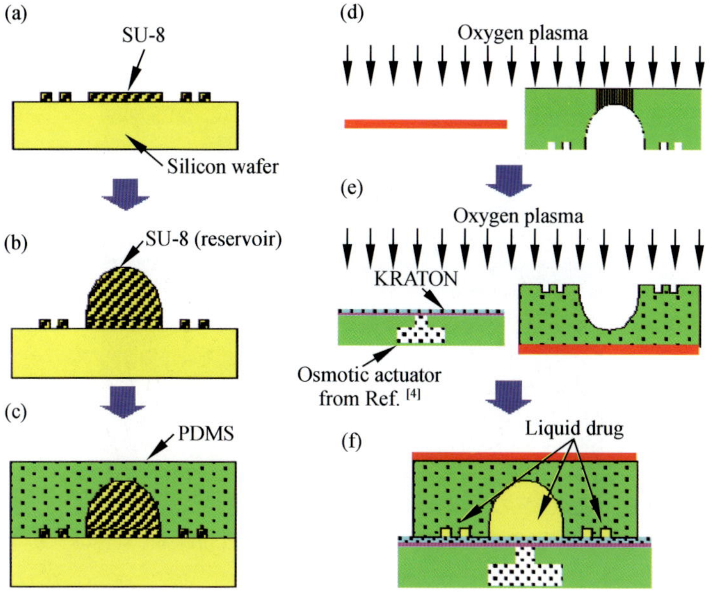

Figure 8.6 Fabrication process of the micro drug delivery system

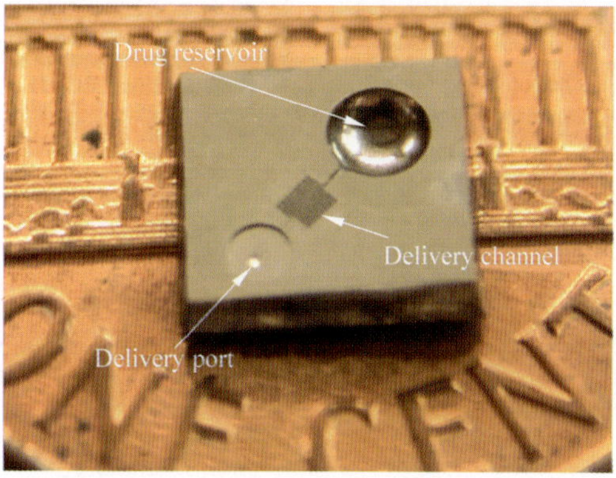

Figure 8.8 The water-powered drug delivery system pictured with a one-cent coin showing the drug reservoir and drug delivery port

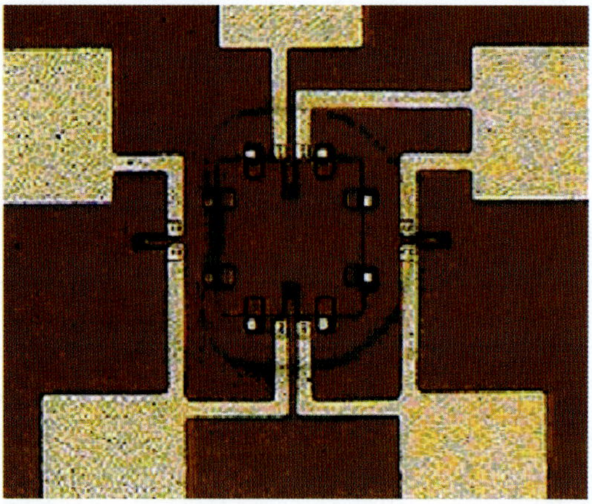

Figure 8.15 Optical photo of a fabricated pressure sensor

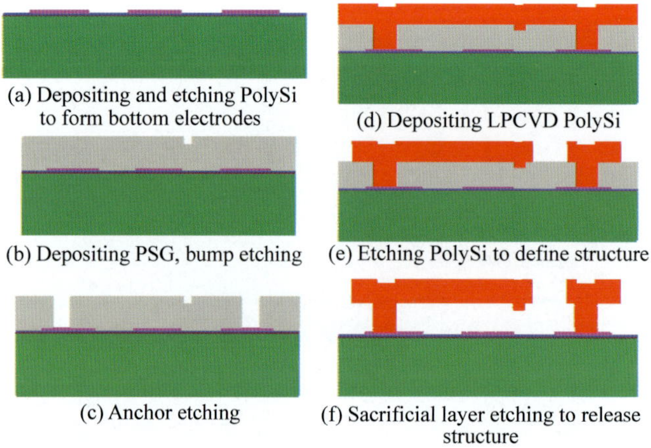
(a) Depositing and etching PolySi to form bottom electrodes
(d) Depositing LPCVD PolySi
(b) Depositing PSG, bump etching
(e) Etching PolySi to define structure
(c) Anchor etching
(f) Sacrificial layer etching to release structure

Figure 9.1 The basic process sequence of silicon surface sacrificial layer technology

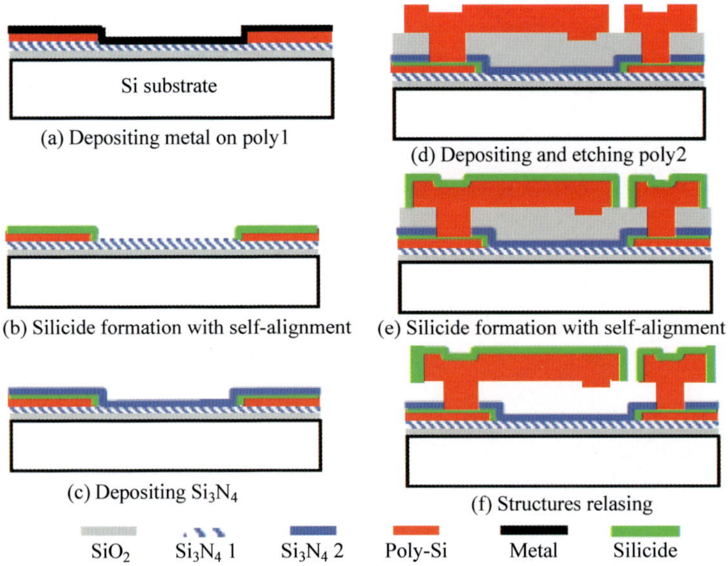

Figure 9.5 Surface micromachining process flow using silicide on both Poly0 and Poly1[44]

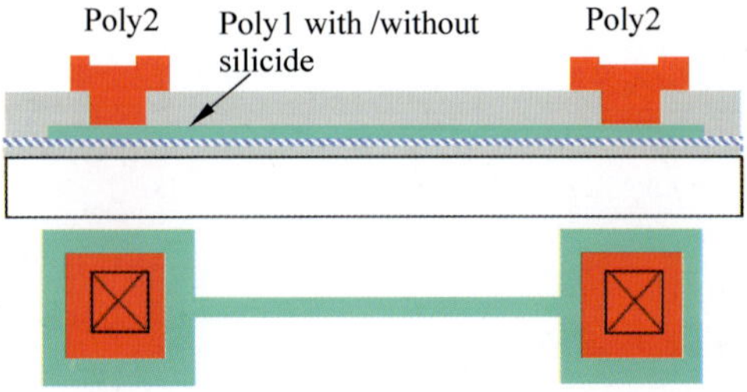

Figure 9.6 Structure to test series resistance of Poly0 (with/without $CoSi_2$) and contact resistance between Poly1 and Poly0 (with/without $CoSi_2$)[44]

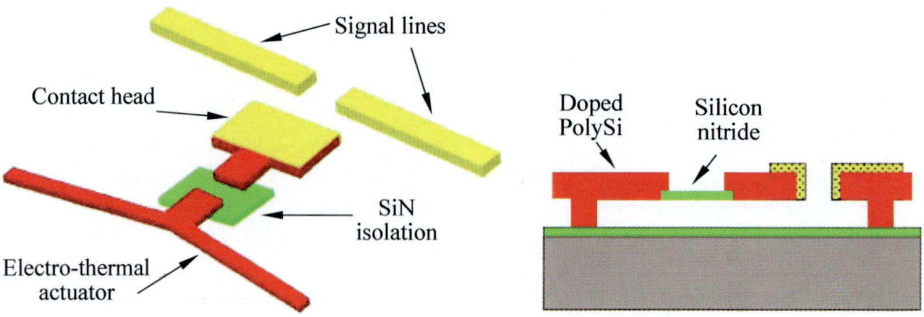

Figure 9.15 A thermal actuated lateral switch with nitride film as the isolation structure[51]

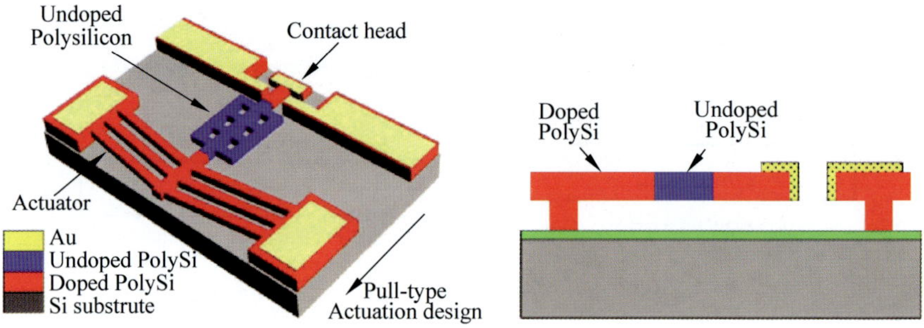

Figure 9.18 a modified thermal actuated lateral switch using undoped polysilicon as isolation structure[49]

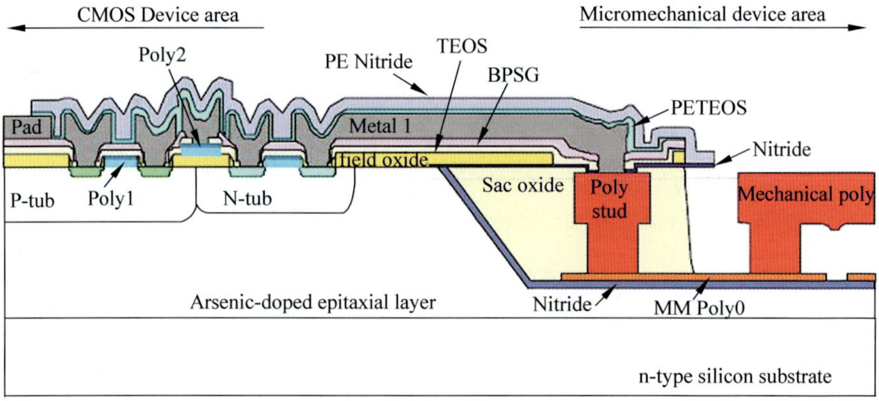

Figure 9.24 Sectional schematic diagram of Pre-CMOS integration technology developed by Sandia (© Sandia National Lab)

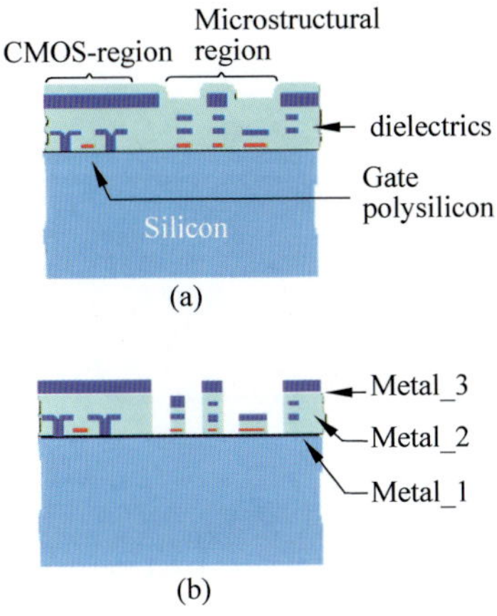

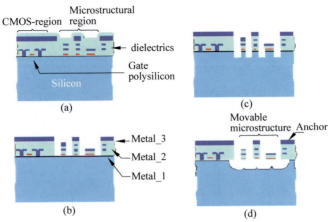

Figure 9.25 Basic process sequence chart of CMOS MEMS technology[69] (© 1996 Elsevier)

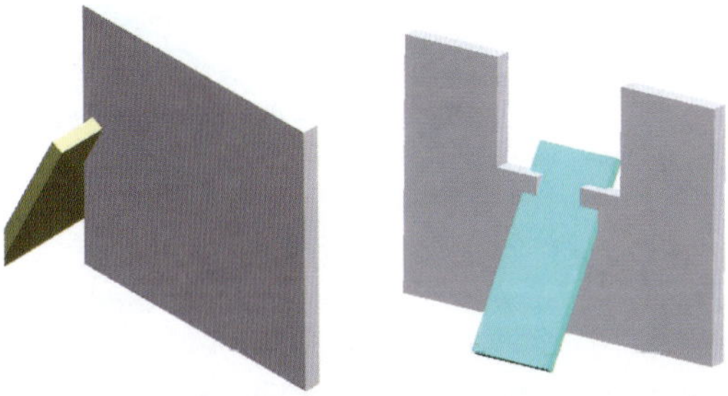

Figure 9.28 Applying latches to fix the off-plate structure

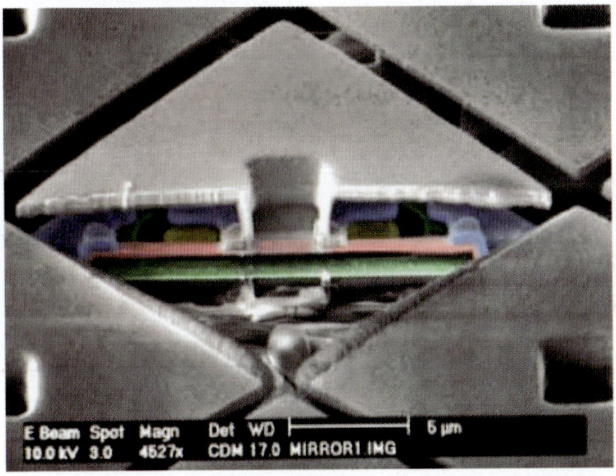

Figure 9.32 Ion mill sectioning of DMD pixel to reveal cross section[82] (© 1996 IEEE)

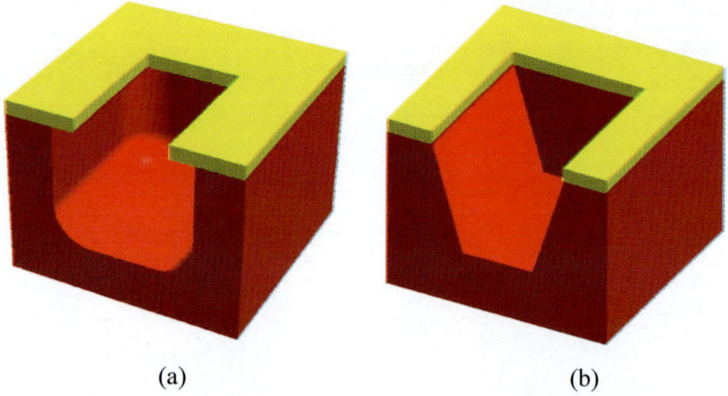

Figure 9.36 Comparison of isotropic: (a) and anisotropic, (b) wet etching of silicon

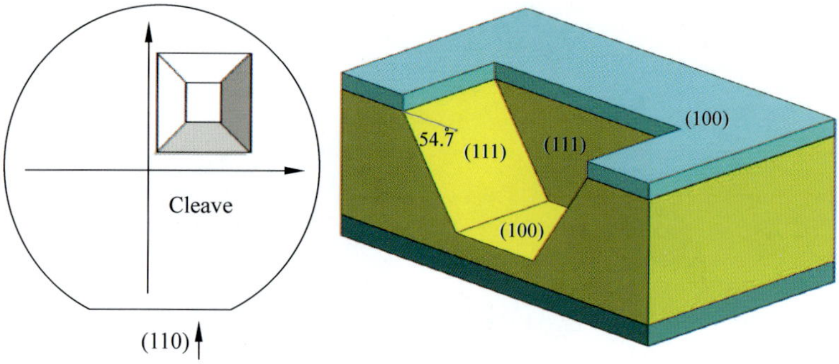

Figure 9.37 Illustration of the anisotropic etching performance of (100) silicon

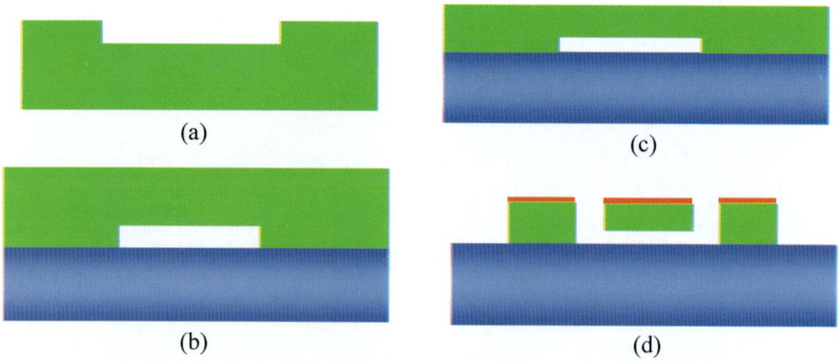

Figure 9.40 Schematic illustration of basic SOG process flow, (a) shallow trench etching, (b) silicon/glass anodic bonding, (c) silicon wafer thinning, (d) deep trench etching to release structure

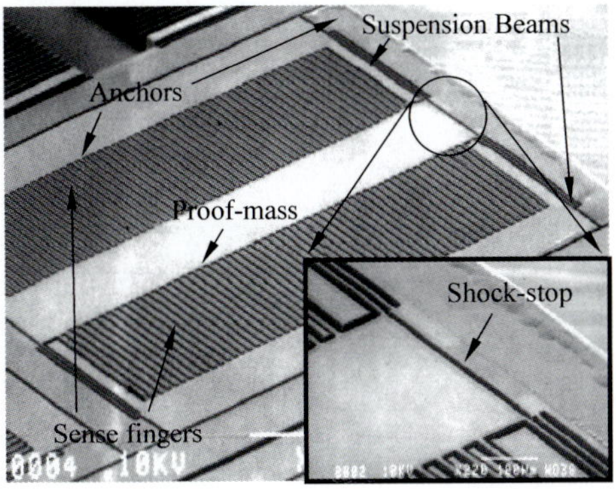

Figure 9.42 Top view of fabricated SOG accelerometer and shock stop[102] (© 1999 IEEE)

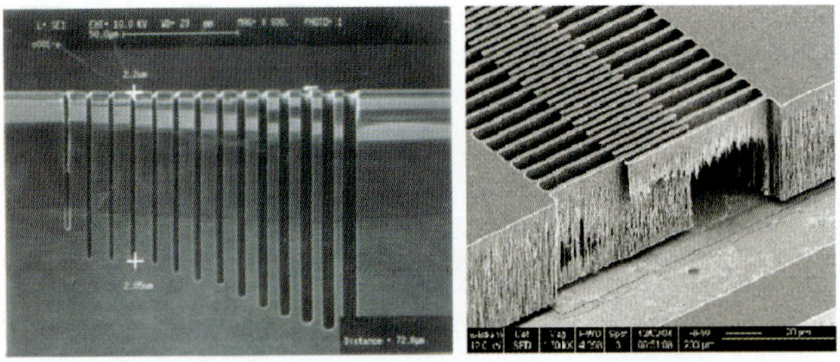

(a) (b)

Figure 9.43 Two important effects in the DRIE process. (a) Lag effect in DRIE Process[133], (b) Footing effect in DRIE process (© 2004 IOP)

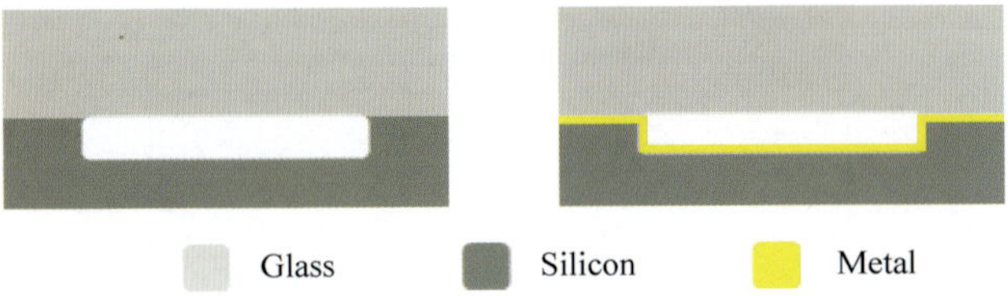

Figure 9.44 Illustration of a shielding metal layer between silicon and glass substrate, which can reduce the footing effect

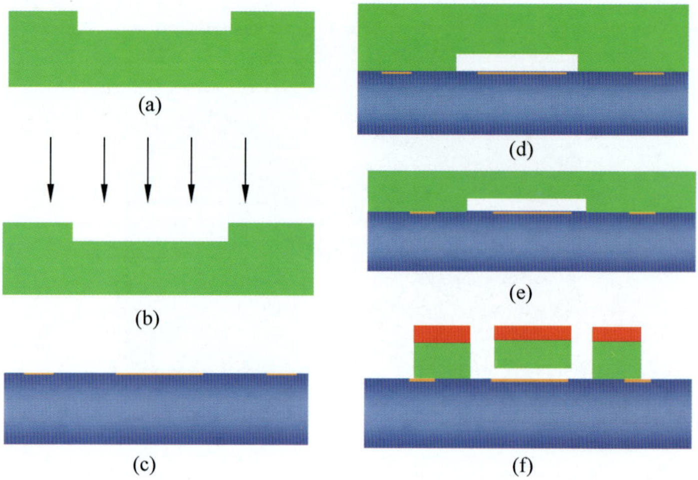

Figure 9.47 A typical SOG process with interconnection on the glass substrate, (a) shallow trench etching, (b) surface doping, (c) life-off to form electrodes, (d) silicon/glass anodic bonding, (e) silicon wafer thinning, (f) deep trench etching to release structure

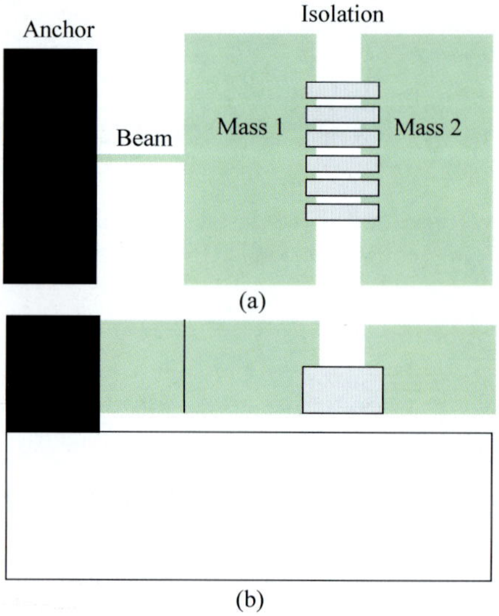

Figure 9.48 A schematic drawing of an isolation structure. A movable microstructure (marked as Mass 1) is linked to a bonded anchor by a flexible beam, while the microstructure is linked to another microstructure (marked as Mass 2) by an isolation structure: (a) is the top view and (b) is cross section view[148]

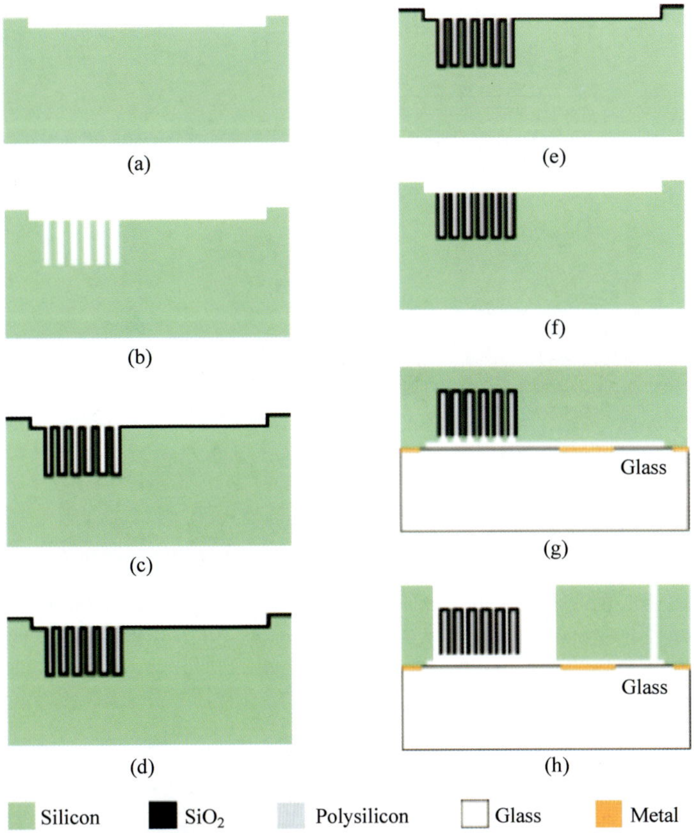

Figure 9.49 The process sequence to achieve the mechanical microstructures with isolation structures[148]

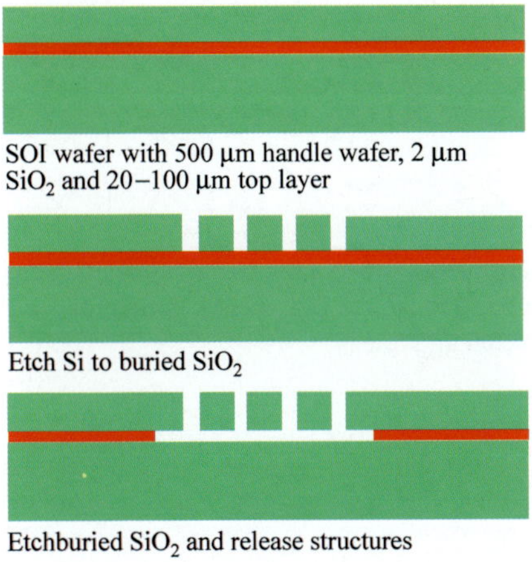

Figure 9.52 Basic SOI-MEMS process flow

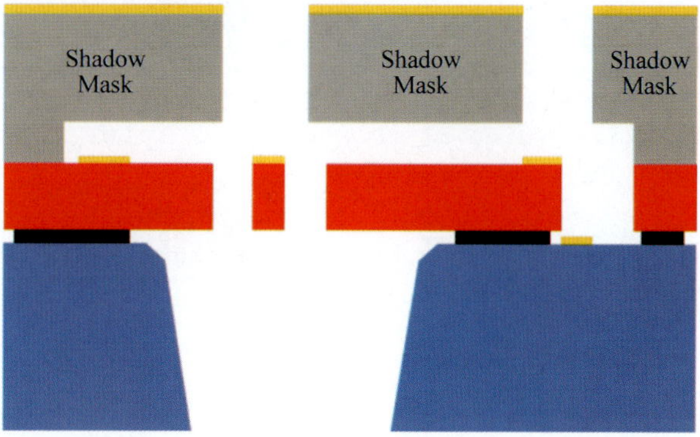

Figure 9.55 The shadow mask is aligned and temporarily bonded to the SOI wafer. The Metal layer, consisting of 50 nm Cr and 600 nm Au, is deposited through the shadow mask (© MEMSCap)

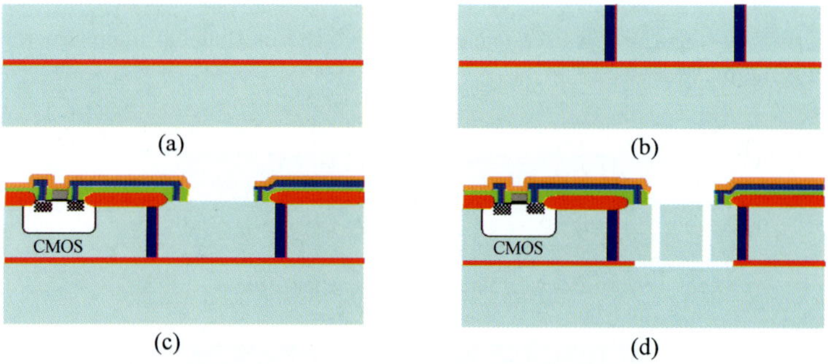

Figure 9.60 The schematic flow of a sacrificial layer technique with SOI substrate, (a) starting SOI wafer, (b) isolation trenches formation, (c) circuit fabrication, (d) MEMS structure etch and release

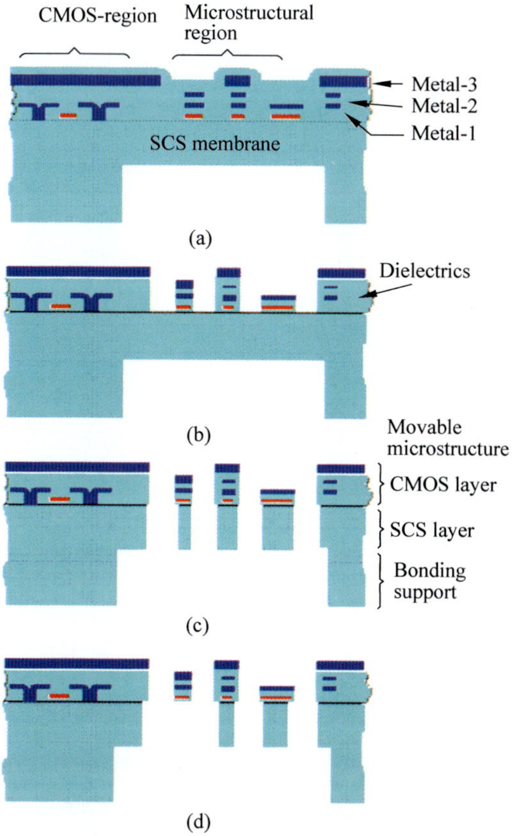

Figure 9.63 DRIE CMOS MEMS process flow (© 2002 IEEE)

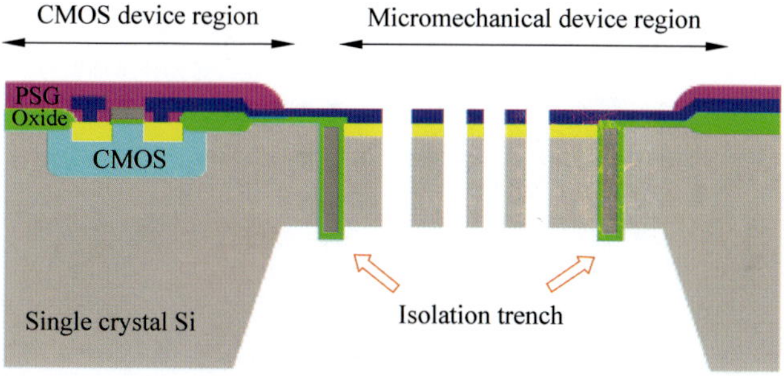

Figure 9.66 A cross-section scheme of the high-aspect-ratio MEMS sensor with CMOS circuits

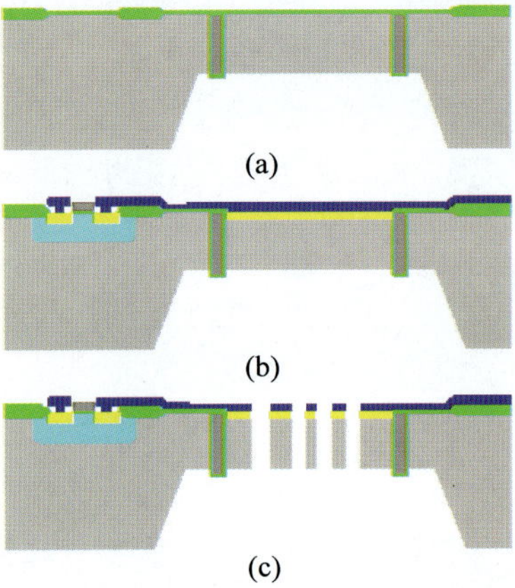

Figure 9.67 The process flow of IBMURIT

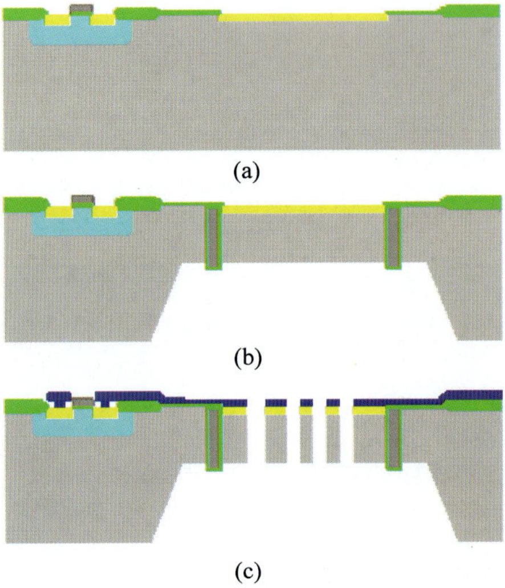

Figure 9.68 The alternative process flow of IBMURIT

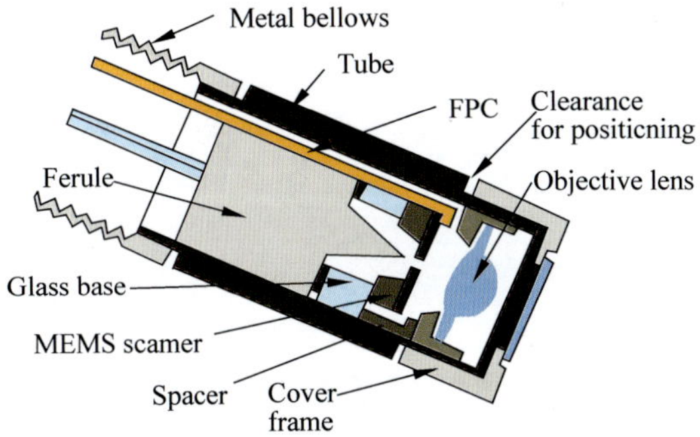

Figure 10.9 A cross sectional drawing of the endoscope head (© 2003 IEEE Picture courtesy of Olympus Optical Company, Ltd. Print from [32] with permission)

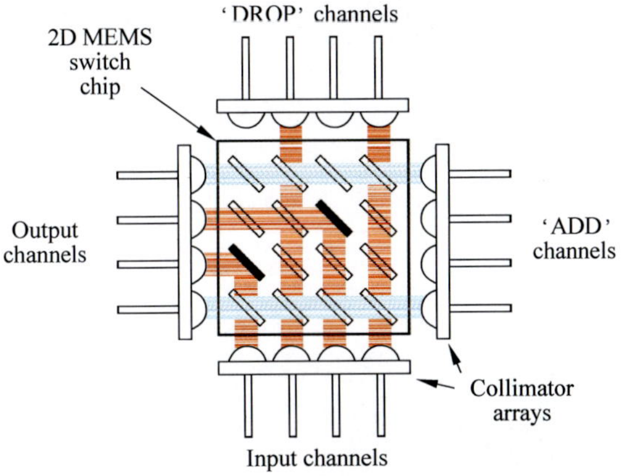

Figure 10.19 Schematic of 2D MEMS optical switches

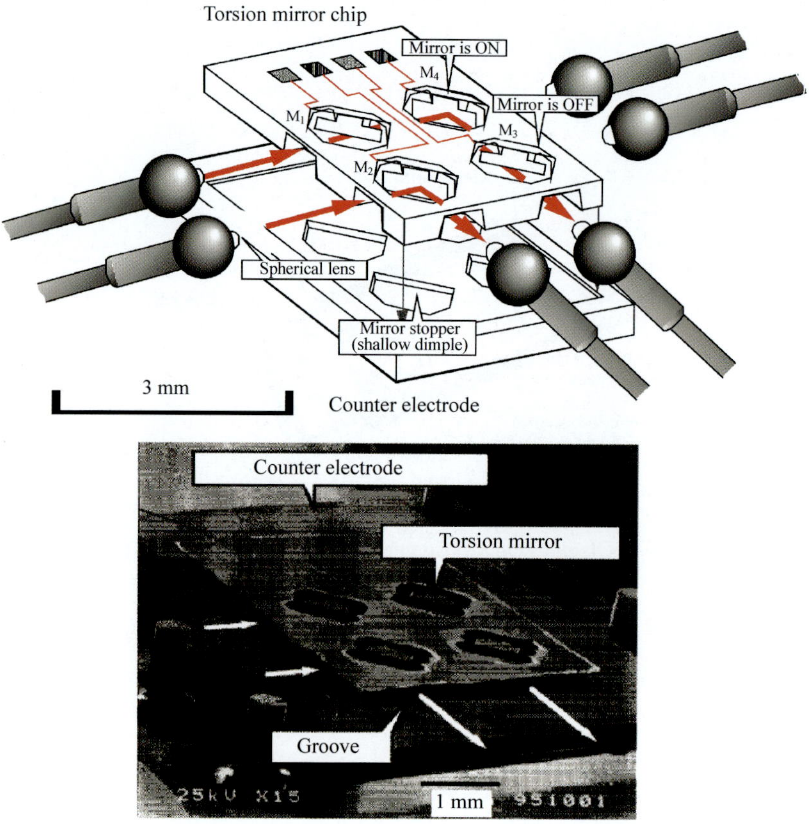

Figure 10.20 Schematic and SEM of bulk-micromachined 2D switch with free-rotating torsion mirrors (© 1999 IEEE Pictures courtesy of Hiroshi Toshiyoshi. Reprinted from [55] with permission)

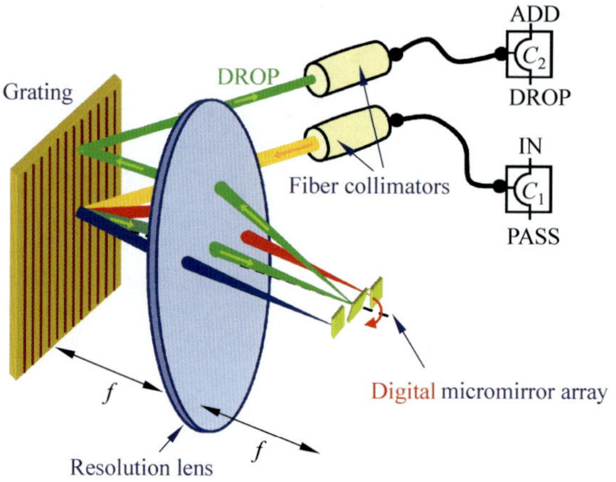

Figure 10.30 Concept of WADM

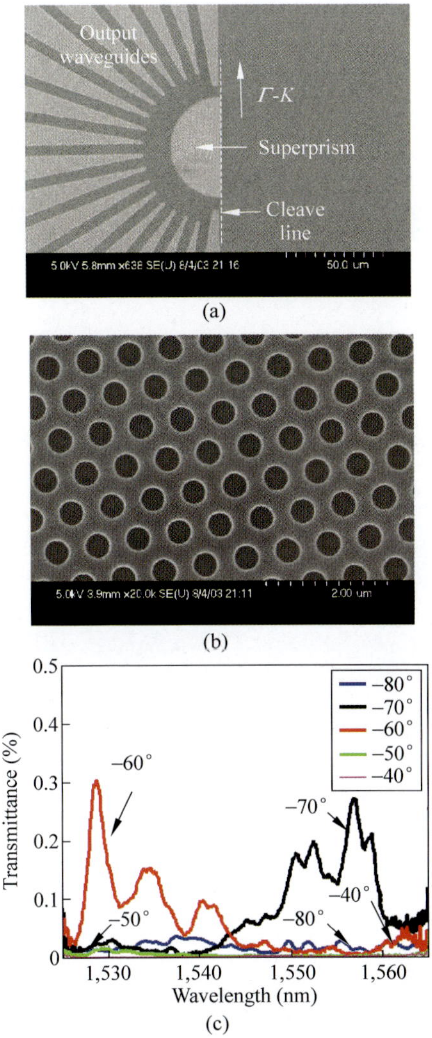

Figure 10.51 (a) SEM of the semicircular PC superprism and surrounding output waveguides, (b) Top view (SEM) of the hexagonal PC lattice, and (c) Transmittance spectra of output light from different waveguides at 12° incident angle. (© 2004 OSA Pictures courtesy of Jin Yao. Reprinted from [157] with permission)

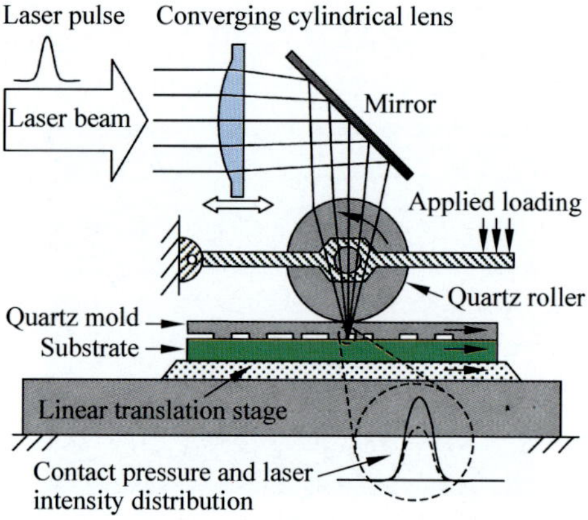

Figure 12.12 Basic idea and setup for roller-based LADI process[37]

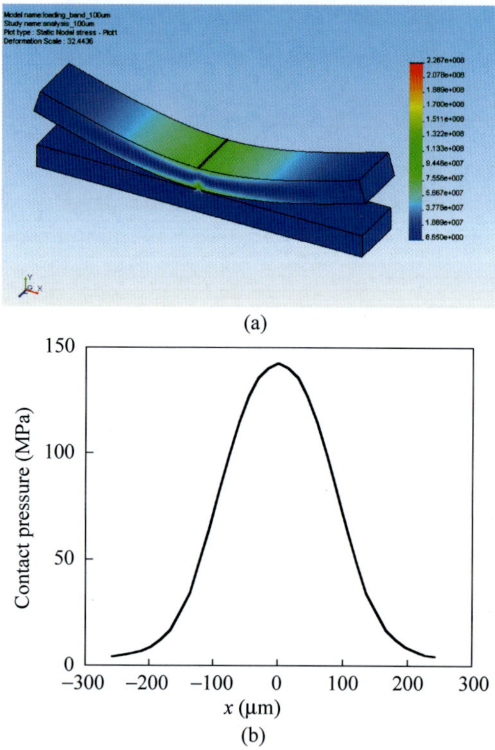

Figure 12.17 The (a) deformation of quartz mold and (b) the contact pressure distribution between mold and substrate in roller-based LADI for an 8 kgf loading force[37]

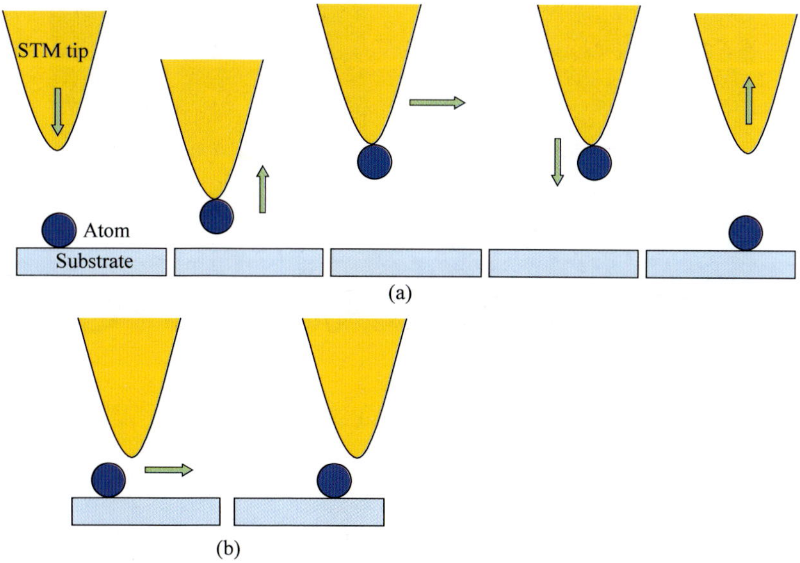

Figure 13.1 Schematic drawing of the nano-manipulation of atoms with STM. (a) Vertical manipulation mode. (b) Lateral manipulation mode

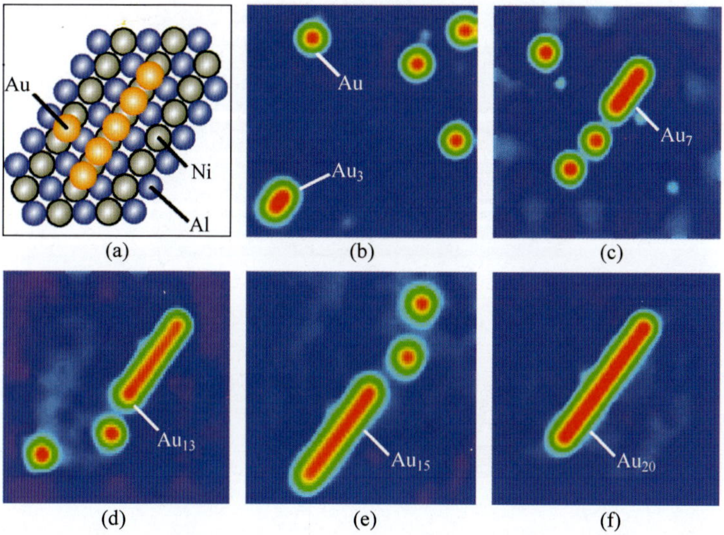

Figure 13.3 Moving and patterning individual Au atoms with STM. A atomic chain was formed with 20 Au atoms[9]

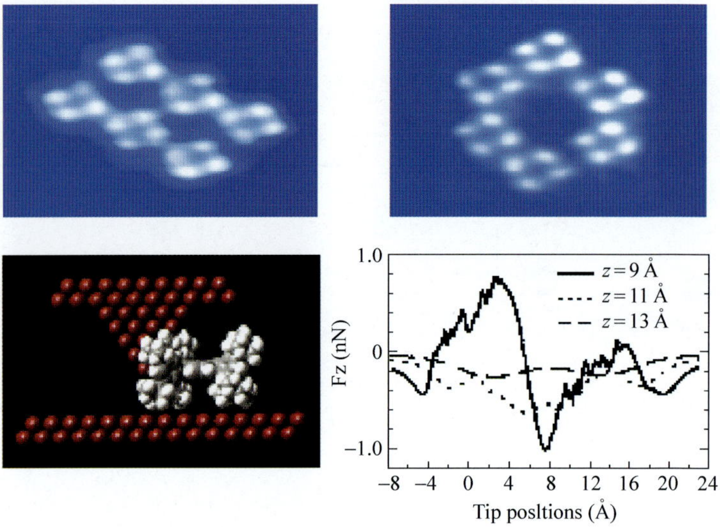

Figure 13.4 (upper) STM images of 6 Cu-TBPP molecules before and after re-arrangement induced by a STM tip. (bottom) The conformation of the Cu-TBPP molecules changed during re-arrangement (bottom left), which was revealed by the force curve (bottom right)[10]

(a)

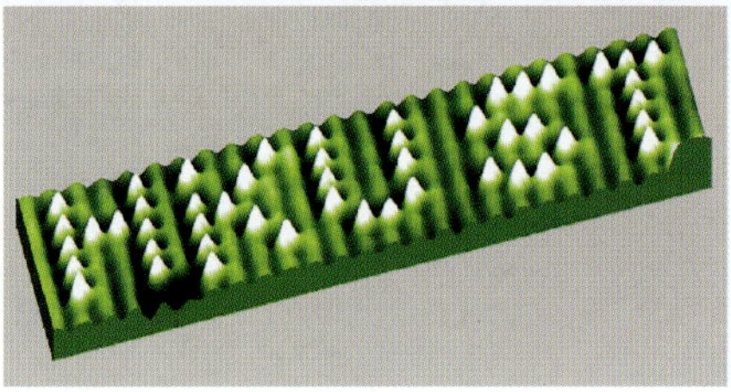

(b)

Figure 13.5 Manipulation of CO molecules with STM. (a) Researchers working with a Low Temperature Omicron STM system; (b) the word 'HKUST' formed with 49 CO molecules on Cu surface. Images were provided by Prof. Xudong Xiao of the Hong Kong University of Science & Technology

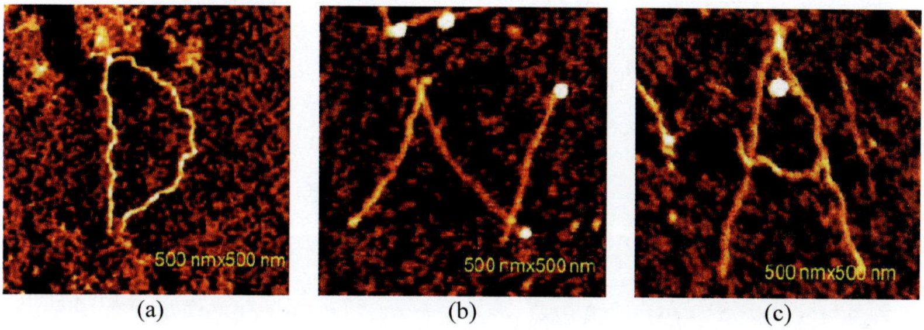

Figure 13.6 Human letters 'D', 'N', and 'A' formed with individual DNA molecules[11]

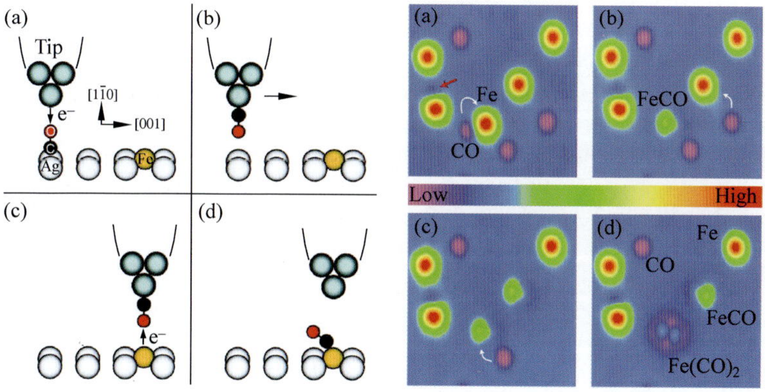

Figure 13.7 Single-molecule reaction induced with STM. (Left) Scheme. (Right) STM images indicating the reaction process. (a) Several Fe atoms and CO molecules on the substrate. (b) One CO molecule reacted with Fe atom to form a FeCO molecules. (c) Two FeCO molecules were formed. (d) One FeCO reacted with another CO and formed a $Fe(CO)_2$[12]

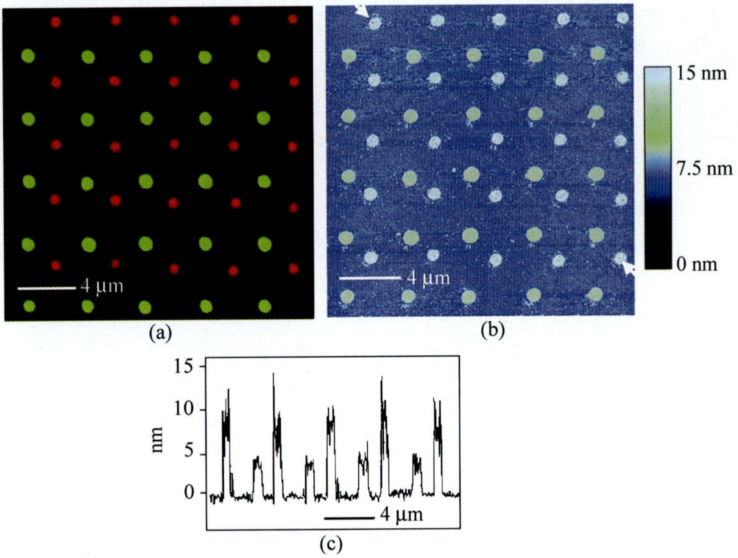

Figure 13.14 DPN-generated biomolecule patterns on substrate showing biological activities. (a) Fluorescent image indicating target DNA molecules binding to their complementary DNA spot. (b) AFM image indicating two kinds of DNA-functionalized Au nanoparticles bound to their complementary DNA spots. (c) Section analysis of the line along the arrows shown in 'B', indicating that two different nanoparticles, with 5 nm and 10 nm in dimensions, respectively, were bound to their complementary DNA spots[27]

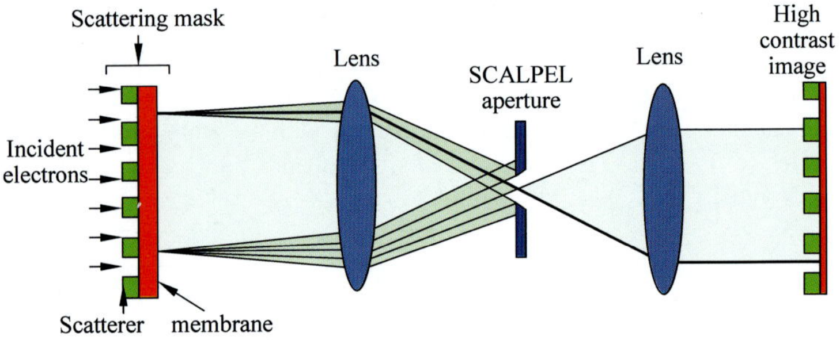

Figure 14.1 Schematic of projection electron-beam lithography system: SCALPEL

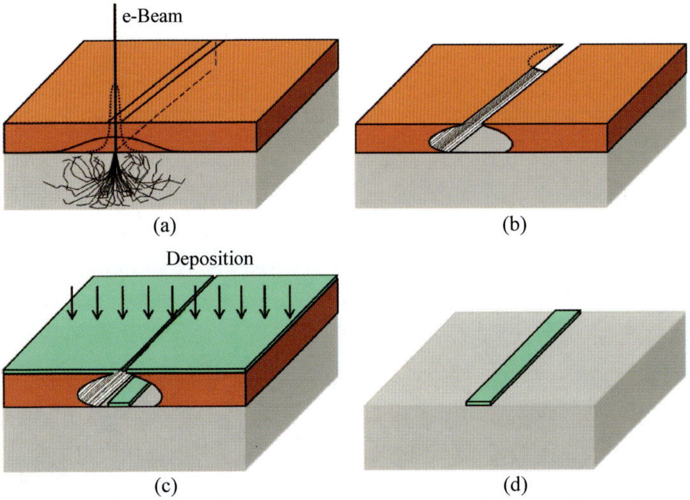

Figure 14.2 Schematic of EBL lift-off process: (a) *e*-beam injection, (b) exposed resist developed and removed, (c) deposition of desired materials by e-gun or vacuum evaporation, (d) lift-off of unwanted materials

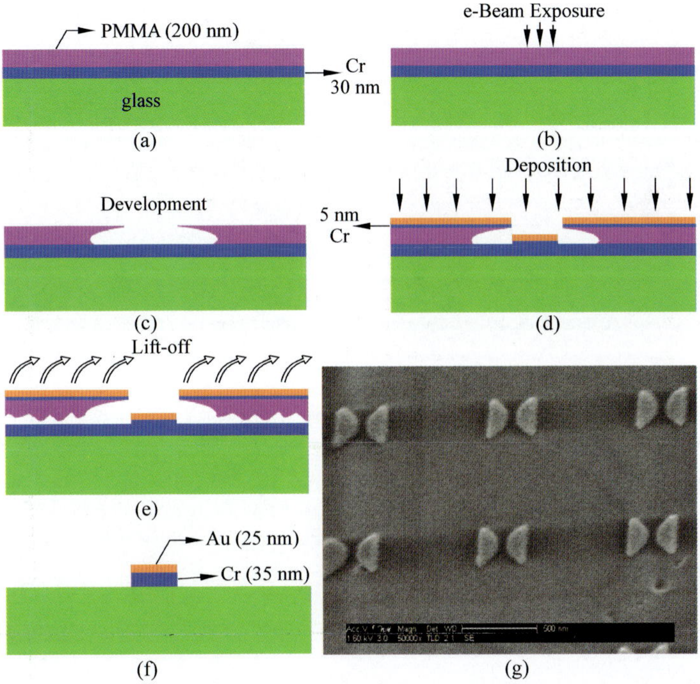

Figure 14.3 Lift-off process using bilayer resist: (a) deposit Cr and spin-coat PMMA, (b) patterning, (c) creating undercut in PMMA, (d) depositing 5 nm Cr and 25 nm Au, (e) removing unwanted materials, (f) wet etching with Au as mask to remove unprotected Cr, (g) SEM image of bowtie array with scale bar of 500 nm

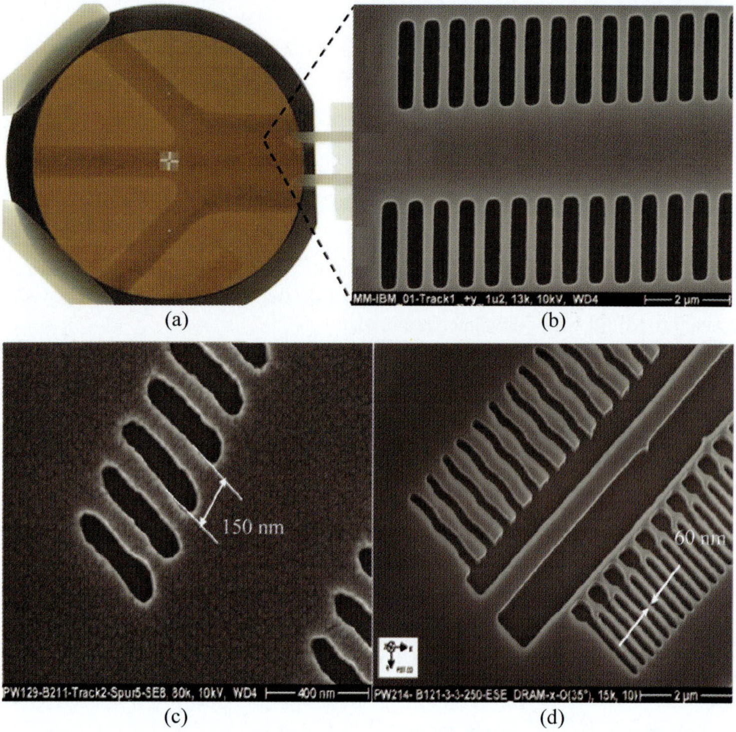

Figure 14.4 Si stencil mask for exposure resolution test: (a) optical image of 150 mm stencil mask fabricated by EBL, (b) SEM image of stencil pattern for resolution test, (c) SEM image of 80 nm wide slot array at a 150 nm period printed by 4X PDT system in 50 nm thick Infineon CARL resist by 45 keV He^+ at 2.0 $\mu C/cm^2$ dose using mask shown in (b), (d) SEM image of DRAM device test pattern with 60 nm narrowest ribs in 230 nm thick Infineon CARL resist (after Loeschner et al.[14])

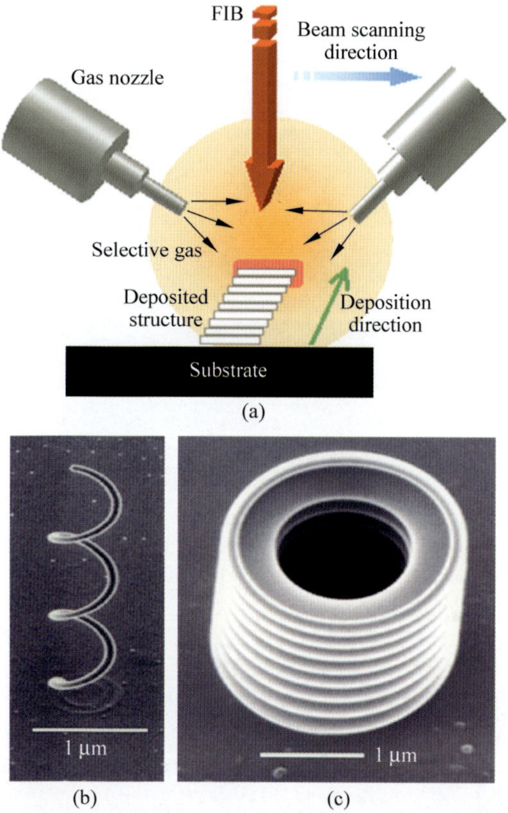

Figure 14.7 Nanostructures fabricated by FIBCVD: (a) schematic of FIBCVD, (b) SEM image of nanocoil with a 600 nm coil diameter, 700 nm coil pitch, and 80 nm wire diameter, (c) nanobellow with a 100 nm thickness, 800 nm pitch, 2750 nm external diameter, and 6,100 nm height (courtesy of Shinji Matsui of Himeji Institute of Technology, Japan)

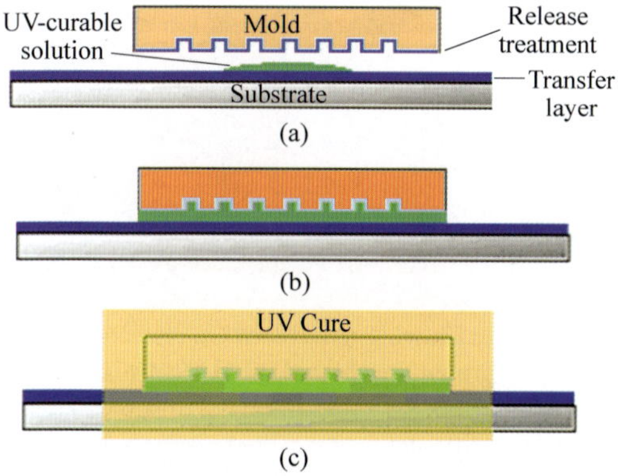

Figure 14.10 Major modified steps in step and flash imprint lithography (SFIL): (a) dispensing UV curable solution, (b) imprinting, (c) UV exposure

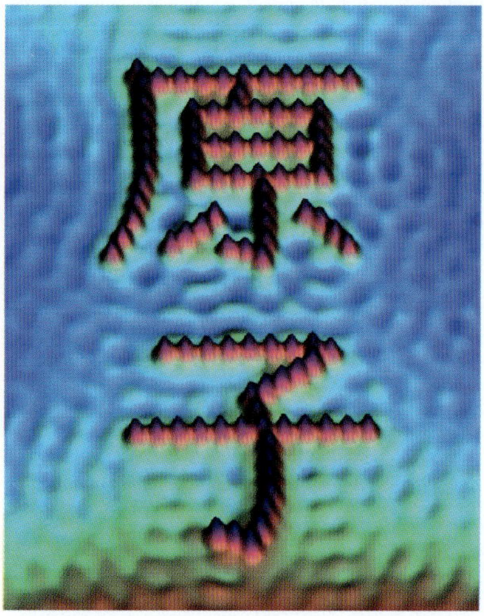

Figure 14.14 STM image of atomic manipulation of iron atoms on Cu(111) surface in writing Chinese characters for 'atom' by C. P. Lutz and D. M. Eigler, to which the literal translation is something like 'original child' (courtesy of IBM Almaden Research Center)

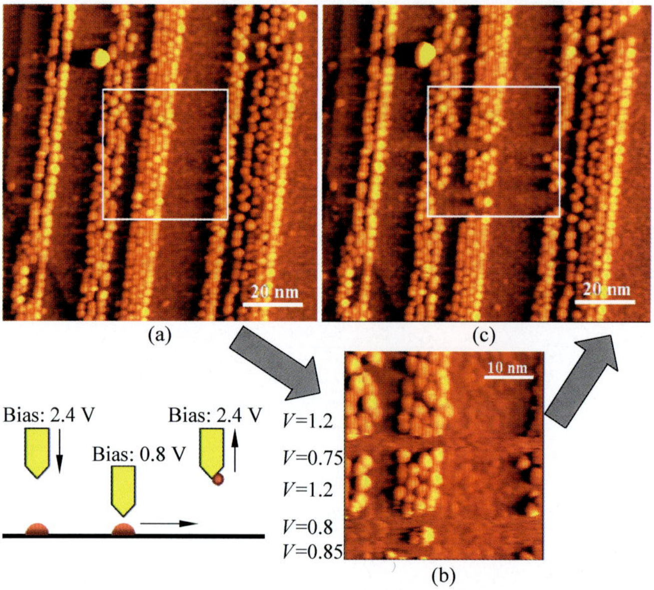

Figure 14.15 STM images showing removal of Co clusters by reducing bias during scanning: (a) Co clusters grown on ordered Al_2O_3/NiAl(100) surface (bias = 2.4 V and tunneling current = 0.8 nA), (b) zoom-in image of square area shown in Panel a, where bias was lowered to different values with $I = 0.8$ nA during scanning, (c) same surface region as in Panel (a) after removal of Co clusters scanned with same imaging parameters (2.4 V, 0.8 nA). The inset cartoon illustrates the procedure (after Tseng et al.[60])

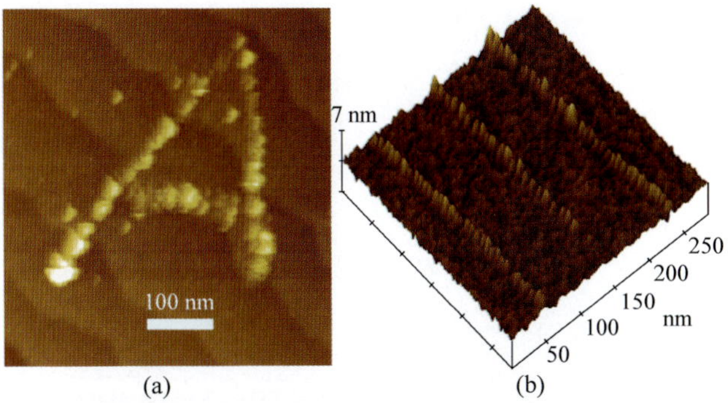

Figure 14.16 Nanostructures on Si substrates by direct STML deposition of sequential dots: (a) STM image of Ag-characters 'A' by Ag-coated tip (courtesy of Daisuke Fujita of National Institute for Materials Science, Japan), (b) AFM image of Au-lines by Au-coated tip (courtesy of H. Abed of Faculté des Sciences de Luminy, France)

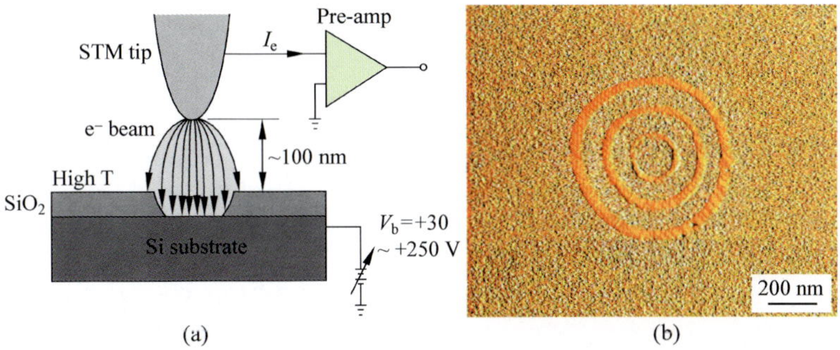

Figure 14.17 Material removal by STM induced thermal decomposition: (a) schematic of decomposition of SiO_2 layer by an STM tip with negative bias, (b) concentric ring pattern with a minimum line width of 25 nm fabricated by STM tip scanning using computer controller (courtesy of Hiroshi Iwasaki of Osaka University, Japan)

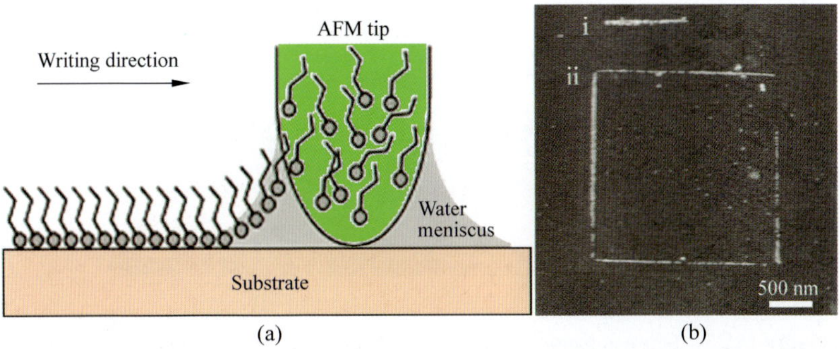

Figure 14.23 Nanostructures fabricated by dip-pen nanolithography (DPN): (a) schematic of DPN, (b) AFM image of Cu nanowires fabricated on mica surface, in which ascorbic acid was dropped onto freshly cleaved mica first, and then writing on mica surface with AFM tip adsorbed with $CuSO_4$ molecules

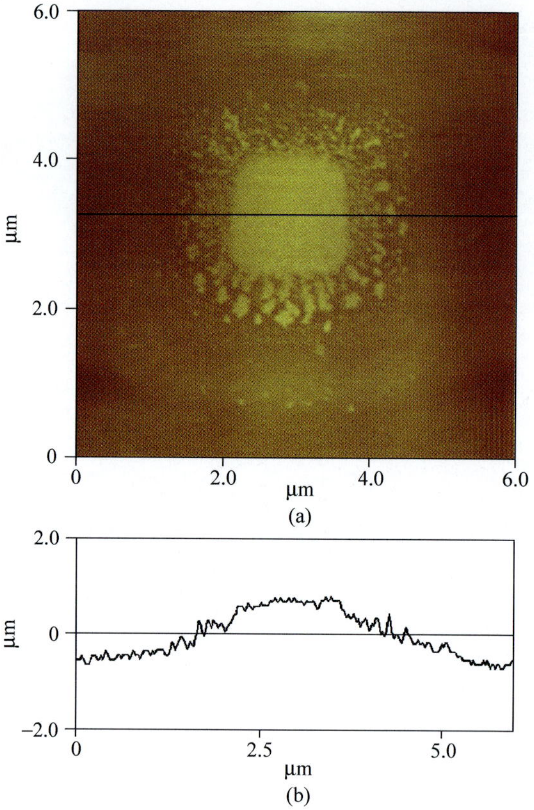

Figure 14.24 Mesa-like nanostructure of BSA on mica surface written by DPN with contact force of 5 nN: (a) AFM image, (b) cross-section profile along the black line shown in (a)

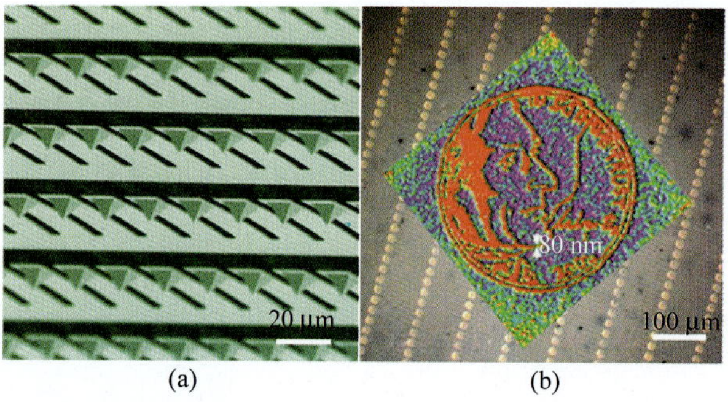

Figure 14.25 Dip-pen nanolithography (DPN) using 55,000 pyramidal tips: (a) SEM image of 2D-tip array, (b) AFM image of miniaturized replica of five-cent coin generated by DPN where background is optical image of part of the 55,000 duplicates were generated on substrate[145]

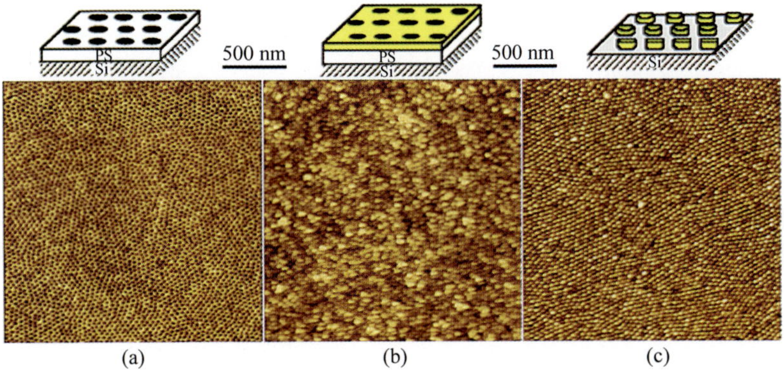

Figure 14.26 Fabrication process for Cr dot arrays: (a) nanoscopic holes in cross-linked polystyrene (PS) matrix following removal of minor component, (b) evaporated Cr onto the PS template, (c) removal of template to yield Cr nanodot array. The height range of AFM images is 10 nm[153]

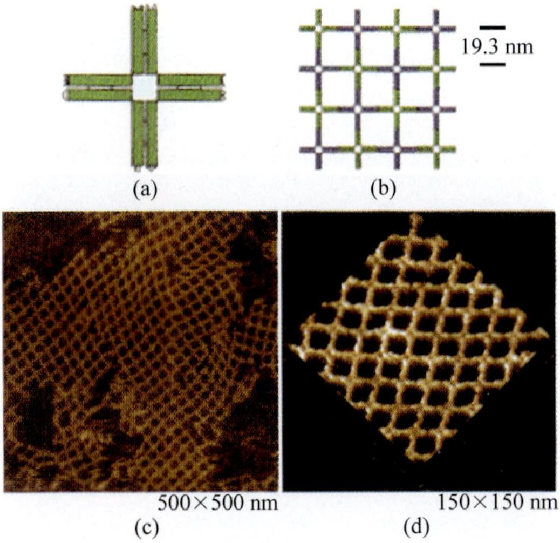

Figure 14.27 Self-assembly of 2D nano-grids with corrugated design: (a) schematic of 4×4 DNA strand component tile, (b) schematic of self-assembled 2D nano-grids, (c) AFM image of self-assembled 2D lattices (nano-grids) displaying a square aspect ratio, (d) surface plot of a magnified region from (c)[163]

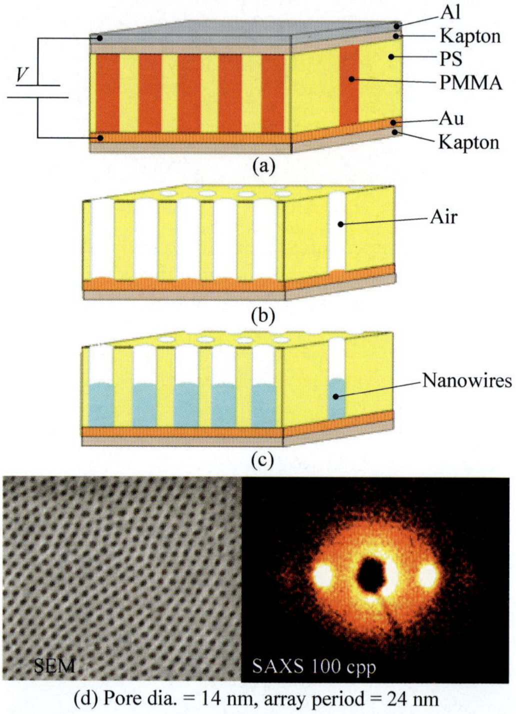

Figure 14.28 Nanopatterning by self assembly: (a) asymmetric diblock copolymer annealed above glass transition temperature of copolymer between two electrodes under applied electric field, forming hexagonal array of cylinders, (b) after removal of the minor component, a nanoporous film being formed, (c) by electrodeposition, nanowires being grown in porous template (after Thurn-Albrecht et al., 2000), (d) SEM and SAXS images of corresponding PS/PMMA template having array period of 24 nm and pore diameter of 14 nm (courtesy of T. P. Russell, UMass Amherst)

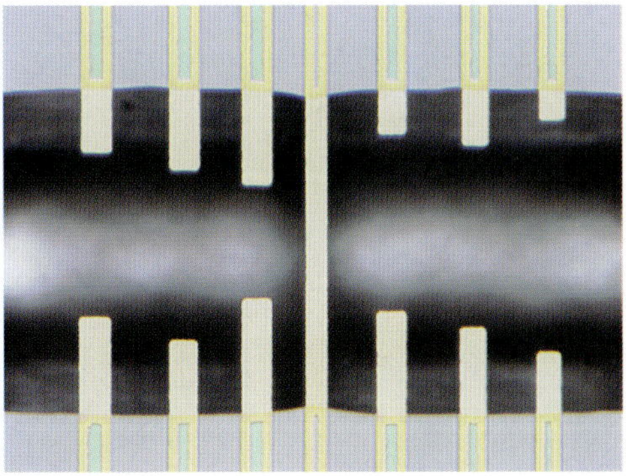

Figure 15.12 Micrograph of the formed 12 nm thick cantilever array

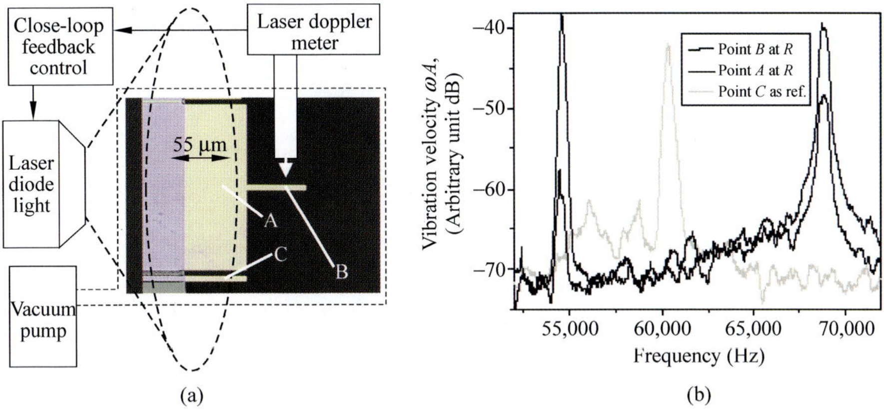

Figure 15.15 (a) Micrograph of a two-degree-of-freedom NEMS resonant cantilever and the schematic of the testing setup; (b) Tested mechanical mode coupling induced sensitivity amplification

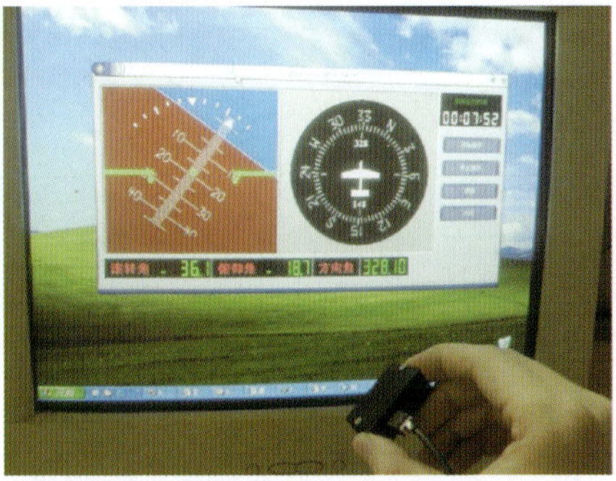

Figure 17.20 Microelectromechanical attitude measurement module and the display interface

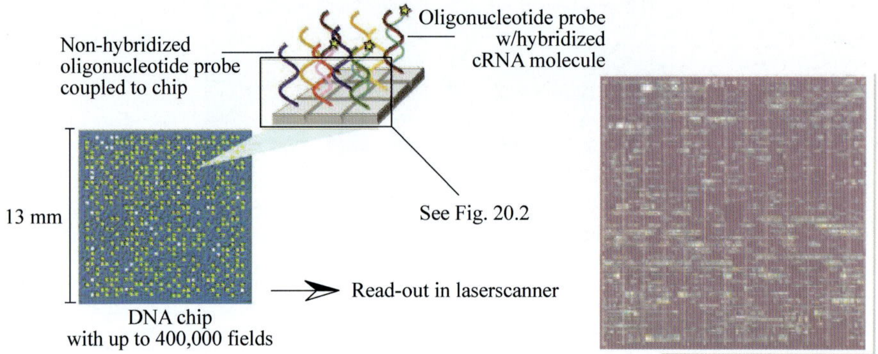

Figure 20.1 Schematic of DNA microarray chip

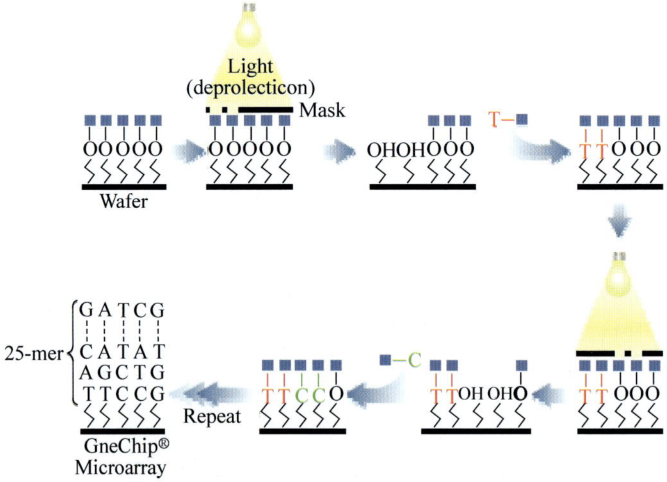

Figure 20.2 Light-directed synthesis strategy used in the manufacture of oligonucleotide microarrays

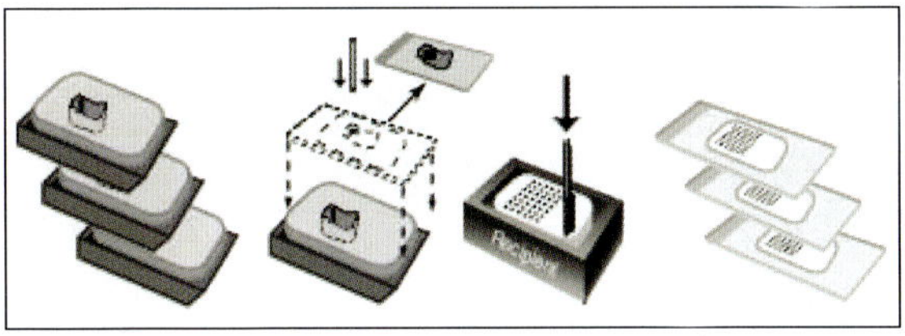

(a)

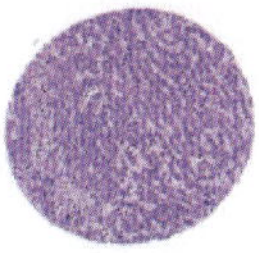

(b) (c) (d)

Figure 20.3 Schematic of fabricating TMA chip and the pictures of TMA chip, (a) general line of fabricating TMA chip, (b) TMA block, (c) TMA slide, (d) tissue spot in the TMA chip

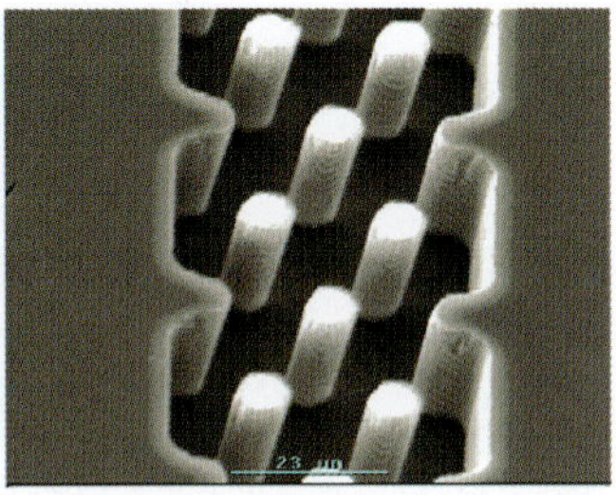

(a) (b)

Figure 20.6 (a) Photograph of multilevel crossflow filtration microchip for blood separation. (b) SEM of micropost array microfluidic chip

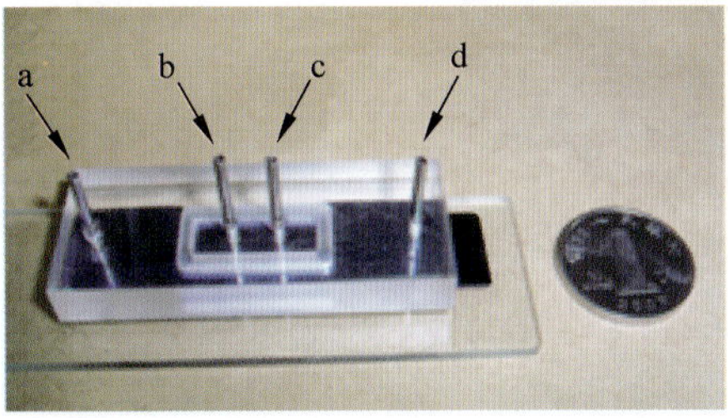

Figure 20.10 Photograph of a sample pretreatment biochip: a. Inlet of whole blood, b. Outlet of red blood cells, c. Inlet of buffers, d. Outlet of waste and DNA

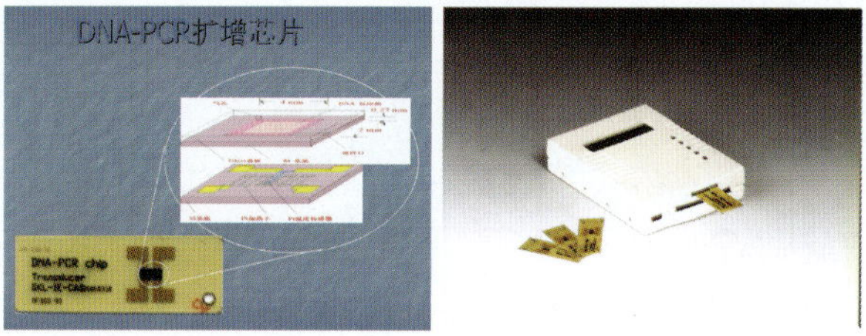

(a) (b)

Figure 20.18 (a) DNA-PCR chip, (b) a miniaturized heat cycler system

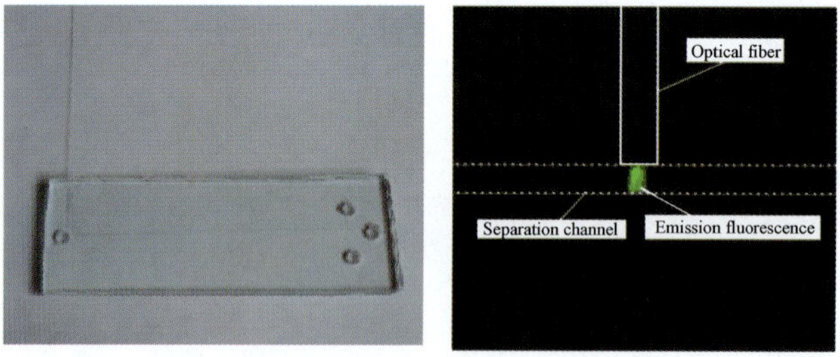

(a) (b)

Figure 20.24 (a) Photograph of integrated PDMS microchips[80]. (b) CCD images of fluorescent emission at the intersection region of microchannel and optical fiber[81]

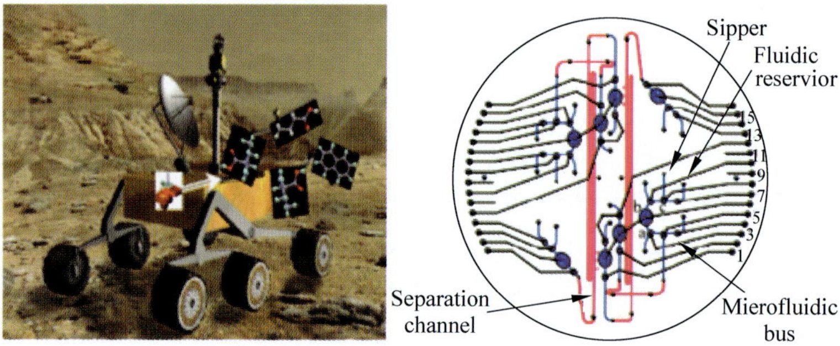

(a) (b)

Figure 20.26 (a) Prototype of microfabricated organic analyzer. (b) Integrated microfluidic chip in MOA

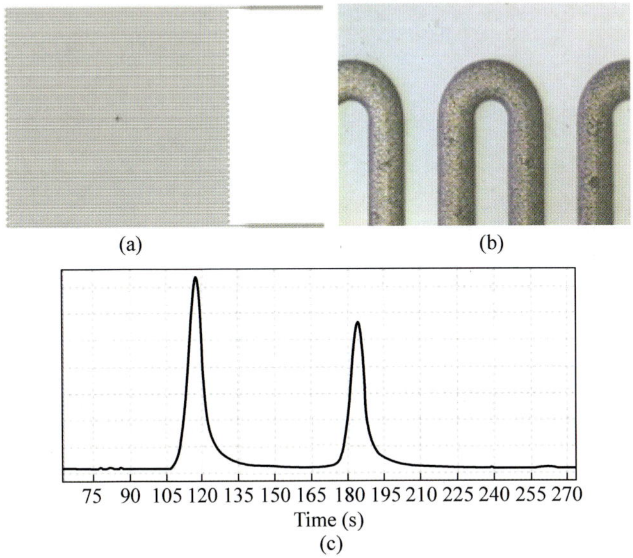

Figure 20.27 (a) Design of a 6 m long column. (b) Photo of the column corner under the microscope. (c) Chromatogram of a 6 m long column

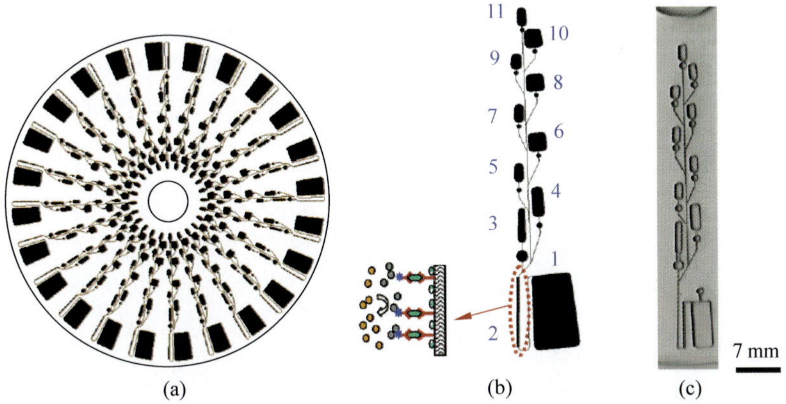

Figure 20.28 Schematics of (a) a CD-ELISA design with 24 sets of assays, (b) a single assay, (1, waste; 2, detection; 3, first antibody; 4, 6, 8, 10, washing; 5, blocking protein; 7, antigen/sample; 9, second antibody; and 11, substrate), and (c) photo of a single assay

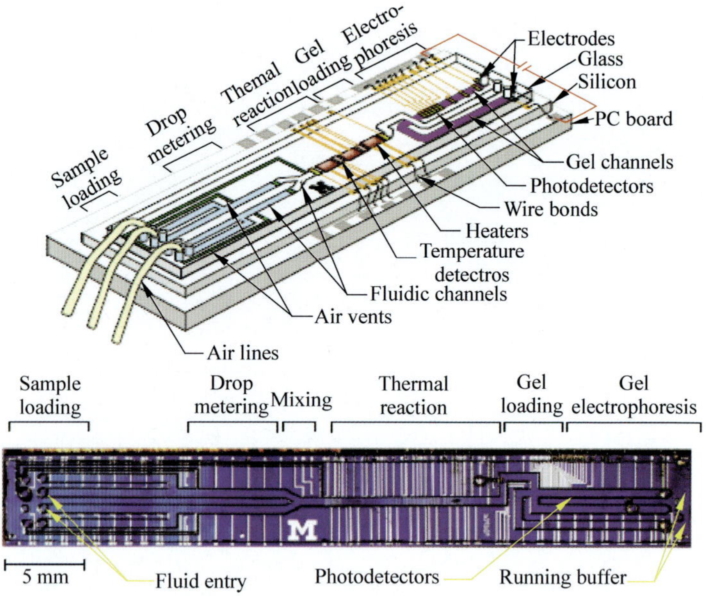

Figure 20.29 Schematic and photograph of an integrated device with a nanoliter liquid injector, a sample mixing and positioning system, a temperature-controlled reaction chamber, an electrophoretic separation system and fluorescence detectors. The device is capable of measuring aqueous reagents and DNA containing solutions, mixing the solutions together, amplifying or digesting the DNA to form discrete products and separating and detecting those products

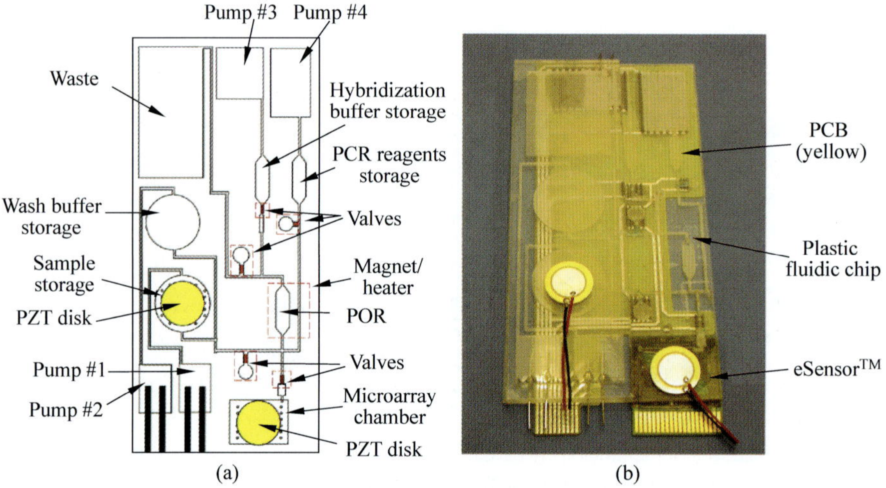

Figure 20.30 (a) Schematic of the plastic microfluidic chip. Pumps 1-3 are electrochemical pumps, and pump 4 is a thermopneumatic pump. (b) Photograph of the integrated device that consists of a plastic fluidic chip, a printed circuit board (PCB), and a Motorola eSensor microarray chip

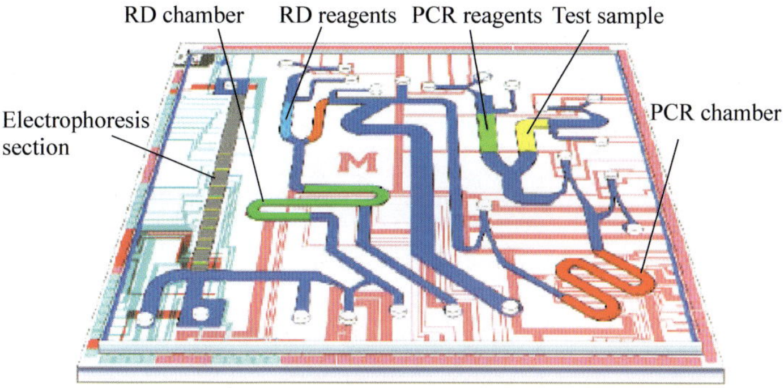

Figure 20.31 Schematic of integrated microfluidic chip

Figure 20.32 Integrated microfluidic chip system for sequencing

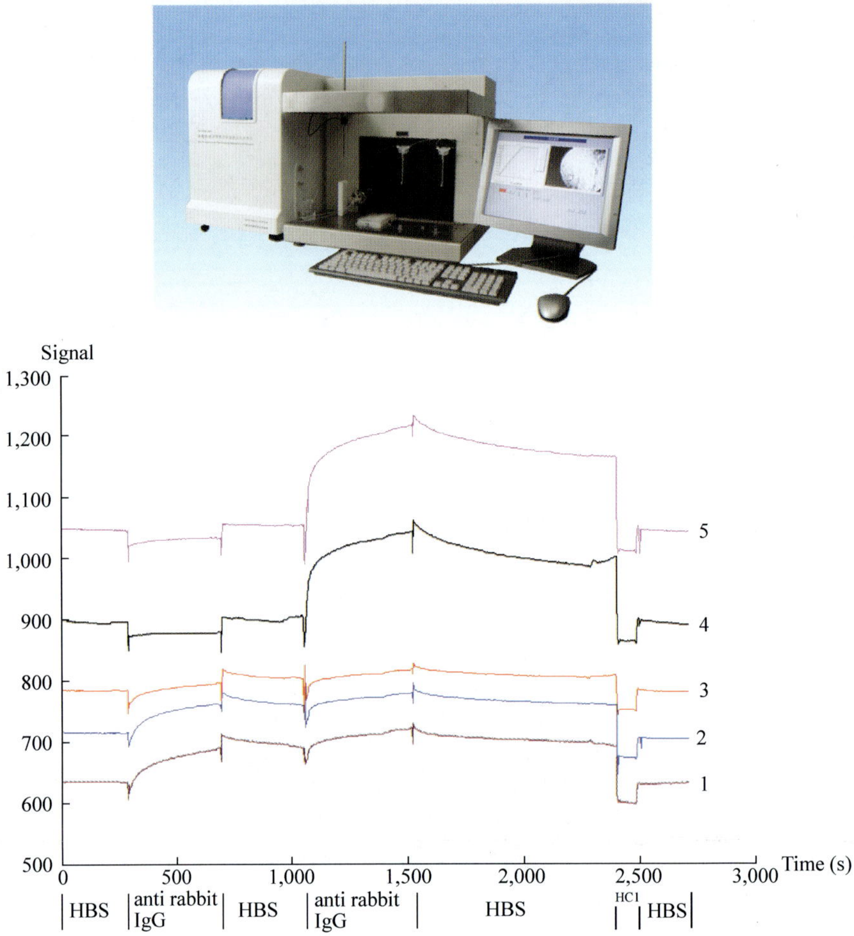

Figure 20.34 Photograph of SPR biochemical analyzer (top) and the SPR testing result (bottom)

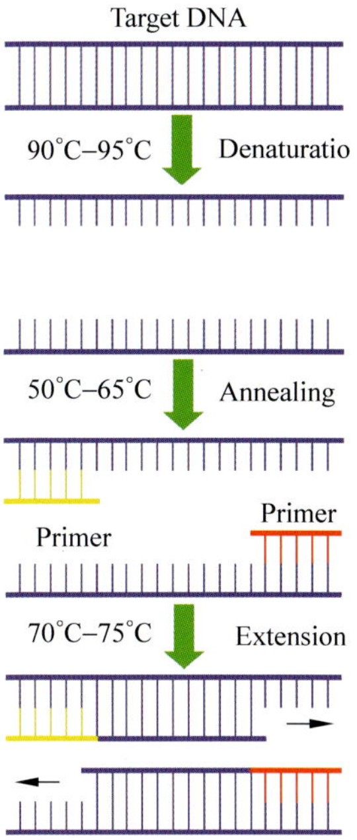

Figure 21.1 Schematic diagram of polymerase chain reaction (PCR) thermocycling. The procedure comprises three steps involving denaturation, annealing, and extension of DNA

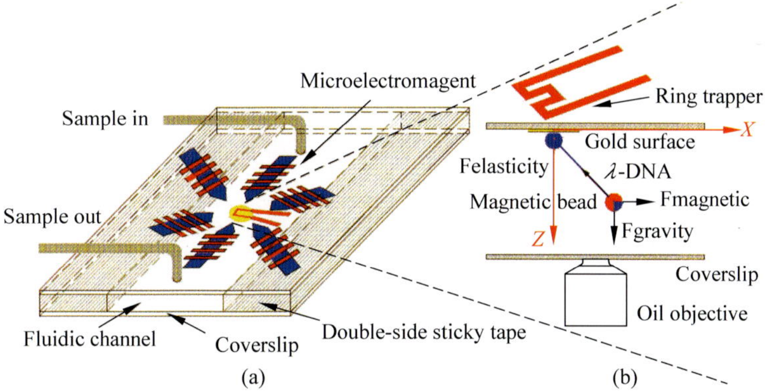

Figure 21.3 (a) Schematic illustration of magnetic tweezers integrated with microelectromagnets, a ring trapper, a fluidic channel, and a gold-patterned surface. (b) Tethered-DNA magnetic bead was in equilibrium under the action of the magnetic force, DNA elastic force, and gravity[86] (© 2006 IOP)

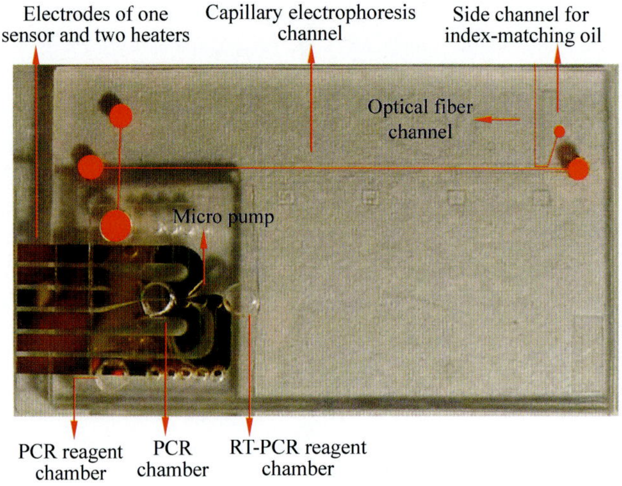

Figure 21.5 A photograph of the integrated microfluidic chip capable of performing DNA/RNA (ribonucleic acid) amplification, electrophoretic separation, and online optical detection of DNA samples[127] (© 2006 WILEY-VCH Verlag GmbH & Co.)

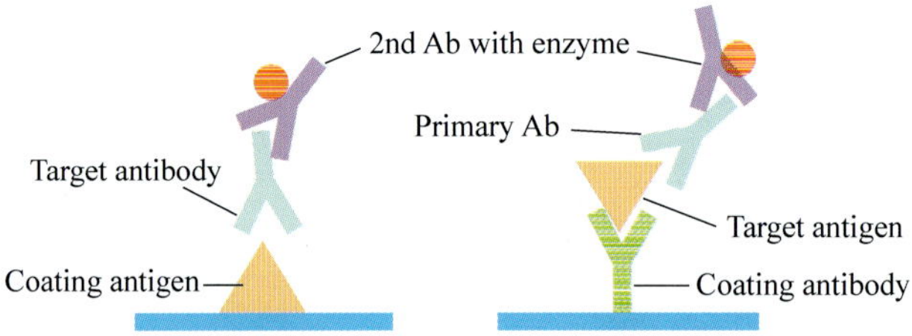

Figure 21.6 A schematic illustration of the operating principle of an enzyme-linked immunosorbent assay (ELISA)